Brylawski

Discrete Mathematics

DISCRETE MATHEMATICS

Kenneth P. Bogart

Dartmouth College

D. C. HEATH AND COMPANY
Lexington, Massachusetts   Toronto

Acquisitions Editor: Mary Lu Walsh

Developmental Editor: Ann Marie Jones

Production Editor: Karen Potischman

Designer: Cornelia Boynton

Production Coordinator: Mike O'Dea

Cover: Henry Reis

There is a growing awareness in the mathematical community that the mathematical needs of students in their first two years of college include a number of subjects not touched on in calculus and touched on only lightly in a traditional high school curriculum. These topics—combinatorics, logic, relations and functions, mathematical induction, graphs and trees, probability, linear algebra, and other modern algebra topics—have in common a step-by-step, or discrete, nature (rather than a continuous nature) and so are referred to as *discrete mathematics*. While these subjects have important applications in the physical, engineering, management, and social sciences, it has been possible to delay their introduction or to treat them in an ad hoc manner as they arise in other courses. However, computer scientists have found that students need to know topics in discrete mathematics in order to fully understand even introductory computer science. The importance of computer science (and therefore discrete mathematics) to computing in other disciplines is becoming more apparent as computers are used in more and more complex situations. Thus discrete mathematics is quickly becoming an essential early ingredient in the college education of many students.

Purpose

After analyzing student needs, a panel of the Mathematical Association of America has issued recommendations for a two-semester course in discrete mathematics. The work of this panel is based first on the panel members' considerable expertise (including Alf Bertziss's and Anthony Ralston's insights published in the *Communications of the ACM* and the *American Mathematical Monthly*), second on prior recommendations of the ACM curriculum committee and IEEE educational activities board and simultaneous recommendations of the ACM task force on computing programs in small colleges, and finally on many other sources including a D. C. Heath survey of approximately 1500 departments of mathematics and computer science. D. C. Heath's survey indicates that present discrete mathematics courses at the elementary level are largely one semester. Recognizing this possibility, the panel has also recommended a syllabus for a one-semester course. This book has been based on the panel recommendations and also addresses the needs outlined in the other studies. The book is designed to be used in a one- or two-semester course and is constructed to allow the instructor of a one-semester course to choose topics according to institutional needs. While the instructor can enrich the course for students who have already had calculus, calculus is not used in any of the exposition and algebra topics traditionally used in calculus are reviewed as they arise. Thus the book is suited to students who have not had calculus and will help prepare them for calculus.

Because computer science or computer use in other fields is important to almost all students taking the course, applications of discrete mathematics to computing are used for motivation throughout the book. Appropriate examples from areas outside computer science help indicate the breadth of applications of discrete mathematics. A central theme in the book is that in order to solve problems by computer, one needs algorithms, and in order to evaluate algorithms, one needs to predict their running time.

Organization

In order to maximize the flexibility of the book, it has been written so that the last section (or sections) in each chapter (other than Chapter 4 on functions) may be omitted without seriously curtailing what can be taught later. Each chapter of the book is divided into sections, which are divided further into subsections (usually two) of approximately equal length and difficulty. The exercises are keyed to subsections, making it easy to adjust the pace of the course to one, two, or three subsections a day, depending on the students' background and the emphasis of the course.

The following table shows the immediate prerequisites for various sections of the book. Of course a prerequisite of a prerequisite is a prerequisite. Except as shown, earlier sections of a chapter are prerequisite for later sections. A section is marked as enriching but not prerequisite if it either provides background for a deeper understanding of the concepts introduced or provides the background needed for an isolated example in that section.

Sections	Immediate Prerequisites	Enriching, but not Prerequisite
1-3, 1-4	1-1, 1-2	
1-5	1-3, 1-4	
2-1, 2-2, 2-3	1-3, 1-4	1-5
3-1, 3-2, 3-3A	1-1, 1-2	
3-3B	3-1, 3-2, 3-3A	
3-4	3-1, 3-2	3-3A
4-1, 4-2, 4-3	3-1, 3-2, 3-3A	
5-1, 5-2	4-1, 4-2, 4-3	2-1, 2-2, 2-3
5-3A	5-1, 5-2	
5-3B	5-3A	
6-1	5-2	
6-2	6-1	
6-3	6-2	
6-4	6-2	
6-5	6-2, 6-4	6-3
7-1, 7-2	6-2, 6-4	5-3A, 6-3, 6-5

Sections	Immediate Prerequisites	Enriching, but not Prerequisite
7-3	7-1, 7-2A	
8-1	6-2, 6-4	
8-2A	8-1	
8-2B, 8-3	5-3A, 8-2A, 7-2	
9-1, 9-2, 9-3	8-1	6-4
9-4	9-1, 9-2, 9-3	5-3B
10-1	5-1, 4-2	
10-2	10-1, 6-1	8-4, 9-1, 9-2, 9-3
10-3	10-1	
10-4, 10-5, 10-6	10-3	
11-1, 11-2	6-2, 6-4	6-3
11-3	11-1, 11-2	7-1, 7-2, 8-1, 8-2A
11-4	11-3	
11-5	11-3, 10-1	10-2
12	10-3, 1-5	9-4, 10-4, 10-5, 10-6, 2-1, 2-2, 2-3

Students with a strong algebra background (such as a thorough preparation for calculus) may find the material on sets, functions, and relations to be largely review. Instructors whose students have such a background may wish to substitute Appendix A, which is a condensed review of these topics from a discrete mathematics point of view, for Sections 1-1 and 1-2, the first half (except for adjacency lists) of Section 3-1, and Sections 4-1 and 4-2.

Contents

Chapter 1 begins with an introduction to sets as truth sets of statements. Later, optional, material in Chapter 1 covers truth tables for the basic connectives and their applications. I have adopted the method of working out truth tables popularized by Kemeny, Snell, et al. in their *Finite Mathematics* series. This method avoids the need to define and analyze subformulas and, in complicated situations, saves the students a good bit of writing. The subject takes on special importance in light of the use of compound statements to control conditional instructions in computer programs. While the topics in Chapter 1 are usually thought of as propositional logic, the applications in programming require the use of variables. For this reason the typical introductory study of propositions is replaced by a parallel study of statements about a universe. Chapter 2 continues the study of logic through rules of inference and the use of quantifiers. The chapter allows the instructor who wishes to concentrate on the nature of proof to spend considerable time there while allowing the instructor whose goals are to help students learn to read proofs and recognize quantifications to proceed more quickly. The treatment of logic is designed to prepare students for later work in the theory of computation, databases, and artificial intelligence. Instructors may find that their students already have an understanding of proof techniques that is appropriate for the goals of their course. In this case it is possible to omit the second half of Chapter 1 and/or Chapter 2 with little or no effect on what can be covered later.

Chapters 3 and 4 are an introduction to relations and functions. Directed graphs (digraphs) and graphs are introduced as tools for the study of relations and symmetric relations, respectively. As there is no standard accepted definition of *digraph* or *graph* in the mathematical community, I've adopted the definitions which fit best with the relational point of view. Equivalence relations are introduced in Chapter 3 and they arise frequently in later chapters; congruence modulo m and partial orderings are also introduced in Chapter 3, but they may be downplayed or omitted as their later use is minor. Instructors who plan to cover Chapter 12 (Abstract Algebra) will want to cover congruence modulo m at some time, however. All of Chapter 4 is fundamental to the remainder of the book. Functions are the basis for the study of permutations and other topics in combinatorics and relative growth rates of functions play an essential role in later algorithm analysis. Students who have had a solid precalculus course can omit or cover quickly all but the last section of Chapter 4; conversely all of Chapter 4 is a good preparation for calculus. The last section introduces the "big Oh" notation which is so useful in discussing algorithms. The functions discussed actually arise in analyzing algorithms, so this section is central to what comes later.

Chapter 5 is a study of the principle of mathematical induction. By Chapter 5 the student has enough background to understand a wide variety of applications. In addition to the sum formulas the student may have seen in algebra, the examples include results about graphs, proving the correctness of algorithms, proving statements about how many steps an algorithm uses, and even specifying algorithms themselves. We also discuss how induction lies at the heart of grammars, which define parts of computer languages. In this context, induction is a core topic in computer science as well as in mathematics! While the study of Chapter 5 is enriched by a study of Chapter 2, Chapter 5 relies only on Sections 1-1 and 1-2, and on Chapters 3 and 4.

Chapter 6 gives the student the basic combinatorial tools used in all counting problems, including counting the number of steps used by an algorithm. We begin by applying the sum and product principles to permutations and combinations, viewed as one-to-one functions and subsets. We move on to discuss a number of applications of basic counting principles, including the binomial theorem. The chapter then unifies a large number of standard applications of the product principle in terms of counting equivalence classes, and introduces multisets (combinations with repetitions). The instructor may choose the brief treatment of multisets at the end of Section 6-2, or the more thorough treatment in Section 6-3 (or both). Chapter 6 concludes with a complete (and optional) discussion of the principle of inclusion and exclusion.

The remaining chapters are largely independent of each other and can be covered as local needs dictate. Chapter 7 covers recurrence relations as a means of unifying and extending previous approaches to solving counting problems. The discussion of first-order recurrence relations and divide-and-conquer algorithms contains important computer science examples (such as binary search and sorting algorithms) and gives the student a new perspective on the importance of logarithms and exponential functions. The treatment of second-order recurrence relations is based on a study of growth problems that includes the Fibonacci numbers in a natural way. Appendix B, on generating functions, is an extension of Chapters 6 and 7. This material unifies many topics in enumeration and is suitable for students with a strong background in algebra. It is especially appropriate for students who have taken or are about to take a course in the calculus of power series.

Chapters 8 and 9 give a solid introduction to graph theory. Chapter 8 begins with trees defined in graph theory terms and quickly progresses to the rooted and binary trees used in computer science. The optional material on two-three trees answers a practical question students may well ask: "What good are binary trees if our data is already (almost) in order?" These two-three trees are special cases of B-trees, a data structure that lies at the heart of modern database management systems. The final section of Chapter 8 covers optimal spanning trees, giving procedures for finding minimum cost communications networks and minimum length paths in graphs.

Chapter 9 introduces a cross-section of other topics in graph theory, and relies on Section 8-1. The instructor who wishes to give a brief overview of graphs may do so by choosing to downplay the role of proofs. On the other hand, for the instructor whose goals include teaching students to write clear and concise proofs, this is an ideal chapter in which to slow down and spend time working on proof technique. The chapter begins with a discussion of various graphical structures and isomorphism. We distinguish between the problem of verifying that a given function is an isomorphism and the problem of determining whether two graphs are isomorphic. This distinction lies at the heart of the definition of the complexity class NP; while it may be unrealistic to try to define and use NP in this course, we present topics in a way that will make them as useful as possible if the student later studies complexity theory. The surprising observation that while Eulerian tours are relatively straightforward to discover, little is known about Hamiltonian tours again motivates a study of complexity theory in later courses. Planarity is now a practical subject since the chips of silicon on which we lay our circuits are planar! Colorability too has its practical aspects in scheduling. We mention briefly how these two subjects combine in the four-color theorem. Directed graphs provide an excellent way to study machines; we introduce finite state machines and automata and study their relationships with the grammars and languages introduced in Chapter 5.

Matrix algebra has applications throughout discrete mathematics. Also, the later study of linear algebra is enhanced by an intuitive understanding of matrix algebra. For these reasons we devote Chapter 10 to matrix algebra. After a discussion of the basic matrix operations we study applications of matrices to graphs, including transitive closures and distances in graphs. (This chapter can be taken up anytime after Section 6-1.) Discussing the solution of systems of equations as matrix equations leads to the inverse of a matrix. Our final topic is determinants, which we approach as numbers used to test the invertibility of matrices. The chapter gives an elementary treatment via row operations.

The subject of probability has many applications throughout the sciences and engineering. Among the reasons it is important in computer science is the concept of expected value. The second most practical question about a program is "How long does it take?" This leads to the concept of the expected value of the running time. While we discuss many applications in the examples, exercises, and problems of Chapter 11, it is possible to illustrate most ideas of probability using simple examples (coin tossing, test taking, and so on). In order to keep the treatment of probability as elementary as possible, we rely on these basic examples for motivation and introduction of new ideas. The discussion of expected value includes a discussion of the expected running time of algorithms and the depth of binary search trees, and culminates in the central limit theorem. Here we illustrate for students the meaning of such common (and misunderstood) phrases as "95% sure." How, for example, can we be 95% sure (or 99.9% sure) that a database will not overflow its alloted space? We conclude our study with another application of matrix algebra, Markov chains.

Abstract algebra and number systems are handled differently in this text than in others. I have found that students regard an unmotivated study of number systems and their properties as an unnecessary rehash of elementary school mathematics, so I prefer to briefly review these topics as they become relevant throughout the text. Definitions of algebraic systems such as groups, semigroups, rings, monoids, and so on, have been saved for the last chapter. The topics chosen are important both in computer science and mainstream mathematics. The treatment begins by identifying abstractions of properties rather than systems. It then introduces the algebraic systems as examples having these properties, and develops the theory of the systems themselves. The properties abstracted are taken up over and over in early chapters of the book for the instructor who chooses to emphasize them, allowing the algebra to appear as part of a natural progression (as, of course, it is). This early exposure includes the treatment of concrete examples of Boolean algebras in Chapter 1, congruence classes in Chapter 3, inductive proofs of facts of arithmetic in Chapter 5, constructions of new machines from old in the problems of Section 9-4, and especially, matrix algebra in Chapter 10. There is a complete but elementary discussion of what we usually call "the first fundamental homomorphism theorem." The concepts of groups, rings, fields, matrices, and cosets are all reinforced by the treatment of error correcting codes in the last section. This chapter is designed to prepare the student for abstract thinking and is ideal preparation for an abstract algebra course.

A few topics that appear often in upper-level discrete mathematics courses have been downplayed or omitted in this book. For example, Karnaugh maps and the Quine-McCluskey procedure for minimizing the number of "logic gates" in a circuit are less important now than they have been in the past. In designing VLSI chips it is not important to minimize logic gates since they occur when "wires" cross in different layers; other design criteria such as heat and deviations from planarity are more important. This is an example in which concepts relevant to one technology are less relevant to another. Minimization of logic gates will be an important topic in digital circuit theory at least until VLSI compilers and chip fabrication technologies become far more available and cheaper. However, this topic is best saved for a specialized course in digital circuits rather than a general course in discrete mathematics.

Exercises and Problems

The **Exercises** have been designed so that each major example or concept has at least two exercises, one odd-numbered and one even-numbered, to go with it. The exercises are intended to give the student mental exercise, and while we hope to make exercises (whether physical or intellectual) interesting and sometimes challenging, we hope above all to make them things that people can and will do. Most exercises give the student one straightforward operation to carry out, as do exercises in courses such as algebra or calculus. Many exercises allow the student to emulate an example or a discussion in the text, leading to further study of the text. However, the process the student finds to emulate is often a thought process, and thus by doing the exercise the student begins to learn to think independently.

For the student (or instructor) not sufficiently challenged by the exercises there is a set of **Problems** at the end of each section. Problems are intended to be interesting, to extend the ideas in the text, to be challenging, and by sometimes including open-ended questions that the student must interpret before answering, to provide a ground for experimentation with generating new questions. Problems allow an instructor to teach a more sophisticated and challenging course.

At the end of each section there is also a fill-in-the-blanks **Concepts Review** with leading questions that will help the student recall major points or definitions from the section just covered. These are helpful for "pulling together" the ideas of a section before attempting the exercises, and also for later review.

The **Review Exercises** at the end of each chapter are exercises in the same sense described above. Some bring together ideas from more than one section of a chapter or ask a question in a different way; most, however, are intended to review what the student has learned in doing earlier exercises.

Solutions to odd-numbered section exercises and to all concepts reviews and chapter review exercises appear in the back of the book, following a list of suggestions for further reading keyed to individual chapters and sections.

Supplements

The **Instructor's Guide** contains solutions to all the even-numbered exercises, discussion of how to do all the problems, possible schedules, and advice and teaching aids for instructors who are relatively new to teaching discrete mathematics.

The book **Introductory Programming for Discrete Mathematics** contains supplementary material on computer programming that illustrates how the ideas of this course are applied in practice. It is intended to be an introduction to computing for students taking a course in discrete mathematics. It can be integrated into a course; however it is also designed for use as a "laboratory manual." While the programs in the book should run in any ANSI standard BASIC that supports recursion and structured programming, they have all been written and tested in True BASIC™. I have collected these programs onto a disk that is ready to run with the user's True BASIC™ package and is available on request from D. C. Heath for the IBM PC™, PC II™, the Apple Macintosh™, the Commodore Amiga™, and the Atari SE™ computers.

The True BASIC™ **Discrete Mathematics software package,** designed and written by John Kemeny, is also available from D. C. Heath. This is a stand-alone program students may use to illustrate various aspects of the course without doing any programming or developing any special computer skills. This program is also ideal for classroom demonstrations of various discrete mathematics topics.

Acknowledgements

This book has been tried out by a wide variety of Dartmouth students and faculty members (ranging from graduate students to full professors); in addition, portions were used at Northeastern University and portions were used in an intensive summer seminar for high school teachers. To all these students and instructors, I offer my thanks for their patience and advice. In addition, a wide variety of people from the mathematics and computer science community have read and commented on portions of the text. They include: David Berman, University of New Orleans; Douglas Campbell, Brigham Young University; Margaret B. Cozzens, Northeastern University; W. E. Deskins, University of Pittsburgh; Thomas A. Dowling, Ohio State University; Andrew G. Earnest, Southern Illinois University; Lyenatte S. Goff, Glendale Community College; Keith Harrow, Brooklyn College, CUNY; Stuart H. Hirshfield, Hamilton College; John Kenelly, Clemson University; Joseph Malkevitch, York College, CUNY; Thomas J. Myers, University of Delaware; John D. Neff, Georgia Institute of Technology; Richard K. Oliver, Indiana State University; Richard Palais, Brandeis University; Fred Roberts, Rutgers University; and Henry M. Walker, Grinnel College. Ann Marie Jones at D. C. Heath played an essential role in helping me integrate this feedback into meaningful change of my original manuscript. Her unique perspective as both an editor and former high school mathematics teacher resulted in better explanations and made my expectations of students far more realistic! Karen Potischman has blended her considerable skills as a production editor with a sympathy for an author's concerns that have made the production process a pleasure. Barry Willenbring has checked my solutions to the odd-numbered and review exercises. To everyone who has helped shape this book, I offer my thanks.

Contents

Discrete Mathematics

CHAPTER 1
Sets and Statements

*I*n this chapter, we learn about sets and statements and how they relate to each other. The truth set of a statement, introduced in this chapter, arises again when we study probability, where it can help us find a numerical measure of how likely the statement is to be true. The concept of truth or falsity of a statement will be an important part of our study of logic in Chapter 2. Throughout the remainder of the book, the concept of a set will be a fundamental building block for the rest of our work, especially our study of relations in Chapter 3, functions in Chapter 4, trees and graphs in Chapters 8 and 9, probability in Chapter 11, and algebra in Chapter 12. It is possible to give a development of the theory of sets analogous to Euclid's development of plane geometry. This approach to set theory can occupy an entire course in mathematics, so instead we rely on our intuition as the foundation of our study of sets.

In this chapter, we introduce the concept of an algorithm—the name for a list of instructions for carrying out a process. This concept will arise in different ways throughout our study. At times we shall develop algorithms to solve certain kinds of problems, and at other times we shall develop tools to understand our algorithms better. We shall see how the truth or falsity of a statement can be used to determine the outcome of an algorithm. We shall learn how to build new statements, called *compound statements*, from old ones. This is especially useful in computer programs, where there are a small number of relatively simple statements we can use to control our algorithms. By building compound statements from these simple ones, we can achieve quite complex goals.

Section 1-1
Statements

⚿ The Idea of a Statement

Discrete mathematics is the mathematics we use to analyze discrete processes.

A **discrete process** is one that can be carried
out in a step-by-step fashion.

Following a recipe, multiplying a three-digit number by a two-digit number, and solving an equation are all examples of discrete processes. Since computers carry out step-by-step processes, discrete mathematics has become an important tool in the science of computing. For an example of a process that is not discrete, think of a ball moving through the air. "Continuous mathematics," such as calculus, is used to analyze such processes.

Algorithms

In studying a discrete process, there are many questions we might try to answer. One of the most basic is, "Exactly how are we supposed to carry out this process?"

A list of step-by-step instructions for carrying
out a process is called an **algorithm.**

As an example of the kinds of instructions used in an algorithm, imagine telling a child who knows the multiplication tables for one-digit numbers how to multiply a one-digit number by a two-digit number. You might say, "Write down the two-digit number. Write down the one-digit number below it. Draw a line below that. Now, multiply the bottom number by the right-hand digit of the top number. If the result has one digit, write down the result below the line. Otherwise, write down the second digit of the result and remember the first digit. . . ." Notice how the last two sentences tell the child to do one thing in one case and a different thing in a second case. An instruction to do one thing if a statement is true ("The result has one digit") and another thing otherwise is called a **conditional** instruction.

The power of computers derives in part from their ability to carry out conditional instructions. To do so, a computer needs to determine the truth or falsity of a statement. The kinds of statements whose truth a computer can determine are limited both by the kind of information that is stored in the computer and the language used to express the statements. A computer using a typical language can determine the truth or falsity of statements such as $x > 0$ or $x < 10$. If we know that x is an integer, then we can find out if it is a positive one-digit number by asking if both $x > 0$ and $x < 10$ hold true. Thus, even though we may not be able to directly ask the computer to check the truth of "x is a one-digit number," we can combine statements to obtain an equivalent statement that the computer can check for us. We begin our study of discrete mathematics by studying statements, how statements may be combined, and how we can determine whether one statement is equivalent to another.

Statements

Statements such as "Seven is a one-digit integer" and "The binary representation of two is 10" have the form of declarative sentences. A declarative sentence can be true, false, or ambiguous. For example,

"Five plus seven is twelve" is true.
"Five plus seven is thirteen" is false.
"Five plus seven is large" is ambiguous.

(The last sentence is ambiguous because of the lack of context. For example, five girls plus seven boys makes a large number of children for a family, but five red grapes plus seven green grapes does not make a large snack.)

From now on, when we use the word **statement**,
we shall mean an unambiguous declarative sentence.

Thus a statement is either true or false.

EXAMPLE 1   Classify each of the following sentences as a true statement, a false statement, or not a statement.

(a) A sentence must contain a verb.
(b) A hydrocarbon contains hydrogen, carbon, and oxygen.
(c) This book is long.
(d) Did you have a party last night?

Solution   Sentence (a) is a *true* statement. Sentence (b) is a *false* statement; though we can see that (b) is unambiguous without knowing chemistry, we need to know a small amount of elementary chemistry to know that a hydrocarbon may not contain oxygen. Sentence (c) is *ambiguous*. (To determine whether (c) is true or false, we need a standard for determining what is and is not long.) Sentence (d) is not a declarative sentence, so it is *not a statement*.   ∎

Statements about Variables

In algebra we learn about variables. The equations we learn to write in algebra are statements containing variables. For example, $x^2 = 4$ is a statement about the variable x, and $x^2 + y^2 = 1$ is a statement about the variables x and y. We also have statements involving variables in computer programming. For example, we noted above that $x > 0$ is a statement whose truth or falsity can be determined by a computer. In natural language, we use variables in a more subtle way. Think of flipping two coins. "The result has heads on both coins" is clearly a statement about the process of flipping two coins, but only after we have flipped the coins do we know which of the four results in Figure 1 occurred.

Figure 1

Thus the word *result* is serving as a variable. In the language we often use in algebra, we could say that the result **varies** over the four possibilities in Figure 1. For our statement about coin flipping to make sense, it had to be made in the context of the *universe* of possible results shown in Figure 1.

The four outcomes shown in Figure 1 form the elements of a set. When we can give an unambiguous description of a collection of objects, we call that collection a **set.** A standard way to represent the set consisting of four outcomes in Figure 1 is {HH, HT, TH, TT}. This shows one unambiguous way to describe a set: make a list of its members. We enclose the list in braces to show where it starts and ends. The order of the list is irrelevant; {TH, HH, TT, HT} is the same set. Suppose we flip two coins three times in a row and get two heads first, two heads second, and two tails third. Then a list of all the outcomes is HH, HH, TT, but the set of outcomes is {HH, TT}. When we list the members of a set, we list each member just once. If we want to record more information, we keep track of our objects with a list, not a set. We use the notation HH $\in$ {HH, HT, TH, TT} to mean that HH is a member of the set listed inside the braces. We read $x \in S$ as "x is a member of S." We would write $H \notin$ {HH, HT, TH, TT} to mean that H is not one of the four members of this set. Another unambiguous way to describe a set is to give a statement that describes its members. Thus

$$\{x \mid x \text{ is a positive integer}\}$$

is a shorthand description of the set of positive integers. We read this as "the set of all x such that x is a positive integer." You may think of the vertical line as standing for "such that." All the statements we make will be about the members of some set. The **universe** for a statement or a discussion is the set whose members are being discussed. Thus we called Figure 1 our universe for coin flipping, and we may say that the natural numbers form our universe when we say, "3 plus 2 is 5." It is possible to make ridiculous statements about a universe, just as it is possible in everyday language. For example, the English sentence "The result has three heads" may be regarded as a statement about flipping a coin twice, but as a statement about this universe it is obviously false and certainly ridiculous.

B Symbolic Statements and Their Compounds

We shall now analyze the process of building statements from simpler ones. To talk about the process in general, it is convenient to use letters (usually p, q, r, or s) to stand for statements. To avoid confusion, we normally use different letters (usually w, x, y, or z) to stand for variables about which we are making statements. If we want to emphasize that a statement is about a variable x, we may use $p(x)$ rather than just p to stand for the statement. (We read $p(x)$ as "p of x" or "p about x.") Thus we can say either "Let p stand for '$x < 10$'" or "Let $p(x)$ be the statement '$x < 10$.'" In the language of algebra, we would say that $w,x,y,$ and z *vary over* our universe and that $p,q,r,$ and s *vary over* statements about our universe. We thus have two different kinds of variables: those that stand for statements and those that stand for members of the universe. We shall, however, consistently use the phrase *statement symbol* for a letter standing for a statement and the word *variable* for a letter standing for a member of our universe. When we say, "Let $p(x)$ stand for '$x < 10$,'" we are using $p(x)$ as our statement symbol and x as our variable. We could also say, "Let p stand for '$x < 10$'"—in this case, p is our statement symbol and x is still our variable.

Compound Statements

We have already mentioned that a computer can determine the truth or falsity of the compound statement "$x > 0$ and $x < 10$." Here we are using the word *and* to construct a new statement from simpler ones. It is traditional to use the symbol $\wedge$ to stand for the word *and*. In this notation, for example, if p stands for the statement "$x < 10$" and q stands for the statement "$x > 0$," then we may say "Let $s = p \wedge q$" in place of saying "Let s be the statement '$x < 10$ and $x > 0$.'" If our universe is the set of integers, then $p \wedge q$ is a way to say "x is a positive one-digit number."

We can also use the word *or* to construct statements from simpler ones. There are two ways the word *or* is used in English. The **inclusive** *or* is being used when someone says, "I will have coffee with breakfast or coffee with lunch." We agree that this statement is true if the person has coffee with one or both meals. We use the symbol $\vee$ to stand for the inclusive *or*. Thus, if p is the statement "I will have coffee with breakfast" and q is the statement "I will have coffee with lunch," we may say "Let $s = p \vee q$" instead of writing "Let s be the statement 'I will have coffee with breakfast or I will have coffee with lunch.'"

The second way the word *or* is used in English is as an **exclusive** *or*. For example, if we order a sundae with one scoop of ice cream, and the clerk behind the counter tells us, "You may have a scoop of vanilla ice cream or a scoop of chocolate ice cream," we know we must choose between the two alternatives—we may not have both. There are a number of traditional symbols for the exclusive *or*; the one we shall use is $\oplus$. Thus if p is the statement "You may have a scoop of vanilla ice cream" and q is the statement "You may have a scoop of chocolate ice cream," $p \oplus q$ stands for the statement "You may have a scoop of vanilla ice cream or you may have a scoop of chocolate ice cream, but not both." In mathematical English, the word *or* is taken to mean inclusive *or* unless there is an indication to the contrary (such as "but not both").

EXAMPLE 2   Let *p* stand for the statement "John drinks cola," and let *q* stand for the statement "John drinks root beer." Write symbolic compound statements using the symbols *p* and *q* that stand for the statements below.

(a) John drinks cola and John drinks root beer.
(b) John drinks cola or John drinks root beer (but not both).

Solution $p \land q$ stands for the statement in (a), and $p \oplus q$ stands for the statement in (b).   ∎

Negation

As well as allowing statements of the form "*p* and *q*" and of the form "*p* or *q*," computer languages typically allow us to determine the truth or falsity of statements of the form "not *p*." Thus, for example, the statement "not $(x < 2)$" is interpreted as "*x* is not less than 2." We shall use the symbol $\neg$ to stand for the word *not*. Thus, if *p* stands for the statement "*x* is less than 2," then $\neg p$ stands for "It is not the case that $x < 2$" or "*x* is not less than 2."

Symbolic Statements

We refer to p, $\neg p$, $p \land q$, $p \oplus q$, and so on as *symbolic statements*.

> A string of symbols that can stand for a statement
> is called a **symbolic statement**.

In a more advanced discussion of logic, symbolic statements would be called *logical formulas*.

> The symbols $\land$, $\lor$, $\oplus$, and $\neg$ are called
> **connective symbols.**
> Symbolic statements containing these symbols are
> called **symbolic compound statements.**

For example, $p \land (q \oplus r)$ is a symbolic compound statement. If we wish to have a single symbol to stand for this symbolic statement, we may write "Let $s = p \land (q \oplus r)$."

EXAMPLE 3   Let *p* stand for the statement "George is at school," let *q* stand for the statement "Sue is at the store," and let *r* stand for the statement "Maria is on the phone." Write the following as symbolic statements.

(a) George is at school or Sue is at the store.
(b) Maria is not on the phone or Sue is at the store.
(c) George is at school and either Maria is on the phone or Sue is at the store.

Solution

(a) $p \lor q$.

(b) $(\neg r) \lor q$.

(c) $p \land (r \lor q)$. Notice that using *either . . . or,* rather than *or* by itself, is a method we use in conversational English to show the order in which the *and* and *or* connectives are to be used. Also notice that the parentheses are essential here in order to avoid ambiguity.   ■

In part (b) of the example, we used parentheses around $\neg r$ for clarity. That is like writing $(-1) \div 4$ for $-1 \div 4$ in arithmetic. According to the standard rules most people use for parentheses, the expression $\neg r \lor q$ is always interpreted as $(\neg r) \lor q$, never as $\neg (r \lor q)$. The standard ways to express this rule are that the $\neg$ sign applies to the first complete statement to its right or, alternatively, to the smallest number of symbols to its right that make sense. For example, r stands for a complete statement, so we interpret $\neg r \lor q$ as $(\neg r) \lor q$. Alternatively, because it makes sense to write $\neg r$, we interpret $\neg r \lor q$ as $(\neg r) \lor q$, and the parentheses are optional. On the other hand, in the symbolic statement $\neg (p \land q) \lor r$, $(p \land q)$ is the first complete statement to the right of the $\neg$ sign, so $\neg (p \land r) \lor r$ is interpreted as $[\neg (p \land q)] \lor r$. This rule is called a **precedence rule;** we say that the operator $\neg$ takes precedence over all other operators. In arithmetic, we say that multiplication takes precedence over addition. In writing symbolic statements, many people assume that *and* takes precedence over *or*, but we shall not make this assumption. We shall always provide enough parentheses to avoid ambiguity.

EXAMPLE 4   Let p, q, and r stand for the same statements as in Example 3. Rewrite the symbolic statements below in grammatical English.

(a) $p \land (\neg q)$. Note: this has the same meaning as $p \land \neg q$.

(b) $r \lor (p \land q)$.

(c) $(\neg p) \land (\neg q)$. Note: this has the same meaning as $\neg p \land \neg q$.

Solution

(a) George is at school and Sue is not at the store.

(b) Maria is on the phone or both George is at school and Sue is at the store. (Note how the word *both* acts like parentheses).

(c) George is not at school and Sue is not at the store. Another answer is: Neither is George at school nor is Sue at the store.   ■

◧ *Truth Sets and Equivalence*

As we saw in Part A, we might use the statement $(x > 1) \land (x < 5)$ about integers in a computer program. Someone else trying to do the same thing might write the statement $(x = 2) \lor (x = 3) \lor (x = 4)$. We see intuitively that these two compound statements are true in exactly the same circumstances. For our purposes, they are equivalent. In order to make good use of the idea of equivalence for statements about variables, we need to make this intuition precise.

Truth Sets

To say that $p(x)$ and $q(x)$ are true in exactly the same circumstances means that each value of x that makes $p(x)$ true also makes $q(x)$ true, and vice versa.

> The set of all values of x in our universe that
> make $p(x)$ true is called the **truth set** of p.

> Two statements about variables are **equivalent** if
> they have exactly the same truth sets.

We write $p(x) \Leftrightarrow q(x)$ as a shorthand for "p and q are equivalent." It is traditional to use an uppercase letter (such as P) to stand for the truth set of the statement denoted by the corresponding lowercase letter (such as p). If p is the statement "The result has one head" about the universe of results of two flips of a coin, then the truth set P of p is {HT, TH}. If q is the statement, "The result has two heads," then the truth set Q of q is {HH}.

One way to show that two such statements are equivalent is to write down the truth set of each and verify that the two sets have exactly the same members. As an example, if we are discussing flipping a coin three times, we can observe that the truth sets of "The result has exactly two heads" and of "The result has exactly one tail" are the same by checking each sequence as below.

Identify sequences with exactly two heads:

HHH   HHT   HTH   THH   HTT   THT   TTH   TTT

Identify sequences with exactly one tail:

HHH   HHT   HTH   THH   HTT   THT   TTH   TTT

This demonstrates convincingly that the two truth sets are equal. In some cases, we can demonstrate that two sets are equal without explicitly writing down representations of the sets. This lets us show that two statements are equivalent even if their truth sets are infinite or so large that we are unwilling to write them down.

For example, consider the possibility of flipping a coin 300 times. You certainly believe that the statement p, "The result has exactly two heads," and the statement q, "The result has exactly 298 tails," are equivalent. However, the method of explicitly writing down all outcomes and circling those in our set would require writing down 2^{300} sequences of H's and T's. (The number 2^{300} is larger than 1 followed by 90 zeros. One way to appreciate the size of this number is to think about how many zeros follow the one in a million, a billion, a trillion, and so on.) How do we convince ourselves that the truth sets of our two statements are indeed equal? Let P be the truth set of p and Q be the truth set of q. Each sequence in either P or Q represents 300 coin flips, so for each sequence the number of H's plus the number of T's must be 300. Now suppose x is a result in P. Then x is a sequence of H's and T's that has two H's. By subtracting, we find that x has 298 T's. Therefore every x in P is also in Q. Now suppose y is an element of Q. Then, by definition, y is a sequence of H's and T's that has 298 T's. By subtraction, y has 2 H's. Thus every y in Q is also in P. Therefore P and Q have exactly the same elements, so that P and Q are the same set. This suggests the **Fundamental Principle of Set Equality:**

> To show that the sets S and T are equal, we may
> show that each element of S is an element of T
> and each element of T is an element of S.

Notation for Sets

We have already used the notation

$$\{x \mid x \text{ is a positive integer}\}$$

to stand for the set of positive integers. This suggests a notation for the truth set of some arbitrary statement $s(x)$ about an element x of a universe. We might write

$$\{x \mid s(x) \text{ is true}\}$$

to stand for the truth set of $s(x)$. If $s(x)$ is the statement "x is a positive integer," however, we would be writing

$$\{x \mid x \text{ is a positive integer is true}\}$$

There is obvious redundancy of language here; to avoid it we can agree to write

$$\{x \mid s(x)\}$$

to stand for the truth set of $s(x)$. This will be our standard notation for truth sets when we want to emphasize the dependence on a variable. It is called **set-builder notation.** (Notice that you can read the braces as "the set of all" and the vertical line as "such that.") When we use a lowercase letter (such as s) alone to stand for a statement, then we will use the corresponding uppercase letter (such as S) to stand for the truth set.

Concepts Review

1. A step-by-step process is called a(n) _____ process.

2. An instruction to do one thing if a statement is true and another thing if a statement is false is called a(n) _____ instruction.

3. An unambiguous declarative sentence is called a(n) _____.

4. A statement must be _____ or _____.

5. The statement "$x \geq 5$" contains a _____.

6. The variable in the statement "The answer key contains two errors" is the phrase _____ _____.

7. The set we are discussing when we make a statement is called the _____ for that statement.

8. The set of elements of the universe that make a statement true is the _____ _____ of the statement.

9. Two statements that have the same truth set are _____.

10. To show that two sets S and T are equal, we show that each element of S is a(n) _____ of T and _____ _____ of T is a(n) _____ of S.

11. $\{x \,|\, s(x)\}$ stands for the set of all x such that $s(x)$ is _____.

Exercises

A   1. Determine whether each of the following sentences is a statement. Notice that one does not need to know what the phrase *binary representation* means in order to determine which sentences are statements.
   (a) The decimal representation of thirteen is 13.
   (b) The decimal representation of thirteen is 15.
   (c) Is the binary representation of three 11?
   (d) Binary representations of numbers are more interesting than decimal representations.
   (e) The decimal representation of thirteen is *cat*.

2. Determine whether each of the following sentences is a statement.
   (a) A teaspoon of sugar dissolves in a 5-ounce cup of coffee.
   (b) An iron nail dissolves in a 5-ounce cup of coffee.
   (c) Coffee tastes better than tea.
   (d) Is coffee consumption harmful to health?
   (e) Caffeine occurs naturally in coffee.

3. For each of the following sentences, the word *result* varies over the universe of outcomes from three flips of a coin. Determine which of the sentences is a statement about the result.
   (a) The result has heads three times.
   (b) The result has tails four times.
   (c) The result has more heads than tails.
   (d) The result is surprising.

4. In the sentences below, the symbol x is allowed to vary over the positive integers (the positive counting numbers). Determine which sentences are statements.
   (a) It is harder to compute x^2 than $x + x + x + x$.
   (b) $x^2 > 0$.
   (c) $x^2 = -1$.
   (d) $(x + 2)(x - 2) = 0$.
   (e) Is $x^2 = 4$?

5. Consider the experiment of flipping a coin three times. Using sequences of letters such as HTH for heads on the first flip, tails on the second, and heads on the third, write down the universe of all possible outcomes of the experiment.

6. Imagine you have a penny, a nickel, and a dime in your pocket. You reach in and remove a coin. Then you reach in and remove another. Using pairs of letters like *PN* for removing first a penny then a nickel, write down the elements of the universe of all possible results. Now assume that you put the first coin back before withdrawing the second one; write down the universe of all possible results.

7. Write a description of how you would tell a child who knows the addition tables for numbers from zero to ten how to add two two-digit numbers.

8. Write a description of how you would tell a child who knows how to subtract one-digit numbers from larger numbers how to subtract a two-digit number from a larger number.

B

9. Let p be the statement "Paul has blond hair," and let q be the statement "Cora has red hair." Write the following statements in grammatical English.
   (a) $p \vee q$
   (b) $p \wedge q$
   (c) $\neg p$
   (d) $p \oplus q$

10. Let p be the statement "Columbus was a genius," and let q be the statement "The *Mayflower* was a yacht." Write the following statements in grammatical English.
    (a) $p \wedge q$
    (b) $\neg q$
    (c) $p \vee q$
    (d) $p \oplus q$

11. Convert the following statements into symbolic form, using p for "Maria has graduated" and q for "George is studying abroad."
    (a) Maria has graduated and George is studying abroad.
    (b) Maria has graduated or George is studying abroad.
    (c) George is not studying abroad.
    (d) Either George is studying abroad or Maria has graduated, but not both.

12. Convert the following statements into symbolic form, using p for $x < -1$ and q for $x^2 > 2$.
    (a) $x^2 > 2$ or $x < -1$, but not both
    (b) $x < -1$ or $x^2 > 2$
    (c) $x < -1$ and $x^2 > 2$
    (d) $x^2 \leq 2$

13. Let p be the statement "Tom is home," let q be the statement "Dinner is served," and let r be the statement "The house is cold." Write down in symbolic form the statements below. Remember that the mathematical interpretation of the word *or* is the inclusive *or*. To say $p \oplus q$ in mathematical English, we must say something equivalent to "p or q, but not both."
    (a) Tom is home and dinner is served.
    (b) Tom is not home and the house is cold.

(c) Dinner is not served or Tom is not home.

(d) Dinner is served and either Tom is not home or the house is cold (or both). (Remember: *p* and either *q* or *r* is a way of saying *p* and (*q* or *r*) in English.)

(e) Tom is home or both dinner is served and the house is cold. (Note again how the *both* in "both *p* and *q*" parenthesizes the statement "*p* and *q*" in English.)

(f) Tom is not home or dinner is served or both the house is not cold and Tom is home.

14. Let *p* be the statement "The company is arriving," let *q* be the statement "The roast is raw," and let *r* be the statement "The potatoes are done." Write the following statements in symbolic form. (Assume that a roast is either raw or done.) See the remarks about the inclusive *or* and about *either* and *both* in the previous problem.

(a) The company is arriving and the roast is raw.

(b) The company is arriving or the potatoes are done.

(c) The potatoes are not done and the roast is raw.

(d) Company is arriving and either the potatoes are done or the roast is raw.

(e) The roast is done or both the company is arriving and the potatoes are not done.

(f) Company is arriving or both the roast is raw and either the potatoes are done or company is arriving.

15. Let *p*, *q*, and *r* be the statements of Exercise 13. Rewrite the following statements in English.

(a) $q \lor r$
(b) $q \land r$
(c) $q \land \neg r$
(d) $q \land (r \lor p)$
(e) $p \lor (r \land q)$
(f) $p \lor (\neg r \land q)$

16. Let *p*, *q*, and *r* be the statements of Exercise 14. Rewrite the following statements in English.

(a) $p \land r$
(b) $q \lor r$
(c) $p \land (q \lor r)$
(d) $p \lor (q \land r)$
(e) $p \land \neg(q \lor r)$
(f) $p \lor (q \lor \neg r)$

C 17. Write down five members of each of the following sets.

(a) $\{x \mid x \text{ is a square of an integer}\}$

(b) $\{x \mid x = 2^y \text{ for some positive integer } y\}$

(c) $\{x \mid x \text{ is an English word with four letters}\}$

18. Write down five members of each of the following sets.

(a) $\{x \mid x \text{ is a cube of an integer}\}$

(b) $\{x \mid x = 3^y \text{ for some positive integer } y\}$

(c) $\{x \mid x \text{ is an English word whose letters appear in alphabetical order}\}$

19. In my pocket there are one nickel, two dimes, and two quarters. I reach in and pull out a coin. Then I reach in and pull out another coin. Using a notation such as *ND* to stand for getting first a nickel then a dime and *QN* for getting first a quarter then a nickel, do the following:

(a) Write down the universe of possible results.

(b) Show the truth set of the statement "I got a total of at least 30 cents," by circling the members of this truth set.

(c) Show the truth set of the statement "I got a dime first," by drawing boxes around the members of this truth set.

20. We remove the ace, king, queen, and jack of spades from an ordinary deck of cards. Using these four cards, we draw a first and second card. Using a notation such as *AK* for getting first the ace then the king, do the following:
    (a) Write down the universe of possible results.
    (b) Show the truth set of the statement "One card we drew was the ace," by circling its members.
    (c) Show the truth set of "We got a king or queen," by drawing boxes around its members.

21. Use the fundamental principle of set equality to show that the set of all results of drawing at least 30 cents in Exercise 19 is equal to the set of all results with at least one quarter.

22. Use the fundamental principle of set equality to show that the set of all results with two face cards in Exercise 20 is equal to the set of all results with no aces.

23. Redo Exercise 19 assuming that I return the first coin to my pocket before drawing the second.

24. Redo Exercise 20 assuming that we return the first card to the' deck before drawing the second.

25. A "word" on a 16-bit computer is a sequence of 16 zeros and ones (called *bits*). Show that the truth set of "This word has exactly 4 ones" equals the truth set of "This word has exactly 12 zeros." Interpret this as a result about equivalence.

26. A "word" on a 16-bit computer is described in Exercise 25. Show that the statement "This word has an even number of ones" is equivalent to "This word has an even number of zeros."

Problems

1. Suppose *U* is the universe of results of flipping a coin twice. Consider the sentence "This sentence about *U* is ambiguous." Is this a statement about *U*?

2. A standard assumption in mathematical work is that whatever universe we are considering does not contain statements about itself. How does this help us avoid deciding whether or not "This sentence is not a statement" is or is not a statement about our universe? Why is it useful to avoid this decision?

3. Other words besides *and, or,* and *not* can be used to connect statements in English to form new statements. From a logical point of view, is the sentence "*p* but *q*" any different from the sentence "*p* and *q*"?

4. Suppose *p* and *q* are statements about a universe *U* with truth sets *P* and *Q*. Can a member of *U* that is not in both the set *P* and the set *Q* make the statement $p \wedge q$ true? Can a member of *U* that is in both the set *P* and the set *Q* make $p \wedge q$ false? How is the truth set of $p \wedge q$ related to the sets *P* and *Q*?

5. Explain how a system of simultaneous equations is a compound statement. How are the truth set of the statement and the solution set of the system of equations related? In terms of their solutions, what does it mean to say that two different systems of equations about the same numerical variables *x, y* and *z* are equivalent as statements?

Section 1-2
Sets

A   Venn Diagrams and Set Operations

There is a convenient kind of diagram, called a **Venn diagram,** that we can use to visualize sets chosen from a universe U. We first draw a rectangle to represent U; inside it we draw circles or other shapes (which we may shade in) to represent sets. Venn diagrams of two sets with elements in common are shown in Figure 2 and Figure 3. (Figure 9, which we shall discuss later, shows a Venn diagram for two sets with no elements in common.)

Figure 2   A Venn diagram for two sets with elements in common.

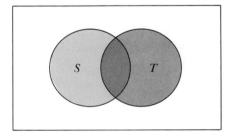

The fact that the two circles in Figure 2 overlap means that the sets they represent have elements in common.

The **intersection** of S and T, denoted by $S \cap T$,
consists of the elements S and T have in common.

In Figure 2, $S \cap T$ is represented by the region shaded.

EXAMPLE 5   A mathematics department is studying the effect of learning some calculus in high school on students' performance in a later course. The set of students who took at least some of their calculus in high school is S = {Adams, Gomez, Nakamura, O'Connor, Wilson}. The set of students who took at least some of their calculus in college is T = {Baker, Nakamura, Smith, Wilson, Wong}. Find $S \cap T$ and explain in words which students it consists of.

Solution   By definition, $S \cap T$ = {Nakamura, Wilson} because Nakamura and Wilson are the only two elements the sets have in common. It is the set of students who have studied some calculus in both high school and college.   ■

Figure 3   The union of two sets is represented by the shaded area.

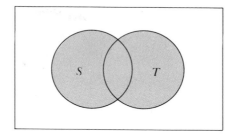

The **union** $S \cup T$ of two sets S and T is the set of
elements in one or the other or both the sets.

In Figure 3, $S \cup T$ is represented by the region shaded.

EXAMPLE 6   If S = {Adams, Gomez, Nakamura, O'Connor, Wilson} and T = {Baker, Nakamura, Smith, Wilson, Wong}, find $S \cup T$.

Solution   By definition, $S \cup T$ = {Adams, Baker, Gomez, Nakamura, O'Connor, Smith, Wilson, Wong}.   ■

Figure 4   A Venn diagram for the complement of a set.

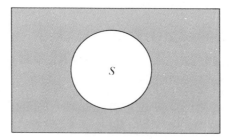

The **complement** of a set S chosen from a universe U
consists of those elements of U that are not in S.

The complement of S is sometimes denoted by S^c, sometimes by $\overline{S}$, sometimes by S', sometimes by $-S$, and sometimes by $\sim S$. We shall use $\sim S$. In Figure 4, the set $\sim S$ is represented by the shaded region. If S and T are sets, then the **set difference** $S \sim T$ consists of the elements of S not in T. Thus $\sim T = U \sim T$. In Figure 5, $S \sim T$ is represented by the region shaded. Notice in Figure 5 that $S \sim T = S \cap (\sim T)$.

Figure 5

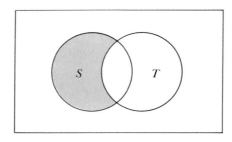

EXAMPLE 7   The mathematics department in Examples 5 and 6 is interested especially in the students who learned all their calculus in high school. This set of students is the set $S \sim T$. Find $S \sim T$.

Solution   To find $S \sim T$, we must remove from S each and every element of T that is also in S. This gives $S \sim T = \{$Adams, Gomez, O'Connor$\}$. ∎

There are a number of important relationships among the operations of complementation, union, and intersection. Among them are **DeMorgan's set laws:**

$$\sim(P \cup Q) = (\sim P) \cap (\sim Q)$$

and

$$\sim(P \cap Q) = (\sim P) \cup (\sim Q)$$

How do we demonstrate the validity of equations like these? We use the fundamental principle of set equality, as shown in Example 8.

EXAMPLE 8   Prove that $\sim(P \cup Q) = \sim P \cap \sim Q$.

Solution   We use our principle that $S = T$ if every element of S is an element of T, and vice versa.

Let $x \in \sim(P \cup Q)$. This means that x is not in $P \cup Q$. By the definition of union, x is not in either P or Q. Thus $x \in \sim P$ and $x \in \sim Q$, so $x \in \sim P \cap \sim Q$ by definition. Thus each x in $\sim(P \cup Q)$ is in $\sim P \cap \sim Q$.

Now let $x \in \sim P \cap \sim Q$. Then $x \in \sim P$ and $x \in \sim Q$. Thus x is not in P and x is not in Q (so it is not in both P and Q either). Therefore x is not in $P \cup Q$, so $x \in \sim(P \cup Q)$. Thus each x in $\sim P \cap \sim Q$ is in $\sim(P \cup Q)$.

By the fundamental principle of set equality, we conclude that $\sim(P \cup Q) = \sim P \cap \sim Q$. ∎

B   Set Operations and Logical Connectives

The notation we use for the set operations union, intersection, and complementation is quite similar to our notation for the logical connectives *and, or,* and *not*. This similarity is intentional; Theorem 1 shows us why. The proof of Theorem 1 gives us another example of how to use the fundamental principle of set equality. (When a proof of a theorem illustrates an important idea, we shall say so.)

Theorem 1   Let p and q be statements and let P and Q be their truth sets. Then

(a) $P \cap Q$ is the truth set of $p \wedge q$.
(b) $P \cup Q$ is the truth set of $p \vee q$.
(c) $\sim P$ is the truth set of $\neg p$.

Proof   We prove only part (a); parts (b) and (c) are proved similarly. First, suppose x is in $P \cap Q$. We shall show that x is in the truth set of $p \wedge q$. Since x is in $P \cap Q$, it is in P and it is in Q. Thus x makes p true and x makes q true. Then x makes $p \wedge q$ true, so x is in the truth set of $p \wedge q$.

Now suppose x is in the truth set of $p \wedge q$. We shall show that x is in $P \cap Q$. Because x makes $p \wedge q$ true, it must make p true and it must make q true. Therefore x is in P and x is in Q. Therefore x is in $P \cap Q$.

Thus $P \cap Q$ and the truth set of $p \wedge q$ have exactly the same elements, so they are the same set.   ∎

Theorem 1 shows why we have made the choice of notation we are using. To convert a logical expression to a set expression, we change all the lowercase statement symbols to uppercase set symbols and the angular connective symbols $\wedge$, $\vee$, and $\neg$ to the curvy connective symbols $\cap$, $\cup$, and $\sim$, respectively. The connection between set operations and logical connectives lets us illustrate facts about equivalence of statements. For example, in Section 1-3 we shall show directly that the symbolic statement $p \wedge (q \vee r)$ is equivalent to the symbolic statement $(p \wedge q) \vee (p \wedge r)$. In this section we shall see how the connection between set operations and logical connectives lets us use Venn diagrams to demonstrate this equivalence. If p, q, and r stand for statements about a variable x, then there is a truth set P for p, a truth set Q for q, and a truth set R for r. By Theorem 1, the truth set for $p \wedge (q \vee r)$ is $P \cap (Q \cup R)$, and the truth set for $(p \wedge q) \vee (p \wedge r)$ is $(P \cap Q) \cup (P \cap R)$. From our definition of equivalence, we see that $p \wedge (q \vee r)$ is equivalent to $(p \wedge q) \vee (p \wedge r)$ if and only if $P \cap (Q \cup R)$ equals $(P \cap Q) \cup (P \cup R)$. (Notice in the last sentence when we talked about statements we used the angular signs $\wedge$ and $\vee$ and the word *equivalent*, but when we talked about sets we used the curved signs $\cap$ and $\cup$ and the word *equals*.) We can use a Venn diagram to visualize the distributive law $P \cap (Q \cup R) = (P \cap Q) \cup (P \cap R)$ for sets; the connection between sets and statements means we are also visualizing the distributive law $p \wedge (q \vee r) \Leftrightarrow (p \wedge q) \vee (p \wedge r)$ for statements. In Figure 6, we show how Venn diagrams for three overlapping sets P, Q, and R may be shaded in to demonstrate the set equality. In Figure 6(a), we shaded both Q and R in gray. Thus $Q \cup R$ is shaded in gray. Next we shade P in color. This means that the region in both P and $Q \cup R$ is shaded in both ways. This region represents $P \cap (Q \cup R)$. That is, $P \cap (Q \cup R)$ is represented by the region shaded in both ways.

In part (b) of Figure 6, $P \cap Q$ is shaded in color and $P \cap R$ is shaded in gray, so that $(P \cap Q) \cup (P \cap R)$ is the entire shaded region in (b). Since the entire shaded region in (b) corresponds to the doubly shaded region in (a), we see that $(P \cap Q) \cup (P \cap R)$ is equal to $P \cap (Q \cup R)$. This shows that the truth set of $(p \wedge q) \vee (p \wedge r)$ equals the truth set of $p \wedge (q \vee r)$. Thus it shows that $(p \wedge q) \vee (p \wedge r)$ and $p \wedge (q \vee r)$ are equivalent.

Figure 6   In (a), the region representing $P \cap (Q \cup R)$ is shaded in both color and gray.
In (b), the region representing $(P \cap Q) \cup (P \cap R)$ is the entire shaded region.

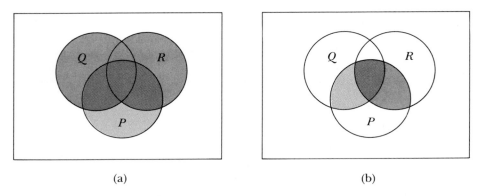

(a)   (b)

The example we have just completed shows how Venn diagrams can give illustrations of complex relationships among sets. The main idea is to represent an expression involving unions, intersections, and complements of two or three sets by using shading to indicate the results of various set operations. When we use Venn diagrams to demonstrate that two sets are equal, it is important that the drawing be consistent with any assumptions we are making. For example, if P and Q are sets that may have elements in common, we must draw overlapping circles to represent P and Q

EXAMPLE 9   Draw a Venn diagram and shade in the region representing the set $P \cup (Q \cap \sim R)$.

Solution   This diagram requires three mutually overlapping circles, as shown in Figure 7(a). In Figure 7(b), we have shaded in color to indicate the set $\sim R$. In Figure 7(c), we have shaded in gray to indicate the region $Q \cap \sim R$; this region is the part of Q shaded as part of $\sim R$. Now in Figure 7(d), we use dots in both the gray region and the region representing P. The dotted region represents $P \cup (Q \cap \sim R)$.   ∎

Figure 7

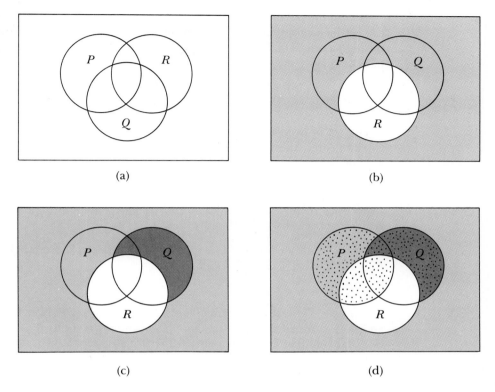

C Subsets

> We say that a set S is a **subset** of the set T
> if each element of S is an element of T.

If S is a subset of T we may say that S *is included in T*. Figure 8 shows a Venn diagram of such a pair of sets.

Figure 8

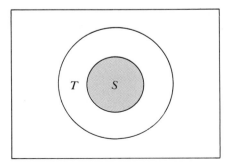

We use the notation $S \subseteq T$ to say that S is a subset of T. The symbol $\subseteq$ is called the **set inclusion** symbol. Note that for every set S, S satisfies the condition that makes it a subset of S, so we have $S \subseteq S$. Notice also that the Fundamental Principle of Set Equality may be rephrased thus:

> To show that two sets S and T are equal, we may
> show that $S \subseteq T$ and $T \subseteq S$.

The set of even numbers is a subset of the set of natural numbers. When we flip two coins, the set of results with no tails is a subset of the set of results with at least one head.

EXAMPLE 10   Let $S = \{a,b,c,d\}$. Let $T = \{a,c,d,e\}$, $R = \{c,d\}$, and $P = \{a,c,d\}$. Which of these sets is a subset of which others?

Solution   Neither S nor T is a subset of any other of the sets. However, $R \subseteq P$, $P \subseteq S$, $P \subseteq T$, $R \subseteq S$, and $R \subseteq T$ as well.   ∎

Example 10 illustrates a fundamental law about subsets. Note that $R \subseteq P$, $P \subseteq T$, and $R \subseteq T$ are all true. In fact, from the two observations $R \subseteq P$ and $P \subseteq T$, we can conclude that every element of R is also an element of T. The **transitive law** states that whenever $R \subseteq P$ and $P \subseteq T$, then $R \subseteq T$ as well. The idea of transitivity will come up again when we study relations.

Relationships between Sets

Notice that the symbolic expressions

$$R \subseteq S \quad \text{or} \quad R = S$$

describe relationships between sets, whereas the symbolic expressions

$$R \cup S \quad \text{or} \quad R \cap S$$

describe operations that give new sets from old ones. The relationship of set inclusion interacts with the set operations, however, as we summarize in Theorem 2. Figures 2, 3, and 8 illustrate the theorem. The proof of Theorem 2 illustrates two fundamental ideas. Part (a) of the proof illustrates how to use the definition of $S \subseteq T$. Part (c) illustrates both this idea and a second major idea. Notice the phrase *if and only if* in part (c). We shall analyze the exact meaning of this phrase later on. For now, our knowledge of English or experience from a course such as geometry tells us that to prove the statement "$R \cup S = S$ if and only if $R \subseteq S$," we must prove that $R \cup S = S$ if $R \subseteq S$ and also prove that $R \cup S = S$ only if $R \subseteq S$.

Theorem 2 Let R and S be sets. Then

  (a) R and S are subsets of $R \cup S$.
  (b) $R \cap S$ is a subset of both R and S.
  (c) $R \cup S = S$ if and only if $R \subseteq S$.
  (d) $R \cap S = R$ if and only if $R \subseteq S$.

Proof

  (a) Since $R \cup S$ consists of the elements of R or S or both, every element of R is also an element of $R \cup S$. Thus $R \subseteq R \cup S$.
  (b) Similar to (a).
  (c) We prove first that $R \cup S = S$ if $R \subseteq S$. For this purpose, assume that $R \subseteq S$. We know already that $S \subseteq R \cup S$. Thus, by the fundamental principle of set equality, if we can also show that $R \cup S \subseteq S$, we will know that $R \cup S = S$. In order to show that each element of $R \cup S$ is an element of S, we suppose x is in $R \cup S$. Then, by the definition of union, x is in R or x is in S. But since $R \subseteq S$, if $x \in R$, then $x \in S$. Thus $x \in S$ in either case. We have just shown that each x in $R \cup S$ is also in S; in symbols, $R \cup S \subseteq S$. This means that $R \cup S = S$.

  Now we prove that $R \cup S = S$ only if $R \subseteq S$. For this purpose, we must show that whenever $R \cup S = S$ holds, then $R \subseteq S$ holds as well. Thus we assume that $R \cup S = S$. However, from part (a) we have $R \subseteq R \cup S$, and since $R \cup S = S$, by substitution we get $R \subseteq S$.
  (d) Similar to (c). ∎

In the proof of Theorem 2, part (c), we illustrated with the sets $R \cup S$ and S how we prove that one set is a subset of another: we show that each x in the first set is also in the second. Example 11 below contains a second example of how to show one set is a subset of another. Notice that the $\subseteq$ sign in Example 11 describes a relationship between the set to its left and the set to its right. The $\subseteq$ is used in expressions involving sets in much the same way the $\leq$ sign is used in expressions involving integers.

EXAMPLE 11 Show that $R \cap (S \cup T) \subseteq S \cup (R \cap T)$.

Solution We must show that each x in $R \cap (S \cup T)$ is also in $S \cup (R \cap T)$. Thus we reason as follows:

  Let $x \in R \cap (S \cup T)$. Then x is in both R and $S \cup T$ by definition. Since x is in $S \cup T$, x is in S or x is in T. This gives us two cases. In the case that x is in S, we get that $x \in S \cup (R \cap T)$ by the definition of union. In the case that x is in T, we get that $x \in R \cap T$ by the definition of intersection and the observation above that $x \in R$. Then, once again, we get $x \in S \cup (R \cap T)$ by the definition of union. Thus in either case, $x \in S \cup (R \cap T)$. Thus each x in $R \cap (S \cup T)$ is in $S \cup (R \cap T)$ as well, so

$$R \cap (S \cup T) \subseteq S \cup (R \cap T) \qquad \blacksquare$$

The Empty Set

Suppose we consider the statements $x > 1$ and $x < 0$ about the universe of natural numbers. The compound statement $(x > 1) \wedge (x < 0)$ is false for every x. Thus its truth set has no elements!

> In order to deal with situations where a truth set has no elements, we use a special set called the **empty set** or **null set,** which has no elements.

Our notation for the empty set is $\varnothing$. (This is the Scandinavian letter pronounced like the o in *work* or the u in *null,* not the Greek phi. It is most convenient to read the symbol $\varnothing$ as "empty.") Thus if P is the truth set of "$x > 1$," and Q is the truth set of "$x < 0$," we would write

$$P \cap Q = \varnothing$$

> We say that two sets S and T are **disjoint** if $S \cap T = \varnothing$.

Thus the truth sets P and Q we just described are disjoint. A Venn diagram of two disjoint sets is shown in Figure 9.

Figure 9

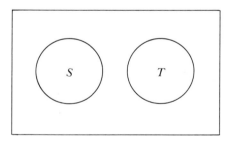

Although the empty set might seem strange at first, it is quite easy to work with. For example, for any set S, $S \cup \varnothing = S$, by the definition of union, and $S \cap \varnothing = \varnothing$, by the definition of intersection. From Theorem 2, we see that this means that $\varnothing \subseteq S$ for every set S.

So far, we have only discussed truth sets of statements about variables. Thus if our universe is the set N of natural numbers, a statement such as

$$(2 + 2 = 4) \wedge (x = x)$$

has the set N as its truth set, but we have not discussed a truth set for a statement such as $2 + 2 = 4$. Some people would say that this statement is true no matter what the (unwritten) variable x stands for, so its truth set is the universe. Others would say that its truth set is so far undefined. Either point of view is valid. In order to allow us the convenience of mixing statements about variables with statements not about variables, we now define truth sets for statements without variables for those who take the second point of view. We define the truth set of a *true* statement about members of a universe U to be the set U itself and the truth set of a *false* statement about members of a universe U to be the empty set.

Concepts Review

1. The _____ of two sets consists of the elements they have in common.

2. The _____ of two sets consists of the elements in at least one of them.

3. The _____ of a set chosen from a universe U consists of the elements in U but not the set.

4. The set of elements in S but not in T is denoted by _____.

5. The sets $S \sim T$ and $S \cap (\sim T)$ are _____.

6. If P is the truth set of p and Q is the truth set of q, then $P \cap Q$ is the truth set of _____.

7. If P is the truth set of p and Q is the truth set of q, then $P \cup Q$ is the truth set of _____.

8. If P is the truth set of p, then $\sim P$ is the truth set of _____.

9. In a discussion of sets and statements, the curved symbols ($\cup$, $\cap$, $\sim$) always go with _____, and the angular symbols ($\vee$, $\wedge$, $\neg$) always go with _____.

10. If every element of S is also an element of T, then S is called a(n) _____ of T.

11. The symbol $\subseteq$ stands for a(n) _____ between sets, whereas the symbol $\cap$ stands for a(n) _____ on sets.

12. The _____ law says that if $S \subseteq T$ and $T \subseteq W$, then $S \subseteq W$.

13. A set with no elements is called the _____ set.

14. Two sets S and T are _____ if $S \cap T = \emptyset$.

Exercises

A In Exercises 1–20 below, let $P = \{a,b,c,d,e,f\}$, $Q = \{a,c,e,g,i,k\}$, $R = \{a,d,g,k\}$, $S = \{c,d,e,f,g,h\}$, and $T = \{d,e,f,g,h\}$. Let the universe U be the alphabet. For Exercises 1–20, find the sets given.

1. $P \cup Q$ 2. $P \cup R$

3. $P \cap Q$ 4. $P \cap R$

5. $P \cup S$ 6. $Q \cup S$

7. $P \cap S$

8. $Q \cap S$

9. $\sim P$

10. $\sim R$

11. $P \sim R$

12. $Q \sim T$

13. $P \cap (Q \cup R)$

14. $P \cup (Q \cap R)$

15. $P \cap (Q \sim S)$

16. $\sim(P \cup T)$

17. $(P \cap Q) \cup (P \cap R)$

18. $(P \cup Q) \cap (P \cup R)$

19. $(P \cap Q) \sim (P \cap S)$

20. $(\sim P) \cap (\sim T)$

21. By using the fundamental principle of set equality, show that $P \cap (Q \cup R) = (P \cap Q) \cup (P \cap R)$ for any sets P, Q, and R.

22. By using the fundamental principle of set equality, show that $\sim(P \cap Q) = \sim P \cup \sim Q$ for any sets P and Q.

B   Now let the letters P, Q, and R stand for arbitrary sets. In Exercises 23–42. draw Venn diagrams and shade in solidly the regions that represent the sets given.

23. $P \cap (\sim Q)$

24. $P \cup (\sim Q)$

25. $P \cap (P \cup Q)$

26. $P \cup (P \cap Q)$

27. $(P \sim Q) \cup (Q \sim P)$

28. $\sim(P \cup Q)$

29. $(P \cup Q) \sim (P \cap Q)$

30. $(\sim P) \cap (\sim Q)$

31. $(P \cap Q) \cap R$

32. $(P \cup Q) \cup R$

33. $P \cup (Q \cap R)$

34. $P \cap (Q \cap R)$

35. $(P \sim Q) \sim (Q \sim P)$

36. $(P \cup Q) \sim (P \cap Q)$

37. $(P \sim Q) \cap (P \cup R)$

38. $(P \sim Q) \cap (P \sim R)$

39. $P \sim (Q \cap R)$

40. $P \sim (Q \cup R)$

41. $(P \cup Q) \sim (Q \cap R)$

42. $(P \cup Q) \sim Q$

In Exercises 43–58, p, q, and r represent arbitrary statements. For each compound statement given, draw a Venn diagram in which you shade in the truth set of the statement given.

43. $p \wedge (\neg p \vee q)$

44. $p \vee (\neg p \wedge q)$

45. $p \wedge \neg(q \vee r)$

46. $p \vee \neg(q \wedge r)$

47. $p \vee (q \wedge r)$

48. $(p \wedge q) \vee (p \wedge r) \vee (q \wedge r)$

49. $p \vee (\neg p \wedge q)$

50. $(p \wedge \neg q) \vee (p \wedge \neg r)$

51. $p \vee (p \wedge (\neg q \vee \neg r))$

52. $(p \vee q) \wedge (p \vee \neg q)$

53. $(p \wedge \neg q) \vee (q \wedge \neg p)$

54. $p \wedge (q \vee r)$

55. Draw two Venn diagrams to represent the following set equalities.
    (a) $\sim(P \cap Q) = (\sim P) \cup (\sim Q)$ (This is one of DeMorgan's two set laws.)
    (b) $P \cup (Q \cap R) = (P \cup Q) \cap (P \cup R)$

56. Draw two Venn diagrams to represent the following set equalities.
    (a) $\sim(P \cup Q) = (\sim P) \cap (\sim Q)$ (This is one of DeMorgan's two set laws.)
    (b) $P \cap ((Q \cup R) \sim (Q \cap R)) = ((P \cap Q) \cup (P \cap R)) \sim (P \cap Q \cap R)$

57. Draw a Venn diagram that illustrates the equivalence $p \vee (q \wedge r) \Leftrightarrow (p \vee q) \wedge (p \wedge r)$.

58. Draw a Venn diagram that illustrates the equivalence $p \vee (q \vee r) \Leftrightarrow (p \vee q) \vee r$.

C 59. Let $P = \{1,2,5,7\}$, $Q = \{2,3,4,5\}$, $R = \{3,4,8,9\}$, $S = \{2,5\}$, and $T = \{1,2,3,4,5,6,7,8,9\}$. Which of these sets is a subset of which other sets?

60. Let $P = \{a,b,c,f\}$, $Q = \{b,d,e,f\}$, $R = \{a,c,d\}$, $S = \{c,d\}$, and $T = \{a,b,c,d,e,f,g\}$. Which of these sets is a subset of which other sets?

61. Which pairs of the sets P, Q, R, S, and T of Exercise 59 are disjoint?

62. Which pairs of the sets P, Q, R, S, and T in Exercise 60 are disjoint?

63. Which of the following statements about the universe of natural numbers have empty truth sets?
    (a) x is even or x is odd.
    (b) x is even and x is odd.
    (c) x is equal to $x^2 - 1$.
    (d) $x^2 = x$.

64. Which of the following statements about the universe of real numbers has an empty truth set?
    (a) $x^2 = 2$ (b) $x^2 + 2 = 1$
    (c) $x^2 > 1$ and $x < \frac{1}{2}$ (d) $x^2 > 1$ and $x^2 < \frac{1}{2}$

In Exercises 65–68, P, Q, and R stand for arbitrary sets. Demonstrate that the relationships given in these exercises hold.

65. $P \cap Q \subseteq P \cap (Q \cup \sim P)$

66. $(P \cup Q) \cap (\sim Q) \subseteq P \cup Q$

67. $(P \cap Q) \sim R \subseteq P \cap (Q \sim R)$

68. $(P \cap Q) \cup (P \cap R) \cup (Q \cap R) \subseteq (P \cup Q) \cap (P \cup R)$

Problems

1. Prove Theorem 1(b).   2. Prove Theorem 1(c).

3. Prove Theorem 2(b).   4. Prove Theorem 2(d).

5. Prove that $S \cup T = (S \sim T) \cup (S \cap T) \cup (T \sim S)$.

6. Find a symbolic statement using the statement symbols p and q with two operators whose truth set is $P \sim Q$.

7. Prove that $(P \sim Q) \cup (Q \sim P) = (P \cup Q) \sim (P \cap Q)$.

8. Give a symbolic statement with one connective symbol whose truth set is the set of Problem 7.

9. For any statement p, the truth set of $p \oplus p$ is empty. Why?

10. For any statement p about a universe U, what is the truth set of $p \oplus \neg p$? Why?

11. One place where set operations are, in effect, used in practical applications is the management of records. For example, a college registrar keeps track of the set of students in a course with an alphabetically ordered class list. In Chapters 5, 7, and 8, we shall see some relatively sophisticated ways of dealing with sets stored as alphabetical lists. Even without any sophisticated thinking, it is clear that keeping track of a set in a computer as a list in alphabetical order lets us determine whether a given student is in a given class by examining, on the average, only half the names in the class list instead of examining all the names on the list. Why is this? Write a computer program that reads as data an alphabetically ordered list of names, asks the user to type in a name, and then reads through the list to determine whether that name is on the class list. Now modify the program so that if the name is not on the list, the computer asks the user if the name should be added to the list, and if the response is yes, inserts the name in the proper place, moving all following names one place up in the list.

12. The set operations of union and intersection correspond to operations a college registrar (as in Problem 11) might need to perform on class lists. In particular, in order to schedule final exams, the registrar needs to know which courses have students in common. Thus the registrar needs to find the intersection of two sets represented by alphabetically ordered lists. It is possible to write a computer program that goes through the two lists and, by the time it has read each name on each list exactly once, prints out all the students the two lists have in common. Write a program that reads two alphabetically ordered lists as data and prints out their intersection in this way.

13. The registrar discussed in Problems 11 and 12 might also need to join two small sections of a course together into one big one. It is possible to write a computer program to go through two alphabetically ordered lists representing sets and print out an alphabetically ordered list representing the union after examining each name on each list only once. Write such a program that reads two alphabetically ordered lists as data and prints out their union in this way.

Section 1-3
Determining the Truth
of Symbolic Statements

A **Truth Tables**

The displays in Figures 10 and 11, called **truth tables**, show us how to determine the truth or falsity of a compound statement with one connective from the truth or falsity of the statements represented by its statement symbols. The top row of a truth table lists the statement symbols used in a compound statement and gives the compound statement. Each of the other rows describes a possible situation and begins by telling us which statement symbols represent true statements in that situation and which represent false statements. We call the top row the *zero row*, the next the *first row*, and so on.

Figure 10   Truth tables.

p	q	$p \oplus q$
T	T	F
T	F	T
F	T	T
F	F	F

(a)

p	q	$p \wedge q$
T	T	T
T	F	F
F	T	F
F	F	F

(b)

p	q	$p \vee q$
T	T	T
T	F	T
F	T	T
F	F	F

(c)

Figure 11   The truth table for negation.

p	$\neg p$
T	F
F	T

EXAMPLE 12   In what situations will the inclusive *or* and exclusive *or* have different truth values?

Solution   The first row of Figure 10(a) and Figure 10(c) end in different symbols, but the other rows are identical. Thus the inclusive *or* and the exclusive *or* have different truth values if and only if both their component statements are true. ∎

Notice that in order to compare two truth tables, we must know that *corresponding rows represent corresponding situations*. By always writing the row beginning TT first, then the TF row next, and so on in reverse alphabetical order, we can be sure that this is the case. Using T and F to stand for true and false and the reverse alphabetical order of the rows derives from the traditional notation of logic. We shall see later that electrical engineering applications suggest using 1 for true and 0 for false; sometimes people who choose this notation use a different standard ordering of the rows. The particular notation used is not important, but it is wise to be aware of the different notations and become comfortable with them.

EXAMPLE 13   Explain why the truth table for $p \wedge q$ contains the entries it does.

Solution   We know that "p and q" is true if and only if p and q are both true. Thus the TT row must end with a T and the other three rows must end with an F.   ■

Truth Tables for Other Compound Statements

For most compound statements, we can't immediately determine when they are true or false, as we did with $p \wedge q$. Thus we need a method to work out a truth table for them. In Figure 12, we illustrate such a method for the compound statement $\neg p \vee q$.

Figure 12

Step 1				
p	q	$\neg$	p	$\vee$	q
T	T		T		T
T	F		T		F
F	T		F		T
F	F		F		F
Step			1		1

Step 2				
p	q	$\neg$	p	$\vee$	q
T	T	F	T		T
T	F	F	T		F
F	T	T	F		T
F	F	T	F		F
Step		2	1		1

Step 3				
p	q	$\neg$	p	$\vee$	q
T	T	F	T	T	T
T	F	F	T	F	F
F	T	T	F	T	T
F	F	T	F	T	F
Step		2	1	3	1

There are three steps shown in Figure 12. In the first step, we wrote the truth values from below p and q on the left beneath the corresponding statement symbols on the right. Then we put a 1 below each column we filled in, to indicate that we had entered values into that column in step 1. In step 2, we took the truth values below p and used them to enter the truth values below the $\neg$ sign, representing the truth values for $\neg p$. We then put a 2 below the column whose values we just *entered*, indicating that its values had been entered in step 2. In step 3, we had two columns of truth values—one below $\neg p$ and one below q—which we used in deciding which truth values to enter in the column below the $\vee$ sign. We put a 3 in the column below the $\vee$ sign to show that its truth values had been entered in the third step. Notice that we highlighted the final column we filled in. The step numbers allow us to show all the steps in one display of the table rather than in three separate displays. They help the reader see the order in which the final table was constructed but are not an essential part of a truth table.

Our next example demonstrates a reason why truth tables are important. Some general-purpose computer languages and some database query languages do not allow us to test directly the truth of $p \oplus q$. If we want to test the truth of a statement of the form $p \oplus q$, we must translate "p or q, but not both" into terms of *and, or,* and *not*. A natural idea to try is to replace *but* by *and*, giving us "p or q and not both p and q." Symbolically this gives us the statement $(p \vee q) \wedge \neg(p \wedge q)$. How can we be sure that testing the truth of this statement will be equivalent to testing the truth of $p \oplus q$?

EXAMPLE 14   Show that $p \oplus q$ and $(p \vee q) \wedge \neg(p \wedge q)$ can replace each other.

Solution   In Figure 13, you see the truth table for $(p \vee q) \wedge \neg(p \wedge q)$. You see that the last column of this table is identical to the last column of the truth table for $p \oplus q$ in Figure 10. Thus $p \oplus q$ and $(p \vee q) \wedge \neg(p \wedge q)$ are true in exactly the same circumstances, so one can replace the other.   ∎

Figure 13

p	q	$(p$	$\vee$	$q)$	$\wedge$	$\neg$	$(p$	$\wedge$	$q)$
T	T	T	T	T	F	F	T	T	T
T	F	T	T	F	T	T	T	F	F
F	T	F	T	T	T	T	F	F	T
F	F	F	F	F	F	T	F	F	F
Step		1	2	1	4	3	1	2	1

We have defined two statements about a universe to be equivalent when they are true in exactly the same circumstances. For two symbolic statements to be true in the same circumstances, their truth tables must have the same final column. Thus we define two symbolic statements to be **equivalent** if their truth tables have the same final column.

EXAMPLE 15   Construct truth tables to show that the symbolic statements $p \wedge (q \vee r)$ and $(p \wedge q) \vee (p \wedge r)$ are equivalent.

Solution   We shall construct two truth tables. We must write eight different patterns of T's and F's below p, q, and r to make sure each possible combination appears once. We arrange the patterns of T and F under p, q, and r using exactly the same reverse alphabetical order for each truth table. Then, when we see that the final columns in the two truth tables are exactly the same, we may conclude that the two symbolic statements are equivalent. The truth tables are shown in Figure 14.   ∎

Figure 14   The truth tables for Example 15.

p q r	p	$\wedge$	$(q$	$\vee$	$r)$
T T T	T	T	T	T	T
T T F	T	T	T	T	F
T F T	T	T	F	T	T
T F F	T	F	F	F	F
F T T	F	F	T	T	T
F T F	F	F	T	T	F
F F T	F	F	F	T	T
F F F	F	F	F	F	F
Step	1	3	1	2	1

p q r	$(p$	$\wedge$	$q)$	$\vee$	$(p$	$\wedge$	$r)$
T T T	T	T	T	T	T	T	T
T T F	T	T	T	T	T	F	F
T F T	T	F	F	T	T	T	T
T F F	T	F	F	F	T	F	F
F T T	F	F	T	F	F	F	T
F T F	F	F	T	F	F	F	F
F F T	F	F	F	F	F	F	T
F F F	F	F	F	F	F	F	F
Step	1	2	1	3	1	2	1

As with statements about a universe, we use the symbol $\Leftrightarrow$ to stand for "is equivalent to." Thus we may write $p \wedge (q \vee r) \Leftrightarrow (p \wedge q) \vee (p \wedge r)$. The $\Leftrightarrow$ sign stands for a *relationship* between two statements, so it is not a symbol for a connective. The $\Leftrightarrow$ sign looks and works much like an equals sign, but we read it as "is equivalent to," *not* "equals."

The equivalence of Example 15 is one of the two **distributive** laws:

$$p \wedge (q \vee r) \Leftrightarrow (p \wedge q) \vee (p \wedge r)$$
$$p \vee (q \wedge r) \Leftrightarrow (p \vee q) \wedge (p \vee r)$$

These are called distributive laws in analogy with $p \cdot (q + r) = p \cdot q + p \cdot r$ of arithmetic. Other important equivalences include DeMorgan's laws:

$$\neg(p \vee q) \Leftrightarrow \neg p \wedge \neg q$$

and

$$\neg(p \wedge q) \Leftrightarrow \neg p \vee \neg q$$

and the **associative** laws

$$p \vee (q \vee r) \Leftrightarrow (p \vee q) \vee r$$

and

$$p \wedge (q \wedge r) \Leftrightarrow (p \wedge q) \wedge r$$

As it is stated, Example 15 appears to be simply an exercise in abstract reasoning. The equivalences stated afterward also seem to be mere theoretical statements. Example 16 shows that the question of Example 15 could arise in designing a computer program.

EXAMPLE 16   Suppose the mathematics department in Examples 5, 6, and 7 has separate records for juniors and seniors. The department needs to merge the list of juniors who have had calculus in high school with the similar list of seniors. Notice that merging these two lists gives a list of the union of these two sets of students. Suppose further that they have two very long alphabetical lists of students, so that they need to use a computer to work with the lists. They need to have the computer read along both lists simultaneously, always choosing the appropriate word in alphabetical order to put into a third list. Show how statements of the form studied in Example 15 can arise in designing the program.

Solution   Let us use "list1" and "list2" to stand for the two lists we need to merge into "list3." As we read along the lists, if we have not yet come to the end of list1 and either we have come to the end of list2 or the name we are examining in list1 comes before the name in list2, then the name in list1 goes into list3 next. To analyze this rather complicated description, we may choose p, q, and r to be the following statements:

p = "we have not come to the end of list1"
q = "we have come to the end of list2"
r = "the name we are examining in list1 comes before the name in list2"

With this choice of p, q, and r, $p \wedge (q \vee r)$ stands for the statement we used to describe when the next name in list3 comes from list1 rather than list2.

Someone else designing the program might say instead that the time when we want to choose the next name in list3 from list1 is the time when we are not at the end of list1 and we are at the end of list2 or the time when we are not at the end of list1 and the word in list1 comes before the word in list2. It takes a careful analysis of the English sentences involved to determine whether the two programs these people design will have the same effect. In symbols, however, the second person is saying that the time when we choose the next word from list1 is the time when $(p \wedge q) \vee (p \wedge r)$ is true. Since we know that $p \wedge (q \vee r)$ is equivalent to $(p \wedge q) \vee (p \wedge r)$, we know that the two program designs will accomplish the same thing.   ■

B   Circuits to Test the Truth of Statements

Switching Circuits

We are all familiar with switches that can be turned off or on by an electronic signal. The switch that makes our telephone ring is an example; it is turned on by someone else's telephone. The channel-changing mechanism in a remote-control television is another. The idea that an electronic signal can turn a switch off or on helps us develop a mental model of how computers operate. Computers represent the truth or falsity of statements by high or low (essentially zero) voltages in memory cells or wires representing the statements. Using these voltages to control switches allows the computer to test for the truth or falsity of compound statements. A circuit to test the truth of $p \wedge q$ would have an input wire for p, one for q, and one output wire with a high voltage if p and q are both high and a low voltage otherwise. In Figure 15, we see such a circuit: a standard *series* connection of switches, controlled by p and q. In this case, we are assuming that a high voltage is one volt and a low voltage is zero volts.

Figure 15

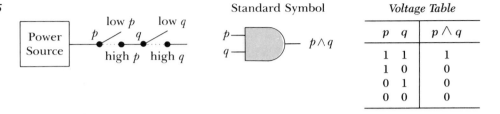

p	q	$p \wedge q$
1	1	1
1	0	0
0	1	0
0	0	0

Common sense (or high school physics) tells us that we can get one volt across this circuit exactly when p and q are both high. This gives us the voltage table that tells us the voltage in the circuit for each combination of voltages in p and q. Notice that replacing 1 by T and 0 by F would give you the truth table for $p \wedge q$. Thus voltage tables are essentially the same thing as truth tables. The "half moon" symbol is shorthand used by engineers to stand for a circuit like this. Such a circuit is called an ***and* gate.**

In Figure 16, we see the standard parallel connection of two switches. Again, common sense (or physics) tells us that we can get some voltage across the circuit if either one or both of the switches are in the *on* position, giving the voltage table shown in Figure 16. Thus, this circuit allows us to test the truth of an inclusive *or*. The standard symbol for this circuit is the "crescent moon" shown in Figure 16. This circuit is usually called an ***or* gate.**

Figure 16

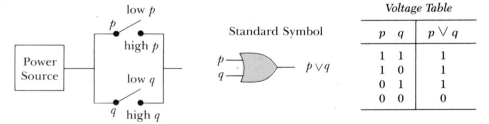

p	q	$p \vee q$
1	1	1
1	0	1
0	1	1
0	0	0

A switch can be turned off electrically as well. Such a switch is used in the **inverter gate** in Figure 17, which has a high voltage if p is false and a low voltage if p is true. The standard symbol for an inverter is a triangle with a circle at its apex. By imagining using these "gates" to connect wires together, we can visualize how to construct computer circuits to test the truth or falsity of various statements without needing any knowledge of electricity.

Figure 17

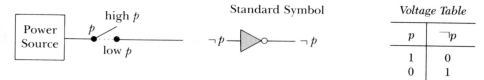

p	$\neg p$
1	0
0	1

Constructing Circuits

EXAMPLE 17   Show how to construct a circuit to check whether $\neg p \vee q$ is true.

Solution   We may use the symbols for *and, or,* and *inverter* gates. In Figure 18, for the first step we do nothing with the input wire for q and put an inverter at the end of the input wire for p. Then, in step 2, we run the output wire from the inverter and the input wire for q into an *or* gate.   ∎

Figure 18

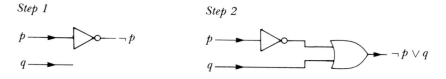

A circuit such as this is called a **combinatorial network,** because it allows us to check the truth of a statement we get by combining other statements into a compound statement.

Recall that we checked the equivalence of $p \oplus q$ with $(p \vee q) \wedge \neg(p \wedge q)$ because computer languages let us use *and,* inclusive *or,* and *not,* but not always exclusive *or.* Now we have seen circuits that let us test for the truth of $p \wedge q$, $p \vee q$, and $\neg p$. We can connect such circuits together in order to get a circuit to test for the truth of $p \oplus q$ by checking the truth of the equivalent statement $(p \vee q) \wedge \neg(p \wedge q)$. Using the standard symbols for *and* gates, *or* gates, and inverters (shown in Figures 14, 15, and 16), we construct a circuit according to the steps shown in Figure 19 (on the next page). Note that in step 2 we "split" the input wires and let wires cross over one another without making contact. Notice how wires can come back together at a gate but nowhere else. A good way to describe these observations is that you may have two arrows going out of a joint in the network, but you can't have two arrows coming in to a joint.

Figure 19

Step 1

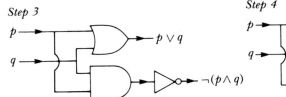

Step 2

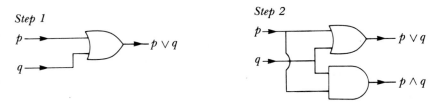

Step 3

Step 4

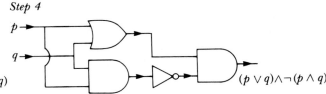

Concepts Review

1. A(n) _____ _____ tells us when a compound symbolic statement is true or false in terms of when the component statement symbols represent true or false statements.

2. Two statements that are true in exactly the same circumstances are _____.

3. Two symbolic statements are _____ if their truth tables have the same final column.

4. The symbol $\Leftrightarrow$ stands for the relationship of _____ between statements.

5. The law $p \wedge (q \vee r) \Leftrightarrow (p \wedge q) \vee (p \wedge r)$ is called a(n) _____ law.

6. The law $\neg(p \vee q) \Leftrightarrow \neg p \wedge \neg q$ is one of _____ laws.

7. The law $(p \vee q) \vee r \Leftrightarrow p \vee (q \vee r)$ is called a(n) _____ law.

8. The circuit that allows us to test the truth of an inclusive *or* is called a(n) _____ _____.

9. The rows of a truth table appear in _____ _____ order.

Exercises

A 1. Explain why the truth table for inclusive *or* contains the entries it does.

2. Explain why the truth table for exclusive *or* contains the entries it does.

3. The logical connective *nor* has the property that p nor q is true when both p and q are false and is false otherwise. Use $p \oslash q$ to stand for p nor q. Write down a truth table for $p \oslash q$.

4. The logical connective *nand* has the property that p nand q is true unless p and q are both true, in which case p nand q is false. Use $p \oslash q$ to stand for p nand q. Write out a truth table for $p \oslash q$.

In Exercises 5–28, write down the truth table for the symbolic compound statement given.

5. $\neg p \vee q$

6. $p \wedge \neg q$

7. $p \wedge (\neg p \vee q)$

8. $q \vee (\neg q \wedge p)$

9. $\neg p \wedge (\neg (p \wedge q))$

10. $\neg (p \wedge (p \vee q))$

11. $p \vee (p \wedge q)$

12. $p \wedge q \wedge (p \oplus q)$

13. $(p \wedge \neg q) \vee (q \wedge \neg q)$

14. $p \oplus (q \wedge \neg p)$

15. $(p \wedge q) \vee (\neg p \wedge \neg q)$

16. $(p \wedge \neg q) \wedge (q \vee \neg p)$

17. $p \oplus (p \vee q)$

18. $\neg (p \oplus q) \wedge p$

19. $p \vee \neg p$

20. $q \wedge \neg q$

21. $p \wedge (q \vee \neg r)$

22. $p \vee (p \wedge (q \vee r))$

23. $p \oplus (q \vee r)$

24. $p \wedge (q \oplus \neg r)$

25. $[(p \wedge q) \vee (p \wedge r)] \vee (q \wedge r)$

26. $(p \vee q) \wedge [(p \vee r) \wedge (q \vee r)]$

27. $(p \oplus q) \wedge \neg (r \oplus q)$

28. $p \wedge ((p \wedge \neg q) \vee (q \wedge \neg p))$

29. Are the statements $p \wedge (q \oplus r)$ and $(p \wedge q) \oplus (p \wedge r)$ equivalent? (Think of the distributive laws.) Using truth tables, show why or why not.

30. Are the statements $p \vee (q \wedge r)$ and $(p \vee q) \wedge (p \vee r)$ equivalent? Using truth tables, show why or why not.

31. Are the statements $p \vee (q \oplus r)$ and $(p \vee q) \oplus (p \vee r)$ equivalent? Why or why not?

32. Are the statements $p \oplus (q \wedge r)$ and $(p \oplus q) \wedge (p \oplus r)$ equivalent? Why or why not?

33. Use truth tables to show the validity of DeMorgan's law: $\neg (p \vee q) \Leftrightarrow \neg p \wedge \neg q$.

34. Use truth tables to show the validity of DeMorgan's law: $\neg (p \wedge q) \Leftrightarrow \neg p \vee \neg q$.

B For each symbolic statement in Exercises 35–44, draw a combinatorial network that has a high voltage output if the statement is true and a low voltage otherwise.

35. $p \wedge \neg q$

36. $\neg p \wedge q$

37. $p \vee (q \vee r)$

38. $p \wedge (q \wedge r)$

39. $\neg (p \wedge q)$

40. $\neg (p \vee q)$

41. $\neg p \vee \neg q$

42. $\neg p \wedge \neg q$

43. $p \wedge (q \vee r)$

44. $p \vee (q \wedge r)$

45. Draw a combinatorial network that will check whether $(p \wedge \neg q) \vee (q \wedge \neg p)$ is true. How does this network relate to the network of Figure 19?

46. Draw a combinatorial network that will check whether $(p \wedge q) \vee (p \wedge r)$ is true. How does this network relate to the network drawn in the answer to Exercise 43?

47. What statement does the combinatorial network in Figure 20(a) check the truth of?

48. What statement does the combinatorial network in Figure 20(b) check the truth of?

Figure 20

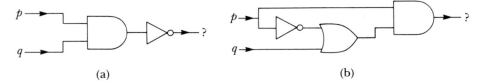

(a)   (b)

Problems

1. Show that a statement p is equivalent to $p \wedge p$, $p \vee p$, and $\neg \neg p$.

2. If a symbolic statement is made up using n different statement symbols, how many rows are in its truth table?

3. What is the maximum possible number of inequivalent symbolic statements made up from two statement symbols?

4. Using only the connectives $\neg$ and $\wedge$, find symbolic statements equivalent to $p \vee q$ and $p \oplus q$.

5. The logical connective *nor* has the property that p nor q is true when p and q are both false, but is false otherwise. Use the symbol $\oslash$ to stand for *nor*. Write out a truth table for $\oslash$, as in Exercise 3, and show how to express *nor* in terms of the $\wedge$, $\vee$, and $\neg$ connectives.

6. The logical connective *nand* denoted by $\oslash$ has the property that $p \oslash q$ is true unless p and q are both true, in which case it is false. Write out a truth table for $\oslash$, as in Exercise 4, and find a way to express *nand* in terms of the $\wedge$, $\vee$, and $\neg$ connectives.

7. Find an expression for $\oplus$ using $\oslash$, $\oslash$, and $\neg$.

8. Suppose that a connective $\triangledown$ has been defined by giving a truth table for $p \triangledown q$. Explain how to find an expression involving the symbols p, q, $\wedge$, $\vee$, and $\neg$ that is equivalent to $p \triangledown q$.

9. Two connectives are *equivalent* if they have the same truth tables. Explain why the connectives $\wedge$, $\vee$, and $\oplus$ are mutually inequivalent connectives. What is the maximum number of mutually inequivalent connectives that we could possibly define?

10. A standard way to arrange switches to turn an emergency system off or (in the case of weapons) to turn it on is to have two switches, each of which must be turned off before the system turns off (or in the case of weapons, each of which must be turned on before the weapon can be used). Show how two switches may be connected to achieve each of these goals.

11. In Figure 21, we show a circuit that takes two inputs x_1 and x_2 and produces two outputs z_1 and z_2. Show that if we regard x_1 and x_2 as binary number digits, then z_2 is the units digit and z_1 is the first digit of the sum $x_1 + x_2$ (this sum again expressed in binary).

Figure 21

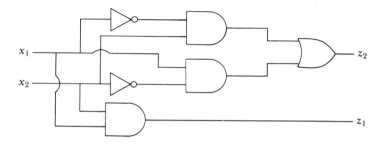

12. See Problem 11 and then design a circuit with four input wires—x_1, x_2, y_1, and y_2— and three output wires—z_1, z_2, and z_3—so that $z_1z_2z_3$ is the binary representation of $x_1x_2 + y_1y_2$, where x_1x_2 stands for the binary number whose digits are x_1 and x_2.

Section 1-4
The Conditional Connectives

A Conditional Statements

The Use of If and Then

So far we have discussed only several simple ways to build up compound statements from more elementary statements. We can connect two clauses in other ways than using a simple connective word. Statements such as "If $x > 6$ then $2x > 13$" occur frequently in mathematical reasoning. Statements such as "I will go downtown only if you go with me" occur frequently in natural language. The word *if* occurs in many different ways in both mathematical and natural language statements. For example, we might see

$$
\begin{array}{ccc}
\text{If } x > 6 & \text{then} & 2x > 13 \\
x > 6 & \text{if} & 2x > 13 \\
x > 6 & \text{only if} & 2x > 13 \\
x > 6 & \text{if and only if} & 2x > 13
\end{array}
$$

Are all four of these uses of the word *if* conceptually different? In order to answer this, let us try to agree on when each of the four kinds of statements below is true and when it is false.

$$
\begin{array}{llll}
\text{If} & p & \text{then} & q \\
& p & \text{if} & q \\
& p & \text{only if} & q \\
& p & \text{if and only if} & q
\end{array}
$$

Of these four statements, people normally find it easiest to agree on the interpretation of the last, so let us begin with it. We shall analyze an example in order to recognize the generally accepted interpretation of *if and only if*. We shall let p be the statement "I go running" and q be the statement "Maria goes running." We abbreviate *if and only if* by the connective symbol $\leftrightarrow$. Under what circumstances will the statement $p \leftrightarrow q$, which stands for "I go running if and only if Maria goes running," be true? In the case that we both run or neither of us runs, we would say that the statement is true. In either case where one of us runs and the other does not, we would say that the statement is false. This gives us the truth table for $p \leftrightarrow q$ shown in Figure 22.

Figure 22   The truth table for $\leftrightarrow$.

p	q	$p \leftrightarrow q$
T	T	T
T	F	F
F	T	F
F	F	T

The Conditional Connective

For other ways of using the word *if*, people often cannot agree on one fixed interpretation. Since we need a precise interpretation in order to give a truth table, we shall analyze how much of the truth table we can fill in on the basis of English usage and then complete the table in the way that is most useful for doing mathematics. Using p for the statement "I go running" and q for the statement "Maria goes running," we abbreviate the statement "If I go running then Maria goes running" by $p \rightarrow q$. What can we agree on about the truth or falsity of the statement $p \rightarrow q$, which stands for "If I go running then Maria goes running"? In the case where Maria and I both run, we would say that the statement is true; this gives us the first line of the truth table in Figure 23 for $p \rightarrow q$. In the case where I go running and Maria does not, we would say that the statement is false. This gives us row 2 of Figure 23. If I do not go running and Maria does not go running, it seems natural to say that the statement is true. This gives us row 4 of the incomplete truth table in Figure 23.

Figure 23   An incomplete truth table for $p \rightarrow q$.

p q	$p \rightarrow q$
T T	T
T F	F
F T	
F F	T

Some people find it difficult to decide on how to fill in the empty last place in Figure 23, others feel it should be filled in with T, and still others feel it should be filled in with F. Since we want $p \rightarrow q$ to represent a *statement*, we *must* fill in a truth value. If we were to put in F, then $p \rightarrow q$ and p $\leftrightarrow$ q would be equivalent, since the completed Figure 23 would be identical to Figure 22. In mathematical reasoning, however, the statement "if p then q" has a different meaning from the statement "p if and only if q." To capture this difference, we must fill in the last truth value as a T, agreeing that $p \rightarrow q$ is true when p is false and q is true. This gives Figure 24(a). Similar analyses for "q if p" (note the order of p and q here) and "p only if q" give the truth tables in Figure 24(b) and (c).

Figure 24   Three variants of the conditional with the same truth tables.

p q	$p \rightarrow q$
T T	T
T F	F
F T	T
F F	T

(a)

p q	q if p
T T	T
T F	F
F T	T
F F	T

(b)

p q	p only if q
T T	T
T F	F
F T	T
F F	T

(c)

The truth tables in Figure 24 show that, from the truth-table point of view, "if p then q," "p only if q," and "q if p" are equivalent, so we use $p \rightarrow q$ to stand for any or all of them. Just as we read "$x + y$" as "x plus y" and "$p \wedge q$" as "p and q," we will normally read "$p \rightarrow q$" as "p only if q." In this way you may think of the arrow as an operator symbol standing for *only if*. (Some people prefer to read the arrow as the word *implies*. This is perfectly acceptable, but, to avoid confusion in situations discussed later, we shall not do so in this book.)

A statement of the form $p \rightarrow q$ is called a
conditional statement; a statement of the form
$p \leftrightarrow q$ is called a **biconditional statement**.

The symbol $\rightarrow$ is called the *conditional connective* symbol, and $\leftrightarrow$ is called the *biconditional connective* symbol.

EXAMPLE 18   Using "I go running" for p, "Maria goes running" for q, and "Rain is falling" for r, write grammatical English translations of the following symbolic statements.

(a) $r \rightarrow p$ (b) $(p \wedge q) \leftrightarrow \neg r$

Solution

(a) Rain is falling only if I go running. Another answer is: If rain is falling, then I go running.
(b) Both I go running and Maria goes running if and only if rain is not falling. Another answer is: Maria and I go running if and only if rain is not falling. (Notice how much easier it is to be precise in a symbolic statement than in an English statement. The use of the word *both* with the word *and* in English corresponds to the parentheses around $p \wedge q$.) ■

EXAMPLE 19   Rewrite the following sentences as symbolic expressions, using the interpretations for p, q, and r in Example 18.

(a) Rain is falling if I go running.
(b) Maria goes running only if both I go running and rain is not falling.
(c) If rain is not falling then Maria goes running and I do not.

Solution

(a) $p \rightarrow r$
(b) $q \rightarrow (p \wedge \neg r)$
(c) $\neg r \rightarrow (q \wedge \neg p)$ ■

We construct a truth table for a symbolic statement involving conditional or biconditional statements in the same way we have constructed other truth tables.

EXAMPLE 20   Construct the truth table for $(p \rightarrow q) \wedge (q \rightarrow p)$. What does it show?

Solution   The truth table is shown in Figure 25. It shows that

$$(p \rightarrow q) \wedge (q \rightarrow p) \Leftrightarrow p \leftrightarrow q$$

In words, $p \leftrightarrow q$ and $(p \rightarrow q) \wedge (q \rightarrow p)$ are equivalent. ■

Figure 25

p	q	$(p$	$\rightarrow$	$q)$	$\wedge$	$(q$	$\rightarrow$	$p)$
T	T	T	T	T	T	T	T	T
T	F	T	F	F	F	F	T	T
F	T	F	T	T	F	T	F	F
F	F	F	T	F	T	F	T	F
	Step	1	2	1	3	1	2	1

Differences between Conditional Statements and Conditional Instructions

In programming languages, the words IF and THEN are generally reserved for conditional instructions of the form

IF statement THEN instruction sequence.

Various languages implement such an instruction in different ways. It is always the case that if the statement is true the computer carries out the instruction sequence. However, if the statement is false, the computer typically *does not* carry out the sequence of instructions. In other words, the computer carries out the instruction sequence *if and only if* the statement is true. Thus a conditional *instruction* is *not* to be interpreted in the same way that a conditional *statement* is.

B Expressing Conditional Connectives in Terms of Other Connectives

In Example 20, we used truth tables to show that the two symbolic statements $p \leftrightarrow q$ and $(p \to q) \wedge (q \to p)$ are equivalent. To check the equivalence of symbolic statements using arrows, we use truth tables in the same way we do to check the equivalence of other symbolic statements. We have also discussed the concept of equivalence for statements about a universe. For the universe of all outcomes of flipping a coin three times, the statement "if there is at least one head then there is at least one tail" is equivalent to the statement "there is at least one tail." Notice that we would not be able to use truth-table analysis to demonstrate this equivalence. To see why, we use p to stand for "there is at least one head" and q to stand for "there is at least one tail." Then we discover that, in symbolic form, we are saying that $p \to q$ and q are equivalent. Figure 26 shows us that $p \to q$ and q are not equivalent as symbolic statements. To show that these two statements about coin flipping are equivalent, we must find the truth sets of $p \to q$ and q; then we must show that these truth sets are equal. For this purpose, we need a way to compute the truth set of $p \to q$ from the truth set of p and the truth set of q.

Figure 26

p	q	p	$\to$	q		p	q	q
T	T	T	T	T		T	T	T
T	F	T	F	F		T	F	F
F	T	F	T	T		F	T	T
F	F	F	T	F		F	F	F

We have already faced a similar situation with $p \oplus q$. We have learned how to express $p \oplus q$ in terms of the connectives $\vee$, $\wedge$, and $\neg$ as $(p \vee q) \wedge \neg(p \wedge q)$. This tells us that the truth set of $p \oplus q$ is $(P \cup Q) \cap \sim(P \cap Q)$. It also gives us a way to check the truth of a statement of the form $p \oplus q$ in a computer language that does not recognize the $\oplus$ connective. Further, it gives a way to describe a circuit to check the truth of $p \oplus q$ using *and* gates, *or* gates, and inverters. These observations suggest that it will be very useful to be able to express $p \to q$ and $p \leftrightarrow q$ in terms of $\vee$, $\wedge$, and $\neg$.

Expressing Conditional Connectives without Arrows

Figure 27 shows the truth table for $p \to q$. Note that $p \to q$ is true except in one case—the case when p is true and q is false. Similarly, $p \vee q$ is true except in one case, though it is a different case. Both statements are true when q is true (and may be false otherwise). Thus it may be possible that $p \to q$ is equivalent to some statement of the form $r \vee q$. Figure 27 shows that this is the case with $r = \neg p$. We formally state this relationship in Theorem 3.

Figure 27   The statements $p \to q$ and $\neg p \vee q$ are equivalent.

p	q	$p \to q$
T	T	T
T	F	F
F	T	T
F	F	T

p	q	$p \vee q$
T	T	T
T	F	T
F	T	T
F	F	F

p	q	$\neg$	p	$\vee$	q
T	T	F	T	T	T
T	F	F	T	F	F
F	T	T	F	T	T
F	F	T	F	T	F
		Step 2	1	3	1

Theorem 3   If p and q are statements, then $p \to q$ is equivalent to $\neg p \vee q$.

Proof   By definition, if the truth tables for two symbolic compound statements have the same final column, then the symbolic statements are equivalent. Figure 27 shows that the truth table for $p \to q$ and the truth table for $\neg p \vee q$ have the same final column. Therefore, $p \to q$ and $\neg p \vee q$ are symbolically equivalent. ∎

How to Get the Truth Set of p → q

According to Theorem 3, if you wish to test the truth of the statement $p \to q$, you may test the truth of $\neg p \vee q$ instead. Since the truth set of $\neg p \vee q$ is $\sim P \cup Q$, the truth set for $p \to q$ is $\sim P \cup Q$. In Example 17 we saw how to construct a circuit to check the truth of $\neg p \vee q$; now we see that the circuit of Example 17 checks the truth of $p \to q$.

EXAMPLE 21   Rewrite the symbolic statement $\neg r \to (s \vee (r \wedge t))$ as an equivalent statement without an arrow.

Solution The symbolic statement given has the form $p \rightarrow q$, where p is $\neg r$ and q is $s \vee (r \wedge t)$. To rewrite the given statement without an arrow, we write $p \rightarrow q$ without an arrow and replace p and q by the appropriate statements. We replace the p in $\neg p \vee q$ with $\neg r$, and we replace the q by $s \vee (r \wedge t)$. This gives the equivalent expression

$$(\neg \neg r) \vee (s \vee (r \wedge t)) \qquad \blacksquare$$

EXAMPLE 22   Rewrite the symbolic statement $(r \wedge s) \leftrightarrow (r \vee s)$ without using any arrows.

Solution The statement $(r \wedge s) \leftrightarrow (r \vee s)$ has the form $p \leftrightarrow q$ with $p = r \wedge s$ and $q = r \vee s$. In Example 20, we showed that $p \leftrightarrow q$ and $(p \rightarrow q) \wedge (q \rightarrow p)$ are equivalent. Furthermore, by substituting $\neg p \vee q$ for $p \rightarrow q$, we can deduce that $p \leftrightarrow q$ and $(\neg p \vee q) \wedge (\neg q \vee p)$ are equivalent. We replace the p's in $(\neg p \vee q) \wedge (\neg q \vee p)$ with $r \wedge s$, and we replace the q's with $r \vee s$, giving

$$(\neg(r \wedge s) \vee (r \vee s)) \wedge (\neg(r \vee s) \vee (r \wedge s)) \qquad \blacksquare$$

EXAMPLE 23   In the experiment of flipping a coin three times, let p be the statement "The first flip comes up heads" and q be the statement "There are at least two heads." Find the truth sets of p, q, and $p \rightarrow q$.

Solution The truth set of p is $P = \{HHH, HHT, HTH, HTT\}$, and the truth set of q is $Q = \{HHH, HHT, HTH, THH\}$. The truth set of $p \rightarrow q$ is the truth set of $\neg p \vee q$, which is

$$\sim P \cup Q = \{TTT, TTH, THT, THH\} \cup \{HHH, HHT, HTH, THH\}$$
$$= \{TTT, TTH, THT, THH, HHH, HHT, HTH\} \qquad \blacksquare$$

Concepts Review

1. A compound statement involving the words *if* and *then* is a(n) _____ statement.

2. The symbol $\rightarrow$ is the symbol for the _____ connective, and $\leftrightarrow$ is the symbol for the _____ connective.

3. The statement $(p \rightarrow q) \wedge (q \rightarrow p)$ is _____ to the statement $p \leftrightarrow q$.

4. The statements "if p then q," "p only if q," and "q if p" are _____ conditional statements.

5. The statement $p \rightarrow q$ is _____ to the statement $\neg p \vee q$.

6. If P is the truth set of p and Q is the truth set of q, then _____ is the truth set of $p \rightarrow q$.

7. The statement $p \leftrightarrow q$ is _____ when p and q are both true and is _____ when p and q are both false.

8. The statement $p \leftrightarrow q$ is _____ if one of p and q is true and the other is false.

9. The statement "p only if q" is true unless p is _____ and q is _____.

Exercises

A   1. A sequence of ten digits, each a zero or a one, is to be sent along a communications channel. Suppose p is the statement "Two (or more) digits are in error," q is the statement "Some digit is in error," and r is the statement "The first digit is in error." Write the following statements in symbolic form. (You don't need to know anything about communications channels.)
   (a) If two (or more) digits are in error, then some digit is in error.
   (b) If some digit is in error, then the first digit is in error.
   (c) If some digit is in error and the first digit is not in error, then two (or more) digits are in error.
   (d) Two (or more) digits are in error if and only if the first digit is in error.
   (e) The first digit is in error exactly when both some digit is in error and two (or more) digits are not in error.
   (f) The first digit is in error only if two (or more) digits are in error.
   (g) The first digit is in error if some digit is in error.
   (h) When the first digit is in error, two (or more) digits are in error.

   2. We flip a penny, a nickel, and a dime. Let p be the statement "The penny comes up heads," let q be the statement "Two (or more) coins come up heads," and let r be the statement "Some coin comes up tails." Write the following statements in symbolic form.
   (a) If the penny comes up heads, then two (or more) coins come up heads.
   (b) Two (or more) coins come up heads if and only if some coin comes up tails.
   (c) If no coin comes up tails, then the penny comes up heads.
   (d) The penny comes up heads if some coin comes up tails.
   (e) The penny comes up heads only if some coin comes up tails.
   (f) If the penny comes up heads and some coin comes up tails, then two (or more) coins come up heads.
   (g) The penny comes up heads exactly when no coin comes up tails.
   (h) When two (or more) coins come up heads, the penny comes up heads.

   3. Let p, q, and r be the statements of Exercise 1. Write the following statements in grammatical English. Do not use the word *implies*.
   (a) $q \rightarrow r$ (b) $p \wedge r \rightarrow q$ (c) $\neg p \wedge q \leftrightarrow r$

   (d) $p \rightarrow q \wedge r$ (e) $\neg q \rightarrow r$ (f) $\neg q \rightarrow \neg r \wedge \neg p$

   4. Let p, q, and r be the statements of Exercise 2. Write the following statements in grammatical English without using the word *implies*.
   (a) $p \rightarrow q$ (b) $(q \rightarrow p) \wedge (p \rightarrow r)$ (c) $(p \wedge \neg r) \leftrightarrow q$

   (d) $(q \rightarrow p) \vee (p \rightarrow r)$ (e) $p \rightarrow q \vee \neg r$ (f) $(p \wedge r) \rightarrow \neg q$

   For Exercises 5–16, construct a truth table for the symbolic statement given.

   5. $(p \rightarrow q) \wedge (p \rightarrow r)$ 6. $(p \rightarrow q) \vee (p \rightarrow r)$

   7. $p \rightarrow (q \wedge r)$ 8. $(p \vee q) \rightarrow r$

   9. $p \rightarrow (q \vee r)$ 10. $(p \wedge q) \rightarrow r$

   11. $p \leftrightarrow q \vee \neg p$ 12. $(p \wedge \neg q) \leftrightarrow (p \rightarrow q)$

   13. $(p \leftrightarrow q) \wedge (q \leftrightarrow r)$ 14. $(p \vee \neg q) \leftrightarrow (p \rightarrow q)$

   15. $p \rightarrow (p \leftrightarrow q)$ 16. $(p \leftrightarrow q) \rightarrow p$

For Exercises 17–22, determine whether the pair of statements is equivalent.

17. $p \leftrightarrow q;\ (p \vee \neg q) \wedge (q \vee \neg p)$

18. $p \wedge (q \rightarrow r);\ (p \wedge q) \rightarrow (p \wedge r)$

19. $p \rightarrow \neg(q \wedge r);\ (q \rightarrow p) \wedge \neg r$

20. $\neg(p \oplus q);\ p \leftrightarrow q$

21. $p \oplus q;\ \neg p \leftrightarrow \neg q$

22. $(p \rightarrow q) \wedge (q \rightarrow r) \wedge (r \rightarrow p);\ (p \leftrightarrow q) \wedge (p \leftrightarrow r)$

B In Exercises 23–32, convert the symbolic statements into statements without arrows or $\oplus$ symbols.

23. $(p \rightarrow q) \wedge (p \rightarrow r)$

24. $(p \rightarrow q) \vee (p \rightarrow r)$

25. $(p \rightarrow q) \wedge (q \rightarrow r)$

26. $(p \rightarrow q) \vee (q \rightarrow r)$

27. $p \rightarrow (q \vee r)$

28. $(p \wedge q) \rightarrow r$

29. $p \leftrightarrow (p \wedge q)$

30. $(p \wedge \neg q) \rightarrow (p \vee q)$

31. $\neg(p \leftrightarrow q)$

32. $(p \rightarrow q) \leftrightarrow (q \rightarrow p)$

Problems

1. On the basis of truth tables for $p \oplus q$ and $p \leftrightarrow q$, find how to express each of these connectives in terms of the other one of these connectives and the $\neg$ symbol.

2. Find a way to express the truth set of $p \rightarrow q$ using only the truth sets P and Q and the symbols $\sim$ and $\cap$.

3. Show that the truth set of $p \leftrightarrow q$ is $(\sim P \cap \sim Q) \cup (P \cap Q)$, where P and Q are the truth sets of p and q.

4. Find statements equivalent to $p \vee q$ and $p \wedge q$ using only the symbols p and q, the $\rightarrow$ symbol, and the $\neg$ symbol.

5. Given a specified final column for the truth table of a new symbolic compound statement $p \triangledown q$, explain how to find an equivalent statement, using the symbols p and q and the connectives $\wedge$, $\vee$, and $\neg$.

6. Find a statement, expressed in terms of p, q, and the connectives $\wedge$, $\vee$, and $\neg$, that you can show is not equivalent to any symbolic statement containing only the connectives $\leftrightarrow$ and $\neg$.

7. Draw combinatorial networks that will determine whether $p \rightarrow q$ and $p \leftrightarrow q$ are true.

Section 1-5
Boolean Algebra

A   Boolean Algebra for Sets

We have seen that to show that two statements about a universe are equivalent, we must sometimes show that two sets are equal. We have also seen that proofs using the fundamental principle of set equality to show that two sets are equal can be time-consuming. Boolean algebra provides us with algebraic properties of set operations that let us verify equations involving sets in much the same ways that ordinary algebra lets us verify equations involving numbers and variables. In Theorem 4, we list some of these properties. We could list many more, but any valid property not listed can be derived algebraically from the properties listed.

Theorem 4   The set operations on subsets of a universe U satisfy the following algebraic laws:

$$P \cup (Q \cup R) = (P \cup Q) \cup R \qquad \text{(Associative laws)} \qquad (1)$$
$$P \cap (Q \cap R) = (P \cap Q) \cap R$$
$$P \cup Q = Q \cup P \qquad \text{(Commutative laws)} \qquad (2)$$
$$P \cap Q = Q \cap P$$
$$P \cap (Q \cup R) = (P \cap Q) \cup (P \cap R) \qquad \text{(Distributive laws)} \qquad (3)$$
$$P \cup (Q \cap R) = (P \cup Q) \cap (P \cup R)$$
$$P \cap (P \cup Q) = P \qquad \text{(Absorptive laws)} \qquad (4)$$
$$P \cup (P \cap Q) = P$$
$$P \cup \varnothing = P \qquad \text{(Identity laws)} \qquad (5)$$
$$P \cap U = P$$
$$P \cup {\sim}P = U \qquad \text{(Inverse laws)} \qquad (6)$$
$$P \cap {\sim}P = \varnothing$$

Proof   Each law can be proved by carefully applying the principle that two sets are equal if each member of one is a member of the other, and vice versa. Each law can also be proved by translating it to the corresponding equations involving $\wedge$, $\vee$, and $\neg$ for statements. Translating laws (1) and (2) gives equivalences that are straightforward to verify by the use of truth tables. The first half of law (3) translates into a statement that we proved earlier.

To give an example of how these laws can be proved using the principle of set equality, we shall now prove the first absorptive law (the first half of law (4)).

Let $x \in P \cap (P \cup Q)$. Then $x \in P$ and $x \in P \cup Q$ by the definition of $\cap$, so certainly $x \in P$. Thus every x in $P \cap (P \cup Q)$ is also in P.

Now suppose $x \in P$. Then $x \in P \cup Q$ by the definition of $\cup$. Therefore, by the definition of $\cap$, $x \in P \cap (P \cup Q)$. Thus, every x in P is in $P \cap (P \cup Q)$. This proves that $P \cap (P \cup Q)$ and P have exactly the same elements, so they are equal.

Law (5) follows immediately from the definitions of union and intersection, and law (6) follows immediately from the definition of ${\sim}P$ as $U \sim P$. ∎

By applying the commutative law, we get many variations on the other laws. For example, $(Q \cup R) \cap P = (Q \cap P) \cup (R \cap P)$. Rather than regard these variations as new laws, we give them the same name as the original law. Thus $(Q \cup R) \cap P = (Q \cap P) \cup (R \cap P)$ is also called a distributive law.

The associative laws (1) tell us that the way we insert parentheses in a repeated union or intersection is unimportant. Thus we may omit parentheses entirely in a repeated union or intersection. This, together with the rule that a $\sim$ sign is applied to the shortest expression to the right of it that makes sense, allows us to avoid writing quite a few parentheses. For example, just as we would write $-x + y + 2$ in place of $((-x) + y) + 2$, we may write $\sim P \cup Q \cup R$ in place of $((\sim P) \cup Q) \cup R$.

When we apply known laws about set operations to derive other ones algebraically, we say we are doing **Boolean algebra.** It is the use of the laws that characterizes Boolean algebra, not the fact that we are working with sets. Analogous laws arise in other contexts; using the laws in those contexts is also called Boolean algebra.

EXAMPLE 24   Use Boolean algebra to prove the *empty intersection property:* $\varnothing \cap P = \varnothing$.

Solution   We write the sequence of equations

$$
\begin{aligned}
\varnothing \cap P &= \varnothing \cap (P \cup \varnothing) && \text{(Law (5) (identity law))} \\
&= \varnothing \cap (\varnothing \cup P) && \text{(Law (2) (commutative law))} \\
&= \varnothing && \text{(Law (4) (absorptive law))}
\end{aligned}
$$
∎

EXAMPLE 25   Use Boolean algebra to prove the *unique identity property:* if $X \cap P = P$ for all subsets P of U, then $X = U$.

Solution   Using $P = U$, we may write

$$
\begin{aligned}
X \cap U &= U \\
X &= U && \text{(identity law)}
\end{aligned}
$$
∎

EXAMPLE 26   Use Boolean algebra to prove the *unique inverse property:* if $X \cap P = \varnothing$ and $X \cup P = U$, then $X = \sim P$.

Solution
$$
\begin{aligned}
X &= X \cap U && \text{(Identity law)} \\
&= X \cap (P \cup \sim P) && \text{(Inverse law)} \\
&= (X \cap P) \cup (X \cap \sim P) && \text{(Distributive law)} \\
&= \varnothing \cup (X \cap \sim P) && \text{(Given property)} \\
&= (P \cap \sim P) \cup (X \cap \sim P) && \text{(Inverse law)} \\
&= (P \cup X) \cap \sim P && \text{(Distributive law)} \\
&= U \cap \sim P && \text{(Given property)} \\
&= \sim P && \text{(Identity law)}
\end{aligned}
$$
∎

Note that in the third to last line of Example 26 we used the phrase *distributive law* to refer to the law we obtain from line 3 by applying the commutative law, just as we said we may after the proof of Theorem 4.

EXAMPLE 27   Use Boolean algebra to prove the *double negation law:* $\sim\sim Q = Q$.

Solution   Apply Example 26 with $P = \sim Q$. It says that if $X \cap \sim Q = \emptyset$ and $X \cup \sim Q = U$, then $X = \sim(\sim Q)$. However, by the inverse law we know that $Q \cap \sim Q = \emptyset$ and $Q \cup \sim Q = U$. According to Example 26, the only set X such that $X \cup \sim Q = U$ and $X \cap \sim Q = \emptyset$ is $\sim(\sim Q)$. Therefore $Q = \sim(\sim Q)$.   ∎

Though proofs like those in Examples 24 through 27 are much "slicker" than proofs involving truth tables or the fundamental principle of set equality, they give rise to a fundamental question: "How do I know which laws to apply in which order when I want to construct a proof?" The answer is that you must rely on your experience and intuition, supplemented by trial-and-error guesses, to discover a sequence of laws that works. This kind of mathematical activity is hard—not only for humans. The fundamental question lies at the heart of the branch of computer science known as artificial intelligence.

B   *Boolean Algebra for Statements*

Questions about statements will often lead us to complicated symbolic statements. Through techniques of Boolean algebra, we can modify expressions to make them considerably simpler. So far, though, we have only studied rules of Boolean algebra for sets. A typical law of Boolean algebra for sets is $P \cap (Q \cap R) = (P \cap Q) \cap R$, the associative law. Let P stand for the truth set of p, Q for the truth set of q, and R for the truth set of r. Then, by Theorem 1, $P \cap (Q \cap R)$ stands for the truth set of $p \wedge (q \wedge r)$, and $(P \cap Q) \cap R$ stands for the truth set of $(p \wedge q) \wedge r$. We know that two statements are equivalent when their truth sets are equal. Therefore, a formula saying that two sets are equal corresponds to a formula saying that two statements are equivalent. Thus

$$P \cap (Q \cap R) = (P \cap Q) \cap R$$

translates to the formula

$$p \wedge (q \wedge r) \Leftrightarrow (p \wedge q) \wedge r$$

We could go through the laws of Boolean algebra for sets and see that the associative, commutative, distributive, and absorptive laws all translate directly into laws about statements. The identity laws and inverse laws of Boolean algebra for sets involve the two special symbols U and $\emptyset$, standing for the universe and empty set, respectively. Since we don't yet have similar special symbols for statements, we cannot yet translate these two laws. It is traditional to let the boldface numeral one (**1**) stand for some statement whose truth set is U—for example, $p \vee \neg p$—and the boldface numeral zero (**0**) stand for some statement whose truth set is $\emptyset$, for example $p \wedge \neg p$. Then all six laws of Boolean algebra can be translated directly for statements.

Theorem 5 The statements about a universe satisfy the following rules.

$$(p \vee q) \vee r \Leftrightarrow p \vee (q \vee r)$$ (Associative laws)
$$(p \wedge q) \wedge r \Leftrightarrow p \wedge (q \wedge r)$$
$$p \vee q \Leftrightarrow q \vee p$$ (Commutative laws)
$$p \wedge q \Leftrightarrow q \wedge p$$
$$p \wedge (q \vee r) \Leftrightarrow (p \wedge q) \vee (p \wedge r)$$ (Distributive laws)
$$p \vee (q \wedge r) \Leftrightarrow (p \vee q) \wedge (p \vee r)$$
$$p \wedge (p \vee q) \Leftrightarrow p$$ (Absorptive laws)
$$p \vee (p \wedge q) \Leftrightarrow q$$
$$p \vee \mathbf{0} \Leftrightarrow p$$ (Identity laws)
$$p \wedge \mathbf{1} \Leftrightarrow p$$
$$p \vee \neg p \Leftrightarrow \mathbf{1}$$ (Inverse laws)
$$p \wedge \neg p \Leftrightarrow \mathbf{0}$$

Proof Each law corresponds to a fact about truth sets given in Theorem 4. ∎

Any algebraic fact we can derive from the laws of Boolean algebra for sets can be similarly translated into a fact about statements. Thus we have:

$$\neg(p \vee q) \Leftrightarrow \neg p \wedge \neg q$$ (DeMorgan's law)
$$\neg(p \wedge q) \Leftrightarrow \neg p \vee \neg q$$
$$\neg\neg p \Leftrightarrow p$$ (Double negation law)
$$p \vee p \Leftrightarrow p$$ (Idempotent properties)
$$p \wedge p \Leftrightarrow p$$
$$\mathbf{0} \wedge p \Leftrightarrow \mathbf{0}$$ (Zero property)
$$\mathbf{1} \vee p \Leftrightarrow \mathbf{1}$$ (One property)

Thus we can use all these algebraic laws to simplify expressions. The next two examples show how to simplify the two expressions we found when we learned how to replace arrow symbols with *and, or,* and *not* symbols.

EXAMPLE 28 Simplify the expression $(\neg\neg r) \vee (s \vee (r \wedge t))$, which we derived in Example 21 in Section 1-4.

Solution In each line below, we apply one rule of Boolean algebra.

$$(\neg\neg r) \vee [s \vee (r \wedge t)] \Leftrightarrow r \vee [s \vee (r \wedge t)]$$ (Double negation)
$$\Leftrightarrow [s \vee (r \wedge t)] \vee r$$ (Commutative law)
$$\Leftrightarrow s \vee [(r \wedge t) \vee r]$$ (Associative law)
$$\Leftrightarrow s \vee r$$ (Absorptive law)

This is a much simpler expression than the one with which we began. ∎

EXAMPLE 29 Simplify the expression

$$(\neg(r \wedge s) \vee (r \vee s)) \wedge (\neg(r \vee s) \vee (r \wedge s))$$

which we derived in Example 22 of Section 1-4.

Solution   In each line below, we apply one rule of Boolean algebra.

$$(\neg(r \wedge s) \vee (r \vee s)) \wedge (\neg(r \vee s) \vee (r \wedge s))$$
$$\Leftrightarrow [(\neg r \vee \neg s) \vee (r \vee s)] \wedge [\neg(r \vee s) \vee (r \wedge s)] \qquad \text{(DeMorgan's law)}$$
$$\Leftrightarrow [(\neg s \vee \neg r) \vee (r \vee s)] \wedge [\neg(r \vee s) \vee (r \wedge s)] \qquad \text{(Commutative law)}$$
$$\Leftrightarrow [(\neg s) \vee (\neg r \vee (r \vee s))] \wedge [\neg(r \vee s) \vee (r \wedge s)] \qquad \text{(Associative law)}$$
$$\Leftrightarrow [(\neg s) \vee (\neg r \vee r) \vee s] \wedge [\neg(r \vee s) \vee (r \wedge s)] \qquad \text{(Associative law)}$$
$$\Leftrightarrow [(\neg s) \vee (1 \vee s)] \wedge [\neg(r \vee s) \vee (r \wedge s)] \qquad \text{(Inverse law)}$$
$$\Leftrightarrow [(\neg s) \vee 1] \wedge [\neg(r \vee s) \vee (r \wedge s)] \qquad \text{(One property)}$$
$$\Leftrightarrow 1 \wedge [\neg(r \vee s) \vee (r \wedge s)] \qquad \text{(One property)}$$
$$\Leftrightarrow \neg(r \vee s) \vee (r \wedge s) \qquad \text{(Identity property)}$$
$$\Leftrightarrow (\neg r \wedge \neg s) \vee (r \wedge s) \qquad \text{(DeMorgan's law)} \qquad \blacksquare$$

Concepts Review

1. The laws $P \cup (Q \cup R) = (P \cup Q) \cup R$ and $(p \vee q) \vee r \Leftrightarrow p \vee (q \vee r)$ are _____ laws.

2. The laws $P \cap Q = Q \cap P$ and $p \wedge q \Leftrightarrow q \wedge p$ are _____ laws.

3. The laws $P \cap (Q \cup R) = (P \cap Q) \cup (P \cap R)$ and $p \wedge (q \vee r) \Leftrightarrow (p \wedge q) \vee (p \wedge r)$ are _____ laws.

4. The laws $P \cap (P \cup Q) = P$ and $p \wedge (p \vee q) \Leftrightarrow p$ are _____ laws.

5. The laws $P \cup \emptyset = P$ and $p \vee 0 \Leftrightarrow p$ are _____ laws.

6. The laws $P \cup \sim P = U$, $P \cap \sim P = \emptyset$, $p \vee \neg p = 1$, $p \wedge \neg p = 0$ are _____ laws.

7. The associative laws allow us to delete some _____ from expressions.

8. The unique identity property tells us that if $X \cap P = P$ for all sets P, then $X = $ _____.

9. The unique inverse property tells us that if $X \cap P = \emptyset$ and $X \cup P = U$, then $X = $ _____.

10. The double negation law tells us that $\neg\neg p$ is equivalent to _____.

11. The relationship of equality for sets corresponds to the relationship of _____ for statements.

12. The idempotent property tells us that $p \wedge p$ is equivalent to _____.

13. DeMorgan's laws tell us that the complement of a union is the _____ of the complements and the _____ of an intersection is the _____ of the _____.

Exercises

A   1. Replace each blank in the proofs that follow with the name of the law of Boolean algebra that justifies the statement preceding the blank. The equations we derive show that $\sim P \cap \sim Q$ has the two inverse properties that make it a complement to $P \cup Q$: namely, its union with $P \cup Q$ is U, and its intersection with $P \cup Q$ is $\emptyset$.

(a) Prove that: $(P \cup Q) \cup (\sim P \cap \sim Q) = U$

$$
\begin{aligned}
(P \cup Q) \cup (\sim P \cap \sim Q) &= ((P \cup Q) \cup \sim P) \cap ((P \cup Q) \cup \sim Q) && (1) \underline{\hspace{2cm}} \\
&= (P \cup (Q \cup \sim P)) \cap (P \cup (Q \cup \sim Q)) && (2) \underline{\hspace{2cm}} \\
&= (P \cup (Q \cup \sim P)) \cap (P \cup U) && (3) \underline{\hspace{2cm}} \\
&= (P \cup (Q \cup \sim P)) \cap U && \text{(See Exercise 3)} \\
&= (P \cup (\sim P \cup Q)) \cap U && (4) \underline{\hspace{2cm}} \\
&= ((P \cup \sim P) \cup Q) \cap U && (5) \underline{\hspace{2cm}} \\
&= (U \cup Q) \cap U && (6) \underline{\hspace{2cm}} \\
&= U \cup U && \text{(See Exercise 3)} \\
&= U && (7) \underline{\hspace{2cm}}
\end{aligned}
$$

(b) Prove that: $(P \cup Q) \cap (\sim P \cap \sim Q) = \emptyset$

$$
\begin{aligned}
(P \cup Q) \cap (\sim P \cap \sim Q) &= (P \cap (\sim P \cap \sim Q)) \cup (Q \cap (\sim P \cap \sim Q)) && (1) \underline{\hspace{2cm}} \\
&= (P \cap (\sim P \cap \sim Q)) \cup (Q \cap (\sim Q \cap \sim P)) && (2) \underline{\hspace{2cm}} \\
&= ((P \cap \sim P) \cap \sim Q) \cup ((Q \cap \sim Q) \cap \sim P) && (3) \underline{\hspace{2cm}} \\
&= (\emptyset \cap \sim Q) \cup (\emptyset \cap P) && (4) \underline{\hspace{2cm}} \\
&= \emptyset \cup \emptyset && \text{(See Example 24)} \\
&= \emptyset && (5) \underline{\hspace{2cm}}
\end{aligned}
$$

2. Replace each blank in the proofs that follow with the name of the law of Boolean algebra that justifies the statement preceding the blank. The equations we derive show that $\sim P \cup \sim Q$ has the two inverse properties that make it a complement to $P \cap Q$.

(a) Prove that $(P \cap Q) \cup (\sim P \cup \sim Q) = U$.

$$
\begin{aligned}
(P \cap Q) \cup (\sim P \cup \sim Q) &= (P \cup (\sim P \cup \sim Q)) \cap (Q \cup (\sim P \cup \sim Q)) && (1) \underline{\hspace{2cm}} \\
&= (P \cup (\sim P \cup \sim Q)) \cap ((\sim P \cup \sim Q) \cup Q) && (2) \underline{\hspace{2cm}} \\
&= ((P \cup \sim P) \cup \sim Q) \cap (\sim P \cup (\sim Q \cup Q)) && (3) \underline{\hspace{2cm}} \\
&= (U \cup \sim Q) \cap (\sim P \cup U) && (4) \underline{\hspace{2cm}} \\
&= U \cap U && \text{(See Exercise 3)} \\
&= U && (5) \underline{\hspace{2cm}}
\end{aligned}
$$

(b) Prove that $(P \cap Q) \cap (\sim P \cup \sim Q) = \emptyset$.

$$
\begin{aligned}
(P \cap Q) \cap (\sim P \cup \sim Q) &= ((P \cap Q) \cap \sim P) \cup ((P \cap Q) \cap \sim Q) && (1) \underline{\hspace{2cm}} \\
&= (\sim P \cap (P \cap Q)) \cup ((P \cap Q) \cap \sim Q) && (2) \underline{\hspace{2cm}} \\
&= ((\sim P \cap P) \cap Q) \cup (P \cap (Q \cap \sim Q)) && (3) \underline{\hspace{2cm}} \\
&= (\emptyset \cap Q) \cup (P \cap \emptyset) && (4) \underline{\hspace{2cm}} \\
&= (\emptyset \cap Q) \cup (\emptyset \cap P) && (5) \underline{\hspace{2cm}} \\
&= \emptyset \cup \emptyset && \text{(See Example 24)} \\
&= \emptyset && (6) \underline{\hspace{2cm}}
\end{aligned}
$$

3. Show that $U \cup P = U$ and $P \cup U = U$. (*Hint:* Study Example 24.) This is called the *universe union property*.

4. Show that $P \cup P = P$. (*Hint:* Write the second P as $P \cap U$ by using an appropriate law.) This is called the *idempotent law for unions*.

5. Show that $P \cup (P \cup Q) = P \cup Q$. (*Hint:* Try the associative law and the previous exercise.)

6. Show the unique identity property: if $X \cup P = P$ for all subsets P of U, then $X = \varnothing$.

7. Show that $P \cap P = P$ for all subsets P of U.

8. Show that $P \cap (P \cap Q) = P \cap Q$.

B   In Exercises 9–12, tell which law of Boolean algebra is being used in each step of the simplification. (Derived laws, such as DeMorgan's laws, may be used.)

9. This proves that $(q \wedge \neg p) \vee (p \wedge \neg q) \Leftrightarrow (q \vee p) \wedge \neg(q \wedge p)$.

$$(q \vee \neg p) \vee (p \wedge \neg q) \Leftrightarrow [(q \wedge \neg p) \vee p] \wedge [(q \wedge \neg p) \vee \neg q] \qquad \text{(a)} \underline{\qquad}$$
$$\Leftrightarrow [(q \vee p) \wedge (\neg p \vee p)] \wedge [(q \vee \neg q) \wedge (\neg p \vee \neg q)] \qquad \text{(b)} \underline{\qquad}$$
$$\Leftrightarrow [(q \vee p) \wedge (\neg p \vee p)] \wedge [\mathbf{1} \wedge (\neg p \vee \neg q)] \qquad \text{(c)} \underline{\qquad}$$
$$\Leftrightarrow [(q \vee p) \wedge \mathbf{1}] \wedge [\mathbf{1} \wedge (\neg p \vee \neg q)] \qquad \text{(d)} \underline{\qquad}$$
$$\Leftrightarrow [(q \vee p) \wedge \mathbf{1}] \wedge [(\neg p \vee \neg q) \wedge \mathbf{1}] \qquad \text{(e)} \underline{\qquad}$$
$$\Leftrightarrow [(q \vee p) \wedge \mathbf{1}] \wedge (\neg p \vee \neg q) \qquad \text{(f)} \underline{\qquad}$$
$$\Leftrightarrow (q \vee p) \wedge (\neg p \vee \neg q) \qquad \text{(g)} \underline{\qquad}$$
$$\Leftrightarrow (q \vee p) \wedge \neg(p \wedge q) \qquad \text{(h)} \underline{\qquad}$$
$$\Leftrightarrow (q \vee p) \wedge \neg(q \wedge p) \qquad \text{(i)} \underline{\qquad}$$

10. $p \wedge p \Leftrightarrow p \wedge (p \vee \mathbf{0})$ (a) $\underline{\qquad}$
    $\Leftrightarrow p$ (b) $\underline{\qquad}$

11. $\mathbf{1} \vee p \Leftrightarrow \mathbf{1} \vee (p \wedge \mathbf{1})$ (a) $\underline{\qquad}$
    $\Leftrightarrow \mathbf{1} \vee (\mathbf{1} \wedge p)$ (b) $\underline{\qquad}$
    $\Leftrightarrow \mathbf{1}$ (c) $\underline{\qquad}$

12. The symbol $p \oplus q$ is not yet defined as part of Boolean algebra. To define it, we may use $p \oplus q$ to stand for the statement $(p \vee q) \wedge \neg(p \wedge q)$, which translates to "$p$ or q and not both p and q." Now we are going to prove the distributive law $(p \oplus q) \wedge r = (p \wedge r) \oplus (q \wedge r)$.

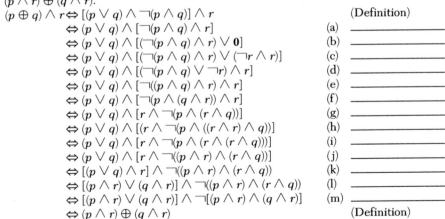

$$(p \oplus q) \wedge r \Leftrightarrow [(p \vee q) \wedge \neg(p \wedge q)] \wedge r \qquad \text{(Definition)}$$
$$\Leftrightarrow (p \vee q) \wedge [\neg(p \wedge q) \wedge r] \qquad \text{(a)} \underline{\qquad}$$
$$\Leftrightarrow (p \vee q) \wedge [(\neg(p \wedge q) \wedge r) \vee \mathbf{0}] \qquad \text{(b)} \underline{\qquad}$$
$$\Leftrightarrow (p \vee q) \wedge [(\neg(p \wedge q) \wedge r) \vee (\neg r \wedge r)] \qquad \text{(c)} \underline{\qquad}$$
$$\Leftrightarrow (p \vee q) \wedge [(\neg(p \wedge q) \vee \neg r) \wedge r] \qquad \text{(d)} \underline{\qquad}$$
$$\Leftrightarrow (p \vee q) \wedge [\neg((p \wedge q) \wedge r) \wedge r] \qquad \text{(e)} \underline{\qquad}$$
$$\Leftrightarrow (p \vee q) \wedge [\neg(p \wedge (q \wedge r)) \wedge r] \qquad \text{(f)} \underline{\qquad}$$
$$\Leftrightarrow (p \vee q) \wedge [r \wedge \neg(p \wedge (r \wedge q))] \qquad \text{(g)} \underline{\qquad}$$
$$\Leftrightarrow (p \vee q) \wedge [(r \wedge \neg(p \wedge ((r \wedge r) \wedge q))] \qquad \text{(h)} \underline{\qquad}$$
$$\Leftrightarrow (p \vee q) \wedge [r \wedge \neg(p \wedge (r \wedge (r \wedge q)))] \qquad \text{(i)} \underline{\qquad}$$
$$\Leftrightarrow (p \vee q) \wedge [r \wedge \neg((p \wedge r) \wedge (r \wedge q))] \qquad \text{(j)} \underline{\qquad}$$
$$\Leftrightarrow [(p \vee q) \wedge r] \wedge \neg((p \wedge r) \wedge (r \wedge q)) \qquad \text{(k)} \underline{\qquad}$$
$$\Leftrightarrow [(p \wedge r) \vee (q \wedge r)] \wedge \neg((p \wedge r) \wedge (r \wedge q)) \qquad \text{(l)} \underline{\qquad}$$
$$\Leftrightarrow [(p \wedge r) \vee (q \wedge r)] \wedge \neg[(p \wedge r) \wedge (q \wedge r)] \qquad \text{(m)} \underline{\qquad}$$
$$\Leftrightarrow (p \wedge r) \oplus (q \wedge r) \qquad \text{(Definition)}$$

In Exercises 13–18, simplify the expressions to equivalent statements that have as few symbols as possible.

13. $(p \vee q) \wedge (\neg p \vee q)$

14. $(p \wedge q) \vee (q \wedge \neg q)$

15. $(p \wedge (p \vee q)) \vee q$

16. $(q \vee (\neg p \wedge q)) \wedge \neg p$

17. $\neg(\neg(p \lor r) \lor \neg(p \lor q))$ 18. $\neg((p \land \neg q) \lor \neg(r \land q))$

19. Prove the unique zero law: if $x \land p \Leftrightarrow 0$ for all p, then $x \Leftrightarrow 0$.

20. Prove the unique identity law: if $x \lor p \Leftrightarrow p$ for all p, then $x \Leftrightarrow 0$.

21. Prove the unique inverse property that if $x \land p \Leftrightarrow 0$ and $x \lor p \Leftrightarrow 1$ then $x = \neg p$.

22. Prove the double negation law that says $\neg\neg p \Leftrightarrow p$.

Problems

1. Use the laws of Boolean algebra to prove that if $p \lor q = q$, then $p \land q = p$. Is the converse statement "If $p \land q = p$, then $p \lor q = q$" true as well?

2. Prove the *four-way associative law:*

$$(p_1 \lor (p_2 \lor p_3)) \lor p_4 \Leftrightarrow (p_1 \lor p_2) \lor (p_3 \lor p_4)$$

3. Prove that $(p \land q) \lor (p \land \neg q) = p$.

4. Prove that $(P \cup Q) \cap (P \cup \sim Q) = P$.

5. Show that $(p_1 \land p_2 \land p_3) \lor (p_1 \land p_2 \land \neg p_3) \Leftrightarrow p_1 \land p_2$.

6. When we are doing Boolean algebra with statement symbols $p_1, p_2, \ldots, p_n$, every symbolic statement that is not equivalent to the statement 0 may be written as $r_1 \lor r_2 \lor \cdots \lor r_m$ with *each* r_i having the form

$$r_i = q_1 \land q_2 \land \cdots \land q_j$$

and each q_k being either one statement symbol p_h or the symbolic statement $\neg p_h$. Explain why.

7. The expression $p \oplus q$ is defined in Exercise 12. Show that $p \oplus 0 \Leftrightarrow p$.

8. Show that $p \oplus p \Leftrightarrow 0$ for each statement p.

9. Prove the associative law $(p \oplus q) \oplus r \Leftrightarrow p \oplus (q \oplus r)$.

10. Show that $p \oplus q$ is equivalent to $(p \land \neg q) \lor (\neg p \land q)$.

Chapter 1
Review Exercises

1. Determine whether or not each of the following sentences is a statement.
   (a) This automobile has driven faster than 70 miles per hour.
   (b) This automobile has driven faster than 700 miles per hour.
   (c) This automobile is beautiful.
   (d) This automobile cost $10,000 when it was new.
   (e) This automobile was expensive when it was new.

2. Determine whether or not each of the following sentences about the universe of integers is a statement about x.
   (a) x is a large number.
   (b) $x + 7 = 10$
   (c) $x^2 = -1$
   (d) $x^2 = x$
   (e) If $x > 7$ then $x^2 < 48$
   (f) If x is large, then x is even.

3. For each of the sentences of Exercise 2 that you determined to be a statement, find its truth set.

4. Consider the process of sending three digits that are zeros or ones across a communication channel. Using a sequence such as 001 to indicate that two zeros and a 1 were received in that order, write down the universe of sequences we may receive.

For Exercises 5 and 6, let p be the statement "This network has seven nodes," q be the statement "This network uses three-bit addresses," and r be the statement "The last bit is a parity check."

5. Write the following statements in symbolic form.
   (a) This network has seven nodes and this network uses three-bit addresses.
   (b) This network has seven nodes and either this network uses three-bit addresses or the last bit is a parity check, but not both.
   (c) This network does not use three-bit addresses, but the last bit is a parity check.
   (d) If the last bit is a parity check, then this network does not use three-bit addresses.
   (e) This network has seven nodes if and only if the last bit is not a parity check bit.
   (f) If this network has seven nodes and the last bit is a parity check, then this network does not use three-bit addresses.

6. Write the following statements in grammatical English.
   (a) $p \wedge (q \vee r)$ (b) $p \vee (q \wedge r)$
   (c) $(p \wedge q) \to \neg r$ (d) $p \leftrightarrow (\neg q \wedge r)$

7. Using the universe of Exercise 4, write out the truth set of each of the following statements.
   (a) The number of zeros is odd.
   (b) The number of zeros is odd and there is at least one 1.
   (c) If the number of zeros is odd, then there is at least one 1.
   (d) The number of zeros is odd if and only if there is at least one 1.

8. Use the fundamental principle of set equality to show that, for the universe of Exercise 4, the statement "The number of zeros is odd" is equivalent to the statement "The number of ones is even."

For Exercises 9–15, let S be the set $\{1,3,5,7,9\}$, T be the set $\{1,2,3,4,5\}$, R be the set $\{0,2,4,6,8\}$, and P be the set $\{3,4,5,6,7\}$.

9. Find $S \cup T$.

10. Find $P \cap R$.

11. Find $P \sim R$.

12. Find $R \cap (S \cup T)$ and $(R \cap S) \cup (R \cap T)$.

13. Find $(R \cup S) \sim (R \cap S)$.

14. Is P a subset of $R \cup S$? Is P a subset of $S \cup T$?

15. Which pair of the sets given is a pair of disjoint sets?

16. Draw Venn diagrams and shade in solidly the area representing the sets given below.
(a) $(R \cup S) \sim R \cap S$ (b) $R \cap (S \cup T)$
(c) $(R \cap S) \cup (R \cap T) \cup (S \cap T)$ (d) $R \cap \sim S$

17. Use Venn diagrams to determine whether the sets $P \cap (R \sim S)$ and $(P \cap R) \sim (P \cap S)$ are equal.

18. Draw Venn diagrams in order to determine whether the statements $p \wedge (q \oplus r)$ and $(p \wedge q) \oplus (p \wedge r)$ are equivalent.

19. Prove that for any three sets P, Q, and R, $P \cap (Q \cup R) \subseteq (P \cap Q) \cup R$.

20. Prove that for any two sets S and T, $S \sim T = S \cap \sim T$.

21. The connective *nif* is denoted by $\uparrow$. The statement p nif q is false except when p is true and q is false, in which case p nif q is true. Write out a truth table for $p \uparrow q$.

In Exercises 22–25, write out truth tables for the symbolic statements given.

22. $\neg p \wedge q$ **23.** $p \wedge [(p \wedge q) \rightarrow q]$

24. $p \wedge \neg(q \wedge r)$ **25.** $p \wedge (q \rightarrow r)$

26. Determine whether the distributive law $p \wedge (q \rightarrow r) \Leftrightarrow (p \wedge q) \rightarrow (p \wedge r)$ is valid.

27. For each of the symbolic statements given, draw a combinatorial network that has a high voltage if the statement is true and a low voltage if the statement is false.
(a) $\neg(p \wedge q)$ (b) $p \wedge (q \oplus r)$ (c) $p \wedge (q \rightarrow r)$

28. Write down the statement whose truth is checked by the network in Figure 28.

Figure 28

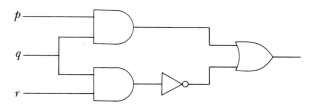

29. Rewrite the statement $(p \rightarrow q) \wedge (q \leftrightarrow r)$ using only the $\wedge$, $\vee$, and $\neg$ connectives.

30. Use truth tables to determine whether $\neg(p \leftrightarrow r)$ is equivalent to $\neg p \leftrightarrow \neg r$.

31. Show how to derive the idempotent laws $P \cap P = P$ and $P \cup P = P$ from the absorptive laws.

32. In the laws of Boolean algebra, we did not mention any properties of $p \oplus q$. In fact, in order to use Boolean algebra to discuss the properties of $p \oplus q$, we may *define $p \oplus q$* to be $(p \wedge \neg q) \vee (\neg p \wedge q)$. The proof below demonstrates that $(p \oplus q) \wedge r = (p \wedge r) \oplus (q \wedge r)$. Fill in the reasons left out. Some reasons may be rules we derived.

$(p \wedge r) \oplus (q \wedge r)$

$= [(p \wedge r) \wedge \neg(q \wedge r)] \vee [\neg(p \wedge r) \wedge (q \wedge r)]$		(Definition)
$= [(p \wedge r) \wedge (\neg q \vee \neg r)] \vee [(\neg p \vee \neg r) \wedge (q \wedge r)]$		(DeMorgan's law)
$= [[(p \wedge r) \wedge \neg q] \vee [(p \wedge r) \wedge \neg r]] \vee [(\neg p \vee \neg r) \wedge (q \wedge r)]$	(a)	_____
$= [[(p \wedge r) \wedge \neg q] \vee [p \wedge (r \wedge \neg r)]] \vee [(\neg p \vee \neg r) \wedge (q \wedge r)]$	(b)	_____
$= [[(p \wedge r) \wedge \neg q] \vee [p \wedge \mathbf{0}]] \vee [(\neg p \vee \neg r) \wedge (q \wedge r)]$	(c)	_____
$= [[(p \wedge r) \wedge \neg q] \vee \mathbf{0}] \vee [(\neg p \vee \neg r) \wedge (q \wedge r)]$	(d)	_____
$= [(p \wedge r) \wedge \neg q] \vee [(\neg p \vee \neg r) \wedge (q \wedge r)]$	(e)	_____
$= [(p \wedge r) \wedge \neg q] \vee [[\neg p \wedge (q \wedge r)] \vee [\neg r \wedge (q \wedge r)]]$	(f)	_____
$= [(p \wedge r) \wedge \neg q] \vee [[\neg p \wedge (q \wedge r)] \vee [(\neg r \wedge q) \wedge r]]$	(g)	_____
$= [(p \wedge r) \wedge \neg q] \vee [[\neg p \wedge (q \wedge r)] \vee [(q \wedge \neg r) \wedge r]]$	(h)	_____
$= [(p \wedge r) \wedge \neg q] \vee [[\neg p \wedge (q \wedge r)] \vee [q \wedge (\neg r \wedge r)]]$	(i)	_____
$= [(p \wedge r) \wedge \neg q] \vee [[\neg p \wedge (q \wedge r)] \vee [q \wedge \mathbf{0}]]$	(j)	_____
$= [(p \wedge r) \wedge \neg q] \vee [[\neg p \wedge (q \wedge r)] \vee \mathbf{0}]$	(k)	_____
$= [(p \wedge r) \wedge \neg q] \vee [\neg p \wedge (q \wedge r)]$	(l)	_____
$= [p \wedge (r \wedge \neg q)] \vee [\neg p \wedge (q \wedge r)]$	(m)	_____
$= [p \wedge (\neg q \wedge r)] \vee [\neg p \wedge (q \wedge r)]$	(n)	_____
$= [(p \wedge \neg q) \wedge r] \vee [\neg p \wedge (q \wedge r)]$	(o)	_____
$= [(p \wedge \neg q) \wedge r] \vee [(\neg p \wedge q) \wedge r]$	(p)	_____
$= [(p \wedge \neg q) \vee (\neg p \wedge q)] \wedge r$	(q)	_____
$= (p \oplus q) \wedge r$	(r)	_____

33. Simplify the expression

$$(p \wedge [(q \wedge r) \vee (q \wedge r \wedge \neg p)]) \vee (p \wedge q \wedge \neg r)$$

to give an expression with exactly three symbols.

34. Using one of the distributive laws and the other laws of Boolean algebra, it is possible to derive the other distributive law. Derive the distributive law $P \cap (Q \cup R) = (P \cap Q) \cup (P \cap R)$ from the distributive law $P \cup (Q \cap R) = (P \cup Q) \cap (P \cup R)$.

CHAPTER 2
Symbolic
Logic

*T*he discussion of statements and their truth and falsity in Chapter 1 constitutes an introduction to the subject of symbolic logic. We think of logic as the study of how to use reasoning to establish the truth of statements. We begin this chapter by demonstrating that even the concept of truth has more than one meaning. Once we have a clearer idea of what we mean by truth, we shall introduce several aspects of symbolic logic aimed at demonstrating the truth of statements. In studying logic, we learn how to show that certain statements are true regardless of what we know about the truth or falsity of their components. An example of such a statement is a mathematical theorem.

Our goal in this chapter is to give you an understanding of why a proof is written the way it is and to establish several patterns of reasoning that occur again and again in proofs. Most of these ideas simply express things you already know. By studying these patterns, you will develop an ability to recognize them explicitly in proofs and remove the shroud of mystery that someone else's proofs nearly always seem to have. If you master the ideas of proof in the carefully structured examples in this chapter, you will find that proofs come more easily in other contexts too. Nothing can substitute for the sense of discovery—"Aha, now I see the idea of it"—but someone who has the idea behind a proof should be able to use the concepts learned in this chapter to convert the idea into a logical explanation that others can follow. For the purposes of this book, such a logical explanation is what we mean by proof.

Section 2-1
Truth, Equivalence, and Implication

A   *Truth and Equivalence*

Since we think of a logical argument as one that convinces us that something is true, it is natural to begin a study of logic by establishing what we mean by truth. Surprisingly, there is more than one thing we can mean when we say a statement is true. For example, consider statements we can make about the universe {HH, HT, TH, TT} of results of two flips of a coin. One true statement we can make is "If a result has exactly one head, then it has exactly one tail." Our statement is an example of what we shall call a universally true statement.

Universal Truth

A statement about a universe U is **universally
true** if it is true for each element of the universe.
A statement is **universally false** if its truth set is empty.

The statement "The result has two heads or the result does not have two heads" is universally true in this sense too, but it is also true in a different way.

To see the other way in which this statement is true, we let p stand for "The result has two heads." Then the statement "The result has two heads or the result does not have two heads" can be rewritten as $p \vee \neg p$. As we confirm in Figure 1(a), the final column of a truth table for $p \vee \neg p$ consists entirely of T's.

Figure 1

p	p	$\vee$	$\neg$	p		p	p	$\wedge$	$\neg$	p
T	T	T	F	T		T	T	F	F	T
F	F	T	T	F		F	F	F	T	F
Step	1	3	2	1		Step	1	3	2	1
		(a)						(b)		

Thus our second example of a true statement is true just because it has the form $p \vee \neg p$. Its truth does not depend on the fact that it was a statement about two flips of a coin. Rather, it is true because of the rules of logic. Logicians say that a statement is **tautologically true** (pronounced *taught*-oh-logically) if it may be written symbolically as a symbolic statement whose truth table has only T's in its final column.

A symbolic statement having only T's in its truth table's final column is called a **tautology** (pronounced taught-*tall*-ogy).

A symbolic statement is a **contradiction** if the final column of its truth table consists entirely of F's.

EXAMPLE 1   Explain why $p \vee \neg p$ is a tautology and $p \wedge \neg p$ is a contradiction.

Solution   As Figure 1(a) shows, the final column of a truth table for $p \vee \neg p$ consists entirely of T's. As Figure 1(b) shows, the final column of a truth table for $p \wedge \neg p$ consists entirely of F's.   ■

Symbolic and Universal Equivalence

Just as there is more than one meaning for the concept of truth, there is more than one meaning for the concept of equivalence. We have given one definition of equivalence for symbolic statements and another definition for statements about a universe. As we shall see in Example 2, we may convert symbolic statements with symbols p, q, . . . into statements about a universe U by substituting a statement about U for p, a statement about U for q, and so on. Suppose we start with two equivalent symbolic statements. Are the statements we get by substituting one statement about U for each symbol equivalent?

EXAMPLE 2   The symbolic statements $\neg(p \vee q)$ and $\neg p \wedge \neg q$ are equivalent. (This is one of DeMorgan's laws.) Substitute the statement $x \leq 0$ for p and $x \geq 10$ for q, using the integers as a universe. Find the truth sets of the resulting statements. Are the resulting statements equivalent?

Solution   For the first symbolic statement, we get $\neg((x \leq 0) \vee (x \geq 10))$. Its truth set is the set of integers that are not either less than or equal to zero or greater than or equal to ten; this is the set of one-digit positive numbers. The symbolic statement $\neg p \wedge \neg q$ becomes $(x > 0) \wedge (x < 10)$; the truth set of this statement about the universe of integers is also the set of positive one-digit integers. Thus the two statements we obtained are equivalent.   ■

The example illustrates the following general principle.

Theorem 1   If s and t are equivalent symbolic statements with statement symbols p, q, . . . , then substituting a statement about a universe U for p, a statement about U for q, and so on yields two statements s' and t' about U that are equivalent.

Proof   To prove that s' and t' are equivalent, we must show that the two statements s' and t' have the same truth set. However, each x in U will make the statement we use for p either true or false, the statement we use for q either true or false, and so on. Thus x determines one and only one row of the truth table for *s* and the corresponding row of the truth table for *t*. Because *s* and *t* are equivalent, the truth tables are identical in the final columns. Thus *x* either makes both *s'* and *t'* true or both *s'* or *t'* false. Therefore *x* is in the truth set of *s'* if and only if it is in the truth set of *t'*. Therefore *s'* and *t'* are equivalent.   ■

B   Implication

We think of logic as the art (or science) of convincing reasoning. We would say that someone is making a "logical argument" if we can see how each statement in the argument follows from earlier statements or generally accepted principles. In a study of logic, we formalize this "follows from" idea as the concept of implication.

Universal Implication

> We say that a statement *p* **implies** a statement *q* if
> *q* is true in every situation that makes *p* true.

If *p* and *q* are statements about variables, we interpret this definition of *implies* to mean that the truth set of *p* is a subset of the truth set of *q*. To emphasize that we are interpreting the word *implies* in this way, we say that *p* **universally implies** *q* when the truth set of *p* is a subset of the truth set of *q*. In this way, we say that any situation in the universe that makes *p* true also makes *q* true. We then write $p \Rightarrow q$ to stand for "*p* implies *q*."

As an example, the truth set of $x > 2$ is a subset of the truth set of $x > 1$, so the statement $x > 2$ implies the statement $x > 1$. This certainly fits our intuitive idea of implication.

EXAMPLE 3   Consider the process of flipping two coins. Does one of the two statements "The result has exactly one head" and "The result does not have two tails" imply the other?

Solution   The statement "The result has exactly one head" is true for the two results shown in Figure 2(a).

Figure 2

(a)   {HT,   TH}
(b) {HH,   HT,   TH}

The statement "The result does not have two tails" has the truth set shown in Figure 2(b). Because each result in Figure 2(a) is also in Figure 2(b), the truth set shown in Figure 2(a) is a subset of the truth set shown in Figure 2(b). Thus by the definition of *implies*, the statement "The result has exactly one head" implies the statement "The result does not have two tails." Again, our definition mirrors intuition.   ■

Suppose now that p is the statement "The result has three heads." Since this statement is false for any result, its truth set is empty. Thus the truth set of p is a subset of the truth set of any statement q. Therefore p implies *any* statement, including "The result has no tails," "The result has two tails," and even "The result has one head." As we see from this example, a universally false statement implies each other statement about its universe.

If p implies q (in symbols, $p \Rightarrow q$) and q implies p ($q \Rightarrow p$), then p and q have the same truth set, so p is equivalent to q ($p \Leftrightarrow q$). Notice how our earlier notation of $\Leftrightarrow$ for equivalence fits neatly with our notation of $\Rightarrow$ for implication.

Symbolic Implication

With symbolic statements s and t, how should we interpret the definition "s implies t if t is true whenever s is true"? For symbolic statements, we say that s implies t (or s *symbolically implies* t) if, when we write down the truth tables for s and t, every row of s's table whose final entry is T corresponds to a row of t's table whose final entry is T. Here is a useful observation about symbolic implication that parallels the statement of Theorem 1:

> If s symbolically implies t and we substitute statements
> about a universe for the symbols in s and t,
> the statement that results from s will automatically
> imply the statement that results from t.

The proof of this is similar to the proof of Theorem 1.

EXAMPLE 4   Show that $p \wedge q$ implies $p \vee (\neg p \wedge q)$.

Solution   To work this example, we write down the two truth tables in Figure 3. The column marked 2 in the first table has one T in row 1 (and only row 1). The column marked 4 in the second table has a T in row 1 (as well as in other rows). Thus whenever $p \wedge q$ is true, $p \wedge (\neg p \vee q)$ is true as well, so $p \wedge q$ implies $p \vee (\neg p \wedge q)$.   ■

Figure 3

p	q	p	$\wedge$	p
T	T	T	T	T
T	F	T	F	F
F	T	F	F	T
F	F	F	F	F
Step		1	2	1

p	q	p	$\vee$	$(\neg$	p	$\wedge$	$q)$
T	T	T	T	F	T	F	T
T	F	T	T	F	T	F	F
F	T	F	T	T	F	T	T
F	F	F	F	T	F	F	F
Step		1	4	2	1	3	1

If we let P be the truth set of p and Q be the truth set of q, we can use a Venn diagram showing $P \cap Q$ and $P \cup (\sim P \cap Q)$ to illustrate the implication of Example 4.

EXAMPLE 5   Draw a Venn diagram to illustrate the implication of Example 4.

Solution   In Figure 4, we shade $P \cap Q$ in color, and we shade $P \cup (\sim P \cap Q)$ in gray. You can see that the gray region includes the entire region shaded in color, visually illustrating that $P \cap Q$ is a subset of $P \cup (\sim P \cap Q)$.   ∎

Figure 4

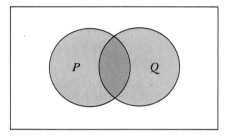

Notice from Figure 4 that $P \cup (\sim P \cap Q) = P \cup Q$, so our implication corresponds to the fact that $P \cap Q \subseteq P \cup Q$. Without drawing the Venn diagram, we might not have recognized this elementary explanation of the implication of Example 4.

Notice that in the notation $p \wedge q \Rightarrow p \vee q$ and in the notation $P \cap Q \subseteq P \cup Q$, the symbols $\Rightarrow$ and $\subseteq$ stand for relationships, and the symbols $\wedge$, $\vee$, $\cap$, and $\cup$ stand for operations. In the same way, symbols such as $=$ and $\leq$ stand for relationships between numbers, whereas symbols such as $+$ stand for operations with numbers. We adopt the same rules for using relationship symbols such as $\Rightarrow$ and $\subseteq$ that we use for relationship symbols such as $=$ and $\leq$. In particular, just as $1 + 4 \leq 3 + 5$ means the same thing as $(1 + 4) \leq (3 + 5)$, $p \wedge q \Rightarrow p \vee q$ means exactly the same thing as $(p \vee q) \Rightarrow (p \wedge q)$, and $P \cap Q \subseteq P \cup Q$ means exactly the same thing as $(P \cap Q) \subseteq (P \cup Q)$. We may express this as a precedence rule, as follows: All operation symbols take precedence over each relationship symbol.

Implication and the Conditional

You have probably noticed the similarity between the symbol $\Rightarrow$ for *implies* and the symbol $\rightarrow$ for *only if*. This similarity is intentional. Because of the way we use the word *implies* in English, it is natural to read $p \rightarrow q$ as "p implies q" as well as "p only if q." Our next two examples show the close connection between the concept of implication and the conditional connective.

EXAMPLE 6   Consider the universe of possible results of two flips of a coin. Let p be the statement "The result has two heads" and let r be the statement "The result has two tails." Find the truth sets of p, of $\neg r$, and of $p \rightarrow \neg r$. Is $p \rightarrow \neg r$ universally true?

Solution   The universe is {HH,HT,TH,TT}. {HH} is the truth set of p. {TT} is the truth set of r, so that {HH,HT,TH} is the truth set of $\neg r$. Now we check each element of the universe to see whether it makes $p \to \neg r$ true: $p \to \neg r$ is true for the result HH because p is true and $\neg r$ is true for HH. For HT, TH, and TT, $p \to \neg r$ is true simply because p is false. Therefore, the truth set of $p \to \neg r$ is the universe and $p \to \neg r$ is universally true.   ■

EXAMPLE 7   Using the statements p and r of Example 6, show that p implies $\neg r$.

Solution   The truth set of p is {HH} and the truth set of $\neg r$ is {HH,HT,TH}, so the truth set of p is a subset of the truth set of $\neg r$. Therefore p implies $\neg r$.   ■

As the two examples suggest, $p \to q$ is a true statement exactly when p implies q. Stated more precisely, this is our next theorem.

Theorem 2   The statement $s \to t$ is (universally, tautologically) true if and only if s (universally, symbolically) implies t.

Proof   (We prove that for symbolic statements s and t, if $s \to t$ is tautologically true, then s symbolically implies t, leaving the other case as a problem.) Suppose $s \to t$ is true. From a truth table for $s \to t$, we see that if $s \to t$ is true, then t must be true whenever s is true. Thus t is true whenever s is true. However, by the definition of *implies*, if t is true whenever s is true, then s implies t. Therefore, s implies t. Thus $s \to t$ is true only if s implies t.

Now suppose s implies t. By the definition of *implies*, t must be true whenever s is true. From a truth table for $s \to t$, we see that if t is true whenever s is true, then $s \to t$ is true. Therefore $s \to t$ is true. Thus s implies t only if $s \to t$ is true.   ■

Because of Theorem 2, many logicians prefer to adopt casual English as the language of logic and read $p \to q$ as "p implies q." In this case, they are using the word *implies* both as the name of a logical connective and as the name of a parallel relationship between statements. It is quite standard in English to have the precise meaning of a word determined by its context. It may be useful to practice using the word in both ways. However, so that the reader doesn't need to figure out from the context how we use the word *imply*, we shall use it only for the name of the logical relationship, not for the name of the logical connective.

Concepts Review

1. A statement about a universe U is _____ true if its truth set is U.

2. A statement about a universe U is universally false if its truth set is _____ .

3. A statement is a(n) _____ if it may be written symbolically as a symbolic statement whose truth table has only T's in its final column.

4. A statement is a(n) _____ if it may be written symbolically as a symbolic statement whose truth table has only F's in its final column.

5. Two statements about a universe are _____ equivalent if they have the same truth set.

6. If we substitute statements about a universe U for the symbols in two symbolically equivalent statements, the statements about U that result are _____ _____ .

7. We say that p _____ q if q is true whenever p is true.

8. We say that p _____ _____ q if the truth set of p is a subset of the truth set of q.

9. If each row of a truth table in which the symbolic statement s is true corresponds to a row of a truth table for the symbolic statement t in which t is true, then s _____ _____ t.

10. The symbol $\Rightarrow$ stands for a(n) _____ between statements, whereas the symbol $\rightarrow$ stands for a(n) _____ for statements.

11. The symbol $\Leftrightarrow$ stands for a(n) _____ between statements, whereas the symbol $\leftrightarrow$ stands for a(n) _____ for statements.

12. If $s \Rightarrow t$, then in a Venn diagram for S and T the circle for S lies _____ the circle for T.

13. If $s \Rightarrow t$, then the statement $s \rightarrow t$ is _____ _____ if s and t are statements about a universe, and $s \rightarrow t$ is a(n) _____ if s and t are symbolic statements.

14. If the statement $s \rightarrow t$ is _____ _____ , then $s \Rightarrow t$ if s and t are statements about a universe. If $s \rightarrow t$ is a(n) _____ , then $s \Rightarrow t$ if s and t are symbolic statements.

Exercises

A 1. Imagine flipping three coins. For each statement below, determine if it is universally true, universally false, or neither by finding its truth set.
   (a) If no tails come up, then the first coin comes up heads.
   (b) The first coin comes up heads and all three coins are tails.
   (c) There is at least one head and at least one tail.
   (d) If there is at least one head, then there is at least one tail.
   (e) If the first two coins are heads, then the last coin is heads.
   (f) If there is at least one head and at least one tail, then the first and second coins are the same or the second and third coins are the same.

2. Consider the following experiment. We *each* choose an integer between 1 and 3 inclusive. This gives us a pair of numbers; for example, (2,1) is a possibility if I choose 2 and you choose 1. Determine whether each of the following statements is universally true, universally false, or neither by finding its truth set.
(a) If the sum of the numbers is 2, then yours minus mine is 0.
(b) If the sum of the numbers is 3, then yours minus mine is 0.
(c) If the sum of the numbers is 4, then yours minus mine is 0.
(d) The sum of the numbers is 5 if their product is 6.
(e) If the sum of the numbers is 6, then the sum of the numbers is 7.
(f) If the sum of the numbers is 7, then the sum of the numbers is 8.

In Exercises 3–14, classify each of the symbolic statements as a tautology, a contradiction, or neither by finding its truth table.

3. $(p \rightarrow q) \wedge (q \rightarrow \neg p)$

4. $(p \rightarrow p) \vee q$

5. $(p \rightarrow q) \vee (q \rightarrow p)$

6. $((p \wedge \neg q) \rightarrow q) \wedge q$

7. $(p \wedge q) \vee (\neg p \rightarrow q)$

8. $(p \rightarrow q) \wedge (q \rightarrow p)$

9. $(p \vee \neg p) \wedge (q \vee \neg q)$

10. $\neg p \wedge (p \vee q) \wedge \neg q$

11. $(p \rightarrow q) \leftrightarrow (p \vee \neg q)$

12. $(p \wedge q) \rightarrow q$

13. $p \wedge ((q \wedge \neg p) \vee (\neg q \wedge \neg p))$

14. $(p \leftrightarrow q) \leftrightarrow (p \oplus q)$

B **15.** Consider the results of tossing a penny, a nickel, and a dime. You may think of the universe as consisting of sequences such as *HTH*, meaning the penny comes up heads, the nickel tails, and the dime heads. By explicitly finding truth sets, find for each pair of statements below if one implies the other and, if so, which implies which.
(a) The nickel comes up heads. The result is not all tails.
(b) There are at least two tails. There is exactly one head.
(c) There are at least two heads. There are at least two tails.
(d) Not all the coins are the same. There are exactly two heads or exactly two tails.
(e) The number of tails plus the number of heads is three. The number of heads and the number of tails are even.

16. Consider rolling two dice, one red and one green. You may think of the universe as pairs such as 6,1, which means the red die has a 6 on top and the green die a 1. For each pair of statements below, analyze truth sets to determine whether one implies the other.
(a) The top faces add to 6. Neither die is a 6.
(b) The top faces add to an odd number. The top of the red die is 1.
(c) The top faces are both even. The sum of the top faces is even.
(d) The top faces add to 1. The top faces add to 13.
(e) The top faces add to 1. The sum of the top faces is 2 or more.

In Exercises 17–28, determine whether one of the symbolic statements in each pair implies the other.

17. $p \wedge q; \ p \oplus q$

18. $(p \vee q) \wedge \neg (p \wedge q); \ p \wedge q$

19. $p \vee q; \ p \oplus q$

20. $p \wedge (q \vee \neg r); \ p \wedge q$

21. $(p \wedge q) \vee r; p \wedge (q \vee r)$

22. $p \wedge (q \vee \neg r); (p \wedge q) \vee (p \wedge \neg r)$

23. $(p \wedge q) \vee r; (p \vee r) \wedge (q \vee r)$

24. $p \wedge (p \vee q \vee r); p$

25. $p \vee q \vee r; p \wedge q$

26. $\neg p \wedge \neg q \wedge (p \vee q); p$

27. $p \wedge (p \vee q \vee r); (p \wedge q) \vee (p \wedge r)$

28. $p \oplus q \oplus r; (p \vee q \vee r) \wedge \neg(p \wedge q \wedge r)$

29–40. For each pair of statements in Exercises 17–28, draw a Venn diagram and tell how it shows that one statement does or does not imply the other.

41. Let s be the first statement and let t be the second statement in each part of Exercise 15. Determine for each part whether $s \to t$ is universally true.

42. Let s be the first statement and let t be the second statement in each part of Exercise 16. Determine for each part whether $s \to t$ is universally true.

In Exercises 43–54, for each pair of symbolic statements s and t in Exercises 17–28, determine whether $s \to t$ or $t \to s$ or both or neither is a tautology.

43. Exercise 17   **44.** Exercise 18   **45.** Exercise 19

46. Exercise 20   **47.** Exercise 21   **48.** Exercise 22

49. Exercise 23   **50.** Exercise 24   **51.** Exercise 25

52. Exercise 26   **53.** Exercise 27   **54.** Exercise 28

Problems

1. Show that if the symbolic statement s symbolically implies the symbolic statement t and we substitute statements about a universe U for the statement symbols, substituting the same statement for a symbol each time it occurs, then the statement resulting from s universally implies the statement resulting from t.

2. Discuss the relationship between equivalence and the $\leftrightarrow$ connective.

3. The *joint denial* of p and q, written as $p \downarrow q$ and read as "neither p nor q," is true when p and q are both false and is false otherwise. (The joint denial is also known as the *Sheffer stroke*.) For each statement given below, explain how to write an equivalent statement in which the only connective is the *joint denial* connective. (The joint denial may appear more than once in an answer.)

(a) $\neg p$

(b) $p \wedge q$

(c) Any statement involving p,q and any of the connectives introduced in the text

4. Given a statement expressed in terms of $\wedge, \vee,$ and $\neg$, its *dual* is obtained by replacing each conjunction ($\wedge$) by a disjunction ($\vee$) and each disjunction ($\vee$) by a conjunction.

Use s' to stand for the dual of s. Thus $[p \wedge (q \vee r)]' = p \vee (q \wedge r)$. Explain why the symbolic compound statements s and t are equivalent if and only if s' and t' are equivalent.

5. Using the duality defined in Problem 4, what is the dual of $p \rightarrow q$? Why?

6. Suppose the only connective appearing in a symbolic compound statement is $\leftrightarrow$. (It may, however, appear more than once, as in $(p \leftrightarrow q) \leftrightarrow r$.) Explain why the statement is a tautology if and only if each statement symbol appears an even number of times.

7. What happens to the result of Problem 6 if negation signs are allowed as well?

8. Show an example of a symbolic compound statement with symbols p and q that may not be expressed by using the $\neg$ and $\leftrightarrow$ connectives alone.

9. Discuss the truth or falsity of the *negation rule:* If a symbolic compound statement s uses only $\neg$, $\vee$, and $\wedge$ connectives, then $\neg s$ may be obtained from s by (1) interchanging $\wedge$ with $\vee$ and (2) replacing each statement symbol by its negation.

10. A portion of a symbolic statement t that makes sense by itself is called a substatement of t. In precise terminology, the symbolic statement s is called a *substatement* or *subformula* of the symbolic statement t if there is a symbolic statement u containing a statement symbol p such that t results from u when p is replaced by (s) (the symbolic statement s in parentheses). Show that if s and s' are equivalent symbolic statements and s is a substatement of the symbolic statement t, then replacing one or more occurrences of (s) by (s') in t yields a symbolic statement t' equivalent to t.

11. Prove the case of Theorem 2 not proved in the text.

Section 2-2
What Is a Proof?

A *Direct Proofs and Counter-Examples*

In this book, a proof of a statement means a convincing argument that the statement is true. Proofs of this kind are often seen outside of mathematics courses. Scientists making predictions on the basis of scientific principles give proofs, in effect, that their predictions follow from their principles. Computer programmers who make assertions that their programs operate according to specifications verify these assertions with a combination of reasoning and experimentation. Historians arguing that a certain sequence of decisions led inevitably to a certain consequence use logical reasoning to prove this point. Thus, though the details of writing a *mathematically* acceptable proof may be the province of mathematicians, the goal of understanding what constitutes a convincing argument should be shared by everyone hoping to use mathematical and scientific principles. We shall now discuss the logical principles that underlie convincing arguments. In order to concentrate on logical principles, we shall not introduce new subject matter at the same time as we discuss the logical principles. Instead, we shall use examples from the proofs in Chapter 1, or involving familiar facts about numbers that you may have seen in elementary school or high school. However, it is important to recognize that the principles behind the proofs we discuss apply to all situations where convincing arguments are needed.

Direct Proofs

Logic is concerned with what makes arguments convincing. We shall discuss a few principles of logic involving compound statements here; our treatment will not include all the principles of reasoning used with compound statements. We have already applied a number of sophisticated techniques of reasoning in proofs we have given in this book. One technique we have used is the *principle of direct inference,* called the *modus ponens* principle by logicians.

> The **principle of direct inference** states that if we
> know that r is true and we know that $r \rightarrow s$ is
> true, we may conclude that s is true as well.

This principle is an example of a *rule of inference*. The proof of Theorem 3 in Section 1-4 shows how the principle of direct inference is used. We wanted to prove that $p \rightarrow q$ is equivalent to $\neg p \vee q$. We expressed the definition of equivalence in an $r \rightarrow s$ form, where r is the statement "The truth tables of $p \rightarrow q$ and $\neg p \vee q$ have the same final column," and s is the statement "$p \rightarrow q$ and $\neg p \vee q$ are equivalent." We then observed that Figure 26 (in Section 1-4) confirmed that statement r was true. Next we observed that $r \rightarrow s$ is true by the definition of equivalence. Then we concluded s; that is, we concluded that $p \rightarrow q$ and $\neg p \vee q$ are equivalent.

We call a mathematical statement a **theorem** if we have a proof that it is true. The most typical kind of mathematical theorem we have is a statement of the form "If p, q, . . . then t," or, more symbolically, $p \wedge q \wedge \ldots \rightarrow t$.

The statements p, q, . . . are called the **hypotheses** and the statement t is called the **conclusion.** To show that such a statement is true, we construct an argument to show that whenever the hypotheses are true, then the conclusion is true. A **direct proof** of the conclusion from the hypotheses is a sequence of statements

first statement
second statement
.
.
.
last statement

in which the last statement is the conclusion, and each other statement is

(a) One of the hypotheses
(b) An accepted mathematical fact, or
(c) The result of applying direct inference to two earlier statements

In writing a proof, we must go through two different processes. The first consists of figuring out what ideas we need to bring together in what ways in order to do the proof. (In other words, figuring out *what* we need to say.) The second process consists of figuring out how to write down these ideas so that the sequence of statements on the paper is a proof. (That is, figuring out *how* to say what we need to say.) In this and most other textbooks, proofs contain a mixture of results from both processes. (In other words, we mix into what we are writing down some explanation of *why* we are writing it down.) For our next proof, we shall divorce the two processes by first explaining what we need to write down and why, then writing down only the statements needed to give a proof using direct inference, as described above.

EXAMPLE 8   Prove that if the integers m and n are each multiples of 3, then $m + n$ is a multiple of 3.

Solution   To begin with, since we are talking about the arithmetic operation of "plus" when we say that $m + n$ is a multiple of 3, we need a way to use arithmetic or algebra to say that m is a multiple of 3 and n is a multiple of 3. To use the symbolism of arithmetic to say m is a multiple of 3, we may say that there is an integer i such that $m = 3i$. In fact, this defines a multiple of 3. Similarly, we may say that there is an integer j such that $n = 3j$. Now we see that $m + n$ may be written as $3i + 3j = 3(i + j)$, and thus by definition $m + n$ is a multiple of 3.

How do we write a proof based on the ideas above so that it has the form of a direct proof? We show how below, indicating in parentheses after each statement how it may be classified among the three kinds of statements allowed in a direct proof.

Assume that m is a multiple of 3 and n is a multiple of 3.	(Hypotheses)
If m is a multiple of 3, then there is an i such that $m = 3i$.	(Accepted fact)
Then $m = 3i$.	(Direct inference)
If n is a multiple of 3, then there is a j such that $m = 3j$.	(Accepted fact)
Then $n = 3j$.	(Direct inference)
If $m = 3i$ and $n = 3j$, then $m + n = 3i + 3j$.	(Accepted fact)
Therefore $m + n = 3i + 3j$.	(Direct inference)
By factoring, $m + n = 3(i + j)$	(Accepted fact)
By definition, if there is an integer k such that $m + n = 3k$, then $m + n$ is a multiple of 3.	(Accepted fact)
Therefore $m + n$ is a multiple of 3.	(Direct inference) ■

Notice how the use of the hypotheses is preceded by the word *assume* and how each use of direct inference is preceded by a word such as *therefore* or *then*. The role of these words is to inform the reader which of the three allowable kinds of statements is being used. Technically, then, the words in parentheses are unnecessary and would not normally appear in a formal proof. Unfortunately, a formal proof written in this way appears awkward and can obscure the thinking behind it.

An informal proof, however, can contain explanations about why certain accepted facts are being used and can rely on generally accepted facts without making explicit reference to them. If we were to outline both a formal proof and a parallel informal proof of the same result, we would expect to get essentially the same outline in each case. (We give an example below of what we mean by an outline of a proof.) Thus an informal proof contains the essence of the argument that appears in a formal proof. After this section of the book, we shall return exclusively to an informal style of proof.

You can see two more direct proofs in the proof of Theorem 2 in the previous section. The first such proof may be summarized in outline form as follows.

> (Suppose) $s \rightarrow t$ is true.
> If $s \rightarrow t$ is true, then t is true whenever s is true.
> If t is true whenever s is true, then s implies t.
> Therefore s implies t.

Here we had two uses of the *modus ponens* principle. Notice in Theorem 2 that, in order to prove a statement of the form $p \leftrightarrow q$, we first proved $p \rightarrow q$ and then proved $q \rightarrow p$. This is a valid approach, because $p \leftrightarrow q$ is equivalent to $(p \rightarrow q) \wedge (q \rightarrow p)$.

Converses

> The statement $q \rightarrow p$ is called the **converse** of the
> statement $p \rightarrow q$.

For example, the converse of the statement "If I am 6 feet tall, then I can reach a 7-foot-high shelf" is the statement "If I can reach a 7-foot-high shelf, then I am 6 feet tall." Notice that the first conditional statement is true, but its converse, the second conditional statement, is false for some people. (For example, a person 5 feet 9 inches tall can reach a 7-foot-high shelf.) We have just shown that we may not assume $q \rightarrow p$ to be true simply because we know that $p \rightarrow q$ is true.

One of the mistakes people make most often when reasoning in unfamiliar circumstances is the result of thinking that they are using a statement of the form $p \rightarrow q$ in their reasoning process when in fact they are accidentally using its converse.

EXAMPLE 9   Find the error in the following argument. "If n is a positive even integer, then $n > 1$. 5 is greater than 1. Therefore, 5 is a positive even integer."

Solution   One way to see a fault in an argument is to write it in symbols. Let p be the statement "n is a positive even integer." Let q be the statement "$n > 1$."

The argument has the following form: "If p, then q. q is true. Therefore, p is true." This argument is invalid, because from $p \to q$ and q we may not conclude p. (The argument could result from mentally substituting $q \to p$ for $p \to q$ and thinking that the argument has the valid form "$q \to p$ and q are true; therefore p is true.") ∎

Counter-Examples

In order to show that $p \to q$ (If I am 6 feet tall, then I can reach a 7-foot-high shelf) does not imply the converse statement $q \to p$, we gave a counter-example to the false assertion that $q \to p$ is true if $p \to q$ is true.

> A **counter-example** to a statement about a
> universe is a member of the universe for which
> the statement is false.

To show that a statement *is* a theorem, we must give a proof; to show that a statement *is not* a theorem, we show that it cannot be proved true by giving a counter-example.

EXAMPLE 10   Is the statement "If n is a positive integer, then n is a sum of one, two, or three squares" a theorem about positive integers?

Solution   The answer turns out to be "No," as we find by experimentation. We see that $2 = 1 + 1$, $3 = 1 + 1 + 1$, 4 is a square, $5 = 4 + 1$, and $6 = 4 + 1 + 1$, but there is no way of writing 7 as a sum of three numbers that are squares. Thus $n = 7$ is a counter-example, so the statement is not a theorem. ∎

B   Indirect Proofs

Various Forms of the Conditional

We have observed that a statement and its converse are not equivalent. In addition to the converse, there are other natural variants to conditional statements. For example, what do we mean when we say, "If I cannot reach a 7-foot-high shelf, then I am not 6 feet tall"? Let us analyze how such a statement relates to our original conditional statement (which in this case is "If I am 6 feet tall, then I can reach a 7-foot-high shelf").

A conditional statement involving just the two clauses p and q or the two clauses $\neg p$ and $\neg q$ can be represented as one of the four forms.

$$p \to q \qquad q \to p \qquad \neg q \to \neg p \qquad \neg p \to \neg q$$

conditional　　**converse**　　**contrapositive**　　**contraconverse**

By writing down the truth tables of these four statements as in Figure 5, we see that a conditional statement is equivalent to its contrapositive. Further, the converse and contraconverse of a conditional statement are equivalent to each other, but not to the original statement. (The contraconverse of a statement is also called its **inverse**.) Thus, despite the richness of language, a conditional statement should have only one of two possible interpretations. Knowing this, we can usually choose the appropriate interpretation quickly.

Figure 5

Conditional

p	q	$p \rightarrow q$
T	T	T
T	F	F
F	T	T
F	F	T

Converse

p	q	$q \rightarrow p$
T	T	T
T	F	T
F	T	F
F	F	T

Contrapositive

p	q	$\neg$	q	$\rightarrow$	$\neg$	p
T	T	F	T	T	F	T
T	F	T	F	F	F	T
F	T	F	T	T	T	F
F	F	T	F	T	T	F
Step		2	1	3	2	1

Contraconverse

p	q	$\neg$	p	$\rightarrow$	$\neg$	q
T	T	F	T	T	F	T
T	F	F	T	T	T	F
F	T	T	F	F	F	T
F	F	T	F	T	T	F
Step		2	1	3	2	1

Contrapositive Inference

EXAMPLE 11   Write the conditional statement "If I cannot reach a 7-foot-high shelf, then I am not 6 feet tall" symbolically. Write down an equivalent symbolic statement with no negations, and interpret this symbolic statement in English.

Solution   The statement given has the form $\neg q \rightarrow \neg p$, where q is "I can reach a 7-foot-high shelf" and p is "I am 6 feet tall." Therefore, it is contrapositive of a statement of the form $p \rightarrow q$; in English, this statement is "If I am 6 feet tall then I can reach a 7-foot-high shelf." ∎

The contrapositive form of conditional statements leads to the principle of **contrapositive inference**:

From $\neg q \rightarrow \neg p$ we may conclude $p \rightarrow q$.

EXAMPLE 12   Prove that, for each member n of the universe of positive integers, if $n^2 > 100$, then $n > 10$.

Solution   (This will be an example of a proof by contrapositive inference. Thus we shall assume the statement "$\neg(n > 10)$" and derive the statement "$\neg(n^2 > 100)$," showing that "$\neg(n > 10)$" implies "$\neg(n^2 > 100)$." Thus we shall have shown that "$\neg(n > 10) \rightarrow \neg(n^2 > 100)$" is true, so that by contrapositive inference, "$n^2 > 100 \rightarrow n > 10$" is true.)

If $n \leq 10$ (that is, if $\neg(n > 10)$), then $n^2 = n \cdot n \leq 10 \cdot 10 = 100$. That is, if n is not greater than 10, n^2 is not greater than 100. Thus (by contrapositive inference) if $n^2 > 100$, then $n > 10$.   ■

Proof by Contradiction

A more common variation of this form of reasoning is the principle of **proof by contradiction.** This rule of inference tells us that

$$\text{From } p \text{ and } (p \wedge \neg q) \rightarrow \neg p \text{ we may conclude } q.$$

Conceptually, the principle of proof by contradiction says that "If by assuming that p and not q are true, we may prove the contradictory statement that p is false, then p must imply q."

EXAMPLE 13   Prove that if $x^2 + x - 2 = 0$, then $x \neq 0$.

Solution   (This is to be an example of proof by contradiction. Thus we will assume that a statement p and another statement $\neg q$ are true and proceed to show that in this case $\neg p$ is true as well.)

Suppose $x^2 + x - 2 = 0$. (This is p.) Assume that $x = 0$. (This is $\neg q$.) This second assumption yields $x^2 + x - 2 = 0^2 + 0 - 2 = -2$, so $x^2 + x - 2 \neq 0$. (This is $\neg p$). This contradicts $x^2 + x - 2 = 0$, so the assumption $x = 0$ is not valid. Therefore $x \neq 0$.   ■

Reduction to Absurdity

In almost the same way, we can derive a contradiction of a known fact.

EXAMPLE 14   Prove that if $x^2 + x - 2 = 0$, then $x \neq 0$.

Solution   (This is an example of another use of contradiction in proofs; we shall explain it below.) Suppose $x^2 + x - 2 = 0$. (This is p.) Assume that $x = 0$. (This is $\neg q$.) Then $0^2 - 0 - 2 = x^2 + x - 2 = 0$, or $-2 = 0$. This is an absurdity, so the assumption $x = 0$ is not valid. Therefore $x \neq 0$.   ■

In this last proof, we began with a statement p. We showed that $p \wedge \neg q$ yielded $-2 = 0$, which contradicts a known fact. In symbols, we showed that $p \wedge \neg q \rightarrow \neg r$, where r is the known fact $-2 \neq 0$. We then concluded that if p is true, then q must be true as well. (Otherwise, we could prove that a tautologically false statement (namely $\neg r \wedge r$) is true!) This form of reasoning is called **reduction to absurdity.** A more formal statement of this rule of inference is that

If r is true, then from p and $p \wedge \neg q \rightarrow \neg r$ we
may conclude q.

Any of the three forms of proof—by contrapositive inference, by contradiction, or by reduction to absurdity—is called an **indirect proof.** (Some logicians prefer to use the phrase *indirect proof* to refer only to proof by contradiction or reduction to absurdity.)

The General Principle of Proof by Contradiction

A traditional example of an indirect proof is one you may have seen when you first learned about rational and irrational numbers. Recall that a **rational** number is one that can be expressed as a (proper or improper) fraction. An **irrational** number is a number that cannot be so expressed.

EXAMPLE 15   Prove that $\sqrt{5}$ is not a rational number.

Solution   First we shall give an informal proof by contradiction; then we shall show how this proof fits into the pattern we have been studying.

Assume that $\sqrt{5}$ is rational. By the *definition of rational numbers,* this means that there are integers m and n such that $\sqrt{5} = m/n$ in lowest terms. Squaring this gives $5 = m^2/n^2$ or $5n^2 = m^2$. When m is factored into prime power factors, m^2 will have the same primes as $5n^2$ has as its prime factors. Thus 5 must be a prime factor of m, so $m = 5k$. Thus $5n^2 = (5k)^2 = 25k^2$, and dividing by 5 gives $n^2 = 5k^2$. This means that 5 is a factor of n. Thus m and n have the common factor of 5. This contradicts the definition of lowest terms. Therefore, the assumption that $\sqrt{5}$ is rational is impossible, so (because a number which is not rational is, by definition, irrational) $\sqrt{5}$ is irrational.   ∎

Notice that the statement "$\sqrt{5}$ is irrational" does not have the form "If p then q." Thus our proof does not fit the pattern we described for proof by contradiction. One way to deal with this is to reword the statement: "If $r = \sqrt{5}$, then r is irrational." Then p is the statement "$r = \sqrt{5}$," and q is the statement "r is irrational." Assuming $\neg q$ gives us $r = m/n$ in lowest terms; assuming both p and $\neg q$ gives us $\sqrt{5} = m/n$ in lowest terms, and the proof proceeds as above.

A second resolution to the fact that the statement "$\sqrt{5}$ is irrational" does not have the form $p \rightarrow q$ is the following **general principle of proof by contradiction:**

If assuming $\neg p$ leads to a contradiction,
then p must be true.

We shall use this more general principle when it is appropriate.

The rules of inference we have discussed belong to a branch of symbolic logic called *propositional logic*. A **proposition** is a statement without variables; propositional logic includes the principles of inference appropriate to such statements. These principles often occur in everyday reasoning and in mathematical proofs. While it may be applied to statements about variables, propositional logic does not provide us with enough tools to construct or understand many mathematical proofs. This is because the rules of inference ignore the possibility of having variables in our statements. In the next section, we shall illustrate the other tools needed.

Concepts Review

1. The principle of _____ _____ tells us that if r and $r \rightarrow s$ are both true, then the statement s is true as well.

2. If we have a proof that a statement is true, then we call that statement a(n) _____ .

3. In a direct proof, each statement is one of the _____, an accepted mathematical fact, or the result of applying _____ _____ to earlier statements.

4. The _____ of the statement $p \rightarrow q$ is the statement $q \rightarrow p$.

5. If $p \rightarrow q$ is true, then $q \rightarrow p$ is [choose one: always, sometimes, never] _____ true.

6. A(n) _____-_____ to a statement about a universe is a member of the universe that makes the statement false.

7. To show that a statement is not universally true, we give a(n) _____- _____ to the statement.

8. A statement and its [choose one: converse, contrapositive, contraconverse] _____ are equivalent.

9. The _____ of the statement $p \rightarrow q$ is the statement $\sim q \rightarrow \sim p$.

10. In the method of proof by _____, we assume that the negation of a statement is true and derive a false consequence.

Exercises

A

1. Find a counter-example to each of the following statements about positive integers n.
   (a) $2n^2 + n = n^3 - n^2 + 3n$
   (b) If n is a prime, then 12 and $n^3 - n^2 + n$ have a common factor.

2. Find a counter-example to each of the following statements about subsets S of $\{a, b, c, d, e\} = U$.
   (a) $S \cap \{a, b, c, d\} = S$
   (b) $S \cap (\{a, b\} \cup \sim S) \neq \emptyset$

3. Construct a direct proof that if m and n are even numbers, then $m + n$ is an even number. (*Hint: n* is even means that $n = 2j$ for some integer j.)

4. Construct a direct proof that if m and n are even numbers, then $m \cdot n$ is an even number.

5. Write down truth tables for $p \leftrightarrow q$ and $(\neg p \lor q) \land (\neg q \lor p)$. Now give a direct proof, patterned after the proof of Theorem 3 of Chapter 1, that if p and q are statements, then $p \leftrightarrow q$ is equivalent to $(\neg p \lor q) \land (\neg q \lor p)$.

6. Write down truth tables for $p \leftrightarrow q$ and $\neg(p \oplus q)$. Now give a direct proof, patterned after the proof of Theorem 3 of Chapter 1, that if p and q are statements, then $p \leftrightarrow q$ is equivalent to $\neg(p \oplus q)$.

7. Prove that if m is even, then m^2 is even.

8. The definition of odd is that n is odd if and only if $n = 2j + 1$ for some j. Construct a proof that if m is odd and n is odd, then $m + n$ is even.

9. Two facts of geometry are: "If angles A, B, and C are the angles of a triangle, then the sum of their measures is 180 degrees," and "If A, B, and C are the angles of one triangle, if A', B', and C' are the angles of a second triangle, and if the measures of A, B, and C equal the measures of A', B', and C', respectively, then the two triangles are similar." Give a proof that "If A, B, and C are the angles of one triangle and A', B', and C' are angles of a second triangle and the measure of A equals the measure of A' and the measure of B equals the measure of B', then the two triangles are similar."

10. We have observed that set inclusion satisfies the transitive law "If $R \subseteq S$ and $S \subseteq T$, then $R \subseteq T$." Using this and any parts of Theorem 2 of Chapter 1 you wish, prove that "If P and Q are sets, then $P \cap Q \subseteq P \cup Q$."

B 11. Write down the converse and then the contrapositive of each of these statements.
   (a) If the hose is 60 feet long, then the hose will reach the tomatoes.
   (b) If George weighs 160 pounds, then Bill weighs at least 210.
   (c) George goes for a walk only if Mary goes for a walk.
   (d) Pamela recites a poem if Andre asks for a poem.

12. Write down the converse and then the contrapositive of each of these statements.
   (a) If n is a prime, then mn is a square.
   (b) If P, Q, and R are colinear, then PQR is not a triangle.
   (c) The diagonals of rhombus R are equal only if rhombus R is a square.
   (d) The diagonals of parallelogram P are equal if parallelogram P is a square.

13. Construct a proof that if m is even and n is odd, then $m + n$ is odd.

14. Construct an indirect proof that if m^2 is even, then m is even.

15. Prove that if $n^2 < 9$, then $n < 3$.

16. Prove indirectly that if m is even, then m^2 is even.

17. Prove that $\sqrt{2}$ is not rational. That is, prove that there are not two numbers m and n such that $m/n = \sqrt{2}$ in lowest terms.

18. Prove that $\sqrt{3}$ is not rational. (See Exercise 17.)

19. Prove that $\sqrt[3]{2}$ is not rational. (See Exercise 17.)

20. Prove that $\sqrt[3]{3}$ is not rational. (See Exercise 17.)

Problems

1. In Problem 4 of Section 2-1, we discussed the dual of a symbolic statement. If we have a proof of a statement t, how may we obtain a proof of the dual statement t?

2. Another principle of inference is the transitive law (also called *hypothetical syllogism*): If we know that $p \to q$ is true and $q \to r$ is true, then we may conclude that $p \to r$ is true. How would use of this principle have simplified Example 8?

3. By using truth tables, verify the transitive law as stated in Problem 2.

4. By using truth tables, verify the principle of constructive dilemma: if $p \lor q$ is true, $p \to q$ is true, and $q \to s$ is true, then $p \lor s$ is true.

5. Use direct inference to prove the principle of transitive inference: from the truth of p, $p \to q$, and $q \to r$ we may conclude r.

6. The principle of the excluded middle is that $p \lor \neg p$ is true for any statement p. Show that the final column of a truth table for $p \lor \neg p$ consists entirely of T's, thus justifying the principle. (In some branches of logic that are not based on such truth-table analysis, this principle is rejected, but we shall not reject it for this book.) Using the principle of the excluded middle as an accepted mathematical fact and the principle of constructive dilemma (Problem 4) as a rule of inference, prove that $(p \to q) \land (q \to r) \to \neg p \lor r$. How does this relate to the transitive law of Problems 2 and 3?

7. Prove that if b and c are integers, then any solution to $x^2 + bx + c = 0$ that is a rational number is also an integer. (*Hint:* The quadratic formula comes very close to doing this for you, but one possible problem remains to be eliminated when you use the quadratic formula.)

8. Prove that there is no largest prime number.

9. The principle of reflexivity states that $p \to p$ is a tautology or, in words, "From the truth of p we may conclude the truth of p." Using the principle of the excluded middle (Problem 6), the principle of reflexivity, and the principle of constructive dilemma (Problem 4), you may construct a direct proof that $(\neg q \to \neg p) \to (\neg p \lor q)$. Do so. What rule of inference have you derived from other rules?

10. The general principle of proof by contradiction may be stated symbolically as $(\neg p \to (q \land \neg q)) \to p$, or in words, "From $\neg p \to (q \land \neg q)$ we may conclude p." Notice that DeMorgan's law applied to $\neg(\neg q \lor q)$ gives $q \land \neg q$. Apply DeMorgan's law and the principle of contrapositive inference to derive the general principle of proof by contradiction.

Section 2-3
Predicate Logic

A   Quantifiers

We have noted that computer languages let us combine statements into meaningful compound statements, and we have learned some of the ways we may use compound statements in reasoning. In addition to forming compound statements, there are other important ways of constructing new statements from old ones. Consider the statement "On an input of x this program stops after producing exactly one output value y." Although this expresses a desirable property of a computer program, it doesn't actually tell us much about whether the program works, because it doesn't tell us about the values of x that make the statement true. A more useful statement is "For all possible inputs x, on an input of x this program stops and produces exactly one output value y." A discouraging but almost equally ·useful statement is "No input x exists for which, on an input of x this program stops and produces exactly one output value y."

Universal Quantification

Similar constructions abound in mathematics. For example, the definition of $P \subseteq Q$ says that every x in P is in Q. For a given x in our universe, we can say that if x is in P, then it is in Q by writing

$$(x \in P) \to (x \in Q)$$

How do we say that each x in P is also in Q? One way is to use a statement of the form

$$\text{For all } x \, [(x \in P) \to (x \in Q)]$$

In words, "For all x (in the universe), if x is in P, then x is in Q." A statement of this form is called a **universally quantified** statement. There is a shorthand symbolism that uses an upside-down A, to remind us of the word *all*. We write

$$\forall x \, [(x \in P) \to (x \in Q)]$$

to stand for the statement "For all x, if $x \in P$, then $x \in Q$." The symbol $\forall$ is called the **universal quantifier symbol.** Thus if $s(x)$ is the statement "On input x, this program stops and produces exactly one output value," we can write $\forall x \, (s(x))$ or $\forall x \, s(x)$ to stand for the statement that "For all x, on input x . . . ."

Existential Quantification

How do we write the statement that no x exists for which the program works? Using a backward E to remind us of the word *exists*, we can write $\neg \exists x \, (s(x))$ or $\neg \exists x \, s(x)$ to stand for "There does not exist an x such that on input x . . . ." We read

$\exists x\ (s(x))$ as "There exists an x such that s of x." The symbol $\exists$ is called the **existential quantifier symbol,** and we say that $\exists x\ (s(x))$ is an *existentially quantified* statement.

EXAMPLE 16   Using $s(x)$ to stand for "$x^2 = 16$," write the statement "There is an x such that $x^2 = 16$" as a symbolic statement.

Solution   We write $\exists x\ (s(x))$.   ∎

EXAMPLE 17   Rewrite the following statements in symbolic form, using the abbreviations $s(x)$ for "x is an even integer," $t(x,y)$ for "$x = 2y$," $p(x)$ for "x is a prime integer," and $r(x)$ for "$x > 2$." Our universe is the universe of positive integers.

(a) If x is an even integer, then there is an integer y such that $x = 2y$.
(b) There is a prime integer x such that $x = 2y$ for some y.
(c) For all prime integers x, if $x > 2$, then x is not an even integer.

Solution   (The idea is to look for phrases for which $s(x)$, $t(x,y)$, and so on are good substitutes and then look for phrases such as *there is, for each,* and *for some*, which we may translate as $\exists$ or $\forall$.)

(a) $s(x) \rightarrow \exists y\ (t(x,y))$; another answer is: $s(x) \rightarrow \exists y\ t(x,y)$
(b) $\exists x\ (p(x) \wedge \exists y\ (t(x,y)))$
(c) This symbolic statement cannot be obtained without rewording the phrase "For all prime integers x," because our universe is the universe of all integers, not the set of prime integers. Since we want to make our statement only about prime integers, we may rewrite our phrase as "For all integers x, if x is a prime, then . . . ."

This variation on the phrase gives us the symbolic statement $\forall x\ (p(x) \rightarrow (r(x) \rightarrow \neg s(x)))$.   ∎

Statements that have quantifiers abound in mathematics. Examine, for example, the definition of a multiple of 3 in Example 8 and the definition of a rational number in Example 15.

Free and Bound Variables

In part (a) of Example 17, only the variable y had a quantifier. We say that y is a **bound variable** in (a) and x is a **free variable** in (a). In (a), we could interpret our statement in one and only one way, regardless of whether we used parentheses to indicate which y-values were quantified by $\exists y$. In (b), one set of parentheses, the parentheses following $\exists x$, was absolutely essential. Without the parentheses, we would not necessarily be saying that the prime number x that we said exists was the same as the number x that was equal to $2y$. (This shows that it is possible for one occurrence of a variable to be bound to a quantifier while another occurrence is not.)

In an expression $\forall x\ (p(x)\ \ldots\ )$ or $\exists x\ (p(x)\ \ldots\ )$, the portion of the expression to which the $\forall x$ or $\exists x$ applies is called the **scope** of the quantifier and will be indicated by parentheses unless it is obvious. (People often treat the signs $\forall$ and $\exists$ as they do the negation sign; namely, if an expression has insufficient parentheses to make it clear, apply $\forall$ or $\exists$ to the shortest list of following symbols that makes sense. In this book we will provide adequate parentheses.)

The variable x is said to be **bound** by $\forall x$ or by $\exists x$ if x lies in the scope of the quantifier. A variable that is not bound by a quantifier is said to be **free.**

EXAMPLE 18   Using the statements of Example 17, rewrite the symbolic statements (a) and (b) in English.

(a) $\forall x\ (p(x) \wedge \exists y\ (t(x,y) \wedge r(x)))$
(b) $\neg\exists x\ (p(x) \wedge \exists y\ (t(x,y)) \vee r(z))$

Solution

(a) For each integer x, x is a prime, and there is an integer y such that x is $2y$ and x is greater than 2.
(b) There is no integer x such that either both x is prime and there is a y such that $x = 2y$ or z is greater than 2.   ■

EXAMPLE 19   In each formula below, describe the scope of each quantifier, and describe which variables are bound and which are free. Note that (a) and (b) come from Example 18.

(a) $\forall x\ (p(x) \wedge \exists y\ (t(x,y) \wedge r(x)))$
(b) $\neg\exists x\ (p(x) \wedge \exists y\ (t(x,y)) \vee r(z))$
(c) $\neg\exists x\ (p(x) \wedge \exists y\ (t(x,y)) \vee r(y))$

Solution   In (a), the scope of $\forall x$ is the remainder of the formula. The scope of $\exists y$ is the formula $(t(x,y) \wedge r(x))$. There are no free variables. In (b), the scope of $\exists x$ is the remainder of the formula, and the scope of $\exists y$ is $(t(x,y))$. The variable z is free, but x and y are bound. In (c), the scopes are the same as in part (b). The y in $r(y)$ is free, but the y in $t(x,y)$ is bound.   ■

Parts (b) and (c) of this example show how much care is needed in interpreting quantified expressions. The statements in (b) and (c) will be equivalent because they will have the same truth set. (In other words, the set of all z that may be used in $r(z)$ to give a true statement in (b) is the same as the set of all y that may be used in $r(y)$ to give a true statement in (c).) The use of the variable y as a bound variable in one part of the expression and a free variable in another part is not incorrect, but it can be quite confusing. Nothing in the rules forbids the use of notation such as we see in statement (c), but nothing prevents us from changing it to less confusing notation, such as that in (b).

Substitution of Constants for Variables

The use of quantifiers is not the only way to specify a statement more precisely. We may also substitute members of the universe for variables, as shown below.

EXAMPLE 20   Let $s(x,y)$ be the statement $x = 3y$. Write the following statements in symbolic form.

(a) There is an x such that $x = 3\cdot4$.
(b) For all y, $15 = 3\cdot y$.
(c) $15 = 3\cdot5$.

Solution

(a) $\exists x\ (s(x,4))$
(b) $\forall y\ (s(15,y))$
(c) $s(15,5)$ ■

If statement (b) in Example 20 appears rather strange, that is because it is false. We shall discuss the truth and falsity of quantified statements shortly.

In the process of substitution of a member of the universe for a variable, the member used for substitution is called a **constant.** There are two important rules to observe in the substitution of constants.

(a) When we substitute a constant for a free variable, we must substitute it for all free occurrences of that variable.
(2) If a statement already has quantifiers, we never substitute a constant for a *bound* variable.

Violating either rule could change the meaning of the statement or render it meaningless.

EXAMPLE 21   Demonstrate how statement (a) below becomes meaningless when we substitute 7 for y and how statement (b) below changes in meaning when we substitute 7 for the first occurrence of y.

(a) $\exists y\ (y = 3\cdot4)$
(b) y is a prime and $y = 3\cdot4$

Solution   (a) becomes the meaningless symbol string $\exists 7\ (7 = 3\cdot4)$. In words, "There exists a seven such that seven equals three times four." (b) becomes the statement "7 is a prime and $y = 3\cdot4$." This statement has {12} as its truth set, whereas the original statement had an empty truth set.   ■

People often say that substituting a constant (a member of the universe) for an occurrence of a variable **binds** that occurrence of the variable to that constant; in this case, that occurrence of the variable is referred to as *bound* to the constant.

This extends the concept of binding and bound variables. In a course of compilers for computer languages, you will learn about a similar but more general concept of binding.

▣ *Truth and Equivalence of Quantified Statements*

The version of logic dealing with quantified statements is called **predicate logic.** The introduction of quantifiers not only extends the expressive power of the statements we can construct but also allows the development of logical principles that explain the reasoning in most mathematical proofs. For example, a proof that uses the fundamental principle of set equality to show that two sets, say S and *T*, are equal might begin with an argument of the form

> Let $x \in S$
> statement 1
> statement 2
> .
> .
> .
> last statement
> Thus $x \in T$
> Therefore, for all x, if x is in S, then x is in T

Following this would be a similar argument in which the roles of S and T would be reversed. Both Example 8 of Section 1-2 and Theorem 1 of Section 1-2 are examples of this kind of proof. The rule of inference underlying this method of reasoning is "If, using the statement $s(x)$ as an assumption, using accepted facts, and using other accepted rules of inference, we may derive the statement $t(x)$, then we may conclude that $\forall x \ (s(x) \rightarrow t(x))$." A thorough study of the rules of inference appropriate to use with quantifiers occupies a major portion of a course in logic, so we shall not attempt such a study. We shall instead follow the tradition in mathematics of using quantified statements informally and relying on our intuition to guide us in interpreting and drawing conclusions from quantified statements.

Quantifiers and Logical Operators

Because a number of standard relationships among quantified statements may not be intuitively clear, we shall supplement our intuition with a brief study of how the two quantifiers relate to each other and to the connective operators $\wedge$, $\vee$, $\rightarrow$, and $\neg$. We need a precise definition of equivalence for quantified expressions so that we can discuss when two expressions are equivalent. We begin with a definition of truth for quantified statements.

> Let $s(x)$ be a statement about x. The statement $\forall x \ (s(x))$
> is true if $s(x)$ is universally true. The statement
> $\forall x \ (s(x))$ is false if $s(x)$ is not universally true. That is,
> $\forall x \ (s(x))$ is false if there is just one counter-example to $s(x)$.

EXAMPLE 22   If $s(x)$ is the statement "$x^2 \geq 0$," and $t(x)$ is the statement "$x \geq 0$" about the integers, is $\forall x\ s(x)$ true? Is $\forall x\ t(x)$ true?

Solution   Since $x^2 \geq 0$ for each integer x, $\forall x\ s(x)$ is true. Since $t(x)$ is false for the integer $x = -1$, $\forall x\ t(x)$ is false.   ■

> The statement $\exists x\ (s(x))$ is **true** if $s(x)$ is true for at least one x in the universe; that is, there is one example which makes $s(x)$ true. $\exists t\ (s(t))$ is **false** if $s(x)$ is false for all x—that is, the truth set of $s(x)$ is empty.

EXAMPLE 23   If $t(x)$ is the statement "$x > 0$" about the integers, is $\exists x\ (t(x))$ true? If $r(x)$ is the statement $x^2 < 0$, is $\exists x\ (r(x))$ true?

Solution   Since 1 is an integer x such that $x > 0$, $\exists x\ (t(x))$ is true. Since $x^2 < 0$ is not true for any integer x, $\exists x\ (r(x))$ is false.   ■

EXAMPLE 24   If p, r, and s are the statements of Example 17, which of the following are true and which are false?

(a) $\forall x\ p(x)$
(b) $\exists x\ p(x)$
(c) $\exists x\ (p(x) \wedge s(x))$
(d) $\exists x\ (p(x) \wedge s(x) \wedge r\ (x))$

Solution

(a) $p(x)$ is the statement "x is a prime integer." False; $x = 4$ is a counter-example.
(b) True; $x = 3$ is an example.
(c) $s(x)$ is the statement "x is an even integer." True; $x = 2$ is an example.
(d) $r(x)$ is the statement "$x > 2$." False; there are no examples.   ■

Equivalence of Quantified Statements

Note that an expression such as $\exists x\ (\neg s(x))$ contains no reference to a universe. Thus we can regard it as an expression capable of representing many different statements about many different universes. Another symbol string capable of representing many different statements about many different universes is $\neg \forall x\ (s(x))$. If we re-express these two formulas with words for the quantifiers, we get "There is an x such that $s(x)$ is not the case" and "It is not the case that for all x, $s(x)$." These two (rather clumsy) sentences say the same thing, so it appears that $\neg \forall x\ (s(x))$ is equivalent to $\exists x\ (\neg s(x))$.

Can we interpret our abstract definition that two statements are equivalent if they are true in exactly the same circumstances so that it applies here?

> We say that the quantified expression q is *equivalent* to the quantified expression p if, no matter which universe

we choose and what statements about this universe
we substitute for statement symbols in q and p, the
resulting statements about the universe are equivalent.

EXAMPLE 25   Explain why $\neg\forall x\ (s(x))$ is equivalent to $\exists x\ (\neg s(x))$.

Solution   The statement $\forall x\ (s(x))$ is true if and only if $s(x)$ is true for all x in the universe. Thus $\neg\forall x\ (s(x))$ is true if and only if there is at least one x for which $s(x)$ is false.

Now $\exists x\ (\neg s(x))$ is true if and only if there is at least one x for which $\neg s(x)$ is true. That is, $\exists x\ (\neg s(x))$ is true if and only if there is at least one x such that $s(x)$ is false.

Thus, no matter which universe we use for $s(x)$, $\neg\forall x\ (s(x))$ and $\exists x\ (\neg s(x))$ will be true for exactly the same statements $s(x)$—that is, in exactly the same circumstances. Thus $\neg\forall x\ (s(x))$ and $\exists x\ (\neg s(x))$ are equivalent for any universe U and statement $s(x)$, so they are equivalent as quantified expressions. ∎

Arguments similar to the one used in the example explain the equivalences in the following theorem.

Theorem 3   The following quantified expressions are equivalent:

(a) $\forall x\ (\neg s(x)) \Leftrightarrow \neg\exists x\ (s(x))$

(b) $(\forall x\ s(x)) \wedge t \Leftrightarrow \forall x\ (s(x) \wedge t)$
$\quad\ (\exists x\ s(x)) \wedge t \Leftrightarrow \exists x\ (s(x) \wedge t)$

(c) $(\forall x\ s(x)) \vee t \Leftrightarrow \forall x\ (s(x) \vee t)$
$\quad\ (\exists x\ s(x)) \vee t \Leftrightarrow \exists x\ (s(x) \vee t)$

(d) $(\forall x\ p(x)) \wedge (\forall x\ q(x)) \Leftrightarrow \forall x\ (p(x) \wedge q(x))$

(e) $(\exists x\ p(x)) \vee (\exists y\ q(y)) \Leftrightarrow \exists x\ (p(x) \vee q(x))$

Proof   Similar to the solution of Example 25. ∎

The theorem is important for what it does not state as well as for what it states. A similar-looking pair of statements not on the list should be suspected of inequivalence until it has been analyzed for equivalence.

EXAMPLE 26   Are the statements $\forall y\ \exists x\ p(x,y)$ and $\exists x\ \forall y\ p(x,y)$ equivalent?

Solution   We suspect they may not be equivalent (because they are not on the list in Theorem 3), so we choose some examples. Let us try the universe U of all integers (remember that this includes the negative ones); let us try $x < y$ for the statement $p(x,y)$. Then $\forall y\ \exists x\ p(x,y)$ is the statement "For each y, there is an x such that $x < y$," and $\exists x\ \forall y\ p(x,y)$ is the statement "There is an x such that for each y, $x < y$." The first statement is true, because for each integer y we may find a smaller one, say $y - 1$. The second statement says that there is a smallest integer

x, but no matter which number we choose for x, x couldn't be less than $x - 1$, so the second statement is false. Thus $\forall y \; \exists x \; p(x,y)$ and $\exists x \; \forall y \; p(x,y)$ are *not* equivalent. ■

Notice that the only difference between the two statements in Example 26 is the order in which $\forall y$ and $\exists x$ appear. This illustrates an important point.

> Interchanging the order in which the quantifiers
> $\forall$ and $\exists$ appear in a statement can significantly
> change the meaning of the statement.

EXAMPLE 27   If the universe for x is the set of students in a class, the universe for y is the set of questions a professor has thought of for a test, and $p(x,y)$ is the statement "Student x cannot answer question y," translate the symbolic statements of Example 26 into English and explain how these translations relate to your answer in Example 26.

Solution   The first statement says that for each question, there is a student who cannot answer that question correctly. The second statement says that there is a student who would answer each question incorrectly. The first statement can be true if no one gets a zero on the test, and the second statement asserts that there is a student who will get a zero. Thus the two statements *cannot* be equivalent. ■

Concepts Review

1. A statement of the form "For all x, $p(x)$" is a(n) _____ _____ statement.

2. A statement of the form "There exists an x such that $p(x)$" is called a(n) _____ _____ statement.

3. The symbol _____ is the existential quantifier symbol.

4. If a quantifier refers to a specific occurrence of a variable, then that occurrence is a(n) _____ variable occurrence.

5. The portion of an expression to which a quantifier applies is called the _____ of the quantifier.

6. By substituting a (constant) member of the universe for a variable, we _____ that variable to that member of the universe.

7. The symbolic statement $\forall x \; (s(x))$ is true if and only if $s(x)$ is _____ _____ .

8. The statement $\exists x \; (s(x))$ is false if and only if the truth set of $s(x)$ is _____ .

9. If there is one example that makes $s(x)$ true, then $\exists x \; (s(x))$ is _____ .

10. Two statements of the form $\neg \exists x \; (s(x))$ and $\forall x \; (\neg s(x))$ are _____ .

Exercises

A **1.** Rewrite the following statements in symbolic form, using $s(x)$ to mean "$x^2 = 5$."
 (a) For each x, $x^2 = 5$.
 (b) There is an x such that $x^2 = 5$.
 (c) There is no x such that $x^2 = 5$.
 (d) For each x, x^2 is different from 5.
 (e) For no x, $x^2 = 5$.

2. Rewrite the following statements in symbolic form, using $s(\text{person})$ to mean "This person is huge."
 (a) There is a person such that this person is huge.
 (b) There is no person such that this person is huge.
 (c) For all persons, this person is not huge.
 (d) For all persons, this person is huge.
 (e) There is a person who is huge.

3. Rewrite the following statements in symbolic form, using the abbreviations $s(x)$ for "x is an even integer," $t(x,y)$ for "$x \leq y$," $r(x)$ for "x is a square," and $q(x,y)$ for "$y = x^2$." The universe for both x and y is the set of positive integers.
 (a) For each y, if there is an x such that $y = x^2$, then y is a square.
 (b) For each x, if there is a y such that $y = x^2$, then x is a square.
 (c) y is a square if there is an x such that $y = x^2$.
 (d) For each x and y, if $y = x^2$, then $x \leq y$.
 (e) There is no x such that x is a square and x is an even integer.

4. Rewrite the following statements in symbolic form, using the abbreviations $p(x,S)$ for "$x \in S$," $q(x,y)$ for "$x = y$," $r(x,S,T)$ for "$x \in S \cap T$," $s(x,S,T)$ for "$x \in S \cup T$," and $t(x,S,T)$ for "$x \in S \sim T$." The universe for x and y is the set of elements of some set, and the universe for S and T is the set of subsets of the same set.
 (a) For each x in $S \cap T$, either $x \in S$ or $x \in T$.
 (b) There is a member x of $S \cup T$ such that either $x \in S \sim T$ or $x \in S \cap T$.
 (c) For all y in $S \sim T$, there is no x in T such that $y \in T$.
 (d) For all z such that $z \in R$, there is either an x such that $x \in S$ and $x = z$ or a y such that $y \in T$ and $y = z$.
 (e) There is no x in $S \sim T$ such that $x \in S$ and $x \notin T$.

5. Using the statement $t(x, y)$ of Exercise 3, write the following in symbolic form.
 (a) For all y, $0 \leq y$.
 (b) $2 \leq 3$.
 (c) $4 \leq 2$.
 (d) For no x is $x \leq 3$.
 (e) There is an x such that $x \leq 4$.

6. Using the statement $p(x,S)$ of Exercise 4, write the following in symbolic form.
 (a) For all S, $2 \in S$.
 (b) There is no x such that $x \in \{1,2,3\}$.
 (c) $6 \in \{1,2,3\}$.
 (d) $2 \in \{1,2,3\}$.
 (e) There is an x such that $x \notin \{1,2,3\}$.

7. In the symbolic expressions below, describe the scope of each quantifier and tell which variables are free and which are bound.
   (a) $\forall x \, (\exists y \, (q(x,y) \wedge r(x)))$
   (b) $\neg \exists x \, (\forall y \, (q(x,y) \wedge t(x,y)) \wedge s(x))$
   (c) $s(u) \wedge (\forall y \, (t(u,y) \vee r(v)) \wedge t(x,v))$
   (d) $\forall x \, (q(x,y) \wedge \exists z \, t(y,z))$

8. In the symbolic expressions below, describe the scope of each quantifier and tell which variables are free and which are bound.
   (a) $q(x,y) \wedge \exists z \, (q(x,z) \vee \forall S \, (\forall T \, r(y,S,T)))$
   (b) $\exists S \, (p(x,S) \rightarrow \forall y \, \forall R \, (q(x,y) \vee t(x,S,R)))$
   (c) $\exists S \, (p(x,R) \vee \neg s(x,R,T))$
   (d) $\exists S \, (p(x,S)) \vee \neg \exists y \, (q(x,y))$

9. Using the statements of Exercise 3, rewrite the symbolic statements of Exercise 7 in English.

10. Using the statements of Exercise 4, rewrite the symbolic statements of Exercise 8 in English.

11. Let $p(x)$ stand for "x is a prime," $q(x)$ stand for "x is even," and $r(x,y)$ stand for "$x = y$." Write down the statement "There is one and only one even prime," using these three symbolic statements and appropriate logical notation. (Use the set of integers for your universe.)

12. Let $p(x,y)$ stand for $x = y^2$, and let $q(z,w)$ stand for $z = w$. Using these symbolic statements and appropriate logical notation, write down the statement "There is one and only one number that is its own square." (Use the set of integers for your universe.)

13. Find and describe the use of a quantifier in the definition of "P is a subset of Q."

14. Find a way to express the definition of "S is empty," using a quantifier explicitly.

B　15. Construct a proof that $S \cap (T \sim U) \subseteq (S \cap T) \sim (S \cap U)$ by starting with the assumption that $x \in S \cap (T \sim U)$ and deriving the conclusion that for all x in the universe, $x \in S \cap (T \sim U) \rightarrow x \in (S \cap T) \sim (S \cap U)$.

16. Construct a proof that $(S \cap T) \sim (S \cap U) \subseteq S \cap (T \sim U)$ by starting with the assumption that $x \in (S \cap T) \sim (S \cap U)$ and concluding as in the previous exercise.

17. Each of the expressions below represents a statement about the integers—positive, negative, and 0. Let $p(x)$ be the statement "x is prime," $q(x)$ be the statement "x is a square," $r(x,y)$ be the statement "$x \leq y$," $s(x,y)$ be the statement "x is a multiple of y," and $t(x,y)$ be the statement "$x = y$." Determine which expressions represent true statements and which represent false statements.
   (a) $\exists x \, (p(x) \wedge \exists y \, (q(y) \wedge r(x,y)))$
   (b) $\forall x \, (p(x) \rightarrow \exists y \, (q(y) \wedge r(x,y)))$
   (c) $\forall x \, (q(x) \rightarrow r(0,x))$
   (d) $\exists x \, (p(x) \wedge \exists y \, (q(y) \wedge t(x,y)))$

18. Each expression below represents a statement about the integers. Using $p(x)$ for "x is prime," $q(x,y)$ for "$x = y^2$," $r(x,y)$ for "$x \leq y$," $s(x,y,z)$ for "$z = xy$," and $t(x,y)$ for

"$x = y$," determine which expressions represent true statements and which represent false statements.

(a) $\forall x \, (\exists y \, (q(x,y) \lor p(x)))$

(b) $\forall x \, (\forall y \, (s(x,x,y) \leftrightarrow q(x,y)))$

(c) $\forall y \, (\exists x \, (q(y,x)))$

(d) $\exists z \, (\exists x \, (\exists y \, (p(x) \land p(y) \land \neg t(x,y))))$

19. Explain why $\forall x \, (\neg s(x))$ is equivalent to $\neg \exists x \, (s(x))$.

20. Explain why $(\forall x \, p(x)) \land (\forall y \, q(y))$ is equivalent to $\forall x \, (p(x) \land q(x))$.

21. Find a reason why $(\forall x \, p(x)) \lor (\forall y \, q(y))$ is not equivalent to $\forall z \, (p(z) \lor q(z))$.

22. Find a reason why $(\exists x \, p(x)) \land (\exists y \, q(y))$ is not equivalent to $\exists z \, (p(z) \land q(z))$.

23. Are the statements $\neg(\forall x \, (p(x) \rightarrow q(x)))$ and $\forall x \, (\neg(p(x)) \rightarrow q(x))$ equivalent?

24. Are the statements $\neg \exists x \, (p(x) \land \neg q(x))$ and $\exists x \, (\neg(p(x) \lor q(x)))$ equivalent?

Problems

1. A list L of numbers consists of five specific numbers $a_1, a_2, a_3, a_4,$ and a_5. Using only the symbols $a_1, a_2, a_3, a_4, a_5, =, \leq, x, \land,$ and $\lor$, write the statement "x is a minimum element of the list L."

2. The symbolism $x \in L$ stands for "x is a member of the list L." Using the symbols 1, 5, $a_i, i, \leq, \forall, L, \land, \rightarrow,$ and $\in$, rewrite the statement of Problem 1. You may assume for this problem that we know that L is a_1, a_2, a_3, a_4, a_5.

3. In Problem 2, change $\leq$ to $<$, change $\forall$ to $\exists$, and allow the symbol $\neg$ as well. Now rewrite the statement of Problem 1.

4. Rather than assuming that the list L of Problem 1 has five specific numbers, assume that it has n specific numbers, where n is a fixed integer (whose value we don't happen to know). Use any appropriate logical or comparison notation (but not dots such as . . .) to

    (a) Write the statement that says that each a_i is a member of L and each member of L is an a_i.

    (b) Write the statement "x is a minimum element of the list L."

5. Use the notation of Problem 1 to say that the list in Problem 1 is sorted into increasing order.

6. Use the notation of Problem 4 to say that the list of Problem 4 is sorted into increasing order.

7. Suppose we have a statement $s(i)$ for every integer i. Discuss the sense in which $\forall i \, (s(i))$ plays the role we would want $s(1) \land s(2) \land s(3) \ldots \land s(i) \land \ldots$ to play if we had defined this second notation. What similar roles does $\exists i \, (s(i))$ play? To what do DeMorgan's laws correspond?

8. This problem is for people who know about limits of sequences. Write the definition of "L is the limit of the sequence of numbers $<a_i>$," using the symbol ϵ to vary over the real numbers, the symbols n and N to vary over the integers, the subtraction symbol, the absolute value symbols and appropriate logical notation.

9. Suppose i is allowed to vary over the universe $\{1,2\}$, and x is allowed to vary over some universe U. Rewrite the statements $s(x) \wedge \exists i \ (r(x,i))$ and $\exists i \ (s(x) \wedge r(x,i))$ without using $\forall$ or $\exists$.

10. In light of Problems 7 and 9, you might expect a certain distributive law to hold for $\exists$. What is it? Discuss whether it holds under any, all, or some circumstances.

11. Use p to stand for the statement "It rains on Sundays." Explain the difference between the statement $\neg p$ and the statement "It does not rain on Sundays." (*Hint:* There are "implicit" quantifiers in these statements.)

12. Suppose $s(x)$ is a statement about a universe U. Does one of the statements $\forall x \ (s(x))$ and $\exists x \ (s(x))$ imply the other? Does your answer depend on whether or not U is empty?

13. Suppose U is the universe of all people and T is the universe of all times. Let $s(x,t)$ stand for "You can fool person x at time t." Write out in symbolic form the statement "You can fool all of the people some of the time, you can fool some of the people all of the time, but you can't fool all of the people all of the time."

Chapter 2
Review Exercises

1. Imagine that a computer sends a message consisting of three digits, each 0 or 1, to another computer. For each statement below, determine whether it is universally true, universally false, or neither by finding its truth set.
   (a) If the first digit is 1, then the sum of the digits is less than or equal to 3.
   (b) The first digit is not 1 or the sum of the digits is an odd number.
   (c) If the sum of the digits is an odd number, then the first or third digit is 1.
   (d) The sum of the digits is odd if and only if there is at least one 1.
   (e) There is at least one 1 if the sum of the digits is odd.
   (f) The sum of the digits is even and the number of nonzero digits is odd.

Classify each of the symbolic statements in Exercises 2–5 as a tautology, a contradiction, or neither by using truth tables.

2. $(p \oplus q) \to (p \vee q)$ 3. $(p \oplus q) \to (p \wedge q)$

4. $\neg[\neg(p \wedge q) \wedge (\neg p \vee q) \wedge p]$ 5. $(p \leftrightarrow q) \to p \wedge q$

6. Imagine the same message system as in Exercise 1. For each pair of statements below, determine whether or not each implies the other. If a pair of statements is equivalent, say so.
   (a) The first digit is 1. The number of 1's is odd.
   (b) The first digit is 1. The sum of the digits is positive.
   (c) If the first digit is 1, then some digit is 0. The sum of the digits is even.
   (d) Each digit after the first digit equal to 1 is also 1. If there is a 0, then the first digit is 0.
   (e) If there is at least one 1, the number of 0's is even. All the digits are 0's.
   (f) The sum of the digits is not 1. If two digits are 0, then all digits are 0.

For each pair of symbolic statements in Exercises 7–10, determine whether or not each implies the other.

7. $p \rightarrow q$; $p \leftrightarrow q$

8. $p \wedge (q \vee r)$; $(p \wedge r) \vee q$

9. $p \wedge (q \oplus r)$; $(p \wedge q) \vee (r \wedge q)$

10. $(p \wedge q) \vee (p \wedge r) \vee (q \wedge r)$, $p \wedge (q \vee r)$

11–14 For each Exercise 7–10, draw a Venn diagram that illustrates your conclusion and explain why it does.

15–18. For each pair s and t of statements in Exercises 7–10, determine whether $s \rightarrow t$ (or $t \rightarrow s$) is a tautology and determine whether $s \leftrightarrow t$ is a tautology.

19. For each pair of statements s and t in Exercise 6, using s for the first statement and t for the second, determine whether $s \rightarrow t$, $t \rightarrow s$, $s \leftrightarrow t$, or none of them is universally true.

20. Find a counter-example to each of the following statements about the sequence of three digits in Exercise 1.
    (a) If the first digit is 1, then the sum of the digits is even.
    (b) The sum of the digits is even if and only if no two consecutive digits are 0.
    (c) The sum of the digits is 2 or two consecutive digits are 0.

21. A number n is a square (by definition) if and only if there is a number i such that $n = i^2$. Construct a direct proof that if m and n are squares, then $m \cdot n$ is a square.

22. Is it possible to construct a proof that, if m and n are squares, then $m + n$ is a square? Why?

23. What are the converse and contrapositive of "If the first digit is in error, then the sum of the digits is odd"?

24. Construct an indirect proof that if $m \cdot n$ is negative, then m is negative or n is negative.

25. Prove that $\sqrt{7}$ is not rational.

26. Recall that the transitive law for subsets of a set states that if $R \subseteq S$ and $S \subseteq T$, then $R \subseteq T$. Given a direct proof that if $P \subseteq R$, $R \subseteq S$, and $S \subseteq T$, then $P \subseteq T$ (the *three-stage transitive law*).

27. Let $p(x,y)$ stand for $x < y$. Let $q(x,S)$ stand for $x \in S$. Let $r(x,y)$ stand for $x = y$. Write the following statements in symbolic form.
    (a) $x \leq y$
    (b) For each x in S, there is an element y in S such that $x \leq y$.
    (c) There is an element z in S such that $z < x$ for each x in S with $x \neq z$.
    (d) There is an element z in S such that $z \geq x$ for each x in S.

28. Write the following statements in English, using the statements of Exercise 27.
    (a) $\forall y \, (q(y,S) \rightarrow p(x,y))$
    (b) $\exists x \, (q(x,s) \wedge \forall y \, ((q(y,s) \wedge \neg r(x,y)) \rightarrow p(x,y)))$
    (c) $\forall x \, (q(x,s) \rightarrow (p(x,y) \vee r(x,y)))$

29. For each symbolic statement in Exercise 28, describe the scope of each quantifier and tell which variables are free and which are bound.

30. Let $p(x, S)$ stand for $x \in S$. Using quantifiers, variables, and p, complete the following definition: Given two sets S and T, $S = T$ if and only if _____ .

31. (a) Construct a proof that $R \cap (S \cup T) \subseteq (R \cap S) \cup (R \cap T)$ by beginning with the assumption that $x \in R \cap (S \cup T)$.

(b) Construct a proof that $(R \cap S) \cup (R \cap T) \subseteq R \cap (S \cup T)$.

(c) Comment on what (a) and (b), taken together, mean.

32. Each of the expressions below represents a statement about the integers. Let $p(x)$ stand for the statement "x is prime," $q(x)$ stand for "$\exists y \, (x = y^2)$," $r(x)$ stand for "$\exists y \, (x = 2y)$," $s(x, y)$ stand for "$x = y$," and $t(x, y)$ stand for "$x < y$." Determine whether each symbolic statement is true or false.

(a) $\forall y \, ((p(y) \land \neg r(y)) \rightarrow t(2, y))$

(b) $\forall y \, ((p(y) \land q(y)) \leftrightarrow r(y))$

(c) $\exists x \, (r(x) \land p(x) \land \forall y \, ((p(y) \land r(y)) \rightarrow s(x, y)))$

(d) $\exists y \, ((p(y) \land \neg r(y)) \land \forall x \, (p(x) \land r(x) \rightarrow t(x, y)))$

33. Give an example that explains why $\neg \exists x \, (p(x))$ is not equivalent to $\exists x \, (\neg p(x))$.

34. Explain why $\exists x \, (p(x)) \lor \exists y \, (q(y))$ is equivalent to $\exists z \, (p(z) \land q(z))$, or give an example to show that they are not equivalent. Does changing $\lor$ to $\land$ change the answer?

35. Explain why $\exists x \, (\forall y \, (p(x) \land q(y)))$ and $\forall y \, \exists x \, (p(x) \land q(y))$ are equivalent, or give an example to show that they are not equivalent.

*T*he concept of a relationship is intuitively quite simple. Relationships such as *is a subset of, is equal to,* and *is the square root of* abound in mathematics. In the real world there are relations of friendship among acquaintances, parent/child relationships, compatibility relationships between computers and other equipment, and so on. The concept of a relationship is so broad that it is difficult to say precisely what we mean by it. By analyzing a situation in which the intuitive idea of a relationship is not adequate to answer a mathematical question, we shall find a very precise way to use sets to specify just what a relationship is. We take this precise definition as the definition of the word *relation*. When we want to use the precise concept, we can so indicate by using the word *relation,* and when we want the intuitive concept, we can use the word *relationship*.

Numerical relationships between variables x and y lead students in high school to draw graphs in the plane with its Cartesian coordinate system. We shall call these graphs *Cartesian graphs* in this book. Many of the relations we study in discrete mathematics are not numerical. There are ways to draw visual representations of these kinds of relations, and these drawings are also called *graphs*. We shall study how drawings called *directed graphs* help us visualize relationships and their properties. (One such property with which you may be familiar is transitivity.) We shall also see how thinking about relationships geometrically gives us insights into new properties that will be important in various applications. One such concept we shall introduce is *reachability*. Another important property of relations, namely symmetry, leads us to the concept of an *undirected graph*. The two concepts of equivalence relations and ordering relations arise in so many mathematical applications that they have been singled out for special study.

Certain ideas from this chapter, especially equivalence relations, pervade our work and will appear in nearly every subject we study. In Chapter 4, we shall use the idea of a relation to give a precise definition of the concept of a function, a cornerstone of modern mathematics. Chapter 8 is devoted to the study of one special kind of graph called a *tree*. Trees are of fundamental importance in computer science and operations research, as well as in the theory of graphs. Chapter 9 is designed to give the reader the flavor of modern graph theory through a study of some of its significant applications. These ideas come up again in Chapter 11, when we see how graph theory and probability theory interact.

There is a more general concept of a relationship among three or more entities that is important in a number of applications, notably database systems in computer science. Although we examine only relations between two entities in this book, our study is designed to lay the foundation for these more general relations also.

Section 3-1
Relations
and Digraphs

A Relations

We have studied two important relationships between statements: implication and equivalence. We have also studied the subset relationship for sets. Relationships among variables are important in algebra and calculus; relationships among figures are important in geometry. So far, we have not needed a precise definition of the word *relationship*. Without such a precise definition, however, it is hard to answer questions about relationships. What do we mean, for example, when we say that two apparently different relationships are the same?

EXAMPLE 1   The formulas $y = x + 2$ and $y = x^4 - 2x^3 - x^2 + 3x + 2$ each describe a relationship between the set $\{-1,0,1,2\}$, which is the universe for x, and the set $\{1,2,3,4\}$, which is the universe for y. Are these relationships different?

Solution   Both formulas relate -1 to 1, 0 to 2, 1 to 3, and 2 to 4. Thus, between the two universes given, they relate exactly the same pairs. In some sense, therefore, they are the same.   ■

The Idea of a Relation

Each of the statements $y = x + 2$ and $y = x^4 - 2x^3 - x^2 + 3x + 2$ has a truth set. Since each statement has two variables, we need to give two values, one for x and one for y, before we can decide the truth or falsity of the statement. Therefore, in order to write the truth sets down, we need a way to record which x-value is related to which y-value. To avoid writing x and y over and over again, let us agree that when we have a value for each variable, we shall write these values as (x,y) with the x-value first and the y-value second. We call the symbol (x,y) an **ordered pair**. Notice that $(-1,1)$ and $(1,-1)$ are *different* ordered pairs. Now the truth set for $y = x + 2$ on our pair of universes is the set of ordered pairs

$$\{(-1,1), (0,2), (1,3), (2,4)\}$$

This is also the truth set of $y = x^4 - 2x^3 - x^2 + 3x + 2$, so on our pair of universes the two statements given by the two formulas are equivalent. For mathematical purposes, our relationships are the same.

> We shall call a set of ordered pairs (a,b), with
> a in A and b in B, a **relation** (or
> **binary relation**) from A to B.
> We call A the **domain** of the relation
> and B the **range** of the relation.

(In some contexts, B is called the **codomain** of the relation.) The set of ordered pairs we gave above is a relation whose domain is $\{-1,0,1,2\}$ and whose range is $\{1,2,3,4\}$. We defined the concept of a relation because we saw potential difficulties in using the word *relationship*. Now, when we need to have the concept of a relationship precisely defined in a given discussion, we will use the word *relation* in place of *relationship*. When an intuitive understanding suffices, we may continue to use the word *relationship*.

EXAMPLE 2   A fraternity has a membership committee consisting of Joe, Frank, and Bill, a house committee consisting of Tony, Joe, Bill, and Andre, and a social committee consisting of Frank, Tony, and Bill. Using initials for the names of people and committees, write down the "is a member of" relation from the set of people to the set of committees.

Solution   Our solution consists of the set of ordered pairs

$$\{(J,M), (F,M), (B,M), (T,H), (J,H), (B,H), (A,H), (F,S), (T,S), (B,S)\} \qquad \blacksquare$$

We say that a relation is a relation **on** a set C if C is both the domain and range of the relation. That is, $A = C = B$ in the definition of a relation.

EXAMPLE 3   We say that a statement p **implies** a statement q if q is true whenever p is true. In this way, we have defined implication to be a relationship between statements. We write $p \Rightarrow q$ for "p implies q." If we determine precisely which statements in a set imply which other statements, we will have a relation. Write down the *implies* relation on the set $S = \{p, q, p \wedge q, p \vee q\}$ of symbolic statements.

Solution   Because p implies itself, the ordered pair (p, p) will be in our relation, as will (q, q), $(p \wedge q, p \wedge q)$, and $(p \vee q, p \vee q)$. Now since $p \Rightarrow p \vee q$ (one way to verify this is to use truth sets), the pair $(p, p \vee q)$ will be in our relation. On the other hand, those two statements paired in reverse order are not in our relation, because $p \vee q$ does not imply p. To determine the remaining pairs in the relation, we check each two elements in S, in both orders, to see if one implies the other. This gives us the set

$$\text{"Implies"} = \mathcal{I} = \{(p, p), (q, q), (p \wedge q, p \wedge q), (p \vee q, p \vee q), (p, p \vee q),$$
$$(q, p \vee q), (p \wedge q, p), (p \wedge q, q), (p \wedge q, p \vee q)\}$$

as the *implies* relation.   ∎

EXAMPLE 4   The relation $\{(1,2), (1,3), (1,4), (2,3), (2,4), (3,4)\}$ is a familiar relation on the set $\{1,2,3,4\}$. What is a standard name for this relation?

Solution   Note that (a,b) is in the relation if and only if $a < b$. Thus our relation is the *less than* relation.   ∎

In two of our examples, there are symbols, namely $\Rightarrow$ and $<$, that we use to stand for our relation. We write $p \Rightarrow q$ and $a < b$ rather than $(p,q) \in \Rightarrow$ or $(a,b) \in$ $<$. Similarly, if R stands for some other relation, we may write aRb rather than $(a,b) \in R$ to say that a is related to b. Notice in all these examples how important it is to remember that (a,b) is a different ordered pair from (b,a). In Example 4, our relation has $(1,2)$ because $1 < 2$ and does not have $(2,1)$ because $2 \not< 1$.

The Cartesian Product

The set of all ordered pairs (a,b) with $a \in A$ and $b \in B$ is called the **Cartesian product** of A and B and is denoted by $A \times B$. (Think about how ordered pairs are used for Cartesian coordinates in the plane; we use the word *Cartesian* here in analogy with the plane.) For example,

$$A \times B = \{1,2\} \times \{a,b,c\} = \{(1,a), (1,b), (1,c), (2,a), (2,b), (2,c)\}$$

The Cartesian product relates every element of A to every element of B. Note that our definition of a relation is equivalent to saying that "A relation from A to B is a subset of the Cartesian product $A \times B$."

B Digraphs

A picture that we use to visualize a relation is often called a *graph*. The first kind of graph we shall study (which is different from the graphs studied in algebra) is called a *directed graph*, or *digraph* for short. In Figure 1, we show digraphs used to visualize the *less than* relation and *less than or equal to* relation on $\{1,2,3,4\}$.

Figure 1 The digraph of the *less than* and *less than or equal to* relation on {1,2,3,4}.

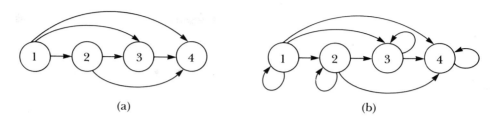

(a)   (b)

To draw a digraph of a relation on a set, we first draw a circle, called a *vertex*, for each member of the domain and range of the relation. In Figure 1, we have four circles, the vertices representing 1, 2, 3, and 4. Next, for each vertex representing a domain element, we draw an arrow, called an *edge*, to each vertex representing a related range element. (As in Figure 1(b), we draw an arrow from a vertex to itself when it represents something related to itself.)

Vertices and Edges of Digraphs

The exact location of the circles or the length or shape of the arrows doesn't tell us anything about the relation. For this reason, it is useful to have a definition of a directed graph that does not mention geometric points or arrows.

We shall say a **directed graph** or **digraph** consists of two sets: a **vertex** set V of elements called **vertices** or **nodes,** and an **edge** set E of ordered pairs of vertices, called **edges.**

(We allow ordered pairs both of whose members are the same.) Notice that the edge set E of a directed graph is simply a relation on the vertex set V. If (x, y) is in E, we say that (x, y) is an edge, x is **adjacent to** y, and y is **adjacent from** x.

EXAMPLE 5   On a certain test, we agree that even if one person scores 5 points below another, it is quite possible that the two people have similar knowledge of the test material. If the scores are Manuel 93, Sarah 89, Rick 84, Carmela 86, and George 80, write down the relation of "possibly similar knowledge" and draw a digraph of it.

Solution   Using initials to stand for people's names, we get the relation {(M,M), (S,S), (R,R), (C,C), (G,G), (M,S), (S,M), (S,R), (R,S), (S,C), (C,S), (R,C), (C,R), (R,G), (G,R)}. Figure 2 is a drawing of the digraph of this relation. ∎

We draw a digraph of a relation from a set A to a set B in the same way, beginning by drawing one circle for each member of the domain and one circle for each element of the range.

Figure 2   The digraph of the relation of Example 5.

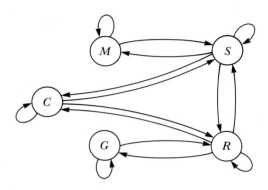

EXAMPLE 6   In Example 2, we discussed a relation between fraternity members and fraternity committees. Draw a digraph of the relation *is a member of* from the set of people to the set of committees.

Solution   Here we need a circle for each person and a circle for each committee. It makes sense to put the circles for people in one row and the circles for committees in another row. We then draw an arrow from each person to each committee he belongs to. In Figure 3, we have a circle (with an initial) for each committee in the top row and a circle (with an initial) for each person in the bottom row.   ■

Figure 3   The graph of the membership relation of Examples 2 and 6.

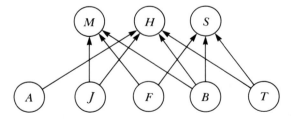

Visualizing relations with digraphs is very useful, but working with really large relations requires a computer. For this purpose, we need a way of representing a digraph that simultaneously permits us to use our geometric intuition and the power of the computer. One representation that is useful in this way is called the *adjacency list* representation.

Adjacency Lists

An **adjacency list** for a vertex is a list of each vertex adjacent from it. To describe a graph by adjacency lists, we write down for each vertex a list beginning with that vertex and then listing all vertices adjacent from it. For example, for vertex S in Example 5, one list we could get is the list $S: S,M,R,C$.

EXAMPLE 7   Write down adjacency lists to represent the graphs in Examples 5 and 6.

Solution   For Example 5, one collection of lists we could get is

$$M: M,S; \quad S: S,M,R,C; \quad R: R,S,C,G; \quad C: C,S,R; \quad G: G,R$$

Another collection of lists we could get is

$$S: C,S,M,R; \quad M: S,M; \quad R: G,C,S,R; \quad G: G,R; \quad C: R,S,C$$

For Example 6, we could get the lists

$$J: M,H; \quad F: M,S; \quad B: M,H,S; \quad T: H,S; \quad A: H; \quad H: \ ; \quad M: \ ; \quad S:$$

The three lists $H: \ ; M: \ ;$ and $S:$ are called **empty lists.** When leaving out empty lists will not cause confusion, people usually do so.   ∎

Notice that we can write down an adjacency list for the vertex S in Example 5 in many different orders. For example, $S: C,S,M,R$ also gives us a list of the vertices adjacent from x. The point is that all we need to know in order to determine which vertices are adjacent from S is the set of vertices adjacent to S. This set may appear in any order in an adjacency list.

◨ Reachability

Directed Walks

Relations and digraphs arise in the study of communications and transportation. The vertices represent locations, and an edge from vertex a to vertex b means that we can send a message or transport goods directly from point a to point b. A drawing of the digraph is like a simplified map of the system we are dealing with. In Chapters 8 and 9, we shall study quite a few of the ideas related to communications and transportation. Here we shall concentrate on one of the most elementary ideas. If we wish to send something from point a to point x, we have to find out if it is possible to reach x from a. If it is possible, we have to find a sequence of edges and vertices we can follow to get from a to x.

A (**directed**) **walk** from vertex a to vertex x
is a sequence of vertices and edges of the form

$$a \ (a,b) \ b \ (b,c) \ c \ . \ . \ . \ w \ (w,x) \ x$$

A shorter way to describe the same walk is the sequence $a \ b \ c \ . \ . \ . \ w \ x$ of vertices; we know we have to use the edge (a,b) to get from a to b, the edge (b,c) to get from b to c, and so on. The word *directed* is included for clarity; in a digraph, the word *walk* means *directed walk*.

If there is a nontrivial directed walk from a to x,
we say that x is **reachable** from a.

(A *trivial* directed walk has one vertex and no edges.)

EXAMPLE 8   Find three different walks from the vertex M to the vertex G in the digraph in Figure 2.

Solution   From vertex M, we can follow an arrow to vertex S. Thus our walk begins as $M(M,S)S$. From S, we have several arrows going out; geometrically it appears that an appropriate arrow to choose leading in the direction of G from S is the arrow from vertex S to vertex R, so we take the arrow from S to R. Now our walk has expanded to $M(M,S)S(S,R)R$. From vertex R we can go to vertex G along an arrow. This gives us

$$M \ (M,S) \ S \ (S,R) \ R \ (R,G) \ G \qquad \text{or} \qquad M \ S \ R \ G$$

as a walk from M to G.

A second walk is

$$M \ (M,S) \ S \ (S,C) \ C \ (C,R) \ R \ (R,G) \ G \qquad \text{or} \qquad M \ S \ C \ R \ G$$

For our third walk, we choose one that "doubles back" on itself:

$$M \ (M,S) \ S \ (S,R) \ R \ (R,C) \ C \ (C,S) \ S \ (S,R) \ R \ (R,G) \ G \qquad \text{or}$$
$$M \ S \ R \ C \ S \ R \ G$$

■

As the example shows, a walk between two vertices needn't be as efficient as possible. The first two walks from M to G in the example are called *paths*.

A (directed) **path** from vertex x to vertex y
is a (directed) walk from x to y in which
no vertex (or edge) appears twice.

EXAMPLE 9   Figure 4 is a digraph of a hypothetical communications system. In discussing digraphs of communications systems, it is customary to use the language of electrical engineering and refer to a vertex as a *node*. We have an arrow joining one node to another if the first can communicate directly to the second.

What nodes are reachable from node E? In other words, to what nodes may node E send a message (possibly indirectly)?

Figure 4

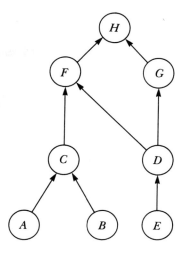

Solution   By following arrows, we see immediately that from E we may reach D, from D we may reach F and G, and from either F or G we may reach H. Thus, from E we may reach D, F, G, and H. Note that E is not reachable from E.   ■

Example 9 suggests an algorithm to find all vertices reachable from a given one. Whenever we want to specify an algorithm precisely, we shall name it, describe the data it is to work on (the **input**) and the data it is to produce (**output**), and finally give the instructions to be carried out. This algorithm is written so that it can be taken either as a description of the visual process or make use of adjacency lists for the original graph.

Algorithm Reach

> Input: A digraph G and a vertex x of G.
> Output: A list of all vertices reachable from x.
> Procedure: Put each vertex adjacent from x on the list.
> Starting with the first vertex in the list, process each vertex z on the list as follows.
> For each vertex y adjacent from z, if y is not already on the list, put it on the list.   ■

Example 9 above shows how the algorithm works. The algorithm is also used in Example 10 below. It is intuitively clear that algorithm Reach produces a list of all the vertices reachable from E, but an actual proof would be difficult to construct with what we know so far. However, the proof of Theorem 1 will be straightforward after we study mathematical induction.

Theorem 1   When algorithm Reach is applied to a vertex x, it produces a list of the vertices reachable from x.

Proof   Delayed until Chapter 5.   ■

The **reachability relation** of a digraph contains the pairs (a,x) such that x is reachable from a.

EXAMPLE 10   Write down the adjacency lists and edge set of the reachability relation for the digraph of Figure 4.

Solution   As in Example 9, applying the Reach algorithm to E will give us the list D,F,G,H, so E: D,F,G,H is the reachability list for E. Applying the Reach algorithm to A, we start with the list A: C. Since C is adjacent to F, we add F, getting A: C,F; since F is adjacent to H, we add H to the list, getting A: C,F,H. Since no more vertices are adjacent from any of C, F, or H, we are done. Applying Reach to the other vertices gives us the reachability lists:

$$E: D,F,G,H; \quad A: C,F,H; \quad B: C,F,H; \quad C: F,H; \quad D: G,F,H; \quad F: H; \quad G: H$$

We convert these adjacency lists into the following edge set for the reachability relation

$$\{(E,D), (E,F), (E,G), (E,H), (A,C), (A,F), (A,H), (B,C), (B,F),$$
$$(B,H), (C,F), (C,H), (D,G), (D,F), (D,H), (F,H), (G,H)\}$$ ■

▣ *Transitivity*

Transitive Relations

The relation of reachability has a property that our original relation need not have had: the property of transitivity.

We say a relation T on a set X is **transitive** if whenever (a,b) and (b,c) are in T, then (a,c) is in T as well

In our other notation, T is transitive if whenever $a\,T\,b$ and $b\,T\,c$, then $a\,T\,c$. In the language of graphs, a relation is transitive if whenever there are edges from a to b and from b to c, then there is an edge from a to c as well. For example, the digraphs in Figure 1 have this property.

EXAMPLE 11   Is the *less than* relation of Example 3 transitive?

Solution   The relation is the set $\{(1,2), (1,3), (1,4), (2,3), (2,4), (3,4)\}$. To check whether the relation is transitive, we need to examine each way of choosing a pair (a,b) and a pair (b,c) in the relation.

If $(a,b) = (1,2)$, then (b,c) can be $(2,3)$ or $(2,4)$. The transitive property applied to $(1,2)$ and $(2,3)$ would require that $(1,3)$ is in the relation, and in fact $(1,3)$ is. The transitive property applied to $(1,2)$ and $(2,4)$ would require that $(1,4)$ be in the relation, and in fact $(1,4)$ is.

We have so far considered the case $(a,b) = (1,2)$; (a,b) could be $(1,3)$ as well, in which case the only choice for (b,c) is $(3,4)$. The transitive property would require that $(1,4)$ be in the relation, and we have seen that this is the case.

The pair (a,b) could be $(2,3)$, in which case (b,c) can only be $(3,4)$. The transitive property would require that $(2,4)$ be in the relation, and this is the case. In the pair (a,b), the entry b cannot be 4, because then there would be no possibility for us to use as the pair (b,c), so we have tested all the possible pairs (a,b) and (b,c). Since each time the pair (a,c) has been in the relation as well, the relation is transitive. ∎

EXAMPLE 12 Is the *can communicate directly to* relation of Example 9 transitive?

Solution The pair (A,C) is in the relation, and so is the pair (C,F), but the pair (A,F) is not. Therefore, the relation is not transitive. ∎

It was a good bit easier to show that this relation was not transitive than it was to show that the preceding example was transitive. To show that a relation is not transitive, we give a counter-example to the transitive law. Checking whether any given relation is transitive may be time-consuming, but it is often possible to show that a certain *kind* of relation is transitive by using a general argument. Our next theorem shows how this happens with a reachability relation.

Theorem 2 If R is a relation and $T(R)$ stands for its reachability relation, then $T(R)$ is transitive.

Proof If b is reachable from a and c is reachable from b, then there are directed walks from a to b and from b to c. Putting these two directed walks together gives a directed walk from a to c, so c is reachable from a. ∎

Transitive Closure

Theorem 2 points out the intimate connection between the concept of reachability and the concept of transitivity. Note, however, that these two concepts *are* different. Transitivity is a property a relation might or might not have. Reachability is the name for a relation defined on the vertices of a digraph; according to Theorem 2, this relation is transitive.

We also call the reachability relation $T(R)$ of a
relation R the **transitive closure** of R.

Why do we use this name? Mathematicians say that we are *closing* a set under an operation if we add into the set all possible results of performing the operation, but we add nothing else in. Because $T(R)$ is transitive, it contains all results of applying the transitive property. However, $T(R)$ contains no other ordered pairs, because every edge in $T(R)$ is either already in R or would be implied by applying the transitive law to the edges in a walk. Thus we form $T(R)$ by "closing" R under application of the transitive law. This is why $T(R)$ is called the *transitive closure* of R.

Notice that computing the transitive closure of a relation means exactly the same thing as computing its reachability relation. Thus in Example 10 we computed the transitive closure of the digraph in Figure 4. *Reachability* and *transitivity* are different concepts, but *transitive closure* and *reachability relation* are simply different names for the same concept.

Concepts Review

1. The symbol (x,y) stands for the _____ _____ whose first element is x and whose second element is y.

2. The _____ _____ of A and B is the set of all ordered pairs (a,b) with a in A and b in B and is denoted by _____.

3. A(n) _____ from A to B is a set of ordered pairs whose first elements are in A and whose second elements are in B.

4. If R is a relation from A to B, then A is called the _____ of R and B is called the _____ of R.

5. A directed graph is used to visualize a(n) _____.

6. A directed graph has a set of _____ and a set of _____.

7. An edge of a digraph is a(n) _____ _____ of vertices.

8. If (x,y) is an edge, then x is _____ _____ y and y is _____ _____ x.

9. A(n) _____ _____ for a vertex names that vertex and all vertices adjacent from it.

10. A(n) _____ _____ from vertex a to vertex x is an alternating sequence of vertices and edges (each edge going from the preceding vertex to the following vertex in the list) that starts with a and ends with x.

11. A vertex x is _____ from a if there is a directed walk from a to x.

12. A directed walk from a to x in which no vertex is repeated is called a(n) _____.

13. We say we can _____ x from a if there is a directed walk from a to x.

14. A relation R is _____ if whenever (a,b) and (b,c) are in R, then (a,c) is in R as well.

15. The reachability relation of a digraph is a(n) _____ relation.

16. The _____ _____ of a relation is another name for its reachability relation.

Exercises

A In Exercises 1–10, write down the set of ordered pairs of the relation described.

1. The *greater than* relation on {1,2,3,4,5}.

2. The *greater than or equal to* relation on {1,2,3,4}.

3. The *equals* relation on {1,2,3,4,5}.

4. The *equals* relation on {a,b,c,d,e}.

5. The *superset* relation ⊇ on the subsets of {1,2}. (We say that A is a **superset** of B if B is a subset of A.)

6. The *less than* relation from the set {1,2,3} to the set {2,3,4}.

7. The relationship between x and y given by y = ±x from the set {0,1,2,3,4} (the universe for x) to the set {−4, −3, −2, −1, 0, 1, 2, 3, 4} (the universe for y).

8. The *has the same number of letters as* relation on the set {hat, glove, shoes, eye, ear}.

9. The *strict subset* relation on the subsets of {a,b,c}. (This relation has a lot of ordered pairs.)

10. The relationship between x and y given by x is related to y if |x − y| ≤ 1 on {1,2,3,4}.

11. The set of ordered pairs {(4,1), (4,2), (4,3), (3,1), (3,2), (2,1)} is a familiar relation on the set {1,2,3,4}. What is this relation usually called?

12. The set of ordered pairs {(1,1), (2,2), (3,3), (4,4) ,(5,5)} is a familiar relation on the set {1,2,3,4,5}. What is this relation usually called?

B 13. Write down the relation corresponding to each digraph in Figure 5.

Figure 5

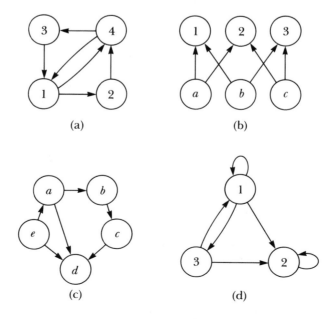

(a)   (b)

(c)   (d)

14. Write down the relation corresponding to each digraph in Figure 6.

Figure 6

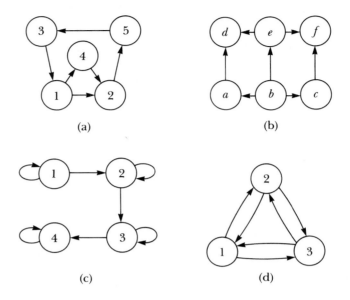

(a)

(b)

(c)

(d)

In Exercises 15–22, draw a digraph of the relations given.

15. The *greater than* relation on {1,2,3,4,5}.

16. The *greater than or equal to* relation on {1,2,3,4}.

17. The *equals* relation on {1,2,3,4,5}.

18. The *superset* relation ⊃ on the subsets of {1,2}.

19. The *has the same number of letters as* relation on the set {hat, glove, shoes, eye, ear}.

20. The *equals* relation on the {a,b,c,d,e}.

21. The *strict subset* relation on the set of all subsets of {a,b,c}.

22. The relation given by "x is related to y if $|x - y| \leq 1$" on {1,2,3,4}.

23. Write down the adjacency lists that represent the digraphs in Figure 5.

24. Write down the adjacency lists that represent the digraphs in Figure 6.

C 25. Find the vertices reachable from vertex 1 in the digraph of Figure 5(a).

26. Find the vertices reachable from vertex a in Figure 5(b).

27. Find the vertices reachable from vertex a in Figure 5(c).

28. Find the vertices reachable from vertex 1 in Figure 5(d).

29. Find the vertices reachable from vertex 1 in Figure 6(a).

30. Find the vertices reachable from vertex *a* in Figure 6(b).

31. Find the vertices reachable from vertex 2 in Figure 6(c).

32. Find the vertices reachable from vertex 2 in Figure 6(d).

33. Find a walk with two edges from vertex 4 to vertex 1 in Figure 5(a). Is this walk a path?

34. Find a walk with three edges from vertex *a* to vertex *d* in Figure 5(c). Is this walk a path?

35. Find a walk with five edges from vertex 4 to vertex 2 in Figure 5(a). Is this walk a path?

36. Find a walk with four edges from vertex 2 to vertex 4 in Figure 6(a). Is this walk a path?

37. What is the largest number of edges in a walk in the digraph in Figure 6(b)?

38. What is the largest number of edges in a walk in the digraph in Figure 5(c)?

39. Write down the reachability relations of the digraphs in Figure 5.

40. Write down the reachability relations of the digraphs in Figure 6.

D Exercises 41–48 refer to the graphs of Figures 5 and 6. For each problem, determine whether the relation of the digraph given is transitive. State why or why not.

41. Figure 5(a)   42. Figure 6(a)

43. Figure 5(b)   44. Figure 6(b)

45. Figure 5(c)   46. Figure 6(c)

47. Figure 5(d)   48. Figure 6(d)

Exercises 49–52 refer to the graphs of Figures 5 and 6. For each problem, draw the transitive closure of the graph indicated.

49. Figure 5(a)   50. Figure 6(a)

51. Figure 5(c)   52. Figure 6(c)

53. The definition of $a > b$ is "$a > b$ means that $a - b$ is positive." Show that the *greater than* relation on any set of numbers is transitive.

54. Use the fact that the *is a subset of* relation is transitive to show that the *implies* relation on the set of statements about a universe is transitive.

In Exercises 55–58, determine whether the relation defined is transitive and explain your answers.

55. Define two numbers x and y to be related if $|x - y| \leq 1$.

56. Define two subsets X and Y of $\{a,b,c,d\}$ to be related if $X \cap Y \neq \varnothing$.

57. Define two integers x and y to be related if $x - y$ is a multiple of 3.

58. Define two integers x and y to be related if $x + y$ is even.

Problems

1. If R is a relation from X to Y and S is a relation from Y to Z, then the relation $R \circ S$ from X to Z has the ordered pair (a,c) if and only if there is an element b in Y such that (a,b) is in R and (b,c) is in S. $R \circ S$ is called the **composition** of R and S. If $R = \{(1,3), (2,4), (4,2), (3,5)\}$ and $S = \{(1,a), (2,b), (3,c), (4,d)\}$, find $R \circ S$.

2. $R \circ S$ is defined in Problem 1. Prove the associative law $(R \circ S) \circ T = R \circ (S \circ T)$.

3. $R \circ S$ is defined in Problem 1. For a relation R on a set X, define $R^2 = R \circ R$, $R^3 = R \circ R^2$, and so on. If X has n elements, show that the transitive closure of R is $R \cup R^2 \cup R^3 \cup \cdots \cup R^{n-1}$.

4. $R \circ S$ is defined in Problem 1. A relation on a set X is called **reflexive** if (x, x) is in the relation for each x in X. Show that if R is a reflexive relation on a set X, then R^{n-1} is the transitive closure of R. (R^n is defined in Problem 3.)

5. What is the maximum possible number of edges in a path in a digraph with n vertices?

6. If there is a walk from x to y, then we define the distance $d(x,y)$ to be the smallest number of edges in any path from x to y. Show that this distance satisfies the rule $d(x,y) \le d(x,z) + d(z,y)$, which in ordinary geometry is called the **triangle inequality**.

7. A **cycle** is a walk whose first and last vertices are equal but whose other vertices and edges are all different. Draw a picture of a digraph that has a three-vertex cycle. If a digraph G has no three-vertex cycles, can its transitive closure have any three-vertex cycles?

8. Cycles are defined in Problem 8. If a digraph has no cycles at all, can its transitive closure have any cycles?

9. Show that the intersection of two transitive relations is transitive. What about the intersection of an arbitrary set of transitive relations?

10. Show that $T(R)$ is the intersection of the set of all transitive relations containing R as a subset.

11. Let X stand for an infinite set. Define a relation R on the *subsets* of X by letting S be related to T if and only if $(S \cup T) \sim (S \cap T)$ is finite. Show that R is transitive. (*Hint:* A Venn diagram will help you tremendously.)

Section 3-2
Symmetric Relations

A   *Symmetric Relations and Graphs*

We say that a relation R is **symmetric** if whenever x is related to y by R, then y is also related to x by R. In our symbolic notation for relations, this translates to the following.

> A relation R is **symmetric** if whenever (x, y)
> is in R, the pair (y, x) is also in R;

equivalently, if whenever $x \, R \, y$, then also $y \, R \, x$. For example, if A is a cousin of B, then B is a cousin of A. As a second example, if A performs essentially as well on a test as B, then B performs essentially as well as A. When we draw a digraph to represent a symmetric relation, each arrow is paired with an arrow going the reverse direction, as in Figure 2, which is the digraph for Example 5 and is repeated below as Figure 7(a).

Figure 7

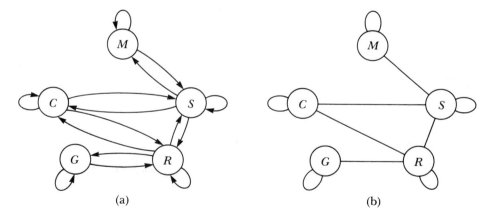

(a)   (b)

In this situation, we could just draw two-headed arrows instead of two arrows; further, we may leave off the arrowheads, since each edge has an arrowhead at each end. Making these replacements give us part (b) of Figure 6. This is a drawing of an *undirected graph*.

What Is a Graph?

In discrete mathematics, it is customary to use the word *graph* to mean undirected graph. In this case, the word *edge* is defined differently so that it is an "undirected" edge. Technically, a **graph** consists of a set V of vertices and a set E of edges; each **edge** is either a two-element subset of V (in which case it is drawn as a line or curve connecting the vertices in a drawing) or a one-element subset of V (in which case it is drawn as a loop connecting the vertex to itself in a drawing). A graph is often called a **simple graph** if it has no one-element edges (loops).

EXAMPLE 13   A sociologist studying a nursery school class has observed who eats snacks together. The students' initials are G, M, J, P, R, S, T, B, A, and L. The data are summarized by the following lists showing who has eaten at least once with whom. G: L, M; L: A, M, G; A: L; M: G, L; S: P; P: S, R; R: P, T; T: R; J: B; B: J. Explain why this relation should be symmetric, show that the data give a symmetric relation, give the edge set of its graph, and draw its graph.

Solution   If child X eats a snack with child Y, then Y is eating a snack with X. Thus the relation should be symmetric. We write down the pairs of the relation as follows:

$$(G, L), (L, G), (G, M), (M, G), (L, A), (A, L), (L, M), (M, L),$$
$$(S, P), (P, S), (P, R), (R, P), (R, T), (T, R), (J, B), (B, J)$$

These are all the pairs given by the lists, and only those pairs. Each two-element set appears in two pairs, side by side, in both possible orders, so the relation is symmetric. The *edge* set of the graph is the set

$$\{\{G, L\}, \{G, M\}, \{L, A\}, \{L, M\}, \{S, P\}, \{P, R\}, \{R, T\}, \{J, B\}\}$$

of the *two-element sets*, not a set of ordered pairs. The graph is shown in Figure 8.   ∎

Figure 8

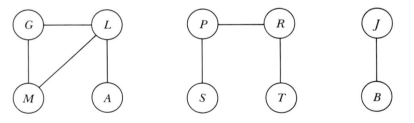

Some other examples of symmetric relations are: being in the same family with, being enrolled in a course with (on the set of people), being on a network with (on the set of computers), representing the same quantity as (on the set of variables), and so on. Whenever we think of one or more properties that objects can share, then we are thinking of a symmetric relation.

Walks in Graphs

Sometimes transportation and communication systems are symmetric. In these cases, if we can send something from point a to point x, then we can send something from point x to point a along the same route in reverse. This leads us to the notion of an (undirected) walk in a graph.

A **walk** is an alternating sequence of vertices and edges

$$a \{a,b\} \, b \, \{b,c\} \ldots w \, \{w,x\} \, x$$

such that each edge connects the vertices
preceding and following it.

As with digraphs, we need only write the list of vertices $abc \ldots wx$ to describe the walk.

We say that x is **connected to** y if there is a walk from x to y.

If we write this walk in reverse order, we get a walk from y to x, so in an undirected graph the relation *is connected to* is a symmetric relation. The definition of the phrase *is connected to* can also be applied to digraphs; in a digraph, this relation need not be symmetric. The concept of reachability applies to graphs as well as digraphs. Clearly, the concepts of reachability and connectivity are closely related; but they are different concepts. We say that a vertex x is connected to itself by the trivial walk consisting of x and no other vertices or edges. This illustrates the only difference between the concepts of reachability and connectivity. A vertex is always connected to itself, but a vertex need not be reachable from itself.

Connected Components

In Figure 8, the graph breaks into three separate parts. These three parts are called *connected components*. What does this mean? First, a set S of vertices is called **connected** if between each two vertices in S there is a walk whose vertices are all in S. Thus $\{G,M\}$ and $\{G,M,A,L\}$ are connected sets, but $\{G,M,A\}$ is not a connected set.

A connected set is called a **connectivity class** if there
is no larger connected set that contains it as a subset.

A graph consisting of a connectivity class and all
edges of G connecting two vertices in the class is
called a **connected component** of G.

Thus in the graph of Figure 8, $\{G,M\}$ is not a connectivity class, but $\{G,M,A,L\}$ is. The set $\{G,M,A,L\}$ together with the edge set $\{\{G,M\}, \{G,L\}, \{L,M\}, \{A,L\}\}$ is a connected component. The fact that a graph always "breaks up into" connected components may be summarized by the following theorem.

Theorem 3   Each vertex of the graph lies in one and only one connected component of the graph.

Proof   First, we show that each vertex has a connected set associated with it in a natural way. Next, we show that this connected set is a connected component. Finally, we show that no different connected component can contain this vertex.

Suppose x is a vertex of the graph. Let S be the set of all vertices connected to x. If $y \in S$ then there is a walk from x to y—or to any vertex on this walk—so there is a walk from x to y using only vertices is S. To see that S is connected, we must show that, for each y and z in S, there is a walk from y to z using only vertices in S. But there are walks from y to x and from x to z using only vertices in S, so putting them together yields the desired walk. Thus S is connected. Now suppose there is a set T of additional vertices we could add to S and get a connected set for $S \cup T$. Then, because $S \cup T$ is connected, for each t in T there is a walk in $S \cup T$ from x to t. Thus, t is connected to x. Thus, by definition t is in S, so $T \subseteq S$. Therefore, S is a connected component, and we have proved that x lies in one connected component. If x also lies in the connected component K, x is connected to each vertex in K by a walk in K, so by definition each k in K is also in S. Therefore $K \subseteq S$. Since S is a connected set containing K, and K is a connected component, $S = K$. Therefore, x lies in only one connected component.   ■

EXAMPLE 14   Write down the connected component containing the vertex A and the connected component connecting the vertex T of the graph of Example 13.

Solution   The connectivity class containing A is the set of all vertices connected to A. This set is $\{A,L,M,G\}$. The edge set of this connected component is $\{\{G,M\}, \{G,L\}, \{L,M\}, \{A,L\}\}$. The connectivity class containing T is the set of all vertices connected to T. This set is $\{R,P,S,T\}$. The edge set of this connected component is $\{\{P,S\} \{P,R\}, \{R,T\}\}$.   ■

Notice in the example that a connectivity class is simply a set of vertices. When we *view* $\{A,L,M,G\}$ in Figure 8 as a set of vertices connected by edges, we are viewing it as a connected component. The point is that a connectivity class is a set, whereas a connected component is a graph. The graph in Figure 7 has only one connected component.

A graph with only one connected component
is called a **connected graph.**

The graph in Figure 7 is connected, and the graph in Figure 8 is not.

To find the connectivity class containing a vertex x, we find vertices connected to x. If there is a walk from x to y, then in the corresponding symmetric relation we could reach y from x. The algorithm Reach was written so that it can be applied to graphs as well as digraphs, so we may use it to find a list of vertices other than x in the connected component containing x.

◨ *Equivalence Relations*

The word *equivalent* is used in many different ways in different mathematical contexts. Nonetheless, there are certain properties we intuitively associate with the word *equivalent*. If we say that x is equivalent to y, then we also expect y to be equivalent to x. Thus we expect a relationship we call *equivalence* to be symmetric. Also, we would always expect an object to be equivalent to itself. We say that a relation R on a set S is **reflexive** if each element of S is related to itself. In symbols, R is reflexive if $(x,x) \in R$ for each x in R or, equivalently, if xRx for each x in R.

EXAMPLE 15   Which of the following relations on $\{1,2,3\}$ is reflexive?

(a) $\{(1,1), (1,2), (2,2), (1,3), (3,2), (3,3)\}$
(b) $\{(1,1), (2,2), (2,3), (3,2), (3,1), (1,3)\}$

Solution   Relation (a) is reflexive because it contains $(1,1)$, $(2,2)$, and $(3,3)$. Relation (b) is not reflexive because it does not contain the pair $(3,3)$.   ■

We have also studied one other property we might associate with the word *equivalent*. If x is equivalent to y and y is equivalent to z, then we expect x and z to be equivalent. Expecting this means that we expect a relation of equivalence to be transitive.

A relation that is reflexive, symmetric, and transitive is called an **equivalence relation.**

EXAMPLE 16   Show that the relationship of equivalence among statements about a universe is an equivalence relation.

Solution   Two statements are equivalent if they have exactly the same truth sets. A statement s has the same truth set as s, so the relation is reflexive. If s has the same truth set as t, then t has the same truth set as s. Therefore, the relation is symmetric. Finally, if r and s have the same truth set and s and t have the same truth set, then r and t have the same truth set. Therefore, the relation is transitive. Thus, the relation of equivalence among statements is an equivalence relation.   ■

EXAMPLE 17   Show that the connectivity relation of a graph is an equivalence relation.

Solution   A vertex is connected to itself by the trivial walk consisting of that vertex alone. Therefore *is connected to* is reflexive. We've already noted that connectivity is symmetric in a *graph*, because if there is a walk from x to y, then the same vertices and edges in reverse order give a walk from y to x. If there is a walk from x to y and a walk from y to z, then these walks may be joined to give a walk from x to z. Therefore, connectivity is transitive. We have just verified that the relation of connectivity has the three properties that make it an equivalence relation.   ■

In a less mathematical context, it is natural to think of two people who get the same scores on a test as equivalent in their abilities on that test. This is another example of an equivalence relation.

EXAMPLE 18   Show that the relation *has the same score as* is an equivalence relation.

Solution   (In the next three sentences, we verify the reflexive, symmetric, and transitive properties.) Each person has the same score as himself or herself. If x and y have the same score, then so do y and x. If x and y have the same score and y and z have the same score, then all three have the same score, so x and z have the same score. Thus we have an equivalence relation.   ■

Graphs of Equivalence Relations

It is possible to recognize from the graph of a relation whether or not it is an equivalence relation.

EXAMPLE 19   On a certain test, the following students got the scores shown: Pat 98, Ram 98, Leroy 98, Maria 98, Kate 86, Sam 86, George 86, Dolly 80, and John 80. Draw the graph of the *has the same score as* relation.

Solution   The graph is shown in Figure 9; initials are used to label the vertices.

Figure 9

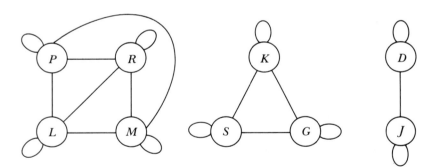

Notice how the connected components of the graph in Figure 9 all have as many edges as possible. Within each component, everything is joined to everything else. One component represents the students who got 98—on this test, these students are mutually equivalent; one component represents those who got 86—on this test, these students are mutually equivalent; and one component represents those who got 80—on this test these students are mutually equivalent. The observation that within a component everything is connected to everything else would tell us that the relation is transitive if we didn't already know it. Why? If (x,y) and (y,z) are edges, then x, y, and z are all in the same component, so (x,z) is an edge as well.

In fact, in the graph of an equivalence relation, the connected components will always have this appearance.

Theorem 4 A graph is the graph of an equivalence relation if and only if each vertex is connected to itself by an edge and each two vertices lying in the same connected component are connected by an edge.

Proof Suppose we have an equivalence relation. Then since it is reflexive, each vertex is joined to itself. If two vertices are in the same connected component, then they are joined by a walk, so (by the transitive property) they are joined by an edge.

Now suppose we have a graph in which each vertex is connected to itself by an edge and each two vertices lying in the same connected component are connected by an edge. The relation of the graph is symmetric; it is reflexive because each vertex is connected to itself by an edge. If $\{x,y\}$ and $\{y,z\}$ are edges, then x and z lie in the same connected component, so that $\{x,z\}$ is an edge. Thus the relation of the graph is an equivalence relation. ∎

EXAMPLE 20 Which of the graphs in Figure 10 is the graph of an equivalence relation?

Figure 10

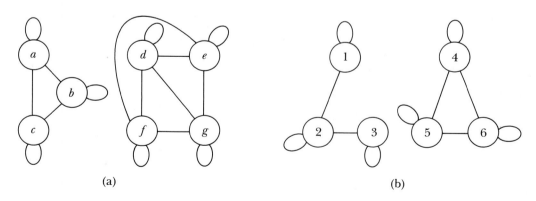

(a)   (b)

Solution Graph (a) is the graph of an equivalence relation, because in each connected component, each pair of vertices is joined by an edge. Graph (b) is not the graph of an equivalence relation, because vertex 1 and vertex 3 are in the same connected component but are not connected by an edge. ∎

A graph is called a **clique** or **complete graph** if each pair of its vertices is connected by an edge. Thus a graph is the graph of an equivalence relation if and only if each connected component is a clique.

Concepts Review

1. A relation is _____ if (x,y) is in the relation whenever (y,x) is in the relation.

2. The edges of a graph are one- or two-element _____.

3. A graph is simple if all its edges are _____ element sets.

4. We say x is connected to y in a graph if there is a(n) _____ from x to y.

5. A set of vertices in a graph is called _____ if each two vertices in the set are joined by a walk whose vertices are in the set.

6. A connected set in a graph is called a(n) _____ _____ of the graph if no larger set that contains it is connected.

7. Every vertex of a graph lies in _____ _____ _____ _____ connected component.

8. A graph with only one connected component is called a(n) _____ graph.

9. A relation on a set X is _____ if (x,x) is in the relation for each x in X.

10. A reflexive, symmetric, and transitive relation is called a(n) _____ _____.

11. The connectivity relation of a graph is a(n) _____ relation.

12. In the graph of an equivalence relation, each two vertices in the same connected component are joined by a(n) _____.

Exercises

A

1. Draw the graphs of the following relations on the set $\{1,2,3,4,5\}$.
   (a) $\{(1,2), (2,1), (2,3), (3,2), (3,4), (4,3), (4,5), (5,4), (5,1), (1,5)\}$
   (b) $\{(1,2), (2,1), (1,3), (3,1), (1,4), (4,1), (1,5), (5,1)\}$
   (c) $\{(1,2), (2,1), (3,4), (4,3), (4,5), (5,4), (3,5), (5,3)\}$
   (d) $\{(1,2), (2,1), (2,3), (3,2), (3,4), (4,3), (2,4), (4,2), (1,4), (4,1)\}$

2. Draw the graphs of the following relations on the set $\{a,b,c,d,e\}$.
   (a) $\{(a,b), (b,c), (c,a), (a,c), (c,b), (b,a), (d,e), (e,d)\}$
   (b) $\{(a,b), (b,a), (b,d), (d,b), (d,e), (e,d), (b,e), (e,b), (a,e), (e,a)\}$
   (c) $\{(b,a), (a,b), (b,c), (c,b), (c,d), (d,c), (c,e), (e,c)\}$
   (d) $\{(a,c), (c,a), (c,e), (e,c), (a,e), (e,a), (b,d), (d,b)\}$

3. Draw the graphs on the set $\{1,2,3,4,5\}$ with the following edge sets.
   (a) $\{\{1,2\}, \{1,3\}, \{1,4\}, \{1,5\}\}$
   (b) $\{\{1\}, \{1,2\}, \{2,3\}, \{2\}, \{3\}, \{4\}, \{4,5\}, \{5\}\}$
   (c) $\{\{1,2\}, \{1,3\}, \{2,3\}, \{2,4\}, \{3,4\}, \{3,5\}, \{4,5\}, \{4,1\}, \{5,1\}, \{5,2\}\}$
   (d) $\{\{1\}, \{1,2\}, \{2,3\}, \{3\}, \{4\}, \{4,5\}, \{5\}\}$

4. Draw the graphs on the set $\{a,b,c,d,e\}$ with the following edge sets.
   (a) $\{\{a,b\}, \{a,c\}, \{a,d\}, \{a,e\}, \{b,c\}, \{c,d\}, \{d,e\}, \{e,b\}\}$
   (b) $\{\{b,c\}, \{b\}, \{c\}, \{c,d\}, \{d\}, \{c\}, \{e\}, \{d,e\}\}$
   (c) $\{\{a,b\}, \{a,c\}, \{a,d\}, \{b,c\}, \{b,d\}, \{d,e\}, \{c,e\}, \{b,e\}, \{a,e\}\}$
   (d) $\{\{a\}, \{a,b\}, \{b,c\}, \{c,a\}, \{d,e\}, \{e\}\}$

5. Write down both the edge set and the symmetric relation of the graphs in Figure 11.

Figure 11

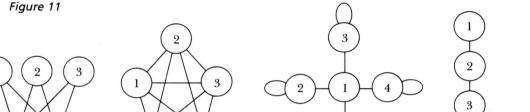

       (a)   (b)   (c)   (d)

6. Write down both the edge set and the symmetric relation of the graphs in Figure 12.

Figure 12

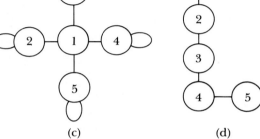

       (a)   (b)   (c)   (d)

7. Find the connectivity classes of the graphs in Exercise 3. State whether or not the graph is connected.

8. Find the connectivity classes of the graphs in Exercise 4. State whether or not the graph is connected.

9. For each of the graphs in Exercise 5, give a walk from vertex 1 to vertex 3 with exactly four edges, or explain why there is no such walk.

10. For each of the graphs in Exercise 6, give a walk from vertex a to vertex c with exactly four edges, or explain why there is no such walk.

11. Determine which graphs in Exercise 1 are connected.

12. Determine which graphs in Exercise 2 are connected.

13. Let V be the set $\{1,2,3,4,5,6\}$. Define the relation R on V by $(x,y) \in R$ if $\dfrac{x+y}{3}$ is an integer.
    (a) Show that R is symmetric.
    (b) Draw the graph of R.
    (c) Write down the connected components of this graph.

14. Let V be the set $\{\{1,2\}, \{3,4\}, \{1,2,3\}, \{4,5\}, \{6,8\}, \{7,8,9\}, \{7\}\}$. Define a relation R on V by $(X,Y) \in R$ if $X \cap Y \neq \varnothing$.
    (a) Show that R is symmetric.
    (b) Draw the graph of R.
    (c) Write down the connected components of this graph.

B 15. Determine if each of the relations described below is an equivalence relation on $\{1,2,3,4,5,6\}$.
    (a) $\{(1,3), (3,5), (5,1), (3,1), (5,3), (1,5), (4,6), (6,4), (4,2), (2,4), (2,6), (6,2), (1.1), (2,2),$
        $(3,3), (4,4), (5,5), (6,6)\}$
    (b) $(x,y) \in R$ if $x - y = \pm 1$
    (c) $(x,y) \in R$ if $|x - y| \leq 1$
    (d) $(x,y) \in R$ if $x^2 - 6x = y^2 - 6y$

16. Determine if each of the relations below is an equivalence relation on $\{-3, -2, -1, 0, 1, 2, 3\}$.
    (a) $\{(-3, -3), (-3, -2), (-2, -2), (-1, -1), (-1,0), (0,0), (0,1), (1, -1), (2,2), (2,3),$
        $(3,3), (-2, -3), (0, -1), (1,0), (-1,1), (3,2)\}$
    (b) $(x,y) \in R$ if $x^2 = y^2$
    (c) $(x,y) \in R$ if $x^2 - y^2 \leq 1$
    (d) $(x,y) \in R$ if $(x - y)^2 \leq 1$

17. For each of the following edge sets of graphs on $\{1,2,3,4,5,6\}$, draw the graph and state whether it is a graph of an equivalence relation and why.
    (a) $\{\{1,1\}, \{1,2\}, \{2,2\}, \{2,3\}, \{3,3\}, \{4,4\}, \{5,5\}, \{5,6\}, \{6,6\}\}$
    (b) $\{\{1,2\}, \{2,3\}, \{1,3\}, \{4,5\}, \{5,6\}, \{4,6\}\}$
    (c) $\{\{1,1\}, \{2,2\}, \{3,3\}, \{4,4\}, \{5,5\}, \{6,6\}\}$

18. For each of the following edge sets of graphs on $\{a,b,c,d,e\}$, draw the graph and state whether it is a graph of an equivalence relation and why.
    (a) $\{\{a,a\}, \{b,b\}, \{c,c\}, \{d,d\}, \{e,e\}, \{a,e\}, \{e,b\}, \{a,b\}, \{c,d\}\}$
    (b) $\{\{a,a\}, \{a,c\}, \{c,c\}, \{c,d\}, \{d,d\}, \{d,a\}, \{e,e\}\}$
    (c) $\{\{a,a\}, \{b,b\}, \{c,c\}, \{d,d\}, \{e,e\}, \{a,b\}, \{b,c\}, \{c,d\}, \{d,a\}, \{a,c\}\}$

19. Consider the relation on the integers $\{1,2,3,4,5,6\}$ given by $(a,b) \in R$ if $a + b$ is a multiple of 3. Explain why R is symmetric, draw the graph of R, and determine whether R is an equivalence relation.

20. Consider the relation on the integers $\{1,2,3,4,5,6\}$ given by $(a,b) \in R$ if $a + b$ is a multiple of 2. Explain why R is symmetric, draw a graph of R, and determine whether R is an equivalence relation.

Problems

1. What is the minimum number of edges possible in a connected graph on an n-vertex set?

2. What is the maximum possible number of edges in a graph on an n-vertex set? A simple graph on an n-vertex set?

3. Is a union of equivalence relations (defined on the same set) an equivalence relation? Is the intersection of equivalence relations (defined on the same set) an equivalence relation?

4. What are the answers to the questions in Problem 3 if the equivalence relations are defined on different sets?

5. When is the transitive closure of a symmetric relation reflexive?

6. Show that if a simple graph has more than $(n - 1)(n - 2)/2$ edges, then it is connected.

7. What is the minimum number of vertices in a simple graph with 30 edges?

8. Three houses must be each connected by underground utility lines to the same sewer connection, the same water connection, and the same natural gas connection. Is it possible to make the connections so that none of the connecting lines crosses another?

9. The *degree* of a vertex in a simple graph is the number of edges it lies in. Show that the sum of the degrees of the vertices is an even number.

10. *Degree* is defined in Problem 9. Show that, in a simple graph, the number of vertices whose degree is odd is an even number.

11. *Degree* is defined in Problem 9. How many vertices will a simple graph have if it has 9 edges and each vertex has degree 3?

12. In a group of nine people, is it possible that each person knows exactly three other people in the group?

Section 3-3
Equivalence Classes
and Congruence Classes

◭ Equivalence Classes

> The connectivity classes of the graph of an
> equivalence relation are called **equivalence classes.**

By examining the equivalence classes of the "same test score" example, we shall
see why they have this name.

EXAMPLE 21   Write down the equivalence classes of the equivalence relation of Example 19 in
which two students were equivalent if they had the same test score.

Solution   We will begin with the equivalence class of Pat. This is the connected
component Pat is in, so it consists of Pat and everyone joined to Pat by an edge.
Using initials, we write this set as $\{P,R,M,L\}$. Notice that this is the set of people
who got 98. The other classes, found similarly, are $\{K,S,G\}$ (the 86s) and $\{D,J\}$
(the 80s). Since we had the graph drawn in Figure 9, we could have just written
down the elements of the connected components by looking at the picture. Notice
how each equivalence class consists of people with mutually equivalent test per-
formances.   ◼

The example shows that if we are given an equivalence relation, it is straightforward to write down the equivalence class containing x. We simply write down
the vertices related to x by the relation.

For equivalence relations, our basic theorem about connected components
(Theorem 3) becomes stronger because of the transitive law. The stronger version
is our next theorem. Here we use V for our universe, to make it easier to think of
the universe as the vertex set of a graph.

Theorem 5   If the relation R is an equivalence relation on a universe V, then V may be divided
up in one and only one way into sets called *equivalence classes* such that

(1)   Each x in V lies in one and only one equivalence class.
(2)   All elements in an equivalence class are equivalent.
(3)   Elements chosen from two different equivalence classes are not equivalent.

Proof   Statement (1) is simply the fact that each x in V lies in one and only one
connected component. Statement (2) follows from the transitive law. Statement (3)
follows from the fact that no edges join elements in two different connected
components.   ◼

Partitions

A collection of sets (none of which is empty) that are disjoint (no two of them have an element in common) and whose union is a set U is called a **partition** of U.

EXAMPLE 22   Which of the following families of subsets of $U = \{1,2,3,4,5,6,7\}$ are partitions and why?

(a) $\{1,2,3\}$, $\{4,6\}$, $\{5,7\}$
(b) $\{1,2,6\}$, $\{4\}$, $\{3,5\}$
(c) $\{2,4,6\}$, $\{1,2,3\}$, $\{5,7\}$
(d) $\{1,2,3,4,6,7\}$, $\{5\}$

Solution   (a) is a partition because the union of the sets is U and they are disjoint. (b) is not a partition because 7 is not in the union of the sets. (c) is not a partition because the element 2 is in both the first and the second set. (d) is a partition because each element between 1 and 7 appears in one and only one of these sets.   ∎

Equivalence classes of equivalence relations always give us partitions. For example, using the equivalence classes from Example 21, we may write

$$\{P,L,R,M\} \cup \{K,S,G\} \cup \{D,J\} = \{P,L,R,M,K,S,G,D,J\}$$

If we write $\mathbb{P} = \{\{P,L,R,M\},\{K,S,G\},\{D,J\}\}$, then we may refer to the partition $\mathbb{P}$ of our set of people. When we have an equivalence relation on a universe U, conclusion 1 of Theorem 5 tells us that the union of the equivalence classes is U and that no two equivalence classes have an element in common. Thus we may restate conclusion 1 as the following theorem.

Theorem 6   The equivalence classes of an equivalence relation on a set U form a partition of U.

Proof   This is a restatement of conclusion 1 of Theorem 5.   ∎

Now suppose we have a set U and we have divided it up into a collection of disjoint sets. For example, using the initials from Example 19, we may write

$$\{P,M,K,D\} \cup \{R,L,S,G,J\} = \{P,L,R,M,K,S,G,D,J\}$$

which represents the partition of our set of people into women and men. Is there an equivalence relation whose equivalence classes are exactly these two sets? We can quickly check that *is the same sex as* is an equivalence relation and has the set of women and the set of men as its equivalence classes. This example demonstrates the general principle stated in the theorem below.

Theorem 7   If $\mathbb{P}$ is a partition of a set U, then there is an equivalence relation whose equivalence classes are the sets of $\mathbb{P}$.

Proof   Define the relation R by putting the ordered pair (x,y) into R if and only if there is a set of $\mathbb{P}$ containing both x and y. (This implies that $(x,y) \notin R$ if x and y are in different sets of $\mathbb{P}$.) This relation is reflexive (because x is in the same set as x), symmetric (because if x is in the same set as y, then y is in the same set as x), and transitive (because if x is in the same set as y and y is in the same set as z, then x is in the same set as z). Thus R is an equivalence relation. For each x, the equivalence class of x is the set of all elements y such that y is related to x—that is, the set of all things in the same set as x. Therefore, the equivalence class will be the set we started with.   ∎

(As pointed out in Problem 12, the relation R defined in the proof is the *only* equivalence relation whose equivalence classes are the sets of $\mathbb{P}$.)

EXAMPLE 23   Given the partition $\{\{1,2\},\ \{5,7,3\},\ \{4,6\}\}$ of $\{1,2,3,4,5,6,7\}$, find an equivalence relation whose equivalence classes are the sets of this partition.

Solution   Since 1 and 2 are in a class together, $(1,2)$ must be in the relation, as $(2,1)$ must be. Also, since 5, 7, and 3 are together, we must have $(5,7)$, $(5,3)$, $(7,3)$, as well as $(7,5)$, $(3,5)$, and $(3,7)$. We must also have $(4,6)$ and $(6,4)$. Finally, since our relation must be reflexive, we must have $(1,1)$, $(2,2)$, and so on. This gives us the set

$$\{(1,1),\ (2,2),\ (3,3),\ (4,4),\ (5,5),\ (6,6),\ (7,7),\ (1,2),\ (2,1),$$
$$(5,7),\ (5,3),\ (7,3),\ (7,5),\ (3,5),\ (3,7),\ (4,6),\ (6,4)\}$$

for our relation.   ∎

B   *Arithmetic Modulo* m

There is an equivalence relation studied in number theory whose importance has been more widely recognized because of its many applications in computing. You may have seen this equivalence relation in elementary school in the guise of "clock arithmetic." For example, you had problems such as "What time will it be in 7 hours if it is now 10:00 A.M.?" You can get the answer 5:00 P.M. by adding 10 to 7, getting 17, and then subtracting 12 to get 5. Similar techniques are useful in many problems involving repeating patterns.

Suppose, for example, you are trying to represent a board game, such as *Monopoly*, in a computer. The board has 40 positions arranged around the 4 sides of a square. Suppose the positions are numbered 0 through 39. You roll dice to determine how many places to move; if you are at place i and roll j dots on the dice, then you move to square $i + j$. But if i is 36 and j is 9, this would say you should go to square 45, and there is no square 45. Instead you go to square 5, because position 40 is equivalent to position 0, position 41 is equivalent to position 1, and so on. Thus, each time we get a number bigger than 39, we convert it to an equivalent number by subtracting 40 from it.

Thus a number x is equivalent to $x + 40$. Going around the board twice would correspond to $x + 80$; going around backwards once would correspond to $x - 40$. Thus the numbers that represent the same positions as the number x are $x + 40n$, where n is any positive or negative integer. The numbers that represent position 5, for example, form the set $\{\ldots -75, -35, 5, 45, 85, \ldots\}$. There is a simple method for determining whether two numbers represent the same square. If $y = x + 40n$, then $y - x = 40n$. Thus x and y are equivalent if and only if $y - x$ is a multiple of 40. For example, 135 is equivalent to 15 because $15 - 135 = -120 = -3\cdot40$. On the other hand, 65 and 115 are not equivalent because $115 - 65 = 50$, which is not a multiple of 40.

Congruence Modulo m

The number 40 is called the **modulus**, and we say that x **is equivalent to** y **modulo 40**, written $x \equiv y \bmod 40$, if $y - x$ is a multiple of 40. Of course, in other situations we may have a different modulus.

> For an arbitrary integer $m > 0$, we say that x is equivalent to y modulo m or x is **congruent** to y modulo m, written $x \equiv y \bmod m$ (or even $x \equiv y$), if $y - x$ is an integer multiple of m.

(We shall use the phrase *congruent modulo m* henceforth.) (In some computer languages Mod(n,m) stands for the remainder we get after dividing n by m. Thus Mod(7,3) = 1 and Mod(12,4) = 0. In this notation we can say that $x \equiv y \bmod m$ if and only if Mod(x,m) = Mod(y,m). In other computer languages, n mod m stands for the remainder we get after dividing m by n. Thus 7 mod 3 = 1. In this notation, we may write $x \equiv y \bmod m$ if and only if x mod $m = y$ mod m. This intuitively appealing notation gives a second meaning to mod m, so that the reader must determine from context whether the congruence relation or the remainder is meant. To avoid possible confusion, we shall use *mod* only for the congruence relation and not for the remainder.)

EXAMPLE 24   Is 87 congruent to 3 mod 12? Is 26 congruent to -13 mod 7?

Solution $87 - 3 = 84 = 7\cdot12$. Therefore $87 \equiv 3 \bmod 12$. For the second question, $26 - (-13) = 39$, which is not a multiple of 7. Thus $26 \not\equiv -13 \bmod 7$.   ∎

We use the three-lined symbol for congruence because its properties are much like those of equality. Three of the similarities with equality may be expressed as follows.

Theorem 8   The relation of congruence modulo m is an equivalence relation.

Proof   Since $x - x = 0 \bmod m$, the relation is reflexive. If $x - y = nm$, then $y - x = (-n)m$, so the relation is symmetric. Finally, if $x - y = nm$ and $y - z = km$, then $x - z = x - y + y - z = nm + km = (n + k)m$. Therefore, our relation is transitive.   ∎

Congruences

A statement that two numerical expressions involving variables are equal is called an *equation*. A statement that two numerical expressions involving variables are congruent is called a **congruence**. Thus, $2x + 4 \equiv x - 1 \bmod 7$ is an example of a congruence. Just as we often need to solve equations, we sometimes need to "solve" congruences.

Two fundamental operations you can perform on an equation (in order to help you solve it) are adding a number to both sides or multiplying both sides of the equation by the same number. So long as that number is an integer, we can do these operations to solve congruences modulo m as well.

Theorem 9   Suppose $x \equiv y \bmod m$ and n is an integer. Then

$$x + n \equiv y + n \bmod m$$

and

$$x \cdot n \equiv y \cdot n \bmod m$$

Proof   If $x \equiv y \bmod m$, then $x - y = km$ for some integer k. Then

$$(x + n) - (y + n) = x - y = km$$

so $x + n \equiv y + n$. We prove that $x \cdot n \equiv y \cdot n$ similarly.   ∎

EXAMPLE 25   Solve the congruence $2x + 4 \equiv x - 1 \bmod 7$.

Solution   We write

$$
\begin{aligned}
2x + 4 &\equiv x - 1 & \bmod 7 \\
(2x + 4) - x &\equiv (x - 1) - x & \bmod 7 \\
x + 4 &\equiv -1 & \bmod 7 \\
(x + 4) - 4 &\equiv (-1) - 4 & \bmod 7 \\
x &\equiv -5 & \bmod 7
\end{aligned}
$$

Since $x + 7$ is congruent to x, we may also write

$$
\begin{aligned}
x + 7 &\equiv -5 + 7 & \bmod 7 \\
x &\equiv 2 & \bmod 7
\end{aligned}
$$

and

$$x + 7 \equiv 2 + 7 \quad \bmod 7$$

or

$$x \equiv 9 \qquad \bmod 7$$ ∎

Is one of these solutions preferred? People often like to choose a solution between 0 and $m - 1$ for a congruence relation; $x \equiv 2$ is called the **principal solution** to the congruence. The **solution set,** which is the set of all numbers x satisfying the congruence, is the infinite set

$$\{ \ldots -12, -5, 2, 9, 16, \ldots \}$$

Notice that this is the equivalence class (also called the *congruence class*) of 2 modulo 7. The **principal element** of a congruence class mod m is the element between 0 and $m - 1$. The principal element of the congruence class of n mod m is the remainder you get when you divide n by m.

To solve equations, we have to be able to divide both sides by a number as well as being able to multiply both sides by a number. We can't always do this for equivalence modulo m, but we often can.

Theorem 10 If $ax \equiv ay$ mod m and the integers a and m have no common factors, then $x \equiv y$ mod m.

Proof Since $ax \equiv ay$ mod m, $ax - ay = km$ for some k. Thus $a(x - y) = km$. Therefore each factor of a is a factor of km. But since no factor of a is a factor of m, each factor of a must be a factor of k (because numbers can be factored in one and only one way). Therefore a is a factor of k, so we may write $k = ak'$. Thus

$$a(x - y) = ak'm$$

and

$$(x - y) = k'm$$

so that $x \equiv y$ mod m. ∎

EXAMPLE 26 Solve the congruence $2x + 4 \equiv 14$ mod 3.

Solution We write

$$
\begin{aligned}
2x + 4 &\equiv 14 && \text{mod } 3 \\
(2x + 4) - 4 &\equiv 14 - 4 && \text{mod } 3 \\
2x + 0 &\equiv 10 && \text{mod } 3 \\
2 \cdot x &\equiv 2 \cdot 5 && \text{mod } 3 \\
x &\equiv 5 && \text{mod } 3 \\
x &\equiv 2 && \text{mod } 3
\end{aligned}
$$

Notice that the first solution we found was $x = 5$. Then we subtracted 3 to get the equivalent principal solution $x = 2$. Any number equivalent to 2 modulo 3 is a solution to our equation; the statement $x \equiv 2$ mod 3 means

$$x \in \{ \ldots, -4, -1, 2, 5, 8, \ldots \}$$

the set of all numbers equivalent to 2 modulo 3. Thus our solution set is the congruence class of 2 modulo 3. ∎

EXAMPLE 27   Find the principal solution of the congruence $2x \equiv 1 \bmod 7$.

Solution   Since we don't have a multiple of 2 on the right-hand side of the congruence, we can't apply Theorem 10. However, we may add 7 to both sides of the congruence, as you see in the second congruence below, and get an even number on the right. Notice that later in the computation we replace $2x + 7$ on the left-hand side of the congruence by $2x$ because $2x + 7$ is congruent to $2x$. We write

$$
\begin{aligned}
2x &\equiv 1 & \bmod 7 \\
2x + 7 &\equiv 1 + 7 & \bmod 7 \\
2x + 7 &\equiv 8 & \bmod 7 \\
2x &\equiv 8 & \bmod 7 \\
2x &\equiv 2{\cdot}4 & \bmod 7 \\
x &\equiv 4 & \bmod 7
\end{aligned}
$$
∎

A similar method lets you solve any congruence of the form $ax \equiv b \bmod m$ whenever a and m have *no common factors*. You add multiples of m to b until you get a number divisible by a—eventually you will—and then divide by a.

EXAMPLE 28   Solve the congruence $4x \equiv 2 \bmod 7$ for its principal solution.

Solution   We write

$$
\begin{aligned}
4x &\equiv 2 & \bmod 7 \\
4x &\equiv 2 + 7 & \bmod 7 \\
4x &\equiv 9 & \bmod 7 \\
4x &\equiv 9 + 7 & \bmod 7 \\
4x &\equiv 16 & \bmod 7 \\
x &\equiv 4 & \bmod 7
\end{aligned}
$$
∎

Concepts Review

1. A connectivity class of a graph of an equivalence relation is called a(n) _____ _____.

2. If we have an equivalence relation R on a set V, then each element of V lies in one and only one _____ _____ of R.

3. All elements in an equivalence class are _____.

4. Elements in different equivalence classes are _____ equivalent.

5. A collection of nonempty disjoint sets whose union is U is called a(n) _____ of U.

6. The equivalence classes of an equivalence relation on U form a(n) _____ of U.

7. For each partition of U, there is an equivalence relation whose _____ _____ are the sets of the partition.

8. If $y - x$ is a multiple of 12, then y is _____ to x _____ 12.

9. The relation of congruence modulo n is a(n) _____ relation.

10. A statement that two numerical expressions involving variables are congruent modulo m is called a(n) _____.

11. The solution set of a congruence is the set of all _____ to the congruence.

12. The principal solution to a congruence modulo m is a number between _____ and _____.

Exercises

A In Exercises 1–4, write the equivalence classes of the equivalence relation given.

1. $\{(1,3), (3,5), (5,1), (3,1), (5,3), (1,5), (4,6), (6,4), (4,2), (2,4), (2,6), (6,2), (1,1), (2,2), (3,3), (4,4), (5,5), (6,6)\}$

2. $\{(1,1), (1,2), (2,1), (2,2), (3,3), (3,4), (4,4), (3,5), (4,5), (4,3), (5,3), (5,4), (5,5), (6,6), (6,7), (7,6), (7,7)\}$

3. $(x,y) \in R$ if $x^2 - 4x = y^2 - 4y$ on the set $\{1,2,3,4,5,6\}$

4. $(x,y) \in R$ if $x^2 = y^2$ on the set $\{-2,-1,0,1,2,3\}$

5. For each of the following partitions of $\{1,2,3,4,5\}$, write down the equivalence relations whose classes are the sets of the partition.
   (a) $\{\{1\}, \{2\}, \{3\}, \{4\}, \{5\}\}$
   (b) $\{\{1,2\}, \{3,4,5\}\}$
   (c) $\{\{1\}, \{2,3\}, \{4,5\}\}$.
   (d) $\{\{1\}, \{2,3,4,5\}\}$

6. For each of the following partitions of $\{a,b,c,d\}$, write down the equivalence relation whose classes are the sets of the partition.
   (a) $\{\{a,b\}, \{c,d\}\}$
   (b) $\{\{a\}, \{b,c,d\}\}$
   (c) $\{\{a,b,c,d\}\}$
   (d) $\{\{a\}, \{b\}, \{c\}, \{d\}\}$

7. Which of the following families of subsets of $\{1,2,3,4,5,6\}$ are partitions of $\{1,2,3,4,5,6\}$?
   (a) $\{\{1,2\}, \{2,3\}, \{3,4\}, \{4,5\}, \{5,6\}\}$
   (b) $\{\{1,2,3\}, \{5\}, \{4,6\}\}$
   (c) $\{\{1,2\}, \{4,5,6\}\}$
   (d) $\{\{1\}, \{5\}, \{6,3\}, \{4,2\}\}$

8. Which of the following families of subsets of $\{a,b,c,d,e,f,g\}$ are partitions of $\{a,b,c,d,e,f,g\}$?
   (a) $\{\{a,g\}, \{b,f\}, \{e,d,c\}\}$
   (b) $\{\{a,f\}, \{b,g\}, \{c,a\}, \{d,e\}\}$
   (c) $\{\{a,b,c\}, \{e\}, \{g,f\}\}$
   (d) $\{\{a,b,c\}, \{d,e,f\}, \{g,h\}\}$

B 9. Determine whether the congruences below are true or false and explain your answer.
   (a) $12 \equiv 75 \bmod 7$
   (b) $12 \equiv 75 \bmod 9$
   (c) $12 \equiv 75 \bmod 3$
   (d) $12 \equiv 75 \bmod 27$
   (e) $12 \equiv 75 \bmod 21$
   (f) $12 \equiv 75 \bmod 63$
   (g) $-6 \equiv 26 \bmod 4$
   (h) $-6 \equiv 8 \bmod 12$
   (i) $-6 \equiv 8 \bmod 14$

10. Determine whether the congruences below are true or false.
   (a) $3 \equiv 75 \bmod 12$
   (b) $3 \equiv 75 \bmod 24$
   (c) $12 \equiv 75 \bmod 8$
   (d) $3 \equiv 75 \bmod 4$
   (e) $3 \equiv 75 \bmod 32$
   (f) $-3 \equiv -75 \bmod 8$
   (g) $-10 \equiv 43 \bmod 7$
   (h) $-10 \equiv 44 \bmod 6$
   (i) $-10 \equiv 44 \bmod 9$

Solve the congruences given in Exercises 11–24. Show the solution set (using three dots for numbers left out) and state the value of the principal solution.

11. $3x + 4 \equiv 2x + 6 \bmod 8$

12. $4x + 2 \equiv 3x + 8 \bmod 11$

13. $3(x - 1) \equiv 2(x + 1) - 2 \bmod 6$

14. $3(x + 2) \equiv 4(x - 1) \bmod 5$

15. $4(x - 1) + 2x \equiv 5(x - 2) + 3 \bmod 7$

16. $3(x - 1) \equiv 2(2x + 3) \bmod 5$

17. $2x + 3 \equiv 7 \bmod 9$

18. $2(x + 2) \equiv 4 \bmod 5$

19. $3x \equiv 2 \bmod 40$

20. $3x \equiv 4 \bmod 7$

21. $3x - 2 \equiv 7 \bmod 8$

22. $5x + 3 \equiv 6x - 1 \bmod 5$

23. $2(3x - 2) \equiv 4x - 1 \bmod 5$

24. $4x \equiv 7 \bmod 9$

25. Find the three smallest members in *absolute* value of the equivalence class mod 9 of each number below. Which of these is the principal element of the equivalence class?
   (a) 21   (b) 17   (c) 11   (d) -3 (e) 0

26. Find the three smallest members in *absolute* value of the equivalence class mod 11 of each number below. Which of these is the principal element of the equivalence class?
   (a) 2   (b) 9   (c) 15   (d) 31   (e) -8

27. Give an example of an x that proves that the following argument is not correct. Note that this is a congruence of the form $ax \equiv b \bmod m$, where a and m have common factors.

$$4x \equiv 8 \bmod 12$$
$$x \equiv 2 \bmod 12$$

28. Give an example of an x that proves that the following argument is not correct. Note that this is an $ax \equiv b \bmod m$, where a and m have common factors.

$$3x \equiv 6 \bmod 15$$
$$x \equiv 2 \bmod 15$$

29. Show that if $x \equiv y \bmod m$, then for any integer n, $x - n \equiv y - n \bmod m$.

30. Show that if $x \equiv y \bmod m$, then for any integer n, $x \cdot n \equiv y \cdot n \bmod m$.

Problems

1. Let R and S be equivalence relations. Is $R \cap S$ an equivalence relation? If so, what are its equivalence classes? If not, why not?

2. Let R and S be equivalence relations. Is $R \cup S$ an equivalence relation? If so what are its equivalence classes? If not, why not?

3. Let $\underline{x}$ stand for the equivalence class of x modulo m. Show that if $x_1 \equiv x \bmod m$ and $y_1 \equiv y \bmod m$, then $x_1 + y_1 \equiv x + y \bmod m$. Why does this tell us that we may define an operation $+$ on equivalence classes by $\underline{x} + \underline{y} = \underline{x + y}$? (Such an operation must operate on two equivalence classes to give us another equivalence class.)

4. Read Problem 3 and then show why we may define an operation $\cdot$ on equivalence classes by $\underline{x} \cdot \underline{y} = \underline{xy}$.

5. Show that if we define R on the set of ordered pairs of positive integers by $([x,y],[z,w]) \in R$ if and only if $xw = zy$, then R is an equivalence relation. What do the equivalence classes of R have to do with rational numbers?

6. Suppose R is an equivalence relation on a set U, with equivalence class partition $\mathbb{P} = \{P_1, P_2, P_3\}$, and S is an equivalence relation on U with equivalence class partition $\mathbb{Q} = \{Q_1, Q_2, Q_3\}$. Show that the nonempty sets among $P_1 \cap Q_1$, $P_2 \cap Q_1$, $P_3 \cap Q_1$, $P_1 \cap Q_2$, $P_2 \cap Q_2$, $P_3 \cap Q_2$, $P_1 \cap Q_3$, $P_2 \cap Q_3$, $P_3 \cap Q_3$ also form a partition of U. This is the equivalence class partition of an equivalence relation T. How is T related to R and S?

7. Generalize Problem 6 to arbitrary equivalence relations R and S.

8. Show that if p is a prime number and n, k, and j are integers between 1 and $p - 1$ (inclusive), then nk and nj are not congruent mod p unless $k = j$.

9. Use the result of Problem 8 to show that if p is a prime and n is an integer between 1 and $p - 1$, then there is an integer k between 1 and $p - 1$ such that $nk \equiv 1 \bmod p$.

10. Generalize the results of Problems 8 and 9 so that in Problem 9 you can replace p by a number m that has no prime factors in common with n.

11. Based on Problem 10, explain why a congruence of the form $ax \equiv b \bmod m$ has a solution if a and m have no common factors.

12. Explain how the proof of Theorem 7 may be modified slightly to show that, given a partition $\mathbb{P}$, there is one and only one equivalence relation whose equivalence classes are the sets of $\mathbb{P}$.

Section 3-4
Partial Orderings

🅐 Order Relations

A large, complicated task can often be broken up into simpler tasks. Typically, some of these tasks must precede certain others. For example, in the task of working out the final grades for a course, recording a student's final exam scores would precede computing the student's average for the course, and computing the student's average for the course would precede determining the student's final grade. If we were writing a computer program to help a teacher make up final grades, our program would have to be designed so as not to conflict with this information about what precedes what.

What can we say about the relation *precedes*? First, a task cannot precede itself. A relation R on a set V is called **reflexive** if (a,a) is in R for each a in V, and R is called **irreflexive** if (a,a) is not in R for any a in V. As the next example shows, saying that a relation is irreflexive is different from saying it is not reflexive.

EXAMPLE 29   Classify each of the relations below as reflexive, irreflexive, or neither. Explain why.

(a) {(1,1), (1,2), (2,3), (2,2), (2,3), (3,3)} defined on {1,2,3}
(b) {(1,1), (1,2), (2,3), (3,3)} defined on {1,2,3,4}
(c) {(1,2), (1,3), (2,3)} defined on {1,2,3}

Solution   (a) is reflexive, because it has the three pairs (1,1), (2,2), and (3,3). (b) is neither, because it has (1,1) and (3,3) but does not have (2,2) or (4,4). (c) is irreflexive, because all its ordered pairs have two different entries.   ■

Precedence and Partial Orderings

Our first observation tells us the *precedes* relation (from above) among tasks must be irreflexive. The second observation we can make is that if task a must precede task b and task b must precede task c, then a must precede c. Thus the *precedes* relation among tasks must be transitive.

> A transitive, irreflexive relation is called a (strict) partial ordering.

EXAMPLE 30   Show that the relation $<$ on the integers is a partial ordering.

Solution   We need to show the relation is both irreflexive and transitive. For this purpose we need a precise definition of $<$. We use the definition of $<$ given by $a < b$ if and only if $b - a$ is positive. Since $x - x = 0$, $x < x$ is not true for any x. Thus the relation is irreflexive. If $a < b$ and $b < c$, then $b - a = p$ and $c - b = q$, with p and q positive numbers. To determine whether $a < c$, we must determine whether $c - a$ is positive. To do this, we solve the equations $b - a = p$ and $c - b = q$ for a and c, and then we write

$$c - a = (q + b) - (b - p) = q + p$$

Notice that $q + p$ is positive, because a sum of positive numbers is positive. Thus $a < c$. Therefore $<$ is a partial ordering.   ■

EXAMPLE 31   The strict subset relation, denoted by $\subset$, is given by the rule $A \subset B$ if $A \subseteq B$ and $A \neq B$. Show that the strict subset relation is a partial ordering. (A is also called a *proper* subset of B if $A \subset B$, but many people do not consider the empty subset a proper subset of any set. For this reason, we shall always say *strict subset*, not *proper subset*.)

Solution   Since $A \subset B$ requires $A \neq B$, the relation must be irreflexive. The transitive property is easy to visualize. In Figure 13, we have $A \subset C$ and $B \subset C$; clearly, $A \subset C$ as well. Using precise definitions requires a bit more work but is necessary to confirm that the picture represents all possible situations. If $A \subset B$ and $B \subset C$, then every element of A is an element of B and every element of B is an element of C; thus $A \subseteq C$. But $A \neq C$, since if $A = C$ the relationships

Figure 13

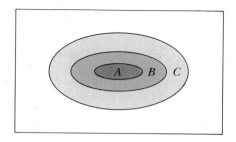

$A \subseteq B \subseteq C$ and $A = C$ imply the relationship $A = B$, contradicting $A \subset B$. Therefore $\subset$ is a partial ordering. ∎

EXAMPLE 32 Show that the relation $\{(1,2), (1,3), (1,4), (1,5), (2,5), (3,5), (4,5)\}$ is a partial ordering.

Solution By inspection, the relation is irreflexive. We must now show (for all possible cases) that if (x,y) and (y,z) are in our relation, then so is (x,z). If we tried to choose $(1,5)$, $(2,5)$, $(3,5)$, or $(4,5)$ for the ordered pair (x,y), then there would be no (y,z), since y would have to be 5—and 5 is not the first entry of any pair. If we choose $(x,y) = (1,2)$, there is exactly one pair to use for (y,z), namely $(2,5)$. The transitive property requires that $(1,5)$ be in the relation, and it is. If we choose $(x,y) = (1,3)$, then $(3,5)$ is our only choice for (y,z); if we choose $(x,y) = (1,4)$, then $(4,5)$ is our only choice for (y,z). Again, in these last two cases, the transitive property tells us that $(1,5)$ should be in the relation, and it is. ∎

Partial Orderings and Total Orderings

Figure 14 shows the digraph of the $<$ relation on $\{1,2,3,4\}$ and the $\subset$ relation on the *subsets* of $\{a,b\}$. At the beginning of the chapter, we saw that the $<$ relation

Figure 14 The digraphs of special cases of Examples 30 and 31.

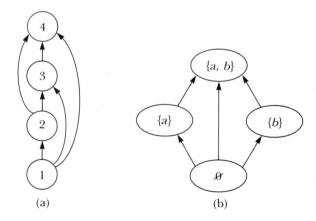

(a)   (b)

on $\{1,2,3,4\}$ is $\{(1,2),(1,3),(1,4),(2,3),(2,4),(3,4)\}$. The ordered pairs of the $\subset$ relation on the subsets of $\{a,b\}$ are:

$$(\varnothing,\{a\}),\ (\varnothing,\{b\}),\ (\varnothing,\{a,b\}),\ (\{a\},\{a,b\}),\ (\{b\},\{a,b\})$$

The pictures point up a difference between the $<$ relation and the $\subset$ relation. The vertices of the $<$ relation seem to line up in a line, reflecting the fact that for each pair m and n of integers, either $m < n$ or $n < m$. However, the sets $\{a\}$ and $\{b\}$ don't line up because, for the sets $\{a\}$ and $\{b\}$, neither $\{a\} \subset \{b\}$ nor $\{b\} \subset \{a\}$. The *less than* relation is called a *total ordering* because the totality of pairs is compared. That is, a partial ordering P of a set X is **total** if, for each distinct x and y in X, either $(x,y) \in P$ or $(y,x) \in P$. Total orderings are also called **linear orderings,** because, as we saw in Figure 14(a), it is possible to arrange the objects being ordered so that they sit (naturally) along a straight line in a drawing of their digraph. Figure 14(b) is a digraph of a partial ordering that we think of as genuinely **partial** because only part of the comparisons possible are actually made.

Notice that in a partial ordering P we cannot simultaneously have $a\,P\,b$ and $b\,P\,a$, for then the transitive law would imply $a\,P\,a$, so the relation would violate the irreflexive law. A relation on a set V that cannot contain both the ordered pairs (a,b) and (b,a) for *any* two elements a and b of V is called **antisymmetric**. (A relation that is not symmetric need not be antisymmetric. Can you give an example of a relation that is neither symmetric nor antisymmetric?) What we just noticed can be rephrased as Theorem 11.

Theorem 11   A partial ordering is antisymmetric.

Proof   Given above.   ∎

Reflexive Partial Orderings

The relations $\le$ and $\subseteq$ are not strict partial orderings because they are reflexive. When working with the ordering of numbers, though, we switch back and forth between $<$ and $\le$, using whichever of these two relations is convenient at the time. It is useful to be able to do similar switching with partial orderings. This leads us to study relations we call *reflexive partial orderings*.

A **reflexive partial ordering** is a
reflexive, antisymmetric, transitive relation.

Just as the transitive closure of a relation may be regarded as the result of "throwing into" the relation all pairs required by the transitive law, the **reflexive closure** of a relation R on X is the relation we get by adding to R all pairs (x,x) with $x \in X$.

EXAMPLE 33   Write out the ordered pairs of the reflexive closure of the $\subset$ relation on $\{a,b\}$. What is the standard notation for this new relation?

Solution The set X being ordered here is the set $\{\emptyset, \{a\}, \{b\}, \{a,b\}\}$, not the set $\{a,b\}$. Thus, using the ordered pairs we already wrote down for the $\subset$ relation, we get the reflexive closure by adding in $(\emptyset,\emptyset)$, $(\{a\}, \{a\})$, $(\{b\}, \{b\})$, and $(\{a,b\}, \{a,b\})$. This gives us the set

$$\{(\emptyset, \emptyset), (\emptyset, \{a\}), (\emptyset, \{b\}), (\emptyset, \{a,b\}), (\{a\}, \{a\}),$$
$$(\{a\}, \{a,b\}), (\{b\}, \{b\}), (\{b\}, \{a,b\}), (\{a,b\}, \{a,b\})\}$$

We recognize this as the $\subseteq$ relation. ∎

Whenever we form the reflexive closure of a strict partial ordering we get a reflexive partial ordering. The phrase *"P is a partial ordering"* means either that P is a partial ordering or that P is a reflexive partial ordering. If it is important to know what kind of partial ordering is being referred to, we should be able to determine that from the context of the phrase.

◧ *Diagrams of Partial Orderings*

In Figure 14, we drew both digraphs with all the arrows pointing upwards. In fact, we can always draw a digraph of a partial ordering in this way. Our next example shows other aspects of the process. In Figure 15, we show a digraph of the sets $\{a,b\}$ $\{b,c\}$ $\{a,b,c\}$ and $\{a,b,c,d\}$, with the subset ordering.

Figure 15

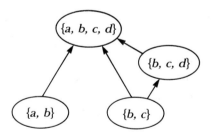

The partial ordering in Figure 15 is different from those in Figure 14 in that it has two elements at the bottom of the diagram. In all three diagrams, the elements at the bottom have no arrows coming into them. Such an element is called *minimal*. In more symbolic terms, if x is in a set ordered by the partial ordering P, we say that x is **minimal** if there is no y such that (y,x) is in P. There is one minimal element in Figure 14(a), namely 1, and one minimal element in Figure 14(b), namely $\emptyset$. There are two minimal elements in Figure 15, namely $\{a,b\}$ and $\{b,c\}$. Notice that in the $<$ relation $\{(1,2), (1,3), (1,4), (2,3), (2,4), (3,4)\}$, 1 is never the second element of an ordered pair. In the set $\{(\emptyset, \{a\}), (\emptyset, \{b\}), (\emptyset, \{a,b\}), (\{a\}, \{a,b\}), (\{b\}, \{a,b\})\}$, $\emptyset$ is never on the right-hand side of an ordered pair. You can check that, in the ordering of Figure 15, neither $\{a,b\}$ nor $\{b,c\}$ is the second element of an ordered pair. Notice how these observations correspond to the formal definition of a minimal element.

How do minimal elements relate to drawings? The minimal elements are at the bottom in each drawing we've seen, so it is natural that the first step in making such a drawing is to identify minimal elements and draw a circle for each one. For the subset ordering of the set {∅, {a}, {b}, {a,b}}, there is one minimal element, namely ∅. We draw this as step 1 in Figure 16. As we describe the remaining steps, we illustrate them for this ordering in Figure 16. After we draw the minimal element or elements, we remove from our partial ordering each ordered pair containing one of the elements drawn.

Figure 16

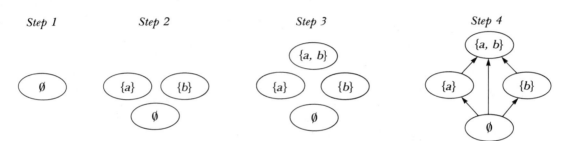

Step 1   Step 2   Step 3   Step 4

For the subset ordering, this leaves us with $P' = \{(\{a\}, \{a,b\}), (\{b\}, \{a,b\})\}$. This new partial ordering will have some new and different minimal elements. For P', our new minimal elements are {a} and {b}. We draw a new row of circles for these new minimal elements above the ones we've already drawn. Now we remove all pairs containing *these* minimal elements from our partial ordering as well. For the subset ordering, this gives us $P'' = ∅$. In this partial ordering, we still have a new minimal element: {a,b} was not minimal before, because it was on the right-hand side of ({a}, {a,b}) and ({b}, {a,b}), but now it doesn't appear as the second element of any ordered pairs—in fact, it doesn't appear in any ordered pairs whatever, because none appear. Since it wasn't minimal until this step, we draw it in now. In general, we would keep repeating this process until P becomes empty and we draw in the circles for the last elements. Finally, as shown in step 4 of Figure 16, when we draw in the arrows representing the relation, all the arrows go upwards.

Covering and Hasse Digraphs

In Figure 17(a), you see the diagram of the subset partial ordering on the subsets of the set {1,2,3}. The picture is reasonably complicated; as part (b) of the figure shows, it is needlessly complicated. The right-hand picture was created from the one on the left by removing arrows implied by the transitive property.

For example, the arrow from {1} to {1,2,3} is implied by applying the transitive property to the arrows from {1} to {1,2} and from {1,2} to {1,2,3}. Even the arrowheads in picture (b) are really unnecessary because all arrows point upwards.

Figure 17 Two representations of the subset ordering.

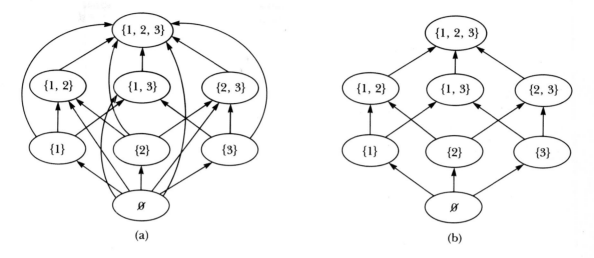

(a)   (b)

The relation we obtain from a partial ordering P by removing pairs implied by the transitive law is called the **covering** relation of P, and a digraph of the covering relation is sometimes called a **Hasse digraph** of P. The **Hasse diagram** (or simply **diagram**) of P is the picture obtained from the Hasse digraph by removing arrowheads (all of which point upwards).

We show the Hasse diagram for the subsets of $\{a,b,c,\}$ in Figure 18.

Figure 18 A Hasse diagram.

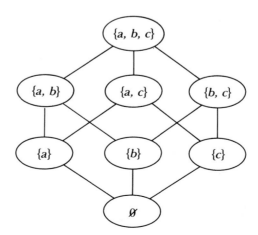

Scheduling and Linear Extensions

Suppose we have some tasks to be carried out and we have one person (or one computer processor) available to carry them out. Suppose we know that some of these tasks must come before some others. How can we find a schedule for carrying out the tasks that violates none of this information? This information will give a partial ordering P of the set T of tasks. Our schedule will, in effect, line the tasks up in a row and say, "Do this one first, then this one," and so on. Thus our schedule gives us a linear ordering L of the tasks. To say that this schedule (L) is consistent with the information given by the partial ordering P is to say that whenever x comes before y in P, then x comes before y in L. Thus each (x,y) in P is in L, so $P \subseteq L$.

> We call a linear ordering L a **linear extension**
> of a partial ordering P if $P \subseteq L$.

EXAMPLE 34   Find a linear extension of the subset ordering on the subsets of $\{a,b,c\}$, as shown in Figure 18.

Solution   A Hasse diagram for a linear ordering is just a vertical line connecting circles representing vertices. We will describe such a Hasse diagram for the linear extension by giving the sets in left-to-right order, as they would be drawn in bottom-to-top order. Using the symbol $<$ to stand for *comes before*, we write

$$\varnothing < \{a\} < \{b\} < \{c\} < \{a,b\} < \{a,c\} < \{b,c\} < \{a,b,c\}$$

How did we choose this linear extension? We wrote down the minimal element $\varnothing$, deleted it from consideration, and got three more minimal elements $\{a\}$, $\{b\}$, and $\{c\}$, wrote them down (in whatever order we chose, in this case alphabetical order), deleted them from consideration, and repeated the process until we had deleted everything.   ■

The process of Example 34 may be summarized as:

(a) Find the minimal elements;
(b) write them down in some order;
(c) remove the minimal elements from the set and remove all pairs containing minimal elements from the ordering;
(d) repeat the process.

Notice that in applying this process, we may list the minimal elements in any given order we choose; if at some stage we have more than one minimal element to consider, then we will have more than one possible linear extension. The process always gives a linear *extension* of a partial ordering, because if (x,y) is in our ordering, x will be written down and deleted from consideration before y becomes minimal. Thus x will come before y in the linear ordering we write down. The process of constructing a linear extension of a partial ordering is sometimes called **topological sorting** in computer science.

Concepts Review

1. A relation R on V is _____ if (a,a) is *not* in R for any a in V.

2. A strict partial ordering is a(n) _____ _____ relation.

3. A partial ordering P on V is called a(n) _____ ordering or a(n) _____ ordering if, for each x and y in V, either $(x,y) \in P$ or $(y,x) \in P$.

4. A relation is _____ if whenever it contains the ordered pair (a,b) (and $a \neq b$) it does not contain the ordered pair (b,a).

5. A(n) _____ _____ _____ is a reflexive, antisymmetric, transitive relation.

6. An element x is _____ relative to the partial ordering P if there is no y with (y,x) in P.

7. An element is minimal if it never appears as the _____ _____ of an ordered pair.

8. We say that y _____ x if (x,y) is in P and $(x,y) \in P$ is not implied by applying the transitive law to other pairs in P.

9. The Hasse digraph of a partial ordering is the digraph of the _____ relation of the partial ordering.

10. The process of topological sorting means finding a(n) _____ _____ of a partial ordering.

Exercises

A

1. The definition of $a > b$ is $a > b$ if $a - b$ is positive. Explain why $>$ is a strict partial ordering.

2. The definition of the *strictly contains* relation is $A \supset B$ if $A \neq B$ and every element of B is also an element of A. Explain why $\supset$ is a strict partial ordering.

3. The definition of $a \geq b$ is $a \geq b$ if $a - b$ is non-negative. Explain why $\geq$ is a reflexive partial ordering.

4. The definition of $A \subseteq B$ is $A \subseteq B$ if every element of A is an element of B. Explain why $\subseteq$ is a reflexive partial ordering.

5. Show that the relation $R = \{(a,b), (a,c), (a,d), (a,e), (a,f), (b,f), (c,f), (d,f), (e,f)\}$ is a strict partial ordering.

6. Show that the relation $\{(a,b), (c,d), (d,e), (c,e)\}$ is a strict partial ordering.

7. Determine whether each of the following relations is a reflexive partial ordering, a strict partial ordering, or neither. In each case, the relation is defined on the set $\{1,2,3,4\}$.
   (a) $\{(1,3), (2,4)\}$
   (b) $\{(1,1), (1,3), (2,2), (2,4)\}$
   (c) $\{(1,2), (2,3), (3,4)\}$
   (d) $\{(1,2), (2,3), (1,3)\}$
   (e) $\{(1,1), (1,2), (2,2), (3,2), (3,3), (3,4), (4,4)\}$
   (f) $\{(2,3)\}$

8. Determine whether each of the following relations is a strict partial ordering, a reflexive partial ordering, or neither. In each case, the relation is defined on the set $\{a,b,c,d\}$.
   (a) $\{(a,b), (b,c)\}$
   (b) $\{(a,b), (c,d)\}$
   (c) $\{(a,a), (b,b), (c,c), (d,d)\}$
   (d) $\{(a,b), (a,c), (b,c), (d,c)\}$
   (e) $\{(a,b), (b,c), (c,d), (d,a)\}$
   (f) $\{(a,b), (c,b), (d,b)\}$

9. Find the reflexive closure of $\{(a,b), (a,c), (a,d), (a,e), (c,c), (e,e), (c,e), (d,e)\}$ on the set $\{a,b,c,d,e\}$.

10. Find the reflexive closure of $\{(1,1), (1,2), (1,3), (2,3), (3,4), (1,4), (2,4)\}$ on the set $\{1,2,3,4\}$.

11. Classify each of the relations below as reflexive, irreflexive, or neither.
    (a) $\{(1,1), (1,2), (2,1), (1,3), (3,1), (3,3)\}$ on $\{1,2,3\}$
    (b) $\{(1,2), (1,4), (1,3), (3,4), (2,4)\}$ on $\{1,2,3,4\}$
    (c) $\{(1,1), (1,2), (2,1), (2,2), (3,3), (2,3)\}$ on $\{1,2,3\}$

12. Classify each of the relations below as reflexive, irreflexive, or neither.
    (a) $\{(1,1), (2,2), (4,4), (1,2), (2,3), (3,3), (1,3)\}$ on $\{1,2,3,4\}$
    (b) $\{(1,1), (1,2), (1,3), (3,1), (1,4), (4,1), (3,3), (4,4)\}$ on $\{1,2,3,4\}$
    (c) $\{(1,3), (3,4), (4,2), (2,3), (4,1)\}$ on $\{1,2,3,4\}$

13. Classify each of the relations in Exercise 11 as symmetric, antisymmetric, or neither.

14. Classify each of the relations in Exercise 12 as symmetric, antisymmetric, or neither.

B 15. For each partial ordering below, specify which elements of $\{1,2,3,4,5\}$ are minimal.
    (a) $\{(1,2), (1,3), (2,3), (4,5)\}$
    (b) $\{(1,2), (1,3), (1,4), (1,5)\}$
    (c) $\{(1,2), (1,3), (2,3), (4,3), (4,5)\}$

16. For each partial ordering below, specify which elements of $\{a,b,c,d,e\}$ are minimal.
    (a) $\{(a,b), (c,d)\}$
    (b) $\{(a,c), (c,b), (a,b), (a,d), (a,e), (d,e)\}$
    (c) $\{(a,c), (e,c), (a,e), (b,d)\}$

17. Draw the digraph of each relation in Exercise 15 in such a way that all arrows point upwards.

18. Draw the digraph of each relation in Exercise 16 in such a way that all arrows point upwards.

19. Draw the Hasse diagram for each partial ordering in Exercise 15.

20. Draw the Hasse diagram for each of the partial orderings in Exercise 16.

21. Draw the Hasse diagram for the $<$ relation on the set $\{1,2,3,4,5\}$.

22. Draw the Hasse diagram for the *alphabetical order* relation on the set $\{cat,bat,hat,dog,pig\}$.

23. The numbers 1, 2, 3, 4, 6, and 12 are the factors of 12. Some of these numbers are factors of each other; for example, 2 is a factor of 4, and 2 is a factor of 12. Write down

the ordered pairs of the *is a factor of* relation on the set $\{1,2,3,4,6,12\}$. Explain why the relation is a reflexive partial ordering and draw its Hasse diagram.

24. The sets $\{1,2\}$, $\{1,2,3\}$, $\{2,3,4\}$, $\{1,2,3,4\}$, and $\varnothing$ are some of the subsets of $\{1,2,3,4\}$. Write down the ordered pairs of the *is a subset of* relation on the set $\{\{1,2\}, \{1,2,3\}, \{2,3,4\}, \{1,2,3,4\}, \varnothing\}$. Explain why the relation is a reflexive partial ordering. Draw the Hasse diagram of the partial ordering.

25. Find a linear extension of each partial ordering in Exercise 15.

26. Find a linear extension of each partial ordering in Exercise 16.

Problems

1. Show that *is a factor of* is a reflexive partial ordering on the set of positive integers. (It is quite standard to say that *m divides n* in place of *m is a factor of n*; in this case, the relation is called the *divides* relation.)

2. Consider the set of ordered pairs of positive integers. We shall define the relation P by $(a,b)\ P\ (c,d)$ if $a \leq c$ and $b \leq d$. That is, $((a,b), (c,d)) \in P$ if and only if $a \leq c$ and $b \leq d$. Show that this is a reflexive partial ordering.

3. Show that the transitive closure of the covering relation of P is P itself.

4. A closed walk in a digraph is a (directed) walk that starts and ends at the same vertex. A one-vertex closed walk with no edges is called *trivial*. Show that the transitive closure of a digraph is a strict partial ordering if and only if the digraph has no closed walks, not even trivial ones.

5. Explain why the definition of the covering relation may be stated as y covers x if (x,y) is in P and there is no z in between x and y.

6. Show that if x and y are elements of a finite set partially ordered by P and $(x,y) \notin P$, then there is a linear extension L of P such that $(y,x) \in L$.

7. Show that a partial ordering of a finite set is the intersection of its set of linear extensions.

8. Show that the subset ordering on the eight subsets of $\{1,2,3\}$ is an intersection of three linear orderings of these eight subsets.

9. Show that the subset ordering on the eight subsets of $\{1,2,3\}$ is not an intersection of two linear orderings of these eight subsets.

10. In drawing a Hasse diagram and in finding a linear extension, we made use of the idea of a minimal element.
    (a) Describe an algorithm that finds one minimal element of a partial ordering, assuming that the partial ordering is given by adjacency lists. Describe an algorithm that finds all minimal elements.
    (b) Repeat (a), assuming that the partial ordering is given as a set of ordered pairs.
    (c) From (a), describe an algorithm to write down a linear extension of the partial ordering.
    (d) From (b), describe an algorithm to write down a linear extension of the partial ordering.

11. There is an important partial ordering called **lexicographic ordering** defined on ordered pairs of integers (or of some other linearly ordered set). We say $(a, b) < (c, d)$ if $a < c$ or $a = c$ and $b < d$.

(a) Show that this is a partial ordering.
(b) Show that this is a linear ordering.
(c) Show that this gives a linear extension of the relation of Problem 2.
(d) Explain how this relates to the order of words in a dictionary.

Chapter 3
Review Exercises

In Exercises 1–3, write down the ordered pairs at the relation specified.

1. $(x,y) \in R$ if $(x^3 - 8x)^2 = (y^3 - 8y)^2$ on the set $\{-3, -2, -1, 0, 1, 2, 3\}$.

2. $(x,y) \in R$ if $(x - y)^2 \leq 4$ on the set $\{-3, -2, -1, 0, 1, 2, 3\}$.

3. The "comes before in numerical order *or* comes before in alphabetic order" relation on the set $\{h, 3, 27, x, 12\}$.

In Exercises 4–6, if the relation specified is an equivalence relation, say so and give its equivalence classes; otherwise, give the properties of an equivalence relation it fails to have and examples of how they fail.

4. The relation of Exercise 1.

5. The relation of Exercise 2.

6. The relation of Exercise 3.

7. Write down the relation corresponding to each digraph in Figure 19.

Figure 19

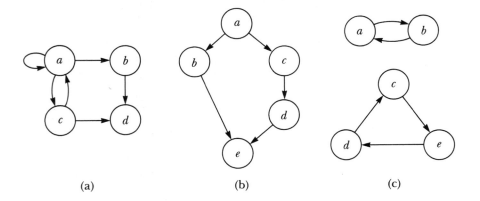

(a)   (b)   (c)

8. Write down the transitive closures of each of the relations in Exercise 7.

9. Draw the digraph of the relation in Exercise 1.

10. Draw the digraph of the relation of Exercise 2.

11. What vertices are reachable from vertex c in Figure 19(a)? From vertex b?

12. What vertices are reachable from vertex a in Figure 19(b)? From vertex d?

13. Find the longest walk (the one with the most edges) you can in Figure 19(b).

14. Find a walk with five edges from vertex a to vertex d in Figure 19(a).

15. For which graphs in Exercise 7 is the transitive closure an equivalence relation? If not, why not? If so, what are its equivalence classes?

16. Define two subsets of $\{1,2,3,4,5,6\}$ to be related if their union is $\{1,2,3,4,5,6\}$. Is this relation reflexive? Irreflexive? Symmetric? Antisymmetric? Transitive?

17. Define two sequences of 0's and 1's from the set below to be related if they have the same number of 0's. Why is this relation an equivalence relation? Draw its graph and write down its equivalence classes.
$$\{110010, 110001, 100010, 100001, 110000, 001110\}$$

18. Is the relation given by "x is related to y" if $x + y$ is a multiple of 4 an equivalence relation on the set $\{1,2,3,4,5,6,7,8\}$? If so, explain why; if not, explain what properties fail. Draw the graph of the relation and write down its connected components.

19. Explain the difference between writing down the symmetric relation corresponding to a graph and writing down the edge set of the graph.

20. Write down the edge set of each graph in Figure 20.

Figure 20

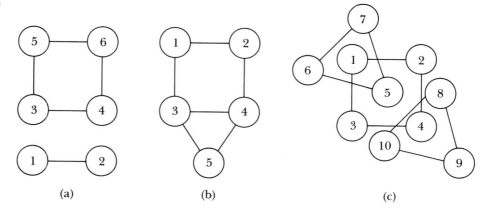

(a)   (b)   (c)

21. Which graphs in Figure 20 are connected? What are the connected components of the other graphs in Figure 20?

22. Write down the equivalence relation whose equivalence class partition is given below.
(a) $\{3\}$, $\{1,5\}$, $\{4,2,6\}$ (b) $\{1\}$, $\{2\}$, $\{3\}$, $\{4\}$

23. Which of the following families of subsets of $\{1,2,3,4,5,6\}$ are partitions of $\{1,2,3,4,5,6\}$?
(a) $\{1,2,3\}$, $\{4,6\}$, $\{2,5\}$ (b) $\{1,4\}$, $\{5,2\}$, $\{6,3\}$
(c) $\{1\}$, $\{2,4\}$, $\{6,3\}$

24. True or false:
(a) $23 \equiv 7 \bmod 9$ (b) $-23 \equiv 4 \bmod 9$
(c) $30 \equiv 3 \bmod 9$ (d) $23 \equiv 41 \bmod 9$

In Exercises 25–28, solve the congruence given. Find the principal solution.

25. $3x + 2 \equiv 2x + 7 \bmod 9$

26. $3x + 7 \equiv 2x + 3 \bmod 9$

27. $6x + 5 \equiv 4x + 7 \bmod 9$

28. $6x - 1 \equiv 2x + 5 \bmod 9$

29. Show why the congruence $6x \equiv 12 \bmod 15$ implies that $x \equiv 2 \bmod 15$, or give a counter-example.

30. Suppose that $x \equiv y \bmod n$. It then follows from the definition of congruence that for any integers a and b, $ax + b \equiv ay + b \bmod m$. Show how it follows.

31. Verify that the relation $\{(c,a), (a,e), (c,e), (b,h), (h,f), (b,f)\}$ is a strict partial ordering of $\{a,b,c,e,f,g,h\}$.

32. Find the reflexive closure of the relation in Exercise 31. What kind of relation have you just written down?

33. We define the relation $\leq$ by $a \leq b$ if $b - a$ is non-negative. Using the facts that the negative of a positive number is negative and that a sum of non-negative numbers is non-negative, show that $\leq$ is a reflexive partial ordering.

34. What are the minimal elements of the partial ordering in Exercise 31?

35. Draw the Hasse diagram of the partial ordering in Exercise 31.

36. What is the relation of the strict partial ordering whose Hasse diagram is shown in Figure 21?

Figure 21

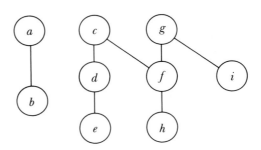

37. Draw the digraph of the *is a factor of* relation on the positive integer factors of 24 in such a way that all arrows point up. Draw the Hasse diagram.

38. Find a linear extension (topological sorting) of the partial ordering in Figure 21.

39. Explain why the $<$ relation on a set of positive integers is always a linear extension of the *is a factor of* relation on the same set of integers.

*T*he idea of a function is central to modern mathematics. The functions studied in high school mathematics include polynomial functions, logarithm functions, exponential functions, and trigonometric functions. All of these are used in discrete mathematics, though sometimes in surprising ways. For example, polynomial, logarithm, and exponential functions play an important role in analyzing how time-consuming an algorithm will be. Applications of this kind lead to the concept of *order of growth* of a function.

In each of the following chapters, functions will arise in different ways. In Chapter 5, we shall see how mathematical induction can be used to establish the order of growth of the time consumed by certain algorithms. In Chapter 6, functions will be used to define what we mean by the size of a set. In Chapter 7, we shall develop sophisticated methods of getting a formula for a function from some rather simple information about the function. In Chapter 8, certain functions will tell us the costs of using various possible communications channels in a communications network, and we shall determine the best channels to use for communication. In Chapter 9, we shall use functions to describe the idea of graphical isomorphism, which tell us when two graphs or digraphs represent relationships that are in essence the same. In Chapter 10, we shall study the determinant function, which is important in geometry, multivariable calculus, and various engineering applications. In Chapter 11, the functions we study will assign probabilities to statements and their truth sets. In Chapter 12, we shall see how the algebraic concept of an operation such as addition or multiplication is still another example of a function. Further, we shall see how the function concept helps us transfer ideas and mathematical structures between similar algebraic situations through the concept of algebraic isomorphism.

The functions described above are just a sampling of what you will find. Understanding functions is essential to understanding discrete mathematics.

Section 4-1
Functions
and Sequences

◢ Functions

One of the most useful kinds of relationships between sets that you have studied in the past is that of a function. When we say that the cost of a bag of potatoes is a function of its weight, we mean that the weight *determines* the cost. When we say that the weight of an object in grams is a function of its weight in ounces, we mean that the weight in ounces *determines* the weight of the object in grams.

In algebra and calculus, we learn to think of a function as a relationship given by a formula, such as $f(x) = x + 2$ or $y = x + 2$. We saw in Section 3-1 that the two apparently different formulas $y = x + 2$ and $y = x^4 - 2x^3 - x^2 + 3x + 2$ described the same relationship between the set $\{-1,0,1,2\}$ and the set $\{1,2,3,4\}$. Since different formulas can define the same relationship, we will not want a definition of functions based on formulas. Instead, we use the concept of a relation (already precisely defined) to define a function as follows.

A **function** from a set D to a set R is a
relation from D to R such that each x in
D is related to one and only one y in R.
D is called the **domain** of the function, and
R is called the **range** of the function.

Since we defined a relation as a set of ordered pairs, we have now defined a function as a special kind of set of ordered pairs. A standard shorthand notation for "f is a function from D to R" is $f: D \rightarrow R$. A standard way to visualize a function (or relation), known as a *cloud diagram*, is shown in Figure 1. We think of a "cloud" as representing vertices in the domain or range; the dots in a cloud represent some but not necessarily all vertices belonging to that cloud. Each arrow represents one ordered pair $(x, f(x))$ in the relation, but not every pair in the relation must be represented. Compare this to how you might use a digraph to visualize a relation.

Figure 1

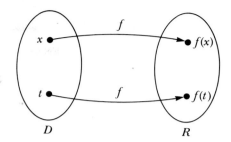

EXAMPLE 1 If $f(x) = x + 2$ is used as a formula that describes a function f from $\{-1,0,1,2\}$ to $\{1,2,3,4\}$, what relation defines f?

Solution As we computed in Section 3-1,

$$f = \{(-1,1),\ (0,2),\ (1,3),\ (2,4)\}$$ ■

The function of Example 1 may be illustrated as in Figure 2.

Figure 2

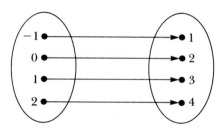

Extending Example 1 as in Section 3-1, if $g(x) = x^4 - 2x^3 - x^2 + 3x + 2$ is used as a formula that describes a function g from $\{-1,0,1,2\}$ to $\{1,2,3,4\}$, then

$$g = \{(-1,1),\ (0,2),\ (1,3),\ (2,4)\}$$

Thus as sets of ordered pairs, f and g are the *same function*, just as they were the same relation. Certainly it is quicker to write $f(x) = x + 2$ than it is to write down a set of ordered pairs. We could not even write down all the ordered pairs in the relation defining f if we used $f(x) = x + 2$ with the set of all integers as its domain. Thus, even though it is useful to have our precise definition in order to make determinations such as whether two functions are equal, we shall usually describe the relation f by writing a description of how to compute the value related to x from the value of x.

> We use the notation $f(x)$ to stand for the value
> in the range that our function f relates
> to the element x of the domain.

We have seen above, with *f* and *g*, two examples of relations that *are* functions. It is natural to ask whether each relation from a set *D* to a set *R* is a function.

EXAMPLE 2   Show that the relation $\{(a,2)\ (a,3)\ (b,4)\ (c,5)\}$ is not a function from $D = \{a,b,c\}$ to $R = \{2,3,4,5\}$.

Solution   The relation relates both the numbers 2 and 3 in the range with the letter *a* in the domain. Thus *a* is not related to only one element in the range. See Figure 3 for help in visualizing this.   ■

Figure 3   Since two arrows leave *a*, this is not a function.

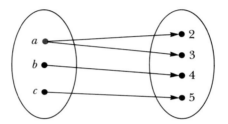

EXAMPLE 3   Show that the relation $\{(a,3),\ (c,2)\}$ from the domain $\{a,b,c\}$ to the range $\{2,3,4,5\}$, is not a function from $\{a,b,c\}$ to $\{2,3,4,5\}$.

Solution   As you see in Figure 4, the element *b* of the domain is not related to any element in the range. Since the relation does not relate each element of the domain to some element of the range, it is not a function.   ■

Figure 4   This is not a function because there is no arrow leaving *b*.

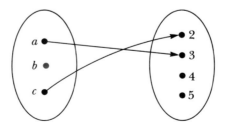

To summarize what Examples 2 and 3 have shown us, to determine if a given relation is a function, we must make two tests.

(1) Is each element of the domain related to an element of the range?

(2) Is no element of the domain related to more than one element of the range?

You may have seen functions of two variables or three variables given by formulas such as

$$f(x,y) = xy + x^2$$

or

$$g(x,y,z) = x + 2y + 3z$$

Are these functions in the sense we just described? Yes; the domain of f is the set of all ordered pairs (x,y) of numbers, and the domain of g is the set of all ordered triples of numbers.

B Properties of Functions

In Figure 5, we see digraphs of four different functions. Note how similar the digraphs are to the cloud diagrams in Figures 1–4.

Figure 5

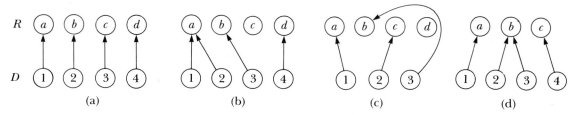

(a)   (b)   (c)   (d)

In each digraph, there is *one and only one* arrow leaving each vertex in the domain. (*Note:* In part (c), the domain is the set {1,2,3}.) This corresponds to the statement that a function relates *one and only one* element of the range to each element of the domain.

In functions (a) and (c), each element of the range receives one arrow or no arrow at all.

> A function is called an **injection** or a **one-to-one** function if different elements of the domain are related to different elements of the range.

Thus a function is one-to-one if each element of the range is related to *at most one* element of the domain. Therefore functions (a) and (c) are one-to-one functions.

In functions (a) and (d), each element of the range receives *at least one* arrow.

A function is called a **surjection** or **onto** function if each element of the range is related to *at least one* element of the domain.

In function (a), each element of the range receives one and only one arrow.

A function is called a **bijection**, a **one-to-one correspondence**, a **one-to-one and onto** function, or a **one-to-one** function from the domain **onto** the range if each element of the range is related to one and only one element of the domain.

The digraph of a relation also shows you when it is not a function, as in Figure 6, which contains the digraphs of the relations of Examples 2 and 3. Notice the similarity of Figure 6 to Figures 3 and 4.

Figure 6   The relations with these digraphs are not functions.

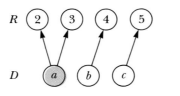   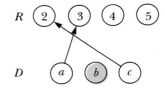

(a) Two arrows leave *a*.   (b) No arrow leaves *b*.

EXAMPLE 4   Which of the relations given below are functions from the domain *D* given to the range *R* given? For the functions, state if they are one-to-one (injections), onto (surjections), or both one-to-one and onto (bijections).

(a) $D = \{a,b,c,d\}$ $R = \{1,2,3,4\}$ $f = \{(a,1),\ (a,2),\ (b,1),\ (c,2),\ (d,3)\}$
(b) $D = \{-2,-1,0,1,2\}$ $R = \{0,1,4\}$ $f(x) = x^2$
(c) $D = \{-2,-1,0,1,2\}$ $R = \{0,1,2,3,4\}$ $f(x) = x^2$
(d) $D = \{0,1,2\}$ $R = \{0,1,4\}$ $f(x) = x^2$
(e) $D = \{0,1,2,3,4\}$ $R = \{0,1,2,3,4\}$ $f = \{(0,4),\ (1,3),\ (2,2),\ (3,1),\ (4,0)\}$
(f) $D = \{a,b,c,d\}$ $R = \{1,2,3,4,5\}$ $f = \{(a,1),\ (b,5),\ (c,4),\ (d,3)\}$
(g) $D = \{a,b,c,d\}$ $R = \{1,2,3,4\}$ $f = \{(a,1),\ (b,2),\ (c,3)\}$

Solution   We give the answers on the basis of the definitions above. In Figure 7, we give digraphs of the relations to show visually what we say in words in the answer. No digraph is needed to give the answer, but notice that the digraph makes the reason for the answer easier to see.

(a) *f* is not a function because 1 and 2 are both related to *a*.
(b) *f* is a function because for each *x*, there is one value *f(x)*. *f* is onto because

Figure 7

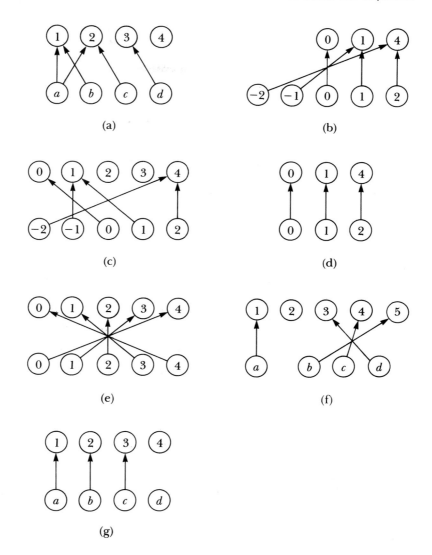

(a)

(b)

(c)

(d)

(e)

(f)

(g)

each of 0, 1, and 4 is the result of squaring a domain value. f is not one-to-one because, for example, $f(-2) = 4$ and $f(2) = 4$.

(c) f is a function, but 3 is not a square of any domain value, so f is not onto. f is not one-to-one for the same reason as in (b).

(d) f is a one-to-one and onto function because each element of D is related to one and only one element of R.

(e) f is a one-to-one and onto function because f relates each domain value to one and only one range value. Note that we could have written $f(x) = 4 - x$.

(f) f is a one-to-one function but is not onto because 2 is not $f(x)$ for any x.

(g) f is not a function because nothing is related to d by f.   ■

The Image of a Function

> The set of range values actually related to some
> domain element is called the **image** of the function.

In digraph (a) of Figure 5, the image is $\{a,b,c,d\}$; in digraph (b), the image is $\{a,b,d\}$; in digraph (c), the image is $\{a,b,c\}$; and in digraph (d), the image is $\{a,b,c\}$. We also say that y is the *image* of x under the function f if $y = f(x)$ (that is, if (x,y) is in f). Each function is a function from its domain onto its image. In Figure 8, you see how to visualize the relationship between the image and the range of a function.

Figure 8

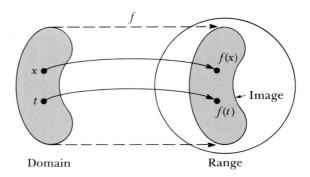

EXAMPLE 5   What is the image of each of the functions in Example 1?

Solution   In (b), the image is $\{0,1,4\}$. This is also the image in (c) and (d). In (e), the image is $\{0,1,2,3,4\}$, and in (f), the image is $\{1,3,4,5\}$.   ■

◖ Sequences, n-tuples, and Sums

Many of the functions we study in discrete mathematics have sets of integers as their domains. We shall see, for example, in Section 3 how the amount of time needed to run a computer program with n items of input data may be profitably studied as a function of the integer n.

> A function whose domain is a set of
> consecutive integers is called a **sequence**.

For example, if $s(i) = i^2$ for each integer $i \geq 0$, then s is a sequence. For historical reasons and for convenience, a special notation has developed for use with sequences. Rather than use the notation $s(i)$ for the value of the sequence s at the integer i, it is customary to use the notation s_i (read as "s-eye" or "s-sub-eye"). It is also typical to refer to s_i as the ith **term** of the sequence and to use $<s_i>$ (read as "the sequence s_i") in place of simply using s to stand for the sequence.

Some examples of how this new notation works should help us avoid confusion.

EXAMPLE 6   Write down the third term of the sequence $<s_i>$ given by $s_i = i(i - 1) + 1$ for $i \geq 1$.

Solution   Since $s_i = i(i - 1) + 1$, $s_3 = 3(2) + 1 = 7$.   ■

EXAMPLE 7   What is the zeroth term of the sequence given by $s_j = j^2 + 2$ for $j \geq 0$? What is term number 3?

Solution   The only possible interpretation of the zeroth term is the term for $j = 0$, which is $s_0 = 0^2 + 2 = 2$. The natural interpretation of term number 3 is s_3, which is $3^2 + 2 = 11$.   ■

In Example 7, we used term number 3 to stand for s_3. Many people prefer to refer to s_3 as the third term of the sequence, even though the first four terms are $s_0 = 2$, $s_1 = 3$, $s_2 = 6$, and $s_3 = 11$. Others prefer to interpret the third term as s_2 in this situation. Whenever there is the possibility that our use of a phrase such as *third term* will be ambiguous, we shall use a phrase such as *term number three* instead.

EXAMPLE 8   Write the first five terms of the sequence given by $s_i = i^2 + 2$ for $i \geq 0$.

Solution   The first five terms will be the terms s_0, s_1, s_2, s_3, and s_4 because the domain is the set of consecutive integers consisting of all integers greater than or equal to 0. Thus the first five terms are 2, 3, 6, 11, and 18.   ■

EXAMPLE 9   Find a formula for the ith term of a sequence that begins as 1, 4, 9, 16, 25, ... For what values of i is your formula valid?

Solution   We see that the sequence of values given is 1^2, 2^2, 3^2, 4^2, 5^2. Thus the natural choice for s_i is that $s_i = i^2$ for $i \geq 1$.   ■

The sequences we have given so far are **infinite** sequences; that is, their domain is an infinite set of consecutive integers. The domain need not be infinite. We frequently have sequences whose domain is the set $N = \{1, 2, \ldots, n\}$. An ordered pair, in fact, may be thought of as a sequence whose domain is $\{1,2\}$, an ordered triple is a sequence whose domain is $\{1,2,3\}$, and so on. A sequence whose domain is $\{1,2,3, \ldots, n\}$ is often called an **n-tuple** (rhymes with *quadruple*).

For example, $s =$ (Sam, Pam, Georgia, William, Dick) is a finite sequence of names and is called a 5-tuple. Notice that we enclosed the list in parentheses.

Recall that a list enclosed in set braces represents a set and the order in which it is listed is irrelevant. Now we see that a list enclosed in parentheses represents an n-tuple, and the order in which it appears is essential. We would say that $s_1 =$ Sam and $s_5 =$ Dick. As this example shows, the values of a sequence needn't be numbers; they may be anything we wish. Any time we have a list of n things in a certain order, it is convenient to think of that list as a sequence or n-tuple.

Summing Finite Sequences

In many applications of discrete mathematics (for example, in the applications to computing in Section 4-3), we need to find sums of sequences. For example, if we need to find out how long it takes to carry out an n-stage process, we must add up the amount of time needed to carry out step number i for all i values between 1 and n. For a different example, if a_i stands for the amount of production at a plant on day i, then the total amount produced over the period from day m through day n (inclusive) is the sum of the value of a_i for all i values between m and n (inclusive). There is a special notation called *summation notation* that is used as a shorthand to describe such sums. We define the notation, which is read as "the sum from i equals m to n of a_i," by the equation

$$\sum_{i=m}^{n} a_i = a_m + a_{m+1} + a_{m+2} + \cdots + a_n$$

In words,

$$\sum_{i=m}^{n} a_i$$

stands for the result of computing a_i for each i between m and n (inclusive) and then adding these values of a_i together.

EXAMPLE 10   Find $\displaystyle\sum_{i=1}^{3} i^2$.

Solution $\displaystyle\sum_{i=1}^{3} i^2 = 1^2 + 2^2 + 3^2 = 1 + 4 + 9 = 14$.   ∎

EXAMPLE 11   Find $\displaystyle\sum_{i=0}^{4} 2i - 1$.

Solution $\displaystyle\sum_{i=0}^{4} 2i - 1 = 2\cdot 0 - 1 + 2\cdot 1 - 1 + 2\cdot 2 - 1 + 2\cdot 3 - 1 + 2\cdot 4 - 1$

$$= -1 + 1 + 3 + 5 + 7 = 15$$ ∎

EXAMPLE 12   Find $\displaystyle\sum_{j=2}^{5} 3^j$.

Solution $\displaystyle\sum_{j=2}^{5} 3^j = 3^2 + 3^3 + 3^4 + 3^5$

$$= 9 + 27 + 81 + 243 = 360 \qquad\blacksquare$$

A sum that will be important to us in Section 4-3 and later applications is

$$1 + 2 + 3 + \cdots + n = \sum_{i=1}^{n} i$$

As a child, the famous mathematician Carl Friedrich Gauss (1777–1855) is said to have noticed that by writing this sum in two different orders, we get

$$
\begin{array}{ccccccccccc}
 & 1 & + & 2 & + & 3 & + \cdots + & n & = & \displaystyle\sum_{i=1}^{n} i \\
+ & n & + & n-1 & + \; n-2 \; + & \cdots & + & 1 & = & \displaystyle\sum_{i=1}^{n} i \\
\hline
 & n+1 & + & n+1 & + \; n+1 \; + & \cdots & + & n+1 & = & 2\displaystyle\sum_{i=1}^{n} i
\end{array}
$$

Since we have n terms, each equal to $n + 1$, added together, we get $n(n + 1)$, giving

$$n(n + 1) = 2\sum_{i=1}^{n} i$$

Dividing by 2 gives the formula

$$\sum_{i=1}^{n} i = \frac{n(n + 1)}{2}$$

Arithmetic Series

One way that Gauss's formula will be important to us is in evaluating a sum of the form

$$\sum_{i=1}^{n} (ai + b)$$

where a and b are constants. Such a sum is called an **arithmetic series** and is often studied in high school algebra. The rules of summation in our next theorem make it straightforward to apply Gauss's formula to obtain the value of an arithmetic series.

Theorem 1   If $<a_n>$ and $<b_n>$ are sequences and c is a constant, then

$$\sum_{i=m}^{n} (a_i + b_i) = \sum_{i=m}^{n} a_i + \sum_{i=m}^{n} b_i$$

$$\sum_{i=m}^{n} ca_i = c \cdot \sum_{i=m}^{n} a_i \quad \text{and}$$

$$\sum_{i=m}^{n} c = (n - m + 1)c$$

Proof   The first statement simply amounts to saying that the order in which we add all the a_i's and b_i's together does not affect their total. The second statement is the distributive law, and the third statement follows from the fact that $\sum_{i=m}^{n} 1$ is a sum of $n - m + 1$ ones.   ∎

Theorem 2   The sum of the arithmetic series $\sum_{i=1}^{n} (ai + b)$ is $an(n + 1)/2 + nb$.

Proof   From Gauss's formula, we get

$$\sum_{i=1}^{n} i = \frac{n(n + 1)}{2}$$

Then

$$\sum_{i=1}^{n} (ai + b) = a\sum_{i=1}^{n} i + \sum_{i=1}^{n} b = a\frac{n(n + 1)}{2} + bn$$ ∎

EXAMPLE 13   Find the sum $\sum_{i=1}^{10} (3i - 1)$.

Solution   We write

$$\sum_{i=1}^{10} 3i - 1 = \frac{3 \cdot 10(11)}{2} + 10 \cdot (-1) = 165 - 10 = 155$$

(Notice that $\sum_{i=1}^{10} 3i - 1$ is, by definition, $2 + 5 + 8 + 11 + 14 + 17 + 20 + 23 + 26 + 29 = 155$. In this case, using our theorems saves us work.)   ∎

Concepts Review

1. A relation from X to Y that associates exactly one member of Y with each member of X is called a(n) _____.

2. The set X in Concept 1 (above) is called the _____ of the _____ and the set Y in Concept 1 is called the _____ of the _____.

3. In the digraph of a function, [at least one, at most one, exactly one, an undetermined number of] _____ edge(s) leave(s) each vertex in the domain.

4. In a(n) _____ function or surjection, [at least one, at most one, exactly one, an undetermined number of] _____ edge(s) enter(s) each vertex in the range.

5. A function in which each element of the domain is related to exactly one element of the range is called a(n) _____ or _____ _____ _____ function.

6. A function that is both one-to-one and onto is called a _____.

7. The _____ of a function is the set of elements in the range that are related to something in the domain.

8. A function is an onto function if its _____ and _____ are the same set.

9. A function whose domain is a consecutive set of integers is called a(n) _____.

10. The notation $\sum_{i=m}^{n} a_i$ means the _____ from i equals _____ to _____ of a_i.

11. A series of the form $\sum_{i=m}^{n} ai + b$ is called a(n) _____ series.

Exercises

A In Exercises 1–12, the formulas represent functions whose domain is the set $\{1,2,3,4,5\}$. For each formula, write down the function it defines as a relation (that is, a set of ordered pairs).

1. $f(x) = x^2$
2. $f(x) = x^2 - x$
3. $g(x) = (2.5 - x)$
4. $f(x) = (3 - x)^2$
5. $h(x) = |x - 3|$
6. $h(x) = |3 - x|$
7. $y = 2x$
8. $y = 3 + x$
9. $y = x^2 - x + 1$
10. $y = x^2 - 5x + 5$
11. $y = \sin(\pi x)$
12. $y = \cos(\pi x)$

13. The **floor function** or **greatest-integer function** of a number x, denoted by $\lfloor x \rfloor$, is the greatest integer less than or equal to x. Thus, $\lfloor -1.5 \rfloor = -2$ and $\lfloor 3.5 \rfloor = 3$. Write down the ordered pairs of the floor function on the domain $\{-2, -1.5, -1, -.5, 0, .5, 1, 1.5, 2\}$.

14. The **ceiling function** or **least-integer function** of a number x, denoted by $\lceil x \rceil$, is the least integer greater than or equal to x. Thus, $\lceil -1.5 \rceil = -1$ and $\lceil 3.5 \rceil = 4$. Write down the ordered pairs of the ceiling function on the domain $\{-2, -1.5, -.5, 0, .5, 1, 1.5, 2\}$.

15. Write out the ordered pairs of the functions given by the rules $f(x) = x^5 - 5x^3 + 6x - 1$, $g(x) = 2x - 1$, and $h(x) = x^3 - 2x - 1$ on the domain $\{-2, -1, 0, 1, 2\}$. Which of these rules are rules for the same function on this domain?

16. Write out the ordered pairs of the functions given by the rules $f(x) = x^3 + x^2 + 2x - 2$, $g(x) = x^5 - 4x^3 + x^2 + 6x - 2$, and $h(x) = 2x^3 + x^2 + x - 2$ on the domain $\{-2, -1, 0, 1, 2\}$. Which of these rules represent the same function on this domain?

B   In Exercises 17–24, we give several pairs of sets D and R and functions from D to R. For each exercise, classify the functions as one-to-one (injections), onto (surjections), both (bijections), or neither, and give their images.

17. $D = \{0,1,2,3\}$ $R = \{a,b,c,d\}$ $\{(0,a), (1,b), (2,c), (3,d)\}$

18. $D = \{a,b,c,d\}$ $R = \{1,2,3,4\}$ $\{(a,1), (b,4), (c,3), (d,2)\}$

19. $D = \{0,1,2,3\}$ $R = \{a,b,c,d\}$ $\{(0,a), (1,a), (2,c), (3,d)\}$

20. $D = \{a,b,c,d\}$ $R = \{1,2,3\}$ $\{(a,1), (b,2), (c,1), (d,2)\}$

21. $D = \{0,1,2,3\}$ $R = \{a,b,c\}$ $\{(0,a), (1,b), (2,c), (3,c)\}$

22. $D = \{a,b,c,d\}$ $R = \{1,2,3\}$ $\{(a,1), (b,2), (c,1), (d,3)\}$

23. $D = \{0,1,2,3\}$ $R = \{a,b,c\}$ $\{(0,a), (1,a), (2,c), (3,c)\}$

24. $D = \{a,b,c\}$ $R = \{1,2,3,4\}$ $\{(a,1), (b,3), (c,4)\}$

In Exercises 25–36, we give several sets D and R and relations from D to R. For each relation, state whether or not it is a function; for each function, state if it is one-to-one and/ or if it is onto, and give its image.

25. $D = \{1,2,3,4,5\}$ $R = \{a,b,c,d,e\}$ $\{(1,a), (2,b), (3,c), (4,c), (5,d)\}$

26. $D = \{1,2,3,4,5\}$ $R = \{a,b,c,d,e\}$ $\{(1,e), (2,c), (3,a), (2,b), (5,d)\}$

27. $D = \{1,2,3,4,5\}$ $R = \{a,b,c,d,e\}$ $\{(1,a), (2,b), (1,c), (3,d), (4,e), (5,d)\}$

28. $D = \{1,2,3,4,5\}$ $R = \{(a,b,c,d,e\}$ $\{(1,e), (2,a), (3,e), (4,a), (5,b)\}$

29. $D = \{1,2,3,4\}$ $R = \{a,b,c,d,e\}$ $\{(2,a), (1,b), (3,e), (4,c)\}$

30. $D = \{1,2,3,4,5\}$ $R = \{a,b,c,d\}$ $\{(1,a), (2,a), (3,d), (4,c), (5,b)\}$

31. $D = \{1,2,3,4,5\}$ $R = \{a,b,c,d\}$ $\{(1,a), (3,b), (2,c), (4,d)\}$

32. $D = \{1,2,3,4,5\}$ $R = \{a,b,c,d\}$ $\{(1,a), (2,b), (2,c), (3,d), (5,d)\}$

33. $D = \{1,2,3,4\}$ $R = \{a,b,c,d,e\}$ $\{(1,a), (2,b), (3,c), (1,d), (4,e)\}$

34. $D = \{1,2,3,4\}$ $R = \{a,b,c,d,e\}$ $\{(1,b), (2,c), (3,d), (4,b)\}$

35. $D = \{1,2,3,4,5\}$ $R = \{a,b,c,d\}$ $\{(1,a), (2,b), (3,c), (4,d), (5,d)\}$

36. $D = \{1,2,3,4\}$ $R = \{a,b,c,d,e\}$ $\{(1,b), (2,e), (3,d), (4,b), (4,a)\}$

In Exercises 37–48, draw the digraphs of the relations given in the exercises specified and use them to explain your answers to those exercises.

37. Exercise 25   38. Exercise 26   39. Exercise 27

40. Exercise 28	**41.** Exercise 29	**42.** Exercise 30
43. Exercise 31	**44.** Exercise 32	**45.** Exercise 33
46. Exercise 34	**47.** Exercise 35	**48.** Exercise 36

C **49.** Let $s_i = i^2 - 1$ for $i \geq 1$. Write down the first five terms of this sequence.

50. Let $s_i = i^2 + 1$ for $i \geq 1$. Write down the first five terms of this sequence.

51. Let $s_i = i^2 + 1$ for $i \geq 0$. Write down the first five terms of this sequence.

52. Let $s_i = i^2 - 1$ for $i \geq 0$. Write down the first five terms of this sequence.

53. If $s_i = \left(\frac{1}{2}\right)^i$, for $i \geq 0$, what is the zeroth term of this sequence? What is term number 5?

54. If $s_i = (2i - 1)^2$ for $i \geq 0$, what is the zeroth term of this sequence? What is term number 4?

55. Find $\sum\limits_{i=1}^{5} 2i^2 + i$

56. Find $\sum\limits_{i=1}^{6} i - 1$

57. Find $\sum\limits_{i=0}^{4} 2^i$

58. Find $\sum\limits_{i=0}^{5} 3i - 1$

59. Find $\sum\limits_{i=3}^{7} i^2 + i$

60. Find $\sum\limits_{i=2}^{5} 2i^2 - i$

61. What is $\sum\limits_{i=1}^{50} (50 - i)$?

62. What is $\sum\limits_{i=0}^{60} i$?

63. What is $\sum\limits_{i=1}^{30} (2i + 2)$?

64. What is $\sum\limits_{i=1}^{30} (2i - 5)$?

65. What is $\sum\limits_{i=0}^{30} (2i - 5)$?

66. What is $\sum\limits_{i=3}^{30} (2i + 2)$?

(Compare with Exercise 64.)

(Compare with Exercise 63.)

67. If $\sum\limits_{i=1}^{n} a_i = 77$ and $\sum\limits_{i=1}^{n} b_i = 14$, what is $\sum\limits_{i=1}^{n} (2a_i - 3b_i)$?

68. If $\sum\limits_{i=1}^{n} a_i = 77$ and $\sum\limits_{i=1}^{n} b_i = 14$, what is $\sum\limits_{i=1}^{n} (3a_i - 2b_i)$?

Problems

1. The sum $\sum\limits_{i=j}^{n} a_i$ is called an *arithmetic series* as long as $a_i = ai + b$. Show that the sum of such an arithmetic series is the number of terms times the average of the first and last terms (term number j and term number n).

2. Suppose that f is a one-to-one function from $S = \{a,b,c,d\}$ to $S = \{a,b,c,d\}$. Show that f is onto.

3. Suppose that f is a one-to-one function from $S = \{1,2,3, \ldots ,n\}$ to $S = \{1,2,3, \ldots ,n\}$. Show that f is onto.

4. Show that if f is a function from an n-element set S to a set with fewer than n elements, then $f(x) = f(y)$ for two distinct elements x and y of S. This is called the *pigeonhole principle* and has surprising applications. For example, explain why, in a group of 13 people, at last 2 will have their birthdays in the same month. What can you conclude about a group of 25 people?

5. How is the size of the image of a function related to the size of the domain? (Assume that the domain is finite.) How is the size of the range of an injection related to the size of the domain?

6. Find the number of functions from $\{1,2,3\}$ to $\{1,2\}$. Find the number of functions from $\{1,2\}$ to $\{1,2,3\}$.

7. Find a formula for the number of functions from an m-element set to an n-element set.

8. Let S be a set and let T be a set of numbers. Let F be the set of all functions from S to T. Show that the relation P, with $(f,g) \in P$ if $f(x) \leq g(x)$ for all x in S, is a reflexive partial ordering of F.

9. Draw the Hasse diagram of the partial ordering P of Problem 8 in the case that $S = \{a,b,c\}$ and $T = \{0,1\}$. Explain why this diagram is similar to Figure 18 in Chapter 3.

10. The sum $f + g$ of two functions whose range is a set of numbers is defined by the rules $(f + g)(x) = f(x) + g(x)$, and the product $f \cdot g$ of two such functions is defined by $(f \cdot g)(x) = f(x)g(x)$. Prove the distributive laws $f \cdot (g + h) = f \cdot g + f \cdot h$ and $(f + g) \cdot h = f \cdot h + g \cdot h$.

Section 4-2
Graphs and Operations on Functions

A   Cartesian Graphs

In algebra, in (analytic) geometry, and in calculus, we often study numerical functions and relations. A **numerical** function is one whose domain and range are both sets of numbers (real, rational, or integer, and so on). Many of these functions play an important role in discrete mathematics as well. We can visualize numerical functions and relations with a third kind of graph called a *Cartesian graph*. To draw such a graph, we must first construct a Cartesian coordinate system on a plane surface. We draw horizontal and vertical number lines, called the x- and y-

axes, so that they intersect at their zero points. We say that a point on the surface has x-coordinate a and y-coordinate b and refer to the point as the point (a,b) if vertical and horizontal lines through the point intersect the x-axis and the y-axis, respectively, at $x = a$ and $y = b$. Several typical examples are shown in Figure 9. Note that (a,b) has two positive coordinates, that the x-coordinate of (c,d) is negative, and that both coordinates of (r,s) are negative.

Figure 9

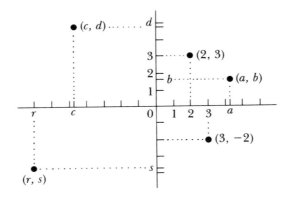

Cartesian Graphs

The **Cartesian graph** of a relation R consists of all points (x,y) in the plane such that x is related to y by R (that is, $(x,y) \in R$ or xRy).

In particular, in the case of a function, (x,y) is on the graph of f if and only if $f(x) = y$. In Figure 10, we show the graph of the *relation* "x is related to y if $x^2 + y^2 = 1$." In Figure 11, we show the graphs of the functions given by $f(x) = x$, $f(x) = x^2$ and $f(x) = x^3$.

Figure 10

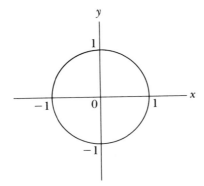

Figure 11

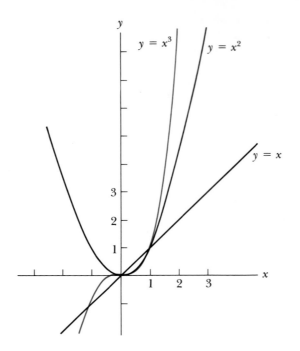

In Figures 12 and 13, we show the graphs of $y = x^2$ and $y = 2^x$ for $x \geq 0$, showing how using different scales on the x- and y-axes can be useful in order to see more information about the functions whose graphs we draw.

Figure 12

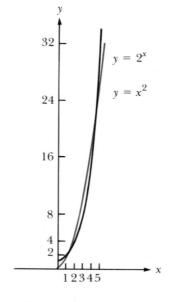

Figure 13

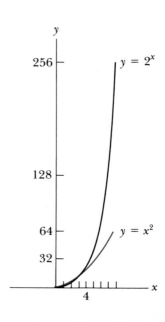

Although Figure 12 could lead us to believe that the graphs of $y = 2^x$ and $y = x^2$ are similar, Figure 13 shows us enough of the two graphs to convince us that they are different. It appears from Figure 13 that the graph of $y = 2^x$ rises *faster* than the graph of $y = x^2$. Similarly, Figure 11 shows us that apparently the graph of $y = x^3$ rises faster than the graph of $y = x^2$, which in turn rises faster than the graph of $y = x$. Later on, we shall describe more precisely this intuitive idea that we can see by examining graphs. These ideas will be especially useful when we begin analyzing algorithms in order to predict how long it will take to run computer programs based on the algorithms.

Discovering Properties of Functions and Relations from Cartesian Graphs

Notice that if, as we show below in Figure 14, we draw a vertical line in Figure 10, it might not cross the graph at all, indicating that some x-values correspond to *no* y-values, and it might cross the graph twice, showing that two y-values correspond to the x-value. This second observation tells us that our graph is *not* the graph of a function, because two y-values correspond to the same x-value.

Figure 14

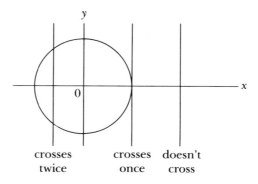

crosses twice   crosses once   doesn't cross

However, you can see in Figure 11 that if we draw any vertical line, it crosses each individual graph *once and only once*. The fact that *each* vertical line crosses the graph means that the domain of the function includes *each* real number. The fact that no vertical line crosses any of the graphs twice means that each x determines only one y on each graph, so each x is related to a unique y by each relation. Thus all three of these relations are functions.

Now consider what happens if we draw a horizontal line through the graphs of Figure 11. If this line is below the x-axis, it doesn't cross the graph of $y = x^2$, showing us that the image of this function contains *no* negative numbers. On the other hand, *each* horizontal line crosses both the graph of $y = x$ and $y = x^3$, so these are functions with *each* real number in their images.

Now a horizontal line above the x-axis crosses the graph of $y = x^2$ twice, telling us that two different x-values correspond to the same y-value. Thus the function given by $f(x) = x^2$ is *not* a one-to-one function. On the other hand, each horizontal line crosses the graph of $y = x^3$ once, telling us that each real number is in the image of the function given by $f(x) = x^3$. Further, each horizontal line crosses the graph of $y = x^3$ *only once*, telling us that the function given by $f(x) = x^3$ is a one-to-one function.

Table 1 shows in summary form what we have learned about how to interpret horizontal and vertical lines through the graph of a relation.

Table 1   Interpreting horizontal and vertical lines through graphs.

	One line doesn't cross	Each crosses once or less	One line crosses more than once
Horizontal line	Not onto	One-to-one	Not one-to-one
Vertical line	Domain not all reals	Relation is a function	Not a function

▣ Composition and Inverses

Composition

In using functions, we combine them in various ways. For example, if $f(x) = \sqrt{x}$ and $g(x) = 1 - x^2$, we may write $f(g(x)) = \sqrt{1 - x^2}$, or $f \circ g(x) = \sqrt{1 - x^2}$. In so doing, we have defined a new relation $f \circ g$.

> The **composition** of a function f with a function g
> is the relation $f \circ g$ (which we read as "f circle g"
> or "f composed with g") that contains the pair (x,y)
> if and only if $y = f(g(x))$ (which we read as "f of g of x").

So that we may compute $f(g(x))$, it is necessary that $g(x)$ be in the domain of f for each x (in the domain of g); in other words, the *image* of g must be a subset of the *domain* of f in order for $f \circ g$ to be defined. Figure 15 should help you visualize composition.

EXAMPLE 14   For each pair of functions below, the image of g is a subset of the domain of f, so that $f \circ g$ is defined. Give the best description you can for the composite function $f \circ g$.

(a) $f = \{(1, -1)\ (2, -2)\ (3, -3)\ (4, -4)\ (5, -6)\}$ $g = \{(1,3)\ (2,4)\ (3,5)\}$

(b) $f(y) = y^3 + 1$ $g(x) = \sqrt[3]{x}$

(c) $f(x) = x^3 + 1$ $g(x) = \sqrt[3]{x - 1}$

Solution   For each part of the problem, we must figure out how to compute $f \circ g(x) = f(g(x))$ for each x in the domain of g. To do so, we first find $g(x)$ and then

Figure 15   The boundary of the image of *g* is dashed; the boundary of the domain of *f* is solid.

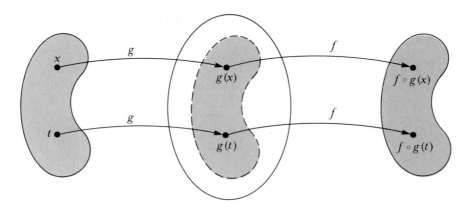

substitute it into the formula for *f*, working from the "inside" of the formula $f(g(x))$ to the outside.

(a) To describe $f \circ g$ as a set of ordered pairs, we need to know $f \circ g(1)$, $f \circ g(2)$, and $f \circ g(3)$

$$f(g(1)) = f(3) = -3$$
$$f(g(2)) = f(4) = -4$$
$$f(g(3)) = f(5) = -6$$

Assembling this information into a set of ordered pairs, we get

$$f \circ g = \{(1, -3),\ (2, -4),\ (3, -6)\}$$

(b) Here we shall try to get a formula for $f \circ g$. We can think of *g* as given by $y = g(x) = \sqrt[3]{x}$. Then $f \circ g(x) = f(g(x)) = f(y) = f(\sqrt[3]{x}) = (\sqrt[3]{x})^3 + 1 = x + 1$.

(c) We write $f \circ g(x) = f(g(x)) = f(\sqrt[3]{x - 1}) = (\sqrt[3]{x - 1})^3 + 1 = x - 1 + 1 = x$. (Notice that the variable used in giving the formula for *f* is irrelevant; what was relevant was that we had to cube the variable and add one.) ∎

EXAMPLE 15   Use the facts that there are 454 g in 1 lb. and 16 oz. in 1 lb. to get a formula for a function that converts weights in ounces to weights in grams.

Solution   Since there are 16 oz. in 1 lb., the weight of an object in pounds is $\frac{1}{16}$ its weight in ounces, thus $p(x) = \frac{1}{16} x$ is a formula to convert weight in ounces to weight in pounds. Further, since 1 lb. is 454 g., the formula $g(x) = 454x$ converts pound weights to gram weights. Thus

$$g \circ p(x) = g(p(x)) = g\left(\frac{1}{16}x\right) = 454 \cdot \left(\frac{1}{16}x\right) = \frac{227}{8} x$$

is a formula for converting weights in ounces to weights in grams. ∎

EXAMPLE 16   Find the compositions $p \circ g$ and $g \circ p$ of the function $p(y) = y/454$, which converts weights in grams to weights in pounds, with the function $g(x) = 454x$, which converts weights in pounds to weights in grams.

Solution $p \circ g(x) = p(g(x)) = p(454x) = \dfrac{454x}{454} = x$

$g \circ p(y) = g(p(y)) = g\left(\dfrac{y}{454}\right) = 454 \cdot \dfrac{y}{454} = y$ ■

> Whenever f and g are two functions such that $f(g(x)) = x$ and $g(f(y)) = y$ for each x in the domain of g and each y in the domain of f, we say that f and g are **inverses** to each other, that f is the **inverse of** g, and that g is the **inverse of** f.

A shorthand notation for this is $f = g^{-1}$ or $g = f^{-1}$. (We read f^{-1} as "f inverse," not "f to the negative one.") The diagram in Figure 16 gives you a way to visualize inverses geometrically.

Figure 16

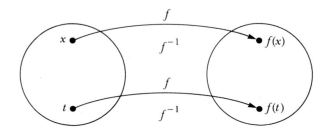

If we are given a function g and a function f, how do we determine whether they are inverses? We simply compute $f(g(x))$ and $g(f(y))$, as in Example 16. But what if we are simply given a function g and we need to know if it has an inverse? Take, for example, $g(x) = x^3$. Since each horizontal line crosses its graph once and only once, we know that for each y there is one and only one x such that $x^3 = y$. (In fact, $x = \sqrt[3]{y}$.)

The remark we made about horizontal lines applies to any function g whose domain and image are sets of real numbers: To determine if g has an inverse, draw its Cartesian graph. If each horizontal line crosses the graph zero times or once, then g has an inverse. Further, if *each* horizontal line crosses the graph once, then the domain of g^{-1} is the set of all real numbers.

Once we know that g has an inverse function f, how do we find f? Let's continue to illustrate the computations with $g(x) = x^3$. Since we want $f(g(x)) = x$, we may define

$$f(y) = \text{the unique } x \text{ such that } x^3 = y \text{ (or in general such that } g(x) = y)$$
$$= \sqrt[3]{y}$$

We know that for each y, this defines exactly one value for $f(y)$, because the function $g(x) = x^3$ is one-to-one. We know that this defines $f(y)$ for every real number y, because the function given by $g(x) = x^3$ is onto, so each y is related to some x.

Now, using z for the variable momentarily, we see that

$$f(g(z)) = \text{the unique } x \text{ such that } g(x) = g(z)$$
$$= z$$

and

$$g(f(y)) = g(\text{the unique } x \text{ such that } g(x) = y)$$
$$= y$$

Thus by defining $f(y) = \sqrt[3]{y}$, we have $f = g^{-1}$ and $g = f^{-1}$. Notice that $f^{-1}(x)$ is not $1/f(x)$.

Our computations have used only the fact that g is a one-to-one function from the real numbers onto the real numbers. Thus, the computations lead us to the general principle stated in Theorem 3.

Theorem 3 A function g from D to R has an inverse if and only if g is one-to-one. The domain of g^{-1} is the image of g.

Proof The proof consists essentially of the computations we made with $g(x) = x^3$ above. ∎

If we know that g has an inverse, how do we find it?

EXAMPLE 17 The function $g(x) = x^3 - 1$ is one-to-one. Find a rule for its inverse function. What is the domain of its inverse function?

Solution For each y, we want the unique x with $x^3 - 1 = y$, so we solve the equation $x^3 - 1 = y$ to get $x = \sqrt[3]{y + 1}$. Thus $g^{-1}(y) = \sqrt[3]{y + 1}$. By Theorem 1, the domain of g^{-1} is all real numbers, because the image of g is the set of all real numbers. ∎

The Graph of the Inverse Function

We showed that if $g(x) = x^3$, then $g^{-1}(y) = \sqrt[3]{y}$. Thus the relation of g consists of all pairs of the form (x, x^3), and the relation of g^{-1} consists of all pairs of the form $(y, \sqrt[3]{y}) = (x^3, x)$. The relationship between the points (x, x^3) on the graph of g and the points (x^3, x) on the graph of g^{-1} suggests a second theorem.

Theorem 4 If g is a one-to-one function, then the points on the graph of g^{-1} may be obtained by interchanging the x- and y-coordinates of the points on the graph of g.

Proof Similar to the observation for the function given by $g(x) = x^3$ above. ∎

EXAMPLE 18   Draw the graph of the two inverse functions given by $g(x) = x^3$ and $f(x) = \sqrt[3]{x}$ on the same axes. How do these graphs relate to the graph of $y = x$?

Solution   The graphs of $y = x$, $g(x) = x^3$, and $f(x) = \sqrt[3]{x}$ are shown in Figure 17. The figure is symmetric with respect to the line $y = x$, because the points (x,x^3) and (x^3,x) are equidistant from the line $y = x$. Thus we may obtain the graph of one function from the graph of the other by "flipping" the figure around the line $y = x$. If you are familiar with the geometric idea of reflecting a figure through a line, you see that a more precise way to say this is that the graph of g is the reflection of f through (or in) the line $y = x$, and vice versa.   ■

Figure 17

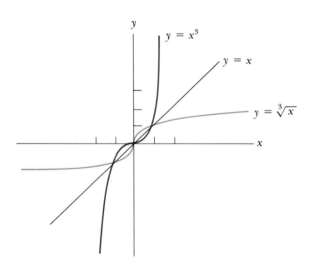

The pattern we see in the example always holds; we obtain the graph of g^{-1} from the graph of g by flipping the entire figure around the line $y = x$. (Using the language of geometry, we say that we obtain the graph of g^{-1} from g by reflecting the graph of g through (or in) the line $y = x$.)

EXAMPLE 19   The function given by $f(x) = 2^x$ is a one-to-one function from the set of real numbers onto the set of positive real numbers. Therefore it has an inverse function, denoted by $y = \log_2(x)$, which is a function from the set of positive real numbers to the set of real numbers. Sketch graphs of $y = 2^x$ and $y = \log_2(x)$ on the same axes.

Solution   In Figure 18, we draw the graph of $y = 2^x$ and flip it around (reflect it through) the line $y = x$ to get the graph of $y = \log_2(x)$.   ■

Figure 18

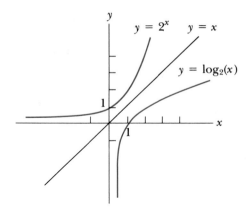

Converting Number Representations

Conversions between two systems of measurement, as in Example 13, always give us pairs of inverse functions. Our final example is of a similar kind, involving the binary and digital representations of numbers. In elementary school we learn the base-10 representation of numbers and often representations in other bases. The decimal (or base-10) representation of a number is the way we usually write it, as a sequence of digits between 0 and 9. For example,

$$134 = 1 \cdot 10^2 + 3 \cdot 10^1 + 4 \cdot 10^0$$

and this formula defines the meaning of the sequence of digits 134. Often other bases for the number system are introduced in elementary or high school. Of these other bases, the base-2 representation has become especially important because of its applications in computing. The base-2 or **binary representation** represents a number as a sequence of ones and zeros (which are called bits rather than digits). Powers of 2 are used in base-2 representations in the way that powers of 10 are used in base-10 representations. For example, 101 is the binary representation for

$$1 \cdot 2^2 + 0 \cdot 2^1 + 1 \cdot 2^0 = 4 + 0 + 1 = 5$$

As a more general example, the four symbols $wxyz$ form the binary representation of

$$w \cdot 2^3 + x \cdot 2^2 + y \cdot 2 + z$$

EXAMPLE 20   Find the binary representation of 3 and of 21.

Solution   Since $3 = 2 + 1$ and $1 = 2^0$, we see that $3 = 1 \cdot 2^1 + 1 \cdot 2^0$. Thus the binary representation of 3 is the sequence 11. Working out the representation of 3 in this way doesn't tell us how to handle other cases such as 21. The trick is to look for the biggest power of 2 in 21. That is 16. (In other words, $2^4 = 16 \leq 21$ but $2^5 = 32 \nleq 21$.) Now we write

$$21 = 16 + 5$$

We repeat the process, this time finding the biggest power of 2 in 5 (which is 2^2 or 4), giving

$$21 = 16 + 4 + 1$$

The biggest power of 2 in 1 is $2^0 = 1$, and 1 appears already as the last term in the sum, so we have 21 as a sum of powers of 2. In expanded notation,

$$21 = 1{\cdot}2^4 + 0{\cdot}2^3 + 1{\cdot}2^2 + 0{\cdot}2^1 + 1{\cdot}2^0$$

Thus the binary representation of 21 is 10101.   ∎

EXAMPLE 21   Find the decimal representation of the number with the binary representation 11010, using $\equiv$ for "represents the same number."

Solution   We write

$$11010 \equiv 1{\cdot}2^4 + 1{\cdot}2^3 + 0{\cdot}1^2 + 1{\cdot}2 + 0{\cdot}2^0 = 16 + 8 + 2 = 26 \qquad ∎$$

To see how this relates to inverse functions, let f be the function that takes the decimal representation of a number and gives us its binary representation. Let g be the function that takes the binary representation of a number and gives us its decimal representation. Then, because each integer has a unique binary representation,

$$f(g(wxyz)) = wxyz$$

(and similarly for different numbers of bits), and because each integer has a unique decimal representation

$$g(f(abc)) = abc$$

(and similarly for different numbers of digits). Thus f and g are inverse functions. This example may be summed up by saying that the representation of the number does not change when converting from binary to decimal and back or converting from decimal to binary and back.

Inverse Images

There is a second important use of the notation f^{-1} that is consistent with inverse functions of one-to-one functions. If f is a function with domain X and image Y, it is natural to speak of the *inverse image* of an element y, defined as follows.

> The **inverse image** of y, denoted by $f^{-1}(\{y\})$, is the set of all elements x such that $f(x) = y$.

EXAMPLE 22   If $f(x) = x^2$ on the real numbers, describe the inverse image of y for each non-negative integer y.

Solution   For $y = 0$, $f^{-1}(\{0\}) = \{0\}$. However, for any other y, both $\sqrt{y}$ and $-\sqrt{y}$ are sent to y by f. Thus for each other y,

$$f^{-1}(\{y\}) = \{-\sqrt{y}, \sqrt{y}\}$$ ■

Since $f(x)$ has exactly one value y, each x in the domain lies in exactly one set $f^{-1}(\{y\})$. Thus the sets $f^{-1}(\{y\})$ form a partition of the domain X. We have learned that each partition is associated with an equivalence relation. Here, x_1 and x_2 are in the same equivalence class $f^{-1}(y)$ if $f(x_1) = y = f(x_2)$.

> The **inverse image equivalence relation**
> for a function f defined on a domain D
> is given by $x \equiv y$ if and only if $f(x) = f(y)$.

EXAMPLE 23   Describe in words the equivalence relation associated with $f(x) = x^2$ in Example 22.

Solution   Two numbers x_1 and x_2 are equivalent if they have the same square.   ■

The braces around the y in $f^{-1}(\{y\})$ tell us that we are talking about an inverse image function, not an inverse function. If a function does not have an inverse and you see the notation $f^{-1}(y)$, it simply means that someone forgot the braces. No confusion is likely even if f does have an inverse for each y, because if f is one-to-one then there is only one x such that $f(x) = y$. Thus the inverse function notation $f^{-1}(y) = x$ and the inverse image function notation $f^{-1}(\{y\}) = \{x\}$ are two different ways to say the same thing about a one-to-one function.

Concepts Review

1. The type of graph studied in algebra is called a(n) _____ graph.

2. The _____ graph of a relation R consists of all points (x,y) in the plane such that x is related to y by R.

3. The graph of $y = 2^x$ rises [significantly faster than, significantly slower than, at the same rate as] _____ the graph of $y = x^2$ as the x gets large.

4. A vertical line drawn through a point in the domain of a function will cross its Cartesian graph [exactly once, at least once, no more than once, an undetermined number of times] _____.

5. If each horizontal line crosses the Cartesian graph of a function at most once, then the function is _____.

6. If each horizontal line crosses the Cartesian graph of a function at least once, then the function is ——————.

7. The function $f \circ g$ defined by $f \circ g(x) = f(g(x))$ is called the —————— of f and g.

8. Before we can define the composition of f and g, we must know that the —————— of g is a subset of the —————— of f.

9. The functions f and g are —————— to each other if $f(g(x)) = x$ and $g(f(y)) = y$ for each x in the —————— of g and each y in the —————— of f.

10. If g is a one-to-one function, then the points on the graph of g^{-1} may be obtained by —————— the x- and y-coordinates of the points on the graph of g.

11. The —————— —————— of a number represents a number as a sequence of zeros and ones.

Exercises

A   In Exercises 1–6, sketch the graphs of the functions given.

1. (a) $f(x) = x^2$ (b) $f(x) = x^2 - 1$ (c) $f(x) = x^2 + 1$

2. (a) $f(x) = |x|$ (b) $f(x) = |x| - 1$ (c) $f(x) = |x| + 1$

3. (a) $f(x) = x^2$ (b) $f(x) = (x - 1)^2$ (c) $f(x) = (x + 1)^2$

4. (a) $f(x) = |x|$ (b) $f(x) = |x - 1|$ (c) $f(x) = |x + 1|$

5. (a) $f(x) = x^2$ (b) $f(x) = -x^2$
     (c) $f(x) = \frac{1}{4}x^2$ (d) $f(x) = 4x^2$

6. (a) $f(x) = |x^2|$ (b) $f(x) = -|x|$
     (c) $f(x) = \frac{1}{2}|x|$ (d) $f(x) = 2|x|$

For Exercises 7–14, state whether the relation in the specified part of Figure 19 is a function.

7. Figure 19(a)   8. Figure 19(b)

9. Figure 19(c)   10. Figure 19(d)

11. Figure 19(e)   12. Figure 19(f)

13. Figure 19(g)   14. Figure 19(h)

For Exercises 15–22, tell whether the function graphed in the specified part of Figure 20 is one-to-one.

15. Figure 20(a)   16. Figure 20(b)

17. Figure 20(c)   18. Figure 20(d)

19. Figure 20(e)   20. Figure 20(f)

21. Figure 20(g)   22. Figure 20(h)

Figure 19

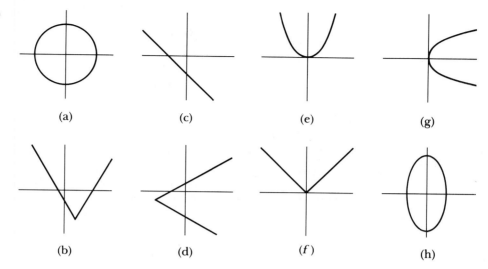

Figure 20

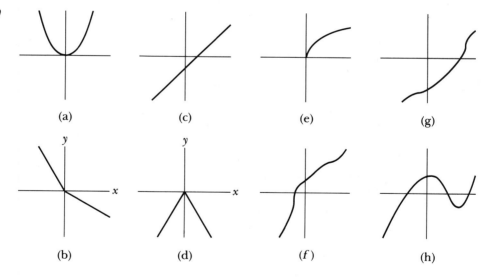

In Exercises 23–30, sketch the Cartesian graphs for each of the pairs of functions given and decide which function is larger for large values of x. (You may wish to use a different scale on the y-axis from that on the x-axis. If so, mark each scale clearly.)

23. $f(x) = \frac{1}{2}x^2$; $g(x) = \sqrt{x}$

24. $f(x) = 2x - 1$; $g(x) = \sqrt{x^2 + 1}$

25. $f(x) = \frac{1}{4}x^4$; $g(x) = 2^x$

26. $f(x) = \sqrt{x/2};$ $g(x) = \log_2(x)$

27. $f(x) = x^2 - 4x;$ $g(x) = 2x^2 - 8$

28. $f(x) = 2^x - 2^{-x}$ $g(x) = x^2$

29. $f(x) = \sqrt{x};$ $g(x) = \log_2(x^2 - 1)$

30. $f(x) = x\sqrt{x} - x;$ $g(x) = x + 1$

31. The greatest-integer or floor function of x, introduced in Exercise 13 of Section 4-1 and denoted by $\lfloor x \rfloor$, is the greatest integer less than or equal to x. Draw the Cartesian graph of $f(x) = \lfloor x \rfloor$ on the domain of all real numbers x between -3 and 3.

32. The least-integer or ceiling function of x, introduced in Exercise 14 of Section 4-1 and denoted by $\lceil x \rceil$, is the least integer greater than or equal to x. Draw the Cartesian graph of $f(x) = \lceil x \rceil$ on the domain of all real numbers x between -3 and 3.

B   In Exercises 33–40, for each pair of functions given, find the composite function $f \circ g$.

33. $f(x) = 2x + 3;$ $g(x) = \frac{1}{2}x$

34. $f(x) = 2 - x^2;$ $g(x) = \sqrt{2 - x}$

35. $f(t) = t^2 - 4;$ $g(x) = x + 2$

36. $f(u) = 2u + 4;$ $g(v) = \dfrac{3v - 1}{2}$

37. $f = \{(1,2), (2,3), (3,4), (4,6)\};$ $g = \{(a,1), (b,2), (c,4), (d,3)\}$

38. $f = \{(a,1), (b,4), (c,6), (d,7)\};$ $g = \{(1,a), (4,b), (6,c)(7,d)\}$

39. $f = \{(1,2), (2,3), (3,4), (4,6), (5,1)\};$ $g = \{(a,1), (b,2), (c,4)\}$

40. $f = \{(1,3) (2,4) (3,4) (4,3)\};$ $g = \{(1,2) (2,3) (3,4)\}$

In Exercises 41–48, for each pair of functions given, determine whether f is the inverse to g.

41. $f(x) = 2x + 2;$ $g(x) = \frac{1}{2}x - 1$

42. $f(x) = x^3 + 1;$ $g(x) = \sqrt[3]{x - 1}$

43. $f(x) = x^3 + 1;$ $g(x) = \sqrt[3]{x} - 1$

44. $f(x) = 3x + 1;$ $g(x) = \frac{1}{3}x - 1$

45. $f = \{(a,1), (b,2), (c,4), (d,3)\};$ $g = \{(1,a), (2,b), (3,d), (4,c)\}$

46. $\{(1,3), (3,5), (5,7), (7,11)\};$ $\{(11,1), (7,5), (5,3), (3,2)\}$

47. $f = \{(1,2), (2,3), (3,4), (4,1)\};$ $g = \{(1,4), (2,1), (3,2), (4,3)\}$

48. $\{(a,b), (c,d), (b,c), (d,a)\};$ $\{(b,a), (a,d), (c,d), (d,c)\}$

49. The floor function or greatest-integer function of x, introduced in Exercise 13 of Section 4-1 and denoted by $\lfloor x \rfloor$, is the greatest integer less than or equal to x. Thus $\lfloor -2.5 \rfloor =$

-3 and $\lfloor 2.5 \rfloor = 2$. The ceiling function of x, introduced in Exercise 14 of Section 4-1 and denoted by $\lceil x \rceil$, is the least integer greater than or equal to x. Thus $\lceil -2.5 \rceil = -2$ and $\lceil 2.5 \rceil = 3$. Find a simpler rule for the composite function given by $f(x) = \lceil \lfloor x \rfloor \rceil$.

50. The floor and ceiling functions were defined in Exercise 49. Find a simpler rule for the composite function given by $f(x) = \lfloor \lceil x \rceil \rfloor$.

51. If $f(x) = \sqrt[3]{x} - 1$, which of the following is a rule for $f^{-1}(x)$?
   (a) $f^{-1}(x) = x^3 + 1$

   (b) $f^{-1}(x) = \dfrac{1}{\sqrt[3]{x} - 1}$

   (c) $f^{-1}(x) = (x - 1)^3$
   (d) $f^{-1}(x) = (x + 1)^3$
   (e) $f^{-1}(x) = x^3 - 1$

52. If $f(x) = (x - 2)^3 + 1$, which of the following is a rule for $f^{-1}(x)$?
   (a) $f^{-1}(x) = \sqrt[3]{x - 2} + 1$

   (b) $f^{-1}(x) = (x - 1)^3 + 2$
   (c) $f^{-1}(x) = \sqrt[3]{x - 1} + 2$

   (d) $f^{-1}(x) = \dfrac{1}{(x - 2)^3 + 1}$

   (e) $f^{-1}(x) = \dfrac{1}{\sqrt[3]{x - 1}} + \dfrac{1}{2}$

53. Find the decimal representation of each number whose binary representation is given below.
   (a) 101   (b) 1111   (c) 1000   (d) 1101

54. Find the decimal representation of each number whose binary representation is given below.
   (a) 111   (b) 10101   (c) 100   (d) 1011

55. Find the binary representation of each number whose decimal representation is given below.
   (a) 8   (b) 7   (c) 10   (d) 11   (e) 17

56. Find the binary representation of each number whose decimal representation is given below.
   (a) 16   (b) 15   (c) 9   (d) 100   (e) 111

57. The rule for converting Fahrenheit temperatures to Celsius temperatures is $g(x) = \frac{5}{9}(x - 32)$. Find the inverse function of g. What conversion does the inverse function provide?

58. The rule for converting Fahrenheit temperatures to Kelvin temperatures is $f(x) = \frac{5}{9}(x + 459)$. Find the inverse function of f. What conversion does the inverse function provide?

59. The rule for converting Kelvin temperatures to Celsius temperatures is $f(x) = x - 273$. The rule for converting Celsius temperatures to Fahrenheit temperatures is $g(x) = \frac{9}{5}x + 32$. Find the rule for converting Kelvin temperatures to Fahrenheit temperatures.

60. The rule for converting Fahrenheit temperatures to Celsius temperatures is $g(x) = \frac{5}{9}(x - 32)$. The rule for converting Celsius temperatures to Kelvin temperatures is $f(x) = x + 273$. Find the rule for converting Fahrenheit temperatures to Kelvin temperatures.

61. Sketch the graph of the function given by $f(x) = (x + 1)^3$ and the line $y = x$; sketch the inverse of the function f.

62. For the domain of all non-negative x, the function g given by $g(x) = \sqrt{x^2 + 1}$ is one-to-one. Sketch the graph of g on this domain, sketch in the graph of $y = x$, and sketch a graph of g^{-1}.

Problems

1. The composition of two functions f and g gives a new function $f \circ g$. Thus, just as multiplication or addition of numbers produces a new number, forming the union or intersection of sets produces a new set, and forming the conjunction or disjunction of two statements produces a new statement, composition of two functions gives a new function. Prove the associative law $(f \circ g) \circ h = f \circ (g \circ h)$ by figuring out what $(f \circ g) \circ h(x)$ is and what $f \circ (g \circ h)(x)$ is.

2. For any domain D, there is a special function i (some people call it i_D), defined by the rule $i(x) = x$ for all x in D. Show that i has the identity property: $f \circ i = f$ for each function with domain D. Because of this property, i is called an **identity function.**

3. This problem is based on Problem 2. The notation $i \circ f$ makes sense. However, the domain of i won't necessarily be the domain of f. How should the domain of i relate to f for $i \circ f$ to make sense? Show that this i has the identity property that $i \circ f = f$.

4. Identity functions were discussed in Problems 2 and 3. If f and g are inverse functions, how do identity functions relate to $f \circ g$ and $g \circ f$?

5. If f and g are functions whose domain is the same set D and whose range is a set of numbers, then (as in Problem 10 of Section 4-1) it makes sense to define a new function $f + g$ by $(f + g)(x) = f(x) + g(x)$. Show that $(f + g) \circ h = f \circ h + g \circ h$. Discuss the possibility of having the distributive law: $f \circ (g + h) = f \circ g + f \circ h$.

6. Define a numerical function z on a domain D by $z(x) = 0$ for all x in D. (z stands for zero.) How should you define $-f$ so that $f + -f = z$? Show that your definition works. What may we say about $f + z$?

7. Suppose we have a digraph of a function f and reverse the directions of all the arrows. If the result is a function, what function must it be?

8. Composition is an idea that makes perfectly good sense for relations. Given a relation R from W to X and a relation S from Y to Z, what condition must hold before we could define $R \circ S$? In that case, how should we define $R \circ S$?

9. The **converse** of a relation R is the set of all (x,y) such that (y,x) is in R. What is the converse of a one-to-one function? Use R^{converse} to stand for the converse of R. Describe the relation we get by forming $R \circ R^{\text{converse}}$. Under what circumstances will $R \circ R^{\text{converse}}$ and $R^{\text{converse}} \circ R$ be the same relation?

10. Given three positive numbers a, b, and c, how will the Cartesian graph of the function given by $g(x) = af(x - b) + c$ be related to the Cartesian graph of the function f?

11. Explain why the composition of two polynomial functions is a polynomial function. How does its degree relate to the degrees of the functions being composed?

Section 4-3 Growth Rates of Functions

🄰 Polynomial Time Algorithms

A **polynomial function of degree n** is a numerical function with a rule of the form

$$f(x) = ax^n + bx^{n-1} + \cdots + cx + d$$

with $a \neq 0$. A polynomial function of degree 1 is sometimes called a **linear function,** because it has the same form as the equation of a straight line with slope m and y-intercept b, namely

$$y = mx + b, \quad \text{or} \quad f(x) = mx + b$$

A **quadratic function** is a polynomial function of degree 2 (that is, $f(x) = ax^2 + bx + c$). A **cubic function** is a polynomial function of degree 3.

A Linear Time Algorithm

In predicting the amount of running time a computer program will take, we often use polynomial functions.

EXAMPLE 24   The algorithm below finds the smallest element in any list of n numbers and moves it to the first position. How many comparisons does the algorithm make? How many times does it exchange numbers?

Algorithm Smallest
     Input: A list L of n numbers in any order whatsoever.
   Output: A list of the same numbers with the smallest one first.
Procedure: For each position i from number 2 to number n in order, do the following:
               If the number in position i is smaller than the number in position 1, exchange it with the number in position 1 and go on to the next i-value.
               Otherwise just go on to the next i-value.

Solution   This algorithm makes $n - 1$ comparisons and, depending on what order the list is in to start with, makes somewhere between 0 and $n - 1$ exchanges. Thus the time a computer program based on this algorithm will take depends on the list. If a comparison takes a units of time, then the program will take at least $(n - 1) \cdot a$ units of time. If an exchange takes b units of time, then the program will take no more than $(n - 1)a + (n - 1)b$ units of time. (Later we'll describe a way to make Smallest more efficient; we don't do so now because the analysis is a bit less complicated this way.)   ■

In Example 24, we see that there will be one linear function f (with $f(n) = (n - 1)a$), and another linear function g (with $g(n) = (n - 1)(a + b)$), such that the running time with n items in the list is between $f(n)$ and $g(n)$. We say that $f(n)$ is a **lower bound** to the running time and $g(n)$ is an **upper bound** to the running time of an algorithm when the running time with n items of input is at least $f(n)$ and no more than $g(n)$.

A Quadratic Time Algorithm

When we study algorithms to accomplish more complicated things, we get more complicated upper and lower bounds (and we sometimes discover these bounds are quite difficult to find). For example, by applying Algorithm Smallest first to positions 1 through n, then two through n, then 3 through n, and so on, we will be able to sort a list into increasing order. This process is called the **selection sort algorithm**.

EXAMPLE 25   Analyze the number of comparisons made by the Selection Sort algorithm. What does this analysis tell us about the total time needed to do all the comparing and exchanging?

Solution   The first time we apply Smallest, we have $n - 1$ comparisons, then $n - 2$, then $n - 3$, and so on. Thus by Gauss's formula, discussed in Sections 4-1 and 5-1, the total number of comparisons is

$$n - 1 + n - 2 + \cdots + 1 = \sum_{i=1}^{n-1} i = \frac{n(n-1)}{2} = \frac{1}{2}n^2 - \frac{1}{2}n$$

Therefore the number of comparisons is a quadratic function of the length n of the list. The number of exchanges is no more than the number of comparisons, so the total time to do all the comparing and exchanging is at least one quadratic function of n (namely $f(n) = \frac{1}{2}a \, (n^2 - n)$ in the notation of Example 24) and is no more than another quadratic function of n.   ■

In our examples, we don't know exactly how long our programs would take, for two reasons. First, we don't know the values of a and b. Second, the computer may need some time to do other things than comparing and exchanging. This second detail depends on a wide variety of factors but usually wouldn't make a linear time bound nonlinear or a quadratic time bound nonquadratic. What good is it to know that our upper bound function is linear or quadratic?

EXAMPLE 26   What is the effect of doubling x on the value of a linear or quadratic function?

Solution   First, suppose $f(x) = mx + b$. To see the effect of doubling x, we write

$$f(2x) = m(2x) + b = 2mx + b \leq 2mx + 2b$$

(if $b > 0$), thus doubling the size of the input will at worst double the running time. With a quadratic function $g(x) = ax^2 + bx + c$, assuming a, b, $c \geq 0$, we get

$$g(2x) = a(4x^2) + b(2x) + c \leq 4ax^2 + 4bx + 4c$$

so doubling the size of the input will at most quadruple the running time.   ■

The Value of Polynomial Time Algorithms

The following example shows the practical effects of the above considerations by discussing four hypothetical programs.

EXAMPLE 27   A professor has four computer programs that deal with a class list. When applied to a list of 30 students, each program runs in approximately one second. Suppose that, for a class of size n, program 1 requires $a \cdot n$ seconds, program 2 requires $b \cdot n^2$ seconds, program 3 requires $c \cdot n^3$ seconds, and program 4 requires $d \cdot 2^n$ seconds. Another professor wishes to use these programs to work with lists of 100 names. How long will each of these programs take?

Solution   Since with 30 students program 1 runs in 1 second, $a \cdot 30 = 1$, so $a = \frac{1}{30}$. Therefore with 100 students, program 1 will require $a \cdot 100 = \frac{100}{30} = 3\frac{1}{3}$ seconds. We reason similarly for program 2, finding that $b(30)^2 = 1$, $b = \frac{1}{900}$; thus for program 2 we use $b \cdot (100)^2 = \frac{100^2}{900} = 11\frac{1}{9}$ seconds. For program 3, since $c(30)^3 = 1$, we get $c = \frac{1}{27000}$. Thus with 100 students, program 3 uses $c \cdot (100)^3 = \frac{1000}{27}$ or about 37 seconds. Because $d \cdot 2^{30} = 1$, we get $d = 2^{-30}$. Thus with 100 students, program 4 uses

$$d \cdot 2^{100} = 2^{-30} \cdot 2^{100} = 2^{70} \text{ seconds}$$

Since $2^{10} = 1024$, we have

$$2^{70} = 2^{7 \cdot 10} = (2^{10})^7 = (1024)^7 > (1000)^7 = 10^{21} = \text{one sextillion}$$

Converting from seconds to centuries, we find that program 4 will take more than 375 billion centuries!   ■

We call an algorithm a **polynomial time algorithm** relative to a numerical parameter n of the input if there is a polynomial function g such that, for each n, $g(n)$ is greater than or equal to the time required to apply the algorithm to an arbitrary problem with this parameter value. **Exponential time algorithms** are similarly defined. In Example 27, the first three programs were based on polynomial time algorithms, and the last program was based on an exponential time algorithm. The example shows us that while polynomial time algorithms may consume significantly more time when the size of the input data is increased, a modest increase in the size of a problem should not render them useless. However, an increase in size that would have an unimportant effect on the time consumed by a polynomial time algorithm can render an exponential time algorithm totally impractical. You may find that looking back at the graphs in Figures 11, 12, and 13 helps you visualize these differences.

B   *Order of Growth of Functions*

Example 27 suggests that if we need to choose an algorithm for use with relatively large amounts of data, we are likely to prefer a linear algorithm to a quadratic one, a quadratic algorithm to a cubic one, and any polynomial time algorithm to an exponential time algorithm. We can, however, give examples of special cases in which these preferences might be reversed.

EXAMPLE 28   Show that when used on 10 or 20 data items, an algorithm that uses $n^2 + 20n$ time units on n data items is preferable to one that uses $100n + 50$ time units.

Solution   For $n = 10$ or 20, the quadratic algorithm uses $10^2 + 20 \cdot 10 = 300$ or $(20)^2 + 20 \cdot 20 = 800$ time units, while the linear algorithm uses 1050 or 2050 time units.   ∎

Even in these cases, however, increasing the number of data items will reverse the relationship. When comparing two computer programs, we are interested in knowing whether one takes twice (or some other multiple) as long as the other. Thus our interest is in the ratio of the time consumed by one program to the time consumed by the other.

EXAMPLE 29   Show that as the number n of data items gets large, the ratio of the time taken by the quadratic algorithm in Example 28 to the time taken by the linear algorithm in Example 28 "becomes infinite," that is, gets larger than any constant we specify.

Solution   The ratio may be written as

$$\frac{n^2 + 20n}{100n + 50} = \frac{n^2\left(1 + \dfrac{20}{n}\right)}{n\left(100 + \dfrac{50}{n}\right)} = n \cdot \frac{1 + \dfrac{20}{n}}{100 + \dfrac{50}{n}}$$

As we increase n, we make the fractions $\frac{20}{n}$ and $\frac{50}{n}$ closer and closer to zero, so the ratio gets closer and closer to $n \cdot \frac{1}{100}$, which is $\frac{n}{100}$. However, $\frac{n}{100}$ will be larger than any constant c we specify, so long as n is more than $100c$. ∎

EXAMPLE 30   Draw a Cartesian graph that illustrates the conclusion of Example 29.

Solution   See Figure 21. ∎

Figure 21   A comparison of $n^2 + 20n$ and $100n + 50$.

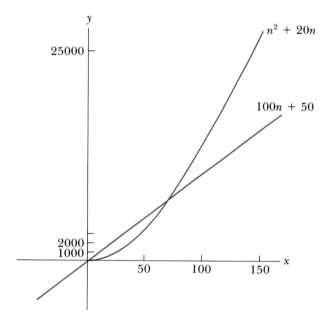

We can make the same sort of argument with any two polynomial functions of different degree; eventually the one of higher degree will become larger (in absolute value) than the one of smaller degree. In fact, the (absolute value of the) ratio of the higher-degree polynomial to the lower-degree polynomial will become infinite—larger than any number we may choose. If all functions that came up in studying algorithms were polynomials, this would make it easy for us to choose general purpose algorithms: We would choose those of lowest degree. However, other functions, such as

$$f(x) = x\log_2 x, \ g(x) = 2^x, \ h(x) = 2^{\sqrt{x}}, \text{ and so on}$$

can arise in studying algorithms. It isn't possible to assign a degree to each of these, but fortunately there is a way to classify functions as to their *order of growth*. (We shall define the idea of order later.) The essential idea is that $f(x)$ grows faster than $g(x)$ if, as x gets large, the ratio of $f(x)$ to $g(x)$ exceeds any constant we choose. What would we mean by "$f(x)$ doesn't grow faster than $g(x)$"? We would mean that we *can* choose a constant such that $f(x)/g(x)$ doesn't exceed that constant for large x-values. There is a special notation, called *big Oh notation*, used to express this idea.

> We say that f is **big Oh** of g, or $f(x)$ is $O(g(x))$, or
> f is $O(g)$, if there is a constant $c > 0$ and a
> number X such that for all $x > X$ $f(x) \leq cg(x)$.

Intuitively, we are saying that, at least for large enough x-values, $f(x)$ is no more than a numerical multiple of $g(x)$. Thus x^2 is $O(x^3)$ (because $x^2 < 1 \cdot x^3$ for $x > 1$), and $2x$ is $O(\frac{1}{3}x)$ (because $2x \leq 6\left(\frac{1}{3}x\right)$ for all x). In an unfortunate (for the beginner) choice of notation, people also write "$f(x) = O(g(x))$" to mean "$f(x)$ is $O(g(x))$." Notice that $f(x) = O(g(x))$ is not an equation in the usual sense. If you try to interpret it as an equation, you will become confused! While this notation can be confusing to the beginner, it also has the potential to be very useful in more advanced situations and is quite standard. Thus we shall not avoid it.

EXAMPLE 31   Show that the function given by $g(n) = 3n^2 + 2n$ is $O(n^2)$.

Solution   Note that for $n \geq 1$,

$$g(n) = 3n^2 + 2n \leq 3n^2 + 2n^2 = 5n^2$$

since $2n < 2n^2$. Therefore, if c is 5 and N is 1, for all $n > N$ it is the case that $g(n) \leq cn^2$. Therefore $g(n)$ is $O(n^2)$.   ■

Order of Growth

We now define when two functions have the same order of growth:

> $f(x)$ **is of order** $g(x)$ means that $f(x) = O(g(x))$ *and* $g(x) = O(f(x))$.

We say an algorithm is an $O(f)$ algorithm if its running time has an $O(f)$ upper bound. It is an **order** f algorithm if the running time has both lower and upper bounds of order f. Our algorithm that found the smallest element in a list of n numbers was an $O(n)$ algorithm; it was also of order n. Our algorithm to sort a list of n numbers was an $O(n^2)$ algorithm. It is also of order n^2.

How would we show that a function $g(x)$ is *not* $O(f(x))$? We would need to show that there is no constant c such that

$$g(x) \leq cf(x)$$

for large x-values. One way to show this is by showing that the ratio $g(x)/f(x)$ becomes infinite as x gets large, because this would imply the impossible result that the constant c is greater than or equal to a function that is becoming infinite. Correspondingly, we could show that $f(x)/g(x)$ approaches 0 as x becomes infinite.

EXAMPLE 32   Which of the following functions are $O(x^2)$? Which of them are of order x^2?

(a) $f(x) = 2x\sqrt{x}$

(b) $f(x) = x^2 + \sqrt{x}$

(c) $f(x) = x^3 + \sqrt{x}$

(d) $f(x) = (x^3 + 1)/x$

Solution

(a) Since $\sqrt{x} \leq x$, $2x\sqrt{x} \leq 2x^2$ when $x \geq 1$. Therefore $f(x) = O(x^2)$. Since $2x\sqrt{x}/x^2 = 2/\sqrt{x}$, and this ratio approaches zero as x becomes infinite, x^2 cannot be $O(2x\sqrt{x})$. Therefore $f(x)$ is not of order x^2.

(b) Since $\sqrt{x} < x^2$ for $x > 1$, $f(x)$ is $O(x^2)$, and since $x^2 + \sqrt{x} > x^2$ for $x > 0$, x^2 is $O(f(x))$. Thus $f(x)$ is of order x^2.

(c) Since there is no number c such that $x^3 < cx^2$ for all large x, $f(x)$ is not $O(x^2)$. Thus $f(x)$ is not of order x^2 either.

(d) Since $f(x) = x^2 + \frac{1}{x}$ and $\frac{1}{x} < x^2$, we see that $f(x) = O(x^2)$ and $x^2 = O(f(x))$, so $f(x)$ has order x^2. ■

We introduced the big Oh notation in order to deal with functions other than polynomial functions. Let us analyze how exponential and logarithmic functions relate to polynomial functions. Figure 18 shows that $x < 2^x$ for all x, and Figure 12 shows that when x is large enough, $2^x > x^2$. The figures don't *prove* these relations, but they suggest that x and x^2 are $O(2^x)$ but are not of the same order as 2^x. Theorem 5 shows that this is the case.

Theorem 5   For any real number r, $x^r = O(2^x)$, but $2^x/x^r$ becomes infinite as x gets large. Further, $\log_2(x) = O(x^r)$ for any real number $r > 0$, but $\dfrac{\log_2(x)}{x^r}$ approaches zero as x gets large.

Proof   (May be omitted without loss of continuity.) In the next chapter we will learn a technique that will let us prove $y^2 < 2^y$ for large y. Dividing the inequality by y gives

$$y < \frac{2^y}{y}$$

Thus, as y gets large, so does $\dfrac{2^y}{y}$. Since the ratio $2^y/y$ becomes infinite as y gets large, substituting $y = \log_2(x)$ gives that $x/\log_2(x)$ becomes infinite as x gets large. Now take logarithms of the ratio $2^x/x^r$ to get

$$\log_2\left(\frac{2^x}{x^r}\right) = \log_2(2^x) - \log_2(x^r) = x - r\log_2(x)$$

Since $\dfrac{x}{\log_2(x)}$ becomes infinite as x gets large, $x - r\log_2(x)$ becomes infinite as well. Since $\log_2(2^x/x^r)$ becomes infinite, $2^x/x^r$ becomes infinite as well. In particular, since $2^x/x^r$ becomes infinite, we see that $x^r < 1 \cdot 2^x$ for large enough x, so that $x^r =$

$O(2^x)$. The last sentence in the statement of the theorem may be derived from the equation $y^{1/r} \leq 2^y$ (for large y) by observing that $z < w$ implies $z^r < w^r$ for $r > 0$ and letting $y = \log_2(x)$.   ∎

EXAMPLE 33   Which of the following functions are $O(x^2)$? Which of them are of order x^2?

(a) $f(x) = 2^{x/2}$ (b) $f(x) = \log_2(x)$ (c) $f(x) = 3x\log_2(x)$

Solution

(a) Since $2^x/x^2$ becomes infinite, we suspect that $2^{x/2}/x^2$ also becomes infinite as x becomes large. To prove it, we note that the square of $2^{x/2}/x^2$ is $2^x/x^4$, and by Theorem 5, this ratio becomes infinite. Therefore $f(x)$ is not $O(x^2)$ and not of order x^2.

(b) Since $\log_2(x) < x$, certainly $\log_2(x) < x^2$ for $x > 0$. Thus $f(x) = O(x^2)$. However, since $\log_2(x)/x^2$ approaches zero as x gets large, x^2 cannot be $O(\log_2(x))$. Therefore $\log_2(x)$ is not of order x^2.

(c) Since $\log_2(x) < x$, $3x\log_2(x) < 3x^2$, so $f(x)$ is $O(x^2)$. However, x^2 is not $O(3x\log_2(x))$ (because $3x\log_2(x)/x^2$ approaches zero as x gets large), and therefore $3x\log_2(x)$ is not of order x^2.   ∎

The chart in Table 2 shows common families of functions and their names in increasing order—each function in the chart is big Oh of all functions below it. The *polylog* functions mentioned in the chart have become very important recently in the analysis of computer programs in which many operations are carried out in parallel.

Table 2   Typical functions in increasing order of growth.

Standard Example of Function	Name
1	constant
$\log_2(\log_2(n))$	log-log
$\log_2(n)$	logarithmic
$(\log_2(n))^k$	polylog
$\sqrt[k]{n}$	root
n	linear
n^2	quadratic
n^k	polynomial
2^n	exponential
$n!$	factorial

Concepts Review

1. A function with a rule of the form $f(x) = ax^n + bx^{n-1} + \cdots + cx + d$ is called a(n) _____ function of _____ n.

2. A quadratic function is a polynomial function of degree _____.

3. A linear function is a polynomial function of degree _____.

4. We say that $f(n)$ is a(n) _____ _____ to the running time of an algorithm operating on n data items and $g(n)$ is a(n) _____ _____ to the running time if the running time with n data items is greater than or equal to $f(n)$ and less than or equal to $g(n)$.

5. A polynomial function grows [(choose one of the following to fill in the blank) at about the same rate, significantly more slowly than, significantly more quickly than] _____ an exponential function.

6. We say that $f(x)$ is _____ if there is a constant c such that $f(x) \le cg(x)$ for large x-values.

7. The interpretation of big Oh notation is that "$f(x)$ is $O(g(x))$" means that f doesn't grow significantly _____ than g.

8. The function f is of order g if f is _____ and g is _____.

9. If $f(x) = \log_2(x)$ and $g(x) = x^r$ with $r > 0$, then [choose $f(x)$ or $g(x)$] _____ is $O([$choose $f(x)$ or $g(x)]$ _____).

10. If $f(x) = 2^x$ and $g(x) = x^r$, then [choose $f(x)$ or $g(x)$] _____ is $O([$choose $f(x)$ or $g(x)]$ _____).

Exercises

A 1. Algorithm Bubbleup below has a predictable effect on the last entry of the list. What is this effect? Apply this algorithm to the list 4,3,2,1 and show the list that results.

Algorithm Bubbleup

Input: A list of n numbers

Output: A list of the same numbers in which the last element of the list is _____.

Procedure: For each position i from 2 to n:

If the element in position $i-1$ of the list is larger than the element in position i of the list, then exchange these two elements and go on to the next i.

Otherwise, just go on to the next i.

2. Algorithm Trickledown below has a predictable effect on the first entry of the list. What is this effect? Apply this algorithm to the list 4,3,2,1 and show the list that results.

Algorithm Trickledown

> Input: A list of n numbers
> Output: A list of the same numbers in which the first element of the list is ____.
> Procedure: For each position i from position $n-1$ down to position 1:
>> If the element in position $i + 1$ of the list is smaller than the element in position i, then exchange these two elements and go on to the next i.
>> Otherwise, go on to the next i.

3. How many comparisons are made in the algorithm of Exercise 1? What is the maximum number of exchanges made?

4. How many comparisons are made in the algorithm of Exercise 2? What is the maximum number of exchanges made?

5. Apply the following algorithm to the list 2,1,5,4,3. Explain what the algorithm does to an arbitrary list of numbers.

Algorithm Bubblesort

> Remark: This is not a good algorithm to use in practice.
> Input: A list of n numbers
> Output: A list of the same numbers in _____.
> Procedure: For each i from n down to 2:
>> Apply algorithm Bubbleup to the portion of the list from position 1 to position i.

6. Apply the following algorithm to the list 3,1,5,2,4. Explain what the algorithm does to an arbitrary list of numbers.

Algorithm Tricklesort

> Remark: This is not a good algorithm to use in practice.
> Input: A list of n numbers
> Output: A list of the same numbers in _____.
> Procedure: For each i from 1 to $n-1$:
>> Apply algorithm Trickledown to the portion of the list from position i to position n.

7. How many comparisons are made in the process of applying algorithm Bubblesort to a list of n numbers?

8. How many comparisons are made in the process of applying algorithm Tricklesort to a list of n numbers?

9. What is the maximum number of exchanges that could be made in the process of applying algorithm Bubblesort to a list of n numbers?

10. What is the maximum number of exchanges that could be made in the process of applying algorithm Tricklesort to a list of n numbers?

11. Two algorithms each take one second on 20 data items. If the time used for n data items is cn^2 for algorithm 1 and $d \cdot 2^n$ for algorithm 2, how long does each algorithm take on 40 data items?

12. Two algorithms each take one second on 20 data items. If the time used for n data items is cn^3 for algorithm 1 and $d \cdot 3^n$ for algorithm 2, how long does each algorithm take on 40 data items?

13. A sorting algorithm that takes $c(n^2 - n)$ seconds on n data items was observed to run for 20 seconds with 64 data items. Another sorting algorithm that takes $dn\log_2(n)$ seconds on n data items was observed to run for 30 seconds with 64 data items. Which method is better to use with 128 data items? With 1024 data items?

14. A sorting algorithm that takes $c(n^2 - n)$ seconds on n data items was observed to run for 1 second with 20 data items. A method that takes $dn\log_2(n)$ seconds on n data items was observed to run for 10 seconds with 20 data items. Which algorithm is better to use for 100 data items? With 1000 data items?

B 15. For each pair of functions below, find a constant c such that $f(x) \leq cg(x)$ for $x > 1$.
   (a) $f(x) = x^2 + x$, $g(x) = x^2$.
   (b) $f(x) = 2\sqrt{x} + 1$, $g(x) = x + x^2$
   (c) $f(x) = x^2 + x + 1$, $g(x) = 2x^3$
   (d) $f(x) = x\sqrt{x} + x^2$, $g(x) = x^2$

16. For each pair of functions below, find a constant c such that $f(n) \leq cg(n)$ for $n > 1$.
   (a) $f(n) = 12n + 3$, $g(n) = 2n - 1$
   (b) $f(n) = n^2 - n + 1$, $g(n) = n^2/2$
   (c) $f(n) = 5n + 1$, $g(n) = (n^2 - n)/2$
   (d) $f(n) = 5\sqrt{n} - 1$, $g(n) = n - \sqrt{n}$

For each pair of functions in Problems 17–24, either $f(x) = O(g(x))$ or $g(x) = O(f(x))$, but not both. Determine which is the case.

17. $f(x) = (x^2 - x)/2$, $g(x) = 6x$

18. $f(x) = x + 2\sqrt{x}$, $g(x) = x^2$

19. $f(x) = x + \log_2(x)$, $g(x) = x\sqrt{x}$

20. $f(x) = x^2 + 3x + 4$, $g(x) = x^3$

21. $f(x) = x\log_2(x)$, $g(x) = x\sqrt{x}/2$

22. $f(x) = x + \log_2(x)$, $g(x) = \sqrt{x}$

23. $f(x) = 2(\log_2(x))^2$, $g(x) = \log_2(x) + 1$

24. $f(x) = 4x\log_2(x) + x$, $g(x) = (x^2 - x)/2$

True or false

_____ 25. $x^2 = O(x^3)$

_____ 26. $n^3 = O(n^2(1 + n^2))$

_____ 27. $x^3 = O(x^2)$

_____ 28. $n^2(1 + \sqrt{n}) = O(n^2)$

_____ 29. $2x^2 + 1 = O(x^2)$

_____ 30. $n^2(1 + \sqrt{n}) = O(n^2\log_2(n))$

_____ 31. $x\log_2(x) = O(x^2)$

_____ 32. $3n^2 + \sqrt{n} = O(n^2)$

_____ 33. $x\log_2(x) = O(x\sqrt{x})$

_____ 34. $3n^2 + \sqrt{n} = O(n + n\sqrt{n} + \sqrt{n})$

_____ 35. $\sqrt{x} = O(\log_2(x))$

_____ 36. $\log_2(n) + \sqrt{n} = O(n)$

_____ 37. $\log_2(x) = O(\sqrt{x})$

_____ 38. $\sqrt{n}\log_2(n) = O(n)$

_____ **39.** $x^{-1} = O(\log_2(x))$ _____ **40.** $n + \sqrt{n} = O(\sqrt{n} \log_2(n))$

_____ **41.** $\log_2(x) = O(x^{-1/2})$ _____ **42.** $\log_2(n) = O(1/n)$

In Exercises 43–50, each function is of order x^k or n^k for some k. What is the smallest such real number k?

43. $x^2 + x$ **44.** $n + \sqrt{n}$

45. $x^2 + x \log_2(x)$ **46.** $\log_2(n) + \sqrt{n}$

47. $\dfrac{x^2 + 2}{1 + x^2}$ **48.** $\dfrac{n^2 + 2n + 1}{3n - 2}$

49. $\dfrac{x^2 + 1}{1 + 2^{-x}}$ **50.** $\dfrac{n^3 + 2^{-n}}{1 + 2n}$

51. For each part of Exercise 15, determine whether the two functions have the same order.

52. For each part of Exercise 16, determine whether the two functions have the same order.

For each pair of functions in Exercises 53–60, explain as carefully as possible what happens to the ratio of $f(x)/g(x)$ or $f(n)/g(n)$ as x or n becomes infinite.

53. $f(x) = 2x + 1$, $g(x) = x/3 - 1$

54. $f(n) = n^2$, $g(n) = n + \sqrt{n} + 2^n$

55. $f(x) = x^2 + 2x$, $g(x) = 100x - 3$

56. $f(n) = n^2 + 1$, $g(n) = 3n^2 + \sqrt{n}$

57. $f(x) = x + \sqrt{x}$, $g(x) = 4x + 2$

58. $f(n) = n \log_2(n) + n^2$, $g(n) = n(\log_2(n))^2 + 1$

59. $f(x) = 2x - 1$, $g(x) = x^2 + 3x + 6$

60. $f(n) = 2n - 1$, $g(n) = 4n + 6$

Problems

1. For each function below, find the smallest integer k and the smallest real number k such that $f(x) = O(x^k)$, or explain why there is no such k.

  (a) $f(x) = \sqrt{x} + 1$ (b) $f(x) = 2^{x/2}$ (c) $f(x) = \log_3(x)$

  (d) $f(x) = 2^{-x}$ (e) $f(x) = \dfrac{x^2 + 1}{x - 2}$ (f) $f(x) = \dfrac{1 + x}{2 + e^{-x}}$

2. For each function below, find the smallest integer k and the smallest real number k such that $f(x) = O(x^k)$, or explain why there is no such k.

  (a) $f(x) = \dfrac{x^2 + x}{x + \sqrt{x}}$ (b) $f(x) = \dfrac{1}{1 + x^2}$ (c) $f(x) = \log_3(x)$

  (d) $f(x) = 2^{-x}$ (for $x \geq 0$)   (e) $f(x) = \dfrac{x}{1 + e^{-x}}$ (f) $f(x) = \dfrac{x \log_2(x)}{1 + x}$

3. Why is $n^2 + \sqrt{n} = O(n^3 - n)$?

4. Explain why $n \cdot \log_2(n) + 2n$ is $O(n\sqrt{n})$.

5. Interpret the "equation" $O(f + g) = O(f) + O(g)$ in such a way that it represents a true statement.

6. Interpret the "equation" $O(f \cdot g) = O(f) \cdot O(g)$ in such a way that it represents a true statement.

7. Table 2 indicates that $n!$ grows faster than 2^n, meaning that $n!/2^n$ becomes infinite as n becomes large. Explain why. What if you replace 2^n by b^n for an arbitrary base b?

8. Express the definition of $f = O(g)$ using quantifiers, the notation of logic, and $<$ and $=$ signs.

9. Consider the problem of computing a table of distances along roads between cities. Use $T(i,j)$ to stand for the distance between city i and city j. For two cities not connected by a road, $T(i,j)$ is the smallest sum of distances between intermediate cities that are connected by roads and lead from city i to city j. The algorithm below, starting with the correct value $T(i,j)$ for cities connected by a road but the value $T(i,j) = \infty$ (or a ridiculously large number) for cities not connected by a road, makes successive approximations to the correct values for $T(i,j)$ until finally all values are correct. What is the smallest k such that for n cities the time taken by the algorithm is $O(n^k)$?

Algorithm Distance
    Input: A table D in which $D(i,j)$ is the distance from city i to city j if a road connects them.
    Output: A table T in which $T(i,j)$ is the distance from city i to city j for any cities.
    Procedure: Start with $T(i,j) = D(i,j)$ for each i and j connected by a road and $T(i,j) = \infty$ otherwise.
        For each i from 1 to n (i will be the number of roads we might use to get between two cities):
            For each j from 1 to n
                For each k from 1 to n
                    For each h from 1 to n
                        If $T(j,h) + D(h,k) < T(j,k)$ then
                            Let $T(j,k) = T(j,h) + D(h,k)$
                        Otherwise don't change anything
                    Go on to the next h
                Go on to the next k
            Go on to the next j
        Go on to the next i.

10. By using only D and replacing the symbol T with D each time it occurs in algorithm Distance in Problem 9, you may reduce the running time of algorithm Distance to $O(n^3 \log_2(n))$. Write down the algorithm (leaving out the now inaccurate parenthetical information) and explain why the number of steps is $O(n^3 \log_2(n))$.

11. It is possible to use a clever trick to carry out the process of Problems 9 and 10 in $O(n^3)$ steps. Find the trick, describe how this version of the algorithm works and explain why it takes $O(n^3)$ steps. (*Hint:* Study algorithm Reach in Section 3-1.)

Chapter 4
Review Exercises

1. Write each function whose rule is given below as a relation with domain $\{0, 1, 2, 3, 4\}$.
   (a) $f(x) = (x-2)^2$ (b) $g(x) = 2^x$ (c) $h(x) = |3-x|$

2. Classify the functions from D to R specified below as one-to-one, onto, both, or neither. Give the image of each function.
   (a) $D = \{0,1,2,3\}$ $R = \{a,b,c\}$ $f = \{(0,a), (1,b), (2,a), (3,c)\}$
   (b) $D = \{0,1,2,3\}$ $R = \{a,b,c\}$ $g = \{(0,a), (1,b), (2,a), (3,b)\}$
   (c) $D = \{0,1,2,3\}$ $R = \{a,b,c,d\}$ $h = \{(0,d), (1,c), (2,d), (3,a)\}$
   (d) $D = \{0,1,2,3\}$ $R = \{a,b,c,d\}$ $f = \{(0,c), (1,d), (2,b), (3,a)\}$
   (e) $D = \{0,1,2,3\}$ $R = \{a,b,c,d,e\}$ $g = \{(0,a), (1,c), (2,b), (3,e)\}$

3. Draw the digraph of each function given in Exercise 2 and explain how it illustrates your answer in Exercise 2.

4. Classify each of the following relations as a function with domain $\{0,1,2,3\}$ or not.
   (a) $\{(0,1), (1,2), (2,1), (3,0)\}$ (b) $\{(0,1), (1,0), (2,3), (3,0), (0,3)\}$
   (c) $\{(0,5), (1,4), (2,3), (3,2)\}$ (d) $\{(0,1), (1,2), (3,4)\}$

5. Draw the digraph of each relation with domain $\{0,1,2,3\}$ given in Exercise 4, assuming that the range and image are equal.

6. The floor and ceiling functions were defined in Exercises 13 and 14 of Section 4-1. If $f(x) = \dfrac{\lfloor x \rfloor + \lceil x \rceil}{2}$, for what values of x is $f(x) = x$?

7. If $f(x) = x^5 - 4x^3 + x^2 + 2x + 1$, $h(x) = 2x^3 + 2x^2 - 6x - 3$, and $g(x) = x^3 + x^2 - 2x + 1$, do any two of these rules define the same function on the domain $\{-2, -1, 0, 1, 2\}$?

8. If $s_i = i(i-1)$ for $i \geq 0$, find the zero$^\text{th}$ term, the fourth term, and the first five terms of this sequence.

9. Find $\displaystyle\sum_{i=1}^{5} 2^{-i}$.

10. Find $\displaystyle\sum_{i=1}^{25} (2i-3)$.

11. Find $\displaystyle\sum_{i=3}^{25} (2i-3)$.

12. If $\displaystyle\sum_{i=1}^{n} a_i = 33$ and $\displaystyle\sum_{i=1}^{n} b_i = 17$, find $\displaystyle\sum_{i=1}^{n} (5a_i - 4b_i)$.

13. Sketch the Cartesian graphs of the functions below and decide which is larger for large values of x. (Use scales on your axes that let you show this behavior in your graph.)
    (a) $f(x) = x^2 + 4x + 2$ $g(x) = 2x^2 - 3$
    (b) $f(x) = x^2$ $g(x) = 2\sqrt{x}$
    (c) $f(x) = \sqrt{x}$ $g(x) = \log_2(x^3)$

14. If $f = \{(a,1), (b,2), (d,3), (c,2), (e,4)\}$ and $g = \{(a,a), (b,a), (c,d), (d,c), (e,e)\}$, what is $f \circ g$?

15. If $f(x) = x - 2$ and g is a function whose domain and range are sets of real numbers, then how does the (Cartesian) graph of $f \circ g$ relate to the (Cartesian) graph of g? How does the graph of $g \circ f$ relate to the graph of g?

16. If $f(x) = (x-1)^3 + 4$, find a rule for the inverse of f. If the domain of f is the set of all real numbers, what is the domain of f^{-1}?

17. Find the binary representation of 13 and 14.

18. Find the decimal representation of the numbers whose binary representations are 1010 and 10001.

19. On the domain of all real numbers between -2 and 2, the function given by $f(x) = 3^x$ is one-to-one. Sketch the graph of f and the line $y = x$ using the same axes, and then use these two graphs to sketch the graph of the inverse function of f.

20. Explain what is in List(Position) after we perform the following algorithm.

   Algorithm Unknown
Input:	A list of n numbers List(1),List(2), . . . ,List(n) not in any special order and a number $j \leq n$.
Output:	A single integer whose name is Position.
Procedure:	Begin with Position = 1.
	For each number i from 2 to j (if there are any):
	If List(i) > List(Position), then let Position = i.
	Go on to the next i. '

21. How many comparisons are made in carrying out algorithm Unknown of Exercise 20 on the list 4,3,7,17,14,8,2 with $j = 5$? In terms of n and j, how many comparisons are made in carrying out algorithm Unknown on a list of length n? What is the maximum number of times we change the value of Position?

22. Apply algorithm Movearound below to the list 4,3,7,17,14,8,2. What list results as output?

   Algorithm Movearound
Input:	A list of n numbers $L(1), L(2)$, . . . ,$L(n)$ not in any special order.
Output:	A list, also called L, of the same numbers.
Procedure:	For each i from 1 to $n - 1$ (if any):
	Apply Unknown to L with $j = n - i + 1$.
	Exchange $L(j)$ with L(Position).
	Go on to the next i.

23. With a list of length n, what is the output of algorithm Movearound in Exercise 22? How many comparisons are made by algorithm Movearound? What is the maximum number of changes of Position made? What is the number of exchanges made?

24. Assume that it takes three times as long to exchange two elements of a list as it takes to compare two elements or to change the value of a variable. (This is a realistic assumption.) Why should you prefer algorithm Movearound to the algorithm Bubblesort of Exercise 5 (or Tricklesort of Exercise 6) of Section 4-3?

25. Three sorting algorithms to sort n items take $a\left(\dfrac{n}{2}\right)^3$, $\dfrac{bn(n+1)}{2}$, and $cn\log_2(n)$ seconds, respectively. Sorting 8 items took 1, 2, and 3 seconds, respectively, with the three

algorithms. Which algorithm is fastest in sorting 16 items? Which is fastest in sorting 32 or more items?

26. For each pair of functions below, find a number c so that $f(x) \le c(g(x))$ for all $x \ge 2$.
    (a) $f(x) = x\sqrt{x}$ $\qquad\qquad$ $g(x) = (x-1)^2$
    (b) $f(x) = x^2$ $\qquad\qquad$ $g(x) = 2(x-1)^2$
    (c) $f(x) = \log_2(x^2 + 2x)$ $\quad$ $g(x) = \sqrt{x}$

27. Which pairs of functions in Exercise 26 have the same order of growth?

28. For each pair of functions below, state whether $f(x) = O(g(x))$, $g(x) = O(f(x))$, f and g have the same order of growth, or none of these.
    (a) $f(x) = x^2 + 3x + 4$ $\qquad$ $g(x) = 6x + 7$
    (b) $f(x) = \sqrt{x}$ $\qquad\qquad$ $g(x) = \log_2(x + 3)$
    (c) $f(x) = x\sqrt{x}$ $\qquad\qquad$ $g(x) = x^2 - x$
    (d) $f(x) = x + x\sqrt{x}$ $\qquad$ $g(x) = 4x\log_2(x^2 + 1)$
    (e) $f(x) = \dfrac{x^2 + 2}{x + 2^{-x}}$ $\qquad$ $g(x) = x + 3$
    (f) $f(x) = 2^x - x^2$ $\qquad$ $g(x) = x^4 + x^2$

*T*he principle of mathematical induction is the primary tool used to prove facts about all the natural numbers. It is not, however, just a tool for number theorists. When we want to verify the truth of a formula involving a natural number n, we need to prove a fact for all natural numbers n. When we want to show that every graph with n vertices has a certain property, we need to prove a fact for all natural numbers n. When we want to demonstrate that a computer program works for any size input, we need to prove a fact for all input sizes—that is, all natural numbers.

Mathematical induction has become far more widely used as computer scientists have employed the idea of definition by induction (called recursive definition) in more and more ways. Mathematical induction lies at the heart of the definitions of modern programming languages. Recursive programming, an important programming technique, is based on recursive definitions of the algorithms to be followed by the programs.

Studying induction gives new meaning to the problem-solving strategy known as *divide and conquer*. Whenever we see how to break up a complicated problem into similar but smaller problems until we get problems so small that we know how to solve them, we are using an inductive strategy. Similarly, whenever we see a way to solve a small version of a problem and how to build the solutions of small problems into the solutions for larger and larger ones, we are again using an inductive strategy. Mathematical induction is the natural tool for demonstrating that such strategies work.

Mathematical induction is a technique we shall use in each of the remaining chapters of this book. Among all the ideas of discrete mathematics, mathematical induction may be the most powerful.

Section 5-1
Proving Algebraic
Statements by Induction

A   Mathematical Induction and Sum Formulas

In one idealized model of a parallel computer, there are many individual processors, each a "computer on a chip." One "master" processor is in control of the whole system. In this model, each processor may send a message to exactly two other processors, and each (except the master processor) may receive a message from exactly one processor. When the master processor has a message to send to the other computers, it first sends it to its two processors, they send it to their two processors in the next stage, and so on. At each stage, machines that have just received the message send it to the two processors they communicate to. We may show that after n such stages of sending messages, the number of processors aware of the message is

$$1 + 2 + 4 + \cdots + 2^n \qquad \text{or} \qquad 2^0 + 2^1 + 2^2 + \cdots + 2^n$$

How can we find this sum? No trick such as Gauss's in Chapter 4 seems to help. However, if we experiment with the sum for various values of n, we see a pattern: $1 + 2 = 3$; $1 + 2 + 4 = 3 + 4 = 7$; $1 + 2 + 4 + 8 = 7 + 8 = 15$; $1 + 2 + 4 + 8 + 16 = 15 + 16 = 31$; $1 + 2 + 4 + 8 + 16 + 32 = 31 + 32 = 63$; and so on. In each of these cases, we added the preceding sum to the term 2^k. It always turned out that the preceding sum was $2^k - 1$. When we added 2^k, we got $(2^k - 1) + 2^k = 2^k + 2^k - 1 = 2 \cdot 2^k - 1 = 2^{k+1} - 1$. It appears that our formula should be

$$1 + 2 + 4 + \cdots + 2^n = 2^{n+1} - 1$$

In our computation, we had a whole sequence of formulas, one formula for each specific value of k that we substituted for n. We saw how each formula could be derived from the immediately preceding one. In other words, we saw how the formula for $n = k$ can be derived from the formula for $n = k - 1$. Thus we expect the pattern to continue forever, so we conclude that the formula is valid for each value of the variable n.

This is the essence of reasoning by mathematical induction. In order to capture the idea behind the argument so that we can use it in other situations, we state the **principle of mathematical induction.**

> Let $s(n)$ be a statement about an integer variable n. If
>   1. the statement $s(1)$ is true, and
>   2. the statement $s(k - 1)$ implies the statement $s(k)$ for each $k > 1$,
> then the statement $s(n)$ is true for all positive integers n.

Now that we have a precise description of the principle behind our argument, let us use it to provide a shorter version of the argument.

EXAMPLE 1 Show that $1 + 2 + 2^2 + \cdots + 2^n = 2^{n+1} - 1$ for each positive integer n.

Solution Let $s(n)$ be the statement $1 + 2 + 2^2 + \cdots + 2^n = 2^{n+1} - 1$. $s(1)$ is the statement $1 + 2 = 2^2 - 1$. Therefore $s(1)$ is true. (The last two sentences are called the **base step** of the proof.)

To show that $s(k - 1)$ implies $s(k)$, we show that $s(l)$ is true whenever $s(k - 1)$ is true. (This is called the **inductive step** of the proof.) Now suppose $s(k - 1)$ is true. (This sentence is called the **inductive hypothesis**.) Thus we are assuming that

$$1 + 2 + 2^2 + \cdots + 2^{k-1} = 2^k - 1$$

(We must show that $s(k)$ (namely $1 + 2 + \cdots + 2^k = 2^{k+1} - 1$) is true. The left-hand side for $s(k)$ ends in 2^k, so the natural thing to do is add 2^k to both sides of the equation that we got from $s(k - 1)$.) Adding 2^k to both sides of the equation for $s(k - 1)$ gives us

$$1 + 2 + 2^2 + \cdots + 2^{k-1} + 2^k = 2^k - 1 + 2^k = 2 \cdot 2^k - 1$$
$$= 2^{k+1} - 1$$

Thus $s(k)$ is true whenever $s(k - 1)$ is true, so $s(k - 1)$ implies $s(k)$.

Therefore, by the principle of mathematical induction, $s(n)$ is true for all positive integers n. That is,

$$1 + 2 + 2^2 + \cdots + 2^n = 2^{n+1} - 1$$

for all positive integers n. (This last paragraph is called the **inductive conclusion**.)

∎

Notice how the proof has three steps. The *base step* is the step that verifies that $s(1)$ is true. The *inductive step* verifies that $s(k - 1)$ implies $s(k)$ by starting with the *inductive hypothesis* that $s(k - 1)$ is true and deriving the truth of $s(k)$. The final step is the *inductive conclusion* that, from the principle of mathematical induction, we may conclude that $s(n)$ is true for all positive integers n. The inductive conclusion is the final step of an inductive proof. It may appear to a casual reader that in an inductive proof we are assuming exactly what we are trying to prove. However, a more careful reader will see that this is not the case; in order to prove that $s(n - 1)$ implies $s(n)$, we must show that *whenever* $s(n - 1)$ is true *then* $s(n)$ is true as well. Therefore, we show that *assuming* the truth of $s(n - 1)$ leads us to conclude the truth of $s(n)$.

Induction with a Different Base

Suppose we try to use induction to prove the statement $s(n)$ given by

$$1 + 2 + \cdots + n - 1 = \frac{n(n - 1)}{2}$$

The left-hand side of the equation is not meaningful unless n is 2 or more. Thus we want to show that $s(n)$ is true for all integers $n \geq 2$ rather than for all positive integers (that is, rather than for all $n \geq 1$). Since we want to prove the statements $s(2)$, $s(3)$, . . . , we want to start with $n = 2$ as our base step. Trying to prove other formulas might lead us in a similar way to other base steps. We accommodate this variety with the following version of the principle of mathematical induction.

> Let $s(n)$ be a statement about an integer variable n. If
> 1. $s(b)$ is true, and
> 2. the statement $s(n - 1)$ implies $s(n)$ for all $n > b$,
> then $s(n)$ is true for all integers $n \geq b$.

EXAMPLE 2 Prove by induction that for $n \geq 2$,

$$1 + 2 + \cdots + n - 1 = \frac{n(n - 1)}{2}$$

Solution The formula holds when $n = 2$, for then it reads $1 = 2 \cdot 1/2$. (This was the base step.) Now assume that the formula holds when $n = k - 1$, giving us

$$1 + 2 + \cdots + (k - 1) - 1 = \frac{(k - 1)(k - 1 - 1)}{2}$$

or

$$1 + 2 + \cdots + k - 2 = \frac{(k - 1)(k - 2)}{2}$$

(That was the inductive hypothesis. Thinking ahead, we note that to get the left-hand side of the formula for $n = k$, we need a $k - 1$ term on the left-hand side. This suggests adding $k - 1$ to both sides of the equation.) Adding $k - 1$ to each side of the equation gives us

$$1 + 2 + \cdots + k - 2 + k - 1 = \frac{(k - 1)(k - 2)}{2} + k - 1$$

$$= \frac{k^2 - 3k + 2 + 2k - 2}{2}$$

$$= \frac{k^2 - k}{2} = \frac{k(k - 1)}{2}$$

This shows the formula holds when $n = k$. (This completes the inductive step.) Therefore, by the principle of mathematical induction, the formula holds for all $n \geq 2$. ∎

EXAMPLE 3 The formula of Example 1 is a special case of the following formula, valid for any number $r \neq 1$.

$$1 + r + \cdots + r^n = \frac{1 - r^{n+1}}{1 - r}$$

Prove this formula for all non-negative integers n.

Solution Our base step will be the case $n = 0$ so that our proof will prove the statement for all non-negative integers, not just for all positive integers. For $n = 0$, the formula yields $1 = \dfrac{1 - r}{1 - r}$, which is certainly true. (This is the base step.)

Now assume the formula is true for $n = k - 1$ (inductive hypothesis); that is, assume that

$$1 + r + r^2 + \cdots + r^{k-1} = \frac{1 - r^{k-1+1}}{1 - r} = \frac{1 - r^k}{1 - r}$$

Adding r^k to both sides (so as to get the sum for the formula with $n = k$ on the left) gives us

$$
\begin{aligned}
1 + r + r^2 + \cdots + r^{k-1} + r^k &= \frac{1 - r^k}{1 - r} + r^k \\
&= \frac{1 - r^k + r^k - r^{k+1}}{1 - r} \\
&= \frac{1 - r^{k+1}}{1 - r}
\end{aligned}
$$

This shows that the formula is true when $n = k$. (This completes the inductive step.) Thus, by the principle of mathematical induction, the formula holds for all non-negative integers n. ∎

The sum in Example 3 is called a **geometric series** with common ratio r. It turns out to be quite important in discrete mathematics and computer science.

B *Proving Inequalities by Induction*

There are a number of important inequalities that can be proved by induction. Practicing with these inequalities will help your understanding of induction; even though the inductive step still consists of doing something (often adding something) to both sides of an equation or inequality, what we must do to both sides is not nearly so clear as it is with sum formulas. We begin with a difficult example.

EXAMPLE 4   Show that $(n + 1)^2 < 2n^2$ for all integers $n \geq 3$.

Solution   (We begin by choosing $n = 3$ for our base step.) If $n = 3$, the formula reads $(3 + 1)^2 < 2 \cdot 3^2$, or $16 < 18$, which is true.

(Next we carry out the inductive step. We begin by making our inductive hypothesis.) Now suppose the inequality is true when $n = k - 1$, so that

$$(k - 1 + 1)^2 < 2(k - 1)^2$$

or

$$k^2 < 2(k^2 - 2k + 1) = 2k^2 - 4k + 2$$

(What should we do now? We compare the inequality above from the case $n = k - 1$ with the inequality we want to prove in the case $n = k$. We want the left-hand side to be $(k + 1)^2$ so that we have the relation with $n = k$ rather than $n = k - 1$. Since $(k + 1)^2 = k^2 + 2k + 1$, the one thing that seems worth trying is adding $2k + 1$ to both sides of the inequality $k^2 < 2k^2 - 4k + 2$.) Adding $2k + 1$ to both sides gives

$$k^2 + 2k + 1 < 2k^2 - 4k + 2 + 2k + 1 = 2k^2 - 2k + 3$$

Since we are working only with those values of k that are greater than 4 (because n is $k - 1$, so $n \geq 3$ gives $k \geq 4$), $2k$ is greater than 3, so $-2k + 3$ is negative. Thus

$$k^2 + 2k + 1 < 2k^2 - 2k + 3 < 2k^2 \qquad \text{or} \qquad (k + 1)^2 < 2k^2$$

Thus whenever the inequality is true for $n = k - 1$ (and $n \geq 3$), the inequality is true for $n = k$ as well. Therefore the inequality is true for all integers $n \geq 3$. ■

The example is interesting in three ways. First, our base step was to verify the inequality for $n = 3$. Second, attempting to use induction led us to consider the inequality $k^2 < 2k^2 - 4k + 2$ and to add $2k + 1$ to the left-hand side. If we hadn't known we wanted to convert the k^2 to $(k + 1)^2$ so as to use induction, we would not have had any way to know it was a good idea to add $2k + 1$ to both sides of the equation. Third, the algebra we needed to apply to finish off the proof was nontrivial; we had to recognize that for the values of k we were considering, the $-2k + 3$ term was negative.

It is useful to note that an apparently trivial change in our statement of the principle of mathematical induction will make the algebraic problems we had in this example "evaporate." In the new version of the principle, we derive the statement $s(k + 1)$ from the statement $s(k)$ rather than deriving the statement $s(k)$ from the statement $s(k - 1)$. The new version of the principle of mathematical induction is as follows.

Suppose $s(n)$ is a statement about an integer variable n. If there is an integer b such that

1. $s(b)$ is true, and
2. the statement $s(k)$ implies the statement $s(k + 1)$ for each $k \geq b$,

then $s(n)$ is true for all $n \geq b$.

EXAMPLE 5 Show that $(n + 1)^2 < 2n^2$ for $n \geq 3$, using this new version of the principle.

Solution If $n = 3$, our formula says that $16 < 18$, which is true. (Now note the change in the inductive hypothesis.) Now suppose the inequality is true when $n = k$, so that

$$(k + 1)^2 < 2k^2 \qquad \text{or} \qquad k^2 + 2k + 1 < 2k^2$$

(For $n = k + 1$ the inequality will be $(k + 2)^2 < 2(k + 1)^2$. Thus we want $k^2 + 4k + 4 < 2(k + 1)^2$, so we add $2k + 3$ to each side of $k^2 + 2k + 1 < 2k^2$.) Adding $2k + 3$ to each side gives us

$$k^2 + 4k + 4 < 2k^2 + 2k + 3$$

(We want the right-hand side to be $2(k + 1)^2 = 2k^2 + 4k + 2$, so we just need to figure out why $2k^2 + 2k + 3 < 2k^2 + 4k + 2$.) Since $k \geq 3$,

$$2k^2 + 2k + 3 \leq 2k^2 + 2k + k \leq 2k^2 + 3k \leq 2k^2 + 4k + 2$$

Therefore

$$k^2 + 4k + 4 < 2k^2 + 4k + 2$$

so that

$$(k + 2)^2 < 2(k + 1)^2$$

Thus our inequality holds for $n = k + 1$, so by the principle of mathematical induction it holds for all $n \geq 3$. ∎

For any given statement, it is not possible to predict whether it will be easier to prove that $s(k - 1)$ implies $s(k)$ or that $s(k)$ implies $s(k + 1)$. Since the algebra will be different, it makes sense to try the other approach if the one you choose first leads to difficulties.

Proving Statements about Order of Growth

We can prove by induction the formula

$$\sum_{i=1}^{n} i^2 = 1^2 + 2^2 + 3^2 + \cdots + n^2 = n(n + 1)(2n + 1)/6$$

for positive integers n. There are similar formulas for sums of cubes, fourth powers, and so on. As you may imagine, the formulas become harder to guess as the exponents get larger. For many purposes, we don't need the actual formula; for example, in analyzing an algorithm, we would most likely need to know only that

$$\sum_{i=1}^{n} i^2 = 1^2 + 2^2 + \cdots + n^2 = O(n^3)$$

Recall this means there is some constant c (a number not depending on n) such that

$$\sum_{i=1}^{n} i^2 \leq cn^3$$

Let us see if we can prove *this* by induction.

EXAMPLE 6   Prove the fact that

$$\sum_{i=1}^{n} i^2 = O(n^3)$$

by using the principle of mathematical induction.

Solution   We wish to prove there is a constant c such that

$$\sum_{i=1}^{n} i^2 \leq cn^3$$

for all positive integers n. How do we decide what to use for c? Experimenting with several values of n, we see that we want to know that

$$\sum_{i=1}^{1} i^2 \leq c \cdot 1^3 = c$$

$$\sum_{i=1}^{2} i^2 \leq c \cdot 2^3 = 8c$$

$$\sum_{i=1}^{3} i^2 \leq c \cdot 3^3 = 27c$$

Expanding the sums on the left gives

$$1 \leq c$$
$$1 + 4 \leq 8c \qquad \text{or} \qquad 5 \leq 8c$$
$$1 + 4 + 9 \leq 27c \qquad \text{or} \qquad 14 \leq 27c$$

Thus it appears that $c = 1$ may work, so we try to prove the statement

$$\sum_{i=1}^{n} i^2 \leq 1 \cdot n^3 = n^3$$

Since

$$\sum_{i=1}^{1} i^2 = 1 \leq 1 \cdot 1^3$$

the inequality is true when $n = 1$.

Now suppose the inequality is true when $n = k$, so that

$$\sum_{i=1}^{k} i^2 \leq k^3$$

Adding $(k + 1)^2$ to both sides of the inequality gives

$$\sum_{i=1}^{k+1} i^2 \leq k^3 + (k + 1)^2$$
$$\leq k^3 + k^2 + 2k + 1$$
$$\leq k^3 + 3k^2 + 3k + 1$$
$$= (k + 1)^3 = 1 \cdot k^3$$

This proves the inequality with $n = k + 1$ as well. Thus by the principle of mathematical induction, the inequality is true for all n, and therefore

$$\sum_{i=1}^{n} i^2 = O(n^3)$$

■ .

Notice that the statement we proved by induction was

$$\sum_{i=1}^{n} i^2 \leq n^3$$

not the statement

$$\sum_{i=1}^{n} i^2 = O(n^3)$$

Thus we needed to have a statement that contained slightly more information than simply

$$\sum_{i=1}^{n} i^2 = O(n^3)$$

in order to use the technique of induction. Once we proved the more detailed statement

$$\sum_{i=1}^{n} i^2 \leq n^3$$

we could immediately conclude that

$$\sum_{i=1}^{n} i^2 = O(n^3)$$

It is not unusual to find that, in order to prove a certain statement, you must first apply induction to prove a slightly more detailed statement, then derive the desired statement from the detailed one you have proved.

Concepts Review

1. The principle of mathematical induction states that if $s(1)$ is true and the statement $s(k - 1)$ _____ the statement _____ for each $k > 1$, then $s(n)$ is true for all integers $n > 0$.

2. The _____ step in an inductive proof consists of verifying $s(1)$ (or verifying $s(b)$ for some b).

3. When we suppose that $s(k - 1)$ is true in an inductive proof, we are making the

   _____ _____.

4. Showing that $s(k - 1)$ implies $s(k)$ is the _____ step of an inductive proof.

5. A(n) _____ series has the form $1 + r + r^2 + \cdots r^n$.

6. The value of the sum $1 + r + r^2 + \cdots + r^n$ is _____.

Exercises

A   1. Identify the base step, the inductive hypothesis, the inductive step, and the inductive conclusion in the proof (below) that

$$0 + 2 + 6 + \cdots + n^2 - n = \frac{n^3 - n}{3}$$

If $n = 1$, the equation becomes $0 = \frac{1 - 1}{3}$, which is true. Therefore, the equation is true when $n = 1$. Now suppose the equation is true when $n = k - 1$. That is, suppose that

$$0 + 2 + 6 + \cdots + (k - 1)^2 - (k - 1) = \frac{(k - 1)^3 - (k - 1)}{3}$$

Adding $k^2 - k$ to both sides of this equation gives

$$0 + 2 + 6 + \cdots + (k - 1)^2 - (k - 1) + k^2 - k = \frac{k^3 - 3k^2 + 3k - 1 - k + 1}{3} + k^2 - k$$

$$= \frac{k^3 - k}{3}$$

Thus our original equation is true when $n = k$. By the principle of mathematical induction, the equation

$$0 + 2 + 6 + \cdots + n^2 - n = \frac{n^3 - n}{3}$$

holds for all positive integers n.

2. Identify the base step, the inductive hypothesis, the inductive step, and the inductive conclusion in the proof (below) that

$$2 + 4 + 6 + \cdots + 2n = n^2 + n$$

If $n = 1$, the formula reads $2 = 1^2 + 1$, which is true. Now assume that the formula is true when $n = k - 1$, so that

$$2 + 4 + \cdots + 2(k - 1) = (k - 1)^2 + k - 1$$

Adding $2k$ to each side gives

$$2 + 4 + \cdots + 2(k - 1) + 2k = (k - 1)^2 + k - 1 + 2k$$
$$= k^2 - 2k + 1 + 3k - 1 = k^2 + k$$

Thus, by the principle of mathematical induction, the formula is true for all positive integers n.

In Exercises 3–12, use induction to prove the formula given for all positive n.

3. $1 + 3 + \cdots + 2n - 1 = n^2$

4. $1 + 4 + 9 + \cdots + n^2 = \dfrac{n(n + 1)(2n + 1)}{6}$

5. $\dfrac{1}{2} + \dfrac{1}{4} + \cdots + \left(\dfrac{1}{2}\right)^n = 1 - \left(\dfrac{1}{2}\right)^n$

6. $3 + 9 + 27 + \cdots + 3^n = \dfrac{3^{n+1} - 3}{2}$

7. $2 - 4 + 8 - 16 + \cdots + (-2)^n = \dfrac{(-2)^{n+1} + 2}{3}$

8. $\dfrac{2}{3} + \dfrac{2}{9} + \cdots + \dfrac{2}{3^n} = 1 - \left(\dfrac{1}{3}\right)^n$

9. $1 + 5 + 9 + \cdots + 4n - 3 = 2n^2 - n$

10. $\dfrac{1}{1 \cdot 2} + \dfrac{1}{2 \cdot 3} + \dfrac{1}{3 \cdot 4} + \cdots + \dfrac{1}{n \cdot (n + 1)} = \dfrac{n}{n + 1}$

11. $1^3 + 2^3 + \cdots + n^3 = \dfrac{n^2(n + 1)^2}{4}$

12. $1 \cdot 2 + 2 \cdot 3 + 3 \cdot 4 + 4 \cdot 5 + \cdots + n(n + 1) = \dfrac{n(n + 1)(n + 2)}{3}$

B   In Exercise 13–16, prove the inequality given.

13. $n^2 < n^3$ if $n > 1$

14. $n^2 + n < n^3$ if $n > 1$

15. $n < 2^n$ if $n \geq 1$

16. $n^2 < 2^n$ if $n > 4$ (In one way of doing this, the result of Example 4 is helpful.)

In Exercises 17–20, prove the "big Oh" statement given.

17. $1^3 + 2^3 + \cdots + n^3 = O(n^4)$

18. $\displaystyle\sum_{i=1}^{n} i^4 = O(n^5)$

19. $1^2 + 3^2 + 5^2 + \cdots + (2n + 1)^2$ (which is $\displaystyle\sum_{i=0}^{n} (2i + 1)^2$) is $O(n^3)$

20. $\displaystyle\sum_{i=1}^{n} (1 + 2i^2)^2 = O(n^5)$.

21. Prove by induction that for any $x > -1$, $(1 + x)^n > 1 + nx$ for all $n \geq 2$.

22. Prove by induction that $\displaystyle\sum_{i=1}^{n} \frac{1}{i^2} \leq 2 - \frac{1}{n}$ for all $n \geq 1$.

Problems

1. Multiply both sides of the inequality $(n - 1)^p < n^p$ by $n - 1$ and use the result to prove that $(n - 1)^{p+1} + n^p < n^{p+1}$. From this, prove that

$$\sum_{i=1}^{n} i^p = O(n^{p+1})$$

2. Show that $\log_2(n) < \sqrt{n}$ for $n \geq 1$.

3. Show that $(n - 1)! > 2^n$ for large values of n, and use this to prove that $2^n/n!$ approaches zero as n becomes infinite.

4. Show that $(n - 1)! > a^n$ for large values of n, and use this to prove that $a^n/n!$ approaches zero as n becomes infinite.

5. Show that $1^3 + 2^3 + 3^3 + \cdots + n^3 = (1 + 2 + 3 + \cdots + n)^2$. How does this relate to Exercise 11 and Gauss's formula?

6. Prove that the number of subsets of an n-element set is 2^n.

7. Find the error in the following proof. Let $s(n)$ be the statement "All elements of an n-element set are equal." Then $s(1)$ is true because all the elements of a one-element set are equal. Now assume that $s(n - 1)$ is true and let N be an n-element set. Then the first $n - 1$ elements of N are equal, and the last $n - 1$ elements of N are equal. Thus all the elements of N must be equal to both the first $n - 1$ elements and the last $n - 1$ elements, so they are all equal.

8. Find the error in the following inductive proof that all positive integers n are equal. The statement is true when $n = 1$, since $1 = 1$. Now suppose the statement is true

for all integers up to and including k. Then $k = k - 1$, so adding 1 to both sides gives $k + 1 = k$. Therefore, by the principle of mathematical induction, $k + 1 = k$ for all integers $k > 0$. Therefore, by transitivity, all positive integers are equal.

9. Prove by using induction appropriately that $n^3 = O\left(\sum_{i=1}^{n} i^2\right)$.

10. (For students who have had calculus.) Use mathematical induction and the product rule to prove the formula for the derivative of x^n.

11. Prove that for any integer $n \geq 0$ and for any two non-negative real numbers a and b,
$$a^n + b^n \geq \left(\frac{a + b}{2}\right)^n.$$

Section 5-2
Other Applications
of Induction

A Strong Induction

When we apply induction in situations rather different from proving formulas, we will sometimes find it convenient to use another form of the principle of mathematical induction, called the **principle of strong** (or *complete*) **mathematical induction.** This form states

Let $s(n)$ be a statement about an integer variable n.
If there is a number b such that
  1. $s(b)$ is true, and
  2. for each $k > b$ the statements $s(b)$ through $s(k - 1)$
  imply the statement $s(k)$,
then $s(n)$ is true for all $n \geq b$.

An example will help to show how strong induction differs from what we've done so far.

EXAMPLE 7 Prove that each positive integer is a prime number, a power of a prime or a product of powers of primes.

Solution Note that a prime number is the first power of a prime, so the statement we are going to prove need only say that each number is a power of a prime or a product of powers of primes. Since we know that $1 = 2^0$, 1 is a power of a prime.

(This was the base step with $b = 1$ and $n = 1$.) Suppose now we know that for all n less than k, n is a prime power or a product of powers of primes. (This was the inductive hypothesis.) Now k is either prime or can be factored as $k = mq$ with $1 < m < k$ and $1 < q < k$. Since m and q are less than k, each is a power of a prime or a product of powers of primes. Thus mq is either a prime power or a product of powers of primes. (This completes the inductive step.) Therefore, by the principle of strong mathematical induction, each positive integer is a power of a prime or a product of powers of primes. (This was the inductive conclusion.)

∎

This example shows how strong induction is useful in proving a statement about an integer n that is not related to the corresponding statement about $n - 1$. For example, the statement that 10 has the prime factorization 2·5 is not related to the statement that 9 is the square of 3. Notice that a proof by strong induction has the same four basic parts that a proof by ordinary induction has. While we could derive the principle of strong mathematical induction from our earlier one, its different appearance makes it useful in situations where we might not have thought to try induction before.

A Non-Numeric Example

EXAMPLE 8   Prove that a connected graph on n vertices has at least $n - 1$ edges.

Solution   We begin by explaining the intuition that would lead us to try strong induction. Notice that removing an edge will either leave a graph that is still connected or a graph with two connected components. If the graph left behind were connected, we would have a connected graph with fewer edges and so be able to induct on the number of edges. On the other hand, if the graph left behind had two connected components, each one would be a connected graph with fewer edges than the original graph, so we should be able to induct on the number of edges again.

This leads us to try to prove the statement by strong induction on the number of edges. To make this easier, we translate the statement "A connected graph with n vertices has at least $n - 1$ edges" into a statement in which the variable is the number of edges rather than the number of vertices. (Since n already stands for the number of vertices and b and k are used in our statement of the principle of strong induction, we use a new letter to stand for the number of edges.) If the graph has m edges, then saying that the number of edges is at least $n - 1$ is saying that $m \geq n - 1$, or $n \leq m + 1$. Thus our statement may be rephrased as "The number of vertices of a connected graph with m edges is at most $m + 1$," and it is this statement we prove by induction on m.

If $m = 0$, we are talking about a connected graph with no edges. Only a single vertex can be a connected graph with no edges, so if $m = 0$, then the number of vertices is no more than $m + 1$. (This was the base step.)

Now suppose the statement is true for all connected graphs with fewer than k edges (that is, when $m < k$). (This is the inductive hypothesis.) Let G be a k-edge graph (that is, a graph with $m = k$) on n vertices. Choose one edge of G and remove it. If the resulting graph is connected, then we have a connected graph with $k - 1$ edges. Since $k - 1$ is less than k, our inductive hypothesis implies that $n \le (k - 1) + 1 = k$, so certainly $m \le k + 1$ is true.

If, on the other hand, removing the edge leaves a disconnected graph G', G' must have exactly two connected components (because more than two components could not be joined back together by just one edge). Suppose the connected components G_1 and G_2 have n_1 and n_2 vertices, respectively, and have m_1 and m_2 edges, respectively. Then $n_1 + n_2 = n$, and $m_1 + m_2 = k - 1$. Since G_1 is connected and $m_1 < k$, our inductive hypothesis implies that $n_1 \le m_1 + 1$. Similarly, $n_2 \le m_2 + 1$. Therefore,

$$n_1 + n_2 \le m_1 + m_2 + 1 + 1$$

so that substituting k for $m_1 + m_2 + 1$ gives

$$n = n_1 + n_2 \le k + 1$$

Thus the statement is true for a graph with k edges as well. (This is the end of the inductive step.) By the principle of mathematical induction, it is true for all graphs. (This is the inductive conclusion.) ∎

Sometimes a proof by strong induction seems to require more than one base step.

EXAMPLE 9 Show that every number greater than or equal to 6 is a sum of a non-negative integral multiple of 3 and a non-negative integral multiple of 4.

Solution We prove the statement $s(n)$ that n is a sum of a non-negative multiple of 3 and a non-negative multiple of 4. (Our base step is the case $n = 6$.) Since $6 = 2 \cdot 3 + 0 \cdot 4$, $s(6)$ is true. Now assume that $s(n)$ is true for all n between 6 and $k - 1$. Since $k - 3 < n$, if $k - 3 \ge 6$, then $k - 3 = a \cdot 3 + b \cdot 4$ for non-negative integers a and b. Then $k = (a + 1)3 + b \cdot 4$. Therefore $s(k)$ is true. (It is tempting to say that by the principle of mathematical induction, $s(k)$ is therefore true for all $k \ge 6$. However, if $k = 7$ or $k = 8$, then $k - 3$ is not greater than or equal to 6. Thus we deal with $k = 7$ and $k = 8$ separately.) Further, if $k - 3 \not\ge 6$ but $k \ge 6$, then $k = 7$ or $k = 8$. Since $7 = 1 \cdot 3 + 1 \cdot 4$ and $8 = 0 \cdot 3 + 2 \cdot 4$, $s(7)$ and $s(8)$ are true as well. (We would have been allowed to use $s(6)$ in proving $s(7)$ and $s(6)$ *and* $s(7)$ in proving $s(8)$, but we didn't need to.) Thus whenever $s(6)$ through $s(k - 1)$ are true, $s(k)$ is true as well. By the principle of strong mathematical induction, $s(n)$ is true for all $n \ge 6$. ∎

You may wish to regard the remarks about $s(7)$ and $s(8)$ as special cases in the proof that $s(6)$ through $s(k - 1)$ imply $s(k)$. That is exactly what they are. However, you may also view them as additional base steps. This is also an appropriate way to view things, because once we have established that $s(6)$, $s(7)$, and $s(8)$ are true, we need only prove $s(n)$ for $n \geq 9$, and if $n \geq 9$, then $n - 3 \geq 6$, and the proof of the first case in Example 9 is all we need.

◻ Recursive Definition

The definition usually used to introduce the summation notation

$$\sum_{i=j}^{n} a_i$$

is that it is the sum of all the values of a_i between $i = j$ and $i = n$. Though accurate, this definition is difficult to use in proofs.

Inductive Definition of Summation Notation

A definition that is much simpler to work with in proofs, although it looks complicated at first, makes use of the principle of induction. We say first,

$$\sum_{i=j}^{j} a_i \quad \text{means} \quad a_j$$

Second, for any $n > j$,

$$\sum_{i=j}^{n} a_i = \left(\sum_{i=j}^{n-1} a_i \right) + a_n \tag{1}$$

EXAMPLE 10   Use the definition just given to evaluate $\displaystyle\sum_{i=1}^{3} r^i$.

Solution   We use Equation (1) twice to write

$$\sum_{i=1}^{3} r^i = \left(\sum_{i=1}^{2} r^i \right) + r^3 = \left(\sum_{i=1}^{1} r^i \right) + r^2 + r^3$$

Finally, we use the base step of the definition, that $\displaystyle\sum_{i=1}^{1} r^i = r^1$, to write

$$\sum_{i=1}^{3} r^i = \left(\sum_{i=1}^{1} r^i \right) + r^2 + r^3 = r^1 + r^2 + r^3$$ ∎

How can we show that the definition before Example 10 defines what the notation means? We use the principle of mathematical induction.

Theorem 1   The notation $\displaystyle\sum_{i=m}^{n} a_i$ is defined for each integer $n \ge m$.

Proof   We let $s(n)$ be the statement

$$\sum_{i=m}^{n} a_i \text{ is defined}$$

Now $s(m)$ is true, for

$$\sum_{i=m}^{m} a_i = a_m$$

Now assume that $s(n - 1)$ is true and $n > m$; Equation (1) shows us that $s(n)$ is true as well. Therefore $s(n)$ is true for all n.   ∎

EXAMPLE 11   Express $\displaystyle\sum_{i=2}^{4} i^2 x^i$ without summation notation.

Solution $\displaystyle\sum_{i=2}^{4} i^2 x^i = \left(\sum_{i=2}^{3} i^2 x^i \right) + 4^2 \cdot x^4 = \left(\sum_{i=2}^{2} i^2 x^i \right) + 3^2 \cdot x^3 + 16x^4$

$$= 2^2 \cdot x^2 + 9x^3 + 16x^4$$

$$= 4x^2 + 9x^3 + 16x^4 \qquad\blacksquare$$

Multiplication and Exponents

We all know intuitively what m times n means for integers m and n. How could we put it into words concisely?

EXAMPLE 12   Give an inductive definition of $m \cdot n$.

Solution   We assume that m is fixed and give a definition by induction on n. We define $m \cdot 1 = m$ and $m \cdot n = m(n - 1) + m$. As in Theorem 1, we could show by induction that this defines $m \cdot n$ for every number $n > 0$. (We could have assumed that n was fixed and done our induction on m equally well.)   ∎

What good is it to define something we already know so well? With this definition, we can actually prove facts about arithmetic that we've been forced to accept on faith up to now.

EXAMPLE 13   Prove the distributive law $(a + b) \cdot n = an + bn$.

Solution   Let $s(n)$ be the statement $(a + b) \cdot n = an + bn$. Then $s(1)$ states that $(a + b) \cdot 1 = a \cdot 1 + b \cdot 1$. But we know that $m \cdot 1 = m$ for each m, so this equation is the true statement $a + b = a + b$. Now suppose $s(n - 1)$ is true, so that $(a + b) \cdot (n - 1) = a \cdot (n - 1) + b \cdot (n - 1)$. We may write

$$
\begin{aligned}
(a + b) \cdot n &= (a + b)(n - 1) + (a + b) & \text{(definition of } (a + b) \cdot n) \\
&= a(n - 1) + b(n - 1) + a + b & \text{(inductive hypothesis)} \\
&= a(n - 1) + a + b(n - 1) + b & \text{(commutative and} \\
& & \text{associative laws)} \\
&= an + bn & \text{(definition of } an \text{ and } bn)
\end{aligned}
$$

Thus by the principle of induction, $(a + b)n = an + bn$ for every positive integer n.   ∎

In a similar way, we could now use the inductive definition of

$$\sum_{i=1}^{n} a_i$$

to prove the distributive law

$$b \cdot \sum_{i=1}^{n} a_i = \sum_{i=1}^{n} ba_i$$

Inductive definitions are also called **recursive** definitions. A major reason for studying recursive definitions is that they make it possible to establish the truth of important facts such as the distributive law in Example 13. (Imagine trying to prove the distributive law without using the inductive definition.) Inductive definitions are useful throughout arithmetic. As another example, by giving an inductive definition of a^n similar to our inductive definition of mn, we can establish the laws of exponents by using mathematical induction. We shall also see that recursive definitions of functions provide a basis for computer programs to compute those functions.

Recursive Definition of Sets

We can describe sets recursively by giving a base step (or steps) describing some members of the set and an inductive step or steps telling us how to use members of the set to construct new members of the set. This is an important technique in the definition of computer languages, a topic we shall consider in more detail in the next section. One classic example of recursive definition is the "well-formed formulas of arithmetic." These are formulas constructed with so many parentheses that there is no chance of misinterpretation. (In fact, as you will see, they have more parentheses than necessary.)

Sentence 1 is the base step. Sentences 2 and 3 are the inductive steps. We use the phrase *number symbol* to mean a sequence of digits that represents a nonnegative number in the usual way. We write

(1) A number symbol is a well-formed formula.
(2) If F is a well-formed formula, then so is $(-F)$.
(3) If F and G are well-formed formulas, then so are $(F + G)$, $(F - G)$, and $(F \cdot G)$.

In the context of defining sets recursively, many people would also write

(4) Nothing else is a well-formed formula.

While this is totally appropriate, it is simply a restatement of the fact that in recursive definition we may apply only the base and inductive steps given to create new members of our set. So that all our uses of induction have the same format, we will not adopt a "closing rule" such as (4) in this book.

EXAMPLE 14   Which of the following are well-formed formulas?

(a) $6 + 3$ (b) $(-(6 + 3))$ (c) $((6 + 3) - 2)$

Solution

(a) This is not a well-formed formula because a well-formed formula containing any one of the symbols $+$, $-$, or $\cdot$ must be formed by using rule (2) or (3) and therefore must be surrounded by parentheses.
(b) The formula is obtained by applying rule (2) to $(6 + 3)$, which is formed by applying rule (3) to the well-formed formulas (by rule (1)) 6 and 3. Thus this is a well-formed formula.
(c) This is formed by applying rule (3) to the well-formed formula $(6 + 3)$ (from above) and the well-formed formula (2) (by rule (1)). Thus it is a well-formed formula. ∎

How would we use the definition of well-formed formulas? We might be writing a program to drill elementary-school students on arithmetic. By generating well-formed formulas and removing the outside parentheses before presenting a formula to the user, our program will produce an arithmetic problem with no possible misinterpretations.

Notice that no integer n was mentioned in the definition of well-formed formulas. Each time we apply rule (2) or (3), we increase the number of plus signs, minus signs, or times signs in our formula by 1. We call these signs **operator signs**. If we had wanted to mention an integer n explicitly, we could have written rule (2) as

(2′) If F is a well-formed formula with n operator signs, then $(-F)$ is a well-formed formula with $n + 1$ operator signs.

We could have written rule (3) similarly. However, mentioning n explicitly in this way simply increases the complexity of the rule without changing the way we apply it, so we have omitted any reference to n.   ,

EXAMPLE 15   Show how to generate a well-formed formula with three operator signs.

Solution   Since operators arise from either rule (2) or rule (3), our formula must be created by three uses of these rules. We get to choose what these uses are. Suppose one of these uses consisted of applying rule (3) with a times sign to get $(F \cdot G)$. Then F and G must have a total of two operators. Let us have two operators for F and none for G. Thus G comes from rule (1); assume that we choose 173 for G. Now F must come from rule (2) or (3); let us choose $(-E)$ for F so that E has one operator. Now E must come from rule (2) or (3); let us choose rule (3) and a minus sign so that $E = A - B$, where A and B have no operators. Since A and B have no operators, they must have come from rule (1). Suppose we choose $A = 10$ and $B = 7$. Then we get $(10 - 7)$ for E, $(-(10 - 7))$ for F, and $((-(10 - 7)) \cdot 173)$ for $F \cdot G$. This is our formula with three operator signs.   ∎

Concepts Review

1. The principle of _____ _____ _____ states that if $s(m)$ is true and if, for each $k > m$, the statements $s(m)$ through $s(k - 1)$ imply $s(k)$, then $s(n)$ is true for all integers $n > m$.

2. The recursive definition of summation tells us that

$$\sum_{i=1}^{1} a_i = a_1 \qquad \text{and} \qquad \sum_{i=1}^{m} a_i = \underline{\qquad}$$

3. A(n) _____ definition of a function f first defines $f(a)$ and then gives $f(n)$ in terms of $f(n - 1)$, for n values larger than a.

4. A(n) _____ definition of a set gives certain members of the set and describes how to construct new members of the set in terms of old members.

5. A(n) _____ _____ _____ of arithmetic is either a number symbol, minus a formula, or the sum, difference, or product of two such formulas.

Exercises

A

1. Give a proof by strong mathematical induction that every integer greater than 1 is a non-negative integer multiple of 2 plus a non-negative integer multiple of 3. (*Hint:* Subtract two from the number if it is bigger than 3.)

2. Give a proof by strong mathematical induction that every integer greater than or equal to 4 is a non-negative integer multiple of 2 plus a non-negative integer multiple of 5. (*Hint:* If the number is bigger than 5, subtract two from it.)

3. Prove that every integer greater than 7 is a non-negative integer multiple of 3 plus a non-negative integer multiple of 5.

4. Prove that every integer greater than 11 is a non-negative integer multiple of 4 plus a non-negative integer multiple of 5.

5. A graph is called a *tree* if it is connected but if removing any edge (no matter which one) leaves a graph that is not connected. Prove that a tree with n vertices has exactly $n - 1$ edges (or equivalently, a tree with m edges has $m + 1$ vertices). (*Hint*: It is possible to induct successfully on either the number of vertices or the number of edges; do whichever seems more convenient to you.)

6. A graph is *uniquely connected* if for each two vertices x and y there is one and only one path in the graph between x and y. Prove that a uniquely connected graph on n vertices has exactly $n - 1$ edges. (See hint to Exercise 5.)

7. Use induction to show that the number of connected components plus the number of edges of a graph is at least the number of vertices.

8. A walk is called an *even walk* if each edge that appears in it is used an even number of times. For example, $a\{a,b\}b\{a,b\}a$ is even. A graph is called a *forest* (for reasons that are not clear here!) if each **closed** walk (a walk starting and ending at the same vertex) is even. Show (by induction) that the number of edges of a forest with n vertices is no more than $n - 1$.

9. Prove (by induction on the number of edges in the walk) that if there is a nontrivial walk from x to y in the digraph of a transitive relation, then (x, y) is in the relation.

10. The kind of polygon we usually draw in geometry is *convex*; that is, any two points in the polygon can be joined by a straight line that lies in the polygon. A basic fact in geometry is that the sum of the degree measures of the angles in an n-vertex convex polygon is $(n - 2)180$. Assume that the result for $n = 3$ has already been proved, and use induction to derive the result in general. (Draw a diagonal to get started.)

B   11. The notation

$$\prod_{i=1}^{n} a_i$$

means the product of the numbers a_i from a_1 to a_n. Give an inductive definition of this notation and write down the value of

$$\prod_{i=1}^{4} i^2$$

12. When we defined the union of sets, we said that the union of a collection of sets was the set of elements that belong to at least one of the sets. In particular, we can write

$$A \cup B = \{x \mid x \in A \text{ or } x \in B\}$$

Give an inductive definition of

$$\bigcup_{i=1}^{n} A_i$$

based only on the definition of $A \cup B$.

13. We define the intersection of two sets A and B by $A \cap B = \{x \mid x \in A \text{ and } x \in B\}$. Give an inductive definition of the notation

$$\bigcap_{i=1}^{n} A_i$$

14. Give an inductive definition of the notation

$$\bigvee_{i=1}^{n} p_i = p_1 \vee p_2 \vee \cdots \vee p_n$$

for the disjunction of n statements.

15. Prove the distributive law

$$A \cap \left(\bigcup_{i=1}^{n} B_i \right) = \bigcup_{i=1}^{n} (A \cap B_i)$$

assuming the two-set distributive law.

16. Prove the distributive law

$$A \cup \left(\bigcap_{i=1}^{n} B_i \right) = \bigcap_{i=1}^{n} (A \cup B_i)$$

assuming the two-set distributive law.

17. Give an inductive definition of a^n for all non-negative n.

18. Give an inductive definition of a^{-n} for all non-negative integers n.

19. Prove the law of exponents $a^m \cdot a^n = a^{m+n}$ by induction on n.

20. Prove the law of exponents $(a^m)^n = a^{mn}$ by induction on n.

21. Prove that the inductive definition of

$$\bigcap_{i=1}^{n} A_i$$

gives the same set as the definition stating that

$$\bigcap_{i=1}^{n} A_i$$

is the set of elements in all the sets A_i.

22. Prove that the two definitions of union in Exercise 12 define the same set.

23. Give an example of a well-formed formula of arithmetic with four operators.

24. Give an example of a well-formed formula of arithmetic with five operators.

25. Is $(2 - (-3))$ a well-formed formula of arithmetic?

26. Is $((4) + (-(2)))$ a well-formed formula of arithmetic?

27. Is $(-((4) + (-(2))))$ a well-formed formula of arithmetic?

28. Is $((4) + (2)) \cdot (-(2))$ a well-formed formula of arithmetic?

29. Give examples of expressions with one, two, and three operators formed according to the rules below.

An expression can be a number.

An expression can be a letter of the alphabet.

An expression can be $-$(expression1) where expression1 is an expression.

An expression can be (expression1) <operator> (expression2) where <operator> is $+$, $\cdot$, $-$, or $/$ and expression1 and expression2 are expressions.

30. Give examples of expressions with one, two, and three operators formed according to the rules below.

An expression can be a number.

An expression can be $\sqrt{\text{expression1}}$ where expression1 is an expression.

An expression can be (expression1) <operator> (expression2) where expression1 and expression2 are expressions and <operator> is $+$, $-$, or $\cdot$.

31. Is $x + 1$ a legal expression described by the rules of Exercise 29?

32. Is $\sqrt{(1) + (3)}$ a legal expression described by the rules of Exercise 30?

33. Is $-((x) \cdot (y) + (1))$ a legal expression described by the rules of Exercise 29?

34. Is $1 + \sqrt{4 - 1}$ a legal expression according to the rules of Exercise 30?

Problems

1. A graph (without loops) is called *uniquely connected* if, given any two vertices u and v, there is one and only one path in the graph beginning at u and ending at v. A vertex has *degree* 1 if it is adjacent to exactly one other vertex. Show that a uniquely connected graph with at least one edge has at least two vertices of degree 1.

2. A digraph is called *uniquely rooted* if there is one and only one vertex r such that for each other vertex v, there is one and only one walk from v to r. The *indegree* of a vertex is the number of edges coming in and the *outdegree* of a vertex is the number of edges going out. Show that a uniquely rooted digraph with at least one edge has at least one vertex of outdegree 1 and indegree 0.

3. Generalize the problem above by showing that if the indegree of the root is i in a uniquely rooted digraph, then the digraph has at least i vertices of indegree 0 and outdegree 1.

4. A cycle in a graph is a walk in which the first and last vertices are the same but no two other vertices (or edges) are equal. A graph with no cycles is called *acyclic*. Show that a connected acyclic graph with two or more vertices has at least two vertices of degree 1.

5. In Exercises 5 and 6, the concepts of *tree* and *uniquely connected* are defined. Prove that a graph is a tree if and only if it is uniquely connected.

6. Write an algorithm whose input is an expression of arithmetic and whose output is the value of the expression if it is legal and is the word *illegal* otherwise.

7. Write an algorithm whose input is an expression of Exercise 30 and whose output is the value of the expression if it is legal (assume the person using the algorithm can do complex number arithmetic) and is the word *illegal* otherwise.

8. Give a proof by induction on the length n of a path from vertex x to vertex y that if y is reachable from x, then the vertex y is on the list of vertices reachable from x produced by algorithm Reach (introduced in Section 3-1).

9. Derive the principle of strong mathematical induction from the ordinary principle of mathematical induction. (*Hint:* Consider proving statements of the form $s(1) \wedge s(2) \wedge \cdots \wedge s(n)$.)

10. In part 3 of the definition of a well-formed formula, the mention of $F - G$ was technically unnecessary. Why? If we delete that mention, do the three rules that result give the same set of well-formed formulas? Explain your answer.

Section 5-3
Applications of Induction in Computer Science

◪ Recursive Algorithms in Computing

The factorial function $n!$ is sometimes defined by saying $n!$ is the product of the first n positive integers. This definition says, for example, that $3! = 1 \cdot 2 \cdot 3$. An inductive definition of the factorial function is

$$0! = 1$$
$$n! = n(n - 1)! \qquad \text{if } n > 0$$

EXAMPLE 16   Compute 3! from the inductive definition.

Solution $3! = 3 \cdot 2! = 3 \cdot 2 \cdot 1! = 3 \cdot 2 \cdot 1 \cdot 0! = 3 \cdot 2 \cdot 1 \cdot 1 = 6.$ ■

The inductive definition gives us a method for computing $n!$ that can be programmed directly in a modern programming language. In Figure 1 you see computer program fragments, one written in a modern version of BASIC and one in Pascal, which compute the factorial function "fact" given by

$$\text{fact}(0) = 1$$
$$\text{fact}(n) = n \cdot \text{fact}(n - 1) \qquad \text{if } n > 0$$

Figure 1

Basic Factorial Function	Pascal Factorial Function

```
DEF fact (n)
   IF n = 0 THEN LET fact = 1
   ELSE LET fact = n*fact(n-1)
   END IF
END DEF
```

```
function Fact (n:integer):integer;
   begin
   if (n = 0)
   then Fact := 1
   else Fact := n*Fact(n-1)
   end;
```

These are examples of what is called **recursive programming**; this means writing computer programs that use inductive definitions. If we ask a computer to use one of these functions to evaluate fact(3), it will do exactly the computations we did above. Just as the computation we made in Example 16 required us to write more than $3! = 3\cdot2\cdot1 = 6$, using one of these recursively defined functions in a computer program would require the computer to do more work than absolutely necessary. However, recursion gives us a straightforward way to express any algorithm that reduces a problem to a "simpler" version of the same problem. Some of these problems have nonrecursive algorithms that are easy to understand and involve less work, but for other such problems the recursive algorithm is the easiest to understand and requires no more work than any other method.

Just as an inductive definition of multiplication makes it easy to prove facts about multiplication, a recursive description of an algorithm often makes it easy to prove important facts about the algorithm—for example, that it does what it is supposed to do! In order to understand recursion, we shall first study it in the context of problems we have solved or could easily solve without recursion (such as computing n factorial) and then apply it to problems that would appear complicated without recursion but are straightforward with recursion. Our next example shows that recursion is not limited to solving numerical problems. A recursive algorithm to find the smallest element in a list may be based on the following idea. The smallest element in a list is either the first element or the smallest element between position 2 and the end of the list.

EXAMPLE 17 Write a recursive algorithm to find the smallest element in a list L of numbers between positions i and j inclusive. Use $L(k)$ to stand for the entry in position k of the list.

Solution

Algorithm Small

Input: A list L of numbers and two positions i and j in the list.
Output: The position k of the smallest number in the list between positions i and j.
Procedure: If $i = j$, then let $k = i$. If $i \neq j$, apply algorithm Small to positions $i + 1$ through j. (This gives a k.) If $L(i) < L(k)$, then change k to i, but if $L(i) \nless L(k)$, do nothing. ∎

EXAMPLE 18 Describe the steps taken in applying algorithm Small to the list 3, 1, 2.

Solution

(a) Begin with $i = 1$ and $j = 3$. Since $i \neq j$, apply Small with $i = 2$ and $j = 3$.
(b) With $i = 2$ and $j = 3$, since $i \neq j$, apply Small with $i = 3$ and $j = 3$.
(c) With $i = 3$ and $j = 3$, let $k = 3$.
(d) Returning to complete the case $i = 2$, compare $L(2)$ with $L(3)$ and change k to 2, since $1 < 2$ (that is, $L(2) < L(3)$).
(e) Returning to complete the case $i = 1$, compare $L(1)$ with $L(2)$ and leave $k = 2$, since $L(1) > L(2)$. ∎

The procedure used in the last two examples is similar to algorithm Smallest in Section 4-3 for finding the minimum element of a list. Here, however, we avoid most of the exchanging inherent in algorithm Smallest. Smallest may be modified to work in the same way; except for that, the differences between the two algorithms are essentially the same as the differences between the computation $3! = 3 \cdot 2 \cdot 1 = 6$ and Example 16. However, algorithm Small has been structured in such a way that we can prove inductively that it works. (With a bit more work, we could also use induction to prove that Smallest works.)

EXAMPLE 19   Prove that algorithm Small finds the position of the smallest element between positions i and j in the list.

Solution   If $j - i = 0$, then algorithm Small sets k equal to the *only* position between i and j; thus it sets k equal to the position of the smallest element between positions i and j. Now assume that when $j - i = n - 1$, Small sets k equal to the position of the smallest element between positions i and j. Consider the case $j - i = n$. Small finds the position of the smallest element between positions $i + 1$ and n (that was the inductive hypothesis) and if the element in position i is smaller, it changes k to i but otherwise leaves k alone. Thus when $j - i = n$, Small finds the position of the smallest element between positions i and j. Thus by the principle of mathematical induction, for all $n \geq 0$, if $j - i = n$, then Small finds the location of the smallest element between positions i and j.   ∎

In Chapter 4, we used algorithm Smallest in discussing the selection sort procedure, though we didn't write the algorithm out explicitly. The idea of selection sort is that we first find the smallest element of the list, next exchange it with the first element and then apply selection sort to the remainder of the list. Notice how easy it is to use the idea as the basis of a recursive algorithm. (It is not difficult to write a version without recursion either, but our goal here is to understand recursion.)

EXAMPLE 20   Write a recursive version of the selection sort algorithm.

Solution

Algorithm Selsort
    Input: A list L and two positions i and j.
    Output: The list obtained from L by sorting the elements between positions i and j into increasing order.
    Procedure: If $i = j$, do nothing.
        Otherwise, use Small to find the location k of the smallest element of L between positions i and j.
        Exchange $L(i)$ and $L(k)$.
        Apply Selsort to positions $i + 1$ through j of L.   ∎

EXAMPLE 21   Prove that algorithm Selsort applied to a list of *n* numbers sorts the list into numerical order.

Solution   Since a list of length 1 is sorted, Selsort applied to a list of length 1 gives a sorted list. Now assume that Selsort applied to a list of length $n - 1$ gives a sorted list. Algorithm Small finds the location *k* of the smallest element. Next we put this smallest element in the correct position (position *i*) and put the entry from position *i* into position *k*. Thus the remaining numbers (other than the smallest one) are now in positions $i + 1$ through *j*. Our inductive hypothesis tells us that applying Selsort to *these* positions gives a list sorted into increasing order, therefore the portion of the list from position *i* through *j* will be sorted into increasing order. Thus, by the principle of mathematical induction, for each *n*, Selsort sorts a list of *n* numbers into increasing order.   ∎

Anyone who has wrestled with the question "Will my program always work?" will recognize the importance of induction as a tool for demonstrating program correctness!

Binary Search

Suppose we have an alphabetically ordered directory of students for a university and want to know if a certain friend is enrolled. We open the directory to see if our friend Sam Stein would be in the last half of the directory or the first half. Suppose Martin is the name of the last person on the page to which we open. Then if Sam is in the book, she is in the last half. Now we take the back half of the directory and open it in the middle. If we find Roe at the bottom of the page, then Sam is in the last quarter of the book. It is clear how we continue to find whether Samantha Stein is in the directory, but it may not be obvious how to describe the process precisely. A recursive description of the process is straightforward.

We will describe an algorithm that determines whether a word is between positions *i* and *j* in an alphabetic list. The notation $\lfloor x \rfloor$ used below means the greatest integer less than or equal to *x*. (The notation $\lfloor x \rfloor$ is read as "floor of *x*.")

Algorithm Binary Search

Input: An alphabetically ordered list, two integers *i* and *j* (with $i \leq j$), and a word.

Output: *Yes* if the word is in the list between positions *i* and *j* (inclusive) and *no* otherwise.

Procedure: If $i = j$, then output *yes* if the word is entry *i* of the list and *no* if not.

Otherwise, if the word comes after entry $\lfloor \frac{i+j}{2} \rfloor$ in alphabetical order, then apply Binary Search to the same list and word using $\lfloor \frac{i+j}{2} \rfloor + 1$ and *j* as the integers.

And, if not, then apply Binary Search to the same list and word using i and $\lfloor \dfrac{i+j}{2} \rfloor$ as the integers.

EXAMPLE 22   Prove that algorithm Binary Search outputs *yes* if the word is between positions i and j and outputs *no* otherwise.

Solution   We prove the statement "If $j - i = n$, then the algorithm outputs *yes* or *no* correctly." If $n = 0$, then $i = j$, and the first sentence of the procedure outputs *yes* or *no* correctly. Suppose that for all n from 0 through $k - 1$, the algorithm outputs *yes* or *no* correctly. If $j - i = k > 0$, then $i < j$ so that

$$\frac{j+i}{2} < j;$$

therefore both

$$\lfloor \frac{j+i}{2} \rfloor - i \quad \text{and} \quad j - (\lfloor \frac{j+i}{2} \rfloor + 1)$$

are less than k. Thus the second sentence of the procedure applies the algorithm to a list of length less than k and thus outputs *yes* or *no* correctly. Therefore, by the principle of mathematical induction, the algorithm always outputs *yes* or *no* correctly.   ■

EXAMPLE 23   Prove that algorithm Binary Search makes $n + 1$ comparisons when applied to a list of length 2^n.

Solution   If $n = 0$, then one comparison is made in applying the first sentence of the procedure. Now assume that k comparisons are made when Binary Search is applied to a list of length 2^{k-1}. When we apply Binary Search to a list of length 2^k, one comparison is made in the second sentence of the procedure in deciding which half of the list to use next. By the inductive hypothesis, k comparisons are made in applying Binary Search to this half of the list, so a total of $k + 1$ comparisons is made. Therefore, by the principle of mathematical induction, for all $n \geq 0$, Binary Search makes $n + 1$ comparisons when applied to a list of length 2^n.   ■

EXAMPLE 24   Give the sequence of comparisons made while searching for the word *cat* in the alphabetically ordered list *animal, bear, cow, dog, elephant*.

Solution   We apply Binary Search with $i = 1$ and $j = 5$, so

$$\lfloor \frac{i+j}{2} \rfloor = \lfloor \frac{1+5}{2} \rfloor = 3$$

Thus the first comparison is, "Does *cat* come after *cow*?" The answer is *no*, so we apply Binary Search with

$$i = 1 \quad \text{and} \quad j = \lfloor \frac{1+5}{2} \rfloor = 3$$

Then, with this new j,

$$\lfloor \frac{i+j}{2} \rfloor = \lfloor \frac{1+3}{2} \rfloor = 2$$

Thus the next comparison is, "Does *cat* come after *bear*?" The answer is *yes*, so we apply Binary Search with

$$i = \lfloor \frac{1+3}{2} \rfloor + 1 = 2 + 1 = 3 \quad \text{and} \quad j = 3$$

Since $i = j$, the next comparison is, "Is *cat* the same as *cow*?" The answer is *no*, so the output is *no* and the process comes to a stop. ∎

EXAMPLE 25   Give the sequence of comparisons made while searching for the word *cow* in the alphabetically ordered list *animal, bear, cow, dog, elephant*.

Solution   Beginning with $i = 1$ and $j = 5$, we have

$$\lfloor \frac{i+j}{2} \rfloor = 3$$

Thus the first comparison is "does cow come after cow?" The answer is *no*, so we apply Binary Search with

$$i = 1 \quad \text{and} \quad j = \lfloor \frac{1+5}{2} \rfloor = 3$$

The next comparison is thus "Does *cow* come after *bear*?" Since the answer is *yes*, we apply Binary Search with

$$i = \lfloor \frac{1+3}{2} \rfloor + 1 = 2 + 1 = 3 \quad \text{and} \quad j = 3$$

Since $i = j$, the next comparison is, "Is *cow* the same as *cow*?" The answer is *yes*, so the output is *yes* and the procedure stops. ∎

The first comparison in Example 25 suggests a change we might make in the Binary Search algorithm to reflect how a person would use it. A person can determine not only whether *cow* comes after *cow*, but also whether *cow* equals *cow* in the same instant of time and thus short-circuit the remainder of the algorithm to save time. You can rewrite the algorithm for the computer in this way also, but with a standard computer (as discussed in Problem 11) this change is counterproductive; it generally wastes time.

B *Using BNF Notation for Recursive Definitions of Sets*

Describing Character Strings

Many applications of computing require a computer to recognize and interpret a sequence of signals it receives as input. Such a sequence might consist of signals from a machine in an automated factory, symbols typed into the computer by a human user, or the symbols that make up a computer program. Often, we may determine inductively whether a sequence of symbols is meaningful by examining how it is built from smaller sequences. For this purpose we would need a recursive definition of the set of meaningful character strings. In general, such a definition can be quite complex.

In describing many such sequences, it is possible to use a notational system developed by John Backus and used by Peter Naur for the description of the programming language Algol. (For this reason, the subject we are about to study is a central topic in a course in compiler design.) The notation is known as **Backus Naur Form**, or **BNF** for short. To illustrate the notation, suppose we need to recognize sequences of symbols representing positive integers for an arithmetic drill program. Below is a BNF description of symbol strings that represent positive integers; an explanation follows the description.

(1) <positive digit>   : = 1 | 2 | 3 | 4 | 5 | 6 | 7 | 8 | 9
(2) <digit>   : = 0 | <positive digit>
(3) <positive integer> : = <positive digit> | <positive integer><digit>

You see in the description that the terms *digit, positive digit,* and *positive integer* are enclosed in angle brackets. The description defines each of these terms; in BNF notation we always enclose a term being defined in angle brackets. Line 1 of the definition is read, "A positive digit can be 1 or 2 or 3 or 4 or 5 or 6 or 7 or 8 or 9." Notice that we read the symbol : = as *can be* and the vertical line | as *or.* The second line is read, "A digit can be zero or a positive digit." The third line is read, "A positive integer can be a positive digit or a positive integer followed by a digit." This illustrates another aspect of BNF notation: When we put the names of two terms being defined side-by-side, we are saying that items with those names may be put side-by-side in the order given. We say we have **concatenated** the items when we put them side-by-side. Notice how lines 1 and 2 of the definition are portions of the base step of an inductive definition, whereas line 3 is an inductive step.

EXAMPLE 26   Show why 1, 10, and 107 represent positive integers.

Solution   By rule (1), the symbol 1 is a positive digit. Thus by rule (3), the symbol 1 represents a positive integer. By rule (2), the symbol 0 is a digit. Since 1 is a positive integer, we may conclude by rule (3) that 10 represents an integer. By rule (1), the symbol 7 is a positive digit, so by rule (2), the symbol 7 is a digit. Since 10 represents a positive integer, we may conclude by rule (3) that 107 represents a positive integer. ∎

EXAMPLE 27 Write an algorithm based on rules (1) through (3) to recognize whether a string of symbols given as input represents a positive integer.

Solution Our algorithm will be inductive; thus rule (3) is the core of the algorithm.

Algorithm PosInt
Input: A string of symbols.
Output: The answer *yes* if the symbol string represents a positive integer and the answer *no* otherwise.
Procedure: If the symbol string has one character, then output *yes* if the character is a member of {1,2,3,4,5,6,7,8,9} and output *no* otherwise.
Otherwise, if the last character is in the set {0,1,2,3,4,5,6,7,8,9}, then remove that last character and give the output that results from applying PosInt to the remaining characters; otherwise output *no* and stop. ∎

EXAMPLE 28 Describe the steps used by algorithm PosInt in determining that 107 represents a positive integer.

Solution The input does not have one character, so we examine the last character and determine that it is in the set {0,1, . . . ,9}. Therefore we remove 7 and apply algorithm PosInt to 10. This has more than one character, so we examine the last character, determine that it is in {0,1, . . . ,9}, and remove it. We apply algorithm PosInt to 1. Since it has one character we get the output *yes* because 1 ∈ {1,2, . . . ,9}. Thus, 107 represents an integer. ∎

EXAMPLE 29 Use algorithm PosInt to show that 10+ does not represent an integer.

Solution This input has more than one character, so we examine the last character. This character (+) is not in {0,1, . . . ,9}, so we output *no*. Thus 10+ does not represent a positive integer. ∎

Describing Formulas

We write the rule

$$<sum> := <positive\ integer> + <positive\ integer>$$

to say, "A sum is a positive integer followed by a plus sign followed by a positive integer." (The two positive integers referred to in that sentence may be different.) To say we should put a named item next to a symbol, we write down the name of the item followed by that symbol. This is similar to the way we have already described to write a rule to concatenate two named items. This process is also called *concatenation*.

EXAMPLE 30   Give a rule we may use with rules (1), (2), and (3) in order to describe all integers, positive, negative, or zero.

Solution   Since an integer is represented by either 0, a positive integer, or a minus sign followed by a positive integer, we may write

(4) <integer> : = 0 | <positive integer> | −<positive integer>.   ∎

To see the power of these techniques, imagine that we are going to design the program for the arithmetic drill we mentioned in connection with well-formed formulas of arithmetic. Recall that we would generate a well-formed formula but remove the outside set of parentheses from it before presenting it to the student. Although BNF makes it easy to describe well-formed formulas, it does not give us a way to say, "Remove the outside set of parentheses." However, it does allow us to describe the ordinary formulas of arithmetic from scratch. Without BNF notation, an inductive description of these formulas would be difficult to follow.

EXAMPLE 31   Using parentheses to show in which order multiple operations are to be carried out, write down rules that we may use with the rules describing numbers so that we describe all expressions of ordinary arithmetic with the operators +, −, ·, and /.

Solution   First, we specify the operators

(5) <operator> : = + | − | · | /

Next, we allow for "simple" expressions such as 3 + 2, −1 + 5 (but not 5 + −1).

(6) <expression> : = <integer>
(7) <expression> : = <integer><operator><positive integer>

Finally, we specify the expressions we get by operating on other expressions.

(8) <expression> : = (<expression>)<operator>(<expression>)
(9) <expression> : = −(<expression>)
(10) <expression> : = <integer><operator>(<expression>)
(11) <expression> : = (<expression>)<operator>(<positive integer>)

These rules let us write down expressions involving division by zero. It is customary to consider such an expression as an allowable expression that has no numerical value.   ∎

Concepts Review

1. A(n) _____ program makes use of an inductive definition.

2. The process of _____ _____ allows us to locate an element in an alphabetical list by successively dividing the list into halves.

3. The notation of _____ _____ form is used to write recursive definitions of character strings.

4. Putting two sequences side by side is known as _____ the sequences.

5. The idea of selection sort is to find the _____ element of the list, put it into the _____ position and apply _____ _____ to the rest of the list.

6. When applied to a list of length 2^n, Binary Search makes _____ comparisons.

7. The symbol $:=$ is read as _____ _____, and the symbol | is read as _____.

Exercises

A

1. Algorithm Bubbleup, which appeared in Exercise 1, Section 4-3 (to which you will need to refer), may be written with a recursive definition. Fill in the procedure in the partial statement of the algorithm below.

   Algorithm Bubble
   Input: A list L of n numbers.
   Output: A list, also called L, of the same numbers, with the largest number in position n.
   Procedure: Exercise.

2. Algorithm Trickledown, which appeared in Exercise 2, Section 4-3 (to which you will need to refer), may be written with a recursive definition. Fill in the procedure in the partial statement of the algorithm below.

   Algorithm Trickle
   Input: A list L of n numbers.
   Output: A list, also called L, of the same numbers, with the smallest element in position 1.
   Procedure: Exercise.

3. Write down a recursive definition of the Bubblesort algorithm, using algorithm Bubble to put the largest element at the end of the list, and then applying Bubblesort to the remainder of the list. (Bubblesort is among the least desirable sorting algorithms in practice, but it is a good example to illustrate the ideas of sorting and recursion.)

4. Write a recursive definition of algorithm Tricklesort, which sorts a list of numbers by using algorithm Trickle in Exercise 2 to put the smallest member of the list in the first position and then applying Tricklesort to the remainder of the list. (See the parenthetical remark about Bubblesort in Exercise 3.)

5. Prove by induction that algorithm Bubble in Exercise 1 works.

6. Prove by induction that algorithm Trickle in Exercise 2 works.

7. Prove by induction that algorithm Bubblesort in Exercise 3 works.

8. Prove by induction that algorithm Tricklesort in Exercise 4 works.

9. We are given the list: ape, bear, cat, dog, goat, hog, horse, pony, rat, tiger. Show the sequence of words that will be examined as entry $\lfloor \frac{i+j}{2} \rfloor$ in applying Binary Search to the list, searching for
   (a) mouse   (b) horse   (c) rat   (d) viper

10. We are given the list: Art, Bess, Chuck, Dan, Erick, Fa, Jorge, Liza, Olivia, Pam, Tony. Show the sequence of names that will be examined as entry $\lfloor \frac{i+j}{2} \rfloor$ in applying Binary Search to the list to search for
    (a) Jorge   (b) Pam   (c) Tony   (d) Anne

B 11. Using rules (1) through (4), explain how to build up the integers 23 and -203.

12. Using rules (1) through (3), explain how to build up the integers 407 and 27.

13. Using algorithm PosInt, show the steps involved in testing each of the following to see whether it represents a positive integer.
    (a) 20   (b) 2 + +0
    (c) + − 1   (d) −301

14. Using algorithm PosInt, show the steps involved in testing each of the following to see whether it represents a positive integer.
    (a) 35   (b) 3 − 5
    (c) 3 − +5   (d) 21 + +0

15. In a number of programming languages, a variable name may consist of a letter followed by any number of symbols, each of which may be a letter, a digit, or an underscore. Using BNF notation, write a definition of legal variable names.

16. In the version of BASIC standardized by the American National Standards Institute, a string variable name must end with a dollar sign and begin with one letter, which may be followed by any number (including 0) of letters, numerals, and underscore characters. Write a definition of legal BASIC string variable names in BNF notation.

17. Write an algorithm to determine whether a string of characters represents a variable name according to the rules of Exercise 15.

18. Write an algorithm to determine whether a string of characters represents a variable name according to the rules of Exercise 16.

19. Write an algorithm to determine whether a character string represents an integer (rather than merely a positive integer).

20. Write an algorithm to determine whether a character string represents a computation with +, −, ·, and /, using integers. Assume that parentheses are used to indicate the order in which operations are carried out, and ignore the possibility of division by zero.

Problems

1. Insertion sort works in the following way. On a list of length 1, you do nothing. On a list of length n, you sort the first $n - 1$ things and then read through the list (usually starting at the last element) to find the place where item number n belongs and put it there. Write a recursive version of the insertion sort algorithm. Use induction to prove that this algorithm works.

2. Show that a list of n items in increasing order and a list of m items in increasing order may be merged into a list of $m + n$ items in increasing order by an algorithm that makes at most $m + n - 1$ comparisons.

3. Write a computer program that implements the algorithm in Problem 2.

4. Devise an algorithm that sorts a list of n items into increasing order by dividing it into two lists of length $\lfloor \frac{n}{2} \rfloor$ and $\lceil \frac{n}{2} \rceil$, sorting them (by applying the same technique to each of them), and applying the algorithm of Problem 2 to merge them into a single list, in increasing order.

5. Prove that the algorithm you devised in Problem 4 works.

6. Show that the algorithm in Problem 4 makes no more than $k \cdot 2^k$ comparisons when n is 2^k.

7. If $n = 2^k$, express the number of comparisons made by the algorithm of Exercise 4 as a function of n. How does this compare with the sorting algorithm we discussed in Chapter 4? How does this compare with the sorting algorithms we discussed in Exercises 1–8 of this section?

8. Compare the number of comparisons made by algorithm Selsort with the maximum number made by algorithm Bubblesort (Exercise 3). Compare the number of exchanges made by each. Which is preferable?

9. The procedure of algorithm Reach (Chapter 3) to find all vertices reachable from a given one in a digraph may be rephrased as follows. "Make a list L of all vertices adjacent from x. Remove x and all arrows leaving it from the digraph. Now for each vertex on the list, apply the Reach algorithm to this vertex and add all the vertices you get to L. Finally, delete any repeats among the vertices in the list L." Prove that this version of the Reach algorithm works.

10. There is a version of Binary Search in which we check whether the word comes after entry $\lfloor i + j \rfloor$, comes before entry $\lfloor i + j \rfloor$, or equals entry $\lfloor i + j \rfloor$. If entry $\lfloor i + j \rfloor$ equals the word for which we are searching, we output *yes* and stop; otherwise we keep going. This requires an extra comparison each time we check whether our word equals entry $\lfloor i + j \rfloor$. Explain why, on the average, this method will be more time-consuming than algorithm Binary Search in the text.

11. The well-formed formulas of arithmetic were defined in Section 5-2, using the phrase *number symbol* as part of the definition. We have now seen how to write BNF descriptions of number symbols. Write a BNF description of the well-formed formulas of arithmetic that incorporates a BNF description of number symbols.

12. Write a BNF description of terminating decimal numbers.

Chapter 5
Review Exercises

1. Identify the base step, inductive hypothesis, inductive step, and inductive conclusion in the following proof that

$$1 \cdot \frac{2}{3} + 2 \cdot \frac{5}{3} + 3 \cdot \frac{8}{3} + 4 \cdot \frac{11}{3} + \cdots + n\left(n - \frac{1}{3}\right) = \frac{n^2(n + 1)}{3}$$

If $n = 1$, our formula reads

$$1\left(1 - \frac{1}{3}\right) = \frac{1^2(1 + 2)}{3}$$

which is true. Therefore the formula holds when $n = 1$. Now suppose the formula is true when $n = k - 1$. In other words suppose that

$$1 \cdot \frac{2}{3} + 2 \cdot \frac{5}{3} + \cdots + (k - 1)\left(k - \frac{4}{3}\right) = \frac{(k - 1)^2 k}{3}$$

Adding $k\left(k - \frac{1}{3}\right)$ to both sides of this equation gives

$$
\begin{aligned}
1 \cdot \frac{2}{3} + 2 \cdot \frac{5}{3} + \cdots + (k - 1)\left(k - \frac{4}{3}\right) + k\left(k - \frac{1}{3}\right) &= \frac{(k - 1)^2 k}{3} + k\left(k - \frac{1}{3}\right) \\
&= \frac{(k^2 - 2k + 1)k}{3} + \frac{3k^2 - k}{3} \\
&= \frac{k^3 - 2k^2 + k + 3k^2 - k}{3} \\
&= \frac{k^3 + k^2}{3} \\
&= \frac{k^2(k + 1)}{3}
\end{aligned}
$$

Thus the formula holds when $n = k$. Therefore, by the principle of mathematical induction, the formula

$$1 \cdot \frac{2}{3} + 2 \cdot \frac{5}{3} + \cdots + n\left(n - \frac{1}{3}\right) = \frac{n^2(n + 1)}{3}$$

holds for all positive integers n.

In Exercises 2–5, use the principle of mathematical induction to prove the formula or inequality given.

2. $\dfrac{1}{3} + \dfrac{1}{9} + \dfrac{1}{27} + \cdots = \dfrac{3^n - 1}{2 \cdot 3^n}$

3. $2 + 10 + 24 + 44 + \cdots + 3n^2 - n = n^2(n + 1)$

4. $n^2 + 3n < n^3$ for $n \geq 3$

5. $n^3 < 2^n$ for $n \geq 10$

6. Prove that $1 \cdot 2 \cdot 3 + 2 \cdot 3 \cdot 4 + \cdots + n(n + 1)(n + 2) = O(n^4)$.

7. Prove that $n^4 = O(1 \cdot 2 \cdot 3 + 2 \cdot 3 \cdot 4 + \cdots + n(n + 1)(n + 2))$.

8. Prove by induction that the maximum number of edges in a graph on n vertices is $\dfrac{n(n + 1)}{2}$. (Remember that a vertex can have an edge connecting it to itself.)

9. A vertex has degree 1 if it lies in an edge only once. A graph (without loops) is uniquely connected if for each pair of vertices x and y, there is one and only one path from x to y in the graph. Prove that if the number of edges in a uniquely connected graph is greater than or equal to 1, then the graph has at least two vertices of degree 1.

10. Give an inductive definition of the conjunction

$$\bigwedge_{i=1}^{n} p_i = p_1 \wedge p_2 \wedge \cdots \wedge p_n$$

of n symbolic statements.

11. Use the inductive definition of Exercise 10 to prove the distributive law that states that

$$q \vee \left(\bigwedge_{i=1}^{n} p_i \right) \quad \text{and} \quad \bigwedge_{i=1}^{n} (q \vee p_i)$$

are equivalent. (You may assume that $q \vee (p_1 \wedge p_2) \equiv (q \vee p_1) \wedge (q \vee p_2)$.)

12. Use the inductive definition of summation notation to prove the distributive law.

$$b \sum_{i=1}^{n} a_i = \sum_{i=1}^{n} b a_i$$

13. Which of the formulas below is a well-formed formula of arithmetic?
(a) $(2 + ((3 - 2) \cdot 4))$ (b) $2 + (4 + 3)$
(c) $((2 \cdot 3) + 4)$ (d) $((3 - 1) + 2)$
(e) $((2 + (3)) \cdot 2)$

14. Give examples of expressions with one, two, and three operator symbols formed according to the following rules.

Any uppercase letter is an expression.
If E is an expression, then $(\sim E)$ is an expression.
If E_1 and E_2 are expressions, then $(E_1 \cup E_2)$ and $(E_1 \cap E_2)$ are expressions.

15. Which of the following are expressions by the rules of Exercise 14?
(a) $(P \cap \sim Q)$ (b) $((\sim(P \cap Q)) \cup R)$ (c) $((P \cap (Q)) \cup R)$ (d) $(\sim(P \cap (Q \cup R)))$

16. The following algorithm takes a numerical list L of length n as input and prints out a number k. What is $L(k)$? Give a proof by induction that this is what $L(k)$ is.

Algorithm Nameless
    Input: A list L of numbers and a number $n > 0$ such that L has at least n entries.
    Output: A number k.

Procedure: If $n = 1$, then let $k = 1$.
  If $n > 1$, then apply Nameless to the list L with the number $n - 1$ to get a number k.
  If $L(n) > L(k)$, then change the value of k to n.
  If $L(n) \leq L(k)$, then do not change k.

17. Algorithm Exercise below has a predictable effect on a list L of length n.

   Algorithm Exercise
      Input: A list L of numbers and a number $n > 0$ such that L has at least n entries.
      Output: A list also called L.
   Procedure: If $n = 1$, do nothing to L.
      If $n > 1$, apply Nameless to L and n.
      Exchange $L(k)$ and $L(n)$.
      Apply Exercise to the new list L, using $n - 1$ as the number.

   What is the effect on L? Give a proof that this is the effect.

18. Describe the sequence of comparisons made in using Binary Search to search for the names below in the list

   Ann, Charles, Robert, Sally, Walter

   (a) Sue   (b) Robert   (c) Ralph   (d) Bill

19. A logical expression may be formed from lowercase letters and any of the symbols $\vee$, $\wedge$, and $\neg$, with parentheses around a compound symbolic statement in the same way that parentheses are put around well-formed formulas of arithmetic. Write a BNF description of logical expressions. (You may use three dots to avoid writing all letters of the alphabet.)

20. A number in "Computer-Scientific" notation consists of an optional minus sign, followed by a non-negative digit, followed by (optionally) a decimal point and a sequence of any number of digits (the last of which is not zero), all followed optionally by a letter e, followed by a plus or minus sign, followed by a representation of a positive integer. Write a BNF description of a number in "Computer-Scientific" notation. This description allows -0 as a number. Change the BNF description to disallow -0.

21. Describe an algorithm based on Exercise 19 to recognize whether a symbol string represents a logical expression.

CHAPTER 6
Basic Counting Techniques

*I*n probability, in the analysis of algorithms, and in many applications of discrete mathematics, we find that we need to know in how many ways a certain kind of process can unfold. The standard techniques for counting the number of outcomes are all based on the idea that two sets have the same size if they are in a one-to-one correspondence with each other. The two most fundamental techniques, the sum and product principles, are ideas that are part of the intuition we develop in understanding addition and multiplication in school. Using these techniques, we shall develop formulas to count functions (also called *n-tuples*), one-to-one functions (also called *permutations*), subsets (also called *combinations*), and some more complicated objects as well. More importantly, we shall see how to use the basic counting principles in a wide variety of circumstances.

We shall see how the idea of a one-to-one and onto function is fundamental to the understanding of counting and how the concept of an equivalence relation helps us organize the solutions to several different counting problems into a coherent whole rather than a grab-bag of special tricks. We shall use Venn diagrams to visualize the technique of "inclusion-exclusion" counting and then, based on what we've learned from the Venn diagrams, develop a formula that works on problems for which Venn diagrams would be impossibly complex.

We shall use our knowledge of counting techniques whenever we try to determine how long an algorithm takes and in making basic computations about mathematical structures such as graphs and trees. Our facility with counting will be exercised to the fullest when we study probability. The principles of counting we learn here would be further extended by a course in combinatorial mathematics; the theory of counting—called *enumeration* in more advanced work—is a deep and rich subject.

Section 6-1
Elementary
Counting Techniques

▨ Counting Principles

The Concept of Size

One of the most useful applications of the idea of a function is that of a counting function. When we talk informally about counting the elements of a set, we think in terms of choosing an element of the set and saying "one," choosing another and saying "two," still another and saying "three," and so on. Thus when we count the elements of an n-element set S, we are setting up a function from the set $N = \{1,2,3, \ldots ,n\}$ onto our set S. This function is one-to-one, because we choose a different element of S each time. Thus we have a bijection (a one-to-one correspondence) from $N = \{1,2,3, \ldots ,n\}$ onto S. We call such a function a **counting function.** We say S has **size** n if there is a counting function from $N = \{1,2,3, \ldots ,n\}$ onto S. In effect, a counting function for S lists the elements of S in a certain order.

EXAMPLE 1   Show two counting functions for the set $\{x,y,z\}$.

Solution   A typical function is $\{(1,x), (2,y), (3,z)\}$, which corresponds to counting in the order x,y,z; another one is $\{(1,y), (2,z), (3,x)\}$, which corresponds to counting in the order y,z,x.   ■

It is a consequence of our definition of size that two sets have the same size if and only if there is a bijection between them. This is the first of several counting principles; we shall call it the **bijection principle.**

EXAMPLE 2   Show that $\{a,b,c\}$ and $\{x,y,z\}$ have the same size.

Solution   A bijection between these two sets is $\{(c,x), (b,y), (a,z)\}$.   ■

A second consequence of the definition of size is the **sum principle,** which we state as a theorem for future reference.

Theorem 1   The size of a union of two disjoint sets is the sum of their sizes.

Proof   Let $S = \{a_1,a_2, \ldots ,a_n\}$ and $T = \{b_1,b_2, \ldots ,b_k\}$. Now suppose $f = \{(1,a_1), \ldots ,(n,a_n)\}$ is a bijection from N to S, $g = \{(1,b_1), \ldots ,(k,b_k)\}$ is a bijection from $K = \{1,2, \ldots ,k\}$ to T, and S and T are disjoint. Then define the function h

to be the set of ordered pairs $\{(1,a_1), (2,a_2), \ldots ,(n,a_n), (n+1,b_1), \ldots ,(n+k,b_k)\}$. Since S and T are disjoint, h is a bijection from $\{1,2, \ldots ,n+k\}$ onto $S \cup T$. ∎

As Example 3 below shows, the sum principle underlies some of the most elementary computations—ones we normally make without needing to think about what principle is appropriate to apply.

EXAMPLE 3   When you use a certain word-processing program to call up a document from a personal computer's storage, you have the choice of a menu named *file* and a menu named *edit*. If you choose the menu named *file*, you are given five activities: save, clone, delete, rename, and quit. If you chose the *edit* menu, you are given seven choices: overstrike mode, insert mode, find, change, move to, spell, style sheet. How many different activities may you request?

Solution   Five filing activities can be chosen, and seven editing activities can be chosen. The sets of filing and editing activities have nothing in common, so the total number of activities is $5 + 7 = 12$. ∎

EXAMPLE 4   A Boy Scout troop committee must have a chairperson and a secretary-treasurer appointed by the chair. If there are six people on the committee, in how many ways may they choose the two different officers?

Solution   A choice of officers will be a pair of people (chair, secretary-treasurer). There are six ways to choose the first person in the pair. Once a chair is chosen, he or she will have five choices for the secretary-treasurer. Thus for each of the six possible chairs, we have a set of five (chair, secretary-treasurer) pairs. This time we have six disjoint sets (rather than two), each with five elements. A natural extension of the sum principle tells us that the union of these six sets has $5+5+5+5+5 = 30$ elements. In Figure 1, you can visualize writing the pairs

Figure 1   Organizing (chair, secretary-treasurer) pairs into stacks with the same chair.

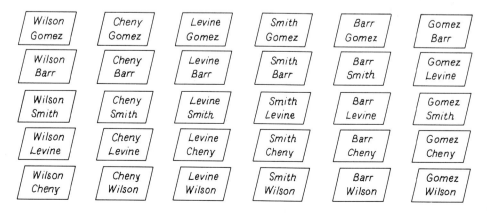

(chair, secretary-treasurer) on slips of paper and making six stacks, one for each possible chair. The stacks represent the six disjoint sets.   ∎

The method we used in the example suggests our next counting principle, called the **product principle.** Theorem 2 is one of several versions of this principle we shall state.

Theorem 2   The union of m disjoint sets, each of size n, has size mn.

Proof   The proof is a classic example of a proof by mathematical induction on m. If m is 1, the theorem states that a set of size n has size n, which is certainly true. Now assume a union of $m - 1$ disjoint sets, each of size n, has size $(m - 1)\cdot n$. We may write the union of m disjoint sets of size n as

$$A_1 \cup \cdots \cup A_m = (A_1 \cup \cdots \cup A_{m-1}) \cup A_m$$

By the induction hypothesis, the set in parentheses has $(m - 1)n$ elements. The set A_m is disjoint from the set in parentheses, so by Theorem 1 the size of $A_1 \cup \cdots \cup A_m$ is $(m - 1)n + n = mn$. Thus by the principle of mathematical induction, the theorem holds for all m.   ∎

EXAMPLE 5   Redo Example 4 using the product principle.

Solution   For each choice of chair we have a set of 5 (chair, secretary-treasurer) pairs with that chair. Thus the set of all possible pairs is the union of six disjoint sets of size 5. Therefore, by the product principle, it has size $6\cdot 5 = 30$.   ∎

It turns out that we may interpret many counting problems as asking for the size of a set of ordered pairs. There is a version of the product principle we could apply directly to such problems. By making the kind of argument we did in the solution of Example 5, we can prove the "ordered pairs" form of the product principle, stated as Theorem 3.

Theorem 3   If m different elements appear as the first elements of ordered pairs in a set S and each first element appears with exactly n different second elements in ordered pairs in S, then S contains exactly mn ordered pairs.

Proof   Similar to the solution of Example 5.   ∎

EXAMPLE 6   Redo Example 4 using Theorem 3.

Solution   Six different people may appear as the first element of a (chair, secretary-treasurer) pair, and each may appear with five different second elements, so we have $6 \cdot 5 = 30$ pairs.   ∎

EXAMPLE 7   The ten-person governing board of the student newspaper and the eight-person editorial committee of the student newspaper must each choose a representative to meet to discuss policy. In how many ways may the pair of representatives be chosen if no governor is on the editorial committee?

Solution   If we give the governing representative first, we have ten choices for the first member of the pair of representatives and eight choices for the second member to go with each first member. Thus we have $10 \cdot 8 = 80$ pairs.   ■

Many problems lead us, as Example 7 did, to consider the set of all ordered pairs whose first element is in a set S and whose second element is in a set T. This set of ordered pairs is denoted by $S \times T$ and called the **Cartesian product** of S and T.

EXAMPLE 8   Write down the Cartesian product of $\{a,b,c\}$ and $\{1,2,3,4\}$.

Solution $\{a,b,c\} \times \{1,2,3,4\} = \{(a,1), (a,2), (a,3), (a,4), (b,1), (b,2), (b,3), (b,4),$ $(c,1), (c,2), (c,3), (c,4)\}$.   ■

By using the method of Example 8, we may show that the size of $S \times T$ is the product of the size of S and the size of T. There is a very useful notation for the size of a set S, using absolute value signs: $|S|$ stands for the size of S and is read as "size of S," *not* "the absolute value of S." For example $|\{cat,pig,cow\}| = 3$. In this notation, our statement about the size of the Cartesian product becomes $|S \times T| = |S| \cdot |T|$. In words, this says, "The size of the product is the product of the sizes." A suggestive example will help us remember this application of the product principle.

EXAMPLE 9   If we have three varieties of bread and five varieties of meat, in how many ways can we make a sandwich using one variety each of bread and meat?

Solution   The sandwiches correspond to ordered pairs (bread variety, meat variety). Thus the number of sandwiches is the size of the Cartesian product of the bread set and meat set, so we have $3 \cdot 5 = 15$ different kinds of sandwiches.   ■

▣ Counting Permutations and Functions

The General Product Principle

We've seen how to use the product principle to compute the number of ways to make a pair of selections—such as the chairperson and secretary-treasurer for a committee. This application leads us to ask, "What if we need a chair, a secretary *and* a treasurer—three people instead of two?" What about a club that needs a president, a vice-president, a secretary, and a treasurer? These problems lead us to count triples—lists of three things—or quadruples—lists of four things. In general, we can imagine problems that ask us to count m-*tuples* (rhymes with quadruples)—lists of *m* things.

The **general product principle,** stated in Theorem 4, extends the product principle from pairs to *m*-tuples.

Theorem 4   Let S be a set of m-tuples such that

(1) There are n_1 different first elements of m-tuples in S.
(2) Given the first $k - 1$ elements of an n-tuple, there are n_k different k^{th} elements appearing with them in n-tuples.

Then there are $\displaystyle\prod_{i=1}^{m} n_i = n_1 \cdot n_2 \cdot \cdots \cdot n_m$ m-tuples in S.

Proof   The proof is by induction on m. If $m = 1$, there is nothing to prove. Suppose the theorem is true for $(m - 1)$-tuples, and let S be a set of m-tuples with the two properties above. Then by the theorem for $(m-1)$-tuples, there are

$$n_1 \cdot n_2 \cdot \cdots \cdot n_{m-1} = \prod_{i=1}^{m-1} n_i$$

ways to choose the first $m - 1$ elements of an m-tuple in S with a given element in position m. For each of the n_m choices for place m, we have a set of $n_1 \cdot n_2 \cdot \cdots \cdot n_{m-1}$ m-tuples that end in that particular choice. Thus the set of all m-tuples is a union of n_m sets, each with $n_1 \cdot n_2 \cdot \cdots \cdot n_{m-1}$ elements; by the product principle, this set has $n_1 \cdot n_2 \cdot \cdots \cdot n_{m-1} \cdot n_m$ m-tuples. Thus, by the principle of mathematical induction, the theorem holds for all m.   ∎

m-*element Permutations*

The problems we used to introduce the general product principle asked for lists of three *different* people or four *different* people in a group. In other words, they asked for one-to-one functions from $\{1,2,3\}$ or $\{1,2,3,4\}$ to a certain set of people.

> We define an **m-element permutation** of a set S
> to be a one-to-one function from the set
> $M = \{1,2, \ldots ,m\}$ to the set S.

Thus an m-element permutation of S is a list of m *distinct* elements of S.

EXAMPLE 10   List all three-element permutations of the four-element set $\{a,b,c,d\}$, representing each permutation as a list of letters.

Solution   We will write our lists in alphabetical order.

$$
\begin{array}{cccccc}
abc & abd & acb & acd & adb & adc \\
bac & bad & bca & bcd & bda & bdc \\
cab & cad & cba & cbd & cda & cdb \\
dab & dac & dba & dbc & dca & dcb
\end{array}
$$
∎

An n-element permutation of an n-element set S
is called simply a **permutation** of S.

EXAMPLE 11   List all permutations of $\{a,b,c\}$, representing each permutation as a list of letters.

Solution

$$
abc \quad acb \quad bac \quad bca \quad cab \quad cba
$$
∎

In effect, we already computed the number of m-element permutations of an n-element set in Theorem 4, but we shall restate the theorem in the language of permutations.

Theorem 5   The number of m-element permutations of an n-element set S is $n!/(n-m)!$. The number of permutations of an n-element set is $n!$.

Proof   We may restate the first sentence of the theorem as, "There are $n!/(n-m)!$ m-tuples of distinct elements chosen from an n-element set S." There are n ways to choose the first element of such an n-tuple. Once we have chosen the first $k-1$ elements of an n-tuple, there are $n-(k-1)=n-k+1$ remaining elements from which we choose the kth member of the n-tuple. Thus there are $n-k+1$ ways to choose the kth member of the n-tuple. Therefore, by Theorem 4, the number of elements in the set of n-tuples is

$$
\prod_{i=1}^{m} (n-i+1) = n\cdot(n-1)\cdot \, \cdots \, \cdot(n-m+1) =
$$

$$
\frac{n\cdot(n-1)\cdot \, \cdots \, \cdot(n-m+1)\cdot(n-m)\cdot \, \cdots \, \cdot1}{(n-m)\cdot(n-m-1)\cdot \, \cdots \, \cdot1} = \frac{n!}{(n-m)!}
$$

The second sentence of the theorem is the special case when $m=n$, and since $0!=1$, the quotient in the first sentence becomes $n!$ in this case.   ∎

The number $n!/(n-k)!$ is often denoted by $(n)_k$ or $P(n,k)$ (for the number of permutations of n things taken k at a time). In Example 12, notice that we do not need to compute $n!$ and $(n-k)!$ in order to compute their ratio, because the $(n-k)!$ cancels out.

EXAMPLE 12   In how many ways can a ten-person club choose three different people to be president, vice-president, and secretary-treasurer?

Solution   We are asking for the number of 3-element permutations of a 10-element set; this number is

$$(10)_3 = \frac{10!}{(10-3)!} = \frac{10!}{7!} = \frac{10 \cdot 9 \cdot 8 \cdot 7 \cdot 6 \cdot \cdots \cdot 1}{7 \cdot 6 \cdot \cdots \cdot 1} = 10 \cdot 9 \cdot 8 = 720 \qquad \blacksquare$$

Other Applications of the Product Principle

There are many applications of the product principle that *do not* involve counting permutations.

EXAMPLE 13   In a test of surface adhesion of paints, six paint varieties were tested using three undercoatings on three different kinds of surfaces. In order to test each combination of factors, how many tests are necessary?

Solution   By the general product principle, we need $6 \cdot 3 \cdot 3 = 54$ tests. $\blacksquare$

EXAMPLE 14   A small database management system consists of three memory devices and four workstations. At any moment, any workstation may make a request for data from any memory device. How many different patterns for simultaneous requests from all the workstations are possible?

Solution   We may view a pattern as a four-tuple consisting of the device requested by workstation 1, the device requested by workstation 2, the device requested by workstation 3, and the device requested by workstation 4. There are three possible entries for the first position of the four-tuple; for each way of choosing this first entry, there are three ways to choose the second entry; for each choice of the first two entries, there are three ways to choose the third; and for each way to choose the first three entries, there are three choices for the fourth entry. Thus we have $3 \cdot 3 \cdot 3 \cdot 3 = 3^4$ four-tuples—3^4 possible patterns of requests for data. $\blacksquare$

In Example 14, we have seen a special case of another pattern that arises frequently.

Theorem 6   The number of functions from an m-element set to an n-element set is n^m.

Proof   We may think of this m-element set as being listed as $a_1, a_2, \ldots, a_m$ by a counting function. Then functions f may be described by m-tuples $(f(a_1), f(a_2), \ldots, f(a_m))$. There are n choices for each $f(a_i)$, so by the product principle there are n^m functions. $\blacksquare$

EXAMPLE 15   Do Example 14 by using Theorem 6.

Solution   We are asking for the number of functions from the set of workstations to the set of memory devices. By Theorem 6, with $m = 4$ and $n = 3$, this number is 3^4.   ■

What is the difference between counting permutations and counting functions? Example 16 illustrates the difference.

EXAMPLE 16   We have five different chairs and seven colors of paint. In how many ways may we paint the chairs if all chairs must be different colors? What if we may use the same color on several (or all) chairs?

Solution   Our paint jobs assign one paint color to each chair, so they are functions from the five-element set of chairs to the seven-element set of colors. Paint jobs with *different* paints on different chairs are one-to-one functions, so there are $P(7,5)$ $= (7)_5 = \frac{7!}{(7-5)!} = 7 \cdot 6 \cdot 5 \cdot 4 \cdot 3 = 2520$ paint jobs with different paints. Paint jobs with repeated colors allowed are merely functions, so there are $7^5 = 16,807$ such paint jobs.   ■

Concepts Review

1. $A(n)$ _____ _____ is a bijection from a set $N = \{1,2, \ldots ,n\}$ onto a set S.

2. A set S has _____ n if there is a counting function from $\{1,2, \ldots ,n\}$ onto S.

3. The principle that two sets have the _____ _____ if there is a bijection between them is called the bijection principle.

4. The _____ _____ states that the size of a union of two disjoint sets is the sum of their sizes.

5. The _____ _____ states that the union of m disjoint sets of size n has size mn.

6. The _____ _____ for ordered pairs tells us that if m different elements appear as the first elements of ordered pairs in a set S and each first element appears with exactly n different second elements, then S contains mn ordered pairs.

7. The _____ _____ of S and T is the set of ordered pairs (x,y), with x in S and y in T.

8. If there are n_1 different first elements of m-tuples in S, and for each way of specifying the first $k - 1$ elements of an m-tuple there are n_k different k^{th} elements of m-tuples with these first $k - 1$ elements, then S contains _____ m-tuples.

9. A k-element _____ of a set S is a one-to-one function from $\{1,2, \ldots ,k\}$ to the set S.

10. The number of m-element permutations of an n-element set is _____.

11. The number of functions from an m-element set to an n-element set is _____.

Exercises

A 1. Write down the ordered pairs of a counting function for the set of alphabet letters from a through g.

2. Write down the ordered pairs of a counting function for the set of alphabet letters from r through z.

3. We can represent three flips of a coin with a list of three letters, each H or T, such as HHT. Let S be the set of all such lists of three letters, each H or T. Let R be the set of *all* subsets of $\{1,2,3\}$. Give a bijection that shows that R and S have the same size.

4. Let R be the set of all functions from $\{1,2,3\}$ to $\{0,1\}$. Let S be the set of all subsets of $\{1,2,3\}$. Give a bijection that shows that R and S have the same size.

5. Let $R = \{a,c\}$ and $S = \{1,2,3,4\}$. Write down $R \times S$. Verify that $|R \times S| = |R| \cdot |S|$.

6. Let $R = \{x,y,z\}$ and $S = \{a,b,c\}$. Write down $R \times S$. Verify that $|R \times S| = |R| \cdot |S|$.

7. In tests of rustproof coatings, each of five different coatings is to be applied to seven different kinds of surfaces. How many tests will be made?

8. In choosing a microcomputer from a certain company, we have a choice of five different main processing units and of three different video displays. These two pieces make a complete system. In how many ways may we choose our system?

9. In how many ways may an eight-member math club choose a president and a secretary (if they must be different)?

10. In how many ways may a 20-member fraternity select a delegate and an alternate for the interfraternity council?

B 11. Compute the ratio $P(20,2) = 20!/18!$ without computing either 20! or 18!.

12. Compute the ratio $(25)_2 = 25!/23!$ without computing either 25! or 23!.

13. What is the value of $(4)_2$? Write down all two-element permutations of a four-element set to show that there are $(4)_2$ of them.

14. What is the value of $(5)_2$? Write down all two-element permutations of a five-element set to show that there are $(5)_2$ of them.

In Exercises 15–38, compute the numbers requested.

15. $P(5,3)$ 16. $P(7,4)$

17. $(6)_3$ 18. $P(7,3)$

19. $(20)_1$ 20. $(7)_3$

21. $P(20,1)$ 22. $(7)_4$

23. $P(15,2)$ 24. $(k)_3$

25. $(20)_2$

26. $P(k,2)$

27. $P(n,2)$

28. $P(22,2)$

29. $P(n,3)$

30. $P(5,5)$

31. $(n)_2$

32. $(3)_3$

33. $P(4,4)$

34. $P(100,1)$

35. $(5)_1$

36. $P(n^2,2)$

37. $(5)_4$

38. $P(n,2)^2$

39. If the club with ten members is to select a president, vice-president, secretary, and treasurer (all different people), in how many ways can they do so?

40. With four kinds of bread, three kinds of cheese, and three kinds of lunch meat, in how many ways may you make a sandwich? (Use one variety of each kind of ingredient.)

41. In how many ways may you pass out three distinct candy bars to four children if no one may get two or more? If you can give any number to any person?

42. In how many ways may you pass out five different pieces of candy to five children if each child must get a piece? If any child can get any number?

43. A pizza may be ordered with any, all, or none of pepperoni, sausage, ground beef, mushrooms, peppers, onions, salami, and anchovies. How many different kinds of pizza are possible?

44. A ten-question true-false test may have any pattern of true and false questions. Among all possible tests, how many patterns of true and false answers are possible?

45. In the local ice cream shop, you may get a sundae with one of ten flavors of ice cream, any one of three flavors of topping, and any (or all or none) of whipped cream, nuts, and a cherry. How many sundaes are possible?

46. The Square Meal Hamburger Shop lets you have your sandwich with one, two, or three beef patties and any of the following toppings: lettuce, tomato, cheese, pickles, special sauce, catsup, mustard, onions. How many different hamburgers are possible?

Problems

1. Show, by describing an appropriate bijection, that the size of a union of three disjoint sets is the sum of their sizes.

2. Show, by an appropriate use of mathematical induction, that the size of a union of n disjoint sets is the sum of their sizes.

3. Show that if R has size n and S has size n, then there is a bijection from R to S.

4. Show that if R has size n and there is a bijection between R and S, then S has size n.

5. Prove Theorem 3.

6. A professor has six test questions. Three form a unit and must be kept together in the order the professor has chosen. In how many ways may the professor arrange the test questions? If the three questions kept together can be asked in any order, then in how many ways may the professor arrange the questions?

7. Three reporters from the school newspaper and three reporters from the school radio station form the panel for a discussion. In how many ways may they be seated in a row behind a table if each of the two groups should sit as three people in a row? In how many ways may they be seated if not one may be adjacent to someone who is from the same group of three?

8. There are a million numbers between 1 and 10^6 (inclusive). How many have only even digits? Only digits different from 1? How many contain at least one digit that is a 1?

9. In a group of n married couples, we wish to choose a pair of people of opposite sexes who are not married to each other. In how many ways may we do this? Suppose we have one child of each couple in the group as well. In how many ways may we pick a man, a woman, and a child who are mutually unrelated?

10. Compute the number of ways to make a stack of five cards from a standard deck of playing cards so that the ace of spades is in the stack. So that at least one ace is in the stack.

11. A license plate has three letters and four numerical digits. How many license plates are possible? How many are possible if the digits and letters must alternate? If the letters must be together in a row? If there are either two or three letters?

12. What is the number of ten-digit numbers in which no two successive digits are equal?

13. Show that if S and T have the same size and R and S have the same size, then R and T have the same size.

14. Prove that the size of a Cartesian product of two sets is the product of their sizes.

Section 6-2
Applications of the
Basic Counting
Principles

◪ Subsets

A surprising variety of problems may be interpreted as asking a question about subsets of a set.

EXAMPLE 17   A teacher asks a twelve-student class for volunteers to work on a project. How many different groups of volunteers may occur?

Solution   To describe the set of volunteers, we write down for each student whether or not he or she volunteers. This gives us a function from the set of students to the set {volunteers, doesn't}. Each different function represents a different set of volunteers, so the number of sets is the number of functions, which is $2^{12} = 4096$. Note that among the possible volunteer sets is the empty set—the set of no volunteers. ∎

The Number of Subsets of a Set

Rather than analyzing each problem involving subsets in the manner above, it will be convenient for us to have a general statement about subsets of a set that we can apply as needed. This is the purpose of Theorem 7.

Theorem 7   A set with n elements has 2^n subsets.

Proof   To specify a subset of an n-element set S, we must specify for each element of S whether it is in the subset or not. By the product principle, there are 2^n such sequences of specifications. ∎

A sequence of specifications, as in the proof of Theorem 7, may be regarded as a function from the n-element set S to the set {not in the subset, in the subset} or, more simply, as a function from S to $\{0,1\}$. This function is called the **characteristic function** of the subset. By Theorem 6, there are 2^n such functions; this gives another proof of Theorem 7.

m-element Subsets of a Set

Problems that lead us to consider subsets often lead us to subsets of a given size. For example, the president of a club may appoint a committee of three people to plan an event. The number of possible committees is the number of 3-element subsets of the set of club members. As another example, it is possible for a computer disk drive to use 16-bit words (sequences of 16 zeros and ones) with information encoded in a special way. With this special encoding, if any single bit is in error, the computer will correct it. Further, if any two bits are in error, the computer will detect this and give us a message saying so. How many patterns of two errors are possible? Such an error pattern is a two-element subset of the set of 16 positions in the computer word, so we are asking, "How many two-element subsets does a 16-element set have?"

To compute the number of m-element subsets of an n-element set, we do not have a clear-cut application of the product principle, but there is a way to apply it indirectly. The method is based on relating m-element permutations and m-element subsets.

Each m-element permutation chosen from an n-element set S is a list of m distinct elements of S. Therefore, it is a list of the elements of an m-element subset of S. A given m-element subset can be listed in $m!$ ways, so the product principle gives us

$$\text{(number of } m\text{-element subsets)} \cdot m! = \text{number of } m\text{-element permutations}$$
$$= (n)_m = \frac{n!}{(n-m)!}$$

Dividing by $m!$ gives

$$\text{(number of } m\text{-element subsets)} = \frac{(n)_m}{m!} = \frac{n!}{m!(n-m)!}$$

We use the symbols $\binom{n}{m}$ or $C(n,m)$ which are read "n choose m" to stand for the number of m-element subsets of an n-element set. Thus we have just shown the following theorem.

Theorem 8   The number of m-element subsets of an n-element set is given by

$$\binom{n}{m} = \frac{n!}{m!(n-m)!}$$

Proof   Given above.   ∎

EXAMPLE 18   What is the number of 2-element subsets of a 16-element set? What is the number of 14-element subsets of a 16-element set?

Solution   We have $\binom{16}{2}$ 2-element subsets. This number is

$$\binom{16}{2} = C(16,2) = \frac{16!}{2! \cdot 14!} = \frac{16 \cdot 15 \cdot 14!}{2! \cdot 14!} = \frac{16 \cdot 15}{2} = 8 \cdot 15 = 120$$

Similarly, we have

$$\binom{16}{14} = C(16,14) = \frac{16!}{14! \cdot 2!} = 120$$

14-element subsets.   ∎

Notice that in the example we did not attempt to compute $16!$ or $14!$; we merely cancelled the $14!$ "out of" the $16!$, leaving only $16 \cdot 15$ to multiply together. Notice also that we got the same answer for both the number of 2-element subsets and the number of 14-element subsets. We could have predicted that equality in advance, for the number of ways to choose 2 elements to be *in* the subset and 14 to be *out* of the subset should be the same as the number of ways to choose 14 to be *in* and 2 to be *out*.

The number $\binom{n}{k}$ is called a **binomial coefficient,** for reasons we shall explain later. People used to (and sometimes still do) call a k-element subset a k-element *combination*. In this context, $(n)_k$ is called "the number of permutations of n things taken k at a time," and $\binom{n}{k}$ is called "the number of combinations of n things taken k at a time." Thus when people talk about "permutations and combinations," they are actually discussing one-to-one functions and subsets.

Extending the examples of choosing officers for a club should help us distinguish intuitively among k-element permutations, k-element subsets, and k-tuples.

EXAMPLE 19   A ten-member club must select a president, a vice-president, and a secretary-treasurer. They must also select a three-member social committee. In how many ways may they make each of these selections? In addition, the club members serve as big brothers or sisters for a children's group. If three new children join that group, in how many ways may the three children select their big brothers or sisters?

Solution   The choice of a president, a vice-president, and a secretary-treasurer gives us a list of three different people, listed in the order that we just listed their titles. Any different list, even with the same people in a different order, corresponds to a different selection. Thus the number of ways to choose officers is the number of 3-element permutations of a 10-element set, namely

$$(10)_3 \,=\, 10{\cdot}9{\cdot}8 \,=\, 720$$

The choice of the three members of the social committee gives us a 3-element set. The order in which we choose the members is irrelevant; choosing the same three people in two different orders gives the same subset. Any different 3-element subset of the ten people gives us a different committee. Thus the number of committees is the number of 3-element subsets (combinations) of a 10-element set, namely

$$\binom{10}{3} \,=\, \frac{10{\cdot}9{\cdot}8}{3{\cdot}2{\cdot}1} \,=\, 120$$

Each child makes a choice from the group of ten people (note that two different children may choose the same member), so the three choices give us a function from the set of three children to the set of ten club members. By Theorem 6, there are $10^3 \,=\, 1000$ such functions. As another way to count the choices, we may regard such a function as a 3-tuple giving the choices of the first, second, and third children, and since each child has ten possible choices we have $10{\cdot}10{\cdot}10 \,=\, 10^3$ such three-tuples.   ■

Another way to see the differences is to write out all k-element permutations, k-element subsets, and k-tuples chosen from a set.

EXAMPLE 20   Write down the 2-element permutations, 2-element subsets, and 2-tuples chosen from the set $\{a,b,c\}$.

Solution

Permutations: *ab   ac   ba   bc   ca   cb*
Subsets: $\{a,b\}$ $\{a,c\}$ $\{b,c\}$
2-tuples: (a,a) (a,b) (a,c) (b,a) (b,b) (b,c) (c,a) (c,b) (c,c) ∎

Multisets

Some problems that appear to call for a subset in fact call for something slightly different, known as a *multiset*. For example, the alphabet letters of the word *roof* are, in alphabetical order $\{f,o,o,r\}$. However, despite our use of braces, we have not written down a set. The *set* of alphabet letters used in the word roof is $\{f,o,r\}$. In some applications (for example, in a computer program to format a document in proportional type) it is important to record how many times each letter occurs. We say that $\{f,o,o,r\}$ is the *multiset* of letters used in *roof*.

> A **multiset** chosen from a set S is specified by a function m from S to the non-negative integers. For each x in S, $m(x)$ is called the **multiplicity** of x. The **size** of the multiset is the sum of the multiplicities of the elements of S.

EXAMPLE 21   What is the multiplicity of each letter of the alphabet in the word *roof*? What is the size of the multiset of letters of *roof*?

Solution   The multiplicity of f is one, of o is two, and of r is one. The multiplicity of each other letter of the alphabet is zero. In symbols, $m(f) = 1$, $m(o) = 2$, $m(r) = 1$, $m(a) = 0$, $m(b) = 0$, $m(c) = 0$, and so on. The size of the multiset is $1 + 2 + 1 = 4$.   ∎

Notice that the characteristic function of a subset T of S is a function that assigns the non-negative integer 0 or 1 to each element of S, assigning a 1 to each element of T and a 0 to all other members of S. Thus we may regard a subset T of a set S as a multiset chosen from S in which the multiplicities are given by the characteristic function of T. It turns out that binomial coefficients are useful in counting the number of k-element multisets chosen from an n-element set.

Theorem 9   The number of k-element multisets chosen from an n-element set is given by

$$\binom{n + k - 1}{k}$$

Proof   A proof similar to the proof of Theorem 8 may be based on the idea of counting equivalence classes of an equivalence relation. A proof that requires less knowledge but gives less insight into general principles is the following. For each multiplicity function m defined on $S = \{x_1, x_2, \ldots x_n\}$, we can define a sequence of $n + k - 1$ ones and zeros as follows. Write down $m(x_1)$ ones, and then write down a zero. Then write down $m(x_2)$ ones and write down a zero. Continue in this way until you have written $m(x_{n-1})$ ones and a zero. Now write down $m(x_n)$ ones and do *not* write another zero. This sequence has $n + k - 1$ entries, and k of these entries are ones. The number of such sequences is the number of ways to choose the k entries that are ones, and this number is $\binom{n + k - 1}{k}$. Since we described a bijection between these sequences and the multiplicity functions of multisets of size k, this is also the number of multisets of size k chosen from S. ∎

EXAMPLE 22   A bin of personal computer disks contains a large supply of disks from four different manufacturers. In how many ways may someone choose six disks from the bin?

Solution   Each selection of six disks may be regarded as a six-element multiset chosen from the set of the four manufacturers. Thus there are

$$\binom{4 + 6 - 1}{6} = \binom{9}{6} = 84 \text{ selections}$$

B   Decomposing Counting Problems

When to Use the Product Principle

The counting problems we have studied so far have involved one application of the sum or product principle or one use of a formula for the number of k-element permutations, k-element subsets, or k-tuples. Real-world problems can be more complicated, however.

EXAMPLE 23   A ten-person club must select a president, a vice-president, and a secretary-treasurer. They must also select a three-person committee. If the officers may *not* serve on the committee, in how many ways may *both* selections be made?

Solution   Once we select the three officers, there will be seven people left from whom we must select a 3-element subset. Thus we will have an ordered pair consisting of a 3-element permutation of a 10-element set for the officers *and* a 3-element subset of a 7-element set for the social committee. We have $(10)_3$ choices for the first member of the ordered pair and $\binom{7}{3}$ choices for the second. Thus, by the product principle, we have

$$(10)_3 \binom{7}{3} = 720 \cdot 35 = 25,200 \text{ selections}$$

Notice, by the way, that $\binom{10}{3}(7)_3 = 120\cdot210 = 25,200$. What method of solving the problem does this equation come from?   ∎

The example suggests the following problem-solving strategy. A problem calls for the product principle if there is a sequence of decisions (or actions) and the *number of* ways of making one is not affected by the actual decisions made for the others. Thus in Example 23, though the actual set of people available for the committee depended on the people chosen as officers, the number of people available to choose from was not dependent on whom we chose for officers.

Tree Diagrams and the Sum Principle

When the situation for a sequence of decisions is less structured than what we've described, it is usually necessary to break the problem into cases, find the number of ways to deal with each case, and add the results together. This means that we are applying the sum principle. A diagram called a **tree diagram** is especially useful for visualizing such a sequence of decisions. Figure 2 is the tree diagram corresponding to the following example.

EXAMPLE 24   We flip a coin. If it comes up heads, we roll a die; if it comes up tails, we flip it again. How many outcomes are possible?

Solution   Figure 2 shows that eight outcomes are possible. This is the sum of the six outcomes in the set of outcomes beginning with heads and the two outcomes in the set of outcomes beginning with tails.   ∎

Figure 2

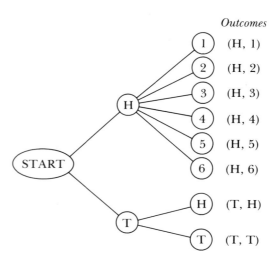

Example 24 was so easy that the diagram was not really necessary. In more complex situations, a tree diagram can be quite useful.

EXAMPLE 25 We have four identical nickels, three identical dimes, and two identical quarters. We select coins until we have 50 cents. In how many ways may we do this?

Solution We choose 0, 1, or 2 quarters, 0, 1, 2, or 3 dimes, and 0, 1, 2, 3, or 4 nickels. However, we choose until we get 50 cents and then stop. Thus our nickel and dime choices will be affected by our quarter choices. Let us divide the problem into three cases: no quarters, 1 quarter, and 2 quarters. These are represented by the circular nodes with 0Q, 1Q, and 2Q in them in Figure 3.

Figure 3 A tree diagram for coin selection.

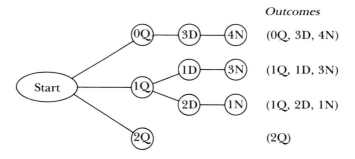

Outcomes

(0Q, 3D, 4N)

(1Q, 1D, 3N)

(1Q, 2D, 1N)

(2Q)

In the case of no quarters, we see that we have no choice but to take all the dimes and nickels. In the case of 1 quarter, we have two subcases, 1 and 2 dimes (what is wrong with 0 dimes or 3 dimes?), which each lead to one selection of coins. In the case of 2 quarters, we have no further selections to make. Thus we have four ways to choose 50 cents. Each choice of coins is completely described by a path through the tree from start to a branch tip, and each such path corresponds to exactly one way to choose the coins. Thus there are four ways to select 50 cents. ∎

There is a subtle point in Example 25. We did not begin with a sequential process—the problem did not say to choose *first* from the quarters, *second* from the dimes, and *third* from the nickels. We imposed this order on the problem by the way we divided it into cases. Each collection of coins adding to 50 cents *will have* either 0, 1, or 2 quarters, so it falls into one of these cases. By the sum principle, the number of selections will be the sum of the numbers in each of these cases. Correspondingly, when we considered dimes, we considered all possible cases; when we considered nickels, we considered all possible cases. How can we be sure we have covered all the cases? We could draw a tree that represents

Figure 4

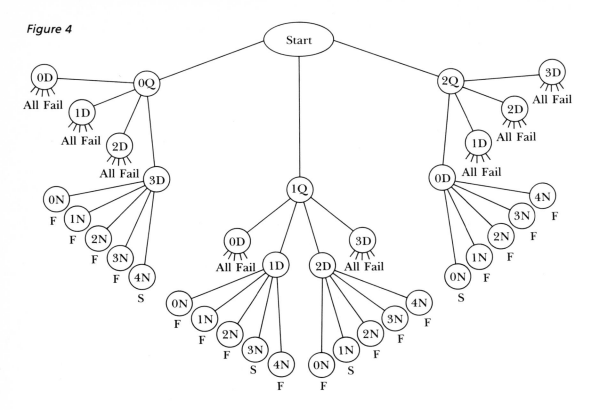

all ways to select coins (that is, it represents the entire *universe* of coin selections) and then go through and label each according to how much that path corresponds to. Part of that approach is illustrated in Figure 4.

We put an F at the end of a path in the tree if that path fails to reach 50 cents. We put an S at the node on the end of a path if that path is successful in reaching 50 cents. Then we count the number of S's to verify the results of Example 25. How big would the tree have been if we had drawn it all? Since there are 3 quarter nodes and 4 dime nodes for each quarter, we would have 3·4 = 12 dime nodes in total, and since there are 5 nickel nodes for each dime node, we would have 12·5 = 60 nickel nodes. Clearly, we should only carry out this painstaking process when we must do so to ensure that each case has been found.

Concepts Review

1. The number of subsets of an n-element set is _____.

2. The number of m-element subsets of an n-element set is _____.

3. The number $\binom{n}{k}$ is called a(n) _____ _____.

4. Another name for the number of k-element subsets of an n-element set is the number of _____ of n things taken k at a time.

5. We use the _____ principle in a problem involving a sequence of decisions if the number of ways of making one of the decisions is not affected by the other decisions that are made.

6. When we break a problem into cases and add together the number of ways of solving each case, we are applying the _____ principle.

7. To specify a(n) _____ chosen from a set x, we assign a non-negative integer $m(x)$ to each element x of S.

8. The number of k-element multisets that may be chosen from an n-element set is _____.

Exercises

A

1. What is the value of $\binom{5}{3}$? Write down all 3-element subsets of a 5-element set to show that there are $\binom{5}{3}$ of them.

2. What is the value of $\binom{6}{2}$? Write down all 2-element subsets of a 6-element set to show that there are $\binom{6}{2}$ of them.

Compute the following numbers.

3. $\binom{6}{3}$ 4. $\binom{7}{4}$ 5. $\binom{20}{19}$ 6. $\binom{7}{3}$

7. $\binom{20}{1}$ 8. $(7)_3$ 9. $\binom{20}{2}$ 10. $(7)_4$

11. $\binom{n}{n-2}$ 12. $\binom{k}{k-3}$ 13. $\binom{n}{2}$ 14. $\binom{k}{3}$

15. $(n)_2$ 16. $(k)_3$ 17. $\binom{655}{654}$ 18. $\binom{25}{23}$

19. $(5)_1$ 20. $\binom{25}{2}$ 21. $(5)_4$ 22. $\binom{801}{799}$

23. $\binom{5}{1}$ 24. $\binom{n^2}{2}$ 25. $\binom{5}{4}$ 26. $\binom{n}{2}^2$

27. If a candy machine has ten different kinds of candy, in how many ways may you select four distinct items?

28. If a computer word has 16 bits, in how many different ways could 3 bits be in error?

29. If you flip a coin eight times, how many different sequences of results with exactly four heads are possible?

30. On a 10-question test, how many patterns of eight correct and two incorrect answers are possible? Eight or more correct answers?

31. From ten people, we must select a committee of three and a committee of four. In how many ways may we do this if the memberships may overlap? In how many ways may we do this if the memberships may not overlap?

32. A teacher with a class of 20 students must select 4 students to enter a science fair and 3 students to enter a writing contest. In how many ways may the teacher make the selections if the two groups may not overlap? What if they may overlap?

33. For most parts below, the problem may be solved by using k-element permutations (or one-to-one functions), k-element subsets, or k-tuples (or functions). For each part, state which method may be used or that none of the three is appropriate.
    (a) In how many ways may five different candy bars be passed out to ten people if no one may receive more than one?
    (b) In how many ways may five different candy bars be passed out to ten people if anyone may get any number of candy bars?
    (c) In how many ways may five identical apples be passed out to ten people if no one may receive more than one?
    (d) In how many ways may five identical apples be passed out to ten people if anyone may get any number of apples?

34. For most parts below, the problem may be solved by using k-element permutations (or one-to-one functions), k-element subsets, or k-tuples (or functions). For each part, state which method may be used. You do not need to know anything about disks, sectors, or reads except for the information given.
    (a) A disk storage device has 16 disks, each of which has many sectors. If a request for data requires reading sectors on 4 *different* disks, in how many ways could the 4 disks be chosen?
    (b) If the 4 sectors needed in part (a) must be read in a certain order, in how many ways could the 4 disks be chosen and read from?
    (c) If the 4 sectors needed in part (a) do not necessarily lie on different disks but must be read in order, in how many ways may the 4 disk reads occur?
    (d) If the 4 sectors do not necessarily lie on the same disks (or on different disks) and do not need to be read in any order, in how many ways may the 4 disk reads occur?

35. Write down the multiplicity function for the multiset of letters chosen from the alphabet in the phrase *practice phrase*.

36. Write down the multiplicity function for the multiset of letters chosen from the alphabet in the phrase *boring but enlightening*.

In Exercises 37–42, compute the number of multisets asked for.

37. 3-element multisets chosen from a 5-element set.

38. 2-element multisets chosen from a 20-element set.

39. 10-element multisets chosen from a 3-element set.

40. 4-element multisets chosen from a 4-element set.

41. 3-element multisets chosen from a 20-element set.

42. 20-element multisets chosen from a 3-element set.

43. A candy store sells five different kinds of chocolate-covered cremes. In how many ways may you select a bag of eight of them?

44. A grocery store has seven different varieties of fruit on display. In how many ways may you select a bag of five pieces of fruit?

45. Find a part of Exercise 33 that may be solved by using multisets.

46. Find a part of Exercise 34 that may be solved by using multisets.

B 47. A group of 12 people must choose a chairperson, who will then select a 3-person executive committee. In how many ways may this process be carried out?

48. A teacher chooses 1 student from a class of 25 students and asks this student to choose 2 others to form a 3-person group to prepare a report. In how many ways may this be done if the student chosen by the teacher is in charge of the group?

49. In how many ways may a committee of three people and a committee of four people be chosen from a club of ten people if the memberships may not overlap? If the memberships may overlap?

50. In how many ways may a teacher with 15 students choose 3 students to compete in a writing contest and 2 students to compete in a speech contest if all 5 students must be different? What if the same students may compete in both contests?

51. In how many ways may a 10-person scout troop committee select a chair, a treasurer, and a 3-person advancement committee if the officers do not serve on the committee?

52. A 20-member fraternity is sponsoring two money-raising projects for charity. For each project, they are giving prizes to the members who come in first, second, and third in the amount of money raised. (The prizes are all different.) In how many ways may the prizes be distributed?

53. We flip a coin until we have two heads or three tails among the outcomes. By using a tree diagram, compute the number of possible sequences of heads and tails we could see.

54. We roll a die until the sum of the top faces is 6 or more. By using a tree diagram, compute the number of possible outcomes.

55. We have coins in two pockets. One has a Canadian nickel, Canadian dime, and Canadian quarter. The other has two identical nickels, two identical dimes, and a quarter, all United States. We choose a pocket and then choose two coins. How many outcomes are possible?

56. A small company has decided to purchase workstations for its top three executives and has reduced the choices to Company D and Company W. All three executives will have to buy from the same company, but they may choose different models. Company D

has four models of workstations and Company W has six models. How many choices are possible?

57. In choosing a sandwich at Speedy Sandwiches, we must decide whether we want a meat sandwich or a meat and cheese sandwich. If there are three choices for bread, five choices for meat, and six choices for cheese, how many sandwiches are possible?

58. In order to go from Camp Bing to Camp Thomas, you must either cross Joe's Peak or go through Narrow's Pass and cross Greene Mountain. There are two trails each from Camp Bing to Joe's Peak and Narrow's Pass. There are three trails from Narrow's Pass to Greene Mountain, two trails from Greene Mountain to Camp Thomas, and two trails from Joe's Peak to Camp Thomas. In how many ways may you plan a hike along trails from Camp Bing to Camp Thomas?

Problems

1. A student has n friends and plans to eat dinner with a different set of four friends for each night of their senior year. If there are 224 evenings on campus during the senior year, what is the smallest n can be?

2. In choosing a three-scoop sundae, you decide on one, two, or three flavors of ice cream, choose your ice cream from among ten varieties, choose from five choices of topping, and say yes or no to whipped cream, nuts, and a cherry. How many different sundaes are possible?

3. A computer-aided instruction program asks a student each question on a list of 20 different questions. For each question, there are 10 choices for the answer. If the student answers the question correctly, the program says so. If the student gets the answer wrong, the program says so and gives the student another chance. If the answer is wrong the second time, then the computer gives the correct answer with a brief explanation and, in any case, goes on to the next question.
   (a) If we observe only the pattern of computer responses, how many different patterns will we see?
   (b) If we observe the pattern of computer and student response, how many different patterns will we see?

4. In how many ways may we choose a 2-, a 3-, and a 4-element set that contain among them all the elements of a 9-element set?

5. In how many ways may we choose three sets of three elements each that among them contain all the elements of a 9-element set?

6. In how many ways may we choose a three-person committee and a four-person committee from among the twenty members of a club if the committees may have at most one member in common?

7. Prove the formula

$$n \binom{n-1}{k} = (k+1) \binom{n}{k+1}$$

and explain how it may be interpreted in terms of selecting $k + 1$ elements, of which one is special, from an n-element set.

8. Show that $C(n,k) \geq C(n,k-1)$ so long as $k \leq \frac{n}{2}$. What does this tell you about the values of k for which $C(n,k)$ is a maximum?

9. We have n apples and another n distinct pieces of fruit. Express the number of ways to choose a snack of k pieces of fruit from among these $2n$ pieces in terms of binomial coefficients.

10. Show that $\binom{n}{r}\binom{r}{k} = \binom{n}{k}\binom{n-k}{r-k}$. Explain what it means in terms of choosing ordered pairs of subsets of an n-element set.

11. How many k-element multisets may be chosen from an n-element set S if each element of S must appear at least once?

Section 6-3
Counting
Equivalence Classes

A Arrangements as Equivalence Classes

In Figure 5, we show a standard way to arrange computers into a communication network called a **one-way** or **single-ring network**. The communications in this network can go from A to B, from B to C, from C to D and then back to A, or start at each of the other three computers and follow the same circular pattern. The permutation $ABCD$ describes this communications pattern. In Figure 6, we show four drawings of this network—one with A on top, one with D on top, and so on.

Figure 5 Two ways of representing a single-ring network.

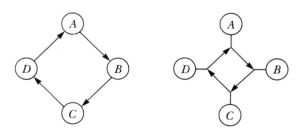

Figure 6   Four different views of the same network.

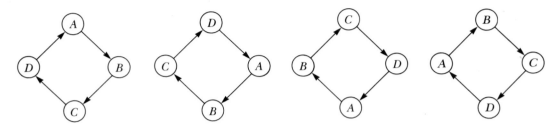

If we start at the top and write down the letters of the computers in the direction of communication, we get a set of four permutations

$$\{ABCD, DABC, CDAB, BCDA\}$$

describing the same communications pattern from different viewpoints. Thus in terms of communication patterns, these four permutations are equivalent.

How many communications patterns are possible? We can't answer the question by counting permutations of the four computers, because different permutations can correspond to the same communications pattern. However, the relation "corresponds to the same communications pattern" is reflexive (any permutation corresponds to the same pattern as itself), symmetric, and transitive. These are the defining properties of an equivalence relation, so the "same pattern" relation is an equivalence relation on the set of permutations of A, B, C, and D. Remember that an equivalence relation on a set divides the set up into *equivalence classes,* sets such that objects in the same set are equivalent but objects in different sets are not. Thus for the "same pattern" relation, two permutations will represent the same pattern if they are in the same class but different patterns if they are in different classes. Therefore, the question "How many communications patterns are possible?" is the same as the question "How many equivalence classes are there?" Once we decide where A must go in the network, the pattern of communications tells us where to put B, C, and D. Thus each equivalence class has four members, one for each placement of A. Since each class has four permutations, we may use the product principle to write.

$$4 \cdot (\text{number of equivalence classes}) = \text{total number of permutations}$$

since every list is in one and only one equivalence class. But each list of the four computers can appear as we list computers beginning with the top position, so we have 4! lists, giving the equation

$$4 \cdot (\text{number of equivalence classes}) = 4!$$

or

$$\text{number of equivalence classes} = \frac{4!}{4} = 6$$

Counting Equal-Sized Equivalence Classes

The observation that led to the equation 4·(number of equivalence classes) = 4! above was that each equivalence class had size 4. If each class had size 2, then 2 times the number of classes would be 4!, and if each class had size 8, then 8 times the number of classes would be 4!. Thus what is important is that all the equivalence classes have the *same size*. The essence of our argument is presented in the next theorem.

Theorem 10   If an equivalence relation on a p-element set has q classes of size r, then $q = p/r$.

Proof   By the product principle, the union of these q disjoint sets of size r has size qr. But the union is the entire p-element set, so $p = qr$, and therefore $q = p/r$.   ∎

EXAMPLE 26   Use Theorem 10 to derive the formula for $\binom{n}{k}$.

Solution   When we computed $\binom{n}{k}$ before, we made use of a correspondence between a subset and the $k!$ permutations of all its elements to get

$$\binom{n}{k} k! = (n)_k$$

Since the number $(n)_k$ is the number of k-element permutations of an n-element set S, this suggests that we may be dealing with an equivalence relation on these permutations. Let us let P be the set of all k-element permutations of S, so the size p of P is $(n)_k$. Define two of these permutations to be equivalent if they are permutations of the same k-element subset of S. Then we have an equivalence relation on P. An equivalence class is the set of all permutations of one k-element subset of S, and therefore has size $k!$. The number of equivalence classes is $\binom{n}{k}$, the number of k-element subsets. Thus when we apply Theorem 10 with $p = (n)_k$, $q = \binom{n}{k}$ and $r = k!$, we get

$$\binom{n}{k} = \frac{(n)_k}{k!}$$ ∎

EXAMPLE 27   An office has five computers that are connected together in a linear network. (This means they will be arranged in five positions on one straight connecting cable. See Figure 7.) Communications can go either way along the cable. In how many different ways may they be arranged?

Figure 7

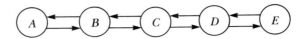

Solution   For the purpose of communications, the arrangement *ABCDE* and the reversed arrangement *EDCBA* are equivalent, because each machine will have exactly the same neighbors. You can show, however, that *EDCBA* is the only other way to list the computers so that each one has the same neighbors as in *ABCDE*. Thus we have an equivalence relation on the permutations of $\{A,B,C,D,E\}$ for which a permutation is equivalent to itself and its reverse. Each equivalence class has two permutations; since we have 5! lists, we get

$$q \cdot 2 = 5!$$

or

$$q = \frac{5!}{2} = 60$$

Thus there are 60 different ways to arrange the computers on the cable.   ∎

EXAMPLE 28   Five computers are to be connected in a double-ring network. A **double-ring** network allows communications between adjacent nodes to go in both directions along the ring (see Figure 8). How many different arrangements are possible now?

Figure 8

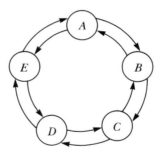

Solution   Two lists showing how the computers are to be connected to the cable are now equivalent if each computer has the same neighbors (considering the first and last elements as neighbors). Let us examine which lists are equivalent to the list *ABCDE*. If we start at each position and read around the ring in a clockwise and then a counter-clockwise direction, then we get the ten permutations

$$\{ABCDE, EABCD, DEABC, CDEAB, BCDEA,$$
$$AEDCB, EDCBA, DCBAE, CBAED, BAEDC\}$$

This set is the equivalence class containing *ABCDE*. How do we know we have listed all the permutations in the equivalence class of *ABCDE*? Once we decide which computer is in the middle spot of a permutation, its two neighbors can be arranged on either side of it in two ways. Then *their* other neighbors each have only one place to go. Since we have five choices for the middle element, we have, by the product principle, $5 \cdot 2 = 10$ lists for a given communications pattern. Thus each equivalence class has size 10. This means the ten permutations listed above are the class containing *ABCDE*. Since there are 5! permutations of the five letters, we get

$$q \cdot 10 = 5! = 120$$
$$q = 12$$

so there are 12 equivalence classes. Thus there are 12 different ways to arrange the computers into a double-ring network. ∎

B *Ordered Distributions and Multisets*

Think about the question, "In how many ways may m distinct jobs be assigned to n computers?" If the order in which each computer does its jobs does *not* matter, then an assignment of jobs to computers is simply a function from the set of jobs to the set of computers. This function tells us for each job which computer does that job. In this case, the number of assignments is n^m, the number of functions from an m-element set to an n-element set. However, it may be that the jobs must be done by a computer in the same order that they are given to the computer.

An *ordered* distribution, which we shall define more precisely later, is a distribution in which the order that objects are received matters. When we talk about distributions of distinct objects (the jobs) to distinct recipients (the computers), we must distinguish the *ordered* distributions from the **unordered distributions,** which are simply functions from the objects to the recipients.

Let us try to visualize the problem of computing the number of ordered distributions as a problem of counting lists. To be specific, suppose we have computers numbered 1, 2, and 3 and jobs denoted by a, b, c, and d. We can use the list $1b2ad3c$ for the distribution in which computer 1 gets job b, computer 2 gets jobs a and d in that order, and computer 3 gets job c. In other words, we list the computers in some order and then insert the jobs into that list, so that the jobs to be done by a given computer are listed, in the order they are to be done, right after the computer. Thus starting with the list 123, there are three places where we can insert job a. Our first step is choosing where job a is to be inserted—for example, by choosing $12a3$. There are now four places where we can insert job b: between 1 and 2, between 2 and a, between a and 3, or after 3. Once we insert job b (for example, choosing $1b2a3$), there are five places for job c, and once we insert job c, there are six places for job d. Thus, by the product principle, the total number of ordered assignments of four jobs to three computers is $3 \cdot 4 \cdot 5 \cdot 6$.

With the example of assigning jobs to computers in mind, we define an **ordered distribution** of the elements of a set S to a set T as a function that assigns a permutation of some (perhaps all or none) of the elements of S to each element of

T in such a way that each element of *S* is in one and only one of these permutations. With the kind of computation we made above, we may then prove the next theorem.

Theorem 11   The number of ordered distributions of a *k*-element set to an *n*-element set is $P(n + k - 1, k)$; that is, $(n + k - 1)!/(n - 1)!$.

Proof   The proof may be patterned on the example above.   ∎

EXAMPLE 29   In how many ways may 12 distinct books be placed on the three shelves of a bookcase, assuming there is room on each shelf for all the books?

Solution   Since putting books onto a shelf in different orders gives different arrangements, the problem is asking for the number of ordered distributions of the books to the shelves. By Theorem 11, this number is $(3 + 12 - 1)!/(3 - 1)!$ $= 14!/2$, which is approximately 44 billion.   ∎

Distributions of Identical Objects

Another kind of distribution problem could ask us to distribute identical objects (apples, boards) to distinct recipients (trick-or-treaters, carpenters). In this problem, the order in which objects are received is irrelevant. To distribute *k* identical objects to *n* recipients, we simply have to specify how many objects each recipient gets, making sure that the total number distributed is *k*. For example, if we have four apples to distribute to three children, we might give four to child 1 and none to the others, or one to child 1, one to child 2, and two to child 3.

In analogy with this example, we define a distribution of *k* identical objects to *n* recipients to be a function *m*, called a **multiplicity function,** from the set $\{x_1, x_2, \ldots, x_n\}$ of recipients to the non-negative integers such that $m(x_1) + m(x_2) + \cdots + m(x_n) = k$. In the examples above, we had two different multiplicity functions. One was $m(x_1) = 4$, $m(x_2) = 0$, $m(x_3) = 0$, and thus $m(x_1) + m(x_2) + m(x_3)$ $= 4 + 0 + 0 = 4$. The second was $m(x_1) = 1$, $m(x_2) = 1$, and $m(x_3) = 2$; thus $m(x_1) + m(x_2) + m(x_3) = 1 + 1 + 2 = 4$.

Multisets

It is not clear from this application why the function is denoted by *m* and called a multiplicity function. Another application of the concept of a multiplicity function is in the definition of a multiset, as in Section 6-2. In order to capture the concept of a "set" in which things can appear a multiple number of times, we defined a **multiset** of size *k*, chosen from a set *S* to be a function *m* from *S* to the non-negative integers such that the sum of the values of *m* is *k*. The number $m(x)$ is called the **multiplicity of *x*.**

EXAMPLE 30   What is the size of the set of letters of Mississippi? What are the multiplicities of *m,p,i,* and *s*? What is the multiplicity of each other alphabet letter? What is the size of the multiset of letters of Mississippi?

Solution   The set of letters of Mississippi is $\{i,m,p,s\}$, so the size of the set of letters is 4. The letter *m* has multiplicity 1; the letter *p* has multiplicity 2; the letters *i* and *s* each have multiplicity 4. Each other alphabet letter has multiplicity 0. Since *m* has multiplicity one, *p* has multiplicity two, and *i* and *s* each have multiplicity four, the size of the multiset of letters is

$$1 + 2 + 4 + 4 = 11$$

Another way to see that the multiset has size 11 is to write it as $\{m,p,p,i,i,i,i,s,s,s,s\}$ and count the symbols.   ∎

EXAMPLE 31   Explain how distributing two apples to Sam, one apple to Chris, no apples to Pat, and three apples to Jamie can be interpreted as a multiset.

Solution   If we write down a person's name once each time we give that person an apple, we get

$$\{\text{Sam, Sam, Chris, Jamie, Jamie, Jamie}\}$$

the multiset with $m(\text{Sam}) = 2$, $m(\text{Chris}) = 1$, $m(\text{Pat}) = 0$, $m(\text{Jamie}) = 3$.   ∎

   If the apples in Example 31 had been an apple, a pear, an orange, a plum, a nectarine, and a peach, each ordered distribution of these fruits would have given us a multiset in the same way. For example, giving an apple and a pear to Sam, an orange to Chris, nothing to Pat, and a peach, a plum, and a nectarine to Jamie gives us the same multiset of people getting fruit as in Example 31. However, many different ordered distributions would give rise to the same multiset. In fact, with *k* different pieces of fruit, we would have *k*! different ordered distributions yielding the same multiset. This kind of reasoning gives us a new proof of the formula for the number of multisets of size *k* chosen from an *n*-element set.

Theorem 12   The number of *k*-element multisets chosen from an *n*-element set is $P(n + k - 1, k)/k!$, which is

$$C(n + k - 1, k) = \binom{n + k - 1}{k} = \frac{(n + k - 1)!}{k!(n - 1)!}$$

Proof   Define two ordered distributions of *k* objects to be equivalent if they yield the same multiset. There are *k*! ordered distributions in each equivalence class, so the number of equivalence classes (and thus the number of multisets) is $P(n + k - 1, k)/k!$.   ∎

EXAMPLE 32   Compute the number of ways that three memory chips with identical defects may be distributed among ten computers built while those chips were in stock. (All three chips may be in one computer.)

Solution   The multiset of computers with defective chips is a 3-element multiset chosen from a 10-element set. There are

$$P(10 + 3 - 1, 3)/3! = \frac{12 \cdot 11 \cdot 10}{3 \cdot 2 \cdot 1} = 220$$

such multisets. Using the second formula in Theorem 12 yields

$$C(10 + 3 - 1, 3) = \frac{12!}{3! \cdot 9!} = \frac{12 \cdot 11 \cdot 10}{3 \cdot 2 \cdot 1} = 220$$

such multisets.   ∎

EXAMPLE 33   In how many ways may we select 13 pieces of fruit from 10 varieties?

Solution   Here we are asking for the number of 13-element multisets we can choose from a 10-element set. By Theorem 12, the number of multisets is

$$\binom{10 + 13 - 1}{13} = \binom{22}{13} = 497,420$$ ∎

How to Approach a Counting Problem

A natural question to ask at this point is, "How do I know which formula to use when?" We shall present several guidelines and a table that summarizes the important formulas. Do not be fooled into believing that *every* counting problem can be solved by one of these formulas. Remember that you must often begin by decomposing a problem into cases, and then solve each case and add the results. What should you do if you cannot decompose the problem easily? If you are faced with a problem in which order matters, you should first ask yourself if you can see a way to use permutations or *n*-tuples. If you don't see any such way, you are likely to need to apply the product principle in some way or other. If you don't see how to apply the product principle directly, ask whether the problem requires counting equivalence classes. If you are faced with a problem in which order is unimportant, you should first ask yourself if you can see a way to use subsets or multisets. If not, you should ask if the problem involves counting equivalence classes. Table 1 summarizes what we know about our formulas. Fortunately, in many (perhaps most) practical problems, one of these approaches will at least get you started.

Table 1

Method	Order	Formula	Typical Problem
k-element subsets of n-element set	Doesn't matter	$\binom{n}{k} = \dfrac{n!}{k!(n-k)!}$	Choose k pieces of fruit of different types from n types.
k-element multisets from n-element set	Doesn't matter	$\binom{n+k-1}{k} = \dfrac{(n+k-1)!}{k!(n-1)!}$	Choose k pieces of fruit, not necessarily of different types, from n types.
r-element equivalence classes of p-element set	Sometimes matters	$q = \dfrac{p}{r}$	Arrange n distinct objects in a circle; here $p = n!$; $r = n$; $q = (n-1)!$.
k-element permutations of an n-element set	Matters	$(n)_k = \dfrac{n!}{(n-k)!}$	k children each choose one piece (*all of different types*) from n types of fruit.
k-tuples chosen from n-element set	Matters	n^k	k children each choose one piece (*not necessarily of different types*) from n types of fruit.
Product principle for k-tuples	Matters	$n_1 \cdot n_2 \cdot n_3 \cdot \;\cdots\; \cdot n_k$	Make a sandwich with n_1 choices for bread, n_2 choices for spread, n_3 choices for meat, n_4 ...
Ordered distributions of k objects to n recipients	Matters	$(n)^k = \dfrac{(n+k-1)!}{(n-1)!}$	Shelve k distinct books on n shelves starting at the left, assuming all would fit on one shelf.

Concepts Review

1. A communications network in which communications go in a fixed direction around a circle is called a(n) _____-_____ or _____-_____ network.

2. In a(n) _____-_____ network, communications may go in both directions around a circle.

3. If an equivalence relation on a set of size p has q equivalence classes of size r, then $q = $ _____.

4. In counting k-element subsets of an n-element set, we have a correspondence between subsets and equivalence classes of k-element _____ of the n-element set.

5. An unordered distribution of a set P of objects to a set R of recipients is a(n) _____ from P to R.

6. An ordered distribution of a set P of objects to a set R of recipients is a(n) _____ that assigns a(n) _____ of a subset of P to each element of R.

7. The number of ordered distributions of a k-element set to an n-element set is

   _____.

8. A(n) _____ function on a set S assigns a non-negative integer to each element of S.

9. A k-element _____ chosen from a set S is a multiplicity function m defined on S such that the sum of the values of m is k.

10. The number of k-element multisets chosen from an n-element set is _____.

Exercises

A

1. In how many ways may six computers be arranged in
   (a) A single-ring network?
   (b) A linear network?
   (c) A double-ring network?

2. In how many ways may seven computers be arranged in
   (a) A linear network?
   (b) A single-ring network?
   (c) A double-ring network?

3. We are going to decorate a circular wastebasket by painting it with exactly four vertical stripes of equal width: one red, one blue, one white, and one yellow. How many patterns are possible?

4. In how many ways may five people be seated around a round table for a game of cards? (For this card game, two arrangements are equivalent if and only if each person has the same *right-hand neighbor* and *left-hand neighbor* in both arrangements.)

5. Explain how the patterns of Exercise 3 may be represented as equivalence classes of an equivalence relation on a set of permutations. Show a typical equivalence class.

6. Explain how the patterns of people in Exercise 4 may be represented as equivalence classes of an equivalence relation on a set of permutations. Show a typical equivalence class.

7. A simple bracelet is a circular wire band with five different colors of plastic tape wrapped around it to make five stripes, one of each color. How can you represent a pattern as an equivalence class of permutations of the five colors? How many bracelets are possible?

8. Four pieces of colored plastic tubing 10 cm long are strung on a string, which is then tied to make a 40 cm-long necklace for a child. If all four pieces are different, then how many patterns are possible?

9. There are $P(4,2) = 12$ two-element permutations of a four-element set $\{a,b,c,d\}$. There are $C(4,2) = 6$ two-element subsets of this set. Each subset corresponds to two equivalent permutations. Write down the six equivalence classes of permutations.

10. There are $P(4,3) = 24$ three-element permutations of a four-element set $\{a,b,c,d\}$. There are $C(4,3) = 4$ two-element subsets of this set. Each subset corresponds to six equivalent permutations. Write down the four equivalence classes of permutations.

11. Give a formula for the number of ways to arrange n computers into a single-ring network.

12. Give a formula for the number of ways to arrange n computers into a double-ring network.

B (*Note:* Exercises 13 through 20 are identical with Exercises 35 through 42 in Section 6-2.)

13. Write down the multiplicity function for the multiset of letters chosen from the alphabet in the phrase *practice phrase*.

14. Write down the multiplicity function for the multiset of letters chosen from the alphabet in the phrase *boring but enlightening*.

In Exercises 15–20, compute the number of multisets asked for.

15. 3-element multisets chosen from a 5-element set.

16. 2-element multisets chosen from a 20-element set.

17. 10-element multisets chosen from a 3-element set.

18. 4-element multisets chosen from a 4-element set.

19. 3-element multisets chosen from a 20-element set.

20. 20-element multisets chosen from a 3-element set.

21. A fruit store stocks six kinds of fruit. In how many ways may you choose a bag of three? What if the three must be different?

22. A candy store sells five different kinds of chocolate-covered cremes. In how many ways

may you select three different ones? In how many ways may you select a bag of three pieces of this candy (not necessarily of different kinds)?

In Exercises 23–26, compute the number of ordered distributions specified.

23. Four objects to five recipients.

24. Three objects to seven recipients.

25. Five objects to four recipients.

26. Seven objects to three recipients.

27. In how many ways may five jobs be assigned to four people if each person must do the assigned jobs in the order in which they are assigned?

28. The order in which wines are tasted affects our perception of their flavor. In how many ways may three people consume seven different sample portions of wine?

29. In how many ways may you pass out ten identical apples to five children?

30. In how many ways may you pass out k identical pieces of candy to n children?

Problems

1. In how many ways may three identical red flowers and three identical white flowers be embroidered around the hem of a skirt? (*Hint:* Do the equivalence classes have the same size?) Show a typical arrangement of each equivalence class.

2. In how many ways may two red beads and four black beads be strung onto a necklace? (See the hint in Problem 1.) Show an arrangement from each equivalence class.

3. What is the answer to Exercise 29 if we require that each child gets at least one apple?

4. What is the answer to Exercise 30 if we require that each child gets at least one piece?

5. A banana split consists of three scoops of ice cream chosen (with repeats allowed) from among ten varieties, covered with three toppings (with repeats allowed) chosen from among eight varieties, all sitting on a split banana. How many banana splits are possible?

6. In how many ways may we arrange n men and n women around a table, alternating men and women?

7. In how many ways may we arrange n men and n women around a table so that the men sit together in a row?

8. In how many ways may we string n distinct red beads and n distinct black beads on a necklace if two beads of the same color may not be side-by-side?

9. In how many ways may the beads in Problem 8 be strung if the black beads are together in a row?

10. In how many different ways may we paint the six faces of a cube with six different colors of paints?

11. Prove Theorem 11.

Section 6-4
The Binomial Theorem
and Pascal's Triangle

A The Binomial Theorem

When we introduced the binomial coefficients $\binom{n}{k}$, we were not able to explain their name. The binomial coefficients get their name from their relationship with powers of a kind of polynomial called a *binomial*. A **binomial** is a polynomial that is a sum of two terms, at least one of which contains a variable. Thus $x + y$, $2x + 1$, $3 - 4x$, and $1 + x^2$ are all examples of binomials. By using the rules you learned in algebra for multiplying polynomial products such as $(x + y)^2 = (x + y)(x + y)$, you may verify the computations below.

$$
\begin{aligned}
(x + y)^0 &= 1 \\
(x + y)^1 &= x + y \\
(x + y)^2 &= x^2 + 2xy + y^2 \\
(x + y)^3 &= x^3 + 3x^2y + 3xy^2 + y^3 \\
(x + y)^4 &= x^4 + 4x^3y + 6x^2y^2 + 4xy^3 + y^4 \\
(x + y)^5 &= x^5 + 5x^4y + 10x^3y^2 + 10x^2y^3 + 5xy^4 + y^5
\end{aligned}
$$

A **monomial** is a polynomial that is *not* a sum of terms. Thus $5x^4y$ and xy^3 are examples of monomials. The number 5 is called the **coefficient** of x^4y in $5x^4y$. Each coefficient of each monomial in the display above is a binomial coefficient. For example, the numbers $1, 4, 6, 4, 1$ are the binomial coefficients $\binom{4}{k}$ for $k = 0, 1, 2, 3, 4$. This suggests the following theorem, called the **binomial theorem.**

Theorem 13   For any non-negative integer n,

$$(x + y)^n = \sum_{k=0}^{n} \binom{n}{k} x^{n-k}y^k = x^n + \binom{n}{1} x^{n-1}y + \cdots + y^n$$

Proof   When we multiply out the product

$$\underbrace{(x + y)(x + y)\cdots(x + y)}_{n\text{ factors}} = (x + y)^n$$

we begin by choosing an x from all the terms and multiplying them all together to get x^n. Next we choose an x from all but one of the terms and choose a y from that term; we multiply the x^{n-1} by y to get $x^{n-1}y$ and add all these $x^{n-1}y$ terms together. How many do we have to add? There are $\binom{n}{1}$ ways to choose the one binomial from which we take y, so we shall be adding $\binom{n}{1}$ terms of the form $x^{n-1}y$ together. So far, then, we have

$$x^n + \binom{n}{1} x^{n-1}y$$

Now we pick an x from $n-2$ of the terms and a y from the other two and multiply them together to get $x^{n-2}y^2$. Adding all these $x^{n-2}y^2$ terms together gives us $\binom{n}{2} x^{n-2}y^2$, so now our sum is

$$x^n + \binom{n}{1} x^{n-1}y + \binom{n}{2} x^{n-2}y^2$$

In general, we have $\binom{n}{k}$ ways to pick an x from $n-k$ of the terms and a y from k terms, giving us the summand

$$\binom{n}{k} x^{n-k}y^k$$

Adding all these summands together gives us

$$\sum_{k=0}^{n} \binom{n}{k} x^{n-k}y^k = (x + y)^n \qquad \blacksquare$$

The proof above contains quite a few preliminary remarks to lead us to the main idea. The core of the proof begins with the words *in general*; the rest of what we wrote is technically unnecessary.

EXAMPLE 34   Write out the expansion of $(x + y)^6$.

Solution   We write $(x + y)^6 = \sum_{k=0}^{6} \binom{6}{k} x^{6-k}y^k$

$$= \binom{6}{0} x^6y^0 + \binom{6}{1} x^5y^1 + \binom{6}{2} x^4y^2 + \binom{6}{3} x^3y^3 + \binom{6}{4} x^2y^4 + \binom{6}{5} xy^5 + \binom{6}{6} y^6$$

$$= x^6 + 6x^5y + 15x^4y^2 + 20x^3y^3 + 15x^2y^4 + 6xy^5 + y^6 \qquad \blacksquare$$

In Example 34, you see a symmetry that shows that the coefficients are the same from right to left as they are from left to right. We pointed out this symmetry when we first introduced binomial coefficients and observed that $\binom{16}{2} = \binom{16}{14}$. The general symmetry rule may be expressed as a theorem.

Theorem 14 $\binom{n}{k} = \binom{n}{n-k}$

Proof The number of ways to select k elements out of n to be *in* a subset is the same as the number of ways to select $n - k$ elements out of n to be *out* of a subset. ∎

EXAMPLE 35 Expand $(2x + 3)^4$.

Solution We write $(2x + 3)^4 = \sum_{i=0}^{4} \binom{4}{i}(2x)^{4-i}3^i$

$$= \binom{4}{0}(2x)^4 + \binom{4}{1}(2x)^3 3^1 + \binom{4}{2}(2x)^2 3^2 + \binom{4}{3}(2x)^1 3^3 + \binom{4}{4}(2x)^0 3^4$$
$$= 1 \cdot 16x^4 + 4 \cdot 8x^3 \cdot 3 + 6 \cdot 4x^2 \cdot 9 + 4 \cdot 2x \cdot 27 + 1 \cdot 1 \cdot 81$$
$$= 16x^4 + 96x^3 + 216x^2 + 216x + 81$$ ∎

EXAMPLE 36 Expand $(1 - x)^5$.

Solution We write

$$(1 - x)^5 = \sum_{i=0}^{5} \binom{5}{i} 1^{5-i}(-x)^i$$
$$= \binom{5}{5} \cdot 1(-x)^0 + \binom{5}{4} \cdot 1(-x)^1 + \binom{5}{3} \cdot 1(-x)^2 +$$
$$\binom{5}{2} \cdot 1(-x)^3 + \binom{5}{1} \cdot 1(-x)^4 + \binom{5}{0} \cdot 1(-x)^5$$
$$= 1 - 5x + 10x^2 - 10x^3 + 5x^4 - x^5$$ ∎

EXAMPLE 37 Use the binomial theorem to show that

$$\binom{6}{0} + \binom{6}{1} + \binom{6}{2} + \binom{6}{3} + \binom{6}{4} + \binom{6}{5} + \binom{6}{6} = 2^6$$

Solution The binomial theorem as we have stated it may be used to compute

$$(x + y)^6 = \binom{6}{0} x^6 + \binom{6}{1} x^5 y + \binom{6}{2} x^4 y^2 + \cdots + \binom{6}{6} y^6$$

How can it be applied to the sum we were given? Note that substituting $x = 1$ and $y = 1$ yields

$$(1 + 1)^6 = \binom{6}{0} 1^6 + \binom{6}{1} 1^5 \cdot 1 + \binom{6}{2} 1^4 \cdot 1^2 + \cdots + \binom{6}{6} 1^6$$

or

$$2^6 = \binom{6}{0} + \binom{6}{1} + \binom{6}{2} + \cdots + \binom{6}{6}$$

■

EXAMPLE 38   What is the coefficient of x^4 in $(2 - 3x)^7$?

Solution   The term involving x^4 will be the term

$$\binom{7}{4} (2)^{7-4} (-3x)^4 = \frac{7 \cdot 6 \cdot 5}{3 \cdot 2 \cdot 1} \cdot 8 \cdot 81 \cdot x^4$$

Thus the coefficient of x^4 is $7 \cdot 5 \cdot 8 \cdot 81 = 22{,}680$.   ■

B   Pascal's Triangle

The binomial theorem makes it reasonable to think about writing out the expansion of $(x + y)^{10}$ or $(x + y)^{12}$, even though multiplying 10 or 12 factors seems unreasonable. However, computing a binomial coefficient such as $\binom{10}{6}$ or $\binom{12}{6}$ by the methods we have available will be time-consuming at best. Further, to write down the expansion, we will need the numbers $\binom{10}{k}$ or $\binom{12}{k}$ for all possible values of k. The symmetry we've already seen cuts our work in half, though—we would need only those binomial coefficients for values of k up to 5 or 6. In Table 2, we've removed the plus signs and powers of x and y from the display of powers of $x + y$ with which we began the section on the binomial theorem, showing only the coefficients so that we can examine them for more patterns. We've also added the row corresponding to $(x + y)^6$. The triangular table we get is called **Pascal's triangle.**

Table 2   Pascal's triangle

```
                        1
                     1     1
                  1     2     1
               1     3     3     1
            1     4     6     4     1
         1     5    10    10     5     1
      1     6    15    20    15     6     1
```

Of course, the symmetry of the binomial coefficients shows in the table, and the 1's along the border correspond to the fact that $\binom{n}{0}$ and $\binom{n}{n}$ are always 1 (because an n-element set has exactly one empty subset and exactly one n-element subset). Further study shows a useful property:

> Each entry in Pascal's triangle is the sum of the two above it to the left and right. We call this property the **Pascal property**.

The table isn't set up in a way that helps us write down a formula to describe the Pascal property. We can visualize a formula for the Pascal property by rewriting Table 2 in a form more like a typical table. In Table 3, the possible values of n are listed in a vertical column to the left-hand side of the table, and the possible values of k are listed in a horizontal row across the top of the table.

Table 3   Pascal's right triangle.

$n\backslash k$	0	1	2	3	4	5	6
0	1	0	0	0	0	0	0
1	1	1	0	0	0	0	0
2	1	2	1	0	0	0	0
3	1	3	3	1	0	0	0
4	1	4	6	4	1	0	0
5	1	5	10	10	5	1	0
6	1	6	15	20	15	6	1

In Table 3, we can see that each entry is the sum of the one directly above it and the one above and to the left of it. For example $\binom{5}{3}$ is the entry in row 5 and column 3, namely 10. This is the sum of 4 and 6, the numbers above it and above and to the left of it. In this table, the number $\binom{n}{k}$ is the entry in row n and column k. (Notice that row zero is the top row and column zero is the leftmost column.) Thus the entry above $\binom{n}{k}$ is $\binom{n-1}{k}$, and the entry above and to the left of $\binom{n}{k}$ is $\binom{n-1}{k-1}$. Therefore the Pascal property states that

$$\binom{n}{k} = \binom{n-1}{k-1} + \binom{n-1}{k}$$

For example, with $n = 5$ and $k = 3$, we get $\binom{5}{3} = \binom{4}{2} + \binom{4}{3} = 6 + 4 = 10$.

Though we are convinced of the truth of this formula by our examples, we have as yet no way to *know* whether the formula fails for some values of n and k. Fortunately, we can prove that the formula holds.

Theorem 15   For all positive integers n and all k between 1 and $n - 1$,

$$\binom{n}{k} = \binom{n-1}{k-1} + \binom{n-1}{k}$$

Proof   The formula tells us that the number of k-element subsets of an n-element set is the sum of the number of $k - 1$-element subsets plus the number of k-element subsets of an $(n - 1)$-element set. We shall prove it by showing that the *set* of k-element subsets is the union of two disjoint sets of subsets, one of size $\binom{n-1}{k-1}$ and one of size $\binom{n-1}{k}$. We may assume that our n-element set is $N = \{1, 2, \ldots, n\}$. The set of k-element subsets may be divided into two parts, the k-element subsets that contain n and the k-element subsets that do not contain n. The number of k-element subsets that do not contain n is the number of k-element subsets of $\{1, 2, \ldots, n - 1\} = N'$, so this number is $\binom{n-1}{k}$. The number of k-element subsets that *do* contain n is the number of $(k - 1)$-element subsets of $\{1, 2, \ldots, n - 1\}$ (this is the number of $(k - 1)$-element subsets we get by removing n from k-element subsets that do contain n), and this number is $\binom{n-1}{k-1}$. Thus by the sum principle,

$$\binom{n}{k} = \binom{n-1}{k-1} + \binom{n-1}{k}$$

∎

This proof is not the only one possible. It is also possible to prove the Pascal relation by using the formula

$$\binom{n}{k} = \frac{n!}{k!(n-k)!}$$

which we derived earlier. To do the proof in this way, try substituting the formula into the right-hand side of the Pascal relation. When you combine terms, you will get the formula for the left-hand side.

Table 4

$n\backslash k$	0	1	2	3	4	5	6	7	8	9
0	1									
1	1									
2	1	2								
3	1	3								
4	1	4	6							
5	1	5	10							
6	1	6	15	20						
7	1	7	21	35						
8	1	8	28	56	70					
9	1	9	36	84	126					
10	1	10	45	120	210	252				
11	1	11	55	165	330	462				
12	1	12	66	220	495	792	924			
13	1	13	78	286	715	1287	1716			
14	1	14	91	364	1001	2002	3003	3432		
15	1	15	105	455	1365	3003	5005	6435		
16	1	16	120	560	1820	4368	8008	11440	12870	
17	1	17	136	680	2380	6188	12376	19448	24310	
18	1	18	153	816	3060	8568	18564	31824	43758	48620
19	1	19	171	969	3876	11628	27132	50388	75582	92378

Using a Table of Binomial Coefficients

By applying the Pascal relation, we get Table 4. To prevent the table from getting too wide too fast, we give values of $\binom{n}{k}$ only for $k \leq \dfrac{n}{2}$.

To find a value such as $\binom{19}{17}$, which is not in the table, we apply the symmetry property, which tells us that $\binom{19}{17} = \binom{19}{2}$. We then look up $\binom{19}{2}$ and find it to be 171.

EXAMPLE 39   Use Table 4 to compute $\binom{20}{17}$.

Solution   We know that

$$\binom{20}{17} = \binom{19}{16} + \binom{19}{17}$$

$$= \binom{19}{3} + \binom{19}{2}$$

$$= 969 + 171 = 1140 \qquad \blacksquare$$

EXAMPLE 40   Use Pascal's triangle to compute $\binom{21}{11}$.

Solution   We know that

$$\binom{21}{11} = \binom{20}{10} + \binom{20}{11}$$
$$= \binom{19}{9} + \binom{19}{10} + \binom{19}{10} + \binom{19}{11}$$
$$= \binom{19}{9} + \binom{19}{9} + \binom{19}{9} + \binom{19}{8}$$
$$= 3 \cdot \binom{19}{9} + \binom{19}{8}$$
$$= 277134 + 75582 = 352716$$

Concepts Review

1. A(n) _____ is a polynomial that is not a sum of terms.

2. A(n) _____ is a polynomial that is a sum of two monomials.

3. The _____ _____ tells us how to expand a power of a binomial.

4. The binomial coefficient $\binom{n}{i}$ is the coefficient of _____ in $(x + y)^n$.

5. The symmetry $\binom{n}{k} = \binom{n}{n-k}$ tells us that the number of ways to choose k elements to be _____ a set equals the number of ways to choose $n - k$ elements that are _____ _____ the set.

6. The Pascal property may be expressed as $\binom{n}{k} =$ _____.

7. In _____ _____, each number is the sum of the two numbers above and to its left and above and to its right.

8. The numbers appearing in _____ _____ are the binomial coefficients.

Exercises

A   In Exercises 1–6, expand the binomial power using the binomial theorem.

1. $(x + y)^7$ 2. $(x + y)^8$ 3. $(x + 2)^4$

4. $(3 - y)^4$ 5. $(2x - 3)^6$ 6. $(2a + 3b)^5$

7. Expand $(\sqrt{2} + \sqrt{3})^4$ and collect like terms.

8. Expand $(\sqrt{2} - \sqrt{3})^4$ and collect like terms.

9. Expand $(x - 1)^8$. Now substitute in $x = 1$ and get a formula for

$$\binom{8}{0} - \binom{8}{1} + \binom{8}{2} - \binom{8}{3} + \binom{8}{4} - \binom{8}{5} + \binom{8}{6} - \binom{8}{7} + \binom{8}{8}$$

10. Expand $(1 - y)^7$. Now substitute in $y = 1$ and obtain a formula for

$$\binom{7}{0} - \binom{7}{1} + \binom{7}{2} - \binom{7}{3} + \binom{7}{4} - \binom{7}{5} + \binom{7}{6} - \binom{7}{7}$$

11. Expand $(x - 1)^n$. Now substitute in $x = 1$ and get a formula for $\binom{n}{0} - \binom{n}{1} + \cdots$.

12. Expand $(-1 + y)^n$. Now substitute in $y = 1$ and get a formula for

$$\binom{n}{n} - \binom{n}{n-1} + \cdots$$

13. Find $\binom{20}{3}$ and $\binom{20}{17}$.

14. Find $\binom{18}{4}$ and $\binom{18}{14}$.

B

15. Find $\binom{12}{3}$, $\binom{12}{9}$ by using Table 4.

16. Find $\binom{14}{5}$, $\binom{14}{9}$ by using Table 4.

17. Write out the *entire* tenth row of the Pascal triangle. (In Table 4, we gave $\binom{10}{k}$ only for $k \leq 5$.)

18. Write out the entire eleventh row of the Pascal triangle. (In Table 4, we gave $\binom{11}{k}$ for $k \leq 5$.)

19. Find $\binom{20}{5}$ and $\binom{20}{15}$.

20. Find $\binom{20}{9}$ and $\binom{20}{10}$.

21. Find $\binom{21}{10}$.

22. Find $\binom{21}{16}$.

23. Prove the symmetry property $\binom{n}{k} = \binom{n}{n-k}$ by using the formula

$$\binom{n}{k} = \frac{n!}{k!(n-k)!}$$

24. Prove the Pascal property by using the formula $\binom{n}{k} = \frac{n!}{k!(n-k)!}$.

25. Use Pascal's triangle to expand $(x + 2)^8$.

26. Use Pascal's triangle to expand $(2 - y)^8$.

Problems

1. Use the binomial theorem to prove that the number of subsets of an n-element set is 2^n. (*Hint:* Expand $(1 + 1)^n$.)

2. Every so often, the Pascal triangle will have a row consisting entirely of odd numbers. Which rows have this property? Can you prove you are correct? (*Hint:* It may be easier to work with rows in which all but the beginning and ending entries are even.)

3. What is $\sum_{i=0}^{10} \binom{10}{i} 3^{10-i}$? What is $\sum_{i=1}^{10} \binom{10}{i} 3^{10-i}$? What is $\sum_{i=0}^{9} \binom{10}{i} 3^{10-i}$?

4. This problem is for people who have had calculus. By taking derivatives, show that

   (a) $\binom{n}{1} + 2 \binom{n}{2} + 3 \binom{n}{3} + \cdots = n2^{n-1}$

   (b) $\binom{n}{1} - 2 \binom{n}{2} + 3 \binom{n}{3} - 4 \binom{n}{4} + \cdots = 0$

5. Use induction on n to prove the binomial theorem for $(x + y)^n$.

6. Apply the binomial theorem to $(1 + x)^n (1 - x^{-1})^n$ to prove that
$$\binom{n}{0}^2 + \binom{n}{1}^2 + \binom{n}{2}^2 + \cdots + \binom{n}{n}^2 = \binom{2n}{n}$$

7. Observe that $\binom{n}{i}^2 = \binom{n}{i}\binom{n}{n-i}$. Rewrite the conclusion of Problem 6 to give an equation you may prove by dividing subsets of $\{1, 2, \ldots, 2n\}$ into subsets of $\{1, 2, \ldots, n\}$ and $\{n+1, \ldots, 2n\}$. Give the proof.

8. Prove that $\binom{n}{0} + \binom{n}{2} + \binom{n}{4} + \cdots = \binom{n}{1} + \binom{n}{3} + \binom{n}{5} + \cdots$.

9. Prove that
$$\binom{m+n}{k} = \binom{m}{0}\binom{n}{k} + \binom{m}{1}\binom{n}{k-1} + \binom{m}{2}\binom{n}{k-2} + \cdots + \binom{m}{k}\binom{n}{0}$$
by using the binomial theorem and the identity $(x + y)^{m+n} = (x+y)^m(x + y)^n$.

10. Give an interpretation of the equation of Problem 9 by using pairs of subsets of a set with $m + n$ elements.

11. The symbol $\binom{n}{i,j,k}$ or $C(n;i,j,k)$ is defined to be $\dfrac{n!}{i!j!k!}$ if $i + j + k = n$ and is defined to be 0 otherwise.

    (a) Show that $\binom{n}{i,j,k} = \binom{n}{i}\binom{n-i}{j}$ if $i + j + k = n$.

    (b) Show that $\binom{n}{i,j,k}$ is the number of ways to divide an n-element set up into a first, a second, and a third part so that the first part has size i, the second part has size j, and the third part has size k.

    (c) Define $C(n;i_1, i_2, \ldots i_k)$ and interpret it as in part (b).

12. Prove the **multinomial theorem,** which states that the coefficient of $x_1^{i_1}x_2^{i_2} \ldots x_k^{i_k}$ in $(x_1 + x_2 + \cdots + x_k)^n$ is $C(n;i_1,i_2, \ldots .i_k)$.

13. Using Problem 12, find the coefficients of x^2y^2z and x^2y^2 in $(x + y + z)^5$ and $(x + y + 3)^5$.

Section 6-5
The Principle of
Inclusion and Exclusion

A Inclusion-Exclusion Formulas and Venn Diagrams

The Size of a Union of Two Sets

Many counting problems deal with a family of subsets of a universe and ask either how many elements of the universe are in the union of these sets or how many are *not* in the union of these sets (that is, are in none of the sets). When we have enough information about how the sets overlap, we can use a method called the *principle of inclusion and exclusion* to answer such questions. For example, in a high school biology class, there are 15 students with dogs, 12 with cats, and 5 with both a dog and a cat. Of the 25 students in the class, how many have one of these kinds of pets and how many have neither kind of pet?

In this problem, we are given the size of the set D of dog owners, the set C of cat owners, and the size of $C \cap D$, the set of those who own both. We shall use B (for both) to stand for $C \cap D$. The problem asks first for the size of $C \cup D$ and then for the size of the complement $\sim(C \cup D)$. The Venn diagram in Figure 9 shows us three disjoint sets whose union is $C \cup D$. These three sets are $B = C \cap D$, $C \sim B$, and $D \sim B$. The problem gave us that the size of $C \cap D$ is 5, which we write as $|C \cap D| = 5$. As the exploded views in Figure 9 show, we can get $|C \sim B|$ by subtracting the size of B from that of C, giving $12 - 5 = 7$,

Figure 9

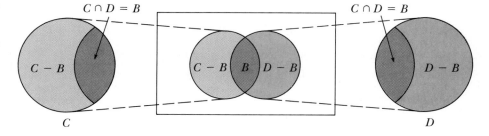

and we can get $|D \sim B|$ by subtracting the size of B from that of D, getting $15 - 5 = 10$. We show the three numbers we just computed in Figure 10; from the figure, it is clear that $|C \cup D| = 7 + 5 + 10 = 22$. The problem also asked us for the size of $\sim(C \cup D)$; Figure 11 shows us that this is the size of $U \sim (C \cup D)$ which is $|U| - |C \cup D| = 25 - 22 = 3$.

Figure 10

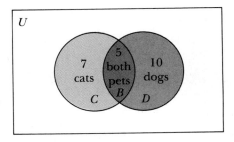

Figure 11

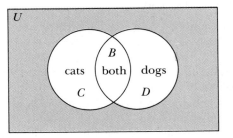

It would be time-consuming to draw a Venn diagram and fill in the numbers each time we have to answer a similar question. By examining the diagram once, we may see a formula that we can always use. If we add together $|C|$ and $|D|$ in hopes of counting the number of elements of $C \cup D$, we will count all the elements of C in $|C|$ and all the elements of D in $|D|$, so the elements in $C \cap D$ are counted twice. Thus the picture suggests $|C \cup D| = |C| + |D| - |C \cap D|$. The discussion below explains precisely why this suggestion is true.

The two exploded views in Figure 9 show us that

$$C = (C \sim B) \cup B \quad \text{and} \quad D = (D \sim B) \cup B$$

Since B is disjoint from $C \sim B$ and $D \sim B$, we get

$$|C| = |C \sim B| + |B| \quad \text{and} \quad |D| = |D \sim B| + B$$

Now simply adding $|C|$ to $|D|$ won't give us $|C \cup D|$, because

$$\begin{aligned} |C| + |D| &= |C \sim B| + |B| + |D \sim B| + |B| \\ &= |C \sim B| + |D \sim B| + 2|B| \end{aligned} \tag{1}$$

while Figure 9 makes it clear that

$$|C \cup D| = |C \sim B| + |D \sim B| + |B| \qquad (2)$$

Subtracting $|B|$ from both sides of Equation (1) gives

$$|C| + |D| - |B| = |C \sim B| + |D \sim B| + |B| \qquad (3)$$

and comparing Equation (2) and Equation (3) gives

$$|C \cup D| = |C| + |D| - |B| \qquad (4)$$
$$|C \cup D| = |C| + |D| - |C \cap D| \qquad (5)$$

Equation (5) is called an **inclusion-exclusion formula** because it includes $|C|$ and $|D|$ with plus signs and then excludes $|C \cap D|$ from this sum by subtracting it out. Applying Equation (5) to our cat-and-dog problem gives

$$|C \cup D| = 12 + 15 - 5 = 22$$

Notice that this method does not require pictures. This does not appear to be an advantage yet, but when we have four or more sets, it will become quite advantageous.

The Size of a Union of Three Sets

EXAMPLE 41   In the biology class discussed above, suppose four students have hamsters, two have hamsters and cats, two have hamsters and dogs, and one has all the pets. Using H to stand for the set of hamster owners, draw a three-set Venn diagram and show the number of pets in each of the seven regions inside the three circles. How many students have at least one of these kinds of pets? How many have none of these kinds of pets?

Figure 12

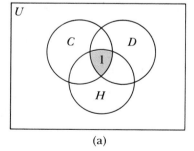
(a)
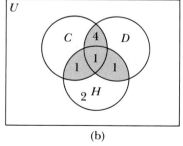
(b)
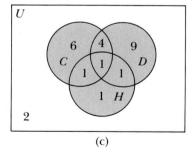
(c)

Solution   In Figure 12, we show three stages of how we may use our knowledge of the problem to fill numbers into the Venn diagram. In part (a), we fill in the only direct knowledge we have, namely that $|C \cap D \cap H| = 1$. Next we have $|C \cap D| = 5$ and $|C \cap D \cap H| = 1$, so we fill in the size of $(C \cap D) \sim$

$(C \cap D \cap H)$, namely $5 - 1 = 4$. Similarly, we fill in the sizes of $(C \cap H) \sim (C \cap D \cap H)$ and $(D \cap H) \sim (C \cap D \cap H)$. To get part (c) of the figure, we use the fact that the set C has 12 elements, of which $4 + 1 + 1 = 6$ are already accounted for, to fill in 6 for the remainder of C. We fill in the 9 and 1 similarly. The total number of pet owners we've shown is $(9 + 6 + 1) + (4 + 1 + 1) + (1) = 16 + 6 + 1 = 23$. Since 25 people are in the class, there are two with none of these pets.   ∎

Example 41 is rather complicated. Fortunately, there is a formula we may use to solve the problem more quickly. Since the formula for the size of the union of two sets was $|C \cup D| = |C| + |D| - |C \cap D|$, it is natural to ask whether

$$|C| + |D| + |H| - |C \cap D| - |C \cap H| - |D \cap H|$$

gives the size of $C \cup D \cup H$. If an element is in C but not D or H, then it contributes once to $|C|$ but not at all to any other term in the expression. (We can make similar statements about elements in *only* D or *only* H.) If an element is in C and D, it contributes once to $|C|$ (with a plus sign), once to $|D|$ (with a plus sign), and once to $|C \cap D|$ (with a minus sign). Thus its overall contribution to the expression is $1 + 1 - 1 = 1$. If an element is in all three sets C, D, and H, then it contributes once to each of $|C|$, $|D|$, and $|H|$ (with a plus sign) and once to each of $|C \cap D|$, $|C \cap H|$, and $|D \cap H|$ (with a minus sign). Thus its overall contribution to the expression is $1 + 1 + 1 - 1 - 1 - 1 = 0$. (We say that it has been excluded as often as it has been included.) If we add $|C \cap D \cap H|$ at the end of the expression, the only elements that will contribute to it are those in all three sets C, D, and H. This gives us our next pair of inclusion-exclusion formulas.

Theorem 16   If C, D, and H are subsets of a universe U, then

$$|C \cup D \cup H| = $$
$$|C| + |D| + |H| - |C \cap D| - |C \cap H| - |D \cap H| + |C \cap D \cap H|$$

and

$$|U \sim (C \cup D \cup H)| = $$
$$|U| - |C| - |D| - |H| + |C \cap D| + |C \cap H| + |D \cap H| - |C \cap D \cap H|$$

Proof   The proof of the first formula was outlined above; the second formula follows by subtraction.   ∎

EXAMPLE 42   Solve the dog-cat-hamster problem of Example 41 by using Theorem 16.

Solution   The set of people owning at least one of these pets is $C \cup D \cup H$; by Theorem 16, this set has size

$$12 + 15 + 4 - 5 - 2 - 2 + 1 = 23$$

The set of people with none of these pets is $U \sim (C \cup D \cup H)$. By Theorem 16, the size of this set is

$$|U \sim (C \cup D \cup H)| = 25 - 12 - 15 - 4 + 5 + 2 + 2 - 1 = 2 \qquad \blacksquare$$

B The Principle of Inclusion and Exclusion

We have seen that we can solve problems asking for the size of a union of two sets or three sets by using Venn diagrams as well as formulas. For four sets, drawing a Venn diagram with circles for the sets will not show us all the overlaps. Figure 13 shows how to draw a four-set Venn diagram using rectangles. We could solve a problem that asks for the size of a union of four sets by filling a number into each of the 15 regions in the set $A \cup B \cup C \cup D$, but it will clearly be faster to use a general formula if we can find one. Furthermore, with 5 or more sets, a Venn diagram showing all the overlaps would be hopelessly complicated; a general formula is the only practical approach here.

Figure 13

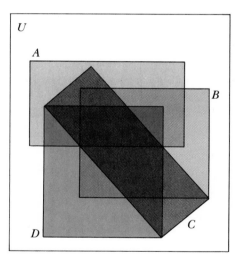

A Formula to Replace Venn Diagrams

From our computations with two and three sets, we can predict what the formula will say. To give a formula for four sets S_1, S_2, S_3, and S_4, we don't yet have a notation to say something like "Add up $|S_i \cap S_j \cap S_k|$ over all ways of choosing three different values i, j, and k." A standard notation to deal with this situation uses the Σ sign as follows:

$$\sum_{i \in N} |S_i| \qquad \text{means} \qquad |S_1| + |S_2| + \cdots + |S_n|$$

$$\sum_{i < j \in N} |S_i \cap S_j| \qquad \text{means} \qquad |S_1 \cap S_2| + |S_1 \cap S_3| + \cdots + |S_2 \cap S_3| +$$

$$\cdots + |S_i \cap S_j| + \cdots + |S_{n-1} \cap S_n|$$

$$\sum_{i < j < k \in N} |S_i \cap S_j \cap S_k| \qquad \text{means} \qquad |S_1 \cap S_2 \cap S_3| + |S_1 \cap S_2 \cap S_4| +$$

$$\cdots + |S_i \cap S_j \cap S_k| + \cdots + |S_{n-2} \cap S_{n-1} \cap S_n|$$

and so on. The general formula that works not only for four sets but for any number n of sets is Theorem 17, the **principle of inclusion and exclusion.**

Theorem 17   If $S_1, S_2, , \ldots , S_n$ are subsets of a universe U, then

$$|S_1 \cup S_2 \cup \cdots \cup S_n| =$$
$$\sum_{i \in N} |S_i| - \sum_{i < j \in N} |S_i \cap S_j| + \sum_{i < j < k \in N} |S_i \cap S_j \cap S_k| - \cdots \quad (6)$$

and

$$|\sim(S_1 \cup S_2 \cup \cdots \cup S_n)| =$$
$$|U| - \sum_{i \in N} |S_i| + \sum_{i < j \in N} (S_i \cap S_j) - \sum_{i < j < k \in N} |S_i \cap S_j \cap S_k| + \cdots \quad (7)$$

Proof   We get one formula from the other by subtraction, so we can prove either one. Formula (6) is set up ideally for proof by induction. In the case $n = 2$, it says that

$$|S_1 \cup S_2| = |S_1| + |S_2| - |S_1 \cap S_2| \quad \text{or} \quad |S \cup T| = |S| + |T| - |S \cap T|$$

which we have already proved.

Now assume that the formula works when $n = k - 1$. To use induction, we must verify that the formula is true when $n = k$. We will first use the formula $|S \cup T| = |S| + |T| - |S \cap T|$ (that is, the case $n = 2$) with $S = S_1 \cup S_2 \cup \cdots \cup S_{k-1}$ and $T = S_k$, which gives us

$$|S_1 \cup S_2 \cup \cdots \cup S_{k-1} \cup S_k|$$
$$= |S \cup T|$$
$$= |S| + |T| - |S \cap T|$$
$$= |S_1 \cup S_2 \cup \cdots \cup S_{k-1}| + |S_k| - |(S_1 \cup S_2 \cup \cdots \cup S_{k-1}) \cap S_k| \quad (8)$$

Now this sum contains three summands. Applying the inductive hypothesis to the first summand gives us all the terms of Equation (6) in the statement of the theorem except for those terms that include S_k. (Note: We have only one way to finish the proof. We must show that the second and third summands give us exactly the terms that have been left out by the first summand.)

The second summand of Formula (8) is one of the left-out terms, namely $|S_k|$. The third summand of Formula (8) may be rewritten by the distributive law

$$|(S_1 \cup S_2 \cup \cdots \cup S_{k-1}) \cap S_k| = |(S_1 \cap S_k) \cup (S_2 \cap S_k) \cup \cdots \cup (S_{k-1} \cap S_k)|$$

This is a union of $k - 1$ sets, so we may apply the inductive hypothesis to it. When we do so, we get an inclusion-exclusion formula in which every term contains something intersected with S_k. In other words, we get exactly the terms $|S_1 \cap S_k|$, $|S_1 \cap S_2 \cap S_k|$, and so on, that were left out by summands 1 and 2. In the formula we get, these terms will appear with a sign opposite from what they have in Equation (6). However, since our third summand has a minus sign, we get the remaining terms of the formula. By the principle of mathematical induction, the formula holds for all values of n. Formula (7) in the theorem follows by subtraction. ∎

EXAMPLE 43   In a hypothetical survey of cancer patients to look for patterns involving consumption of various substances, we ask people about regular use of tobacco, alcohol, coffee, and cured meat. Figure 14 shows a possible set of results for people who fall into various categories.

Figure 14

Substance	T	A	C	M	TA	TC	TM	AC	AM	CM	TAC	TAM	TCM	ACM	TACM
No. of people	10	12	13	17	6	8	7	7	8	7	5	4	5	4	3

If everyone participating in the study made use of at least one of the substances on a regular basis, how many people participated in the study?

Solution   Using the inclusion-exclusion formula for the size of a union, we write

$$|T \cup A \cup C \cup M| = 10 + 12 + 13 + 17 - 6 - 8 - 7 - 7 - 8 - 7 +$$
$$5 + 4 + 5 + 4 - 3 = 24$$ ∎

Example 43 shows how we may use the inclusion-exclusion formulas in place of Venn diagrams. Our next example shows how we can apply the inclusion-exclusion formulas to problems involving a variable for the number of sets.

EXAMPLE 44   A teacher collects n test papers, shuffles them, and hands them back to the class to grade. In what fraction of the ways to hand back the tests do no students receive their own tests?

Solution   We may think of the students as being numbered 1, 2, . . . , n. We are asking how many permutations of the set $N = \{1, 2, . . . ,n\}$ map no element to itself, because each way of handing the tests back can be represented as a permutation mapping student *i* to student *j* if student *i*'s name is on the paper student *j* receives. Such a permutation that maps no element to itself is called a **derangement.**

One strategy is to take the total number of distributions of papers (which is $n!$) and subtract the number that give a student his or her own paper. However, if we do this exclusion for each student, we will, for example, subtract out *twice* those that give Pam *and* Pat their own papers—once for Pam and once for Pat. Thus, we see an inclusion-exclusion pattern emerging, so we try to rephrase the problem in terms of sets that correspond to giving someone his or her own paper (or to not giving someone his or her own paper).

Thus we let S_i be the set of distributions of the papers so that student *i*'s name is on the paper student *i* gets. (In terms of permutations, S_i is the set of permutations that *do* map *i* to itself.) Now we want to know how many distributions are in *none* of the sets S_i. To find this, we apply Formula (7) in Theorem 17. For this purpose, we will need the size of S_i, $S_i \cap S_j$, $S_i \cap S_j \cap S_k$, and so on. The size of S_i is $(n-1)!$ because there are $(n-1)!$ permutations of the integers 1 through n that map *i* to *i*. (For example, the permutations in S_n correspond naturally to the permutations of the set $\{1, 2, \ldots, n-1\}$.) Similarly, there are $(n-2)!$ permutations of the integers 1 through n that map *i* to *i* and *j* to *j*, so if $i \neq j$, $|S_i \cap S_j| = (n-2)!$. The same kind of reasoning tells us that the intersection of *k* different sets S_i will have size $(n-k)!$. Thus each $|S_i|$ is $(n-1)!$, each $|S_i \cap S_j|$ is $(n-2)!$, and so on. Since there are $\binom{n}{1}$ ways to choose *i*, there are $\binom{n}{1}$ terms of the form $|S_i|$. Since there are $\binom{n}{2}$ ways to choose *i* and *j*, there are $\binom{n}{2}$ terms of the form $|S_i \cap S_j|$, and so on. When we substitute into Equation (7) in Theorem 17, we get

$$|\sim(S_1 \cup S_2 \cup \cdots \cup S_n)| = |U| - \sum_{i \in N} |S_i| + \sum_{i < j \in N} |S_i \cap S_j| - \cdots$$

$$= n! - \binom{n}{1}(n-1)! + \binom{n}{2}(n-2)! - \binom{n}{3}(n-3)! + \cdots$$

$$= \sum_{i=0}^{n} (-1)^i \binom{n}{i}(n-i)! = \sum_{i=0}^{n} (-1)^i \frac{n!}{i!(n-i)!}(n-i)!$$

$$= \sum_{i=0}^{n} (-1)^i \frac{n!}{i!}$$

This is the number of distributions in which no one gets his or her own paper. Since the total number of distributions is $n!$, the fraction of distributions in which no one receives his or her own paper is

$$\sum_{i=0}^{n} \frac{(-1)^i}{i!} = 1 - 1 + \frac{1}{2} - \frac{1}{6} \cdots$$

Those who have studied power series in calculus will note that this is the power series expansion for the natural exponential function e^x evaluated at $x = -1$. Thus the fraction approaches $e^{-1} = 1/e$ (which is a little more than a third) as n gets large. ■

Example 44 shows a second benefit of our algebraic formulation of the principle of inclusion and exclusion. Not only can we find numerical values; we may also derive general formulas.

Concepts Review

1. The size of a union of two sets C and D is given by the formula $|C \cup D|$ = _____.

2. The inclusion-exclusion formula for three sets tells us that $|R \cup S \cup T|$ = _____.

3. A permutation of $\{1,2, \ldots ,n\}$ that maps no element to itself is called a(n) _____.

4. The notation _____ stands for the sum over all i and j in N with $i < j$ of $|S_i \cap S_j|$.

5. The _____ _____ formula tells us that
$$|S_1 \cup S_2 \cup \cdots \cup S_n| = \sum_{i \in N} |S_i| \underline{\hspace{2cm}} \underline{\hspace{2cm}} - \cdots$$

Exercises

A

1. If $|A| = 10$, $|B| = 12$, and $|A \cap B| = 7$, what is $|A \cup B|$? Further, if $|U| = 20$, what is $|\sim(A \cup B)|$?

2. If $|S| = 20$, $|T| = 25$, and $|S \cap T| = 9$, what is $|S \cup T|$? If $|U| = 40$, what is $|\sim(S \cup T)|$?

3. If $|A| = 10$, $|B| = 12$, and $|A \cup B| = 20$, what is $|A \cap B|$?

4. If $|A| = 10$, $|B| = 20$, and $|A \cup B| = 25$, what is $|A \cap B|$?

5. Given three sets R, S, and T such that $|R \cap S \cap T| = 2$, $|R \cap S| = 6$, $|S \cap T| = 7$, $|R \cap T| = 5$, $|R| = 17$, $|S| = 17$, $|T| = 17$, find $|S \cup T|$. If $|U| = 48$, find $|\sim(S \cup T)|$. Find $|R \cup S \cup T|$ and $|\sim(R \cup S \cup T)|$.

6. Given three sets, S_1, S_2, and S_3 such that $|S_1 \cap S_2 \cap S_3| = 3$, $|S_1 \cap S_2| = 9$, $|S_1 \cap S_3| = 7$, $|S_2 \cap S_3| = 8$, $|S_1| = 20$, $|S_2| = 23$, and $|S_3| = 20$, find $|S_1 \cup S_2 \cup S_3|$. If $|U| = 42$, find $|\sim(S_1 \cup S_2 \cup S_3)|$.

7. In Exercise 5, find the size of $R \cup S$. Find the size of $T \sim (R \cup S)$. (*Hint:* Put the sizes into the Venn diagram.)

8. In Exercise 6, find the size of $S_1 \cup S_2$, $S_1 \sim S_2$, and $S_3 \sim (S_1 \cup S_2)$.

9. Among 60 pet owners responding to a survey, 30 owned cats, 25 owned dogs, and 5 owned both. How many respondents had a dog or cat? How many had neither?

10. To do this exercise, you do not need to know the meaning of the words *byte, error,* or *parity check error.* In an analysis of error patterns in 64 stored erroneous bytes of computer data, 34 had an even number of errors, 12 had errors in the parity check

position, and 6 had both a parity check error and an even number of errors. How many bytes had an odd number of errors, none of which were in the parity check position?

11. A used car dealer has 20 cars on the lot. Nine have automatic transmission, 11 have power steering, and 8 have power brakes. Seven have both automatic transmission and power steering, 4 have automatic transmission and power brakes, 5 have power steering and power brakes, and 3 have automatic transmission, power steering and power brakes. Draw a Venn diagram; using the initials *T, S,* and *B,* label the region that corresponds to each combination of features. How many cars are "stripped"—that is, have none of these features?

12. Among 31 varieties of corn tested, 14 had uneven ears, 17 had incomplete germination, and 11 had weak stalks. Six had uneven ears and incomplete germination, 5 had weak stalks and incomplete germination, and 7 had uneven ears and weak stalks. Two varieties had all three defects. How many had none of these defects? Draw a Venn diagram; using the initials *U, I,* and *W,* show which regions represent which combinations of defects.

B   13. Copy the Venn diagram in Figure 13 and shade in the following four regions: $A \cap B \cap C$, $(A \cap B \cap C) \sim (A \cap B \cap C \cap D)$, $A \cap B \cap \sim C$, $(A \cap B) \cup (C \cap D)$.

14. Copy the Venn diagram in Figure 13 and shade in the following regions: $B \cap C \cap D$, $(B \cap C \cap D) \sim (A \cap B \cap C \cap D)$, $B \cap C \cap \sim A$, $(B \cap C) \cup (A \cap D)$.

15. Experimental garden plots were treated with four substances: lime, potash, urea, and phosphate. Some were treated with each combination of these substances. Figure 15, which uses *L* for lime, *P* for potash, *U* for urea, and *F* for phosphate, shows how many plots received each combination of substances. The plots that received none of the substances were control plots. If there were 36 plots in total, how many plots were control plots?

Figure 15

Substances	L	P	U	F	LP	LU	LF	PU	PF	UF	LPU	LUF	LPF	PUF	LPUF
Number	20	19	17	16	14	14	12	12	11	10	10	8	9	7	5

16. In a study of association of food with migraine headaches, researchers studied four substances: chocolate, ripened cheese, monosodium glutamate, and alcohol. They asked a group of headache sufferers whether they consumed each of these substances regularly. The (hypothetical) data are given in Figure 16. If 50 people participated in the study, how many used none of the substances?

Figure 16

Substances	C	R	A	M	CR	CA	CM	RA	RM	AM	CRA	CAM	CRM	RAM	CRAM
Number	18	21	18	18	14	13	12	13	12	11	10	9	8	7	6

17. Use the data in Exercise 15 to fill in a copy of the Venn diagram in Figure 13, giving the size of each region.

18. Use the data in Exercise 16 to fill in a copy of the Venn diagram in Figure 13, giving the size of each region.

19. Five children bring story books to nursery school, and the books become hopelessly mixed up. In how many ways may the children take the books home so that everyone has a book that belongs to someone else?

20. Six people bring gifts for a grab-bag at a party. In how many ways of distributing the gifts (one to each person) will at least one person receive the gift he or she brought?

21. Experimental garden plots are to be treated with lime, urea, potash, and phosphate. The experimental design calls for 32 plots to be treated with each of the substances (and perhaps others), 16 plots with each two of the substances (and perhaps others), 8 plots with each three of the substances (and perhaps others), and four plots with all four of the substances. What is the total number of garden plots needed?

22. In a testing program for interaction of food substances in triggering migraine headaches, the substances studied are phenylethylamine, tyramine, monosodium glutamate, and papain. The experimental design calls for 56 people to ingest each individual substance (and perhaps others), 24 people to ingest each two substances (and perhaps others), 8 people to ingest each three substances (and perhaps others), and 4 people to ingest all four substances. How many people are required for the experiment?

23. In Exercise 21, if the researcher had wanted to have 32 plots treated with each individual substance, 29 plots treated with each two substances, 12 plots treated with (at least) each three substances, and 6 plots treated with (at least) all four, the experiment would be impossible. Show why by attempting to compute the number of garden plots used.

24. In Exercise 22, suppose the experimental design called for 60 people to ingest each individual substance, 56 to ingest each two substances (or more), 48 to ingest each three substances (or more) and 36 to ingest all four. Show that such a design is impossible by showing that the total number of subjects involved is equal to the number of subjects taking any given substance. (Why does this show that the design is impossible?)

25. A fraternity has a costume party in which each person must make a costume using a sheet. One rule of the party is, however, that at a certain point the sheets must all be removed. If the sheets become totally mixed up, in how many ways may *n* partygoers each go home with a sheet belonging to someone else?

26. A programmer accidentally neglected to coordinate a program to print addresses for envelopes with a program to print letters, so that letters end up being put in envelopes randomly. If there are *n* letters, in how many ways may *n* letters be put into envelopes so that no one receives the letter intended for that person?

27. Five children bring one candy bar each (all different) to a treasure hunt game at camp. The counselor hides the candy and the children look for it. Whoever finds a candy bar eats it. In how many ways may the children find and eat the candy if no one eats the candy he or she brought? (A child may find more than one or find none.)

28. At a "silent auction" bake sale, each person brings one dish and makes a sealed bid on all the dishes. For each dish, the highest bidder wins, If six people participate, in how many ways may the bidding come out so that at least one person gets the contribution he or she made?

29. If we want to pass out eight identical apples to Sam, Jo, and Pat so that Jo gets three or more, we give out three apples to Jo and then pass out the remaining five apples in $C(5 + 3 - 1, 5)$ ways. In how many ways may we pass out eight identical apples to Sam, Jo, and Pat so that no one gets five or more?

30. How many four-letter "nonsense words" may we make with the letters $\{a,b,c,d,e\}$ if no letter can be used three or more times? (*Hint:* How many nonsense words *do* use the letter a three or more times?)

31. In how many ways may eight distinct pieces of candy be passed out to four children so that each child gets at least one piece?

32. A four-person family has seven housekeeping jobs to do. In how many ways may the jobs be assigned to the family members if each person does at least one job?

Problems

1. A **fixed point** of a function $f: N \rightarrow N$ is an element X of N such that $f(x) = x$. How many functions from an n-element set to itself have no fixed points?

2. In how many k-element multisets chosen from an n-element set does no element have multiplicity more than m?

3. In how many ways may k books be arranged on n shelves so that no shelf gets more than m books?

4. A marriage counselor seats n couples around a table for a discussion so that no one is next to his or her spouse. (However, men or women may be side-by-side.) In how many ways may this be done?

5. At a dinner party, n married couples are seated around a table, alternating sex, so that no one is next to his or her spouse. In how many ways may this be done? (This is a classic problem, known as the *Ménage problem*. Most published solutions are beyond the level of this text. However, it may be done in a way similar to the solution of Problem 4 without any special mathematical knowledge.)

6. There are n children in a nursery school who play in the snow and get their mittens wet. The mittens are put on a radiator to dry and become hopelessly mixed up. In how many ways may the children return home so that each child is wearing two (not necessarily matched) mittens that belong to another child or children?

7. In Problem 6, each child must take a left mitten and a right mitten. The students also get their socks wet and put them on another radiator to dry. As the reader might predict, the socks become hopelessly mixed up. Explain how the question "In how many ways may the children return home so that each child is wearing two socks (not necessarily matched), at least one of which is another child's?" differs from the question of Problem 6, and answer this question.

8. A group of n people sit around a table for a meeting, get up for a break, and return to the table. In how many ways may they return so that no one is to the right of the same person in both the first and second seatings?

9. Show that the number of functions from an n-element set onto a k-element set is given by

$$\sum_{i=0}^{k} (-1)^i \binom{k}{i} (k-i)^n$$

10. In how many ways may we pass out k identical apples to n children if no child is to get more than three apples?

11. Let $S_1, S_2, \ldots S_n$ be subsets of a universe U such that each S_i has the same size m_1, all intersections $S_i \cap S_j$ have the same size m_2, and so on. Show that

$$|S_1 \cup S_2 \cup \cdots \cup S_n| = \sum_{i=1}^{n} \binom{n}{i} (-1)^{i-1} m_i$$

and further, if $m_0 = |U|$, then

$$|\sim(S_1 \cup S_2 \cup \cdots \cup S_n)| = \sum_{i=0}^{n} \binom{n}{i} (-1)^i m_i$$

12. Explain how Problem 11 simplifies problems such as 8, 9, 10, and the problem of derangements.

Chapter 6
Review Exercises

1. Write down the ordered pairs of a counting function for the set $\{a,s,d,f,g,h,j,k,l\}$.

2. The symbols $1,2,10,11,12,20,21,22$ stand for the so-called *ternary representations* of the numbers one through eight. Describe a bijection between these symbols and the usual symbols $1,2,\ldots,8$ for these numbers. (*Note:* You don't need to understand ternary representations to do this problem. If you do know about them, try to use what you know in your solution.)

3. How many elements should the set $\{1,2,3\} \times \{a,z\}$ have? Write them down.

4. A certain personal computer manufacturer offers three different central processors, four different memory configurations, five different video displays, and four different disk drive configurations. Each of these is compatible with the others, so they may be combined in any way to form a system. How many systems are possible?

In Exercises 5–10, compute the numbers requested.

5. $P(10,8)$ 6. $(n)_3$ 7. $P(6,6)$

8. $\binom{6}{4}$ 9. $C(n,3)$ 10. $\binom{n}{n-3}$

11. A kindergarten teacher needs to select three different students from a class of 20 to be a horse, a tree, and a troll in a school play. In how many ways may he do this?

12. A college professor must select 3 students from a 20-student calculus class to compete in an intramural problem-solving contest. In how many ways may she do this?

13. The neighborhood beautification committee has been given a pine tree, a red maple tree, and a pin-oak tree. In how many ways may they distribute them among ten families for planting if no family may get more than one? What if any family can get any number of them?

14. The committee of Exercise 13 has been given three identical silver birches. In how many ways may they distribute them among ten families for planting if no family may get more than one? What if any family may receive any number of trees?

15. A computer printer has six switches, each with two positions. One switch controls draft versus high quality, one controls pica versus elite type size, and the other four control various compatibility settings for use with various types of computers. In how many different ways may the six switches be set?

16. Eight scouts have been organized into a patrol for a jamboree. They must choose their officers: a patrol leader, an assistant patrol leader, and a quartermaster. They must also choose a 4-person team to participate in a skills contest. In how many ways may they make these choices if no one on the team may be an officer? What if officers may be team members?

17. In the situations below, most questions may be answered by using k-element permutations, k-tuples, k-element subsets, or k-element multisets. For each question, state which method is most appropriate; if none is appropriate, say so. State the relevant formula. The problems concern the assignment of certain processing tasks among the processors of a multiprocessor computer. All you need to understand about the computer is that the processors may all be distinguished from one another.
    (a) In how many ways may k distinct tasks be distributed among n processors so that no processor gets more than one?
    (b) In how many ways may k distinct tasks be distributed among n processors if each processor may receive any number of the tasks and tasks may be done appropriately in any order or even simultaneously?
    (c) In how many ways may k distinct tasks be distributed among n processors if each processor may receive any of the tasks in any order and must do the tasks it receives in the order that they are received?
    (d) In how many ways may k identical tasks be distributed among n processors in such a way that no processor gets more than one?
    (e) In how many ways may k identical tasks be distributed among n processors if any processor may receive any number of tasks?

18. Three processors in a multiprocessing computer each generate a bit (a bit is either a zero or one) in sequence. If the number of one-bits generated already is even, then the processor chooses a zero or one at random. Otherwise the machine repeats the previous bit. Draw a tree diagram with three stages, showing the possible bits generated by processors one, two, and three. How many outcomes are possible?

19. In how many ways may seven computers be arranged into a single-ring network? A double-ring network? A linear network with two-way communication?

20. Write down the multiplicity function for the multiset of letters (chosen from the alphabet) appearing in *sample phrase*.

21. In how many ways may we arrange three deans, four students, two professors, and two staff people in a circle if the deans must be in a row, the students must be in a row, the professors must be in a row, and the staff people must be in a row?

22. Write down the expansion of $(x + y)^9$.

23. Write down and simplify the expansion of $(3x - 2)^5$.

24. Write down the formula for $(x + 1)^5$. Substitute in $x = 1$ to get a formula that gives us a certain sum of binomial coefficients. How may this formula be interpreted as a formula about subsets of a 5-element set?

25. Use Table 4 to obtain values of the following.

(a) $\binom{18}{12}$ (b) $\binom{20}{5}$ (c) $\binom{20}{15}$ (d) $\binom{21}{5}$

26. We have two oranges, three apples, and five pears. In how many ways may we pass them out to ten children so that each child gets one?

27. A hypothetical survey of 25 faculty members with computers showed that 18 had external floppy-disk drives, 8 had external hard-disk drives, and 5 had both. How many had some kind of external storage device? How many had neither kind of external storage device?

28. After the survey of Exercise 27 was completed, it was learned that several faculty members in the group were experimenting with CD (laser) storage devices. In particular, five people had CD storage devices, three people had both hard-disk and CD storage, two people had both floppy-disk and CD storage, and one person had all three. How many people had no external storage device?

29. How many people in Exercise 28 had CD storage but no other kind of external storage device? How many had both CD and hard-disk external storage but no floppy-disk external storage?

30. Six students are to submit their best idea for a term project to their laboratory instructor. On the basis of which students have which strengths, the instructor will choose one project for each of the students. In how many ways may the instructor assign the proposed projects so that no one receives the project he or she proposed? Assume that the six projects are all different, but the same project may be assigned to more than one person.

31. Redo Problem 30, making the assumption that each person must be assigned a different project but still assuming that all the projects are different.

32. A classroom has n desks but $m < n$ students using it for a two-hour seminar. In the middle of the seminar, there is a five-minute break. In how many ways may the students sit when they return from the break if no student sits at the desk he or she occupied before the break?

*W*e have learned how thinking inductively helps us solve problems by reducing a problem involving an integer n to the same kind of problem with a smaller value of n. In many applications, it is important to know the number of different ways in which a problem may be solved. When we can construct the solutions inductively, we can also count them inductively. Since so many problems have inductive solutions, this provides a unifying idea that both explains similarities among many of the problems we have already solved and suggests solutions to more complex problems that we have not yet approached.

The idea of a recurrence equation is that it expresses the nth term of a sequence of numbers in terms of the preceding terms. How do we use this idea? A certain kind of problem leads us to a recurrence equation. By standard techniques, we can determine all sequences that obey this equation and then specialize to the sequence that solves our problem.

Many different applications lead us to similar recurrence equations. For example, radioactive decay, population growth, compound interest, and the analyses of certain algorithms can all lead us to the same kinds of recurrence equations. In particular, when using probability theory to determine how much time certain algorithms or processes should be expected to take, one discovers that principles of probability lead naturally to certain recurrence equations. In more advanced work, counting graphs and trees with certain properties, one finds that the structure of the graphs or trees leads once again to recurrence relations that describe the numbers of interest.

The study of recurrence relations depends on quite a few of the ideas we have studied earlier, but mathematical induction will be the tool that underlies our work.

Section 7-1
First-Order Recurrences and Exponential Functions

Ⓐ   Recurrence Equations

We begin our study of recurrence equations by showing how several problems we've solved by whatever technique seemed appropriate can all be viewed as solving a certain kind of equation that describes how the terms of a sequence relate to each other. The examples we use demonstrate certain properties that recurrence equations may or may not have—properties that help us classify our eventual solution techniques.

The Selection Sort Recurrence

We discussed the selection sort algorithm for sorting a list of n numbers into increasing order. Let us use C_n to stand for the number of comparisons made in sorting n items. Recall that the technique of selection sort is first to find the smallest element of the list (for which purpose we use $n-1$ comparisons), exchange that smallest element with the first element, and then carry out the selection sort process on the remaining $n-1$ elements. (Notice the inductive nature of this description.) Since the number of comparisons we make with these remaining $n-1$ elements is C_{n-1}, the total number of comparisons is given by the equation

$$C_n = n-1 + C_{n-1}$$

We also know that $C_1 = 0$, because no comparisons are made to sort a one-element list.

The Subset Recurrence

Now consider a second problem, that of computing the number of subsets of the set $N = \{1,2, \ldots ,n\}$. Let us use S_n to stand for the number of subsets of N. We can get an equation relating S_n to S_{n-1} from the observation that a subset of N either contains n or does not. A subset of N does not contain n if and only if it is also a subset of $N' = \{1,2, \ldots ,n-1\}$. Thus the number of subsets of N that do not contain n is S_{n-1}. A subset of N *does* contain n if and only if it consists of a subset of N' with n added to it. Thus the number of subsets of N that do contain n is also S_{n-1}. By using the sum principle, we get

$$S_n = \text{(number of subsets not containing } n) + \text{(number of subsets containing } n)$$
$$= S_{n-1} + S_{n-1}$$
$$= 2S_{n-1}$$

We also know that $S_0 = 1$, because the empty set has only itself for a subset.

The Bijection Recurrence

Finally consider the problem of computing the number of bijections (one-to-one and onto functions) from $N = \{1,2, \ldots ,n\}$ to an n-element set. We have n choices for $f(n)$; we must map the elements of $N' = \{1,2, \ldots ,n-1\}$ bijectively to the remaining $n-1$ elements of the set. There are b_{n-1} ways to do this. Thus by the product principle,

$$b_n = \text{(number of choices for } f(n))\cdot\text{(number of bijections between } N' \text{ and}$$
$$\text{the remaining elements)}$$
$$= nb_{n-1}$$

We also know that $b_1 = 1$, for there is exactly one bijection between two one-element sets.

   In each of these cases we discussed a sequence of numbers and discovered an equation that would let us compute the nth term of the sequence from the $(n-1)^{\text{th}}$ term of the sequence. In addition, we had the zeroth or first term of the sequence. These correspond to the inductive step and the base step in an inductive proof that there is one and only one sequence satisfying our conditions. Thus we can compute the values of the sequence from the information given.

EXAMPLE 1   Compute the first five terms of the sequence $S_n = 2S_{n-1}$, given above for subsets, starting with term 0.

Solution   The first five terms will be term number 0 through term number 4. We are given $S_0 = 1$. We may now write:

$$S_1 = 2S_0 = 2{\cdot}1 = 2$$
$$S_2 = 2S_1 = 2{\cdot}2 = 4$$
$$S_3 = 2S_2 = 2{\cdot}4 = 8$$
$$S_4 = 2S_3 = 2{\cdot}8 = 16$$

■

The Idea of Recurrence Equations

An equation that allows us to compute the nth term
of a sequence $<a_n>$ from the preceding terms (the terms
a_{n-1}, a_{n-2}, etc.) is called a **recurrence** or **recurrence equation**
(or sometimes *recurrence relation* or *difference equation*).

The three examples we gave of recurrence equations allowed us to compute the value of a_n from the value of a_{n-1} (and perhaps the value of n) without using a_{n-2} or any other earlier values of a_i. A recurrence equation is called a **first-order** recurrence equation if it allows us to compute a_n from a_{n-1}. A recurrence equation is called an rth**-order** recurrence equation if it allows us to compute a_n from the preceding r terms $(a_{n-1}, a_{n-2}, \ldots, a_{n-r})$.

EXAMPLE 2   What is the order of each of the following recurrence equations?

(a) $a_n = 3a_{n-1} + n^2$
(b) $a_n = na_{n-1} + 2^n$
(c) $a_n = \sqrt{a_{n-1}} + a_{n-2}^2$
(d) $a_n = a_{n-1} + a_{n-2} + \cdots + a_1$

Solution   Equations (a) and (b) are first-order recurrence equations. Equation (c) is a second-order recurrence equation, because a_n is computed using both a_{n-1} and a_{n-2}. Equation (d) has no order whatsoever, because it tells us how to use *all* the preceding terms to compute a_n, not just some fixed number r of preceding terms.   ∎

Linear Recurrence Equations

An important property that our sorting, subset, and bijection recurrence equations jhad is the property of linearity.

> A first-order recurrence equation is called **linear**
> if there are functions $b(n)$ and $d(n)$
> such that the recurrence may be written
>
> $$a_n = b(n)\, a_{n-1} + d(n)$$

(We write $b(n)$ and $d(n)$ rather than b_n and d_n to emphasize that it is the sequence $<a_n>$ that is being described.) A **linear recurrence equation** is one of the form

$$a_n = b_1(n)a_{n-1} + b_2(n)a_{n-2} + \cdots + b_0(n)a_0 + d(n)$$

Here $d(n)$ is called the **driving function** of the recurrence.

EXAMPLE 3   Which of the recurrence equations in Example 2 are linear and why?

Solution

(a) is linear; we have $b(n) = 3$ and $d(n) = n^2$.
(b) is linear; we have $b(n) = n$ and $d(n) = 2^n$.
(c) is not linear; neither a_{n-1} nor a_{n-2} appears to the first power.
(d) is linear; we have $b_i(n) = 1$ for each i and $d(n) = 0$.   ∎

Solutions of Recurrence Equations

We computed in an earlier chapter that the sequence C_n (satisfying $C_n = C_{n-1} + n - 1$) with which we began this section is given by

$$C_n = \frac{n(n-1)}{2}$$

Notice that in fact this gives $C_1 = 1 \cdot 0/2 = 0$, as required. To see that this formula for C_n satisfies $C_n = C_{n-1} + n - 1$, we add $n - 1$ to what the formula gives for C_{n-1}, getting

$$C_{n-1} + n - 1 = \frac{(n-1)(n-2)}{2} + n - 1$$

$$= \frac{n^2 - 3n + 2 + 2n - 2}{2}$$

$$= \frac{n^2 - n}{2}$$

$$= C_n$$

Thus the function $C_n = n(n-1)/2$ satisfies both the condition $C_1 = 0$ and the recurrence equation.

> A function f is called a **solution** to a recurrence
> equation if substituting $f(n)$ for a_n in the
> recurrence equation gives a valid equation for all n.

We have just verified that the function given by $C_n = n(n-1)/2$ is a solution to the recurrence relation $C_n = C_{n-1} + n - 1$.

The remainder of our study of recurrence equations will focus on methods for *finding* solutions to various types (first-order, linear, and so on) of recurrence equations that typically arise in practical problems.

B First-Order Linear Homogeneous Recurrence Equations

We've defined a first-order linear recurrence equation to be one of the form

$$a_n = b(n)\, a_{n-1} + d(n)$$

In two of our three motivating examples, the subset recurrence $S_n = 2S_{n-1}$ and the bijection recurrence $b_n = nb_{n-1}$, the term $d(n)$ was zero.

> A first-order linear recurrence is
> called **homogeneous** if $d(n) = 0$.

(*Homogeneous* is defined similarly for higher-order recurrence relations.)

EXAMPLE 4   Classify the following recurrence relations as homogeneous or not:

(a) $t_n = (n-1) t_{n-1}$ (b) $t_n = n t_{n-1} - t_{n-1}$

(c) $a_n = a_{n-1} - a_{n-2}$ (d) $a_n = a_{n-1} - (n-2)$

Solution   Recurrence (a) is homogeneous by definition. Recurrence (b) is simply a way to rewrite (a), so it is homogeneous. Recurrence (c) is also homogeneous (because each term contains an a_i). Recurrence (d) is *not* homogeneous; here $d(n) = -(n-2)$. ∎

Constant Coefficient Recurrences

Two of our motivating examples, the subset recurrence $S_n - 2S_{n-1}$ and the comparison recurrence $C_n = C_{n-1} + n - 1$, had still another property different from being homogeneous.

> A first-order linear recurrence is a **constant coefficient** recurrence if $b(n)$ is constant.

(The term is defined analogously for higher-order linear recurrence relations.) Notice that $C_n = C_{n-1} + n - 1$ is called a constant coefficient recurrence despite the fact that $n - 1$ is *not* a constant; the defining property is that the coefficient of C_{n-1}, in this case 1, is constant.

EXAMPLE 5   Classify the following recurrence relations as constant coefficient or not.

(a) $a_n = 3a_{n-1}$ (b) $a_n = 2a_{n-1} + n$

(c) $a_n = n a_{n-1} + 2$ (d) $a_n + a_{n-1} = 2a_{n-2} + n^2$

Solution   Recurrence (a) is constant coefficient because 3 is constant. Recurrence (b) is constant coefficient because 2 is constant. Recurrence (c) is not constant coefficient because n is not constant. Recurrence (d) is constant coefficient because, when we write it in the usual form, the coefficient of a_{n-1} is -1 and the coefficient of a_{n-2} is 2. ∎

The Homogeneous Constant Coefficient Case

Among our three motivating examples, only the subset relation, $S_n = 2S_{n-1}$ is a first-order linear homogeneous recurrence with constant coefficients. Such a recurrence must have the form

$$a_n = b a_{n-1}$$

where b is a constant. This kind of recurrence relation arises from a wide variety of applications. For example, if V_n is the value after n years of a savings certificate that pays 10% interest compounded annually, the statement that we add 10% to the value each year becomes

$$V_n = V_{n-1} + .10V_{n-1} = 1.1V_{n-1}$$

Similarly, in radioactive decay, the amount of radioactive material present decreases by a fixed percentage during one unit of time. That is, a fixed fraction p of the radioactive material decays in one unit of time. If a_n stands for the amount of material present after n units of time, then we may write

$$a_n = a_{n-1} - pa_{n-1} = (1-p)a_{n-1}$$

Solving the Recurrence

The recurrence relation $a_n = ba_{n-1}$ may remind us of the inductive step in the definition of b^n. Namely, we define b^0 to be 1 and then define b^n to be $b \cdot b^{n-1}$. Just as we can use induction to show that this uniquely defines b^n, we may prove that the recurrence relation $a_n = ba_{n-1}$ and just one value a_m of the sequence $<a_i>$ uniquely determines the sequence.

Theorem 1   If the sequence $<a_i>$ satisfies $a_n = ba_{n-1}$ for $n > m$ and $a_m = c$, then $a_n = cb^{n-m}$ for all $n > m$.

Proof   We prove by induction that the sequence satisfies this formula. If $n = m$, then the formula gives $a_n = cb^0 = a_m$, so the formula is valid for $n = m$. Now suppose the formula is valid when $n = k-1$. This gives us

$$a_{k-1} = cb^{k-1-m}$$

and substituting this for a_{k-1} in the recurrence $a_k = ba_{k-1}$ gives us

$$a_k = bcb^{k-1-m} = cb^{k-m}$$

Thus the formula holds when $n = k$, so by the principle of mathematical induction, it is valid for all n.   ∎

General Solutions

We have defined a sequence satisfying a recurrence equation to be a *solution* to that recurrence equation. We have just shown that there is one and only one solution to a recurrence relation $a_n = ba_{n-1}$ with a specified value for one term a_m. We call the formula

$$a_n = cb^{n-m}$$

a *general solution*.

> A formula involving certain constants is called a
> **general solution** to the recurrence if every solution
> may be obtained from the formula by assigning
> specific numerical values to the constants.

EXAMPLE 6   Use Theorem 1 to show that a set has 2^n subsets.

Solution   The number S_n of subsets of an n-element set satisfies $S_n = 2S_{n-1}$. Also $S_0 = 1$. Therefore, by Theorem 1, $S_n = 1 \cdot 2^{n-0} = 2^n$.   ■

Non-Constant Coefficients

The recurrence relation $b_n = nb_{n-1}$ is a homogeneous recurrence relation in which the coefficient of b_{n-1} is *not* constant but is the variable n. This recurrence relation is totally parallel to the inductive step in an inductive definition of $n!$, namely the step $n! = n(n-1)!$. In addition, we verified that for bijections $b_1 = 1$. Since $1! = 1$ as well, we could prove by induction that if $b_1 = 1$ and $b_n = nb_{n-1}$, then $b_n = n!$.

The situation with a general recurrence relation $a_n = c(n)a_{n-1}$ is quite similar. The inductive definition of product notation

$$\prod_{i=m}^{n} c(i) = c(m) \cdot c(m+1) \ldots c(n-1)\, c(n)$$

is

$$\prod_{i=m}^{m} c(i) = c(m) \text{ and } \prod_{i=m}^{n} c(i) = \left(\prod_{i=m}^{n-1} c(i) \right) \cdot c(n) \qquad \text{for } n > m$$

Then, just as with the bijection recurrence, we may prove by induction the following theorem.

Theorem 2   If the sequence $\langle a_n \rangle$ satisfies $a_n = c(n)a_{n-1}$ for $n > m$ and $a_m = c$, then

$$a_i = c \prod_{i=m+1}^{n} c(i)$$

Proof   An application of mathematical induction.   ■

EXAMPLE 7   Use Theorem 2 to explain why $b_n = n!$ is the solution for the bijection recurrence $b_n = nb_{n-1}$ with $b_1 = 1$.

Solution   To use the formula in Theorem 2, we let $c(n) = n$ and take $m = 1$. Replacing a_n with b_n in the formula, we get

$$b_n = 1 \cdot \prod_{i=1+1}^{n} i = \prod_{i=2}^{n} i = i!$$ ■

Notice that in Example 7 we referred to the recurrence equation $b_n = nb_{n-1}$ and also to the fact that $b_1 = 1$. The fact that $b_1 = 1$ is called an **initial condition** (because it tells us the initial or first term of the sequence). Had we not known that $b_1 = 1$, we could only have written $b_n = cn!$, where c stands for the value of b_1. Without an initial condition, we can find only the **general solution** to the recurrence relation. To find the **particular solution** that solves a certain problem, we must use the information in the problem to determine the constant c. The facts we use to determine c are called the *initial conditions* of the problem.

C Exponential Functions and Logarithms

We have seen how sequences of the form $a_n = cb^n$ arise as solutions to practical problems that give recurrence relations of the form $a_n = ba_{n-1}$. In our study of induction, we showed how b^n was defined inductively for non-negative integers n and how induction helps prove the rules of exponents

$$b^{m+n} = b^m b^n \quad \text{and} \quad (b^m)^n = b^{mn}$$

In fact, b^x can be defined for any real number x so long as $b \geq 0$.

Rules of Exponents

In algebra you may have learned that the rule of exponents

$$b^{x+y} = b^x b^y \tag{1}$$

can be used to show that $b^{-n} = 1/b^n$ (by substituting n for x and $-n$ for y in Equation (1)). You may also have learned that the rule of exponents

$$(b^x)^y = b^{xy} \tag{2}$$

tells you that $b^{1/q} = \sqrt[q]{b}$, so that $b^{p/q} = \left(\sqrt[q]{b}\right)^p$. Thus defining b^x for a rational number $x = p/q$ is part of algebra. Example 8 shows some of the ways in which we learn in algebra to use rules (1) and (2) of exponents.

EXAMPLE 8   Simplify the following

(a) $(b^4 b^2)^3$
(b) $\sqrt{b^2 \cdot b^4}$
(c) $2^{1/2} \cdot 4^{1/4} \cdot 3^{-1} \cdot 27^{2/3}$

Solution
(a) $(b^4 b^2)^3 = (b^{4+2})^3 = (b^6)^3 = b^{18}$
(b) $\sqrt{b^2 \cdot b^4} = (b^{4+2})^{1/2} = (b^6)^{1/2} = b^3$
(c) $2^{1/2} \cdot 4^{1/4} \cdot 3^{-1} \cdot 27^{2/3} = 2^{1/2} \cdot (2^2)^{1/4} \cdot 3^{-1} \cdot (3^3)^{2/3}$
$$= 2^{1/2} \cdot 2^{2/4} \cdot 3^{-1} \cdot 3^{6/3}$$
$$= 2^{1/2} \cdot 2^{1/2} \cdot 3^{-1} \cdot 3^2$$
$$= 2 \cdot 3 = 6 \qquad \blacksquare$$

Defining b^x for other x-values (such as $x = \sqrt{2}$) requires some knowledge of continuous mathematics. For example, in calculus you learn how to define b^x so that the graph of the function given by the formula $f(x) = b^x$ is a smooth curve, such as the one shown in Figure 1 for $b = 2$.

Figure 1   The graph of the base-2 exponential function.

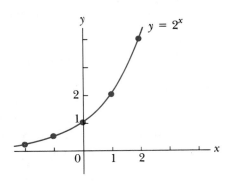

Logarithm Functions

Figure 1 illustrates that if $f(x) = b^x$ and $b > 1$, then f is a one-to-one function whose domain is the real numbers and whose image is the positive real numbers. Thus f has an inverse function f^{-1} whose domain is the positive real numbers and whose image is the set of all real numbers.

> The inverse function to the exponential function $f(x) = b^x$ is called the **base-b logarithm** function.

We write $x = \log_b(y)$ to mean $y = b^x$ or $x = f^{-1}(y)$. Thus $\log_b(b^x) = x$.

EXAMPLE 9   Use the definition of logarithms to find the following.

(a) $\log_{10}(100)$ (b) $\log_2(16)$ (c) $\log_3\left(\frac{1}{9}\right)$
(d) $2^{\log_2(5)}$ (e) $\log_2(4^3)$

Solution
(a) $\log_{10}(100) = \log_{10}(10^2) = 2$
(b) $\log_2(16) = \log_2(2^4) = 4$
(c) $\log_3\left(\frac{1}{9}\right) = \log_3(3^{-2}) = -2$
(d) $2^{\log_2(5)} = 5$
(e) $\log_2(4^3) = \log_2((2^2)^3) = \log_2(2^6) = 6$ ∎

The rules of exponents (1) and (2) above translate into basic rules for logarithms.

Theorem 3   For each b, u, and v greater than 0, and each real number r

$$\log_b(uv) = \log_b(u) + \log_b(v) \tag{3}$$

and

$$\log_b(u^r) = r\log_b(u) \tag{4}$$

Proof Let $u = b^x$ and $v = b^y$. (The definition of the base-b logarithm tells us that $x = \log_b(u)$ and $y = \log_b(v)$.) Thus by rule (1) above, $uv = b^x b^y = b^{x+y}$. Since $\log_b(b^{x+y}) = x + y$, this gives

$$\log_b(uv) = \log_b(b^{x+y}) = x + y = \log_b(u) + \log_b(v)$$

Rule (4) is proved similarly. ∎

EXAMPLE 10   Use the fact that $\log_{10}(2) = .301$ (approximately) and $\log_{10}(3) = .477$ (approximately) to compute $\log_{10}(6)$.

Solution $\log_{10}(6) = \log_{10}(2 \cdot 3) = \log_{10}(2) + \log_{10}(3) = .301 + .477 = .778$. ∎

EXAMPLE 11   Use the fact that $\log_{10}(2) = .301$ (approximately) to compute $\log_{10}(8)$.

Solution $\log_{10}(8) = \log_{10}(2^3) = 3\log_{10}(2) = 3 \cdot (.301) = .903$. ∎

EXAMPLE 12   Use the fact that $-\log_2(9) = \log_2\left(\frac{1}{9}\right)$ to simplify $\log_2(18) - \log_2(9)$.

Solution $\log_2(18) - \log_2(9) = \log_2(18) + \log_2\left(\frac{1}{9}\right)$
$$= \log_2\left(18 \cdot \frac{1}{9}\right)$$
$$= \log_2(2)$$
$$= 1$$
∎

Using Logarithms to Solve Exponential Equations

The fact that logarithms are inverses to exponential functions is useful in solving equations involving exponential functions.

EXAMPLE 13   How long does it take for money invested in a savings certificate at 10% to double?

Solution   If the amount initially invested is a, then after x years the value of the certificate is $a(1.1)^x$. Therefore the question may be rephrased: "For what x is $a(1.1)^x = 2a$?" Dividing by a gives

$$(1.1)^x = 2$$

and taking logarithms to the base b gives

$$\log_b(1.1)^x = \log_b(2)$$
$$x\log_b(1.1) = \log_b(2) \qquad \text{or}$$
$$x = \log_b(2)/\log_b(1.1)$$

Notice the surprising byproduct: the ratio $\log_b(2)/\log_b(1.1)$ equals x regardless of the value of b; it does not depend on b. By using a convenient base and either a table of logarithms, a calculator, or a computer, we get

$$x = 7.27 \qquad \text{(approximately)}$$
∎

As Example 13 shows, for some problems the base we use for logarithms is not important. In other problems there is one base that is best. For example, in calculus the natural logarithm (whose base is the number $e = 2.71828...$) is most important, whereas in discrete mathematics and computer science base-2 logarithms arise most often. Calculators and computers typically compute (approximately) base-10 logarithms and base-e logarithms. Fortunately, it is possible to compute base-2 logarithms from base-10 logarithms, so we can convert the information given by the calculator or computer into base 2.

EXAMPLE 14   Find a formula to compute base-2 logarithms from base-10 logarithms.

Solution   Recall that $y = 2^x$ if and only if x is the base-2 logarithm of y. Taking base-10 logarithms of both sides gives $\log_{10}(y) = x \log_{10}(2)$. Substituting the equivalent value $\log_2(y)$ for x gives $\log_{10}(y) = \log_2(y)\log_{10}(2)$. Dividing by $\log_{10}(2)$ gives

$$\log_2(y) = \frac{\log_{10}(y)}{\log_{10}(2)}$$

■

EXAMPLE 15   Find an approximate value for $\log_2(3)$ by using base-10 logarithms.

Solution   We were given in Example 10 that $\log_{10}(3) = .477$ and $\log_{10}(2) = .301$, approximately. By applying the formula of Example 14, we get

$$\log_2(3) = \frac{\log_{10}(3)}{\log_{10}(2)} = \frac{.477}{.301} = 1.585 \qquad \text{(approximately)}$$

■

Order of Growth

When we discussed the order of growth of functions, we observed without proof that for large numbers x, $2^x > x^2$.

EXAMPLE 16   Show that $2^n > n^2$ for all $n > 4$.

Solution   We use induction, starting with $n = 5$. If $n = 5$, the inequality reads $32 > 25$, which is true. Now assume that $2^k > k^2$ and $k > 4$. Since $k > 4$, $k^2 > 4k > 2k + 1$. Thus we may write

$$2^{k+1} = 2 \cdot 2^k > 2 \cdot k^2 = k^2 + k^2 > k^2 + 2k + 1 = (k + 1)^2$$

Thus $2^{k+1} > (k + 1)^2$, so by the principle of mathematical induction, $2^n > n^2$ for all n.

■

Similar proofs show that so long as $b > 1$, $b^n > n^2$ for large n. Thus, for large n, $b^n/n > n$, so that the ratio of b^n to n becomes infinite as n gets large. As we did for exponential functions with base 2 in Chapter 4, Theorem 15, we may prove the following theorem.

Theorem 4   If $b > 1$, then $x^r = O(b^x)$ for all real numbers r, and b^x is not $O(x^r)$ for any r. Further, $\log_b(x) = O(x^r)$ for any $r > 0$, and for any $r > 0$, x^r is not $O(\log_b(x))$.

Proof   Similar to Theorem 15 of Chapter 4.   ■

EXAMPLE 17   Classify the following as true or false.

(a) $x^2 = O(3^x)$ (b) $2^x = O(x^4)$
(c) $\log_3(x) = O(x)$ (d) $\log_{10}(x) = O(\sqrt{x})$
(e) $x^2 = O(\log_2(x))$ (f) $x^2 = O(\log_3(x^9))$

Solution

(a) true   (b) false
(c) true   (d) true (here r is $\frac{1}{2}$, and $\frac{1}{2} > 0$)
(e) false   (f) false (*Note:* $\log_3(x^9) = 9\log_3(x)$; then
                                                        Theorem 4 applies)   ■

Concepts Review

1. A(n) _____ equation for the sequence $<a_n>$ is an equation that allows us to compute a_n from values of a_k with $k < n$.

2. A(n) _____ _____ recurrence equation for the sequence $<a_n>$ allows us to compute a_n from a_{n-1}.

3. A recurrence equation has _____ r if it allows us to compute a_n from a_{n-1}, $a_{n-2}, \ldots$ through a_{n-r}.

4. A recurrence equation is _____ if a_n may be written $a_n = b_1(n)a_{n-1} + b_2(n)a_{n-2} + \cdots + d(n)$.

5. The function $d(n)$ in (4) is called the _____ function of the recurrence equation.

6. (Choose the appropriate answer from the possibilities in square braces.) To say that the recurrence equation in (4) is a *constant* coefficient equation means that the expression(s) $[a_i; b_i(n); d(i); b_i(n)$ and $d(i); a_i$ and $b_i(n); a_i$ and $d(i); a_i, b_i(n)$ and $d(i)]$ _____ are all constant.

7. The equation in (4) is called _____ if $d(i) = 0$ for all i.

8. A(n) _____ to a recurrence equation is a sequence that, when substituted into the recurrence relation, yields a true statement.

9. A(n) _____ _____ is a formula involving constants such that each solution may be obtained by assigning specific numerical values to these constants.

10. The _____ function to the base b is the inverse of the exponential function $f(x) = b^x$.

Exercises

A   1. In Exercise 3 of Section 5-3, we discussed algorithm Bubblesort. Explain why it is that if c_n is the number of comparisons this algorithm makes with an n-element list, then

$$c_n = n - 1 + c_{n-1}$$

2. In Exercise 4 of Section 5-3, we discussed algorithm Tricklesort. Explain why it is that if c_n is the number of comparisons this algorithm makes with an n-element list, then

$$c_n = n - 1 + c_{n-1}$$

3. Let J_n be the number of ways to assign n jobs to three computers. Explain why $J_n = 3J_{n-1}$.

4. Let f_n be the number of functions from an n-element set to an m-element set. Explain why $f_n = mf_{n-1}$.

5. What is the order (if any) of each of the following recurrence relations?
   (a) $t_n = nt_{n-1}$ (b) $t_n = nt_{n-1} + (n-1)t_{n-2}$
   (c) $t_n = nt_{n-2} - n$ (d) $t_n = t_1 + 2t_2 + 3t_3 + \cdots + (n-1)t_{n-1}$
   (e) $t_n = t_{n-1}^2 + n^2$ (f) $t_n = 2t_{n-1} + t_{n-2}^2$

6. What is the order (if any) of each of the following recurrence relations?
   (a) $a_n = a_{n-1} + a_{n-2}$ (b) $a_n - a_{n-1} = a_{n-2}$
   (c) $a_n = 3a_{n-1} + n$ (d) $a_n = a_{n-1}^2 + n^2 - 2$
   (e) $a_n = a_{n-1} - a_{n-2} + a_{n-3} - a_{n-4} + \cdots \pm a_1$
   (f) $a_n = (a_{n-1} + a_{n-2})(a_{n-1} - a_{n-2})$

7. Which recurrence relations in Exercise 5 are linear?

8. Which recurrence relations in Exercise 6 are linear?

9. If $c_n = c_{n-1} + n - 1$, write out the first five terms of the sequence $<c_i>$, beginning with $c_1 = 0$.

10. If $b_n = nb_{n-1}$, write out the first five terms of the sequence $<b_i>$, beginning with $b_1 = 1$.

11. Given $S_0 = 1$ and $S_1 = 1$, compute the first eight terms of the sequence $<S_i>$ with $S_n = S_{n-1} + S_{n-2}$, starting with S_0.

12. Given $S_0 = 1$ and $S_1 = 2$, compute the first eight terms of the sequence $<S_i>$ with $S_n = S_{n-1} + S_{n-2}$, starting with S_0.

13. Verify that $b_n = n!$ is a solution to the recurrence equation $b_n = nb_{n-1}$. (In the text, we verified that $C_n = n(n-1)/2$ is a solution to $C_n = C_{n-1} + n - 1$.)

14. Verify that $S_n = 2^n$ is a solution to the recurrence equation $S_n = 2S_{n-1}$.

15. Verify that $S_n = 3 \cdot 2^{n-1} - 1$ is a solution to the recurrence relation $S_i = 2S_{i-1} + 1$.

16. Verify that $t_n = 2 - 7 \cdot \left(\frac{1}{2}\right)^n$ is a solution to the recurrence relation $t_i = \frac{1}{2}t_{i-1} + 1$.

B   17. Classify each of the following recurrence equations as homogeneous or nonhomogeneous.
   (a) $S_n = 2S_{n-1} + 1$ (b) $S_n = \frac{1}{2}S_{n-1}$
   (c) $t_n = nt_{n-1} + t_{n-2}$ (d) $nt_n = t_{n-1} + 1$
   (e) $S_n - S_{n-1} = 2(S_{n-1} - S_{n-2})$ (f) $S_n = n^2 S_{n-1}$

18. Classify each of the following recurrence equations as homogeneous or nonhomogeneous.
    (a) $S_n = \frac{1}{2}S_{n-1}$
    (b) $S_n = (n-1)S_{n-1}$
    (c) $S_n = S_{n-1} + 0.15 \, S_{n-1}$
    (d) $S_n = S_{n-1} + 2S_{n-2}$
    (e) $S_n = n^2 \, S_{n-1}$
    (f) $S_n = S_{n-1} + S_{n-2} + 1$

19. Classify each recurrence equation of Exercise 17 as constant coefficient or not.

20. Classify each recurrence equation of Exercise 18 as constant coefficient or not.

21. In the absence of constraints, a growing biological population will grow by a fixed percentage each year. Show that if this percentage is p percent per year, then the size S_n of the population after n years is given by $S_n = (1 + .01p)S_{n-1}$.

22. In certain chemical reactions, a fixed percentage (approximately) of a reactant is consumed in a given time period. Assuming that 1% of a reactant is consumed per second, write a recurrence relation for the amount of that reactant present after n seconds of reaction time.

23. If $10,000 is deposited at 10% compounded annually for 20 years, how much is it worth at the end of those 20 years? (You will need a calculator for this.)

24. If 10% of a radioactive substance decays to nonradioactive material each year, how much of a sample of 100 grams is still radioactive ten years later? (A calculator is recommended for this.)

25. If $a_n = 3a_{n-1}$ and $a_0 = 2$, find a_i for $i = 1,2,3,4,5$.

26. If $a_n = \frac{1}{2}a_{n-1}$ and $a_1 = 4$, find a_i for $i = 2,3,4,5,6$.

27. Find a formula for the sequence $<a_n>$ described in Exercise 25.

28. Find a formula for the sequence $<a_n>$ described in Exercise 26.

29. A sequence $a_0, a_1, a_2, \ldots$ satisfies $a_i = 2a_{i-1}$, and $a_5 = 96$. What is a_0?

30. A sequence $a_0, a_1, a_2, \ldots$ satisfies $a_i = .5a_{i-1}$, and $a_6 = 1.5$. What is a_0?

31. Suppose that $a_n = \sqrt{n}a_{n-1}$ and $a_1 = 4$. Give a formula for a_n valid for $n \geq 2$.

32. Suppose that $a_n = n^2 a_{n-1}$ and $a_2 = 3$. Give a formula for a_n valid for $n \geq 2$.

C 33. Sketch the graph of the exponential function f given by $f(x) = 3^x$.

34. Sketch the graph of the exponential function f given by $f(x) = 4^x$.

Use rules (1) and (2) for exponents to simplify each expression given in Exercises 35–46 to one of the form b^r.

35. 10^{3+2}

36. $(10^2)^3$

37. $(10^3/10^2)10^5$

38. $2^2 \cdot 2^{7-5}$

39. $(2^3)^3$

40. $(2^3 \cdot 2^2)^5/4^3$

41. $(10^3 \cdot 10^{-1})^4$

42. $\sqrt{10^3}$

43. $(10\sqrt{10})^3/100$

44. $2^2 \cdot \sqrt[3]{64}$

45. $(2\sqrt{2})^4$

46. $(2\sqrt[3]{2})^2 \cdot (\sqrt{2})^5$

47. The base-10 logarithm of 5 is approximately .699. What is the base-10 logarithm of 15 (approximately)? (There is useful information in Example 10.)

48. What is the base-10 logarithm of 18 (approximately)? (There is useful information in Example 10.)

49. The base-10 logarithm of 5 is approximately .699. What is the base-10 logarithm of 25 (approximately)?

50. What is the base-10 logarithm of 36 (approximately)? (There is useful information in Example 10.)

51. The base-10 logarithms of 2 and 5 are approximately .301 and .699. Why is it not surprising that the sum of these two numbers is 1?

52. The base-10 logarithm of 4 and 5 are approximately .602 and .699. Why is it not surprising that the sum of these two numbers is 1.301, which happens to be (approximately) 1 plus the base-10 logarithm of 2?

53. Find a formula for computing base-3 logarithms from base-10 logarithms.

54. Find a formula for computing base-2 logarithms from base-e (natural) logarithms.

Simplify the expressions in Exercises 55–72.

55. $(a^4)^2$

56. $(a^4 \cdot a^3)^2$

57. $\dfrac{2^3 + 3^{-1} \cdot 27^{1/3}}{2^2}$

58. $(b^3)^4 \cdot b^{-7}$

59. $(b^5 b^3)^4$

60. $\dfrac{5^3 \cdot 3^2 \cdot 2^4}{(60)^2}$

61. $3^{\log_3(7)}$

62. $4^{\log_2(3)}$

63. $2^{\log_4(3)}$

64. $(81)^{3/4}$

65. $2^{\log_2(17)}$

66. $\log_2(2^5)$

67. $\log_3(21) - \log_3(7)$

68. $\log_2(4^{2x+1})$

69. $\log_6(15) + \log_6(4)$

70. $\log_3(9^{a-b})$

71. $\log_2(20) - \log_2(15) + \log_2(12)$

72. $9^{\log_3(x^2)}$

73. A radioactive substance decays in such a way that 10% of its weight is rendered non-radioactive after one day. Find a formula for the amount present after x days, and find the half life—that is, find the number of days it takes for 50% of the material to be rendered nonradioactive.

74. A physicist has isolated a radioactive substance that she thinks is new. She wants to compute the half-life (see Exercise 73) of the substance to see if it is the half-life of any known substance. In 17 seconds, 0.05 grams of the substance decayed to a mixture containing only 0.004 grams of the substance. Find a formula for the amount present after t seconds and find the half-life.

75. For how many years must $10,000 be deposited in a savings certificate at 10% annual interest (compounded annually) to become worth $25,000?

76. A bacteria population increases by 20% in one day. How many days will it take to at least double?

77. If the half-life of a radioactive substance is 3 days, in how many days does all but at most 10% decay?

78. If a bacteria population doubles in 3 days, in how many days would it be 10 times its original size or more?

79. After one year, 12% interest compounded monthly is the same as 1% interest computed and paid monthly for a year. If $10,000 is deposited at 12% compounded monthly, what is it worth at the end of one year? What is the effective annual interest rate (the percentage by which the $10,000 increased)?

80. Is there a time period over which we can compound 10% interest to achieve an effective annual rate (actual percentage of increase in value over one year) of 10.5%, 11%, 12%?

Problems

1. Verify that $a_n = 2^n$ and $b_n = (-2)^n$ are each solutions to the recurrence equation $a_n = 4a_{n-2}$, valid for $n \geq 2$.

2. Verify that $a_n = (2i)^n$ and $b_n = (-2i)^n$, where $i = \sqrt{-1}$, are each solutions to the recurrence equation $a_n = -4a_{n-2}$, valid for $n \geq 2$.

3. In climbing stairs, a child jumps up one stair or two stairs at a time, with the number of stairs on one jump independent of the number on any other jump. Find a second-order recurrence relation for the number s_n of ways to climb n steps.

4. We draw n mutually intersecting circles in the plane (think of a 2- or 3-set Venn diagram, for example) so that each one crosses each other one twice and no three have a boundary point in common. The picture divides the plane into regions whose boundaries are portions of the circles' boundaries, and each time we add a new circle it intersects as many regions previously in the drawing as possible. Show that a recurrence relation for the number of regions r_n in the drawing is $r_n = r_{n-1} + 2(n-1)$. What does this say about the possibility of drawing a 4-set Venn diagram with circles?

5. A group of $2n$ people is to be divided into pairs for games of chess. Write a recurrence equation for the number d_n of ways of dividing $2n$ people up into pairs.

6. Repeat Problem 5, dividing $4n$ people into groups of four for a game of bridge.

7. Pascal's relation is a two-variable recurrence equation for the binomial coefficients $C(n,k)$. Pascal's relation states that $C(n,k) = C(n-1,k-1) + C(n-1,k)$. Find a two-variable recurrence equation for the number $M(n,k)$ of k-element multisets chosen from an n-element set.

8. Find a two-variable recurrence equation for the number $F(n,m)$ of functions from an n-element set *onto* an m-element set.

9. Find a two-variable recurrence equation for the number of k-element subsets of the integers 1 through n that *do not* contain two successive integers.

10. The **Bell number** $B(n)$ is the number of partitions of an n-element set. Find a recurrence relation that expresses $B(n)$ in terms of $B(1)$ through $B(n-1)$.

11. The **Stirling number** $S(n,k)$ is the number of partitions of an n-element set into exactly k nonempty sets. Find a two-variable recurrence relation for $S(n,k)$.

12. Show that the number a_n of ways to completely parenthesize the expression $r_1 \cdot r_2 \cdot \ldots \cdot r_n$ (that is, to insert parentheses so that the expression may be evaluated by successively multiplying together two terms as indicated, such as $((r_1 r_2) \cdot r_3) \cdot r_4)$ satisfies the recurrence $a_n = a_{n-1}a_1 + a_{n-2}a_2 + \cdots + a_1 a_{n-1}$, valid for $n \geq 2$.

13. A group of n children bring story books to nursery school. During school the books become hopelessly mixed up. Give a recurrence equation for the number of ways the children may take books home so that no one takes home the book he or she brought.

14. Explain why $a^{\log_c(n)} = n^{\log_c(a)}$.

Section 7-2
First-Order
Linear Recurrences

A   The Solution of First-Order Linear Recurrences

We do not yet have a general recurrence-solving method that we can apply to the recurrence $c_n = c_{n-1} + n - 1$. In the language we introduced in Section 7-1 for classification of recurrences, this is a constant coefficient first-order linear non-homogeneous recurrence. In general, such a recurrence would have the form

$$s_n = b s_{n-1} + d(n)$$

Assume that we have such a recurrence, valid for integers $n > 0$. Let us compute s_3. Since the recurrence tells us that $s_3 = b s_2 + d(3)$ and $s_2 = b s_1 + d(2)$, we get, by substitution of s_2 into the formula for s_3

$$s_3 = b(b s_1 + d(2)) + d(3) = b^2 s_1 + b d(2) + d(3)$$

Since $s_1 = b s_0 + d(1)$, we substitute this into the formula for s_3 to get

$$s_3 = b^2(b s_0 + d(1)) + b d(2) + d(3)$$
$$= b^3 s_0 + b^2 d(1) + b d(2) + d(3)$$

Note that the first summand is the general solution to the corresponding homogeneous equation $s_n' = b s_{n-1}'$. The remaining terms are a polynomial in b. The powers on b do not appear to relate easily to the numbers inside the parentheses after d. However, factoring b^3 out of the entire formula gives us the suggestive formula

$$s_3 = b^3(s_0 + d(1)b^{-1} + d(2)b^{-2} + d(3)b^{-3})$$

This form suggests that

$$s_4 = b^4(s_0 + d(1)b^{-1} + d(2)b^{-2} + d(3)b^{-3} + d(4)b^{-4})$$

The General Solution with Constant Coefficients

The pattern we see leads us to the formula for the general solution to the recurrence.

Theorem 5   The general solution to the recurrence equation

$$s_n = bs_{n-1} + d(n), \qquad \text{valid for } n > 0$$

is

$$s_n = b^n\left(s_0 + \sum_{i=1}^{n} d(i)b^{-i}\right), \qquad \text{valid for } n > 0$$

Proof   For $n = 1$, the formula gives $s_1 = b(s_0 + d_1 b^{-1}) = s_0 b + d(1)$, which is exactly what the recurrence gives us. Now assume that $n > 1$ and

$$s_{n-1} = b^{n-1}\left(s_0 + \sum_{i=1}^{n-1} d(i)b^{-i}\right)$$

Since $s_n = bs_{n-1} + d(n)$, substitution gives

$$s_n = b\left[b^{n-1}\left(s_0 + \sum_{i=1}^{n-1} d(i)b^{-i}\right)\right] + d(n)$$

$$= b^n\left(s_0 + \sum_{i=1}^{n-1} d(i)b^{-i}\right) + b^n b^{-n} d(n)$$

$$= b^n\left(s_0 + \sum_{i=1}^{n} d(i)b^{-i}\right)$$

Thus by the principle of mathematical induction, our formula is valid for all n. ∎

Since the undetermined constant in the formula for the solution is s_0, the initial value of the sequence, we call any condition that lets us determine this constant an *initial condition* (as in Section 7-1).

EXAMPLE 18   Find a solution to the recurrence relation

$$t_k = 2t_{k-1} + 2^k, \qquad \text{valid for } k > 0$$

with the initial condition $t_0 = 1$.

Solution   First, we apply Theorem 5 to derive the general solution

$$t_k = 2^k \left(t_0 + \sum_{i=1}^{k} 2^i 2^{-i} \right)$$

$$= 2^k \left(t_0 + \sum_{i=1}^{k} 1 \right)$$

$$= 2^k (t_0 + k)$$

$$= t_0 2^k + k 2^k$$

Now $t_0 = 1$, so

$$t_k = 2^k + k 2^k = (k + 1) 2^k \qquad \blacksquare$$

EXAMPLE 19   Find the solution to the selection sort recurrence

$$c_n = c_{n-1} + n - 1$$

with the initial condition $c_1 = 0$.

Solution   We derived this recurrence for lists of length n. Since a list of length 0 is meaningless, the recurrence is valid for $n > 1$ rather than $n > 0$. We take the point of view that we are going to derive a solution that would be valid for $n = 0$ as well *if* c_0 were meaningful. This lets us apply Theorem 5. In the notation of Theorem 5, we have $b = 1$ and $d(n) = n - 1$, giving us the general solution

$$c_n = 1^n \left(c_0 + \sum_{i=1}^{n} (i - 1) 1^{-i} \right)$$

$$= c_0 + \sum_{i=1}^{n} (i - 1)$$

$$= c_0 + \frac{n(n - 1)}{2}$$

Now $c_1 = 0$. Substituting this into our general solution gives

$$0 = c_1 = c_0 + \frac{1(1 - 1)}{2} = c_0$$

Thus the solution satisfying the initial condition $c_1 = 0$ is $c_n = \dfrac{n(n - 1)}{2}$. Note that we used a condition on c_1 to determine c_0. $\blacksquare$

The General First-Order Linear Recurrence

There is a formula for the general solution for the most general form a linear recurrence can have, namely

$$s_n = b(n) s_{n-1} + d(n)$$

One important application of this kind of recurrence arises in the probability problem of analyzing how long the popular sorting algorithm known as Quicksort should be expected to take to sort a list of n items.

Theorem 6 If $a_n = b(n)a_{n-1} + d(n)$, valid for $n > 0$, then

$$a_n = \left(\prod_{i=1}^{n} b(i) \right) \left[a_0 + \sum_{i=1}^{n} d(i) \prod_{j=1}^{i} \frac{1}{b(j)} \right]$$

Proof The proof follows the pattern of Theorem 5. ∎

EXAMPLE 20 Find a formula for the general solution to the recurrence $a_n = na_{n-1} + n!$.

Solution In our general solution, we substitute i for $b(i)$ and $i!$ for $d(i)$. This gives

$$a_n = \left(\prod_{i=1}^{n} i \right) \left[a_0 + \sum_{i=1}^{n} i! \frac{1}{\prod\limits_{j=1}^{i} j} \right]$$

$$= n! \left[a_0 + \sum_{i=1}^{n} \frac{i!}{i!} \right]$$

$$= n! (a_0 + n)$$ ∎

B Recurrences from Divide-and-Conquer Algorithms

An algorithm that solves a problem by breaking it up into a number of instances of the same kind of problem with a smaller input parameter, solving these problems, and then reassembling the solutions of these problems into a solution of the original problem is called a **divide-and-conquer algorithm** or **decomposition algorithm**. There are two classic examples of such algorithms.

Binary Search

In **binary search,** we look for a word in an alphabetically ordered list as follows. First we compare it with the middle element to see whether it should be in the first or the second half. Then we search for it in the appropriate half. In this way we take halves again and again. When the list has been halved until our current piece has length 1, we simply compare our identifier to the one element in our current piece. It takes one comparison to divide the problem in half, and when we get done the problem is solved without needing any reassembling, so if c_n is the number of comparisons we make, we may write

$$c_n = c_{n/2} + 1 \qquad (n \text{ even and } n > 0)$$

Merge Sort

Another important decomposition algorithm is the sorting technique known as **merge sort.** The merge sort algorithm has the following divide-and-conquer description.

> If a list has only one entry, it is already sorted.
> Otherwise it may be broken into two lists about
> half as long, each of these may be sorted, and
> then the two sorted lists may be merged together
> to form a single sorted list.

In order to merge the two halves, we may use the following algorithm, which is based on the discussion in Example 16 of Chapter 1.

Algorithm Merge
    Input: Two lists L_1 and L_2 of length p and q, respectively, and sorted into increasing order.
    Output: One list L_3 sorted into increasing order.
    Procedure: Start with i and j equal to 1.
    For each k from 1 to $p + q$, do the following:
        If $i \leq p$ and $(j > q$ or $L_1(i)$ comes before $L_2(j))$, then do the following:
            Let $L_3(k) = L_1(i)$.
            Replace i by $i + 1$.
        Otherwise,
            Let $L_3(k) = L_2(j)$.
            Replace j by $j + 1$.
    Go on to the next k-value if there is one.

Recall that selection sort requires some multiple of $n(n-1)/2$ units of computer time to sort a list of length n because it makes $n(n-1)/2$ comparisons. The merge sort algorithm makes significantly fewer comparisons when n is large. We can demonstrate this by deriving a recurrence relation for the number of comparisons that merge sort makes in the most complicated case and solving the recurrence.

The number of comparisons needed to sort a list of length n is equal to the amount of time needed to break it in half, plus the amount of time needed to sort each half, plus the amount of time needed to merge the two sorted halves. If we use s_n to stand for the maximum number of comparisons required to sort a list of length n, then $s_{n/2}$ stands for the maximum number of comparisons needed to sort a list half as long. The number of comparisons made by algorithm Merge is at most three comparisons for each value of k. Thus the number of comparisons needed to merge two lists is no more than three times the sum of their lengths. Since no comparisons are needed to break the list in half, and each half-list requires $s_{n/2}$ comparisons, the total number of comparisons is no more than the solution (with $s_0 = 0$) to the equation

$$s_n = 2s_{n/2} + 3n$$

Divide-and-Conquer Recurrence

We call a recurrence a **divide-and-conquer** recurrence
if it has the form $s_n = bs_{n/a} + d(n)$ for integer $a > 1$.

We shall use our two examples that have $a = 2$ to demonstrate how to solve a divide-and-conquer recurrence.

In both the binary search recurrence relation

$$c_n = c_{n/2} + 1$$

and the merge sort recurrence relation

$$s_n = 2s_{n/2} + 3n$$

the relation makes sense only for even values of n. To make sure all the values of n we consider are even, it is convenient to restrict our studies of these recurrences to values of n that are powers of 2. (In the general case we restrict n to be a power of a.)

When we restrict n to be a power of 2, we can convert each of these recurrence relations into a form we recognize. We begin by substituting 2^k for n to get

$$c_{2^k} = c_{2^{k-1}} + 1 \qquad \text{and}$$
$$s_{2^k} = 2s_{2^{k-1}} + 3 \cdot 2^k$$

Letting $v_k = c_{2^k}$ and $u_k = s_{2^k}$, we get the first-order linear relations

$$v_k = v_{k-1} + 1 \qquad \text{and}$$
$$u_k = 2u_{k-1} + 3 \cdot 2^k$$

Since these are first-order linear recurrences, we may write down their general solutions immediately. Assuming that the relations are valid for all $k > 0$ (what are we assuming about n here?) we apply Theorem 5 to get

$$v_k = v_0 + k \qquad \text{and}$$

$$u_k = 2^k \left(u_0 + 3 \cdot \sum_{i=1}^{k} 2^i \cdot 2^{-i} \right)$$
$$= 2^k (u_0 + 3k)$$

However, the original recurrence relations were expressed in terms of n. Since $n = 2^k$, we have $k = \log_2(n)$. Making the substitutions $v_0 = c_{2^0} = c_1$, $u_0 = s_{2^0} = s_1$, $n = 2^k$, and $k = \log_2(n)$, we get

$$c_n = c_1 + \log_2(n) \qquad \text{and}$$
$$s_n = n(s_1 + 3\log_2(n)) = s_1 n + 3n\log_2(n)$$

These solutions are valid for those values of n that are powers of 2. Notice how both solutions involve logarithms. Since the logarithm function grows so slowly, divide-and-conquer algorithms have the potential to be quite efficient. (However, using a divide-and-conquer method does not guarantee speed.) In particular, the fact that merge sort requires $O(n \log_2(n))$ comparisons for a list of length n, while other algorithms such as selection sort and bubblesort require on the order of n^2 comparisons, means that merge sort will be significantly faster for sorting long lists. (There are other sorting algorithms that make $O(n\log_2(n))$ comparisons and do not require the rather cumbersome merging process. They take more effort to understand and may have their own disadvantages, but in most (except for the largest) practical applications you will see one of them rather than merge sort.)

Converting to First-Order in General

EXAMPLE 21   Convert the recurrence relation

$$t_n = 3t_{n/2} + n^2$$

to a first-order linear recurrence and specify for which values of n the conversion is valid.

Solution   Since we wish to convert the $t_{n/2}$ to an s_{k-1}, we want to let $n = 2^k$. Then we let $s_k = t_n$. Note that $n/2 = 2^k/2 = 2^{k-1}$ so that $t_{n/2} = s_{k-1}$. This gives us

$$s_k = 3\,s_{k-1} + \left(2^k\right)^2$$
$$s_k = 3\,s_{k-1} + 2^{2k}$$
$$s_k = 3\,s_{k-1} + 4^k$$

This conversion is valid for values of n that are powers of 2.   ■

EXAMPLE 22   Find the general solution to the divide-and-conquer recurrence of Example 21 by making use of the conversion made in Example 21.

Solution   By Theorem 5, the solution for s_k is

$$s_k = 3^k\left(s_0 + \sum_{i=1}^{k} 3^{-i}4^i\right)$$

$$= 3^k\left(s_0 + \sum_{i=1}^{k}\left(\frac{4}{3}\right)^i\right)$$

$$= 3^k\left(s_0 + \frac{\dfrac{4}{3} - \left(\dfrac{4}{3}\right)^{k+1}}{1 - \dfrac{4}{3}}\right)$$

$$= 3^k\left[s_0 - 3\left(\frac{4}{3} - \left(\frac{4}{3}\right)^{k+1}\right)\right]$$

$$= 3^k\left[s_0 - 4 + 4\cdot\left(\frac{4}{3}\right)^k\right]$$

$$= s_0 \cdot 3^k - 4\cdot 3^k + 4\cdot 4^k$$

Since n is 2^k, we may write $4^k = 2^{k^2} = (2^k)^2 = n^2$ and

$$3^k = \left(2^{\log_2(3)}\right)^k = (2^k)^{\log_2(3)} = n^{\log_2(3)}$$

This gives

$$t_n = (t_1 - 4)n^{\log_2(3)} + 4n^2 \qquad\blacksquare$$

EXAMPLE 23   Find the particular solution to the divide-and-conquer recurrence of Example 21 that has $t_1 = 4$. First use the formula for s_k, then the formula for t_n.

Solution   Since $2^0 = 1$, $s_0 = t_1 = 4$. This gives us

$$s_k = 3^k\left(4\cdot\left(\frac{4}{3}\right)^k\right)$$

$$= 4^{k+1}$$

This is *not* the solution for t_n, however. Since $2^k = n$, we convert the 4^{k+1} into a power of 2 in order to change from s_k to t_n. Since $4 = 2^2$, we get

$$t_n = s_k = 4^{k+1} = 2^{2k+2}$$

$$= 2^{2k}\cdot 2^2$$

$$= (2^k)^2\cdot 2^2$$

$$= 4n^2$$

A way to get the same results with less work with exponents is to use the fact that $k = \log_2(n)$, giving

$$t_n = s_k = 4^{k+1} = 4^{\log_2(n)+1} = 4 \cdot 4^{\log_2(n)}$$
$$= 4 \cdot 2^{2 \cdot \log_2(n)}$$
$$= 4(2^{\log_2(n)})^2$$
$$= 4n^2$$

Since $t_1 = 4$, the formula for t_n gives us $t_n = 4n^2$ directly. It is always worth examining several approaches to solving a problem in order to choose the one that requires the least algebra! ∎

C   Growth Rates of Solutions

We have written the formula

$$s_n = b^n \left(s_0 + \sum_{i=1}^{n} b^{-i} d(i) \right)$$

as the general solution to a first-order linear constant coefficient recurrence relation

$$s_n = bs_{n-1} + d(n)$$

What the Solution Tells Us

Does the formula make it easier to obtain a numerical value for a certain term s_n, say s_{10}? To find out, let us analyze how much computation is involved. To compute s_{10} from the formula, we have to compute $d(1)$ through $d(10)$, compute b^{-1} through b^{-10}, multiply the b^i and $d(i)$ terms together, add these all up, and do another addition and multiplication. Thus we have 10 additions, 11 multiplications, 10 evaluations of $d(i)$, and 11 powers of b to compute. To compute s_{10} by using the recurrence equation 10 times, we have 10 multiplications, 10 additions, and 10 computations of $d(i)$. The formula involves *more* work! In the examples we have done, however, the summation in the formula has been one we can convert to a simpler expression. Such a simplification not only makes computation easier but allows us to observe that our solution is, say, a constant times b^n, or has an $n^2 b^n$ term in it, or perhaps is only a multiple of n. Thus a formula can tell us how fast a solution grows as a function of n. As we have seen with our earlier work on the analysis of algorithms, it is this information that is most useful to us.

EXAMPLE 24 If $s_i = 2s_{i-1} + i2^i$ and $s_0 = 0$, how fast will s_n grow as a function of n?

Solution We use the formula to write

$$s_n = 2^n \left(s_0 + \sum_{i=1}^{n} 2^{-i} \cdot i2^i \right) = \frac{2^n \, n(n+1)}{2}$$

Thus $s_n = O(n^2 2^n)$, and in fact since $s_n > \frac{1}{2} n^2 2^n$, s_n is of order $n^2 2^n$. ∎

EXAMPLE 25 If s_n satisfies the recurrence

$$s_n = 2s_{n/2} + n$$

which is similar to the merge sort recurrence, how fast will s_n grow as a function of n?

Solution We can solve the recurrence to see that $s_n = s_1 n + n\log_2(n)$. Thus, since $n \le n\log_2(n)$ for $n \ge 2$, we have $s_n = O(n\log_2(n))$. Also, $s_n \ge n\log_2(n)$, so $n\log_2(n) = O(s_n)$. Therefore, s_n is of order $n\log_2(n)$. ∎

Predicting General Patterns of Growth

If the recurrence in Example 24 had been $s_n = 2s_{n-1} + \sqrt{i} \, 2^i$, then substituting into the formula would give us the sum $\sum_{i=1}^{n} \sqrt{i}$, a sum we do not recognize. Thus it would be useful if we could get some information about the solution without using the formula. In the theorem below, we make several observations in general about the rate of growth of the solution; these observations are sufficient information about the growth rate of the solution in many practical problems.

Theorem 7 The solution s_n of the recurrence relation $s_n = bs_{n-1} + d(n)$ has the following growth properties.

(1) If $d(i) = O(c^i)$ where $0 < c < b$, then $s_n = O(b^n)$, and s_n is of order b^n if $d(i) > 0$ for all i.

(2) If $d(i) = O(b^i)$, then $s_n = O(nb^n)$.

(3) If $b^i = O(d(i))$, then $s_n = O\left(\left(\sum_{i=1}^{n} d(i) \right)^2 \right)$.

(4) If $d(i)$ is of order b^i, then s_n is of order nb^n.

Proof   For statement (1), note that for some k

$$\sum_{i=1}^{n} d(i)b^{-i} \leq k \sum_{i=0}^{n} \frac{c^i}{b^i} \leq k \frac{b}{b-c}$$

Substituting this into the formula of Theorem 5 shows that $s_n = O(b^n)$. However, $s_n \geq s_0 b^n$ if $d(i) > 0$ for all i. For statement (2), note that for some k

$$\sum_{i=1}^{n} d(i)b^{-i} \leq k \sum_{i=1}^{n} b^i b^{-i} = kn$$

Using this with the formula of Theorem 5 gives $s_n \leq b^n(s_0 + kn) = O(nb^n)$. For statement (3), rewrite s_n as

$$s_n = \left[s_0 b^n + \sum_{i=1}^{n} d(i)b^{n-i} \right] \leq \left[s_0 b^n + k \sum_{i=1}^{n} d(i)d(n-i) \right]$$

$$\leq \left[s_0 b^n + 2k\left(\sum_{i=1}^{n} d(i) \right)^2 \right] = O\left[\left(\sum_{i=1}^{n} d(i) \right)^2 \right]$$

and for statement (4)

$$s_n = b^n s_0 + \sum_{i=1}^{n} d(i)b^{n-i} \geq b^n s_0 + k \sum_{i=1}^{n} b^n \geq knb^n \qquad \blacksquare$$

EXAMPLE 26   What does Theorem 7 tell us about the order of growth of a sequence satisfying the following recurrence?

$$s_n = 3s_{n-1} + \frac{2^n}{n^2}$$

Solution   Since $2^n/n^2 < 2^n$ and $2 < 3$, statement (1) applies, and since $2^n/n^2 > 0$, statement (1) tells us that s_n is of order 3^n. (Imagine trying to simplify the formula for the general solution of this recurrence in order to understand how the solution grows!) $\blacksquare$

EXAMPLE 27   What does Theorem 7 tell us about the order of growth of solutions to the merge sort recurrence $t_n = 2t_{n/2} + 3n$?

Solution   To apply Theorem 7, we must make our conversion of t_n to a first-order linear recurrence. Letting $n = 2^k$ and $s_k = t_n$, we obtain $s_k = 2s_{k-1} + 2^k - 1$. Thus $d(i)$ has order 2^i, so s_k has order $k2^k$, and converting from k to n gives us that t_n has order $n\log_2(n)$. $\blacksquare$

Growth Rates for Divide-and-Conquer Recurrences

Example 27 suggests that it would be useful to have general results about the growth rate of solutions to divide-and-conquer recurrences of the form

$$t_n = bt_{n/a} + d(n)$$

Each of the parts of Theorem 7 converts to give information about solutions to this recurrence. Parts (1), (2), and (4) have the most natural translations; we give these translations in Theorem 8.

Theorem 8 The solution t_n of the recurrence relation $t_n = bt_{n/a} + d(n)$, valid for $n = a^k$ and $k \geq 0$, has the following growth properties.

(1) If $d(i) = O\left(i^{\log_a(c)}\right)$ where $c < b$, then $t_n = O\left(n^{\log_a(b)}\right)$, and if $d(i) \geq 0$, then t_n has order $n^{\log_a(b)}$.

(2) If $d(i) = O\left(i^{\log_a(b)}\right)$, then $t_n = O(n^{\log_a(b)} \log_a(n))$.

(3) If $d(i)$ is of order $i^{\log_a(b)}$, then t_n is of order $n\log_a(n)$.

Proof First we translate the recurrence on t to $s_k = bs_{k-1} + d(a^k)$, using $n = a^k$ and $t_n = s_k$. Then we observe that the conditions on $d(i)$ and b^i translate to conditions on $d(a^i)$ and b^i. Finally, we use the fact that

$$b^{\log_a(n)} = a^{\log_a(b)\log_a(n)} = n^{\log_a(b)}$$ ■

Note that Theorem 8 tells us immediately that merge sort is an order $n\log_2(n)$ algorithm.

Concepts Review

1. Conditions on the values of a_i that allow us to determine the first r values of a sequence governed by an rth-order recurrence relation are called _____ conditions.

2. A(n) _____ _____ _____ algorithm breaks a problem up into smaller problems, solves the smaller problems, and then reassembles the solutions into a solution of the original problem.

3. The _____ sort algorithm sorts a list by breaking it in half, sorting each half, and then merging the two sorted lists together.

4. A formula for the solution to a recurrence is generally more important for what it tells us about the _____ rate of the solution than it is for calculating numerical values of the solution.

5. If $s_n = bs_{n-1} + d(n)$ and $d(i) = O(b^i)$, then $s_n = O(\underline{\hspace{1.5cm}})$.

6. If $t_n = bs_{n/b} + d(n)$ and $d(i) = O(i)$, then $t_n = O(\underline{\hspace{1.5cm}})$.

Exercises

A   In Exercises 1–8 below, find a general solution to the given recurrence relation and then find the particular solution satisfying the given initial condition.

1. $s_n = 3s_{n-1} + 3^n$; $s_0 = 1$ 2. $a_n = 2a_{n-1} + 2^n$; $a_0 = 3$

3. $s_n = 3s_{n-1} + n3^n$; $s_1 = 4$ 4. $c_n - 2c_{n-1} = n2^n$; $c_3 = 4$

5. $s_n = 2s_{n-1} + 1$; $s_0 = 1$ (Recall the formula for the sum $1 + r + r^2 + \cdots + r^n$.)

6. $a_n = 3a_{n-1} + 1$; $a_0 = 2$ 7. $s_n = \frac{1}{2}s_{n-1} + 2^n$; $s_0 = 4$

8. $s_n = 3s_{n-1} + \frac{1}{3^n}$; $s_0 = \frac{1}{3}$

9. A contract to buy something with a loan at 12% interest works as follows. At the end of each month of the contract, 1% (which is $\frac{1}{12}$ of 12%) of the outstanding balance is added to the balance, and a payment, say \$200, is subtracted. Write a recurrence that describes this process.

10. In a payroll savings plan, someone deposits \$100 at the end of each month, and the savings institution pays 12% interest compounded monthly. Write a recurrence that describes the value of the account after n months.

11. One tenth of the material in a dump for nuclear waste decomposes into inactive material in one year, and 300 pounds of new material are added at the end of each year. Write a recurrence that describes the total amount of active material in the dump.

12. A state fish hatchery puts 2000 fish at the end of each year into a certain lake. The fish population doubles each year naturally. Write a recurrence that describes the fish population each year.

B   For Exercises 13–18, convert the recurrence to a first-order linear recurrence and specify for which values of n the conversion is valid.

13. $a_n = a_{n/3} + 2$ 14. $t_n = t_{n/4} + 3$

15. $a_n = 2a_{n/3} + n$ 16. $t_n = 3t_{n/4} + n$

17. $a_n = 3a_{n/3} + 1$ 18. $s_n = 2a_{n/3} + 1$

19. Solve the recurrence in Exercise 13 for the solution that has $a_1 = 3$.

20. Solve the recurrence in Exercise 14 for the solution that has $t_1 = 2$.

21. Find the general solution for the recurrence in Exercise 15.

22. Find the general solution for the recurrence in Exercise 16.

23. Find the solution to the recurrence in Exercise 17 that has $a_2 = 6$.

24. Find the solution to the recurrence in Exercise 18 that has $s_2 = 6$.

25. Explain why specifying that $a_0 = 4$ does not determine a unique solution for the recurrence you solved for a general solution in Exercise 21.

26. Explain why specifying $t_0 = 4$ does not determine a unique solution from the general solution you found to the recurrence in Exercise 22.

27. Finding the nth power of an integer i by successive multiplications by i requires $n-1$ multiplications. Assuming $n = 2^k$, describe a divide-and-conquer algorithm such that if s_n is the number of multiplications to find the nth power, then

$$s_n = s_{n/2} + 1$$

Solve this recurrence to determine the number of multiplications required by this method. Is this algorithm desirable?

28. Finding the product of a list of n integers by successive multiplications requires $n-1$ multiplications. Assuming $n = 2^k$, describe a divide-and-conquer algorithm for which the number of multiplications satisfies

$$m_n = 2m_{n/2} + 1$$

Solve this recurrence to determine the number of multiplications needed for a list of length n. Is this algorithm desirable?

C 29. If $s_n = 3s_{n-1} + 3^n$, write down the general solution and show directly that $s_n = O(n \cdot 3^n)$.

30. If $s_n = 3s_{n-1} + 2^n$, write down the general solution and show directly that it is $O(3^n)$.

31. Recall that $1 + 2^2 + 3^2 + \cdots + n^2 = O(n^3)$. Write down the solution to the recurrence $s_n = 2s_{n-1} + n^2 2^{n-1}$ and explain why it is $O(n^3 2^n)$.

32. Write down the solution to $s_n = 2s_{n-1} + 3$ and explain why $s_n = O(2^n)$.

33. Suppose that $s_n = 2s_{n-1} + n^2$. What is the order of growth of s_n?

34. Suppose that $s_n = 3s_{n-1} + n^3$. What is the order of growth of s_n?

35. Suppose that $s_i = 3s_{i-1} + i2^i$. What is the order of growth of s_n?

36. If $s_n = 3s_{n-1} + n^2 2^n$, what is the order of growth of s_n?

37. If $s_n = 3s_{n-1} + \dfrac{n+1}{n+2} 3^n$, what is the order of growth of s_n?

38. If $s_n = 2s_{n-1} + \dfrac{1+n^2}{3+n^2} 2^{n-1}$, what is the order of growth of s_n?

39. If $a_n = 2a_{n/3} + \sqrt{n}$, what is the order of growth of a_n?

40. If $t_n = 3a_{n/2} + n\sqrt{n}$, what is the order of growth of a_n?

Problems

1. Discuss the differences between Exercise 27 and Exercise 28.

2. Two mutually intersecting lines divide the plane into four regions. Let a_n be the maximum number of regions the plane can be divided into by n mutually intersecting straight lines. Find a recurrence for a_n and solve it. (*Hint*: $n - 1$ lines divide the plane into a_{n-1} regions. As you draw in the nth line, it starts cutting a new region in half each time it crosses a line.)

3. Find a recurrence for the number of closed regions formed by n mutually intersecting circles on a piece of paper so that each two intersect in two places along their circumference. (See Problem 2 for a hint.) For example, with one circle, a_1 is 1, with two circles a_2 is 3, and with three regions a_3 is 7. Solve this recurrence.

4. The Towers of Hanoi puzzle consists of a board with three pegs and n rings, as shown in Figure 2. The object of the game is to move all the rings from one peg to another, one at a time, moving each ring to any peg you wish but never placing a ring on top of a smaller one. Let a_n be the number of moves required with n rings. Find and solve a recurrence for a_n. (Think about how you could use mathematical induction on n to prove there is a way to solve the problem.)

Figure 2   The Towers of Hanoi.

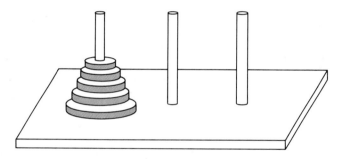

5. Discuss the effect of having four pegs rather than three for the Towers of Hanoi.

6. Discuss the effect on the number of moves needed to solve the Towers of Hanoi of a rule saying that a disk may be moved from one peg only to an adjacent peg (that is, you may not move a disk in one move from the first to the last peg).

7. A group of $2n$ people is to be divided into pairs for a game of chess. Find and solve a recurrence relation for the number of ways that this may be done.

8. A group of $4n$ people is to be divided into groups of four for bridge. Find and solve a recurrence relation for the number of ways that this may be done.

9. We have a list of 2^n items. We want to find the largest and smallest members of the list. If $n = 1$, we find the largest and smallest member of the list with one comparison. If $n > 1$, we break the list into two equal parts, find the largest and smallest entries of each part, and then compare the two largest and smallest entries we get, so as to find the largest and smallest entries of the entire list. Find and solve a recurrence relation for the number of comparisons this algorithm makes.

10. A **parallel algorithm** for summing a sequence of numbers works as follows. Split the sequence in half. Simultaneously (with two different computer processors) sum each half, then add the sums together. When the sequence has length 1, do nothing, for you have its sum. Assume that splitting a sequence takes a units of time and adding two numbers takes b units of time. (We assume that the times for any other operations necessary to implement the algorithm are included in the splitting time.) Find a recur-

rence for the amount of time needed to sum n numbers. Assuming that n is a power of two, solve the recurrence.

11. Read Problem 10 and then design a parallel algorithm to find the minimum of a list of numbers. Show that the time needed for a list of n numbers is $O(\log_2(n))$, assuming n is a power of 2.

12. Analyze the time needed by a revised merge sort algorithm by finding a recurrence based on the idea that after splitting a list into two halves, the two halves are sorted simultaneously but then merged by the same merge procedure used in the standard version of merge sort.

13. Prove Theorem 6.

Section 7-3
Second-Order
Linear Recurrences

▲ Examples of Second-Order Recurrences

We have concentrated so far on first-order recurrences. We shall now give several examples to show how second-order linear recurrence equations can arise. Our first example is centuries old, first worked out by Fibonacci, and is the original source of a sequence of numbers that has proved fascinating to amateur and professional mathematicians alike: the **Fibonacci sequence.**

The Fibonacci Sequence

EXAMPLE 28   We are observing a hypothetical population of rabbits, beginning with one pair of newborn rabbits. When a rabbit in this population is less than one month old, it cannot reproduce, but during the second and each succeeding month of life, each pair of rabbits gives rise to one new pair of rabbits. Figure 3 shows a way to visualize this. How many pairs of rabbits are present at the end of 1, 2, 3, 4, and 5 months? Write a recurrence for the number of pairs of rabbits present after n months, assuming that none die.

Solution   The number of pairs of rabbits present at the end of each month is summarized in Table 1, which we shall now explain. We begin with newborn rabbits so that at the end of month 0, we have one pair of immature rabbits. Since they are immature, we still have one pair after one month. However, they have become mature. During the second month, this pair has a pair of newborn rabbits, so we have one pair of newborn rabbits and one pair of mature rabbits at the end

Figure 3

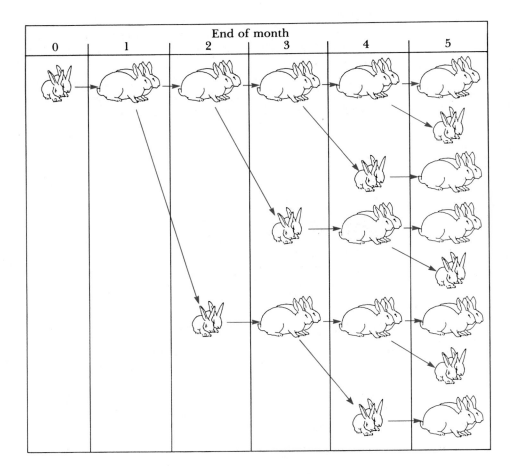

Table 1   A Summary of the Solution to Example 28.

Month	Pairs of newborn rabbits at month's end	Pairs of mature rabbits at month's end	Total number of pairs of rabbits at month's end
0	1	0	1
1	0	1	1
2	1	1	2
3	1	2	3
4	2	3	5
5	3	5	8
.	.	.	.
.	.	.	.
.	.	.	.

of two months. During the third month, the mature rabbits reproduce and the newborns mature, so after three months we have two pairs of mature rabbits and one pair of newborns. In month 4, two pairs of rabbits have newborns and one pair matures, for a total of five pairs of rabbits at the end of month 4. Finally, three of these pairs reproduce during month 5, giving us a total of eight pairs of rabbits at the end of month 5. Using r_n to stand for the number of pairs of rabbits present at the end of month n, we see that the terms r_0, r_1, r_2, r_3, r_4, r_5 of our sequence are 1, 1, 2, 3, 5, 8. Notice that each term of the sequence (beyond the second) is the sum of the two preceding terms. It appears that $<r_n>$ satisfies $r_n = r_{n-1} + r_{n-2}$ for $n \geq 2$. To explain why this recurrence is satisfied, note that the rabbits that have offspring during month n are those who have at least a month's worth of maturity. Thus they are exactly the rabbits who were present throughout month $n - 1$. To be present at the beginning of month $n - 1$, they must have been present at the end of month $n - 2$. Thus r_{n-2} is the number of pairs of offspring produced during month n, and the equation $r_n = r_{n-1} + r_{n-2}$ states that all rabbits present at the end of month $n - 1$ are still present at the end of month n, and all the mature rabbits have offspring as well.

Once we know the two values of $r_0 = 1$ and $r_1 = 1$, we can derive the remaining terms of the sequence by applying the rule $r_n = r_{n-1} + r_{n-2}$. The values of r_0 and r_1 are called *initial conditions*. ■

> The **Fibonacci sequence** is the solution to
> $r_n = r_{n-1} + r_{n-2}$ with the initial conditions
> $r_0 = 1$ and $r_1 = 1$.

Second-Order Recurrences as Models for Plant Growth

Our next two examples involve the growth of woody plants. New wood grows primarily on wood that has grown in the previous year. We idealize this by assuming (for these examples) that all new wood springs from the previous year's growth. One way to measure the overall size of a woody plant is by the total length of all its branches. It is this measure of size we shall consider in the next two examples.

EXAMPLE 29   In a certain hypothetical variety of woody plant, the amount of new growth formed in a given year is exactly equal to the previous year's amount of growth. Let t_n be the total length of all the branches after n years. Write a recurrence equation describing t_n.

Solution   During year n, the previous year's growth is $t_{n-1} - t_{n-2}$. Thus the amount of new growth in year n is $t_{n-1} - t_{n-2}$, and the amount of wood already present at the beginning of month n is t_{n-1}. Thus the total length of wood present at the end of month n is given by

$$t_n = t_{n-1} + (t_{n-1} - t_{n-2}) = 2t_{n-1} - t_{n-2} \quad \text{and}$$
$$t_n - 2t_{n-1} + t_{n-2} = 0$$

■

EXAMPLE 30   In a certain hypothetical woody plant, the new growth in a given year is exactly twice the preceding year's growth. Figure 4 shows a way to visualize this. Write a recurrence equation for s_n, the sum of the lengths of all the branches after n years.

Figure 4

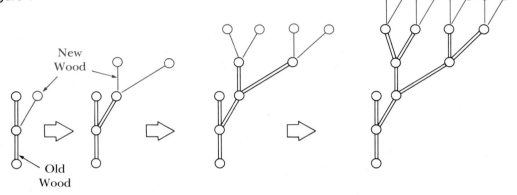

Solution   Last year's growth is $s_{n-1} - s_{n-2}$, as in Example 29. Therefore the new growth in year n is $2(s_{n-1} - s_{n-2})$. This plus the old growth already present is equal to s_n, so we write

$$s_n = 2(s_{n-1} - s_{n-2}) + s_{n-1} = 3s_{n-1} - 2s_{n-2} \qquad \text{or}$$
$$s_n - 3s_{n-1} + 2s_{n-2} = 0 \qquad\qquad \blacksquare$$

Examples 29 and 30 illustrate the fact that we don't need to know anything about initial conditions in order to write down a recurrence relation.

Finding Solutions

Our three examples are all second-order linear homogeneous recurrences with constant coefficients. You may recall that each solution to a first-order linear recurrence $s_n = bs_{n-1}$ was of the form $s_n = cb^n$ for some constant c. Thus it is natural to ask if Examples 28–30 have multiples of exponential functions as solutions. We explore this possibility in Example 31.

EXAMPLE 31   What conditions, if any, on b and c will make the sequence $s_n = cb^n$ a solution to the recurrence $s_n - 3s_{n-1} + 2s_{n-2} = 0$ of Example 30?

Solution   If $s_n = cb^n$ is a solution, then substitution gives us

$$cb^n - 3cb^{n-1} + 2cb^{n-2} = 0$$

Now if either $c = 0$ or $b = 0$, we are asking whether $s_n = 0$ is a solution to $s_n - 3s_{n-1} + 2s_{n-2} = 0$, and the answer is *yes*. If neither c nor b is 0, we may divide by c and by b^{n-2} to get

$$b^2 - 3b + 2 = 0 \qquad \text{or, by factoring,} \qquad (b-1)(b-2) = 0$$

Thus if $cb^n = s_n$ is a solution, then $b = 1$ or $b = 2$. In fact, if c_1 is a constant, then substituting $c_1 1^n$ in for s_n in the left-hand side of the recurrence gives

$$c_1 \cdot 1^n - 3c_1 \cdot 1^{n-1} + 2c_1 \cdot 1^{n-2} = c_1(1 - 3 + 2) = 0 \tag{1}$$

Similarly, if c_2 is a constant, then

$$c_2 \cdot 2^n - 3c_2 \cdot 2^{n-1} + 2c_2 \cdot 2^{n-2} = c_2 \cdot 2^{n-2}(4 - 6 + 2) = 0 \tag{2}$$

Thus $c_1 \cdot 1^n = c_1$ *is* a solution for any value of the constant c_1, and $c_2 \cdot 2^n$ *is* a solution for any value of the constant c_2. Thus $c \cdot b^n$ is a solution if and only if $b = 1$ or $b = 2$, but c may have any value (including 0).   ∎

As the example shows, the recurrence relation itself gives us no information about c. As was the case with first-order recurrences, initial conditions will determine appropriate values for c. However, before we can give a description of how to use initial conditions, we must be sure our solutions are general enough to include all possibilities. Are the solutions we found in the example the only ones possible? No, for if we add Equations (1) and (2), we see that $c_1 \cdot 1^n + c_2 \cdot 2^n = c_1 + c_2 \cdot 2^n$ is a solution for any choice of c_1 and c_2. Our next example shows why this observation is important.

EXAMPLE 32   Suppose that we begin with a plant with 2 feet of old wood and 1 foot of new wood, satisfying the assumptions of Example 30. Find a formula for the total length of wood present after n years.

Solution   We look for a formula of the form $c_1 + c_2 \cdot 2^n = t_n$. How do we find c_1 and c_2? Notice that $t_0 = 3$, since we start with a total of 3 feet of wood. This gives the equation

$$3 = c_1 + c_2 \cdot 2^0 = c_1 + c_2 \tag{3}$$

This gives us one equation involving the two unknown quantities c_1 and c_2. If we can get another equation involving the unknowns c_1 and c_2, then we should be able to solve for c_1 and c_2. If we knew the value of t_1, this would give us another equation. In the first year, the 1 foot of new wood will grow 2 more feet of wood, giving us a total of 5 feet. Thus $t_1 = 5$. This gives us

$$5 = c_1 + c_2 \cdot 2^1 = c_1 + 2c_2 \tag{4}$$

Subtracting Equation (3) from Equation (4) gives $c_2 = 2$, and substitution gives $c_1 = 1$. Thus our formula is $t_n = 1 + 2 \cdot 2^n$. Notice that this is *not* a solution of the type we studied in Example 31.   ∎

In Example 32, we used the information $t_0 = 3$ and $t_1 = 5$ to determine the constants c_1 and c_2. Facts that determine t_0 and t_1 will always let us find c_1 and c_2. As is the case with first-order recurrences, such facts are called *initial conditions*.

B   ### *Second-Order Linear Homogeneous Recurrences*

We saw that the sequences $s_n = 1$ and $t_n = 2^n$ are both solutions to the recurrence relation $s_n - 3s_{n-1} + 2s_{n-2} = 0$. We then observed that for any choice of c_1 and c_2 the sequence $<c_1 s_n + c_2 t_n>$, called a **linear combination** of $<s_n>$ and $<t_n>$, is another solution to the recurrence relation. This observation was useful because it made it possible to find a solution with $s_0 = 3$ and $s_1 = 5$. Our observation is a special case of the general principle that a linear combination of solutions to a homogeneous linear recurrence is still a solution.

Linear Combinations of Solutions

Theorem 9   If $<s_i>$ and $<t_i>$ are sequences that satisfy the linear homogeneous recurrence

$$a_n = \sum_{i=0}^{n-1} b_i(n)a_i$$

then for any choice of constants c_1 and c_2, the sequence given by $a_i = c_1 s_i + c_2 t_i$ also satisfies the recurrence.

Proof   We know that

$$s_n = \sum_{i=0}^{n-1} b_i(n)s_i \qquad \text{and} \qquad t_n = \sum_{i=0}^{n-1} b_i(n)t_i$$

Multiplying the first equation by c_1 and the second by c_2 and adding, we get

$$c_1 s_n + c_2 t_n = c_1 \sum_{i=0}^{n-1} b_i(n)s_i + c_2 \sum_{i=0}^{n-1} b_i(n)t_i$$

$$= \sum_{i=0}^{n-1} c_1 b_i(n)s_i + \sum_{i=0}^{n-1} c_2 b_i(n)t_i$$

$$= \sum_{i=0}^{n-1} (c_1 b_i(n)s_i + c_2 b_i(n)t_i)$$

$$= \sum_{i=0}^{n-1} b_i(n)(c_1 s_i + c_2 t_i) \qquad\blacksquare$$

EXAMPLE 33   Explain why $c_1 2^n + c_2(-2)^n$ is a solution to the recurrence $s_n = 4s_{n-2}$ for any choice of c_1 and c_2.

Solution   Note that $2^n = 2^2 \cdot 2^{n-2}$ and $(-2)^n = 2^2(-2)^{n-2}$. Therefore $s_n = 2^n$ and $t_n = (-2)^n$ are both solutions to the recurrence $s_n = 4s_{n-2}$. Then Theorem 9 tells us that $c_1 2^n + c_2(-2)^n$ is a solution also. $\blacksquare$

Exponential Solutions to Second-Order Linear Recurrences

We have seen examples where an exponential function is a solution to a recurrence of the form

$$a_n + ba_{n-1} + ca_{n-2} = 0 \tag{5}$$

which is a second-order linear homogeneous recurrence relation. Since $a_n = b^n$ is a solution to $a_n = ba_{n-1}$, we might guess that $a_n = b^n$ is also a solution to the recurrence (5) above. This guess is rarely correct, even though (5) has a solution of the form $a_n = r^n$ for some value of r. To see why, we simply substitute r^n for a_n, as in the proof of the theorem below.

Theorem 10   The sequence $a_n = r^n$ is a nonzero solution to the recurrence relation $a_n + ba_{n-1} + ca_{n-2} = 0$ if and only if r is a root of the equation $x^2 + bx + c = 0$.

Proof   Assume that $a_n = r^n$ is a solution to $a_n + ba_{n-1} + ca_{n-2} = 0$. Then $r^n + br^{n-1} + cr^{n-2} = 0$. The value $r = 0$ corresponds to the zero solution $a_n = 0$ for all n; if $r \neq 0$, then we may divide by r^{n-2} to get $r^2 + br + c = 0$. Therefore r is a root of the equation $x^2 + bx + c = 0$.

Now suppose r is a root of the equation $x^2 + bx + c = 0$. Then we multiply the equation $r^2 + br + c = 0$ by r^{n-2} to get $r^n + br^{n-1} + cr^{n-2} = 0$. This shows that $a_n = r^n$ is a solution to the recurrence. ∎

EXAMPLE 34   Which exponential functions are solutions to the recurrence $a_n = a_{n-1} - 6a_{n-2}$?

Solution   We rewrite the recurrence as $a_n - a_{n-1} + 6a_{n-2} = 0$. By Theorem 2, r^n is a solution if and only if r is a root of the equation $x^2 - x + 6 = 0$. This factors as $(x - 3)(x + 2) = 0$, so $a_n = r^n$ is a solution if and only if $r = 3$ or $r = 2$. ∎

Obtaining All the Solutions

We can prove by induction that the recurrence $a_n + ba_{n-1} + ca_{n-2} = 0$ describes one and only one sequence once the values a_0 and a_1 are specified. The values a_0 and a_1 are referred to as **initial values,** and facts that let us determine a_0 and a_1 are called *initial conditions*. We can now state a theorem that completely describes the solutions to the recurrence $a_n + ba_{n-1} + ca_{n-2} = 0$ in most cases.

Theorem 11   If the equation $x^2 + bx + c$ has two different roots, r_1 and r_2, then each solution to the recurrence relation $a_n + ba_{n-1} + ca_{n-2} = 0$ may be written as $c_1 r_1{}^n + c_2 r_2{}^n$ for some choice of c_1 and c_2.

Proof We know (by induction) that once a_0 and a_1 are given, there is one and only one solution to the recurrence. We also know by Theorems 9 and 10 that if r_1 and r_2 are roots of the polynomial $x^2 + bx + c$, then for any constants c_1 and c_2, $c_1 r_1{}^n + c_2 r_2{}^n$ is a solution to the recurrence. Substituting $n = 0$ and $n = 1$ into this solution and setting the results equal to a_0 and a_1 gives

$$c_1 r_1{}^0 + c_2 r_2{}^0 = a_0$$
$$c_1 r_1{}^1 + c_2 r_2{}^1 = a_1 \quad \text{or}$$
$$c_1 + 2c_2 = a_0$$
$$c_1 r_1 + c_2 r_2 = a_1$$

From the study of simultaneous equations in algebra, we know that if r_1 and r_2 are different, we may find one and only one solution to these equations for c_1 and c_2. Thus these values of c_1 and c_2 must make $c_1 r_1{}^n + c_2 r_2{}^n$ the unique solution to the recurrence determined by the values of a_0 and a_1. ∎

> Because of its role in determining the solutions to the recurrence equation $a_n + ba_{n-1} + ca_{n-2} = 0$, the polynomial $x^2 + bx + c$ is called the **characteristic polynomial** of the recurrence equation.

EXAMPLE 35 Solve the Fibonacci equation $a_n = a_{n-1} + a_{n-2}$, assuming that we begin with 1 pair of baby rabbits.

Solution The recurrence may be rewritten as $a_n - a_{n-1} - a_{n-2} = 0$. The quadratic formula tells us that $x^2 - x - 1 = 0$ if and only if

$$x = \frac{1 \pm \sqrt{1+4}}{2} = \frac{1 + \sqrt{5}}{2} \text{ or } \frac{1 - \sqrt{5}}{2}$$

Thus the general solution to the Fibonacci equation is

$$a_n = c_1 \left(\frac{1 + \sqrt{5}}{2} \right)^n + c_2 \left(\frac{1 - \sqrt{5}}{2} \right)^n$$

It is surprising that we have $\sqrt{5}$ involved in c_n—if we start out with an integer number of rabbits, we must continue to have an integer number of rabbits. We assume that we start with one pair of baby rabbits. Then a_0 is 1. The rabbits are immature, so a_1 is 1 also. The equation $a_0 = 1$ gives us

$$1 = c_1 \left(\frac{1 + \sqrt{5}}{2} \right)^0 + c_2 \left(\frac{1 - \sqrt{5}}{2} \right)^0 \quad \text{or} \quad 1 = c_1 + c_2$$

The equation $a_1 = 1$ gives

$$1 = c_1 \left(\frac{1 + \sqrt{5}}{2} \right)^1 + c_2 \left(\frac{1 - \sqrt{5}}{2} \right)^1$$

Solving our equations for c_1 and c_2, we get

$$c_1 = \frac{1}{\sqrt{5}} \frac{1 + \sqrt{5}}{2} \quad \text{and} \quad c_2 = \frac{1}{\sqrt{5}} \frac{\sqrt{5} - 1}{2}$$

Thus

$$a_n = \frac{1}{\sqrt{5}} \left(\frac{1 + \sqrt{5}}{2} \right)^{n+1} - \frac{1}{\sqrt{5}} \left(\frac{1 - \sqrt{5}}{2} \right)^{n+1}$$

A little experimentation should convince you that the square roots of 5 will always cancel out, as they must. Since we know that the a_n we found satisfies our recurrence relation and its initial conditions, and since once we specify a_0 and a_1, the other values of a_n are *all* completely determined by the recurrence relation, we know that our answer must be correct. ∎

In general, to solve a recurrence of the form $a_n + ba_{n-1} + ca_{n-2} = 0$, we solve the equation $x^2 + bx + c$. If this equation has two roots r_1 and r_2, then each solution to the recurrence has the form $c_1 r_1^n + c_2 r_2^n$ for some choice of c_1 and c_2. We call the expression $c_1 r_1^n + c_2 r_2^n$ the **general solution** to the recurrence relation. If the equation has only one root r, then each solution has the form $c_1 r^n + c_2 n r^n$. We outline a proof of this fact in the problems following this section and another proof in the problems for Appendix B.

Concepts Review

1. The _____ sequence consists of the solutions to the equation $a_n = a_{n-1} + a_{n-2}$ that have $a_0 = 1$ and $a_1 = 1$.

2. If $<s_n>$ and $<t_n>$ are sequences, then the sequence $<c_1 s_n + c_2 t_n>$ is called a(n) _____ _____ of the sequences $<s_n>$ and $<t_n>$.

3. If $<s_n>$ and $<t_n>$ are solutions to a homogeneous linear recurrence equation, then so is any _____ _____ of $<s_n>$ and $<t_n>$.

4. If the exponential function $a_n = r^n$ is a solution to the recurrence equation $a_n + ba_{n-1} + ca_{n-2} = 0$, then r is a solution to the quadratic equation _____.

5. If the quadratic equation in (4) has two distinct roots r_1 and r_2, then the general solution to the recurrence equation is _____.

6. If the quadratic equation in (4) has only one root, then the general solution to the recurrence equation is _____.

7. The characteristic polynomial of the recurrence equation $a_n + ba_{n-1} + ca_{n-2} = 0$ is the polynomial _____.

Exercises

A 1. If $s_n + 2s_{n-1} + s_{n-2} = 0$ and $s_0 = 1$ and $s_1 = 3$, find s_2, s_3, s_4, and s_5.

2. If $s_n - 5s_{n-1} + 6s_{n-2} = 0$ and $s_0 = 4$ and $s_1 = 6$, find s_2, s_3, s_4, and s_5.

In Exercises 3–10, state whether or not the recurrence is a second-order linear homogeneous recurrence with constant coefficients.

3. $s_n + 2s_{n-1} + s_{n-2} = 0$

4. $s_n + 4s_{n-1} + 4s_{n-2} = 0$

5. $s_n + ns_{n-1} + s_{n-2} = 0$

6. $s_n = 5s_{n-1} - 6$

7. $s_n + 2s_{n-1} + 2 = 0$

8. $s_n = 5s_{n-1} - 6s_{n-2}$

9. $s_n + s_{n-2} - n = 0$

10. $s_n = 5s_{n-2}$

In Exercises 11–28, classify each recurrence relation as linear or not, homogeneous or not, constant coefficient or not, and determine its order if it has one.

11. $s_n = s_{n-1} - s_{n-2}$

12. $s_n = s_{n-1} \cdot s_{n-2}$

13. $a_n = 3a_n - 2a_{n-2}$

14. $t_n = na_n + a_{n-1}$

15. $a_n = n^2 a_n + na_{n-1} + n!$

16. $a_n = a_n - a_{n-1} + a_{n-2}^2$

17. $a_n = \sum_{i=1}^{n-1} ia_i$

18. $s_n = s_{n/2} + s_{n/4}$

19. $s_n = s_{n/2} + n^2$

20. $s_{n+1} = (s_n + s_{n-1})(s_n - s_{n-1})$

21. $s_{n+2} = s_{n+1} + s_{n-1} + 2^n$

22. $s_n = 3s_{n-1} + 2s_{n-3}$

23. $a_n = n^2 a_{n-1} + n^3 a_{n-2}$

24. $t_n = \sum_{i=1}^{n} t_i$

25. $a_{n+3} = a_{n+2} - a_{n+1}$

26. $t_n = (t_{n-1} - 2)(t_{n-2} - 1)$

27. $s_n = 2s_{n/2} + 4s_{n/4} + 2^n$

28. $s_{n^2} = s_n + s_{n-1}$

29. In the plant growth example of Examples 29 and 30, suppose each foot of year-old wood produces 1.5 feet of new wood. Write the recurrence relation for the total length of wood (t_n) present after n years.

30. In the plant growth example of Examples 29 and 30, suppose each foot of year-old wood produces 3 feet of new wood. Write a recurrence describing the amount t_n of wood present after n years.

31. In the Fibonacci example, suppose that each pair of mature rabbits produces two new rabbits in the next month. Write down the recurrence that results.

32. In the Fibonacci example, suppose that each pair of mature rabbits produces three new rabbits in the next month. Write down the recurrence that results.

33. In the Fibonacci example, suppose that a one-month old pair of rabbits produces a new pair of rabbits and a pair of rabbits two months old or older produces *two* new pairs of rabbits. Write the recurrence that results.

34. In the plant growth example of Examples 29 and 30, suppose that each foot of year-old wood produces 2 feet of new wood, each foot of two-year-old wood produces 1 foot of new wood, and wood more than two years old produces no new wood. Write the recurrence for the total length of wood t_n present in the plant after n years.

35. Find the conditions, if any, on b and c that make $c \cdot b^n$ a solution to the recurrence $s_n - 5s_{n-1} + 6s_{n-2} = 0$.

36. Find the conditions, if any, on b and c that make $c \cdot b^n$ a solution to the recurrence $s_n - 6s_{n-1} + 8s_{n-2} = 0$.

37. Find the conditions, if any, on b and c that make $c \cdot b^n$ a solution to the recurrence $s_n - 4s_{n-1} + 4s_{n-2} = 0$.

38. Find the conditions, if any, on b and c that make $c \cdot b^n$ a solution to the recurrence $s_n + 2s_{n-1} + s_{n-2} = 0$.

39. Find a solution to the recurrence of Exercise 35 with $s_0 = 2$ and $s_1 = 5$.

40. Find a solution to the recurrence of Exercise 36 with $s_0 = 0$ and $s_1 = 2$.

B   Find the general solution of the recurrences in Exercises 41–48.

41. $a_n = 5a_{n-1} - 6a_{n-2}$ 42. $a_n = a_{n-1} + 6a_{n-2}$

43. $s_n = 6s_{n-1} - 5s_{n-2}$ 44. $t_{n+2} = 4t_{n+1} - 3t_n$

45. $a_n = 4a_{n-1} + 5a_{n-2}$ 46. $a_n = 7a_{n-1} - 12a_{n-2}$

47. $s_{n+2} = s_{n+1} + 12s_n$ 48. $t_{n+1} = 2t_n + 3t_{n-1}$

For the recurrence relations in Exercises 41–48, find the solution satisfying the condition specified in Exercises 49–56.

49. Exercise 41: $a_0 = 0$; $a_1 = 1$ 50. Exercise 42: $a_1 = 4$; $a_2 = 22$

51. Exercise 43: $s_1 = 0$; $s_2 = 20$ 52. Exercise 44: $t_0 = -1$; $t_1 = 3$

53. Exercise 45: $a_0 = 4$; $a_1 = 8$ 54. Exercise 46: $a_1 = 2$; $a_2 = 2$

55. Exercise 47: $s_0 = 5$; $s_1 = 6$ 56. Exercise 48: $t_1 = 4$; $t_2 = 8$

In Exercises 57–64, find the general solution to the recurrence relation given.

57. $a_n = 3a_{n-1} - a_{n-2}$ 58. $s_n = 2s_{n-1} + 2s_{n-2}$

59. $s_n = 4s_{n-1} - 2s_{n-2}$ 60. $t_{n+2} = 5t_{n+1} - 5t_n$

61. $a_n = a_{n-1} - a_{n-2}$ 62. $s_{n+2} = 3s_{n+1} - 3s_n$

63. $a_n = 4a_{n-1} - 5a_{n-2}$ 64. $s_{n+2} = s_{n+1} - s_n$

In Exercises 65–72, find the solution to the recurrence in the exercise given satisfying the conditions given.

65. Exercise 57: $a_0 = 4$; $a_1 = 6$ 66. Exercise 58: $s_0 = 2$; $s_1 = 2$

67. Exercise 59: $s_1 = 0$; $s_2 = -4$ 68. Exercise 60: $t_0 = 2$; $t_1 = 5$

69. Exercise 61: $a_0 = 0$; $a_1 = 1$

70. Exercise 62: $s_1 = 0$; $s_2 = 6$

71. Exercise 63: $a_1 = 2$; $a_2 = -2$

72. Exercise 64: $s_0 = 4$; $s_1 = 2$

Problems

1. Verify that if the characteristic polynomial of the recurrence equation $a_n + ba_{n-1} + ca_{n-2} = 0$ has only one root r, then the sequence $a_n = nr^n$ is a solution to the recurrence.

2. Use the result of Problem 1 to show that $s_n = c_1 r^n + c_2 nr^n$ is the general solution to a second-order linear homogeneous recurrence equation if the characteristic polynomial has exactly one root r.

3. A special-purpose computer can do one of three types of jobs. Job 1 takes one second, and jobs 2 and 3 take two seconds. Give a recurrence equation for the number of arrangements of jobs possible in n seconds. Solve this recurrence equation.

4. Find and solve a recurrence equation for the number of sequences of n zeros and ones with no consecutive ones.

5. Find and solve a recurrence equation for the number of sequences of n zeros, ones, and minus ones with no consecutive minus ones.

6. The Fibonacci numbers F_n are the sequence of numbers satisfying $a_n = a_{n-1} + a_{n-2}$ with $a_0 = a_1 = 1$. Show that

$$\sum_{i=0}^{n-2} F_i = F_n - 1$$

7. The sequence F_n is defined in Problem 6. Show that

$$\sum_{i=0}^{n} F_{2i} = F_{2n+1}$$

8. Show that

$$a_n = \sum_{k=0}^{n} \binom{n-k}{k}$$

is a solution to the Fibonacci recurrence equation.

9. Let s_n be any sequence that satisfies the recurrence equation

$$s_n + as_{n-1} + bs_{n-2} = c(n)$$

Let u_n be the general solution to

$$t_n + at_{n-1} + bt_{n-2} = 0$$

Show that $s_n + u_n$ is a solution to the original recurrence equation.

10. Discuss how to solve a recurrence equation of the form

$$s_n + as_{n-1} + bs_{n-2} + cs_{n-3} = 0$$

11. Apply the technique you developed in Problem 10 to the recurrence equation $a_n - 2a_{n-1} - a_{n-2} + 2a_{n-3} = 0$.

12. Apply the technique you developed in Problem 10 to the recurrence equation $a_n - 3a_{n-1} - 4a_{n-2} + 12a_{n-3} = 0$.

13. Apply the binomial theorem to show that the solution shown for the Fibonacci equation in Example 35 is always an integer.

Chapter 7
Review Exercises

1. The Insertion Sort algorithm may be described as follows. To sort a list of length 1, do nothing. To sort a list of length n, first apply insertion sort to the first $n - 1$ entries. Next insert the last element into the correct position by working your way from position $n - 1$ down to position 1, if necessary, moving an element right one place if it should come after the element you are trying to insert. When you find the first element that does *not* come after the one you are trying to insert, put the element you are trying to insert right after it. In the worst possible situation, how many comparisons will you make in trying to insert a word into an already sorted list of length $n - 1$? How many will you make in the best possible situation? Explain why in the worst possible case the number of comparisons w_n made in sorting an n-element list by using insertion sort satisfies the recurrence

$$w_n = w_{n-1} + n - 1$$

Explain why the number of comparisons b_n made in the best possible case of applying insertion sort to an n-element list satisfies the recurrence

$$b_n = b_{n-1} + 1$$

2. Find a recurrence for the number j_n of ways to assign n jobs to m computers, assuming that the jobs and the computers are distinguishable and that any computer may be assigned any number of jobs. Assume that the order in which the jobs are assigned is irrelevant. (If you have studied ordered distributions, you will find it useful to solve the same problem assuming that the order in which the jobs are assigned is relevant.)

In Exercises 3–10, classify each recurrence equation according to (a) its order if it has one; (b) whether or not it is linear and, if it is linear, whether or not it is constant coefficient; (c) whether or not it is homogeneous.

3. $a_n = 3a_{n-1}$

4. $a_n = n^2 a_{n-1}$

5. $a_n = a_{n-1} + n^2$

6. $a_n = a_{n-1} - a_{n-2}$

7. $a_n = a_{n-1} - a_{n-2} - n^2$

8. $a_n^2 = a_{n-1}$

9. $a_{n+1} = a_{n-1}^2$

10. $a_n = a_{n-1} - a_{n-2} + a_{n-3} - a_{n-4} + \cdots \pm a_0$

11. If $a_0 = 3$, what are the first five terms of the sequence a_i given by Exercise 3? By Exercise 4?

12. Use substitution to verify that $a_n = n^2(n + 1)^2/4$ is a solution to the recurrence equation

$$a_n = a_{n-1} + n^3$$

13. If $a_n = (n + 1)a_{n-1}$ and $a_0 = 1$, find a formula for a_n valid for $n \geq 0$.

In Exercises 14–17, simplify the expression given.

14. $(2^3 \cdot 4^2)^2$

15. $2^{\log_2(5)}$

16. $4^{\log_2(5)}$

17. $\log_2(50) - \log_2(25)$

18. The base-10 logarithm of 2 is approximately .301 and the base-10 logarithm of 5 is approximately .699. What is an approximate value for the base-10 logarithm of 40?

19. Find a formula for computing base-8 logarithms from base-10 logarithms.

20. A radioactive substance decays in such a way that 20% of the material present becomes nonradioactive in one hour. Find a formula for the amount present after n hours, given that you start with an amount a_0. What is the half-life of the substance?

21. Find a formula for the value of a \$1000 savings certificate after n years if it pays 8% annual interest (compounded annually). How long does it take for the value of the certificate to double?

In Exercises 22–24, find the general solution to the recurrence relation given and then find the particular solution satisfying the initial conditions given.

22. $s_n = 3s_{n-1} + 2^n$ $s_0 = 3$

23. $s_n = 3s_{n-1} + 1$ $s_1 = 6$

24. $s_n = 3s_{n-1} + 3^n$ $s_2 = 6$

25. Let a_n stand for the amount of money deposited in a savings account in a certain bank. Assume that the owner of the account deposits \$200 annually and the account pays 8% interest annually. Give a recurrence relation that describes a_n. Assuming that the savings account begins at \$1000, find a formula for its value after n years. Find how many years it takes to reach a value of \$3000. (Your answer will require the use of logarithms; use a calculator to get a numerical value.)

For Exercises 26–29, convert the recurrence to a first-order linear recurrence and specify for which values of n the conversion is valid.

26. $t_n = 3t_{n/2} + 4$

27. $a_n = 3a_{n/3} + 4$

28. $c_n = 3c_{n/4} + 4$

29. $c_n = 3c_{n/2} + n$

For Exercises 30–33, solve the specified recurrence for the values of n you specified in Exercises 26–29, using the initial condition given.

30. Exercise 26: $t_1 = 1$

31. Exercise 27: $a_3 = 7$

32. Exercise 28: $c_1 = 1$

33. Exercise 29: $c_4 = 28$

34. If $s_n = 3s_{n-1} + n^2$, what is the order of growth of s_n?

35. If $a_i = 3a_{i-1} + i^2 2^i$, what is the order of growth of a_i?

36. If $a_i = 2a_{i-1} + i3^i$, what is the order of growth of a_i?

37. If $t_n = 3t_{n/2} + \sqrt{n}$, what is the order of growth of t_n?

38. If $t_n = 3t_{n/2} + n^2$, what is the order of growth of t_n?

39. Suppose $a_n = a_{n-1} + 6a_{n-2}$ and $a_0 = 1$, $a_1 = 2$. Find a_3, a_4, a_5, and a_6.

40. Use substitution to verify that one solution to the recurrence of Exercise 39 is $a_n = 3^n$.

41. Find the general solution to the recurrence of Exercise 39 and find the particular solution with $a_0 = 1$ and $a_1 = 2$.

42. A bank is trying to encourage people to leave money in its savings certificate. It offers to pay 8% interest on all money deposited, plus a 2% bonus on money that has been in the account for one year or more. Write a recurrence that describes the amount present in an account after n years. Use your recurrence to calculate the value of an account that started at $1000 after 5 years.

*T*here is a special kind of graph called a *tree*, which appears in many of the applications of graph theory. Trees first arose in the study of properties of molecules in chemistry and in the study of voltages in circuits, and they are now used in a wide variety of ways in computer science. The concept of a binary tree is useful in the evaluation of formulas, in the study of alphabetically ordered lists, and in the study of so-called branching processes. The concept of a spanning tree is important in the context of efficient communication, in the determination of distances between vertices in a transportation system, and in the abstract study of graphs. In fact, the properties of trees often provide the base step in inductive proofs of results about graphs.

Our study of trees takes up where our study of reachability and connectivity in graphs left off. We begin with a study of efficient ways to design a communication network. Such networks often have a center of communications; this leads us to the notion of a rooted tree. When we carefully analyze the meaning of efficient communication, we discover that there are two different practical criteria we might use for efficiency. This leads us to two different kinds of rooted spanning trees of so-called weighted graphs: minimum total weight spanning trees and minimum distance (or minimum path weight) spanning trees. Among the most important kinds of rooted trees we study are the binary search trees, structures that we can use in the design and implementation of computer programs to process ordered lists of data efficiently. Trees will also play an important role in our study of graphs.

Trees are one of the most important unifying ideas in graph theory and computer science.

Section 8-1
Trees and
Spanning Trees

▲ Trees

We introduce the concept of a tree with a typical application. Suppose you are responsible for laying out coaxial cable to connect the buildings on a college campus so that a television signal originating in one building can be sent to any other building on campus. You can represent the network you plan with a graph that has one vertex (in Electrical Engineering language, one node) for each building and an edge between two vertices if and only if the corresponding buildings are to be joined by cable. Since you want to be able to send a signal from each building to each other building, the graph will have a walk from each vertex to each other vertex. In the language of Chapter 3, this means that your graph will be connected. An edge $\{x,y\}$ that could be erased leaving x and y connected by a walk would correspond to wasted cable. Thus you would not want such "redundant" edges in your graph.

The Concept of a Tree

A **tree** is a connected graph with the property that for each edge $\{x,y\}$, removing $\{x,y\}$ from the edge set (and *nothing* from the vertex set) gives a graph in which x and y are not connected.

Our description of the television network graph above tells us that it will be a tree.

EXAMPLE 1   Determine which graphs in Figure 1 are trees.

Figure 1

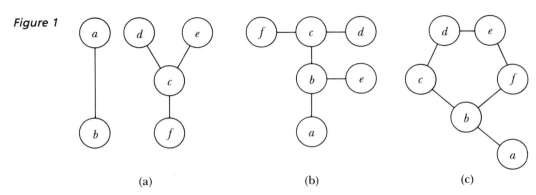

(a)   (b)   (c)

Solution   Graph (a) is not connected, so it is not a tree. Graph (b) is connected. Removing edge $\{a,b\}$ leaves a graph in which a and b are not connected; in the same way, removing *any other* edge in graph (b) leaves a graph in which its endpoints are not connected. Thus graph (b) is a tree. Graph (c) is connected. However, removing *one* of the edges $\{b,c\}$, $\{c,d\}$, $\{d,e\}$, $\{e,f\}$, or $\{f,b\}$ leaves a connected graph. Therefore graph (c) is not a tree. ■

Cycles

The "ring" of vertices b,c,d,e,f in graph (c) of Figure 1 appears to be the reason the graph is not a tree. Such configurations are called *cycles*. To be more precise,

A **closed walk** in a graph is a walk
$$v_0\, e_1\, v_1\, e_2 \ldots v_{n-1}\, e_n\, v_0$$
that starts and ends at the same vertex v_0.

A closed walk is called a **cycle** if $v_i \neq v_j$ and $e_i \neq e_j$ for each distinct i and j less than n.

In graph (c) of Figure 1, b,c,d,e,f,b is the sequence of vertices of a cycle. If *all* the edges and vertices of a graph form a cycle, then we say that the graph itself *is a cycle*. Thus graph (c) of Figure 1 is not a cycle, but the four graphs in Figure 2 are cycles.

Figure 2   Several cycles.

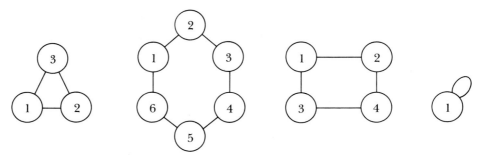

Paths

A walk in which all the vertices (and edges)
are different is called a **path**.

Thus the sequence a,b,c,d represents a path in graph (b) of Figure 1, and the sequence a,b,c,d,e,f represents a path in graph (c) of Figure 1.

EXAMPLE 2   For each of the first three graphs of Figure 2, how many paths are there from vertex 1 to vertex 2?

Solution   1{1,2}2 is always one path, and there is a second path around the cycle, for instance 1{1,3}3{2,3}2 in the first graph. Any other walk between vertices 1 and 2 will have to repeat some vertex. Thus, there are exactly two paths between vertices 1 and 2 in each of the first three graphs of Figure 2.   ∎

In contrast to Example 2, you see in part (b) of Figure 1 that it is possible to find one and only one path connecting each pair of vertices. As our next theorem shows, the observations we have made about paths and cycles in trees serve to characterize trees.

Other Descriptions of Trees

Theorem 1   The following statements about a simple graph G are equivalent.

(1) G is a tree.
(2) For each pair of vertices x and y of G, there is a unique path from x to y.
(3) G is connected and has no cycles.

Proof   We shall prove that statement (1) implies statement (2), then that statement (2) implies statement (3), and also that statement (3) implies statement (1). By the transitivity of "implies," each of the statements will imply each other one, so we will have proved that they are all equivalent.

To prove that (1) implies (2), suppose 1 is true and 2 is false so that G is a tree but there are vertices x and y such that there are two different paths from x to y. Thus there must be an edge $e = \{u,v\}$ on one path but not on the other. Now the portion of the path from x to y preceding e is a walk between x and u, and the portion of the path following e is a walk from v to y. These two walks together with the other path from x to y constitute a walk from u to v that does not include e. Thus removing e leaves a graph in which u and v are connected, contradicting (1). Therefore (1) implies (2).

Now to show that (2) implies (3), assume that for each pair of vertices x and y of G there is a unique path from x to y. Then G must be connected. If G had a cycle, two adjacent vertices on that cycle would be connected by two different paths, as in Example 2. This contradicts what we just assumed, so G can have no cycles. Thus statement (2) implies statement (3).

Now assume that G is connected and has no cycles. If there were an edge $e = \{x,y\}$ such that it could be removed and leave x and y connected, then there would be a path from x to y not using e. Following this path from x to y and then following e from y back to x gives us a cycle. This would contradict our assumption that statement (3) is true, so statement (3) implies statement (1).   ∎

When a graph is given to us by its edge set or adjacency lists, it may not be easy to detect whether or not it is a tree. However, by drawing the graph we can see if it is a tree.

EXAMPLE 3   Draw the graphs described by the adjacency lists below. Which is a tree?

G: 1:2,3;   2:1,3,4,5;   3:2;   4:2,6;   5:2,6;   6:4,5.
H: 1:3;   2:3,4,5;   3:2;   4:2;   5:2,6;   6:5.

Solution   We see from our drawings in Figure 3 that both graphs are connected but only the first has a cycle, so H is a tree and G is not.   ■

Figure 3   Drawing two graphs from adjacency lists.

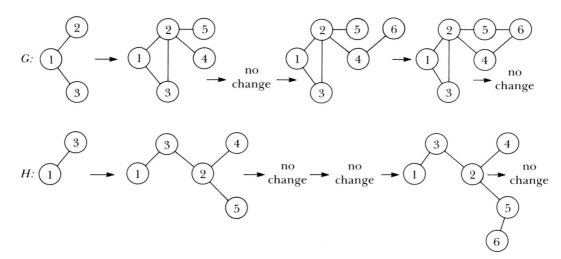

B   Spanning Trees

We began our study of trees with the idea of connecting buildings on a campus together for a television broadcast system. Frequently, some of the buildings on a campus are already connected by utility tunnels for steam, electricity, telephone, and so on. In such a case, we would want to route our television cable through the existing tunnels rather than create new ones. This gives us a graph theoretic problem. We have a graph whose vertices correspond to buildings and whose edges correspond to tunnels. Planning a broadcast system whose cables go through tunnels is the same as choosing a tree on the same vertex set whose edges are all "tunnel" edges.

The Concept of a Spanning Tree

This leads us to the idea of a spanning tree. Given a graph G with vertex set V and edge set E, we define a **spanning tree** of G to be a tree whose vertex set is V and whose edge set is a *subset* of E.

EXAMPLE 4   Find spanning trees of the graphs in Figure 3.

Solution   These graphs both have the same vertex set. The graph H is a tree, so it is a spanning tree of itself. Every edge of H is also an edge of G, so H is also a spanning tree of G.   ■

How would we find a spanning tree of G if we hadn't already been given the tree H? One idea is to start at some vertex and build up the tree one edge at a time. We might start at vertex 2 and choose edge {2,3}. Having 2 and 3 in our tree now, we might next choose edge {1,3} and increase our vertex set to {1,2,3}. Now we *can't* choose edge {1,3} as a tree edge because we would get a cycle among edges we choose. To keep building a tree, we would choose edge {2,5} or {2,4}, and so on. This approach may be described precisely by algorithm Spantree.

An Algorithm to Find Spanning Trees

Algorithm Spantree

    Input   A graph G with a vertex set V and edge set E, and an element x in V.

    Output   The edge set F of a spanning tree of G.

    Procedure   Let $V' = \{x\}$. Let $F = \varnothing$. Repeat the following steps until step 1 becomes impossible.

    (1) Choose an edge e from a vertex v in V' to a vertex y not in V'.

    (2) Add y to V'.

    (3) Add e to F.

Theorem 2   Algorithm Spantree produces a spanning tree of a connected graph.

Proof   We begin with a connected graph on the vertex set V' with the one vertex x. Each time we choose an edge, we choose an edge that has one vertex in the connected graph, so the new graph we get with the new vertex set V' is connected. Since we never choose an edge with two vertices in V', we will never choose all the edges of a cycle of G. Thus, F is always the edge set of a tree. Now when step 1 is impossible, no element of V' is adjacent in G to any element of $V \sim V'$. Therefore V' is a connected component of G. Thus, if we begin with a connected graph G, we will have $V' = V$ when we are done, so we get a spanning tree of G.   ■

The proof of Theorem 2 actually proves more than Theorem 2; we describe the stronger result in Theorem 3.

Theorem 3   Algorithm Spantree produces a spanning tree of the connected component of G containing x.

Proof   Given in the proof of Theorem 2.   ■

EXAMPLE 5   Apply algorithm Spantree with $x = a$ to the graph with adjacency list representation:

$$a: b,d,e \qquad b: a,d \qquad c: d,e,f$$
$$d: a,b,c,f \qquad e: a,c \qquad f: c,d$$

Use adjacency lists to keep track of the edge set F of the spanning tree. Draw the graph and the spanning tree you construct.

Solution   To start, $V' = \{a\}$. Let us choose $\{a,b\}$ in step 1. This gives us adjacency lists *a: b* and *b: a*; now $V' = \{a,b\}$.

A second natural edge to choose is $\{a,d\}$. This gives us $V' = \{a,b,d\}$ and the adjacency lists

$$a: b,d \qquad b: a \qquad d: a$$

Now we might as well continue choosing edges from a's adjacency list, so we choose edge $\{a,e\}$. This gives us $V' = \{a,b,d,e\}$ and the adjacency lists

$$a: b,d,e \qquad b: a \qquad d: a \qquad e: a$$

Now we have chosen all the edges we can using a's adjacency list; let us try to use b as our vertex in V' for step 1. Since only a and d are on b's adjacency list and both are in V', we can't use b in step 1. Since d was the next vertex after b that we put into the tree, let us choose to examine d's edges next. We see that d is adjacent to a and b, but they are in V'. Since d is adjacent to c and f (which are not in V'), we next choose $\{d,c\}$ and $\{d,f\}$, obtaining

$$a: b,d,e \qquad b: a \qquad d: a,c \qquad e: a \qquad c: d$$
$$a: b,d,e \qquad b: a \qquad d: a,c,f \qquad e: a \qquad c: d \qquad f: d$$

Now step 1 is impossible, and the work of the algorithm is complete. We draw the graph and its spanning tree in Figure 4.   ∎

Figure 4   The graph and spanning tree of Example 5.

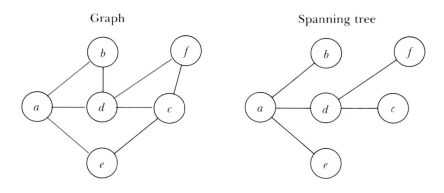

Graph

Spanning tree

The Number of Edges of a Tree

In applying algorithm Spantree, we start with one vertex in a tree and build the tree in steps, adding one vertex and one edge in each step. Thus the tree we get from Spantree will have one fewer edge than it has vertices. Our next theorem shows this is a property of trees in general, not just trees the algorithm produces.

Theorem 4   A tree with n vertices has $n - 1$ edges.

Proof   The proof is by induction on n. A tree with one vertex has no edges. (A graph with one vertex can only have a loop for an edge, but a loop gives a cycle with one edge.) Now suppose inductively that when k is less than n, a tree on k vertices has $k - 1$ edges. Let G be a tree with n vertices. If we choose an edge e of G and remove it, the resulting graph has two connected components. Let k be the number of vertices of one and m be the number of vertices of the other. Neither connected component can have a cycle, so each is a tree. Since k and m must both be less than n, our inductive hypothesis tells us these components have $k - 1$ and $m - 1$ edges, respectively. G has one more edge than these two trees together, so it has

$$k - 1 + m - 1 + 1 = k + m - 1 = n - 1$$

edges. Thus, by mathematical induction, a tree on n vertices has $n - 1$ edges for any $n > 0$.   ∎

In fact, a connected graph with n vertices and $n - 1$ edges *must be* a tree and a graph with n vertices, $n - 1$ edges, and no cycles *must be* a tree as well. We could thus insert these two statements into the list in Theorem 1 of equivalent ways to say that a graph is a tree.

Theorem 5   The following two statements about a graph G with n vertices are equivalent to the statement "G is a tree."

(a) G is connected and has $n - 1$ edges.
(b) G has $n - 1$ edges and no cycles.

Proof   The statement "G is a tree" implies both statement (a) and statement (b). Proving that (a) or (b) implies that G is a tree is a straightforward application of "proof by contradiction."   ∎

Concepts Review

1. A(n) _____ is a connected graph with the property that removing any edge {*x,y*} from its edge set leaves a graph in which *x* and *y* are not connected.

2. A(n) _____ _____ in a graph is a walk that starts and ends at the same vertex.

3. A closed walk is called a _____ if no two vertices or edges other than the first and last vertex are equal (but the first and last vertex *are* equal).

4. A(n) _____ _____ of a graph *G* with vertex set *V* and edge set *E* is a tree whose vertex set is *V* and whose edge set is a subset of *E*.

5. A tree with *n* vertices has _____ edges.

6. A connected graph with *n* vertices and _____ edges is a tree.

7. A graph on *n* vertices with _____ edges and no cycles is a tree.

8. A connected graph with no cycles is called a(n) _____.

9. In a tree, for each pair of vertices *x* and *y* there is a unique _____ between *x* and *y*.

Exercises

A

1. Draw an example of a cycle on 8 vertices.

2. Draw an example of a cycle on 9 vertices.

3. Below we give the edge sets of several graphs on the vertex set {1,2,3,4,5,6}. Draw the graphs and locate all cycles (if any). State whether or not the graph is a tree.
   (a) {{1,2}, {1,3}, {2,4}, {3,6}, {4,6}, {3,5}, {4,5}}
   (b) {{1,2}, {1,3}, {2,4}, {4,6}, {3,5}}
   (c) {{1,2}, {3,6}, {4,6}, {4,5}, {3,5}}
   (d) {{1,2}, {2,3}, {3,4}, {3,5}, {1,5}, {4,6}, {2,6}}

4. Below are the edge sets of several graphs on the vertex set {*a,b,c,d,e,f*}. Draw the graphs and locate all cycles (if any). State whether or not the graph is a tree.
   (a) {{*a,b*}, {*e,d*}, {*b,c*}, {*d,f*}, {*a,c*}, {*e,f*}}
   (b) {{*a,b*}, {*e,d*}, {*b,c*}, {*c,d*}, {*d,f*}, {*a,c*}, {*e,f*}}
   (c) {{*a,b*}, {*a,c*}, {*c,d*}, {*d,b*}}
   (d) {{*a,b*}, {*a,d*}, {*a,c*}, {*e,f*}, {*b,c*}, {*b,d*}, {*c,d*}}

5. For each graph you have drawn in Exercise 3, find all paths from vertex 1 to vertex 6, or explain why none exists.

6. For each graph you have drawn in Exercise 4, find all paths from vertex *a* to vertex *d*, or explain why none exists.

7. Draw the graphs represented by adjacency lists below. Identify which graphs are trees.
   (a) 1: 2,3,5;   2: 1,4;   3: 1,4;   4: 2,3,5;   5: 1,4
   (b) 1: 2,3;   2: 1;   3: 1,4;   4: 3,5;   5: 4
   (c) 1: 2,3,4,5; 2: 1;   3: 1;   4: 1;   5: 1

8. Draw the graphs represented by adjacency lists below. Identify which graphs are trees.
   (a) *a: b;*   *b: a,c;*   *c: b,d;*   *d: c,e;*   *e: d,f;*   *f: e*
   (b) *a: b,f;*   *b: a,c;*   *c: b,d;*   *d: c,e;*   *e: d,f;*   *f: a,e*
   (c) *a: b,c,d,e;* *b: a,c,d,e;*   *c: a,b,d;*   *d: a,b,c,e;*   *e: a,b,d*

9. Find a closed walk with 6 edges in each graph of Exercise 7. (The closed walk need not be a cycle.)

10. Find a closed walk with 6 edges in each graph of Exercise 8. (The closed walk need not be a cycle.)

11. How many paths are there from vertex 1 to vertex 5 in the graphs of Exercise 7?

12. How many paths are there from vertex *a* to vertex *e* in the graphs of Exercise 8?

B 13. Let *G* be the graph on vertex set {1,2,3,4,5} with the following edge set: {{1,2}, {1,3}, {1,4}, {3,4}, {4,5}, {2,5}, {2,3}}. Which of the edge sets below are edge sets of spanning trees of *G*?
   (a) {{1,3}, {3,4}, {4,5}, {5,2}, {1,2}}
   (b) {{1,3}, {1,2}, {1,4}, {1,5}}
   (c) {{1,2}, {1,3}, {3,4}, {4,5}}
   (d) {{1,3}, {3,2}, {3,4}, {4,5}}

14. Let *G* be the graph on the vertex set {a,b,c,d,e,f} with edged set {{a,d}, {a,e}, {b,d}, {b,e}, {b,f}, {c,e}, {c,f}, {e,f}, {e,d}}. Which of the edge sets below are edge sets of spanning trees of *G*?
   (a) {{b,d}, {b,e}, {b,f}, {a,d}, {c,f}}
   (b) {{a,d}, {a,e}, {a,b}, {b,f}, {c,f}}
   (c) {{a,d}, {a,e}, {b,d}, {b,f}, {c,f}, {c,e}}
   (d) {{a,e}, {b,e}, {c,e}, {d,e}, {f,e}}

15. Apply algorithm Spantree to each graph whose edge set is given below and either find one connected component or a spanning tree of the graph.
   (a) {{1,2}, {1,3}, {2,4}, {3,6}, {4,6}, {3,5}, {4,5}}
   (b) {{1,2}, {1,3}, {2,4}, {4,6}, {3,5}}
   (c) {{1,2}, {3,6}, {4,6}, {4,5}, {3,5}}
   (d) {{1,2}, {2,3}, {3,4}, {3,5}, {1,5}, {4,6}, {2,6}}

16. Apply algorithm Spantree to each graph whose edge set is given below and either find one connected component or a spanning tree of the graph.
   (a) {{a,b}, {e,d}, {b,c}, {d,f}, {a,c}, {e,f}}
   (b) {{a,b}, {e,d}, {b,c}, {c,d}, {d,f}, {a,c}, {e,f}}
   (c) {{a,b}, {a,c}, {c,d}, {d,b}}
   (d) {{a,b}, {a,d}, {a,c}, {e,f}, {b,c}, {b,d}, {c,d}}

17. Without drawing the graphs, apply algorithm Spantree to the following adjacency lists and answer the following questions. Is the graph connected? If so, write down adjacency lists for a spanning tree. Is the graph a tree? (*Hint:* What is the spanning tree of a tree?) Does the graph have any cycles? (*Note:* You don't need to *find* any cycles—only answer whether there are cycles.)
   (a) 1: 2,3,5   2: 1,4   3: 1,4,6   4: 2,3   5: 1,6   6: 3,5
   (b) 1: 2,5   2: 1,3,6   3: 2,5,4   4: 3,6   5: 1,3   6: 2,4

(c)	1: 2,3	2: 1,3	3: 1,2	4: 5,6	5: 4,6	6: 4,5
(d)	1: 2	2: 1,3,4	3: 2,5	4: 2,6	5: 3	6: 4

18. Without drawing the graph, apply algorithm Spantree to each of the graphs given by adjacency lists below. Answer the following questions. Is the graph connected? If so, give adjacency lists of a spanning tree, and if not, give one connected component. Is the graph a tree? Does the graph have cycles?

(a)	*a: c*	*b: c*	*c: a,b,d*	*d: c,f,e*	*f: d*	*e: d*
(b)	*a: b,e*	*b: a,d,f*	*c: e,d*	*d: c,b,f*	*e: a,c*	*f: b,d*
(c)	*a: b,c,d*	*b: a,d*	*c: a,d*	*d: a,c,b*	*e: f*	*f: e*
(d)	*a: b,c,d,e*	*b: a,c,d,e*	*c: a,f,b*	*d: a,b,e,f*	*e: a,b,d,f*	*f: e,c,d*

Problems

1. A vertex has degree 1 if it is adjacent to exactly one other vertex. Prove by induction that a tree has at least two vertices of degree 1.

2. A graph with the property that removing any edge increases the number of connected components is called a *forest*. Show that the following statements are equivalent.
   (a) G is a forest.
   (b) There is at most one path between any two vertices of G.
   (c) G has no cycles.

3. Prove that a graph with no cycles is a tree if and only if there is no two-element set of its vertices that may be added to its edge set to give a new graph with no cycles.

4. Theorem 4 may be proved by applying algorithm Spantree to a tree G. The result is a spanning tree of G. You can prove that if G is a tree, any spanning tree of G contains every edge G contains. (In other words, any spanning tree of G must be G itself.) Give this proof.

5. The degree of a vertex in a simple graph is the number of edges it lies in. Show that a connected simple graph in which each vertex has degree 2 is a cycle.

6. Give a complete proof of Theorem 5(a).

7. Give a complete proof of Theorem 5(b).

8. Show that a connected graph with $m > 0$ vertices is a cycle if each pair of points may be joined by exactly two paths.

9. Use algorithm Spantree to explain why every tree has at least one vertex of degree 1.

10. Suppose that in algorithm Spantree we modify step 1 so that once we begin choosing edges e from a certain vertex v, then at each subsequent repetition of step 1 we choose an edge e connecting *this same* vertex v to a vertex y not in V' until such choices become impossible. (At this time we are free to choose a new vertex v in V'.) The resulting tree is called a *breadth first search* tree, and the process of constructing the tree is called *breadth first search*.
    (a) Determine whether or not breadth first search was used in Example 5.
    (b) How do breadth first search and adjacency lists relate?
    (c) Prove by induction on the number of vertices in the tree that at each stage of construction of a breadth first search tree, the path from vertex x to vertex y in the

tree has no more edges than any other path from x to y in the graph. In other words, prove that the path from x to y in the tree is a shortest path from x to y in the graph. (*Note:* This part of the problem arises again in the next section; some additional concepts introduced there make it easier.)

11. Suppose that in applying step 1 of algorithm Spantree, we always choose from all members of V' the vertex v most recently added to V' and adjacent to something not in V'. Then our spanning tree is called a *depth first search* tree, and the process of constructing the tree is called *depth first search*.
    (a) Construct a depth first search tree for the graph of Example 5.
    (b) A traditional rule of thumb for finding your way out of a maze is to place your left hand on the wall beside you and start walking, never moving your hand away from the wall and going wherever the wall leads you. Explain how this relates to depth first search.

Section 8-2
Rooted Trees

A The Concept of a Rooted Tree

In many applications of trees, the vertices represent possible stages of some process we are carrying out. One of these vertices can be singled out as representing the start of the process.

> A tree in which a vertex has been singled out
> is called a **rooted tree,** and the vertex
> singled out is called the **root.**

The use of the word *node* in place of the word *vertex* is especially prevalent in the literature about rooted trees. The tree diagrams we drew to represent the possible ways to carry out a sequence of steps are examples of rooted trees. Figure 5 shows the rooted tree we drew in Chapter 4 to describe the following simple multistage process. We flip a coin. If it comes up heads, we roll a die; if it comes up tails, we flip it again.

Figure 5

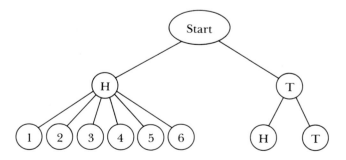

Basic Terminology

When a person's descendants don't intermarry, the family tree diagram of all the descendants is another example of a rooted tree. In fact, adopting the language of family trees for rooted trees improves our understanding of them. In Figure 6 we have drawn a typical rooted tree which we will use to illustrate this language

Figure 6

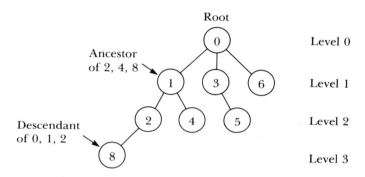

By Theorem 1 there is one and only one path from r to a chosen vertex x in the tree. We say that y is an **ancestor** of x and x is a **descendant** of y if y is on the path from the root r to the vertex x. In Figure 5, for example, vertex 8 is a descendant of vertex 1, and vertex 1 is an ancestor of vertex 8. Vertex 4 is *not* an ancestor of vertex 8. We don't, however, call a vertex an ancestor or descendant of itself. We say that a descendant x of a vertex y is a **child** of y and y is a **parent** of x if x and y are connected by an edge of the tree. Thus 8 is a child of 2, but 8 is not a child of vertex 1 or vertex 0. Vertex 2 is a parent of vertex 8, and vertex 1 is a parent of vertex 2, but vertex 1 is not a parent of vertex 8. In our picture we see vertices with 0, 1, 2, or 3 children, but each vertex other than the root has one and only one parent. In fact, this is a fundamental property of rooted trees.

Theorem 6 In a rooted tree, each vertex other than the root has one and only one parent.

Proof There is one and only one path from the root to a vertex x. On that path, only one vertex is adjacent to x in the tree. (We would get a cycle if two vertices were adjacent to x.) Thus x has one and only one parent. ∎

In a family, if person A is an ancestor of person B and person B is an ancestor of person C, then A is an ancestor of C. Further, we don't call a person an ancestor of himself or herself. In the language of Chapter 3, we've just said that the ancestor relation is transitive and irreflexive. A transitive irreflexive relation is called a *partial ordering*. Thus the ancestor relation is a partial ordering in a family with no intermarriage. The same holds true for the ancestor relation for rooted trees.

Theorem 7   The ancestor relation and descendant relation of a rooted tree are partial orderings of the vertex set of the tree.

Proof   By definition, the ancestor relation is irreflexive. To show that the ancestor relation is transitive, suppose x is an ancestor of y and y is an ancestor of z in the rooted tree with root r. The one and only one path from r to z contains y. The portion of this path from r to y is the one and only one path from r to y, so it contains x. Therefore x is on the path from r to z and is an ancestor of z. The argument for the descendant relation is similar.   ∎

Internal and External Nodes

A node of a tree with no children
is called an **external node.**

It may also be called a *leaf* or a *terminal node;* other nodes are called *internal* (or *interior*) nodes. Thus 0, 1, 2, and 3 are internal nodes of the tree of Figure 2, and 8, 4, 5, and 6 are external nodes of this tree. People often draw circles for internal nodes and squares for external nodes, as we show in Figure 7.

Figure 7

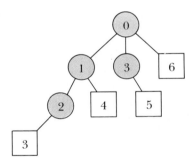

Levels

The drawing of the tree in Figure 6 suggests that the vertices of a tree fall into levels; the parent/child relation lets us make this idea precise.

The **level** of the root node is 0; the **level** of any
other node is one plus the level of its parent.

This recursively defines the level of any vertex. (In other words, we could prove by mathematical induction that this assigns one and only one integer, called the *level*, to each vertex.) In Figure 6 we have indicated the levels of the vertices. The **height** or **depth** of the tree is the largest of the levels of the vertices; it is said to be infinite if there is no largest level.

The terminology also suggests how we can draw a graph of any rooted tree. First draw a circle for the root. Next draw a row of circles below the root for the level 1 vertices and connect them to their parent. Now draw a row of circles for the level 2 vertices, putting the children of a given level 1 vertex in a row directly below it. Connect vertices to their parents and repeat the process. In this way, we can draw the graph so that we descend along lines of the graph to get from a vertex to one of its descendants. This process can be carried out so that the edges never cross over each other, so our rooted tree looks just like the root system of a natural tree. If we turn it upside down, it looks just like the branch system of a natural tree. This similarity is the reason trees got their name.

EXAMPLE 6 Draw the rooted trees that result from choosing first vertex 2 and then vertex 6 as roots in the tree shown in Figure 8.

Figure 8 A tree.

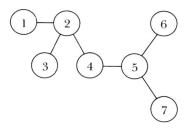

Solution The two rooted trees appear in Figure 9. ■

Figure 9 Two rooted trees from the same tree.

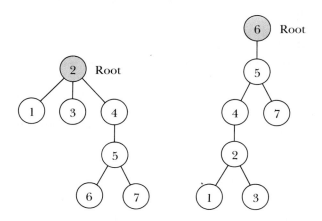

▣ *Binary Trees*

A special kind of rooted tree called a *binary tree* arises when we analyze a sequence of decisions with two (or sometimes three) possibilities. Figure 10 shows the binary tree of possible outcomes a tennis match could have. Notice that each internal node of the tree has exactly two children. Notice also how edges going left have a different meaning from edges going right.

Figure 10   A "best two out of three" tennis match.

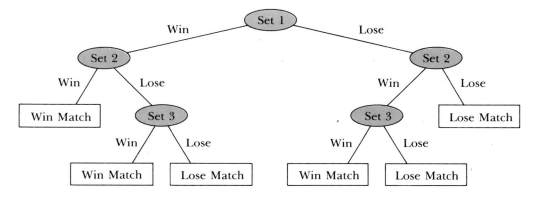

The Concept of a Binary Tree

A **binary tree** is a rooted tree in which each
internal node has exactly two children,
one designated a right child and one
designated a left child.

In Figure 11(a), node 1 is the root, node 2 is the left child of the root, and node 4 is the right child of node 3. (See Problem 8 for an alternate definition of a binary tree.)

The binary tree in Figure 11(b) is a *different* binary tree, for in it, vertex 3 is the *left* child of vertex 1 and vertex 2 is the *right* child of vertex 1. The **right** (or left) **subtree** of a vertex consists of the right (or left) child of the vertex and all its descendants; there is a triangle around the right subtree of vertex 3 in Figure 11(a). The binary trees we have drawn so far have all their external vertices at two successive levels (levels 2 and 3 in the examples). A well-balanced binary tree is one whose external nodes are at the same level or at two successive levels. We shall draw an unbalanced tree later.

Binary Search

Recall the Binary Search algorithm for determining whether (and where) a target word is in an alphabetically-ordered list of words. Figure 12 shows how we can

Figure 11 Two different binary trees.

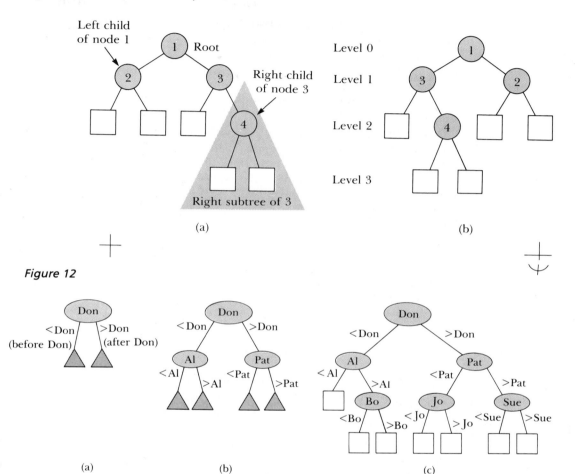

(a)

(b)

Figure 12

(a)

(b)

(c)

use a binary tree to illustrate the steps of Binary Search on the list Al, Bo, Don, Jo, Pat, Sue. When a list has $2n$ entries, we shall start our search at entry n; when it has $2n + 1$ entries, we shall use entry $n + 1$ as the starting point. We use a slightly different (and somewhat less efficient) version of Binary Search here from the version introduced in Chapter 5; with this version, the pictures are quite suggestive. Each time we compare our target word to a word in the list, we determine whether the target comes before, comes after, or equals the word we are examining.

Tree (a) shows how we begin our binary search. We find Don if Don is our target. We start a new binary search on part of the list to the *left* of Don if our target comes before Don. We start a new binary search on the part of the list to the *right* of Don if the name comes after Don. The triangle denotes an "unexplored" portion of the tree.

In tree (b) we see two different possibilities. We pick Al as the starting point in the list Al, Bo. If the target comes after Al, there is still a possible place for it to the right of Al, so we draw a triangle. If the target comes before Al, there is no room for it in the list since Al is first, so we draw an empty rectangle indicating that the target is not in the list.

Tree (c) shows all the other possibilities for finding or not finding an element in the list.

Notice that the tree we constructed is well-balanced. We can prove by induction on n that the binary tree representing binary search on an n-element (alphabetically) ordered list is well-balanced. Thus, if its external nodes are at level k and perhaps $k + 1$, the tree has at least $1 + 2 + 2^2 + \cdots + 2^{k-1}$ internal nodes and at most $1 + 2 + 2^2 + \cdots + 2^{k-1} + 2^k$ internal nodes. Since each element of the list appears in some internal node, using the formula

$$1 + r + r^2 + \cdots + r^n = \frac{1 - r^{n+1}}{1 - r}$$

for the sum of a geometric series (discussed in Chapter 5 and Chapter 7) gives

$$2^k - 1 \leq n \leq 2^{k+1} - 1$$

Adding 1 and taking logarithms gives

$$k \leq \log_2(n + 1) \leq k + 1$$

Since the number of levels of the tree is the maximum number of comparisons we need in order to find whether (and where) an element is in the list, we see from the tree that binary search on an n-element list takes at most $\log_2(n + 1)$ comparisons. Thus, for example, if n is about 1000, we need at most $10 = \log_2(1024)$ comparisons to find an entry with binary search, whereas we might need as many as 1000 comparisons to search the list sequentially (that is, one entry at a time in order).

Binary Search Trees

Although binary search allows us to quickly determine whether or where a word is in an ordered list, if we find a word (say Abe for the list of Figure 12) *not* in the list and try to insert it where binary search says it should go (before Al in the list of Figure 12), we might have to move most or all elements of the list to make room for it. This means that inserting a word into the correct place could be quite time-consuming. Figure 12 suggests another strategy. If there were some way we could store the words in a tree rather than just a list, then to insert Abe we would convert Al's left child to an internal node, write in Abe, and give this node two empty children. Similarly, to insert Zoe in the list we would convert Sue's right child to an internal node, write in Zoe, and give this node two empty children.

The scheme we just described will give us a structure for storing an ordered list of n data items that usually lets us test for membership in the list in computer time proportional to $\log_2(n)$ and also add elements that we have discovered are not members to the list in an amount of time that doesn't increase at all as the list increases in length. The structure we have found is called a **binary search tree.** A binary search tree for a list L of words (or any other totally ordered set L) is a binary tree whose internal nodes are in a one-to-one correspondence with the elements of L in such a way that each nonempty node has the following property, called the *binary search property:*

A node has the **binary search property** if all
elements corresponding to its left (or right)
subtree come before (or after) its element in order.

Notice that at each stage of the construction of Figure 12, each vertex had the binary search property. Based on the binary search property, we may use algorithm Searchtree below to look for a word in a binary search tree.

Algorithm Searchtree
　　Input　A binary search tree and a word.
　　Output　The word *found* and the location if the word is in the tree.
　　　　　　The word *not* and the location where the word belongs if the word is not in the tree.
　Procedure　If the word is the same as the word in the root, then output *found* and the location of the root.
　　　　　　Otherwise, if the root has no children, output *not* and the location of the root.
　　　　　　Otherwise, if the word comes after the word in the root, apply Searchtree to the right subtree of the root.
　　　　　　Otherwise, apply Searchtree to the left subtree of the root.

Unfortunately, it is possible to construct unbalanced binary search trees. In Figure 13, we show the result of inserting Al into the *empty* binary search tree— the tree with one empty node—and then inserting Bo, then Don, and so on through the list of Figure 12. To learn whether Tom is in this tree, we would have to examine each internal node, just as if we were to go through the list one element at a time. However, by using probability it is possible to show that *on the average,* a search in a binary search tree requires only $O(\log_2(n))$ comparisons.

Figure 13   A skewed binary search tree.

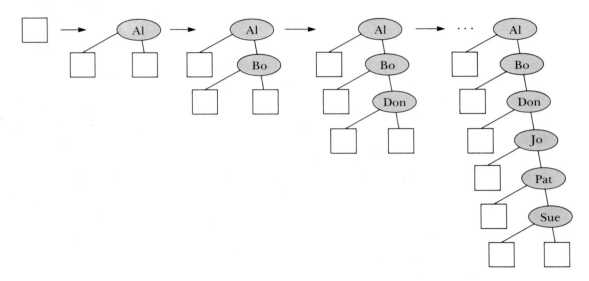

Concepts Review

1. A tree in which a vertex has been singled out is called a _____ tree and the vertex singled out is called the _____.

2. The vertex y is a(n) _____ of the vertex x, and the vertex x is a(n) _____ of the vertex y if y is on the _____ path from x to the root of the rooted tree.

3. A descendant x of a vertex y is called a(n) _____ of y if y and x are connected by an edge.

4. If x is a child of y, then y is a(n) _____ of x.

5. In a rooted tree, each vertex other than the root has _____ _____ _____ _____ parent.

6. The _____ relation and _____ relation of a rooted tree are partial orderings.

7. A node with no children is called a(n) _____ node or a(n) _____ node.

8. A node of a rooted tree with at least one child is called a(n) _____ node.

9. The _____ of a node is one more than the _____ of its parent.

10. The _____ or _____ of a finite tree is the largest of the levels of its vertices.

11. A(n) _____ tree is a rooted tree in which each internal node has two children, one designated as a(n) _____ child and the other designated as a(n) _____ child.

12. The right subtree of a node in a binary tree consists of the _____ _____ of the node together with all its _____.

13. A binary search tree for a list *L* of words has its internal nodes in a one-to-one correspondence with the elements of *L* in such a way that all words in the left subtree of a node _____ _____ the word in that node and all words in the right subtree of a node _____ _____ the word in that node.

Exercises

A   1. Draw the rooted tree that represents the process of flipping a coin three times.

2. Draw the rooted tree that represents the process of choosing a sequence of three bits. A bit is either a 0 or a 1.

3. Draw each of the trees whose edge set is listed below as a rooted tree with root vertex 1.
   (a) {{2,5}, {2,6}, {2,7}, {1,2}, {1,3}, {4,8}, {4,9}, {1,4}}
   (b) {{2,1}, {3,1}, {4,1}, {5,1}, {5,6}, {5,7}}
   (c) {{2,5}, {4,5}, {5,6}, {1,5}, {1,3}, {1,7}}

4. Draw each of the trees whose edge set is listed below as a rooted tree with root vertex *a*.
   (a) {{a,b}, {a,e}, {c,h}, {e,h}, {d,g}, {f,g}, {a,g}}
   (b) {{a,h}, {b,c}, {c,e}, {c,g}, {d,g}, {f,g}, {e,h}}
   (c) {{a,b}, {c,e}, {d,e}, {e,h}, {f,a}, {g,a}, {e,a}}

5. In Figure 14, vertex 1 is taken as the root vertex. What are the children of vertex 2? The ancestors of vertex 2? The descendants of vertex 2?

Figure 14

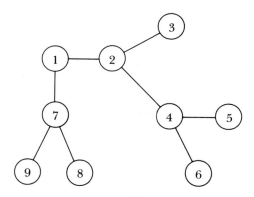

6. In Figure 14, vertex 5 is taken as the root. What are the children of vertex 2? The ancestors of vertex 2? The descendants of vertex 2?

7. In Figure 14, vertex 1 is taken as the root. What is the level of each vertex of the tree? What is the height of the tree?

8. In Figure 14, vertex 5 is taken as the root. What is the level of each vertex of the tree? What is the height of the tree?

9. In Figure 14, vertex 1 is taken as the root. What are the internal vertices of the tree? What are the external vertices of the tree?

10. In Figure 14, vertex 5 is taken as the root. What are the internal nodes of the resulting rooted tree? What are the external nodes of the resulting rooted tree?

B   11. In the binary tree of Figure 15, answer the following questions:
(a) What is the right child of vertex 3?
(b) What is the left child of vertex 4?
(c) What nodes are in the left subtree of vertex 2?
(d) What nodes are in the right subtree of vertex 3?

Figure 15

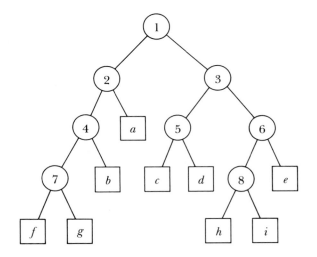

12. In the binary tree of Figure 15, answer the following questions:
(a) What is the left child of vertex 6?
(b) What is the right child of vertex 6?
(c) What nodes are in the left subtree of vertex 1?
(d) What nodes are in the right subtree of vertex 6?

13. Draw the binary tree that shows the possible outcomes of the "best three out of five games" for baseball playoffs.

14. Draw the binary tree that shows the possible outcomes of a "modified best three out of five" match, in which you must win two games in a row or three games out of five to win the match.

15. Draw the binary tree that illustrates the possible outcomes of binary search on the list

Abe, Al, Don, Hal, Jo, Pat, Sue, Tom

16. Draw the binary tree that illustrates the possible outcomes of binary search on the list

Abe, Al, Don, Hal, Jo, Pat, Sue, Tom, Zoe

17. Show the binary tree that results from adding Paul and Sam in that order to the binary search tree you constructed in Exercise 15. (Do this by converting external nodes to internal nodes.) Will this be the same tree you would get if you redid Exercise 15 with Paul and Sam in the list of Exercise 15 in alphabetical order?

18. Show the binary tree that results from adding Paul and Sam to the binary search tree you constructed in Exercise 16. (Do this by converting external nodes to internal nodes.) Will this be the same as the tree you would get if you redid Exercise 16 with Paul and Sam in the list in alphabetical order?

19. Beginning with an empty binary search tree, show the tree that results from inserting the words *egg, bread, cinnamon, vanilla, milk,* and *sugar* into the tree in that order, one at a time.

20. Beginning with an empty binary search tree, show the tree that results from inserting the words of Exercise 19 in reverse alphabetical order into the tree, one at a time.

21. Find two other ways to insert the words of Exercise 19 into a binary search tree, one word at a time, so that the result looks exactly the same as the tree of Exercise 19.

22. Explain why there are no other ways to insert the words of Exercise 19 into a tree to give a result that looks exactly the same as the tree of Exercise 20.

Problems

1. Some nodes of a tree will be internal nodes no matter which vertex we choose as a root. Which vertices are these?

2. Explain how intermarriage among the descendants of an individual can keep the family tree of descendants of that person from being a rooted tree.

3. Prove by induction that the tree illustrating the outcomes of binary search on an ordered list of n items is well balanced.

4. A binary tree is called *height balanced* or simply *balanced* if it is a single node or if, for each node, the heights of its right and left subtrees differ by at most one and the right and left subtrees are balanced. Show that a well-balanced tree is height-balanced but a height-balanced tree need not be well-balanced.

5. Prove that the definition of level assigns one and only one number, called the *level*, to each vertex of a finite rooted tree.

6. A binary tree is called a *full* or *complete* binary tree if all its external nodes are at the same level. If a full binary tree has m levels, how many nodes does it have?

7. Prove that the number of external nodes of a binary tree is one more than the number of internal nodes.

8. Here is an alternate definition of a binary tree. Since it is not obvious until part (b) that this defines essentially the same kind of tree we've been working with, we refer to it as a *bintree* for now. A bintree is either empty or consists of a root node, a left subtree which is a bintree, and a right subtree which is a bintree.

(a) Explain why this recursively defines the concept of a bintree.

(b) Describe a one-to-one correspondence between bintrees and binary trees in which the bintree "looks like" the internal nodes of the binary tree.

(c) Describe how to prove by induction that you have defined a one-to-one correspondence.

(d) Show that with your correspondence from part (b), if x and y in the binary tree correspond to x' and y' in the bintree, then x is a left (right) child of y if and only if x' is the root of the left (right) subtree of y'.

9. A breadth first search tree was defined in Problem 10 of Section 8-1. It is a rooted tree whose root vertex is the element x given as input to the algorithm. A *cross edge* for a rooted spanning tree of a graph G is an edge $\{x, y\}$ of G such that neither is x a descendant of y nor is y a descendant of x.

(a) Show that after a breadth first search of a graph G, each edge of the graph is either a tree edge or a cross edge.

(b) Show that the levels of the vertices of G in the rooted tree that comes from breadth first search are the distances of the vertices from x in G. Relate this to Problem 10(b) in Section 8-1.

10. Depth first search is defined in Problem 11 of Section 8-1. Cross edges are defined in Problem 9 above. Show that there are no cross edges for a depth first search spanning tree of a graph.

11. An *articulation point* of a graph is a vertex with the property that if you remove it and all edges containing it from the graph, the resulting graph has more connected components than before. Explain why x is an articulation point if and only if in a depth first search tree centered at x, x has more than one child.

Section 8-3
Using Rooted Trees
in Computing

A Traversing Trees

A typical use for a list of names is a class list for a course. Two things we want to do with such a list are to find if someone is in the class and to add someone to the class. We have seen how we can do both these operations quickly by storing the list in a binary search tree. When we are keeping track of students, another thing we shall want to do is to get the list in alphabetical order. The binary search tree we constructed in the last section is shown in Figure 16. It hardly has the appearance of being in alphabetical order. However, thinking about smaller examples suggests a way to see a semblance of alphabetical order in a binary search tree.

Figure 16

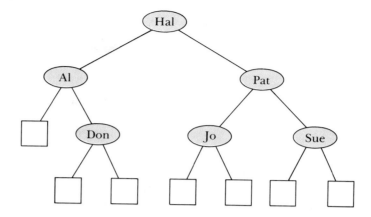

For a tree with one nonempty node, we just write the name in the node. For a node with nonempty children, the left child comes first, then the root node, and then the right child.

Printing the Words in a Binary Search Tree in Alphabetical Order

More generally, by the definition of a binary search tree, the contents of the entire left subtree of a node precede the contents of that node in alphabetical order. Also, the entire contents of the right subtree follow the contents of that node in alphabetical order. Thus, so long as we have an algorithm that will print the left subtree in order, then print the root, and then print the right subtree in order, we will be able to use it to print out the contents of the tree in alphabetical order. Fortunately, this is enough of a description to allow us to write down an algorithm we shall call PrintInOrder, which takes a binary search tree and prints the contents of its nodes out in alphabetical order. We have written the algorithm so that it applies to any binary tree, not only to a binary search tree.

Algorithm PrintInOrder

      Input: A binary tree T.

    Output: A sorted list of the contents of the nodes.

  Procedure: If the root of T is internal, then apply PrintInOrder to the left subtree of the root.

                  Print the contents of the root, if any.

                  If the root of T is internal, then apply PrintInOrder to the right subtree of the root.

EXAMPLE 7   Write down the sequence of letters produced by PrintInOrder when it is applied to the tree in Figure 17.

Figure 17

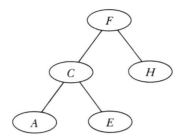

Solution   Because the root is internal, we first apply PrintInOrder to the subtree with root node C. Because C is internal, we first apply PrintInOrder to the subtree with root node A. (Because A is external, we do not attempt to apply PrintInOrder to its nonexistent left subtree.) Next, we print A, and because node A is external, we have completed all steps of PrintInOrder applied to the tree with root A. Thus we go on to the next step. That is, we return to applying PrintInOrder to the tree with root node C. The next step is to print the contents of the root of this subtree, so we print out C. Next we apply PrintInOrder to the tree with root node E. This node is external, so we print its contents (E) and return to applying PrintInOrder to the tree with root node C. However, we have carried out the last step of *this* application of PrintInOrder, so now the next step will continue the application of PrintInOrder to the tree with root node F. We have completed applying PrintInOrder to the left subtree of the root, so our next step is to print the contents of the root node (F). Following that, the next step is applying PrintInOrder to the tree with root node H. Node H is external, so we print it out. But now, when we return to continue the application of PrintInOrder to the tree with root Node F, we have carried out the last step of this application of PrintInOrder and have no other application to return to, so we stop. The sequence of letters we print is $ACEFH$.   ■

EXAMPLE 8   What is printed when we apply PrintInOrder to the tree of Figure 16?

Solution   The details of the work are similar to those of Example 7, except that when we reach an external node, it contains nothing for us to print, so we return to the previous application of PrintInOrder. Thus we print out the sequence Al, Don, Hal, Jo, Pat, Sue.   ■

Algorithm PrintInOrder carries out one step at each external node (printing the contents if any) and three steps at each internal node (initiating work on the left subtree, printing the contents if any, and initiating work on the right subtree). Thus, an upper bound on the amount of computer time it takes is proportional to the number of nodes of the tree. This means that if we keep a list such as a class list in a binary search tree, we can not only quickly add a name to the list and find a name in the list, but also print out the list in an amount of time proportional to the length of the list.

Tree Traversals

We say we are **traversing** a tree when we examine each of its vertices individually. A **tree traversal algorithm** is thus an algorithm in which we examine each vertex individually. Algorithm PrintInOrder is an example of a tree traversal algorithm.

In briefest outline, our printing algorithm reads

> Traverse left subtree
> Process current node
> Traverse right subtree

Notice that in this outline we are allowing any kind of process to be applied to the current node.

Since the action we are taking is in between the left and right traversals, the name **inorder tree traversal algorithm** is appropriate for any algorithm that can be outlined in this way. An algorithm whose outline is

> Process current node
> Traverse left subtree
> Traverse right subtree

is called a **preorder tree traversal algorithm,** and an algorithm whose outline is

> Traverse left subtree
> Traverse right subtree
> Process current node

is called a **postorder tree traversal algorithm.** Notice that we could shorten the preorder and postorder algorithms to a two-line outline each:

Preorder	*Postorder*
Process current node	Traverse all subtrees of current node
Traverse all subtrees of current node	Process current node

This shows that it is natural to talk about preorder and postorder traversals of arbitrary rooted trees. Inorder traversals, however, make the most sense only in the context of binary trees. Typically, when we are traversing a tree there is some natural order in which the children of a vertex occur. Such a tree is called an **ordered tree.** With an ordered tree, we take the children in this order when traversing the tree.

Applications of Preorder and Postorder Traversals

Preorder, inorder, and postorder traversals arise in many ways in computer science. Our next two examples show how preorder and postorder traversals relate to the evaluation of formulas. The examples deal only with well-formed formulas, introduced in Chapter 5. The usual formulas of arithmetic require more work but use similar principles.

EXAMPLE 9   A binary well-formed formula (of integer arithmetic) is either a number symbol, a variable symbol, or a formula of the form (*f*<operator>*g*) whose *f* and *g* are well-formed formulas and whose operator is +, −, or ·. We construct the tree of the formula by the rules:

(1) The tree of a number or variable symbol is a node containing that symbol.
(2) The tree of a formula of the form (*f*<operator>*g*) is formed by constructing a node and writing the operator into it, constructing the tree of *f* as the left subtree of this node and constructing the tree of *g* as the right subtree of this node.

Show how the tree of the formula ((3 + 7) · (17 − 6)) is constructed. In what order are we traversing the nodes of the tree as we construct it?

Solution   The steps of the construction are shown in Figure 18. The order is that of a preorder traversal.   ■

Figure 18

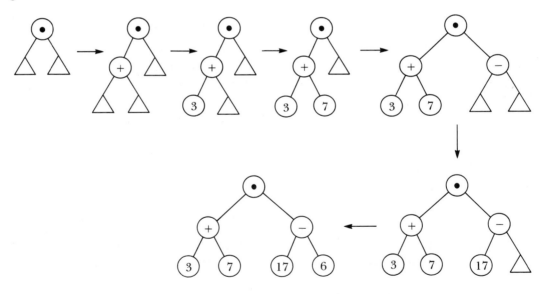

EXAMPLE 10   Carry out a postorder traversal of Figure 18 and, at each internal node, process that node by replacing the symbol in it by the result of performing that operation on the numbers in the child nodes. What does the result represent?

Solution   We show in Figure 19 only the steps representing internal nodes. The number in the root of the final tree is the value of the formula.   ■

Figure 19

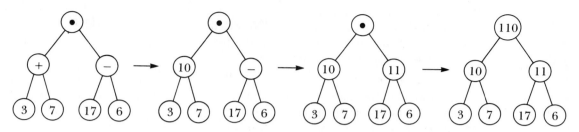

⬛ Two-Three Trees

The major disadvantage of binary search trees in computer applications is that, although on the average we need to perform only $O(n\log_2(n))$ operations to construct an n-node binary search tree, it is possible for a list of data items (in alphabetical order, for example) to require on the order of n^2 operations to construct, or n operations to search for something in, an n-node binary search tree. By using a slightly more complicated tree we shall call a binary-ternary search tree, we can overcome this disadvantage.

Binary-Ternary Trees

A **binary-ternary tree** or **B-T tree** is a rooted tree in which each internal node has either two children, one called the left child and one called the right child, or three children, one called the left child, one called the middle child, and one called the right child. A typical binary-ternary tree is shown in Figure 20, where the internal nodes are shown as circles and the external nodes are shown as rectangles.

A node is called a **binary node** if it has two children and a **ternary node** if it has three children. Typical binary and ternary nodes are shown in Figure 20.

Figure 20   A typical binary-ternary tree.

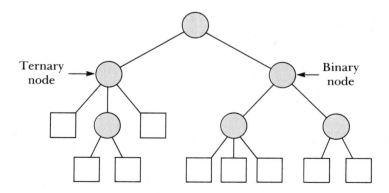

Binary-Ternary Search Trees

A **binary-ternary search tree** for an ordered list of words is a binary-ternary tree in which each binary node is associated with one word of the list and each ternary node is associated with two words of the list (we say a node *contains* the words associated with it) in such a way that:

- Each word in the left subtree of a node comes before the contents of the node;
- Each word in the middle subtree of a ternary node comes between the two words contained in the node; and
- Each word in the right subtree of a node comes after the contents of that node.

A typical binary-ternary search tree using alphabet letters in place of words is shown in Figure 21. The numbering of the internal nodes is there simply so we can refer to specific nodes later on.

Figure 21   A typical binary-ternary search tree.

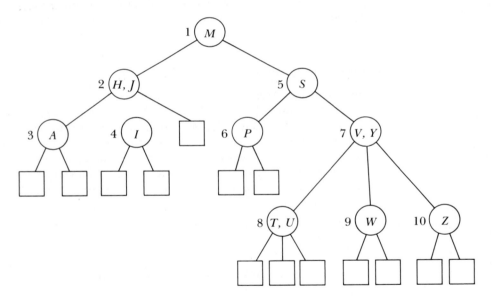

The algorithm for finding a word in a B-T search tree is analogous to the algorithm for finding a word in a binary search tree.

EXAMPLE 11   Describe the steps made in searching for the symbol *I* in the B-T search tree of Figure 21.

Solution   *I* comes before *M*, so we look in node 1's left child. *I* comes between *H* and *J*, so we look in node 2's middle child. We find *I* in this node. Using the numbers to the left of the nodes, we can describe the sequence of nodes examined as 1,2,4. ∎

EXAMPLE 12 Describe the sequence of nodes examined in searching for the letter X in the tree of Figure 21.

Solution X comes after M, so we examine node 5. X comes after S, so we examine node 7. X comes between V and Y, so we examine node 9. X comes after W, so we examine the right child of node 9 and discover that X is not in the tree. ∎

Two-Three Trees

Now it is possible to add words to a B-T search tree in a manner similar to the way we added words to a binary search tree. If we do so, we will have the same kinds of problems we had with binary search trees. By using a technique known as *node splitting*, we will instead come up with special kinds of B-T trees called *2-3 trees* (read "two, three" trees, not "two minus three" trees). This is a special case of a data structure called a B-tree, which is the basis for modern file management software for computers.

In the process of adding a word to a 2-3 tree, we temporarily allow one node of the tree to become **quaternary**—that is, to have four children (a first, a second, a third, and a fourth child)—and to contain three data items. When this happens, we no longer have a 2-3 tree. The technique of splitting is what allows us to convert the tree back to a binary-ternary tree. To add a word to a 2-3 tree, we search for the word until we arrive at an empty node. Then, rather than putting the word into the empty node, we put the word into the *parent* of the empty node and give the parent one more empty child. Two possibilities occur, as shown in Figure 22. In part (a) of the figure, you see that if the parent is binary, then inserting the new item (L in the figure) simply makes the node ternary, and we are done. If the parent node is ternary, as in part (b) of the figure, then inserting the new item (K in the figure) has given us a quaternary node, so we no longer have a B-T tree (or a 2-3 tree).

A quaternary node has three data items. To split a quaternary node, we replace it with two binary nodes containing the first and last data items, put the middle data item into *its* parent node, and make both binary nodes into children of this parent. As Figure 23 shows, carrying this process out on the tree of Figure 22(b) gives us a tree with a different quaternary node.

It may not appear that we have accomplished much, but we now have a quaternary node for the root of the tree. We give the root a new and temporarily empty parent, getting the tree in part (a) of Figure 24, and then we split the quaternary node, promoting the data item K into the root. This is shown in part (b) of Figure 24.

Thus, whenever we have a quaternary node, we may split it and move its middle data item up one level. If we move the middle data item into a binary node, then that binary node becomes ternary, and we are done. Otherwise we keep splitting until the root is quaternary and then split the root, as in Figure 24.

Figure 22   Inserting a new letter into a 2-3 tree.

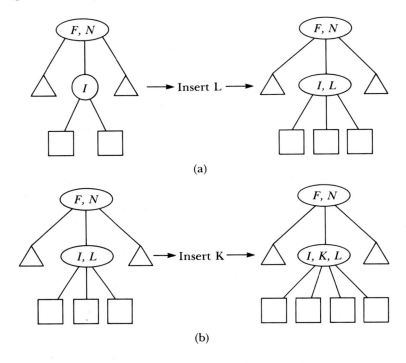

(a)

(b)

Figure 23   The result of splitting the *IKL* node and promoting the data item *K*.

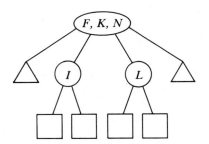

The Time Needed for Operations on 2-3 Trees

Now we can define the term 2-3 tree. A **2-3 tree** is the result of starting with an empty node and constructing a B-T tree by inserting a list of data items, one at a time, as described above. Notice that when we split the root, all the levels of *all* the other vertices go up by 1. This lets us use mathematical induction to prove the following theorem.

Figure 24 Adding an empty root to allow us to split a quaternary root and promote its middle data item.

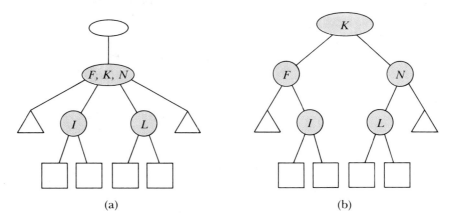

(a)   (b)

Theorem 8   In a 2-3 tree, all the external nodes have the same level.

Proof   Problem 3.   ∎

We showed that if all the external nodes of a binary tree are at level n or level $n + 1$, then the tree has between $2^n - 1$ and $2^{n+1} - 1$ interior nodes. In much the same way, we may prove the next theorem.

Theorem 9   In a 2-3 tree of depth n (that is, whose external nodes all have level n) the number of internal nodes is at least $2^{n+1} - 1$ and at most $\dfrac{3^{n+1} - 1}{2}$ nodes.

Proof   Problem 4.   ∎

From Theorem 9, we may derive Theorem 10.

Theorem 10   A 2-3 tree with m nodes has depth at most $\log_2(m + 1) - 1$ and at least $\log_3 (2m + 1) - 1$.

Proof   Problem 5.   ∎

Theorem 10 tells us that to locate an item in a 2-3 tree containing n data items or to insert an item into a 2-3 tree containing n data items takes at most $O(\log_2(n))$ operations. Thus constructing an n-node 2-3 tree takes at most $n \log_2(n)$ operations. By modifying inorder traversal so that it can apply to 2-3 trees, we can use 2-3 trees as the basis for a sorting algorithm to sort n data items in $O(n \log_2(n))$ steps. Thus 2-3 trees allow us to achieve all the goals we have set for the use of binary trees.

Concepts Review

1. When we examine each of the vertices of a tree individually, we are _____ the tree.

2. A(n) _____ tree traversal algorithm processes the current node, traverses the left subtree, and then traverses the right subtree.

3. A(n) _____ tree traversal traverses the left subtree of the current node, traverses the right subtree of the current node, and then processes the current node.

4. A(n) _____ tree traversal algorithm traverses the left subtree of the current node, processes the current node, and then traverses the right subtree of the current node.

5. A tree in which the children of a node occur in a certain order as the first child, second child, and so on is called a(n) _____ tree.

6. In a(n) _____-_____ tree, each internal node has either a right and a left child or a right, a middle, and a left child.

7. A(n) _____-_____ _____ tree has a word associated with each binary node and two words associated with each ternary node in such a way that the words associated with nodes in the left subtree of a vertex _____ _____ the word(s) in that vertex, the words associated with nodes in the middle subtree of a vertex are _____ the words in a ternary node, and the words associated with the nodes in the right subtree of a vertex _____ _____ the word(s) in that vertex.

8. A 2-3 tree is a special kind of _____-_____ search tree.

9. A node we split in inserting a word into a 2-3 tree is always a(n) _____ node, which prevents the tree from being a 2-3 tree.

10. A(n) _____-_____ tree is a B-T search tree formed by using the process of splitting quaternary nodes and converting binary nodes to ternary nodes.

11. A two-three tree with m nodes has depth at most _____ and at least _____.

Exercises

A
1. Write down the letters in the nodes of the tree in Figure 25 in the order they would be processed in an inorder tree traversal.

2. Write down the numbers in the nodes of the tree in Figure 26 in the order they would be processed in an inorder tree traversal.

3. Write down the letters in the tree in Figure 25 in the order they would be processed in a preorder tree traversal.

4. Write down the numbers in the nodes of the tree in Figure 26 in the order they would be processed in a preorder tree traversal.

Figure 25

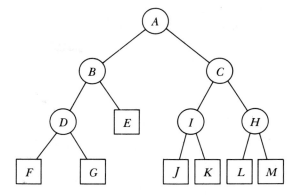

Figure 26

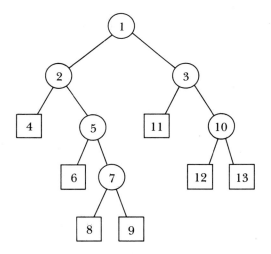

5. Write down the letters in the nodes in the tree of Figure 25 in the order they would be processed in a postorder tree traversal.

6. Write down the numbers in the nodes in the tree in Figure 26 in the order they would be processed in a postorder tree traversal.

7. Construct a binary search tree by starting with the empty tree and inserting the words *circle, square, sphere, rectangle, hexagon, pentagon, parallelogram,* and *triangle,* one at a time in that order. Write down the words in the tree in the order that they would be processed by an inorder tree traversal. What is special about this order?

8. Construct a binary search tree by starting with an empty tree and inserting the phrases *disk drive, tape drive, central processor, workstation, printer, plotter, display,* and *modem,* one at a time in that order. Write down the phrases in the tree in the order that they would be processed by an inorder tree traversal. What is special about this order?

9. The tree in Figure 27 shows the interrelationships among schools and departments in a hypothetical university. Write down the names of the nodes of the tree in preorder sequence. How does preorder sequence relate to the organization of a university catalog?

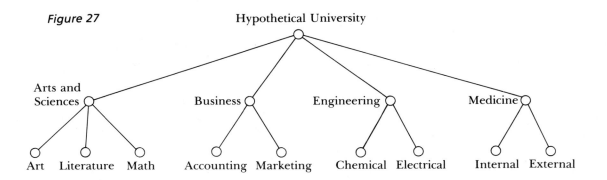

Figure 27

10. The tree in Figure 28 shows the relationship among the mowers, subassemblies, and parts of a hypothetical lawn-mower company. Write down the names of the nodes of the tree in preorder sequence. How does preorder sequence relate to the organization of a parts catalog?

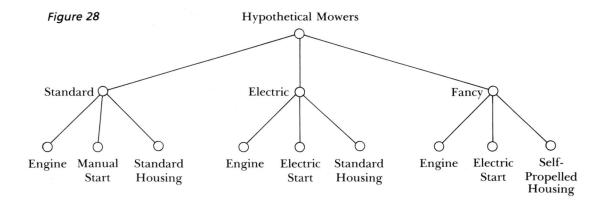

Figure 28

For each of the well-formed formulas in Exercises 11–22, write down the expression tree that corresponds to it.

11. $(43 - 26)$ **12.** $(3 + 7)$

13. $(43 + 77)$ **14.** $(7 - 3)$

15. $((17 + 3) \cdot 6)$

16. $((7 + 3) \cdot 41)$

17. $((17 + 2) - 4)$

18. $((7 - 3) + (2 \cdot 7))$

19. $((17 + 3) \cdot (14 - 2))$

20. $(((7 + 3) \cdot (2 - 1)) + (3 - (7 \cdot 2)))$

21. $(((17 + 3) \cdot (17 + 3)) \cdot (17 + 3))$

22. $(((7 + 1) \cdot (7 + 2)) \cdot (7 + 3))$

For each exercise referred to in Exercises 23–34, show the steps of evaluating the expression tree by a postorder traversal.

23. Exercise 11.

24. Exercise 12.

25. Exercise 13.

26. Exercise 14.

27. Exercise 15.

28. Exercise 16.

29. Exercise 17.

30. Exercise 18.

31. Exercise 19.

32. Exercise 20.

33. Exercise 21.

34. Exercise 22.

B **35.** In the binary-ternary tree in Figure 21, show the sequence of nodes examined in looking for the symbol T in the tree.

36. In the binary-ternary tree in Figure 21, show the sequence of nodes examined in looking for the symbol Z in the tree.

37. Show the sequence of nodes examined in looking for the symbol R in the tree of Figure 21.

38. Show the sequence of nodes examined in searching for the symbol D in the tree of Figure 21.

39. Show the tree that results from inserting the letter B into the 2-3 tree of Figure 29.

Figure 29

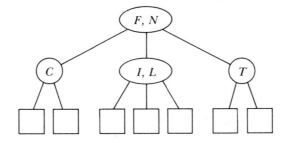

40. Show the tree that results from inserting the letter R into the 2-3 tree of Figure 29.

41. Show the tree that results from inserting the letter G into the 2-3 tree of Figure 29.

42. Show the tree that results from inserting the letter *M* into the 2-3 tree of Figure 29.

43. Write down nine words in alphabetical order. Show the 2-3 tree that results from beginning with an empty node and inserting the words, one at a time, in the order you have given. Now show the binary search tree you get by using the standard method for inserting words into a binary search tree, starting with an empty node and inserting the words, one at a time, in the order you have given.

44. Write down nine words in reverse alphabetical order. Show the 2-3 tree that results from beginning with an empty node and inserting these words, one at a time, in the order you have given. Now show the binary search tree you get by using the standard method for binary search trees, starting with an empty node and inserting the words, one at a time, in the order you have given.

Problems

1. What are the maximum and minimum possible number of nodes in a binary-ternary tree of depth *n*?

2. In a binary-ternary tree with one ternary node and depth *n*, where must the ternary node be to have the maximum possible number of vertices in the tree? What is this maximum possible number of vertices?

3. Prove Theorem 8.

4. Prove Theorem 9.

5. Prove Theorem 10.

6. Write out an algorithm for printing out the words in a 2-3 tree in alphabetical order.

7. Write out an algorithm for inserting a word into a 2-3 tree by the method of splitting when necessary.

8. Find two different binary search trees that give the same sequence of words when the words are printed out in the order of an inorder traversal.

9. Find two different binary search trees for which printing out the words in the order of a preorder traversal gives the same list. Could you find two such trees for a postorder traversal? Why?

10. Is it possible to find two different binary search trees such that when you print out their nodes in the order of a preorder traversal you get the same two lists, and when you print out their nodes in the order of an inorder traversal you get the same two lists?

11. Is it possible to find two different binary search trees such that when you print out their nodes in the order of a preorder traversal you get the same two lists, and when you print out their nodes in the order of a postorder traversal you get the same two lists?

12. A "two-pan balance" tells us that two objects have the same weight or which one is heavier. Given *n* coins, of which *n* − 1 are identical and one is lighter than the rest, what is the minimum number of weighings needed to find the light coin? If we do not

know that one coin is light, but only that one coin is different in weight, how many weighings are needed? (*Hint:* It is easier to get started if you assume that n is a power of two.)

Section 8-4
Minimizing Total Cost
and Path Length
in Spanning Trees

◰ Minimum Total Weight Spanning Trees

We began our study of spanning trees with the observation that a spanning tree of a graph representing a communications network allows us to use a minimum number of edges in communicating among all the nodes of the network. Since an edge represents a connection that must be built, each edge has a certain cost associated with it. Thus using a minimum number of edges lets us make our communications at a minimum cost. Since each edge represents a different real-world connection, and some real-world connections will be less costly to construct than others, different spanning trees will have different construction costs. What we want to construct, then, is a spanning tree of minimum cost. Other kinds of real-world problems are similar. If a bus company wants to introduce shuttle bus service among n cities (or n locations in a city), using a minimum number of buses but allowing a rider to get from any city to any other city, then a spanning tree of the graph of possible routes will allow the n locations to be connected with $n-1$ shuttle buses. Presumably, there is some demand (measured numerically as the number of people per day) for service between each pair of cities where a direct connection is possible. The bus company will want to serve as many customers as possible on *direct* routes, so it will want to choose the spanning tree that serves the *maximum* number of passengers possible on direct routes.

Weighted Graphs and Spanning Trees

In either of the two problems, we have a graph and we have a number associated with each edge. A graph that has a number $w(e)$ associated with each edge e is called a **weighted graph,** and $w(e)$ is called the **weight** of edge e. In Figure 30, we show the standard way to draw a weighted graph.

In these two problems, we also had a number associated with each spanning tree, namely the sum of the weights of its edges. In one problem, we wanted this sum to be a minimum and in the other problem we wanted the sum to be a

Figure 30   A weighted graph.

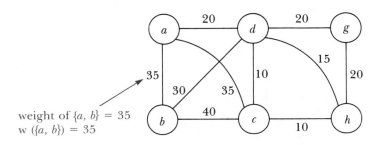

weight of $\{a, b\}$ = 35
w $(\{a, b\})$ = 35

maximum. It turns out that we can make the sum a maximum with a small change in the algorithm we use to make the sum a minimum. A **minimum total weight spanning tree** (often called a *minimum spanning tree*) of a weighted graph G is a spanning tree of G with the property that the sum of the weights of its edges is no more than the sum of the weights of the edges of each other spanning tree of G. The sum of the weights of the edges of a tree is called the **total weight** of the tree.

EXAMPLE 13   In Figure 30, the edge set $\{\{a,b\}, \{a,c\}, \{a,d\}, \{d,g\}, \{d,h\}\}$ is the edge set of a spanning tree. What is its total weight? Is this a minimum total weight spanning tree?

Solution   We see that $w(\{a,b\})$ = 35, $w(\{a,c\})$ = 35, $w(\{a,d\})$ = 20, $w(\{d,g\})$ = 20, and $w(\{d,h\})$ = 15, so the total weight is $35 + 35 + 20 + 20 + 15 = 125$. We can remove edge $\{a,c\}$ from the spanning tree and replace it with edge $\{d,c\}$. This reduces the total weight of the tree to 100. Thus the tree given is not a minimum total weight spanning tree.   ■

Finding Minimum Total Weight Spanning Trees

We can adapt algorithm Spantree to find spanning trees of minimum total weight. Algorithm MTWTree (for Minimum Total Weight *tree*) below will let us find a minimum total weight spanning tree. It is called a "greedy" algorithm because it always makes the least costly (most advantageous) choice possible, with no concern about blocking possible future choices.

Algorithm MTWTree
    Input: A weighted graph G with vertex set V and edge set E and a vertex x of G.
    Output: The vertex set V' and edge set E' of a minimum total weight spanning tree of the connected component of G containing x.
    Procedure: Start with $V' = \{x\}$, $E' = \varnothing$.

Repeat the steps below until there is no edge e connecting a vertex x in V' to a vertex y not in V'.

(1) Choose such an edge $e = \{x,y\}$ of minimum weight with $x \in V'$ and $y \notin V'$.

(2) Put y into V' and e into E'.

EXAMPLE 14   Find a minimum total weight spanning tree for the weighted graph shown in Figure 30. What is its total weight?

Solution   We shall start the process at $x = a$. Thus we begin with $V' = \{a\}$ and $E' = \varnothing$. The edge $\{a,d\}$ is the minimum weight edge with one vertex in V'. Thus we change V' to $\{a,d\}$ and E' to $\{\{a,d\}\}$. Now the least weight edge leaving V' is $\{d,c\}$, so V' becomes $\{a,d,c\}$ and E' becomes $\{\{a,d\}, \{d,c\}\}$. Now the least weight edge leaving V' is $\{c,h\}$, so V' becomes $\{a,d,c,h\}$ and E' becomes $\{\{a,d\}, \{d,c\},$ $\{c,h\}\}$. Now we have the two choices $\{d,g\}$ and $\{g,h\}$ of weight 20 for the minimum weight edge leaving V'. The algorithm doesn't tell us which to choose, so we choose whichever we please, say $\{d,g\}$, so V' is $\{a,d,c,g,h\}$ and E' is $\{\{a,d\}, \{d,c\}, \{c,h\},$ $\{d,g\}\}$. Finally, $\{d,b\}$ is now the least weight edge leaving V', so V' becomes V and E' becomes $\{\{a,d\}, \{d,c\}, \{c,h\}, \{d,g\}, \{b,d\}\}$. The total weight of the tree is 90. ∎

Why the Algorithm Works

In order to show that the algorithm always works, it will be convenient to introduce some extra notation. The sets V' and E' change each time we work through steps 1 and 2 of the algorithm. In the next theorem, we use V'_i to stand for the ith set V', and E'_i to stand for the ith set E'. Thus $V'_0 = \{x\}$ and $E'_0 = \varnothing$. We let e_i stand for the ith edge added to E', so $E_i = \{e_1, e_2, \ldots, e_i\}$ for $i = 1, 2, \ldots, |V| - 1$.

Theorem 11   Let E'_i stand for the ith edge set produced by the algorithm MTWTree from the graph G. Then for each i there is a minimum cost spanning tree whose edge set contains E'_i.

Proof   First note that E'_0 is empty, so there must be a minimum cost spanning tree whose edge set contains E'_0 as a subset. Now suppose G has a minimum weight spanning tree with edge set E' containing the edges in $E'_{i-1}\{e_1, e_2, \ldots, e_{i-1}\}$. If E' contains e_i as well, the conclusion of the theorem holds. Otherwise, adding e_i to E' produces a unique cycle that contains the edge $e_i = \{x_j, x_i\}$. The edge e_i leads out of the set $V'_{i-1} = \{x_0, x_1, \ldots, x_{i-1}\}$, so at least one other edge of the cycle, say e', must also lead out of V_{i-1}. Removing e' from E' and replacing it with e_i produces a connected graph, which, because it has the right number of edges, is a tree. However, e_i had minimum weight among all edges leaving V_{i-1}, so the new tree, which contains $e_1, e_2, \ldots, e_{i-1}, e_i$, must also be a minimum weight spanning tree. Therefore, the theorem follows by the principle of mathematical induction. ∎

For a reasonably large graph with many edges, step 1 of the algorithm may be time-consuming. The time used will depend on how we find the edges connecting a vertex in V' to a vertex not in V' and how we find the minimum cost edge. In our example, we used geometric inspection to determine the available edges and then "looked at" the set of available edges to choose one with minimum weight. In a practical situation, we would be likely to use a computer to keep track of the graph and select our minimum weight spanning tree. If we simply tried to program the steps of MTWTree directly, we might decide to test each edge to see if it goes between V' and V-V' and, as we go through these edges, keep track of the least weight edge we have seen so far. Thus we would have $O(|E|)$ comparisons each time we go through steps 1 and 2. Further, we would go through steps 1 and 2 once for each vertex other than our center x, so we would have $O(|V|)$ repetitions of these steps. Thus we would have an $O(|V|)O(|E|)$ algorithm. It is possible to program the algorithm so that we have only $O(|V|)$ computations each time we carry out steps 1 and 2. This method, due to Prim, is outlined in the problems.

B Minimum Path Length Spanning Trees

There are other important examples of situations where some spanning trees of a graph are more useful than others. For example, if we were going to use the spanning tree to send and receive information between a central database and workstations on a computer network, it would be desirable to get information back and forth quickly. In this way, we ensure that if one user updates a certain item, the other users will have the benefit of this update as soon as possible. The more edges a message travels along, the longer it takes to reach its destination. The minimum number of edges in a path from x to y in a graph is called the **distance** from x to y. In our spanning tree, we want the distance from the central database to each other node to be as small as possible.

EXAMPLE 15   Find the distance from vertex a to vertex c in Figure 31.

Figure 31

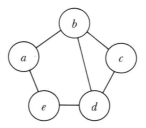

Solution   There are one path of length 2, two paths of length 3, and one path of length 4 from vertex a to vertex c in Figure 31. Thus the distance from a to c is two.   ∎

A problem similar to designing a database network arises if our graph represents a transportation network and we have a vertex representing a central warehouse, from which we dispatch a truck as needed to carry a delivery (as quickly as possible) to a node of the network. In a real-world transportation network (and perhaps in a real-world computer network also), different edges of the graph will represent transportation links with different lengths, perhaps different speed limits, and perhaps other differences. We will once again have a weighted graph—that is, a graph with numbers assigned to the edges. The numbers on the edges could represent transportation times, or they could represent actual geographical distances.

Weighted Distance

We define the (weighted) **length** of a walk in a weighted graph to be the sum of the weights of its edges, and we define the **distance** from a vertex x to a vertex y to be the length of a minimum length path from x to y. Thus to solve the problem of finding the fastest route from x to y, we want to find a path whose length *is* the distance from x to y.

In Example 15, we examined all paths from a to c to find the shortest path from a to c. The same technique works in a weighted graph. However, for a large graph with many edges, examining all paths might result in examining every subset to determine whether it is a path and, if so, if it is of minimum weight. Since there are 2^n subsets of an n-element vertex set, this could be quite time-consuming even for relatively small graphs. Fortunately, it is possible to construct a spanning tree of a (weighted) graph so that the distance from a vertex x to another vertex y in the tree is the same as the distance from x to y in G. Then we do not need to examine paths at all to find a shortest path from x to y; the unique path in the tree *is* a shortest path from x to y.

Minimum Path Weight Spanning Trees

We define a **minimum path weight spanning tree** of a weighted graph G centered at the vertex x to be a spanning tree such that the weighted length of the path from x to any other vertex y in the tree is the distance from x to y in G. The following variation of algorithm Spantree finds a minimum path weight spanning tree for a weighted graph *with non-negative weights*. (To apply it to a non-weighted graph to find shortest paths, simply assign weight 1 to each edge.)

Algorithm MPWTree

Input: A weighted graph G and a vertex x.

Output: The vertex set V' and edge set E' of a minimum path weight spanning tree centered at x of the connected component of G containing the vertex x.

Remark: $D(z)$ will stand for the distance from x to z in the tree; V' will be the vertex set; and E' will be the edge set of the tree.

Procedure: Let $V' = \{x\}$. Let $E' = \varnothing$. Let $D(x) = 0$.

Repeat the steps below until there is no edge $\{z,y\}$ with $z \in V'$, $y \notin V'$.

(1) Choose an edge $\{z,y\}$ with $z \in V'$, $y \notin V'$ such that $D(z) + w(z,y)$ is minimum.

(2) Put y into V', put $\{z,y\}$ into E'.
Let $D(y) = D(z) + w(z,y)$.

EXAMPLE 16   Find the edge set of a minimum path weight spanning tree centered at vertex a in the graph of Figure 30.

Solution   We start with $V' = \{a\}$, $D(a) = 0$, and $E' = \emptyset$. Of all edges leading away from a, $\{a,d\}$ has least weight, so $D(a) + w(\{a,d\})$ is a minimum for this edge. Thus E' becomes $\{\{a,d\}\}$, V' becomes $\{a,d\}$, and we set $D(d) = 0 + 20 = 20$. Now both $D(a) + w(\{a,b\})$ and $D(a) + w(\{a,c\})$ are 35, while $D(d) + w(\{d,c\}) = 20 + 10 = 30$, which is less, and in fact $\{d,c\}$ makes this sum a minimum. Thus we change E' to $\{\{a,d\}, \{d,c\}\}$ and V' to $\{a,c,d\}$, and we set $D(c) = 30$. Now two choices make our $D(z) + w(z,y)$ sum equal to 35: the choices $\{z,y\} = \{a,b\}$ and $\{z,y\} = \{d,h\}$. (Notice that $\{z,y\} = \{a,c\}$ is not allowed now, because a and c are both in V'.) Suppose we choose $\{a,b\}$ to add next. Then E' becomes $\{\{a,d\},\{d,c\},\{a,b\}\}$ and V' becomes $\{a,b,c,d\}$. Now $\{d,h\}$ is our only candidate making $D(z) + w(z,y)$ a minimum, so we change E' to $\{\{a,d\}, \{d,c\}, \{a,b\}, \{d,h\}\}$ and V' to $\{a,b,c,d,h\}$. Now we have only one choice for $\{z,y\}$, namely $\{d,g\}$, giving $D(d) + w(\{d,g\}) = 20 + 20 = 40$, so we change E' to $\{\{a,d\}, \{d,c\}, \{a,b\}, \{d,h\}, \{d,g\}\}$, and V' becomes V. Thus E' is the edge set of our minimum path weight spanning tree rooted at a. ∎

EXAMPLE 17   Find a path of minimum weight from a to h in the graph of Figure 30.

Solution   In Figure 32 we draw the tree of Example 16 as a rooted tree. We see that the path in the tree from h back to the root (a) is $h\{d,h\}d\{a,d\}a$, which has length $w(d,h) + w(a,d) = 15 + 20 = 35$. ∎

Figure 32

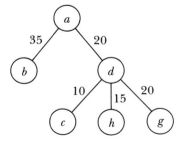

The strategy we use to find a minimum path weight spanning tree is called a "greedy" strategy, because at each stage we make the least costly choice possible at that stage without regard for its consequences for future stages. It is an interesting fact that the algorithm works for weighted graphs with non-negative weights, but for some graphs with some negative weights the algorithm may not work. We explore these ideas in the problems.

In our example, we used geometric observation to determine the edge (z, y) that makes $D(z) + w(z, y)$ a minimum. In a computer program, we might examine each edge, searching for the one that makes the sum smallest. Since we would do this once each time we add a new vertex to the tree, we would have $O(|V|)$ minima to find, each minimum taking perhaps $O(|E|)$ units of time to find. Thus it appears we have an $O(|V|) \cdot O(|E|) = O(|V| \cdot |E|)$ algorithm. In fact, by doing some of the minimum-finding work for each vertex outside V' as we go along, we can reduce the time needed to carry out the algorithm to $O(|V|^2)$. This idea, which is due to E. W. Dijkstra, is explored in the problems.

Concepts Review

1. A graph in which a number has been assigned to each edge is called a(n) _____ graph.

2. A(n) _____ _____ _____ spanning tree of G is a spanning tree such that the sum of the weights of its edges is no more than the sum of the weights of the edges of any other spanning trees.

3. A(n) _____ method is one that makes the most desirable choice at each stage regardless of the possible consequences for later choices.

4. The _____ between two vertices in a graph is the number of edges in a shortest path between those two vertices.

5. The _____ of a walk in a weighted graph is the sum of the weights of its edges.

6. The _____ between two vertices of a weighted graph is the minimum value of the sum of the weights of the edges on a path between the two vertices.

7. In a(n) _____ _____ _____ spanning tree centered at a vertex x of a graph G, the distance from x to y in the graph and the spanning tree are equal for each vertex y.

Exercises

A 1. What is the weight of edge $\{a, b\}$ in Figure 33? Which edge has the least weight?

2. What is the weight of edge $\{e, f\}$ in Figure 33? Which edge has the maximum weight?

3. What is the weight of the spanning tree of Figure 33 with edges $\{a, b\}$, $\{b, d\}$, $\{b, e\}$, $\{a, c\}$, and $\{c, f\}$? Is this a minimum total weight spanning tree?

4. What is the weight of the spanning tree of Figure 33 with edges $\{e, f\}$, $\{b, f\}$, $\{a, b\}$, $\{a, c\}$, and $\{b, d\}$? Is this a maximum total weight spanning tree?

Figure 33

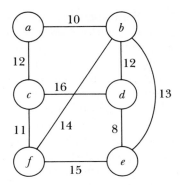

5. Find a minimum total weight spanning tree centered at vertex *c* in the graph of Figure 33.

6. Find a maximum total weight spanning tree centered at vertex *c* in the graph of Figure 33.

7. Find a minimum total weight spanning tree centered at vertex *d* in the graph of Figure 33. Is the total weight of this tree the same as the total weight of the tree you found in Exercise 5? How does your answer relate to Theorem 11?

8. Find a maximum total weight spanning tree centered at vertex *b* in the graph of Figure 33. Is the total weight of this tree the same as the total weight of the tree you found in Exercise 6? How does your answer relate to Theorem 11?

9. The *weighted adjacency list a: b,3,c,4,g,3* means that vertex *a* is connected to *b* by an edge of weight 3, *a* is connected to *c* by an edge of weight 4, and *a* is connected to *g* by an edge of weight 3. Given the weighted adjacency lists *a: b,3,c,4,g,3; b: a,3,d,2,c,4; c: a,4,b,4,d,4,f,4; d: b,2,c,4,g,2; f: c,4,g,3; g: a,3,d,2,f,3*, find a minimum total weight spanning tree centered at vertex *d*.

10. Weighted adjacency lists are described in Exercise 9. Given the weighted adjacency lists *a: c,2,f,3,b,4; b: a,4,f,1; c: a,2,d,2,f,2; d: c,2,f,2; f: b,1,a,3,c,2,d,2*, find a minimum total weight spanning tree centered at vertex *f*.

B   11. Show that the distance from *a* to *d* in the graph of Figure 34 is 3 by writing down all paths from *a* to *d* and choosing the shortest one.

Figure 34

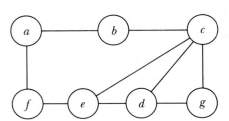

12. Show that the distance from a to g in Figure 34 is 3 by writing down all paths from a to g and choosing the shortest one.

13. In Figure 35, we show a graph with the edges of a spanning tree shown in black and the other edges in color. This tree is not a minimum path weight spanning tree centered at b. Explain why.

Figure 35

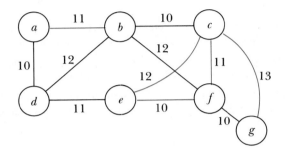

14. In Figure 36, we show a graph with the edges of a spanning tree shown in black and the other edges in color. This tree is not a minimum path weight spanning tree centered at b. Explain why.

Figure 36

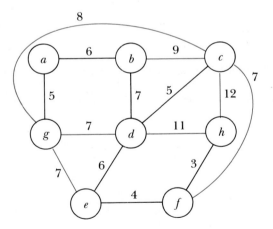

15. Find a minimum path weight spanning tree centered at vertex b of the graph in Figure 35.

16. Find a minimum path weight spanning tree centered at vertex b of the graph of Figure 36.

17. Use your tree from Exercise 15 to find a minimum length path from vertex b to vertex g in Figure 35. What is its length?

18. Use the tree you found in Exercise 16 to find a minimum length path from vertex b to vertex f in Figure 36.

Exercises 19 and 20 show the answer to the natural question, "Why did we learn two different methods for finding minimum weight spanning trees? Won't one algorithm solve both problems?" The answer is that neither algorithm solves the kind of problem the other algorithm solves; Exercises 19 and 20 show that MPWTree does not produce minimum length paths.

19. Find a minimum total weight spanning tree centered at b in the graph of Figure 35. Show that the path from b to d in this tree is not a minimum length path from b to d.

20. Find a minimum total weight spanning tree centered at b in the graph of Figure 36. Show that the path from b to h in this tree is not a minimum length path from b to h.

21. Apply algorithm MPWTree to the graph in Figure 37 to find a tree centered at d. Show that there is a path from d to c in the graph that has a smaller length than the path in the tree.

Figure 37

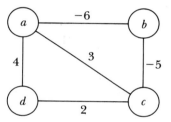

22. Apply algorithm MPWTree to the graph in Figure 38 to find a tree centered at a. Is it possible to find a path in the graph from a to b that has a smaller length than the path in the tree? Is it possible to find such a path if the tree is centered at some other vertex?

Figure 38

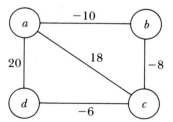

Problems

1. Suppose we choose a set E' of edges of a graph as follows. Start with $E' = \emptyset$. Repeat the following step until $|E'| = |V| - 1$. Choose a minimum cost edge in the set of all edges that may be added (individually, not collectively) to E' without creating a cycle and add this edge to E'. (If E' is $\{\{1,2\},\{2,3\}\}$ we *cannot* add $\{1,3\}$, but we can add $\{3,4\}$ without creating a cycle.) Show that E' is the edge set of a minimum total weight

spanning tree. (This is the basis for Kruskal's algorithm (introduced by J. B. Kruskal in 1956), which begins by sorting the edges into order of increasing cost. Kruskal's algorithm next uses a rather advanced technique involving connected components to check the edges one at a time and select those that do not form a cycle with previously selected edges.)

2. To make step 1 in algorithm MTWTree efficient, we use some additional information. For each v in V but not V', we let $L(v)$ (for "least of v") be the vertex z in the set V' for which $w(\{z,v\})$ is a minimum. To start out, V' has the single vertex x, so $L(v)$ is x if (x,v) is an edge. If $\{x,v\}$ is not an edge, we don't define $L(v)$. Now each time we add an element y to V', we check each $L(v)$ to see if $L(v)$ should be changed to y. (This takes $O(|V|)$ steps). This lets us find the $\{x,y\}$ of minimum weight with $O(|V|)$ steps by checking $w(L(y),y)$ for each y not in V'. Rewrite algorithm MTWTree to use this method and show how it works on the graph of Figure 30. This method is usually called Prim's algorithm because it was introduced by R. C. Prim in 1957; it was also suggested by E. W. Dijkstra in 1959.

3. Give a general statement explaining when the problem demonstrated in Exercises 21 and 22 can arise in a weighted graph.

4. A very important part of the proof that the algorithm MPWTree works for graphs with no edges of negative weight is the *triangle inequality*. We use $d(x,y)$ to stand for the length of a shortest path from x to y. The triangle inequality is the statement that $d(x,z) \leq d(x,y) + d(y,z)$. Prove that the triangle inequality holds for weighted graphs with no edges of negative weight.

5. Use the triangle inequality to show that if z is on a minimum length path from x to y then $d(x,z) \leq d(x,y)$.

6. Prove that algorithm MPWTree produces a minimum path weight spanning tree of a connected weighted graph with non-negative weights. (*Hint:* Assume that there is a path from x to a vertex y in the graph that is shorter than the path from x to y in the tree. Now, with the help of Problem 5, you may show that y should have been added to the tree along with the last edge of this shorter path, a contradiction.)

7. Give an example analogous to Exercises 19 and 20 to show that a tree produced by algorithm MPWTree need not be a minimum total weight spanning tree.

8. State precisely the version of MTWTree that finds spanning trees of maximum total weight. Prove that it finds a spanning tree of maximum total weight.

9. We gave no examples or exercises showing how to use MPWTree to find paths of maximum weight. Can it be modified for this purpose?

10. A quick implementation of algorithm MPWTree is based on the following ideas of Dijkstra. We define $D(z)$ not only for each vertex z in the tree but also for each vertex z outside the tree that is adjacent to something in the tree. Initially, when V' consists of x alone, $D(z)$ is $w(x,z)$ for each z connected to x. Later on, in repeating steps 1 and 2, when we add a vertex y to the tree, we define a new value of $D(v)$ for each vertex v adjacent to y, the minimum of the current value (if any) of $D(v)$ and the sum $D(y) + w(v,y)$. This means that in step 1 the $D(z) + w(v,y)$ is actually $D(y)$, so in step 1 we choose the y that makes $D(y)$ a minimum. This lets us examine each vertex once in choosing y rather than examining each edge once.
   (a) Rewrite algorithm MPWTree so that it uses these ideas.
   (b) Show that the revised algorithm is an $O(|V|^2)$ algorithm.

Chapter 8
Review Exercises

For Exercises 1–5, draw the graph, locate all cycles (if any), and specify whether the graph is a tree.

1. $V = \{1,2,3,4,5,6\}$ $E = \{\{1,2\}, \{1,3\}, \{1,4\}, \{4,5\}, \{4,6\}, \{5,6\}, \{2,3\}\}$

2. $V = \{1,2,3,4,5,6,7\}$ $E = \{\{1,3\}, \{2,3\}, \{3,4\}, \{4,5\}, \{4,6\}, \{4,7\}\}$

3. 1: 2,3,4;   2: 1;   3: 1;   4: 1;   5:

4. 1: 2,3,6;   2: 1;   3: 1,4,5;   4: 3;   5: 3;   6: 1

5. 1: 2,3;   2: 1,4,3;   3: 1,2,4;   4: 2,3

6. Find all paths from vertex 1 to vertex 5 in the graph of Exercise 1.

7. Which of the following are edge sets of spanning trees of the graph in Exercise 1?
   (a) $\{\{1,2\}, \{1,3\}, \{1,4\}, \{4,6\}, \{4,5\}\}$
   (b) $\{\{1,2\}, \{1,3\}, \{2,3\}, \{4,6\}, \{5,6\}\}$
   (c) $\{\{2,3\}, \{3,1\}, \{1,4\}, \{4,6\}, \{5,6\}\}$
   (d) $\{\{1,2\}, \{1,3\}, \{4,6\}, \{5,6\}\}$

8. Without drawing the graph, apply algorithm Spantree to the following graphs, starting with vertex 1, and answer the following questions. Is the graph connected? If so, what are the adjacency lists of a spanning tree? If not, what connected component have you found?
   (a) $\{\{1,5\}, \{1,2\}, \{2,4\}, \{4,5\}, \{2,3\}, \{3,4\}\}$
   (b) $\{\{1,2\}, \{2,3\}, \{3,4\}, \{4,1\}, \{2,4\}, \{5,6\}\}$
   (c) 1: 2,3;   2: 1,4;   3: 1,4;   4: 2,3,5,6;   5: 4,6;   6: 4,5
   (d) 1: 2,3;   2: 1,3;   3: 1,2;   4: 5,6,7;   5: 4,6,7;   6: 4,5,7;   7: 4,5,6

9. A nickel, a dime, and a quarter are in a hat. We carry out the process of selecting first one coin and then a second. Draw the rooted tree that illustrates this process, assuming we put the first coin back before drawing the second. Draw the rooted tree that illustrates this process, assuming we do not put the first coin back before drawing the second.

10. Draw the tree with vertex set $\{1,2,3,4,5,6,7\}$ and edge set $\{\{1,2\}, \{2,4\}, \{2,3\}, \{3,5\}, \{3,6\}, \{3,7\}\}$ as a rooted tree with root vertex 1. Repeat the exercise with root vertex 3.

11. In the rooted trees of Exercise 10, answer these questions for each root. What are the children of vertex 2? What are the descendants of vertex 2? What are the ancestors of vertex 5? What are the internal vertices of the rooted tree? What are the external vertices of the rooted tree?

12. In the tree of Figure 39, draw the left subtree of vertex a. What is the right child of vertex c? Which vertices have empty left children?

Figure 39

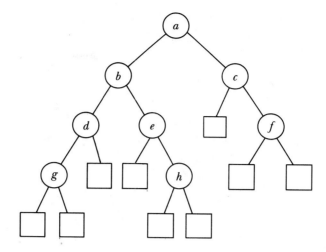

13. Draw the binary tree that represents the possible outcomes of binary search on the ten-element list A,C,F,G,J,K,R,S,X,Z. Would the tree itself look any different if we had used some different alphabetically ordered list with ten elements?

14. Using the method of converting external nodes to internal nodes, add a vertex containing N to the binary search tree of Exercise 13. Now use this method to add a vertex containing M to the tree. Finally, add a vertex containing P to the tree. Would the final tree look different if we had first added M, then P, and then N?

15. Beginning with an empty binary search tree and adding one vertex at a time, show the binary search tree that results from inserting the vertices E,C,D,A,J,M,H into a binary search tree, in that order. Show the tree that results from inserting the same vertices, but in alphabetical order. Which of these trees could result from inserting the vertices in some other order? Show such an order.

16. Write down the letters stored in the nonempty vertices of the binary tree in Figure 39 in the order of a preorder traversal, then an inorder traversal, and then a postorder traversal.

17. If you write the letters stored in the nonempty nodes of one of the binary search trees you constructed in Exercise 15 in the order of an inorder traversal, what list of letters will you get? Does it matter which tree of Exercise 15 you use?

18. Draw the expression tree of the well-formed formula $((17 + 3)\cdot(44 - (3\cdot8)))$.

19. Show the steps involved in using a postorder traversal of the expression tree you drew in Exercise 18 to evaluate the expression.

20. Draw the 2-3 tree that results from inserting the letters of Exercise 15 into a 2-3 tree, one at a time, in the order given in Exercise 15.

21. Draw the 2-3 tree that results from inserting the letters of Exercise 15 into a 2-3 tree, one at a time, in alphabetical order.

22. Find the distance from vertex 1 to vertex 7 in the graph of Figure 40 by writing down a list of all paths from vertex 1 to vertex 7 and choosing one of minimum length.

Figure 40

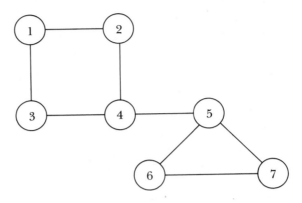

23. How many more paths would you have to write down in Exercise 22 if there were an edge between vertices 4 and 6?

24. In Figure 41, the number adjacent to each edge is its weight. Is the tree whose edges are the edges from d to each other vertex a minimum total weight spanning tree of the graph?

Figure 41

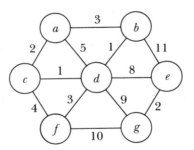

25. In Figure 41, is the tree whose edges are the edges from d to each other vertex a minimum path weight spanning tree centered at vertex d?

26. Find a minimum total weight spanning tree of the graph in Figure 41 by using algorithm MTWTree. Show (in whatever way you choose) the order in which vertices and edges are selected for membership in the tree.

27. Use algorithm MPWTree to find a minimum path weight spanning tree centered at vertex g in the graph of Figure 41. Show (in whatever way you choose) the order in which vertices and edges are selected for membership in the tree.

28. Although we have no algorithms to find structures other than trees of minimum weight in a weighted graph, problems might lead us to do so. For example, if we are designing aircraft holding patterns we may want cycles that minimize fuel consumption. Find a minimum total weight cycle in the graph of Figure 41.

*W*e introduced digraphs and graphs in order to have visual representations of relations. The origins of graph theory include chemistry, geography, recreational mathematics, and geometry. Now graphs are important because of their many applications in operations research and management science, in computer science, in behavioral science, and even in attempts in physics to build fundamental theories to explain the interactions of the universe.

In this chapter, we shall introduce several important kinds of applications of graph theory that relate to a wide variety of practical problems. The relationship of graph theory to chemistry leads us to study multigraphs as well as graphs and to the concept of isomorphic graphs—graphs that are essentially the same even if they do not appear geometrically to be so. We then study questions about tours in graphs. In advanced work in computer science, the Eulerian and Hamiltonian tour problems we introduce here could be used as prototypes for the complexity classes known to computer scientists as P and NP. The problem of coloring graphs has both theoretical and practical overtones. In the practical vein, scheduling events leads us to the concept of coloring. In a theoretical vein, we are able to explain the meaning of the famous four-color theorem for planar graphs. The study of planar graphs may appear to be an exercise in abstract geometry, but the problems of designing circuits on computer chips have given knowledge about planar graphs and related topics a central role in the applications of mathematics to computer science.

Graph theory is a major unifying idea in discrete mathematics and its applications. Graphs are part of the basic tool kit of specialists in operations research, computer science, and mathematical behavioral science.

Section 9-1
Basic Concepts
of Graph Theory

◼ Graphs and Multigraphs

We introduced graph theory in Chapter 3 for the study of relations. Relations, as such, had not even been studied abstractly when graph theory began. One origin of graph theory is the molecular concept of matter in chemistry. A brief discussion of this concept will lead us to several important ideas in graph theory.

An Overview of the Molecular Concept of Matter

All recognizable matter is built up of small particles called *molecules*. A molecule itself is built from smaller particles called *atoms*. In Figure 1, you see several chemical diagrams of chemical compounds. These are examples of hydrocarbons, substances whose atoms are either carbon atoms or hydrogen atoms. The compound called normal butane is an example of a so-called saturated hydrocarbon. The mathematician Cayley developed the concept of trees, the subject of Chapter 8, while he was studying saturated hydrocarbons. In the diagrams of Figure 1, an H stands for a hydrogen atom, and a C stands for a carbon atom. Each line represents a *chemical bond*, a relationship of mutual attraction between two atoms. (The chemical bonds in benzene are more complex than the diagram indicates; trying to explain the diagram has led chemists to a better understanding of benzene

Figure 1

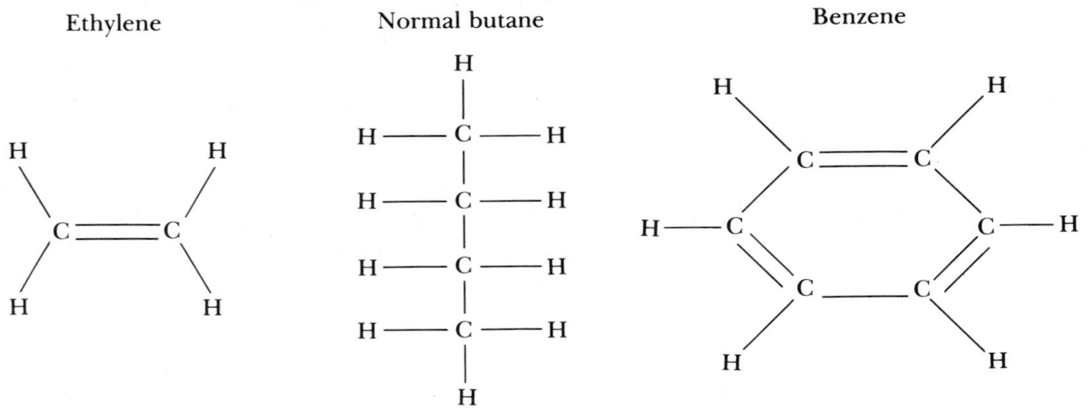

Ethylene   Normal butane   Benzene

and the nature of chemical bonds.) The chemical diagrams are quite similar to graphs. A graph has a set of vertices and a set of edges.

Figure 2

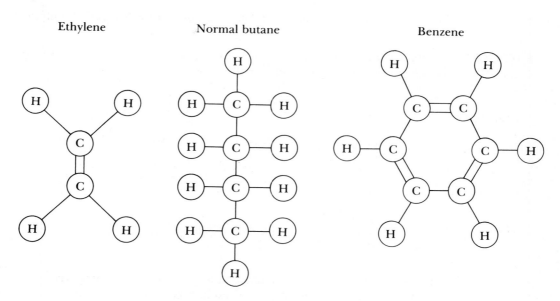

Ethylene

Normal butane

Benzene

In Figure 2, we may think of the circles we have drawn as vertices and the lines representing bonds as edges. We have redrawn the diagram of ethylene in Figure 3, numbering the carbon atoms and hydrogen atoms so that we can distinguish among them.

Figure 3

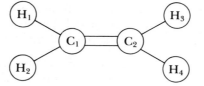

We can now use $\{C_1, C_2, H_1, H_2, H_3, H_4\}$ as a vertex set. When we write down the two-element sets corresponding to edges, we get $\{\{C_1, H_1\}, \{C_1, H_2\}, \{C_2, H_3\}, \{C_2, H_4\}, \{C_1, C_2\}, \{C_1, C_2\}\}$. In the terminology of Chapter 6, this is a multiset rather than a set, because the edge $\{C_1, C_2\}$ appears twice. In the language of multisets, the edge $\{C_1, C_2\}$ has multiplicity 2. In this way, chemical diagrams lead us to the concept of a multigraph.

Multigraphs

A **multigraph** consists of a vertex set V and a
multiset E of two-element multisets chosen from
V and called **edges**.

Since a set is a special kind of multiset, a graph is a special kind of multigraph.

EXAMPLE 1   Several typical multigraphs are shown in Figure 4. Which of these are graphs? Which are simple graphs (graphs without loops, as in Chapter 3)?

Figure 4

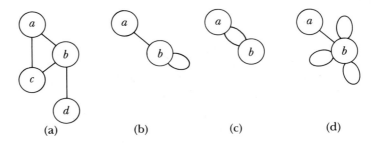

(a)   (b)   (c)   (d)

Solution   Multigraph (a) is a simple graph, because it has no loops and each edge appears just once. Multigraph (b) is a graph, because each edge appears just once, but it is not simple, because the two-element multiset $\{b,b\}$ is a loop. Multigraphs (c) and (d) are not graphs, because in (c) the edge $\{a,b\}$ appears twice and in (d) the edge $\{b,b\}$ appears three times. ■

As the example shows, a multigraph may have several edges joining two vertices a and b and any number of loops at any vertex. Further, by saying that an edge is a two-element multiset, we allow a loop to be represented by $\{b,b\}$, which captures the idea of an edge from b to b better than the one-element set $\{b\}$ we had to use to represent it in Chapter 3. Thus we can restate the definition of a graph from Chapter 3 in more natural terminology as follows:

A **graph** consists of a set V of elements called *vertices* and a
set E of two-element multisets chosen from V and called *edges*.
A graph is **simple** if each edge is a two-element set.

Multidigraphs

Recall that a **digraph** consists of a set V and a set of ordered pairs of elements of V called *edges*.

We define a **multidigraph** as a set V together
with a multiset E of ordered pairs of elements of V.

Figure 5

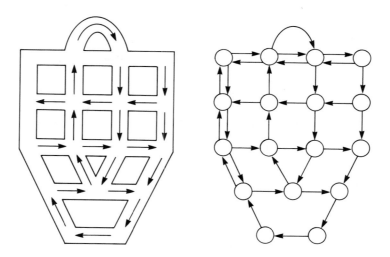

Figure 5 shows a map of a hypothetical network of one-way streets in a city; next to the map is a multidigraph that represents the map. The vertices of the multidigraph represent street corners. The edges represent the permissible direction of travel along the streets. You should be able to identify why the multidigraph is not a digraph.

Graph theory encompasses multigraphs and multidigraphs as well as graphs and digraphs. The basic ideas of graph theory—walks, paths, cycles, connectivity, reachability, and spanning and search trees—all apply to multigraphs and multidigraphs as they did for graphs and digraphs.

B Isomorphism

In the study of butane, a hydrocarbon whose molecules each contain 4 carbon atoms and 10 hydrogen atoms, chemists discovered two substances with slightly different chemical properties, each having 10 hydrogen atoms and 4 carbon atoms. Two natural questions are "How is this possible?" and "Is it possible that there are more than two forms of butane?" The first question is answered by the drawings in Figure 6. Those two drawings both contain 4 carbon and 10 hydrogen atoms, but they don't look alike. Perhaps the difference in appearance accounts for a difference in chemical properties. To use graph theory to study such differences, we need a precise way to say that two graphs are (or aren't) essentially the same.

Isomorphic and Nonisomorphic Graphs

In Figure 7, we see several drawings of graphs. The first two drawings represent a symmetric relation that relates vertex 1 to vertex 2, vertex 2 to vertex 3, and vertex 3 to vertex 4.

Figure 6   Two isomers of butane.

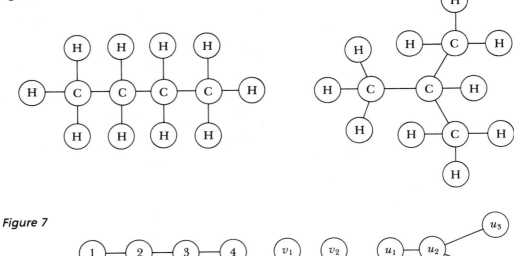

Figure 7

(a)   (b)   (c)

Although drawing (b) has a different appearance from (a), by moving vertex v_1 to the right and vertex v_4 to the left and adjusting the lengths of edges we get a geometric figure congruent to drawing (a). To say that the two drawings are congruent means that we can make the vertices and edges of one correspond to those of the other in such a way that corresponding edges join corresponding vertices. We don't need geometric ideas to discuss such correspondences; a correspondence between the vertices of two graphs is just a one-to-one function from one vertex set onto the other. To say that edges correspond when vertices do is to say that if the vertex x corresponds to x' and y corresponds to y', then $\{x,y\}$ is an edge if and only if $\{x',y'\}$ is an edge. This kind of correspondence is called an *isomorphism*.

> An **isomorphism** is a one-to-one function f from the vertex set of a (multi)graph G to the vertex set of the (multi)graph H such that there is an edge in G from x to y if and only if there is an edge in H from $f(x)$ to $f(y)$ (of the same multiplicity).

Simply substituting digraph for graph gives us the definition of isomorphism for (multi)digraphs. We say that G and H are **isomorphic** if there is an isomorphism from G to H. (*Iso* is a Greek prefix whose meaning is basically "same"; *morph* is also from the Greek, meaning basically "shape" or "form.")

EXAMPLE 2   Show that the function f given by $f(i) = v_i$ is an isomorphism between the graphs drawn in (a) and (b) of Figure 7.

Solution $\{1,2\}$ is an edge of (a), and $\{f(1), f(2)\}$ is $\{v_1, v_2\}$, which is an edge of (b). Similarly, $\{2,3\}$ and $\{3,4\}$ are edges of (a), and $\{f(2), f(3)\} = \{v_2, v_3\}$ and $\{f(3), f(4)\} = \{v_3, v_4\}$ are edges of (b). No other set is an edge of (a) or (b), so $\{i,j\}$ is an edge of (a) if and only if $\{f(i), f(j)\}$ is an edge of (b). Therefore f is an isomorphism.   ∎

EXAMPLE 3   Show that the function f given by $f(i) = u_i$ is not an isomorphism from the graph in (a) of Figure 7 to the graph of (c) in Figure 7.

Solution $\{3,4\}$ is an edge of (a), but $\{f(3), f(4)\} = \{u_3, u_4\}$ is not an edge of (c).   ∎

The Concept of Degree

In Example 3, we have not settled whether the graphs of (a) and (c) in Figure 7 are isomorphic; we have only settled whether one function is an isomorphism. In fact, drawing (c) looks different because it has one vertex that appears in three edges, whereas drawing (a) has *no* vertex that lies in three edges.

> The number of times a vertex appears in edges
> of a multigraph is called its **degree**.

In other words, the *degree* of a vertex x is the number of two-vertex edges x lies in plus twice the number of loops x lies in (since it appears twice in a loop). Because of the theorem below, we say that an isomorphism *preserves* the degrees of vertices.

Theorem 1   If f is an isomorphism from G to H, then the degree of a vertex x in G is equal to the degree of $f(x)$ in H.

Proof $\{f(x), z\}$ is an edge of H if and only if $\{x, f^{-1}(z)\}$ is an edge of G (by the definition of isomorphism).   ∎

The theorem applies to multigraphs as well, though the proof must be modified to mention multiplicity of edges. The theorem also applies to digraphs, though the proof must be modified to mention $(f(x), z)$ and $(z, f(x))$. More important in digraphs is the *indegree* of x, the number of edges (z, x) in the edge set, and the *outdegree* of x, the number of edges (x, z) in the edge set. The theorem can be rewritten for digraphs to show that if f is an isomorphism from a digraph G to a digraph H, then x and $f(x)$ have the same indegree in G and H and x and $f(x)$ have the same outdegree in G and H.

EXAMPLE 4   Find an isomorphism between the two digraphs in Figure 8. What are the indegree and outdegree of vertex 1 and of the vertex that corresponds to it?

Figure 8

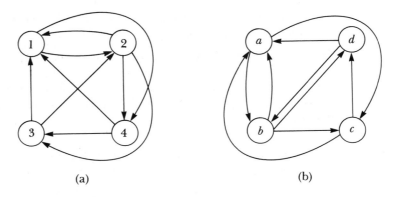

(a)   (b)

Solution   1 and *a* both have three edges coming in; 2 and *b* both have three edges going out. The other four vertices all have two edges coming in and going out. Thus we see that we want $f(1) = a$ $f(2) = b$. To decide $f(3)$, we observe that 3 has arrows to 1 and 2 and *d* has arrows to *a* and *b*, so we try $f(3) = d$ $f(4) = c$. It is straightforward to check by inspection that (i,j) is an edge if and only if $(f(i), f(j))$ is an edge.   ∎

Showing That Graphs Are Not Isomorphic

EXAMPLE 5   Show that graphs (a) and (c) in Figure 7 are not isomorphic.

Solution   Vertex 2 of (a) has degree 2, so if there is an isomorphism f from (a) to (c), vertex $f(2)$ should have degree 2 in (c). However, each vertex in (c) has degree 1 or 3, so there is no vertex that can be $f(2)$. Thus there is no isomorphism f between the graphs.   ∎

The example shows us the only practical means for demonstrating that one graph is *not* isomorphic to another. We find a property (such as having a vertex of degree 2) that *should* be preserved by an isomorphism and then show that only one of the graphs has that property. Don't be fooled into thinking that we must always examine degrees of vertices. In Figure 9, we show two nonisomorphic graphs whose vertices all have degree 3.

EXAMPLE 6   Show that the two graphs shown in Figure 9 are not isomorphic.

Solution   One property we may observe in drawing (a) of Figure 9 is that a_1, a_2, and a_3 are all connected to each other. Thus if f is an isomorphism, $f(a_1)$, $f(a_2)$, and $f(a_3)$ must all be joined by edges. However, if we choose three vertices in (b), at least two must be in the top layer or at least two must be in the bottom layer.

Figure 9

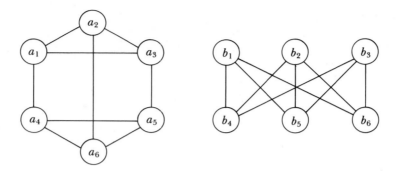

But two vertices in the same layer are not connected. Thus no three vertices b_i, b_j, and b_k may all be joined by edges, so no $\{b_i, b_j, b_k\}$ may be $\{f(a_1), f(a_2), f(a_3)\}$. Thus no isomorphism f is possible. ∎

Concepts Review

1. A(n) _____ consists of a vertex set V and a multiset E of two-element multisets chosen from V and called *edges*.

2. A(n) _____ consists of a vertex set V and a multiset E of ordered pairs chosen from V and called *edges*.

3. A(n) _____ is a one-to-one function from the vertex set of a graph G onto the vertex set of a graph H such that $\{x,y\}$ is an edge of G if and only if $\{f(x), f(y)\}$ is an edge of H.

4. If there is an isomorphism from G to H, then G and H are said to be _____.

5. The degree of a vertex of a multigraph is the _____ of _____ element edges plus _____ the _____ of _____ element edges in which the vertex lies.

6. If f is an isomorphism from G to H, then the degree of x in G and $f(x)$ in H are

   _____.

7. The _____ of a vertex x in a digraph is the number of edges (x,y) it lies in.

Exercises

A In Exercises 1–6, state whether the drawing specified is a drawing of a graph, a simple graph or just a multigraph.

1. Figure 10(a)   2. Figure 10(b)   3. Figure 10(c)

4. Figure 10(d)   5. Figure 10(e)   6. Figure 10(f)

Figure 10

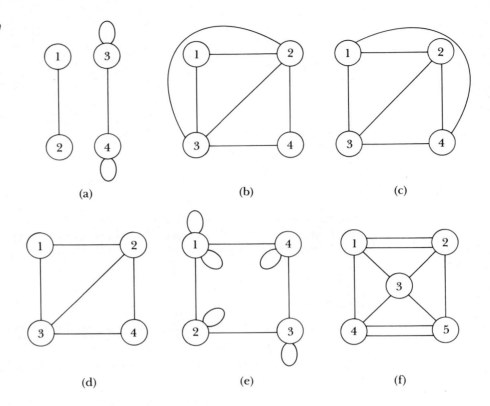

(a)　　　　　　　　(b)　　　　　　　　(c)

(d)　　　　　　　　(e)　　　　　　　　(f)

In Exercises 7–12, write down the edge multisets of the multigraph specified.

7. Figure 10(a)　　　　　**8.** Figure 10(b)　　　　　**9.** Figure 10(c)

10. Figure 10(d)　　　　**11.** Figure 10(e)　　　　**12.** Figure 10(f)

In Exercises 13–18, classify each of the multidigraphs given as digraphs or multidigraphs.

13. Figure 11(a)　　　　**14.** Figure 11(b)　　　　**15.** Figure 11(c)

16. Figure 11(d)　　　　**17.** Figure 11(e)　　　　**18.** Figure 11(f)

In Exercises 19–24, write down the edge multiset of the multigraph specified.

19. Figure 11(a)　　　　**20.** Figure 11(b)　　　　**21.** Figure 11(c)

22. Figure 11(d)　　　　**23.** Figure 11(e)　　　　**24.** Figure 11(f)

In Exercises 25–30, draw the multigraph on $\{1,2,3,4,5,6\}$ or $\{a,b,c,d,e\}$ with the edges given. Classify each one as connected or not connected (defined in Chapter 3).

25. $\{\{1,2\}, \{1,2\}, \{2,3\}, \{3,4\}, \{3,4\}, \{4,5\}, \{5,6\}, \{5,6\}, \{6,1\}\}$

26. $\{\{1,2\}, \{2,2\}, \{2,2\}, \{1,3\}, \{2,3\}, \{3,4\}, \{3,4\}, \{4,5\}, \{5,6\}\}$

Figure 11

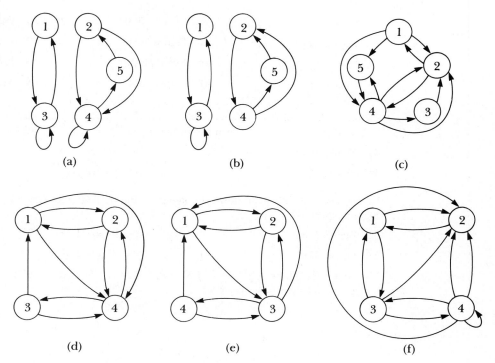

(a) (b) (c)

(d) (e) (f)

27. {{1,2}, {2,3}, {3,1}, {3,1}, {4,5}, {4,5}, {5,6}, {6,1}}

28. {{a,b}, {b,c}, {c,a}, {d,e}, {d,e}}

29. {{a,b}, {a,b}, {b,c}, {b,c}, {c,a}, {c,a}, {a,e}, {b,d}}

30. {{a,a}, {b,b}, {b,b}, {c,d}, {d,e}, {e,a}, {a,e}}

In Exercises 31–36, draw the multidigraph on {1,2,3,4,5} or {a,b,c,d,e} with the edges specified. Determine the vertices reachable from vertex 1 or vertex a.

31. {(1,2), (1,2), (2,1), (2,3), (2,3), (3,1), (4,5), (5,4), (5,5), (5,5)}

32. {(1,2), (2,3), (3,4), (4,5), (5,1), (1,5), (4,5), (4,3), (2,3), (2,1)}

33. {(1,2), (2,3), (2,3), (4,3), (4,3), (5,4)}

34. {(a,b), (b,c), (c,a), (d,e), (d,e), (e,d), (e,d)}

35. {(a,b), (b,c), (d,c), (e,d), (c,e), (c,a), (a,a), (a,a), (e,e), (e,e)}

36. {(a,b), (a,b), (c,d), (d,c), (e,e)}

We can use adjacency lists to describe multidigraphs as well as graphs. For example, the list a: b,b,c,d,d means that there are two edges from a to b, one from a to c, and two from a to d. Give an adjacency list representation for each multigraph or multidigraph specified in Exercises 37–48.

37. Figure 10(a)	**38.** Figure 10(b)	**39.** Figure 10(c)
40. Figure 10(d)	**41.** Figure 10(e)	**42.** Figure 10(f)
43. Figure 11(a)	**44.** Figure 11(b)	**45.** Figure 11(c)
46. Figure 11(d)	**47.** Figure 11(e)	**48.** Figure 11(f)

B   In Exercises 49–52, write down the degree of each vertex in the multigraph specified.

49. Figure 10(a)   **50.** Figure 10(b)

51. Figure 10(c)   **52.** Figure 10(f)

In Exercises 53–56, write down the indegree and outdegree of each vertex in the multidigraph specified.

53. Figure 11(a)   **54.** Figure 11(c)

55. Figure 11(d)   **56.** Figure 11(f)

57. Show that $f(1) = a$, $f(2) = b$, $f(3) = c$, $f(4) = e$, $f(5) = d$ is an isomorphism between graphs (a) and (b) in Figure 12.

Figure 12

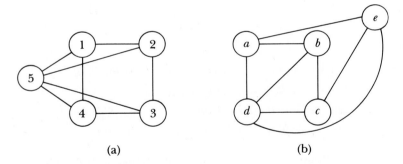

(a)   (b)

58. Show that $f(1) = b$, $f(2) = a$, $f(3) = e$, $f(4) = c$, $f(5) = d$ gives an isomorphism between graphs (a) and (b) in Figure 12.

59. Show that $f(1) = a$, $f(2) = b$, $f(3) = d$, $f(4) = c$, $f(5) = e$ does not describe an isomorphism between graphs (a) and (b) in Figure 12.

60. Show that $f(1) = a$, $f(2) = b$, $f(3) = c$, $f(4) = d$, $f(5) = e$ does not describe an isomorphism between graphs (a) and (b) in Figure 12.

In Exercises 61–64, show that the graphs in the figures specified are not isomorphic.

61. Figure 13   **62.** Figure 14

63. Figure 15   **64.** Figure 16

Figure 13

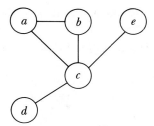
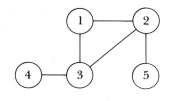

Figure 14

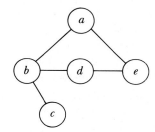
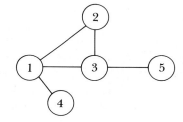

Figure 15

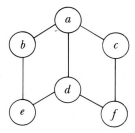
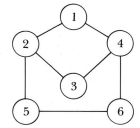

Figure 16

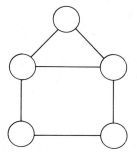
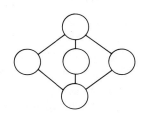

65. Show that if f is an isomorphism from G to H, then the number of vertices of G is equal to the number of vertices of H.

66. Show that if f is an isomorphism from G to H, then the number of edges of G is equal to the number of edges of H.

67. The edge sets of three digraphs are given below. Which of these digraphs are isomorphic to which others (and which pairs are *not* isomorphic)?
    (a) $\{(a,b),\ (b,d),\ (d,c),\ (c,a),\ (d,a),\ (c,b)\}$
    (b) $\{(1,2),\ (2,3),\ (2,4),\ (4,3),\ (3,1),\ (4,1)\}$
    (c) $\{(w,x),\ (x,y),\ (y,z),\ (z,w),\ (x,z),\ (y,w)\}$

68. The edge sets of three digraphs are given below. Which of these digraphs are isomorphic to which others (and which pairs are not isomorphic)?
    (a) $\{(1,4),\ (4,2),\ (2,1),\ (3,1),\ (3,2),\ (3,4)\}$
    (b) $\{(1,3),\ (4,3),\ (3,2),\ (4,2),\ (4,1),\ (2,1)\}$
    (c) $\{(2,1),\ (1,4),\ (2,4),\ (1,3),\ (4,3),\ (2,3)\}$

69. If G and H are isomorphic digraphs and G is a digraph of a transitive relation, explain why H must be a digraph of a transitive relation.

70. If G and H are isomorphic digraphs and G is a digraph of a symmetric relation, explain why H must be a digraph of a symmetric relation.

71. Find two nonisomorphic spanning trees of the graph in Figure 17.

Figure 17

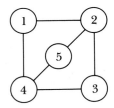

Figure 18

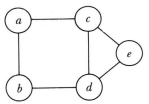

72. Find two nonisomorphic spanning trees of the graph in Figure 18.

Problems

1. It is a fact that if an n-vertex graph is connected, then it has at least $n-1$ edges. Is this true for multigraphs?

2. It is a fact that if a graph on n vertices has more than $\binom{n-1}{2}+1$ edges, then it is connected. Prove this. Is the same statement true for multigraphs?

3. What is the maximum number of edges possible in a graph on n vertices? A simple graph on n vertices? Why does this question not make sense for multigraphs?

4. What is the maximum number of edges possible in a digraph on n vertices? A simple digraph (that is, having no arrows from a vertex to itself) on n vertices? Why does this question not make sense for multidigraphs?

5. What is the largest number of edges possible in a simple graph that is not connected?

6. A graph with *n* vertices, *n* − 1 edges, and no cycles is a tree. Explain why this statement remains true if we replace the word *graph* with *multigraph*.

7. Explain why the sum of the degrees at the vertices in a multigraph is twice the number of edges.

8. Explain why the sum of the indegrees of vertices in a digraph equals the sum of the outdegrees of vertices in the digraph.

9. Give a proof by mathematical induction that a connected graph in which each vertex has degree 2 must be a cycle. Is this true if you replace the word *graph* with *multigraph*?

10. Give a proof by mathematical induction that a connected graph with *n* vertices and *n* edges is a cycle. Is this true if you replace the word *graph* with *multigraph*?

11. Show that the relation "is isomorphic to" is an equivalence relation on the set of graphs with a given vertex set. Is this true for multigraphs as well?

12. Show that if *G* and *H* are isomorphic and *G* has a cycle on three vertices, then *H* has a cycle on three vertices. What can you say about a cycle on any number *m* of vertices?

Section 9-2
Tours in Graphs

◼ Eulerian Walks

In an article generally acknowledged to be one of the origins of graph theory [reprinted in *Graph Theory 1736–1936* by Biggs, Lloyd, and Wilson (Clarendon, 1976)], Leonhard Euler (pronounced "oiler") described a geographic problem, which he offered as an elementary and entertaining example of what he called "the geometry of position." The *Königsberg bridge problem* concerns the town of Königsberg in Prussia (now Kaliningrad in Russia), which is shown in a schematic map (circa 1700) in Figure 19(a). Euler tells us that the citizens amused themselves

Figure 19

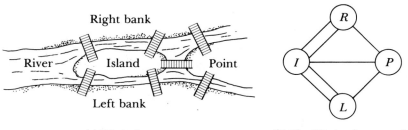

(a) Königsberg

(b) The Könisgsberg graph

by trying to find a walk through town that crossed each of the seven bridges once and only once (and, hopefully, ended where it started). Euler stated that such a walk is impossible.

Representing a Map by a Graph

In Figure 19(b), we show a multigraph whose vertices represent the four land masses and whose edges represent the seven bridges. A walk through the multigraph that includes each edge corresponds to a walk through Königsberg that crosses each bridge.

EXAMPLE 7   Draw a graph to represent the map in Figure 20 and use inspection to find a walk that uses each edge exactly once. Use this to describe a walk that crosses each bridge in Figure 20 exactly once.

Figure 20

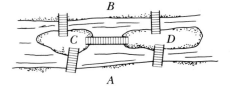

Figure 21

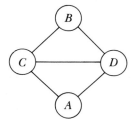

Solution   The graph will have four vertices, one representing each land mass, and five edges, one representing each bridge. We show the graph in Figure 21. The sequence of vertices and edges $C\{C,D\}D\{D,A\}A\{A,C\}C\{C,B\}B\{B,D\}D$ includes each edge exactly once, so it is the desired walk. This corresponds to beginning on island C, crossing the bridge to D, then crossing to A, crossing to C, then to B, and finally to D.   ■

Eulerian Walks and Tours

Notice that the walk in the graph of Figure 21 did not start and end at the same place.

> A walk through a (multi)graph that includes each edge once
> (for each time it appears in the edge multiset) is called
> an **Eulerian** ("oil *air* ian") **walk**. A closed Eulerian walk
> is called an **Eulerian tour**.

Thus, in Example 7, we found an Eulerian walk but not an Eulerian tour. In fact, the graph of Figure 21 does not have an Eulerian tour, as the following theorem shows.

Theorem 2 If a connected multigraph has an Eulerian tour, then the degree of each vertex is an even number.

Proof With the exception of the first and last vertex, each vertex in the Eulerian tour is preceded and followed by two edges each time it appears. Because each edge is in the walk, the number of times each such vertex appears in edges of the graph is even. Thus each such vertex has even degree. But the first and last vertex are the same, and this vertex appears in one edge at the beginning of the walk, one at the end, and an even number (perhaps zero) in between. Thus this vertex has even degree also. ∎

EXAMPLE 8 Does the graph in Example 7 have an Eulerian tour?

Solution No, because it has two vertices of degree three. ∎

Theorem 3 If a connected multigraph has an Eulerian walk that is not a tour, then it has exactly two vertices of odd degree.

Proof Similar to the proof of Theorem 2. ∎

EXAMPLE 9 Does the graph of Königsberg have an Eulerian walk?

Solution No, because there are four vertices of odd degree. ∎

We have some results we can use to show that a graph does not have an Eulerian tour or walk, but how can we show that a graph *does* have one?

EXAMPLE 10 Construct an Eulerian walk in the graph of Figure 22(a).

Figure 22

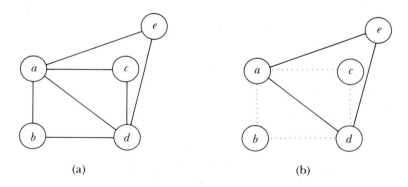

(a)   (b)

Solution Let us begin by constructing a closed walk with no concern for whether it is Eulerian. We might, for example, choose the walk $b\{b,d\}d\{d,c\}c\{c,a\}a\{a,b\}b$. This walk is shown by the dotted edges in Figure 22(b). If we ignore these edges, we can see an obvious closed walk using the remaining edges, namely $a\{a,d\}d\{d,e\}e\{e,a\}a$. Now if we insert this entire closed walk for a in the original walk, we get the walk $b\{b,d\}d\{d,c\}c\{c,a\}a\{a,d\}d\{d,e\}e\{e,a\}a\{a,b\}b$. This walk is an Eulerian tour.   ∎

An Algorithm to Construct a Tour

The process in the example may be described as follows. Start at a vertex and construct a walk by adding edges and vertices until you return to the starting vertex. (So long as all vertices have even degree, we can do this; we shall explain why momentarily.) Remove these edges from the graph. Now repeat the process to get a new closed walk starting and ending at some vertex x on the original walk. Replace the vertex x in the original closed walk with this entire new closed walk. Repeat this process until you run out of edges, and you will have an Eulerian tour. We have given most of the proof of the following theorem.

Theorem 4   If, in a connected multigraph, each vertex has even degree, then the multigraph has an Eulerian tour.

Proof   The process used to construct the tour is described above. First we show that the original walk can be continued until it closes. Each vertex on the original walk has an even degree, but each time the walk enters a vertex other than the first, that vertex has so far appeared in an odd number of edges of the walk. (Both in *and* out some number of times, and then in but not yet out.) Since each vertex has even degree, there is an edge by which we can leave the vertex. Thus we can continue the walk until it returns to the first vertex. After we delete the edges of this walk, each connected component of the resulting graph contains a vertex of the original walk. (Think about removing the edges one at a time.) Removing the edges of the walk reduces each degree by an even number, so each degree remains even. Thus we can continue the process until no edges remain. Inserting each closed walk we get into the walk we already have lets us build a walk that includes all the edges.   ∎

B   Edge Tours

Suppose the edges of a graph represent roads, and the vertices represent intersections. To deliver the mail along these roads, we would have to drive on each street at least once. An Eulerian tour permits us to drive on each road exactly once and return to our starting place without any wasted trips. However, we have seen that not all graphs have Eulerian tours.

> An **edge tour** of a (multi)graph is a closed walk
> that includes each edge *at least once*
> (for each time it appears in the edge set).

The problem of finding an edge tour of a multigraph with as few edges as possible may be thus regarded as finding the least expensive mail delivery route. In the real world, different roads will have different lengths. Thus the best mail delivery route would be an edge tour whose total mileage is a minimum.

Minimum Weight Tours

We introduced the term *weighted graph* to mean a graph with numbers assigned to the edges. Finding an edge tour of minimum total weight in a weighted graph has become known as the *Chinese postman problem* because M. K. Kwan pointed out (in the first issue of the journal *Chinese Mathematics*) how the problem relates to mail delivery. The problem arises in many other applications as well; routing school buses along rural roads, sending garbage trucks or snowplows through cities, and testing all the links of a communications network are examples where minimum weight edge tours are useful.

EXAMPLE 11   In Figure 23, we show a multigraph of roads and intersections over which a school bus must be routed. One routing for the school bus to cover each road is 1-2-4-3-1-4-3-1-4-5-6-7-8-5-6-7-8-9-5-8-9-5-4-1. (The hyphens stand for edges.) What is the weight of this tour if all edges have weight 1?

Solution   Since there are 23 edges in this tour, the weight of the tour is 23.   ■

Figure 23

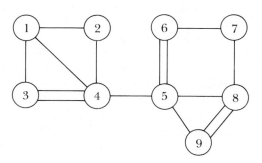

EXAMPLE 12   Use dotted lines to show the walk of Example 11 in Figure 23 and show the multigraph that results from deleting the *solid* edges.

Solution   Shown in Figure 24.   ■

The dotted-edge multigraph in Figure 24(b) has an Eulerian tour, since each vertex has even degree. In fact, the tour of Example 11 is an Eulerian tour of this modified multigraph. This multigraph is similar to the multigraph of Figure 23, except that some edges, such as {1,3}, have been doubled and one, {1,4}, has been

Figure 24

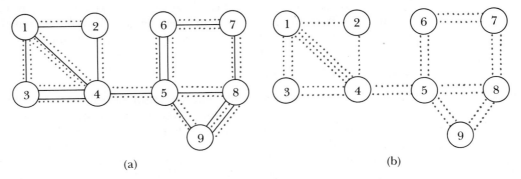

(a)   (b)

tripled. Thus the multigraph in Figure 24(b) is obtained by adding copies of existing edges to the multigraph in Figure 23 until the resulting multigraph has an Eulerian tour. This Eulerian tour gives us the edge tour of the original multigraph. In Figure 25, we have shown the multigraph of Figure 24(b) with edges also in the original graph shown as solid. This figure shows that we added eight edges to the multigraph of Figure 23 in order to get our Eulerian tour. If there were a way to add fewer edges to the multigraph in Figure 23 to get an Eulerian tour, that tour would be a lower-weight edge tour for Figure 23. With this in mind, let us examine how we may add edges to Figure 23 in order to convert all the degrees to even numbers. Adding the edge {1,3} and {4,5} to Figure 23 gives us the first graph in Figure 26.

Could we double just one more edge and have no vertices of odd degree? No, because the two leftover vertices, 6 and 9, are a distance 2 apart. This suggests that we add two more edges, as in Figure 26(b). This multigraph has no vertices of odd degree, so it has an Eulerian walk. By experimenting with doubling edges touching vertices of odd degree, we can see that any way of doubling edges to make the graph Eulerian will require at least four edges. Any Eulerian tour in the multigraph of Figure 26(b) will be a solution to the school bus problem and a better tour than the one we rather randomly chose in Example 11.

Figure 25

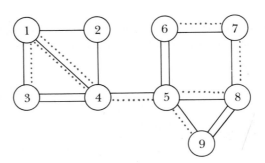

Figure 26

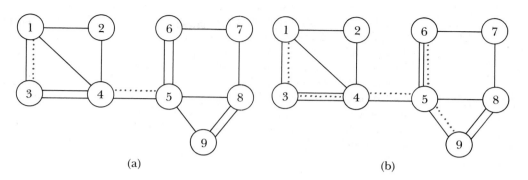

(a)   (b)

EXAMPLE 13   Find a minimum weight edge tour of Figure 23 by finding an Eulerian tour of Figure 26(b).

Solution   In Figure 27, we show the process of finding and erasing closed walks until we run out of edges. Putting this sequence of closed walks together gives us 1-4-3-1-2-4-5-6-7-8-9-5-6-5-8-9-5-4-3-1. ■

Figure 27   The arrows show the closed walk about to be removed.

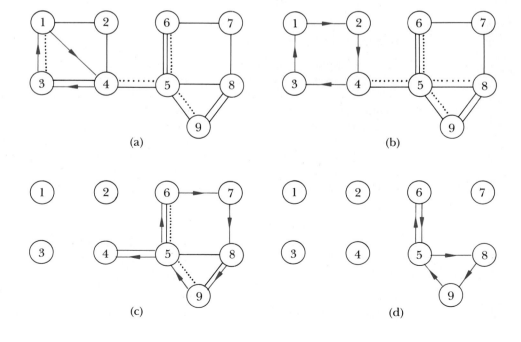

(a)   (b)

(c)   (d)

We used a trial-and-error process of experimentation to find the minimum-sized set of edges to add to the multigraph in Figure 23 to make it Eulerian. For small weighted graphs, trial-and-error procedures are fine for people to use. However, they are not well suited to use on a computer. We could, of course, check each set of edges to determine whether it could be doubled in order to make the graph Eulerian. However, the number of sets of edges is $2^{|E|}$; even with a computer, this amount of checking is formidable. There is a polynomial time algorithm for finding a set of edges to double, but explaining this algorithm uses more graph theory than we have space to cover. [The book *Graph Theory, An Algorithmic Approach* by Nicos Cristofides (Academic Press, New York, 1975) covers the tools needed to develop such an algorithm.]

C   *Vertex Tours*

Just as some problems call for us to visit all the edges of a graph, others call for us to visit all the vertices.

> A closed walk that visits all vertices of a
> (multi)(di)graph is called a **vertex tour**.

The best-known example is called the *traveling salesman problem*. We have a weighted graph whose vertices represent cities and whose edges represent air routes between the cities. The number on an edge is the cost of a ticket on that air route. The problem is to choose a walk that visits each city, returns to its starting place, and costs as little as possible.

Hamiltonian Tours

In some applications, we don't need to concern ourselves with weights on the edges. For example, if we have a number of computers tied into a communications network, we may wish to choose a set of communications links that lets us put the computers into a single-ring network. Recall that a single-ring network is an arrangement of the computers in a "communications circle" such that messages may be passed along the circle in one direction. Since the links are already constructed, the cost of the links we use is unlikely to be a consideration; our only problem is to construct a walk, starting and ending at the same vertex, that includes each other vertex exactly once. The edges of this walk will be the links of the ring network.

> A closed walk that contains each vertex (except the first and
> last) of a graph exactly once is called a **Hamiltonian tour** of
> the graph. A path that contains each vertex of the graph
> once and only once is called a **Hamiltonian path**.

Hamiltonian tours and paths are named after William Rowan Hamilton, who invented a game called "Around the World." The game required the players to find a Hamiltonian tour of a graph representing an imaginary transportation network among the cities of the world.

EXAMPLE 14 Which of the following sequences of vertices and edges are Hamiltonian tours of the graph in Figure 28?

Figure 28

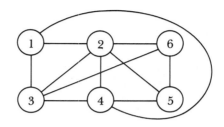

(a) 1{1,2}2{2,4}3{3,6}6{6,5}5{5,4}4{4,1}1
(b) 3{3,4}4{4,5}5{5,2}2{1,2}1{1,6}6{6,3}3
(c) 1{1,2}2{2,5}5{5,4}4{2,4}2{2,6}6{6,3}3{3,1}1
(d) 5{2,5}2{4,2}4{3,4}3{1,3}1{1,6}6{6,5}5
(e) 1{2,1}2{5,2}5{5,4}4{4,3}3{3,1}1

Solution   Since {4,1} is not an edge, (a) is not a walk and thus is not a Hamiltonian tour. Sequence (b) is a Hamiltonian tour because it is a closed walk and each vertex appears exactly once. Sequence (c) is not a Hamiltonian tour because vertex 2 appears twice. Sequence (d) is a Hamiltonian tour. Sequence (e) is not a Hamiltonian tour because vertex 6 does not appear at all. ∎

EXAMPLE 15 With the following weights on the edges, which of the vertex tours in Example 14 is the least weight tour?

Edge	{1,2}	{1,3}	{1,6}	{2,3}	{2,4}	{2,5}	{2,6}	{3,4}	{3,6}	{4,5}	{4,6}	{5,6}
Weight	1	1	4	3	2	1	1	2	2	1	3	3

Solution   The vertex tours are (b), (c), and (d). The total weight of (b) is $2 + 1 + 1 + 1 + 4 + 2 = 11$. The total weight of (c) is 9. The total weight of (d) is 13. Thus the least cost vertex tour among those given is tour (c). ∎

Example 15 suggests that a minimum cost vertex tour need not be Hamiltonian. In fact this is the case.

EXAMPLE 16 Find a minimum cost vertex tour in the graph of Figure 29.

Solution   The walk 1{1,2}2{1,2}1{1,3}3{1,3}1{1,4}4{1,4}1 has total weight $1 + 1 + 1 + 1 + 2 + 2 = 8$. It is a vertex tour. It has minimum cost because a tour

Figure 29

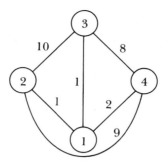

containing any other edge would have total weight more than 8, since it would have an edge of weight 8 or more. ∎

In some applications, of course, we will want to choose a minimum cost Hamiltonian tour rather than simply a minimum cost vertex tour.

EXAMPLE 17   The graph in Figure 29 shows a hypothetical network of air connections between cities. The numbers along the edges represent costs. Each of the air flights takes about the same amount of time. Among all the vertex tours taking a minimum amount of time, find the one that is cheapest.

Solution   A minimum time vertex tour will be a Hamiltonian tour. Thus we want to find a minimum cost Hamiltonian tour. This will be a four-vertex cycle, called a *four-cycle* for short. (In Section 8-1, we defined a cycle to be a closed walk without repeated vertices or edges.) However, a four-vertex cycle does not have three mutually intersecting edges, so one of the edges $\{1,2\}$, $\{1,3\}$, and $\{1,4\}$ is not in the cycle. Deleting the edge $\{1,2\}$ leaves a graph without a four cycle. Deleting either $\{1,3\}$ or $\{1,4\}$ leaves a four cycle; the cheaper one is the four cycle $1\{1,2\}2\{2,4\}4\{3,4\}3\{1,3\}1$, so this is the minimum cost Hamiltonian tour. ∎

Determining Whether a Graph Has a Hamiltonian Tour

Recall that we have a simple way to check whether a graph has an Eulerian tour; we check whether every vertex has even degree. There are no similar results for Hamiltonian tours, but there are results telling us that certain graphs have Hamiltonian tours. A typical result about the existence of Hamiltonian tours is the following theorem.

Theorem 5   If, in a graph with $n > 2$ vertices, each vertex has degree $n/2$ or more, then the graph has a Hamiltonian tour.

Figure 30   The edges $\{x_1,y\}$, $\{x_1,x_i\}$ and $\{x_{i-1},y\}$ are shown as colored lines. Dotted lines represent the other vertices on the walk. Other edges of H' are not shown.

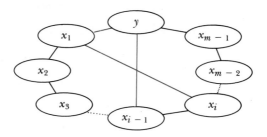

Proof   Certainly, if the graph were complete in the sense that *each* pair of vertices is an edge, taking a list of the vertices in any order would give a Hamiltonian tour. Thus if there is a counter example H to the theorem, we may add edges to H one at a time until we get a graph H' with a Hamiltonian cycle. (This cycle is illustrated in Figure 30.) Let G be the graph that we get from H' by deleting the last edge $\{x,y\}$ we added. Then G is a counter-example to the theorem, and since each edge of H is an edge of G, each vertex of G has degree $n/2$ or more. (G might in fact be H.) Since H' has a Hamiltonian cycle, and removing $\{x,y\}$ destroys that Hamiltonian cycle, the cycle must have consisted of a path from x to y including *all* the vertices together with the edge $\{x,y\}$. Thus G has the path

$$x = x_1\{x_1,x_2\}x_2 \cdots \{x_{n-1},x_n\}x_n = y$$

which includes all the vertices. Note that if x_i is adjacent to x and x_{i-1} is adjacent to y, then (as you can see in Figure 30) the cycle

$$x_1\{x_1,x_2\} \cdots x_{i-1}\{x_{i-1},y\}y\{y,x_{n-1}\}x_{n-1}\{x_{n-1},x_{n-2}\} \cdots x_i\{x_i,x_1\}x_1$$

is a Hamiltonian cycle. Thus for each x_i adjacent to x, x_{i-1} is *not* adjacent to y. Since there are $n/2$ or more vertices adjacent to x, there are at least $n/2$ vertices *not* adjacent to y between x_1 and x_{n-1}. But then fewer than $n/2$ vertices remain to be adjacent to y, contradicting the hypothesis that y has degree $n/2$ or more. Thus the assumption that there was a counter-example is incorrect; this proves the theorem.   ∎

The proof of the theorem is called an **existence proof** because it shows that something exists without showing how to construct it. In contrast, the proof we gave to show that Eulerian tours exist when all vertices have even degree was **constructive**, because it could be used as the basis for an algorithm to construct the tours that it proved to exist. All known algorithms for constructing Hamiltonian tours are quite time-consuming.

Concepts Review

1. A(n) _____ walk in a multigraph includes each edge of the multigraph (as often as its multiplicity).

2. A closed Eulerian walk is called a(n) _____ _____.

3. If a connected multigraph has an Eulerian tour, then each vertex has a(n) _____ _____ as its degree.

4. If a connected multigraph has an Eulerian walk (but not an Eulerian tour), then the graph has _____ vertices of odd degree.

5. A(n) _____ _____ of a multigraph is a closed walk that includes each edge at least once (for each time it appears in the edge multiset).

6. The Chinese postman problem is the problem of finding a(n) _____ _____ edge tour of a weighted graph or digraph.

7. A Hamiltonian tour of a multigraph includes each vertex (except the first and last) _____ _____.

8. A path that includes each vertex once and only once is called a(n) _____ _____.

Exercises

A   1. Draw a multigraph whose vertices represent the land masses and whose edges represent the bridges in the map of Figure 31(a).

Figure 31

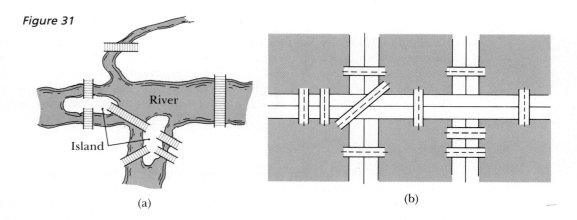

(a)   (b)

2. A city is divided by interstate highways as shown in Figure 31(b). A system of overpasses allows city traffic to pass from region to region. Draw the graph whose vertices represent the 6 regions of the city and whose edges represent the 10 overpasses.

3. Use inspection to write down the vertices and edges of an Eulerian walk in the graph you drew in Exercise 1. (You will need to assign labels to the vertices.)

4. Use inspection to write down the vertices and edges of an Eulerian walk in the graph you drew in Exercise 2. (*Hint:* Start in the vertex that corresponds to the upper left-hand corner.) (You will need to assign labels to the vertices.)

5. Does the graph you drew in Exercise 1 have an Eulerian tour?

6. Does the graph you drew in Exercise 2 have an Eulerian tour?

7. In the late eighteenth century, another bridge was built in Figure 19, connecting the left bank to the right bank. Did this make an Eulerian walk possible? Did this make an Eulerian tour possible?

8. In Figure 19, suppose another bridge was built connecting the island to the point. Does this make an Eulerian walk possible? Does this make an Eulerian tour possible?

9. Find an Eulerian walk or tour in the multigraph of Figure 32(a).

Figure 32

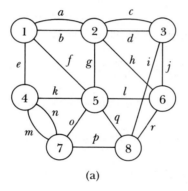

(a)

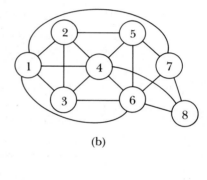

(b)

10. Find an Eulerian walk or tour in the multigraph of Figure 32(b).

11. Redraw Figure 31(a) with one more bridge so that it has an Eulerian tour.

12. Why is it impossible to build one more highway overpass in Figure 31(b) in order to construct a network that has an Eulerian tour?

B **13.** Find the total weight of the edge tour 1-2-3-4-1-5-2-3-4-5-1 in Figure 33.

Figure 33

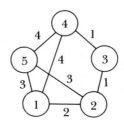

14. Find the total weight of the edge tour 1-5-4-3-5-1-3-2-4-5-1-2-1-5-1 in Figure 34.

Figure 34

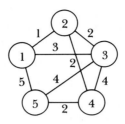

15. Which of the following is an edge tour of the graph in Figure 33?
    (a) 1-2-3-4-5-2-1-4-5-1   (b) 1-2-3-4-1-5-2-3-4-1
    (c) 1-5-4-1-5-2-3-4-1-2-1   (d) 1-4-3-2-5-4-1-5-4-3-2-1

16. Which of the following is an edge tour of the graph in Figure 34?
    (a) 1-2-3-4-5-1-3-2-4-5-3-1   (b) 1-2-3-4-2-3-4-5-3-1
    (c) 1-5-3-1-2-3-4-5-3-4-1   (d) 1-5-3-1-2-3-4-5-1-2-4-5-1

17. Show how to make the graph of Figure 33 have an Eulerian tour by duplicating two edges of the graph.

18. Show how to make the graph of Figure 34 have an Eulerian tour by duplicating two edges of the graph.

19. Find a minimum cost set of edges to duplicate in order to make the graph of Figure 33 have an Eulerian tour.

20. Find a minimum cost set of edges to duplicate in order to make the graph of Figure 34 have an Eulerian tour.

21. Change the weight of edge {3,4} to 3 and repeat Exercise 19.

22. Change the weight of edges {1,2}, {2,4}, and {4,5} to 7 and repeat Exercise 20.

23. Find a minimum weight edge tour for the graph of Figure 33.

24. Find a minimum weight edge tour for the graph of Figure 34.

25. Find a minimum weight edge tour for the graph of Figure 33 using the weights of Exercise 21.

26. Find a minimum weight edge tour for the graph of Figure 34 using the weights of Exercise 22.

C 27. For each sequence below of vertices and edges of the graph in Figure 35, state whether the sequence is a vertex tour, a Hamiltonian tour, a Hamiltonian path, or none of these.
    (a) 1{1,2}2{2,6}6{5,6}5{3,5}3{3,4}4{1,4}1
    (b) 1{1,2}2{2,4}4{4,3}3{3,5}5{5,6}6{6,1}1
    (c) 1{1,2}2{2,3}3{3,4}4{4,1}1{1,5}5{5,6}6
    (d) 1{1,5}5{5,6}6{2,6}2{2,3}3{3,4}4{1,4}1
    (e) 1{1,2}2{2,6}6{6,5}5{4,5}4{3,4}3

Figure 35

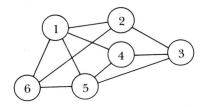

28. For each sequence below of vertices and edges of the graph in Figure 35, state whether the sequence is a vertex tour, a Hamiltonian tour, a Hamiltonian path, or none of these.
    (a) 5{3,5}3{3,4}4{4,1}1{1,2}2{2,6}6{5,6}5
    (b) 5{5,6}6{2,6}2{2,3}3{3,4}4{4,6}6{6,1}1{1,5}5
    (c) 5{5,3}3{3,4}4{4,1}1{1,6}6{6,2}2
    (d) 5{5,4}4{4,1}1{1,2}2{2,6}6{1,6}6{5,6}5
    (e) 5{3,5}3{3,4}4{4,1}1{1,6}6{2,6}2{2,3}3{3,5}5

29. Among the following vertex tours of the weighted graph of Figure 36, find the one of least total weight.
    (a) 1-6-4-5-3-2-1
    (b) 1-3-4-6-4-5-4-3-2-1
    (c) 1-2-3-2-1-3-4-5-4-6-4-1
    (d) 1-2-3-1-4-5-4-6-1
    (e) 1-2-3-5-4-6-1

Figure 36

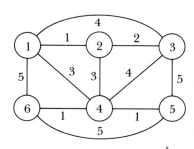

30. Among the following vertex tours of the weighted graph of Figure 36, find the one of minimum total weight.
    (a) 3-5-4-6-1-2-3
    (b) 3-1-2-4-6-5-3
    (c) 3-2-1-4-6-4-5-4-3
    (d) 4-5-6-1-3-2-4
    (e) 4-2-1-2-3-2-4-6-4-5-4

31. Among the Hamiltonian tours in Exercise 29, find one of minimum weight.

32. Among the Hamiltonian tours in Exercise 30, find one of minimum weight.

33. Find *all* Hamiltonian tours starting and ending at vertex 1 in the graph of Figure 37.

Figure 37

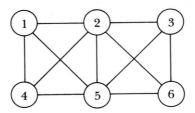

34. Find all Hamiltonian tours starting and ending at vertex 4 in the graph of Figure 38.

Figure 38

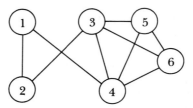

35. Draw an example of a connected graph with 6 vertices and 9 edges that does not have a Hamiltonian tour but whose vertices all have degree 2 or more.

36. Draw an example of a connected graph with 7 vertices and 12 edges that does not have a Hamiltonian tour but whose vertices all have degree 2 or more.

Problems

1. The concepts of Eulerian walk and Eulerian tour have been defined in such a way that the definitions apply to digraphs as well. Show that if a digraph (or multidigraph) has an Eulerian tour, then every vertex has equal indegree and outdegree.

2. A multidigraph is said to be *weakly connected* if erasing all the arrowheads leaves a connected graph. Show that a weakly connected digraph has an Eulerian tour if each vertex has equal indegree and outdegree.

3. In the game of dominoes, we play with rectangular tiles with dots representing numbers at each end. In one version of the game, we place tiles end to end in such a way that the ends match. If each two-element multiset of numbers between zero (a blank) and 6 appears exactly once on a domino, is it possible to use all the dominoes in this game?

4. Give a proof of Theorem 3 similar to the proof of Theorem 2.

5. Give a proof of Theorem 3 by adding an edge connecting the two vertices of odd degree, applying Theorem 2, and then removing that edge.

6. There are 8 sequences (x_1, x_2, x_3) of three zeros and ones. Draw a digraph of these sequences by drawing an arrow from (x_1, x_2, x_3) to each different sequence of the form (x_2, x_3, y). Here y can stand for 0 or 1. Thus $(1, 0, 0)$ has an arrow to $(0, 0, 0)$ and $(0, 0, 1)$, because x_2 and x_3 are both 0. Note, we do not draw arrows from a vertex to itself. Thus there is no arrow from $(0, 0, 0)$ to $(0, 0, 0)$. Show that this graph has an Eulerian tour.

Use the Eulerian tour to write down 8 zeros and ones around the circumference of a circle so that each of the eight possible arcs with three numbers on it represents one of the sequences. Thus, for example, 000 will be on an arc, 001 will be on an arc, and so on.

7. Show that if a graph has k vertices of odd degree, then k is even.

8. Show that if a graph has k vertices of odd degree, then the number of vertices in an edge tour is at least $|E| + \frac{k}{2}$.

9. Can a weighted graph have two different Eulerian tours with different costs? Give an example or show why not.

10. Discuss the minimum size of an edge tour of a complete graph on n vertices (one in which each pair of vertices is an edge) for all values of n.

11. Draw an example of a graph that has a Hamiltonian path but not a Hamiltonian tour.

12. Show that if in a graph with $n > 2$ vertices the sum of the degrees of each two vertices is n or more, then the graph has a Hamiltonian tour.

13. A Hamiltonian tour in a digraph is defined in the same way as a Hamiltonian tour in a graph. Show that if for each 2 vertices x and y the outdegree of x plus the indegree of y is n or more, then the digraph has a Hamiltonian tour.

14. If we put arrows on all the edges of a complete graph on n vertices (see Problem 10), will the resulting digraph be sure to have a Hamiltonian path?

Section 9-3
Coloring
and Planarity

◢ Intersection Graphs and Graph Coloring

One way in which graphs come up in applications is in the study of interactions among people, processes, time periods, responsibilities, and so on.

EXAMPLE 18 In scheduling a language achievement contest, we have language proficiency exams in French, German, and Spanish and literature exams in French, German, Spanish, and Latin. Table 1 shows which of eight hypothetical students have entered which exams. Draw a graph that illustrates which tests have students in common with which other tests.

Solution In Figure 39, we have drawn a vertex for each of the seven examinations. For each student, we have then drawn an edge between two exams if that student

Table 1

Exam	Students 1	2	3	4	5	6	7	8
FP	X		X			X	X	X
GP			X		X			
SP		X		X		X	X	
FL	X			X				X
GL			X					
SL				X		X		
LL	X	X				X	X	X

Figure 39

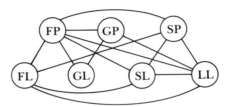

is enrolled in both exams. We draw just one edge between two vertices even if the two tests have more than one student in common. ■

Intersection Graphs

The kind of graph we have drawn in Figure 40 is called an *intersection graph*. A graph is called an **intersection graph** if we may associate sets to the vertices in such a way that two vertices are joined by an edge if and only if their sets have a nonempty intersection.

Figure 40

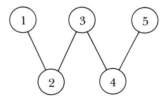

EXAMPLE 19   What sets may be associated to the vertices of the graph in Figure 39 to represent it as an intersection graph?

Solution   We drew an edge between two vertices if their tests had at least one student in common. This suggests that the intersections of sets should show the students which are in common. Thus it is natural to associate with each test the set of students taking that test. Doing so gives us FP:{1,3,6,7,8}, GP:{3,5}, SP:{2,4,6,7}, FL:{1,4,8}, GL:{3}, SL:{4,6}, LL:{1,2,5,6,7}. Notice, for example, that the set associated with FP has a nonempty intersection with the sets for GP, SP, FL, GL, SL, and LL. Therefore, there should be an edge from FP to each of the other vertices. We see in Figure 39 that this is the case. For each other vertex we may show that its edges correspond to its intersections with other sets. ■

Coloring

How do we make use of an intersection graph? One typical use is illustrated by the interactions described in Example 18. The problem we would naturally face in Example 18 is scheduling the exams so that a student won't have to be in two different exams at the same time. Thus we want an assignment of time slots to exams so that two exams with a student in common will not be scheduled in the same time slot. For reasons not relevant here, such an assignment is called a coloring.

Given a graph G with vertex set V and an edge set E, a **coloring** of G with color set C is a function f from V to C. We call the elements of C **colors.**

A coloring function f is a **proper coloring** of G if
$f(x) \neq f(y)$ whenever x and y are joined by
an edge in E.

In Example 18, we want to properly color the graph using the set of time slots as our set of colors. Let us return to Example 18 after some less complicated examples.

EXAMPLE 20   Show how to properly color the graph in Figure 40 with the three colors red, black, and gray.

Solution   In Figure 41, we show a way to assign the color red first, then gray, and finally black. Notice that we assigned the color red to two nonadjacent vertices, then gray to two nonadjacent vertices, and finally black to the remaining vertex. Thus no two adjacent vertices have the same color. ■

Figure 41

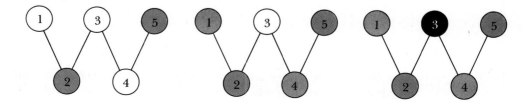

EXAMPLE 21   Show a way to properly color the graph of Figure 40 with two colors.

Solution   We may color vertices 2 and 4 with red because they are not adjacent. We may color vertices 1, 3, and 5 black because no two of them are adjacent.   ■

As Examples 20 and 21 show, different proper colorings might use different numbers of colors.

The **chromatic number** of a graph is the minimum number of colors needed in any proper coloring.

EXAMPLE 22   What is the chromatic number of the graph in Figure 40?

Solution   One color cannot be used in Figure 40, but Example 21 shows that we can find a proper coloring with two colors. Thus the chromatic number is two.   ■

In general, determining the chromatic number of a graph is rather difficult. For one kind of graph, a *complete* graph on n vertices, the chromatic number is obvious. A **complete graph** on n vertices consists of n vertices, each two of which are connected by an edge. A complete graph whose vertices and edges are all vertices and edges of G is called a **clique** of G.

Theorem 6   If G contains a clique on n vertices, then the chromatic number of G is at least n.

Proof   No two of the n vertices in the complete graph may be the same color, so a proper coloring requires at least n colors.   ■

EXAMPLE 23   Find the chromatic number of the graph in Figure 39.

Solution   The 5 vertices FP, FL, SP, SL, and LL are all mutually interconnected. Therefore, the graph has chromatic number at least 5. The scheme FP:R, GP:G, SL:G, SP:B, GL:B, FL:Y, LL:W is a proper coloring of the graph with five colors. Therefore the chromatic number is 5.   ■

EXAMPLE 24   Use the coloring of Exercise 23 to give a schedule of the exams in Example 18.

Solution   Each color represents a different time slot. Thus we may schedule French Proficiency in period 1, German Proficiency and Spanish Literature in period 2, SP and GL in period 3, FL in period 4, and LL in period 5. Any permutation of these time periods is also appropriate.   ■

B *Planarity*

The drawings we give of graphs are always on flat surfaces—on *planes*. Some of the drawings, such as graphs (b) and (c) in Figure 42, are more difficult to visualize than others because their edges cross over each other. In fact, drawing (b) is

Figure 42

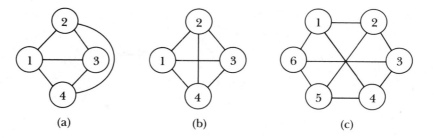

(a)   (b)   (c)

needlessly complicated, because if we were to route the edge {2,4} *around* vertex 3, we would get the drawing in Figure 42(a). Thus (a) and (b) are drawings of the same graph.

> A drawing of a graph is called a **planar drawing** if the lines representing edges do not cross. A graph that has a planar drawing is called a **planar graph.**

EXAMPLE 25   Show that the graph drawn in Figure 42(b) is planar.

Solution   Figure 42(a) is a planar drawing of the graph in Figure 42(b).   ■

EXAMPLE 26   Show that the graph drawn in Figure 42(c) is not planar.

Solution   Suppose we have a planar drawing; we shall show that this leads to a contradiction. In the drawing, the vertices 1 through 6 form a six-sided figure, which has an inside and an outside. If the edge {1,4} crosses through the inside, then neither the edge {2,5} nor {3,6} may cross through the inside. If the edge {2,5} crosses through the outside of the figure, then the edge {3,6} may not cross through the outside. But {1,4} and {2,5} must be drawn somewhere without crossing each other, so one must be on the inside and the other must be on the outside. Therefore, there is nowhere to draw the edge {3,6}; we have a contradiction.   ■

Euler's Formula

When we draw a graph on a plane surface, it divides the surface up into regions. For example, in Figure 43(a), we see a "triangular" region bounded by the cycle 4{4,5}5{5,6}6{6,4}4. Another region is bounded by the cycle 1-2-4-5-1 and has edge {2,3} and vertex 3 "sticking out" into it. Another drawing of the same graph is shown in Figure 43(b). Both drawings divide the plane into four regions, one entirely outside the drawing and the others polygons with cycles of the graph forming their boundaries.

When Euler studied planar drawings, he called these regions **faces.** He noticed that no matter how you redraw a planar drawing, the number of faces is always the same. He also saw that when the drawing is connected, the number (f) of faces

Figure 43

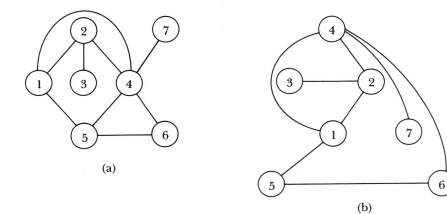

(a)

(b)

is always determined by the number (v) of vertices and the number (e) of edges by the formula, now called **Euler's formula,**

$$v - e + f = 2$$

Theorem 7   If a planar drawing of a connected multigraph G with v vertices and e edges has f faces, then $v - e + f = 2$.

Proof   We prove the result by induction on the number of faces. If the outside face is the only face, then G can have no cycles, so G is a tree because it is connected. Then $e = v - 1$ and $f = 1$, so $v - e + f = 2$.

Now assume that G has at least two faces and suppose $\{x,y\}$ is an edge on the boundary of two faces. Removing the edge (but not its vertices) leaves a connected graph with $e - 1$ edges and $f - 1$ faces (because two faces have just become one). (The graph is still connected, because we removed just one edge of a closed walk.) We may assume inductively that $v - (e - 1) + (f - 1) = 2$, but simplifying gives us $v - e + f = 2$. Thus, by the principle of mathematical induction, the formula is true for all connected planar graphs.   ∎

EXAMPLE 27   If a connected planar graph has 7 vertices and 9 edges, how many faces must a planar drawing have?

Solution   Since $7 - 9 + f = 2$, we obtain $f = 2 + 2 = 4$. In fact, we see in Figure 43 that the two drawings have 7 vertices, 9 edges, and 4 faces.   ∎

Our next theorem lets us derive a useful inequality that makes some applications of Euler's formula easier.

Theorem 8   In a simple planar graph with v vertices, e edges, and f faces, $3f \leq 2e$.

Proof The proof consists of carefully using the facts that each face has at least three edges on its boundary and each edge touches at most two faces. ■

We shall call the inequality below in Theorem 9 **Euler's inequality.**

Theorem 9 In a simple planar graph with v vertices and e edges, $e \le 3v - 6$.

Proof We solve $v - e + f = 2$ for f, getting $f = 2 + e - v$. We substitute this into $3f \le 2e$, getting

$$6 + 3e - 3v \le 2e \qquad \text{or} \qquad e \le 3v - 6$$ ■

EXAMPLE 28 A complete graph on 5 vertices has each two-element subset of its 5-element vertex set as an edge. A picture is in Figure 44. Show that this graph, denoted by K_5, is not planar.

Figure 44 The complete graph on five vertices.

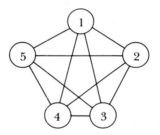

Solution The graph K_5 has 5 vertices. Since each two-element set is an edge, the graph has $\binom{5}{2} = 10$ edges. Thus e is 10 and $3v - 6$ is 9, so $e \not\le 3v - 6$. By Theorem 9, K_5 cannot be planar. ■

In the nineteenth century, a popular problem of recreational mathematics was the question, "Can you always color a map of a world with four colors in such a way that countries that share a boundary line have different colors?". One attempted proof was published by a respected mathematician; years later the proof was found to be in error. The problem is equivalent to asking whether every planar graph has a proper coloring with four colors. The *four-color problem* led to many developments in graph theory. In 1976, Kenneth Apel and Wolfgang Haken announced that by extensive use of a computer they had been able to demonstrate that a planar graph may indeed be properly colored with four colors. As yet, no one has found a proof that does not use a computer in a significant way. [See the article, "The Four Color Problem," by Apel and Haken, in the book *Mathematics Today,* edited by Lynn Arthur Steen (Springer-Verlag, 1978) for a fascinating historical overview of the work leading to the proof.]

Concepts Review

1. A graph is called a(n) _____ _____ if we may associate sets to the vertices in such a way that two vertices are joined by an edge if and only if their sets have a(n) _____ _____.

2. A(n) _____ _____ of G is a function f from the vertex set of G to a set C such that $f(x) \neq f(y)$ if x and y are joined by a(n) _____.

3. The _____ _____ of a graph is the minimum number of colors used in any _____ _____.

4. A complete graph contained in a multigraph G is called a(n) _____ of G.

5. If G contains an n-vertex clique, then the _____ _____ of G is at least n.

6. A(n) _____ _____ of a graph is a drawing of the graph in a plane such that lines representing edges do not _____.

7. A graph is planar if it has a(n) _____ _____.

8. The regions into which a drawing of a connected graph divides a plane are called the _____ of the drawing.

9. In _____ formula, $v - e + f =$ _____, v stands for the number of _____, e for the number of _____, and f for the number of _____.

Exercises

A

1. Draw the intersection graph whose vertices and edges are determined by the following sets: $\{1,2,3\}$, $\{1,2,3,4\}$, $\{1,3,5,7\}$, $\{1,4,5,6\}$, $\{2,4,6\}$, $\{3,5,7\}$, $\{1,4,7\}$.

2. Draw the intersection graph whose vertices and edges are determined by the following sets: $\{a\}$, $\{a,b,c\}$, $\{a,c,d\}$, $\{a,d,e\}$, $\{a,e,f\}$, $\{a,f,b\}$.

3. We are scheduling a track meet with 6 events and 10 participants. Table 2 shows which participants have entered which events. Draw a graph whose vertices represent the events and whose edges show which events have contestants in common.

Table 2

Events	\multicolumn{10}{c}{Participants}
	1	2	3	4	5	6	7	8	9	10
1		X		X				X	X	X
2	X	X	X	X	X	X	X	X		
3	X	X	X	X	X					X
4					X	X			X	
5	X			X	X		X	X		X
6							X	X	X	X

4. A computer program with 7 procedures uses 6 data files. The files used by each procedure are shown in Table 3. Draw a graph whose vertices represent the procedures and whose edges show which procedures use at least one file in common.

Table 3

Procedures	Files					
	1	2	3	4	5	6
1		X		X		
2	X		X	X	X	
3		X	X			X
4	X		X	X		
5		X	X			X
6	X					X
7		X			X	X

5. Write down the set of contestants for each of the six events shown in Table 2.

6. Write down the set of files used by each of the procedures shown in Table 3.

7. Draw the intersection graph for the sets in Exercise 5. How should this graph relate to the one drawn in Exercise 3?

8. Draw the intersection graph for the sets in Exercise 6. How should this relate to the graph drawn in Exercise 4?

9. Find a proper coloring using the colors red, green, and blue for Figure 45.

Figure 45

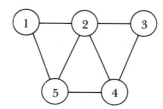

10. Find a proper coloring using the colors red, green, and blue for Figure 46.

Figure 46

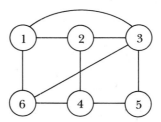

11. Find the chromatic number of the graph in Figure 45.

12. Find the chromatic number of the graph in Figure 46.

B   In Exercises 13–16, determine whether the graph specified is planar. Give a planar drawing or explain why the graph is not planar.

13. Figure 47   14. Figure 48

15. Figure 49   16. Figure 50

Figure 47

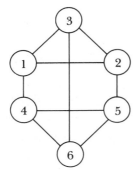

Figure 48

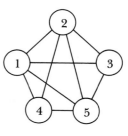

Figure 49

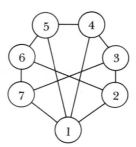

Figure 50

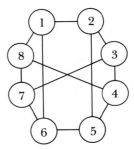

17. Find a planar drawing (by trial and error) of the graph with edge set {{1,2}, {2,3}, {3,4}, {4,5}, {1,5}, {1,4}, {2,5}, {2,4}, {3,5}} and vertex set {1,2,3,4,5}.

18. Find a planar drawing of the graph on {1,2,3,4,5,6} with adjacency lists 1:2,3,4; 2:1,5,6; 3:1,5; 4:1,5,6; 5:2,3,4; 6:2,4.

19. If a planar graph has 10 vertices and 20 edges, how many faces does it have?

20. If a planar graph has 12 vertices and 18 edges, how many faces does it have?

21. Show that the graph in Figure 49 satisfies the formula $e \leq 3v - 6$. Does this mean that the graph in Figure 49 is planar? Explain why or why not.

22. Show that the graph in Figure 50 satisfies the formula $e \leq 3v - 6$. Does this mean that the graph in Figure 50 is planar? Explain why or why not.

23. Is the graph in Figure 51 planar?

24. Is the graph in Figure 52 planar?

Figure 51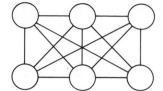

Figure 52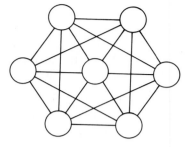

Problems

1. A graph is called *bipartite* if its vertex set may be divided into two parts V_1 and V_2 such that each edge connects a vertex in V_1 with a vertex in V_2. Figure 9(b) shows a traditional way to view a bipartite graph. Show that the chromatic number of a bipartite graph is two.

2. Show that a graph whose chromatic number is two is a bipartite graph.

3. If a graph contains a five-vertex cycle, can its chromatic number be two?

4. What is the chromatic number of a tree with two or more vertices?

5. What is the chromatic number of a cycle with an even number of vertices? With an odd number of vertices?

6. What is the chromatic number of a complete graph on n vertices? (A *complete graph* on a vertex set V is one having each two-element subset of V as an edge.)

7. What is the maximum possible number of edges in a graph with n vertices and chromatic number $n-1$?

8. Can a graph with a loop have a proper coloring?

9. We say an edge *contacts* a face if that edge touches that face. A *contact pair* is an ordered pair $(\{x,y\}, F)$ such that F is a face and $\{x,y\}$ is an edge that contacts F.
   (a) Show that in a simple planar graph the number of contact pairs is at least $3f$, three times the number of faces.
   (b) Show that in a simple planar graph the number of contact pairs is at most $2e$, twice the number of edges.
   (c) Complete the proof of the inequality $3f \leq 2e$.

10. Contact pairs are defined in Problem 9.
    (a) Show that if a simple planar graph has no three-vertex cycles (three-cycles), then the number of contact pairs is at least $4f$.
    (b) Show that if a simple planar graph has no three-cycles, then $2f \leq e$.
    (c) Show that if a simple planar graph has no three-cycles, then $e \leq 2v - 4$.
    (d) A *complete bipartite graph* with two parts of size 3 is, by definition, a graph whose vertex set is a union of two disjoint parts each of size 3 such that each vertex in one part is connected to each vertex in the other part, but no vertex is connected to another vertex in the same part. The standard notation for this graph is $K_{3,3}$. Draw $K_{3,3}$. Show that $K_{3,3}$ is not planar.

11. Is it possible to make a planar graph from a complete graph on five vertices by removing one edge? Is it possible to make a planar graph from a complete graph on six vertices by removing two edges?

12. Show that if a planar graph has two connected components, then $v - e + f = 3$. State and prove the corresponding formula for a graph with k connected components.

13. Sketch a cube with its vertices numbered 1 through 8. Now draw a planar graph with $\{1,2,3,4,5,6,7,8\}$ as its vertex set and with $\{i,j\}$ an edge if and only if i and j are connected by an edge of the cube.
    (a) Show that there is a one-to-one correspondence between the faces of the graph and the faces of the cube.
    (b) An icosahedron is a 20-sided three-dimensional figure whose faces all are triangles. How many edges does it have? How many vertices does it have?
    (c) A dodecahedron is a 12-sided figure in three dimensions whose faces are all pentagons. How many vertices and edges does it have?

14. (a) Show that if every vertex of a graph has degree six or more, then the number e of edges is at least three times the number v of vertices.
    (b) Show that a planar graph has at least one vertex of degree five or less.

15. Use the result of part (b) of the previous problem to show by induction that every planar graph has a proper coloring using six or fewer colors.

Section 9-4
Digraphs
and Machines

A Machine Digraphs

An important application of digraphs is to give a model for the inner workings of an "intelligent" machine such as a computer. One such machine is the device used in an "exact change lane" at a toll booth on a highway or bridge. This machine adds up the values of the coins dropped into it until the total value is the required toll and then signals the driver to go ahead. Figure 53 shows a digraph of a machine to collect an exact toll of 25 cents.

Figure 53   A digraph of an "exact change" toll counter.

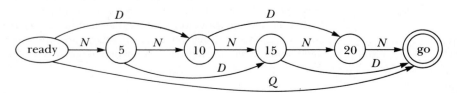

How Digraphs Can Represent Machines

When we use a digraph to represent a machine, we call its vertices the **states** of a machine. Thus the machine represented in Figure 53 has a ready state, a five-cent state, a ten-cent state, a fifteen-cent state, a twenty-cent state, and a go state. When a driver arrives at the machine, it is in its ready state, waiting for someone to put in some change. The legal inputs (things the driver may put into it) are nickels, dimes, and quarters. Each time the machine receives an input, it can change its state on the basis of that input. For example, if it is in the five-cent state and receives an input of a dime, it will change to the fifteen-cent state. Each edge of the digraph represents such a state change; the label on the edge shows the input that leads to that change of states.

Rather than try to give a precise meaning to the word *machine*, we will define the term *machine digraph*.

> We define a **machine digraph** with **state set** *S* and
> **input alphabet** *I* to be a digraph whose vertex set
> is *S* and whose edges are labeled with elements
> chosen from *I*.

(We allow an edge to have more than one label.) Figure 53 shows a machine digraph with state set {ready, 5, 10, 15, 20, go} and input alphabet {*N, D, Q*}.

This digraph does not represent a toll-counting machine perfectly. A person may very well drop a quarter into the machine even if the machine is in state 5, 10, 15, or 20. Since the action of the machine with such an input is not determined, we say that this example is a *nondeterministic machine*. (A more formal definition will come later.) Our next example makes our model of the machine more realistic but more complicated.

EXAMPLE 29   Draw a machine digraph for a toll-counting machine that will allow a driver to go as long as the driver deposits twenty-five cents *or more*.

Solution   To the graph drawn in Figure 53 we must add arrows indicating that the machine moves to state "go" if we input a dime in state 20 or a quarter in state 5, 10, 15, or 20. Further, if we put in more money in state "go," the machine stays in state "go." This is shown in Figure 54. ■

Figure 54

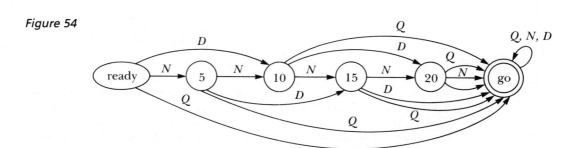

Notice that in Figure 54 we have three edges leaving each vertex, with one and only one edge for each possible input. We say that a machine digraph is a digraph of a **deterministic machine** if for each vertex there is a one-to-one correspondence between the labels on the outgoing edges and the input alphabet. Thus the machine in Figure 54 is deterministic. A machine is **nondeterministic** if it is not deterministic.

Automata

In both Figure 53 and Figure 54, we drew an extra circle around the vertex "go." This is because this state indicates that the machine has accepted our money and will let us go. When we want to indicate that a machine has reached a goal when it arrives at a certain state, we call that state an **accepting state** and draw a circle around it in the machine digraph.

> An **automaton** (plural: automata) is a machine
> with a selected set of states called accepting
> states and a single state called a starting state.

Thus Figure 53 and Figure 54 are digraphs of automata. A **finite state machine** or **finite automaton** is one with a finite number of states. Just as we can give a toll-counting machine a sequence of coins, we can give any automaton a sequence of characters from its input alphabet. We call a finite sequence of the characters a **character string.** We say that the automaton *accepts* a character string if, when it starts in its starting state and receives this sequence of inputs, the machine arrives at an accepting state.

EXAMPLE 30   Describe the state set, the input alphabet and the set of character strings accepted by the deterministic automaton in Figure 55.

Figure 55

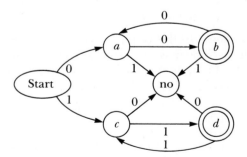

Solution   The state set is {start, no, a,b,c,d}. The accepting states are b and d. The input alphabet is {0,1}, since the edges leaving each vertex have the label 0 or the label 1. A sequence that leads us to state b can have only zeros. We can prove by induction on the number of zeros that a sequence of zeros leads us to state a if it has an odd number of zeros and to state *b* if it has an even number of zeros. Thus a character string consisting of all zeros is accepted if and only if it has an even number of zeros. Similarly, a string consisting of all ones is accepted if and only if it has an even number of ones. Thus a string is accepted if and only if it consists of an even number of zeros or it consists of an even number of ones. ∎

The Language of a Machine

The set of character strings accepted by a machine is called the **language** of the machine. This terminology is appropriate because automata may be designed so that the language they accept, for example, is a certain portion of a computer language. To design an automaton to accept a certain language, we must understand how to build up character strings in that language, one character at a time.

EXAMPLE 31   Draw a digraph of a machine with input alphabet {*a*,*b*} that accepts those sequences of letters that do not have the same letter twice in a row.

Solution   We need to have a state that says the last input was an *a* and we have not had the same letter twice in a row, and a state that says the last input was a *b* and we have not had the same letter twice in a row. We can use just one state to say that one of the letters has appeared twice in a row. We draw an oval around each vertex that is an accepting vertex to distinguish the accepting from the non-accepting vertices. We show the digraph in Figure 56. ∎

Figure 56

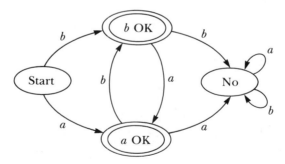

The example also hints at why the digraph model of a machine is so useful: states can operate as "memory" cells. The state *a OK*, for example, remembers that the last input was an *a* and that the input string up to that point was OK. With a finite state machine, we can't necessarily devise a way for the machine to remember everything we want. There might conceivably be an infinite supply of things that potentially need to be remembered, whereas we can use only a finite number of states. We can, however, make the machine "remember" some facts about arbitrarily long input strings—such as the fact that the input string has been OK up until now.

▣ Machines, Grammars, and Languages

We have seen how a machine may be used to describe a language (a set of character strings). When we studied induction, we learned to use the BNF (Backus-Naur Form) notation to give an inductive definition of a set of character strings. In our current terminology, the BNF notation gives an inductive description of a language. The BNF description of a set allows us to write a recursive algorithm to test a character string in order to determine if it is in the set. The digraph of a machine lets us write down directly a BNF description of the language of the machine.

The Notation of BNF

We review briefly the notation of BNF and introduce some new terminology. In using BNF notation, we enclose terms being defined in angle brackets. We shall now call such terms **nonterminal symbols.** The characters used in the character strings are called **terminal symbols.** We use BNF notation to describe rules for building up symbol strings. These rules, called **productions,** have the form of two symbol strings separated by the symbol $:=$. These are **replacement rules.** For example, the rules

$$a{<}A{>} := c{<}B{>}d$$
$$<B> := aa$$
$$<\text{start}> := a{<}A{>}c$$

let us make the replacements

$$<\text{start}> := a{<}A{>}c := c{<}B{>}dc := caadc$$

Grammars

A **phrase structure grammar** for a language is a set of productions we may use to derive each word in the language (and only those words) by making a sequence of replacements, each sequence beginning with a fixed nonterminal symbol we call the "start symbol." The language of an automaton has a straightforward grammar.

EXAMPLE 32   Write down a grammar to describe the language of the automaton shown in Figure 57 and give an informal description of the language.

Figure 57

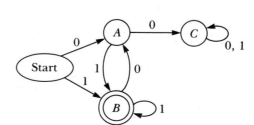

Solution Each production in our grammar will describe a possible change of state the machine will make with a given input. For example

$$<\text{start}> := 0<A>$$

says that if we input 0 when the machine is in the start state, the machine will move to state A. Similarly, we have

$$<\text{start}> := 1<B>$$

Recall that we may combine these productions using a vertical line for *or* to write

$$<\text{start}> := 0<A>|1<B>$$

To describe the state changes from state A, B, or C, we write

$$<A> := 0<C>|1<B>$$
$$<B> := 1<B>|0<A>$$
$$<C> := 0<C>|1<C>$$

Each production tells us how to add a symbol to a symbol string in the language. However, whenever the machine changes to an accepting state, it may stop, and our productions do not show this. To show that we may stop in state B, we write one more production:

$$<B> := \lambda$$

The symbol λ, the Greek letter lambda, stands for an *empty string*, a string with no characters. Replacing a nonterminal symbol with λ gives a string with no nonterminal symbols, so we stop. Once we have replaced a nonterminal symbol with λ, we stop writing λ, so that only the string we had before using λ appears.

We describe the language of the machine by examining Figure 57. We may get to state B only on an input of 1 and may stay in state B on an input of 1. With an input of 0, we may go to state A; from state A we go permanently to state C if we get a zero. Therefore, to get an accepted string if we are in state A, we must get an input of 1. Thus an input of 0 must be followed by an input of 1 in an accepted string. Therefore, an accepted string cannot have two zeros in a row. Since we must end in state B to accept a string, an accepted string must end in a 1. Therefore, the language accepted by the machine is the set of all strings of zeros and ones ending with a one and not having two zeros in a row. ■

Regular Grammars

Notice that there are only two kinds of productions in the grammar in Example 32. The left-hand side of each production consists of exactly one nonterminal symbol. Each right-hand side consists of one terminal symbol followed by one nonterminal symbol or else just the symbol λ. A grammar is called **regular** if each production has one of these forms.

Theorem 10   The language of an automaton has a regular grammar.

Proof   We treat each state of the machine as a nonterminal symbol. We treat each character of the input language as a terminal symbol. For each edge from state A to state B with label a, we write the production $<A> := a<B>$. For each accepting state A, we write the production $<A> := \lambda$. For each walk from the start state to an accepting state, there is a sequence of substitutions that produces the character string of labels on the edges of the walk. Since each production corresponds to an edge, each sequence of substitutions in which the last substitutes λ for a nonterminal symbol produces the character string of labels on the edges of a walk from the start state to an accepting state. Thus the grammar we have described generates the language of the automaton. By definition, the grammar is regular.   ■

By reversing the arguments presented in the proof of Theorem 10, we may prove Theorem 11.

Theorem 11   For each regular grammar, there is an automaton that has the same language.

Proof   We introduce a vertex for each nonterminal symbol of the grammar. Each production of the form $<A> := a<B>$ gives an edge from vertex A to vertex B with label a. For each production of the form $<A> := \lambda$, we regard A as an accepting state. We may show that this machine has the same language as the grammar by arguments similar to those in Theorem 10.   ■

EXAMPLE 33   Draw a digraph of a machine that accepts the language generated by the grammar below. What language is generated?

$$<\text{start}> := a<A> | b<B>$$
$$<A> := a<\text{start}> | \lambda$$
$$<B> := b<\text{start}> | \lambda$$

Solution   Our vertices are "start," A, and B. Our edges go from "start" to A, from "start" to B, and from A and B back to "start." States A and B are accepting. This gives the digraph shown in Figure 58. The walks from "start" to A or B contain

Figure 58

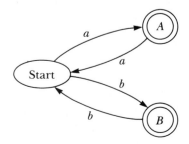

each label an even number of times each time it appears. Thus the language consists of all sequences of a's and b's in which each letter occurs an even number of times in a row each time it appears except that the final character appears an odd number of times in its last appearance. ∎

Concepts Review

1. When a digraph is used to represent a machine, the vertices are called the _____ of the machine.

2. The _____ _____ of a machine digraph is the set of symbols appearing as labels on its edges.

3. A machine is _____ if the labels on the outgoing edges from a vertex consist of the entire input alphabet, each symbol used once.

4. A(n) _____ is a finite state machine with a set of accepting states and a fixed starting state.

5. An automaton _____ a character string if receiving this character string as input would lead the machine from the start state to an accepting state.

6. The symbols that may appear in character strings accepted by a machine are called _____ symbols.

7. The rules used to replace one symbol string by another in a BNF description of a language are called _____.

8. A grammar is called _____ if each production has exactly one nonterminal symbol on the left-hand side and has either the symbol for the empty string or one terminal symbol followed by one nonterminal symbol as its right-hand side.

9. The language of an automaton has a(n) _____ _____.

10. For each _____ grammar there is a(n) _____ that accepts the language of the grammar.

Exercises

A

1. Draw the digraph for a machine that accepts nickels and dimes to get exact change for twenty cents.

2. Draw the digraph for a machine that accepts nickels, dimes, and quarters to get exact change for thirty cents.

3. Draw the digraph for a machine that accepts nickels, dimes, and quarters to get twenty cents or more.

4. Draw the digraph for a machine that accepts nickels, dimes, and quarters to get thirty cents or more.

5. Write down each character string in the language of the machine whose digraph you drew in Exercise 1. (Use *N* for nickel and *D* for dime.)

6. Write down each character string in the language of the machine drawn in Figure 53.

7. What is the state set, input alphabet, and the language accepted by the deterministic automaton whose digraph is drawn in Figure 59?

Figure 59

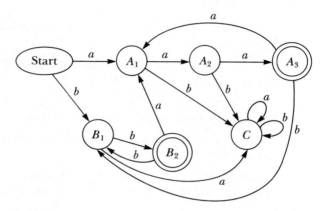

8. What are the state set, the input alphabet, and the language accepted by the deterministic automaton whose digraph is drawn in Figure 60?

Figure 60

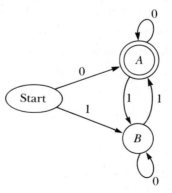

9. Draw a digraph of an automaton with input alphabet {0,1} that accepts any character string with an even positive number of ones.

10. Draw a digraph of an automaton with input alphabet {0,1} that accepts all character strings that do not have three or more ones in a row.

B **11.** Show a sequence of replacements that derives the character string *abba* from the grammar below.

$$<A> := a<B>a|a|a<A>a|aa$$
$$<B> := b<A>b|b|b<B>b|bb$$
$$<Start> := A|B$$

12. Show a sequence of replacements that derives the character string *aabaa* from the grammar in Exercise 11.

13. Write down the productions of a grammar that determines the same language as the deterministic automaton in Figure 61. Describe the language.

Figure 61

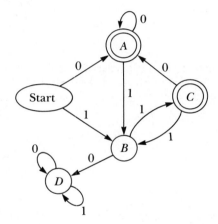

14. Write down the productions of a grammar that determines the same language as the deterministic automaton in Figure 62. Describe the language.

Figure 62

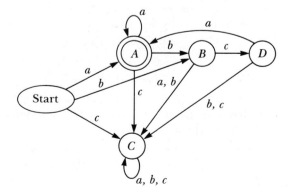

15. Write down a grammar that generates the same language as the nondeterministic automaton in Figure 63. Describe its language.

Figure 63

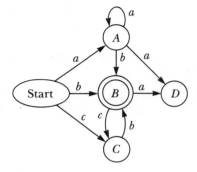

16. Write down a grammar that generates the same language as the nondeterministic automaton in Figure 64. Describe its language.

Figure 64

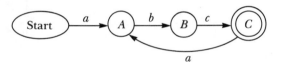

17. Draw the digraph of an automaton that has the language given by the grammar below. Is the automaton deterministic? Is the grammar regular? Describe informally the language generated by this grammar.

$$<\text{Start}> := 1<A>|0<B> \qquad <A> := 1<A>|0<C>|\lambda$$
$$<C> := 1<A>|0<B> \qquad <B> := 1<B>|0<B>|\lambda$$

18. Draw the digraph of an automaton that has the language given by the grammar below. Is the automaton deterministic? Is the grammar regular? Describe informally the language generated by this grammar.

$$<\text{Start}> := 1<A>|0<B> \qquad <A> := 1<C>|0<B>|\lambda$$
$$<C> := 0<D>|1<A> \qquad <D> := 0<B>|1<C>$$
$$<B> := 0<B>|1<B>$$

19. Draw the digraph of an automaton that determines the same language as the grammar below. Is the automaton deterministic? Is the grammar regular? Describe the language determined by the grammar.

$$<\text{Start}> := 0<A>|1<C> \qquad <A> := 0<B> \qquad <B> := <0><\text{Start}>|\lambda$$
$$<C> := 1<D> \qquad <D> := 1<\text{Start}>|\lambda$$

20. Draw the digraph of an automaton that determines the same language as the grammar below. Is the automaton deterministic? Is the grammar regular? Describe the language of the grammar.

$$<Start> := 0<A>|1<C>|0<D> \qquad <A> := 1<B>$$
$$<B> := 0<Start>|1<E> \qquad <C> := 0<D>$$
$$<D> := 0<E>|1<Start> \qquad <E> := \lambda$$

Problems

1. A *partially deterministic machine* is one in which for each state there is *at most one* edge with a given label leaving that state. Give an example of a partially deterministic machine with four states. Show how to convert it into a deterministic machine with five states that accepts exactly the same language.

2. Show that a partially deterministic machine (defined in Problem 1) may be converted into a deterministic machine that accepts the same language by adding one state and appropriate labeled edges.

3. Draw an example of a nondeterministic automaton with input alphabet $\{0,1\}$ that is *not* partially deterministic and has three states. Using your example, draw a new machine with seven states, one for each nonempty subset of the original set of states. Draw an arrow from the set S to the set T with the label 0 if T is the set of all states the original machine can reach from a state in S with input 0. Draw an arrow from the set S to the set T with the label 1 if T is the set of all states the original machine can reach from a state in S with input 1. Make a state of the new machine accepting if it contains an accepting state of the old machine. Use $\{<Start>\}$ as your start state. Show that the new machine accepts exactly the same language as the old one. Why is the new machine deterministic?

4. Based on Problem 3, prove that for each finite automaton there is a deterministic finite automaton that accepts exactly the same language.

5. Based on Problems 3 and 4, explain why a language has a regular grammar if and only if it is the language of a deterministic finite automaton.

6. Two automata are said to be *equivalent* if they accept exactly the same languages.
   (a) Explain why equivalence is an equivalence relation.
   (b) Recall that congruence mod n has the property that if $y \equiv z \mod n$, then $x + y \equiv x + z \mod n$. We say we have *composed* machine M with machine N at state s if s is a state of M and we create a new machine denoted by MsN by replacing the start state of N with the state s. If N_1 is equivalent to N_2, is MsN_1 equivalent to MsN_2?

7. The *sum* $M + N$ of two automata M and N is a machine whose digraph has one new start state (called START) and all the vertices and edges of both M and N. In addition, for each old edge $(start,s)$ with label L in *either* start state of M or N, the new digraph has one new edge $(START,s)$ with label L. In this new digraph, the two old start states are no longer designated as start states. (If two states have the same name, say A, in both machines, the corresponding states are given the names AM and AN.)
   (a) Draw the sum of the machines of Figures 60 and 61.

(b) Is it the case that if N_1 is equivalent to N_2 (see Problem 6), then $M + N_1$ is equivalent to $M + N_2$?

(c) Describe the language of the sum of two machines.

8. The *concatenation* of two automata M with N, denoted by $M{\cdot}N$, is the machine whose digraph has all the vertices and edges of M and N, whose start state is the start state of M, whose accepting states are the accepting states of N, and which has the following edges as well. For each accepting state a of M there is an edge (a,s) with label L for each edge (start,s) with label L in the machine N.

(a) Draw the concatenation of the machine M of Figure 60 and the machine N of Figure 61.

(b) Draw the concatenation of the machine N of Figure 61 and the machine M of Figure 60.

(c) If N_1 and N_2 are equivalent (see Problem 6), are $M{\cdot}N_1$ and $M{\cdot}N_2$ equivalent?

(d) If N_1 and N_2 are equivalent, are $N_1{\cdot}M$ and $N_2{\cdot}M$ equivalent?

(e) Describe the language of $M{\cdot}N$.

9. Use $\equiv$ to stand for the equivalence of Problem 6. Discuss the truth or falsity of the commutative laws $M + N \equiv N + M$; $M{\cdot}N \equiv N{\cdot}M$. Does it make sense to discuss a commutative law for MsN in Problem 6?

10. Use $\equiv$ to stand for the equivalence of Problem 6. Discuss the truth or falsity of the following associative laws: $(MsN)tP \equiv Ms(NtP)$, $(M + N) + P \equiv M + (N + P)$, and $(M{\cdot}N){\cdot}P \equiv M{\cdot}(N{\cdot}P)$.

11. Discuss the validity of distributive laws among the operations of Problems 6, 7, and 8.

Chapter 9
Review Exercises

1. Below are several edge sets. Some are for graphs, some are for simple graphs, and some are only for multigraphs. All use the vertex set $\{1,2,3,4,5,6\}$. Draw each and classify it in a simple graph, a graph, or a multigraph.. Classify each as connected or not connected.

(a) $\{\{1,2\}, \{1,3\}, \{2,3\}, \{4,5\}, \{5,1\}, \{4,6\}\}$

(b) $\{\{1,1\}, \{1,2\}, \{2,3\}, \{2,3\}, \{3,4\}, \{3,4\}, \{4,5\}, \{4,5\}, \{5,6\}, \{6,6\}\}$

(c) $\{\{1,1\}, \{2,3\}, \{3,4\}, \{4,5\}, \{6,6\}\}$

(d) $\{\{1,4\}, \{1,5\}, \{1,6\}, \{2,4\}, \{2,5\}, \{2,6\}, \{3,4\}, \{3,5\}, \{3,6\}\}$

2. Draw the multidigraphs given by the following edge sets. Classify the edge sets as edge sets of digraphs or multidigraphs. Determine the vertices reachable from vertex 1 and the vertices reachable from vertex 5. The vertex set is $\{1,2,3,4,5\}$.

(a) $\{(1,2), (2,1), (1,3), (3,4), (4,3), (4,5), (5,5)\}$

(b) $\{(1,1), (1,2), (2,2), (2,1), (3,4), (4,5), (5,3), (3,5)\}$

(c) $\{(1,2), (2,3), (2,3), (3,4), (3,4), (4,5)\}$

3. Give adjacency lists for the multigraphs or multidigraphs specified below.

(a) Exercise 1(a)   (b) Exercise 1(b)

(c) Exercise 2(a)   (d) Exercise 2(c)

4. Show that the function f given by $f(i) = a_i$ is an isomorphism from the graph G in Figure 65 to the graph H in Figure 65. Describe a different function g that is also an isomorphism.

Figure 65

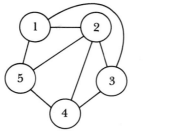
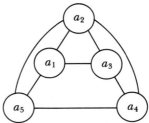

5. Suppose $f(1) = a_3$ $f(3) = a_1$ $f(2) = a_2$ $f(4) = a_4$ $f(5) = a_5$. Determine whether or not f is an isomorphism from G to H in Figure 65.

6. Determine whether or not the two graphs in Figure 66 are isomorphic.

Figure 66

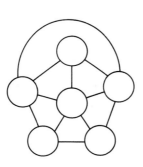
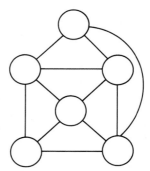

7. Determine whether or not the two graphs in Figure 67 are isomorphic, giving an isomorphism if there is one or a reason if there is not.

Figure 67

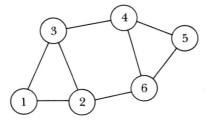
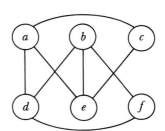

8. Determine whether or not the two graphs in Figure 68 are isomorphic, giving an isomorphism if there is one or a reason if there is not.

Figure 68

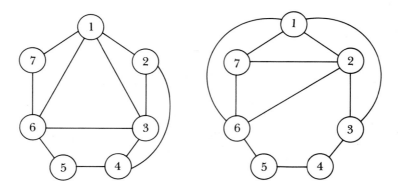

9. Explain why if f is an isomorphism from a digraph G to a digraph H and y is reachable from x in G, then $f(y)$ is reachable from $f(x)$ in H.

10. Explain why it is that if G and H are isomorphic, then the number of four-element cycles in G is equal to the number of four-element cycles in H.

11. Draw the multigraph whose vertices represent the land masses and whose edges represent the bridges in Figure 69.

Figure 69

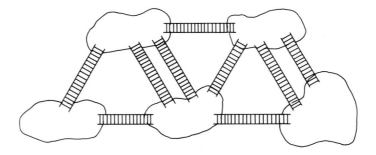

12. Does the multigraph you drew in Exercise 11 have an Eulerian walk? Does it have an Eulerian tour?

13. Use inspection to write down an Eulerian walk or tour of the graph you drew in Exercise 11.

14. Is there any one bridge that can be removed in Figure 69 so that the resulting graph has an Eulerian tour? If so, draw the graph of the modified picture. If not, why not?

15. In how many ways may you add one edge to the multigraph you drew in Exercise 11 so that the resulting graph has neither an Eulerian walk nor an Eulerian tour?

16. Find the weight of the edge tour 1-2-4-3-7-1-8-6-2-5-6-5-1-4-3-2-1 in Figure 70.

17. Show how to make the graph of Figure 70 have an Eulerian tour by duplicating three edges.

Figure 70

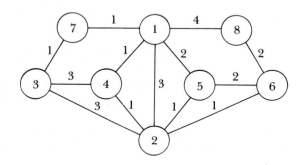

18. What is the cost of an edge tour of Figure 70 based on the Eulerian tour you found in Exercise 17?

19. Find a minimum weight edge tour for the graph of Figure 70.

20. Find a Hamiltonian tour of the graph in Figure 70.

21. What is the weight of the Hamiltonian tour you found in Exercise 20?

22. For each of the following sequences of vertices, determine whether it is a vertex tour of Figure 70, a Hamiltonian tour of Figure 70, a Hamiltonian path of Figure 70, or none of the above.
    (a) 1-8-6-5-2-3-4-7-1
    (b) 1-7-3-2-4-1-8-6-5
    (c) 4-2-3-7-1-8-6-5
    (d) 1-8-6-2-4-3-7-1

23. For each Hamiltonian path you found in Exercise 22, what is its weight?

24. Explain why a Hamiltonian path in Figure 70 cannot contain all the weight 1 edges.

25. Based on Exercise 24, it is possible to state what the minimum weight of any Hamiltonian path in Figure 70 can be. Determine this weight and find a Hamiltonian path of this weight.

26. Draw the intersection graph whose vertices and edges are determined by the following sets: {2,5,4,6}, {1,3}, {2,5,6}, {1,3,4,6}, {1,5,6}, {1,3,4,5}.

27. In a hypothetical college, certain committees meet every other week. In Table 4, we show which professors (who are on more than one committee) are on which committees.

Table 4

Committees	Professors								
	A	B	C	D	E	F	G	H	I
1	X		X		X		X	X	
2		X	X	X		X		X	
3					X		X		X
4	X	X	X			X			
5				X	X			X	
6				X		X	X		X

Draw a graph whose vertices represent the committees and whose edges show which committees have professors in common.

28. For each committee, write down the set of professors on that committee and draw the intersection graph of these sets. How does this graph relate to the graph of Exercise 27?

29. Find a proper coloring (using red, blue, and green) of the graph in Figure 71. Explain how this coloring relates to possible schedules for committee meetings.

Figure 71

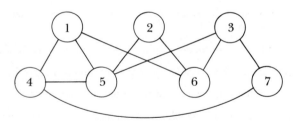

30. What is the chromatic number of the graph you drew in Exercises 27 and 28?

31. Find a planar drawing of the graph in Figure 71 or explain why it is not planar.

32. Is the graph in Figure 72 planar?

33. If a planar graph has 9 vertices and 12 edges, how many faces must it have?

34. Does the graph in Figure 73 satisfy $e \le 3v - 6$? Is this graph planar? Explain why or why not.

35. A candy machine sells candy for 35 cents. Draw the digraph of a machine that accepts nickels, dimes, and quarters to get exact change for 35 cents.

36. Using N, D, and Q, write down each character string in the language of the machine in Exercise 35. (There are pretty many, but you may indicate the general patterns if you prefer rather than writing them all down.) Explain how this language relates to making change for 35 cents.

37. Is the automaton drawn in Figure 74 deterministic? What is its state set? Its input alphabet? Describe the strings it accepts.

Figure 72

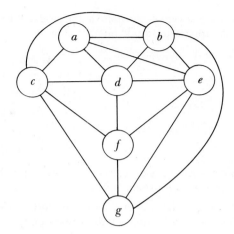

Figure 73

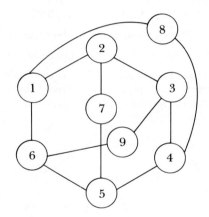

Figure 74

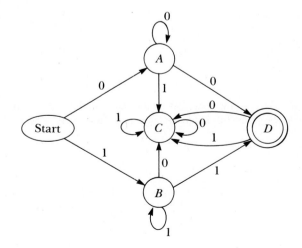

38. Draw a deterministic finite automaton that has $\{0,1\}$ for its input alphabet and accepts any string with an odd number of ones.

39. Given the grammar

$$<\text{Start}> := a<A_1>|b<B>$$
$$<A_1> := a<A_2>|b<B>$$
$$<A_2> := a<A_3>|b<B>$$
$$<A_3> := \lambda|a<A_3>|b<B>$$
$$<B> := b<B>|a<A_1>$$

show a sequence of replacements leading to the string *bbbaaa*. Is there a sequence of replacements leading to *bbaa*?

40. Draw an automaton that recognizes the language generated by the grammar in Exercise 39. Is the automaton you drew deterministic?

41. What happens to the language generated by the machine of Figure 74 if we delete state *D* and make states *A* and *B* accepting?

42. Write down a grammar for the language of the machine described in Exercise 41.

43. Is the grammar of Exercise 39 regular?

44. Is the machine of Figure 75 regular? Is it deterministic? Write down a grammar for the language accepted by the machine. What is the language accepted by the machine? Is there an automaton with three vertices rather than four in its digraph that generates the same language?

Figure 75

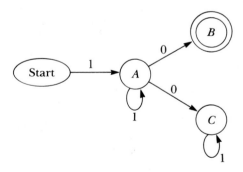

45. Give a grammar that generates the language accepted by the machine in Figure 76. Describe this language informally. In what ways does the machine fail to be deterministic?

Figure 76

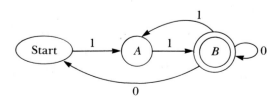

46. Given the grammar below, find a finite state automaton that accepts the language generated by the grammar.

$$<\text{Start}> := a<A>|b<B>$$
$$<B> := \lambda|b<B>|a<A>|a<A'>$$
$$<A> := b<B>|a<A'>$$
$$<A'> := b<B>$$

Describe the language informally.

*I*n this chapter, we shall study the concept of a matrix, one of the fundamental tools of discrete mathematics and of a great deal of continuous mathematics as well. You may have seen matrices in connection with the solution of equations, and we explain exactly how that application of matrices works. However, matrices have fascinating applications in the theory of graphs, in geometry, and even in probability. Matrices also provide an excellent data structure for use in computer programs. We shall see how the answers to certain practical questions can be found by applying standard arithmetic operations on matrices.

We begin our study of matrices with a study of their arithmetic and some of the algebraic properties this arithmetic has. We can immediately apply this arithmetic to the concept of transitive closure and other problems in graph theory. Next, we make a careful study of the role of matrices in solving systems of equations. We develop a technique that can be used by a person or programmed onto a computer to determine all solutions to any system of linear equations. Our study of equation-solving leads us to the concept of an invertible matrix and the inverse of such a matrix. This idea has intellectual appeal, since it extends ideas from arithmetic and ordinary algebra, as well as vast practical significance. Many practical applications of invertibility require more knowledge than we can provide here, but in Chapter 11 we illustrate how useful inverse matrices can be in understanding Markov chains in probability. In order to determine whether matrices are invertible, we introduce the concept of a determinant. The reader may have been introduced to the time-consuming and detailed application of determinants to the solution of systems of two or three linear equations in two or three unknowns. Since we have more efficient methods for solving equations, we do not pursue this application, but rather the application of determining invertibility.

Section 10-1
Matrix Arithmetic

A Sums and Numerical Products

A horizontal list of numbers such as

$$[1,2,3] \quad [-x,y] \quad [2+x,\ 3-y,\ 2x+z,\ y-z] \quad \text{or} \quad [3]$$

is often called a **row matrix**, and a vertical list of numbers such as

$$\begin{bmatrix} x-y \\ z+2x \end{bmatrix} \quad \begin{bmatrix} 3 \\ 6 \\ 9 \end{bmatrix} \quad \begin{bmatrix} 10 \\ 20 \\ 0 \\ 30 \\ 0 \end{bmatrix} \quad [-17] \quad \text{or} \quad \begin{bmatrix} 0.5 \\ 0.66 \\ 17 \\ 3.53 \end{bmatrix}$$

is often called a **column matrix**. A rectangle of numbers such as

$$\begin{bmatrix} 1 & 0 \\ 2 & 3 \end{bmatrix} \quad \begin{bmatrix} x & 0 & 0 \\ 0 & y & 0 \\ 0 & 0 & z \end{bmatrix} \quad \begin{bmatrix} 10 & 20 & 30 \\ 5 & 25 & 30 \end{bmatrix} \quad \begin{bmatrix} 0.1 & 2.3 \\ 3.4 & 0.5 \\ 1.1 & 5.5 \\ 6 & 1 \end{bmatrix}$$

is called a **matrix**. The first matrix above is called a two-by-two matrix; the other three are a three-by-three, a two-by-three and a four-by-two matrix, respectively. An **m-by-n (or $m \times n$) matrix** consists of m rows of n numbers each. We will normally enclose the entries of a matrix in rectangular braces, as above.

We can use matrices (the plural of *matrix*) to keep track of related quantities. For example, if a store is ordering small, medium, large, and jumbo eggs, it might use the column matrix

$$\begin{bmatrix} 10 \\ 20 \\ 80 \\ 30 \end{bmatrix} = Q$$

to keep track of the fact that it is ordering 10 dozen small eggs, 20 dozen medium eggs, 80 dozen large eggs, and 30 dozen jumbo eggs. We often use an uppercase letter to denote a matrix; here we have called our matrix Q to stand for quantity.

Matrix Addition

We form the **sum** of two *m*-by-*n* matrices by adding corresponding entries. We form the **difference** by subtracting corresponding entries. For example,

$$\begin{bmatrix} 1 & 2 \\ -1 & 1 \end{bmatrix} + \begin{bmatrix} 1 & 2 \\ 2 & 3 \end{bmatrix} = \begin{bmatrix} 2 & 4 \\ 1 & 4 \end{bmatrix}$$

$$\begin{bmatrix} 1 & 2 \\ -1 & 1 \end{bmatrix} - \begin{bmatrix} 1 & 2 \\ 2 & 3 \end{bmatrix} = \begin{bmatrix} 0 & 0 \\ -3 & -2 \end{bmatrix}$$

Note that we have only defined the sum for two matrices that are *both* *m*-by-*n* matrices.

EXAMPLE 1　If *A*, *B*, *C*, and *D* are the matrices below, which of the sums *A* + *B*, *B* + *C*, and *C* + *D* are defined?

$$A = \begin{bmatrix} 1 \\ 2 \end{bmatrix} \qquad B = [3,4] \qquad C = \begin{bmatrix} 1 & 2 \\ 3 & 4 \end{bmatrix} \qquad D = \begin{bmatrix} 1 & -1 \\ 0 & 1 \end{bmatrix}$$

Solution　We say that two matrices have the same shape if they have the same number of rows and the same number of columns. *A* and *B* do not have the same shape, so *A* + *B* is *not* defined. *B* and *C* do not have the same shape, so *B* + *C* is *not* defined. *C* and *D* *do* have the same shape, so *C* + *D* *is* defined.　■

There are rules for addition, such as *a* + *b* = *b* + *a* (the commutative law) and (*a*+*b*) + *c* = *a* + (*b*+*c*) (the associative law), that we use without consciously thinking about them when we do arithmetic. Fortunately, because matrix addition is just repeated numerical addition, these standard laws of addition apply to matrix addition as well.

Numerical Multiplication

To multiply a matrix *M* by a real number *r*, we multiply each entry of *M* by *r*.

EXAMPLE 2　If the wholesale prices for small, medium, large, and jumbo eggs (by the dozen) are given by the matrix [.60　.70　.80　.90], what matrix would represent the prices after a 10% increase?

Solution　Increasing each price by 10% is the same as multiplying each price by 1.1, so our new price matrix would be

$$(1.1)P = 1.1[.60 \quad .70 \quad .80 \quad .90] = [.66 \quad .77 \quad .88 \quad .99]$$　■

Notice that adding $-1 \cdot M$ to *M* gives the all-zeros matrix which we denote by *0* and call the *zero matrix*, so $-1 \cdot M$ is the matrix we would naturally think of as $-M$.

Row-Column Products

There is an important operation called *multiplication of matrices,* which may be applied in a wide variety of problems. We begin our study of this operation with an example. We have seen that a store ordering small, medium, large, and jumbo eggs might use the column matrix

$$Q = \begin{bmatrix} 10 \\ 20 \\ 80 \\ 30 \end{bmatrix}$$

to keep track of the fact that they are ordering 10 dozen small eggs, 20 dozen medium eggs, 80 dozen large eggs, and 30 dozen jumbo eggs. Let us assume that the egg wholesaler uses the matrix

$$P = [.60 \quad .70 \quad .80 \quad .90]$$

of Example 2 for the wholesale prices of small, medium, large, and jumbo eggs.

With these prices, how much would the order for eggs cost the store? We have to add up the prices times the quantities for each size of egg to get

$$\begin{aligned} \text{Cost} &= .60 \cdot 10 \ + .70 \cdot 20 + .80 \cdot 80 + .90 \cdot 30 \\ &= \ \ 6.00 \ + \ 14.00 + \ 64.00 + \ 27.00 \\ &= \ 111.00 \end{aligned}$$

In effect, we are multiplying the price matrix times the quantity matrix, giving

$$\text{Cost} = P \cdot Q$$

There is a way to define multiplication of matrices so that, with this multiplication rule, the cost matrix *is* the price matrix times the quantity matrix. In particular, if R is a row matrix with n entries $r_1, r_2, \ldots, r_n$ and C is a column matrix with n entries $c_1, c_2, \ldots, c_n$, then we define the **product** RC by

$$[r_1, r_2, \ldots, r_n] \cdot \begin{bmatrix} c_1 \\ c_2 \\ \cdot \\ \cdot \\ \cdot \\ c_n \end{bmatrix} = R \cdot C = r_1 c_1 + r_2 c_2 + \cdots + r_n c_n$$

Thus when we multiply a row matrix on the left by a column matrix on the right, we get a number. We can, if we wish, think of this number as a matrix with just one entry, namely $[r_1 c_1 + r_2 c_2 + \cdots + r_n c_n]$. In the example below, we use $R1$ and $R2$ rather than R_1 and R_2 to stand for two row matrices, because there is no possibility of confusion between $R1$ and the first entry r_1 of a matrix R.

EXAMPLE 3   Using the matrices

$$R1 = [1 \quad 2 \quad 4] \\ R2 = [5 \quad 4 \quad 2 \quad 3] \qquad C1 = \begin{bmatrix} 3 \\ 2 \\ -1 \end{bmatrix} \qquad C2 = \begin{bmatrix} 1 \\ -1 \\ -1 \\ 1 \end{bmatrix}$$

compute $R1C1$ and $R2C2$. Explain why the product $R1C2$ cannot be computed.

Solution $R1C1 = 1 \cdot 3 + 2 \cdot 2 + 4 \cdot (-1) = 3$; $R2C2 = 5 \cdot 1 - 4 \cdot 1 - 2 \cdot 1 + 3 \cdot 1$ $= 2$. The product $R1C2$ cannot be computed because $R1$ has three entries and $C2$ has four entries, and we cannot compute a product of a row matrix by a column matrix unless they have the same number of entries.   ∎

B   *Matrix Products*

The *row-column product* described is a special case of a more general multiplication on matrices. To show how this more general operation arises, we expand our egg wholesaler example. The prices of eggs may change each week. In Table 1, we give (hypothetical) wholesale prices of eggs over a four-week period. The matrix that follows the table is obtained from the table by deleting the labels from the horizontal rows and vertical columns of the table and placing rectangular brackets around the body of the table. We now use P to stand for this matrix.

Table 1

	Sm	Med	Lg	Jum
Week 1	.60	.70	.80	.90
Week 2	.55	.65	.75	.85
Week 3	.60	.75	.85	.95
Week 4	.65	.70	.85	.95

$$\begin{bmatrix} .60 & .70 & .80 & .90 \\ .55 & .65 & .75 & .85 \\ .60 & .75 & .85 & .95 \\ .65 & .70 & .85 & .95 \end{bmatrix} = P$$

As the table shows, each row of the matrix represents a different week of prices for eggs.

Let us now assume that the wholesaler deals with three stores and that each store has a standard weekly order for eggs, as shown in Table 2. The matrix following the table is simply the body of the table. We now use Q to stand for this matrix.

Table 2

	Store 1	Store 2	Store 3
Sm	10	20	20
Med	20	30	40
Lg	80	160	100
Jum	30	40	40

$$\begin{bmatrix} 10 & 20 & 20 \\ 20 & 30 & 40 \\ 80 & 160 & 100 \\ 30 & 40 & 40 \end{bmatrix} = Q$$

Now row i (which we denote by Ri) of Table 1 (matrix P) tells us the prices of eggs in week i. On the other hand, column j (which we denote by Cj) of Table 2 (matrix Q) tells us the standing weekly order of eggs for store j. Thus if we form the product of the row matrix Ri with the column matrix Cj, the result is the cost in week i of the order for eggs from store j. Thus, for example, $R2C3$ is the cost in week 2 of the order from store 3. In order to keep track of our wholesaler's weekly billings, we should form the matrix in which the entry in row i and column j is the bill in week i for store j; we have seen that this is the product of Ri with Cj. For example, the entry in row 2 and column 3 will be the product of $R2$ and $C3$. This leads to the following definition.

The General Matrix Product

The **product** of a matrix M with rows $R1, R2, \ldots, Rm,$
each of length n, times a matrix N with columns
$C1, C2, \ldots, Ck$, each of length n, is the matrix
whose entry in row i and column j is $Ri \cdot Cj$.

Symbolically, we write

$$M \cdot N = \begin{bmatrix} -R1- \\ -R2- \\ \vdots \\ -Ri- \\ \vdots \\ -Rm- \end{bmatrix} \cdot \begin{bmatrix} | & | & & | & & | \\ C1 & C2 & \cdots & Cj & \cdots & Ck \\ | & | & & | & & | \end{bmatrix}$$

$$= \begin{bmatrix} R1 \cdot C1 & \cdots & R1 \cdot Cj & \cdots & R1 \cdot Ck \\ Ri \cdot C1 & \cdots & Ri \cdot Cj & \cdots & Ri \cdot Ck \\ Rm \cdot C1 & \cdots & Rm \cdot Cj & \cdots & Rm \cdot Ck \end{bmatrix} \begin{matrix} \\ \leftarrow \text{ row } i \\ \\ \end{matrix}$$

(with column j indicated above the middle column)

In particular,

$$\begin{bmatrix} -R1- \\ -R2- \end{bmatrix} \begin{bmatrix} | & | & | \\ C1 & C2 & C3 \\ | & | & | \end{bmatrix} = \begin{bmatrix} R1C1 & R1C2 & R1C3 \\ R2C1 & R2C2 & R2C3 \end{bmatrix}$$

(This shows why we first defined the product only for a row matrix on the left by a column matrix on the right. That definition helps us remember that the entry in *row i* and *column j* of the product MN is *row i* of M times *column j* of N.)

EXAMPLE 4   If $M = \begin{bmatrix} 1 & 2 \\ 2 & -1 \end{bmatrix}$ and $N = \begin{bmatrix} 3 & -2 & 1 \\ 1 & 2 & -3 \end{bmatrix}$, compute the product MN and explain why the product NM cannot be computed.

Solution   We highlight a typical entry, the entry in row 2 and column 3.

$$MN = \begin{bmatrix} 1 & 2 \\ 2 & -1 \end{bmatrix} \begin{bmatrix} 3 & -2 & 1 \\ 1 & 2 & -3 \end{bmatrix}$$

$$= \begin{bmatrix} 1 \cdot 3 + 2 \cdot 1 & -2 \cdot 1 + 2 \cdot 2 & 1 \cdot 1 - 2 \cdot 3 \\ 2 \cdot 3 - 1 \cdot 1 & -2 \cdot 2 - 1 \cdot 2 & 2 \cdot 1 + (-1)(-3) \end{bmatrix}$$

$$= \begin{bmatrix} 3 + 2 & -2 + 4 & 1 - 6 \\ 6 - 1 & -4 - 2 & 2 + 3 \end{bmatrix} = \begin{bmatrix} 5 & 2 & -5 \\ 5 & -6 & 5 \end{bmatrix}$$

The product NM cannot be computed because the rows of N have three entries and the columns of M have two entries.   ∎

EXAMPLE 5   If P and Q are the matrices below, compute $P \cdot Q$ and $Q \cdot P$.

$$P = \begin{bmatrix} 1 & 2 \\ -2 & 3 \end{bmatrix}, \qquad Q = \begin{bmatrix} 1 & -1 \\ 2 & 2 \end{bmatrix}$$

Solution

$$P \cdot Q = \begin{bmatrix} 1 & 2 \\ -2 & 3 \end{bmatrix} \begin{bmatrix} 1 & -1 \\ 2 & 2 \end{bmatrix} = \begin{bmatrix} 1 + 4 & -1 + 4 \\ -2 + 6 & 2 + 6 \end{bmatrix} = \begin{bmatrix} 5 & 3 \\ 4 & 8 \end{bmatrix}$$

$$Q \cdot P = \begin{bmatrix} 1 & -1 \\ 2 & 2 \end{bmatrix} \begin{bmatrix} 1 & 2 \\ -2 & 3 \end{bmatrix} = \begin{bmatrix} 1 + 2 & 2 - 3 \\ 2 - 4 & 4 + 6 \end{bmatrix} = \begin{bmatrix} 3 & -1 \\ -2 & 10 \end{bmatrix}$$ ∎

Example 5 shows one of the more interesting features of matrix multiplication. The commutative law $P \cdot Q = Q \cdot P$ that holds for multiplication of numbers *need not work* for multiplication of matrices. (In fact it *usually does not* work for matrix multiplication.)

The Identity Matrix

EXAMPLE 6   Using the matrix I shown below and the matrices P and Q of Example 5, compute IP and QI.

$$I = \begin{bmatrix} 1 & 0 \\ 0 & 1 \end{bmatrix}$$

Solution   We write

$$IP = \begin{bmatrix} 1 & 0 \\ 0 & 1 \end{bmatrix}\begin{bmatrix} 1 & 2 \\ -2 & 3 \end{bmatrix} = \begin{bmatrix} 1{\cdot}1 + 0(-2) & 1{\cdot}2 + 0{\cdot}3 \\ 0{\cdot}1 + 1(-2) & 0{\cdot}2 + 1{\cdot}3 \end{bmatrix} = \begin{bmatrix} 1 & 2 \\ -2 & 3 \end{bmatrix}$$

We also write

$$QI = \begin{bmatrix} 1 & -1 \\ 2 & 2 \end{bmatrix}\begin{bmatrix} 1 & 0 \\ 0 & 1 \end{bmatrix} = \begin{bmatrix} 1{\cdot}1 + (-1){\cdot}0 & 1{\cdot}0 + (-1){\cdot}1 \\ 2{\cdot}1 + 2{\cdot}0 & 2{\cdot}0 + 2{\cdot}1 \end{bmatrix} = \begin{bmatrix} 1 & -1 \\ 2 & 2 \end{bmatrix}$$

Thus $IP = P$ and $QI = Q$.   ∎

In Example 6, we see an analogy between matrix multiplication and numerical multiplication that *does* work. The matrix I behaves like the number 1. We can describe this analogy more generally with a bit more terminology. An n-by-n matrix is called a **square matrix.** The **main diagonal** of an n-by-n matrix consists of the entries in row 1 and column 1, row 2 and column 2, and in general row i and column i for each i from 1 to n. (See Figure 1.) An **identity matrix** is a square matrix with ones as its main diagonal entries and zeros as all its other entries. Thus the matrix I in Example 6 is a two-by-two identity matrix. I is a standard symbol for an identity matrix of any size. It follows from the definition of matrix multiplication that $MI = M$ and $IM = M$ whenever the products are defined.

Figure 1

Square matrix

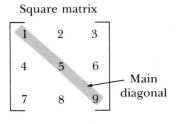

Four by four identity matrix

$$\begin{bmatrix} 1 & 0 & 0 & 0 \\ 0 & 1 & 0 & 0 \\ 0 & 0 & 1 & 0 \\ 0 & 0 & 0 & 1 \end{bmatrix}$$

Double-Subscript Notation

It is inconvenient to speak of "the element in row i and column j of the matrix M" to refer to this entry. In **double-subscript notation** for a matrix M, people use either

$$M_{ij} \quad \text{or} \quad m_{ij}$$

(read as "em sub eye jay" or "em eye jay") to stand for the entry in row i and column j of a matrix M. There are times when an uppercase letter M is most appropriate and times when a lowercase letter m is most appropriate; usually it is a matter of choice. Thus a matrix M with three rows and four columns would be written

$$\begin{bmatrix} M_{11} & M_{12} & M_{13} & M_{14} \\ M_{21} & M_{22} & M_{23} & M_{24} \\ M_{31} & M_{32} & M_{33} & M_{34} \end{bmatrix}$$

EXAMPLE 7   In the matrix M below, what are M_{21} and M_{13}?

$$M = \begin{bmatrix} 1 & 3 & 5 \\ -1 & 6 & 4 \\ 2 & -3 & 1 \end{bmatrix}$$

Solution M_{21} is -1, the element in row 2 and column 1, and M_{13} is 5, the element in row 1 and column 3.   ■

If M has rows $R1, R2, \ldots$ and N has columns $C1, C2, \ldots$, then we use double-subscript notation to write the definition of the product MN as

$$(MN)_{ij} = RiCj$$

which says, "The i,j entry of MN is the product of row i of M with column j of N." We can also write

$$(MN)_{ij} = \sum_{k=1}^{n} M_{ik}N_{kj}$$

which is a more explicit way to describe the product of row i with column j.

EXAMPLE 8   Write down the double-subscript representation for a 2-by-2 matrix M, a 2-by-2 matrix N, and the product MN.

Solution   We write

$$\begin{bmatrix} m_{11} & m_{12} \\ m_{21} & m_{22} \end{bmatrix} \begin{bmatrix} n_{11} & n_{12} \\ n_{21} & n_{22} \end{bmatrix} = \begin{bmatrix} m_{11}n_{11} + m_{12}n_{21} & m_{11}n_{12} + m_{12}n_{22} \\ m_{21}n_{11} + m_{22}n_{21} & m_{21}n_{12} + m_{22}n_{22} \end{bmatrix}$$ ■

Note that in Example 8 the element $(MN)_{12}$ is given by $m_{11}n_{12} + m_{12}n_{22}$, which is what we get by expanding the notation

$$\sum_{k=1}^{2} m_{1k}n_{k2}$$

We sometimes need to use double-subscript notation and the double-subscript formula for matrix multiplication in symbolic computations, as for example in the proof of the **distributive law for matrix multiplication**.

Theorem 1   If A and B are m-by-n matrices and C is an n-by-p matrix, then $(A + B)C = AC + BC$.

Proof   We compute the entry in row i and column j of $(A + B)C$ and of $AC + BC$. First, we use the fact that $(A+B)_{ik} = A_{ik} + B_{ik}$ to write

$$((A+B)C)_{ij} = \sum_{k=1}^{n} (A+B)_{ik}C_{kj} = \sum_{k=1}^{n} (A_{ik}+B_{ik})C_{kj} = \sum_{k=1}^{n} A_{ik}C_{kj} + \sum_{k=1}^{n} B_{ik}C_{kj}$$

Second, we use the fact that $(AC + BC)_{ij} = (AC)_{ij} + (BC)_{ij}$ and the double-subscript formula for matrix multiplication to write

$$(AC+BC)_{ij} = (AC)_{ij} + (BC)_{ij} = \sum_{k=1}^{n} A_{ik}C_{kj} + \sum_{k=1}^{n} B_{ik}C_{kj}$$

This shows that $((A + B)C)_{ij} = (AC + BC)_{ij}$ for each i and j, so the matrices $(A + B)C$ and $AC + BC$ have exactly the same entries. Thus they are equal. ∎

EXAMPLE 9   Using the matrices M, P, and Q of Examples 4 and 5, compute the matrix product $(M + P)Q$ and the sum $MQ + PQ$ to show that they are equal.

Solution

$$(M+P)Q = \left(\begin{bmatrix} 1 & 2 \\ 2 & -1 \end{bmatrix} + \begin{bmatrix} 1 & 2 \\ -2 & 3 \end{bmatrix} \right) \begin{bmatrix} 1 & -1 \\ 2 & 2 \end{bmatrix}$$

$$= \begin{bmatrix} 2 & 4 \\ 0 & 2 \end{bmatrix} \begin{bmatrix} 1 & -1 \\ 2 & 2 \end{bmatrix} = \begin{bmatrix} 10 & 6 \\ 4 & 4 \end{bmatrix}$$

$$MQ+PQ = \begin{bmatrix} 1 & 2 \\ 2 & -1 \end{bmatrix} \begin{bmatrix} 1 & -1 \\ 2 & 2 \end{bmatrix} + \begin{bmatrix} 1 & 2 \\ -2 & 3 \end{bmatrix} \begin{bmatrix} 1 & -1 \\ 2 & 2 \end{bmatrix}$$

$$= \begin{bmatrix} 5 & 3 \\ 0 & -4 \end{bmatrix} + \begin{bmatrix} 5 & 3 \\ 4 & 8 \end{bmatrix} = \begin{bmatrix} 10 & 6 \\ 4 & 4 \end{bmatrix}$$

∎

The other major law of arithmetic, the **associative law of multiplication**, $(MN)P = M(NP)$, may also be proved by using double-subscript notation and the double-subscript formula for matrix multiplication.

Concepts Review

1. An array of numbers in a rectangle is called a(n) _____.

2. To find the _____ of two matrices we add the corresponding entries.

3. An *m*-by-*n* matrix has _____ rows and _____ columns.

4. The product of a row matrix with entries r_1 through r_n times a column matrix with entries c_1 through c_n is given by the formula $R{\cdot}C =$ _____.

5. To multiply an *m*-by-*n* matrix times an *r*-by-*s* matrix, we must have _____ equal to _____.

6. The entry in row *i* and column *j* of the matrix product *MN* is the product of _____ _____ of *M* with _____ _____ of *N*.

7. In double-subscript notation, m_{ij} stands for the entry in _____ *i* and _____ *j* of the matrix *M*.

8. The _____ _____ of an *n*-by-*n* matrix *A* consists of $A_{11}, A_{22}, \ldots, A_{nn}$.

9. A(n) _____ matrix has ones on the main diagonal and zeros off the main diagonal and when multiplied by the matrix *A* gives the result _____.

10. The formula

$$\sum_{j=1}^{n} A_{ij}B_{jk}$$

is a formula which allows us to compute the entry in row _____ and column _____ of the matrix _____.

Exercises

A For Exercises 1 through 46 below, use the matrices

$$R = [1 \quad 2 \quad 2 \quad 1] \quad S = [1 \quad -1 \quad 1 \quad 0] \qquad C = \begin{bmatrix} 1 \\ 3 \\ 3 \\ 1 \end{bmatrix} \quad D = \begin{bmatrix} 1 \\ 2 \\ -1 \\ 2 \end{bmatrix} \quad E = \begin{bmatrix} 2 \\ 0 \\ 1 \\ 2 \end{bmatrix}$$
$$T = [1 \quad 0 \quad 1 \quad 0] \quad 0 = [0 \quad 0 \quad 0 \quad 0]$$

1. Find $R + S$ and $R - T$.

2. Find $T + S$ and $R - S$.

3. Verify that $(R + S) + T = R + (S + T)$.

4. Verify that $(C + D) + E = C + (D + E)$.

5. Find the sum $S + 0$ and explain what this illustrates.

6. Find the sum $0 + R$ and explain what this illustrates.

In Exercises 7 through 46 below, use the matrices above and also the matrices

$$L = \begin{bmatrix} 2 & 1 \\ 0 & 2 \end{bmatrix} \quad M = \begin{bmatrix} 1 & 2 \\ -1 & 1 \\ 2 & 0 \\ 0 & 1 \end{bmatrix} \quad N = \begin{bmatrix} 1 & 4 \\ 4 & 1 \end{bmatrix} \quad P = \begin{bmatrix} 1 & 3 & 1 & 0 \\ 1 & -1 & 1 & 0 \\ 2 & 0 & 0 & 1 \end{bmatrix} \quad Q = \begin{bmatrix} 1 & -1 \\ 2 & 1 \end{bmatrix}$$

In Exercises 7 through 14, state whether the given sum is defined.

7. $L + M$

8. $M + N$

9. $L + N$

10. $L + Q$

11. $P + Q$

12. $R + T$

13. $M + C + D$

14. $R + T + S + P$

15. Find $L - N$ and $L + N$.

16. Find $N + Q$ and $Q - N$.

17. Find the product RC.

18. Find the product RD.

19. Find the product SD.

20. Find the product TC.

B For Exercises 21 through 46 below, use the matrices in Part A above.

21. Find the product PC.

22. Find the product PD.

23. N^2 means N times N. Find N^2 and N^4.

24. Find L^2 and L^4.

25. Find the product $P(C + E)$ and the sum $PC + PE$. What does this illustrate?

26. Find the product $P(D + E)$ and the sum $PD + PE$. What does this illustrate?

In Exercises 27 through 32, which of the products are defined?

27. MC

28. PC

29. QE

30. MD

31. QC

32. PE

33. Find the product MN. Is the product NM defined?

34. Find the product PM. Is the product MP defined?

35. Find the product NQ and the product QN. What does this illustrate?

36. Find the product LQ and the product QL. What does this illustrate?

37. Find the products $(LN)Q$ and $L(NQ)$. What does this illustrate?

38. Find the products $(TM)L$ and $T(ML)$. What does this illustrate?

39. Find the product $(R + S)M$ and the sum $RM + SM$. What does this illustrate?

40. Find the product $L(N + Q)$ and the sum $LN + LQ$. What does this illustrate?

41. Write down the 3-by-3 identity matrix I and compute the product IP.

42. Write down the 4-by-4 identity matrix I and compute the product PI.

43. What is P_{13}? What is P_{31}?

44. What is M_{12}? What is M_{21}?

45. Find the value of the following.

$$\sum_{k=1}^{2} M_{1k}Q_{k2}$$

In what row and column of MQ do we find this entry?

46. Find the value of the following.

$$\sum_{k=1}^{4} P_{3k}M_{k2}$$

In what row and column of PM do we find this entry?

Problems

1. Prove the distributive law $A(B+C) = AB + AC$ for two-by-two matrices.

2. Prove the associative law $A(BC) = (AB)C$ for all matrices A, B, and C such that the products are defined. (*Hint:* The i,j entry of either side may be shown to be

$$\sum_{k=1}^{n} \sum_{h=1}^{m} a_{ik}b_{kh}c_{hj}$$

or a similar (and equal) sum.)

3. Suppose A is a two-by-two matrix such that $AB = BA$ for *all* two-by-two matrices B. What can you say about A?

4. The cancellation rule—If $AB = AC$ and $A \neq 0$, then $B = C$—works for numbers. Give an example to show that it does not work for matrices.

5. Find an example of a matrix A with $A \neq \pm I$ but $A^2 = I$.

6. Show that the cancellation rule—If $A + C = A + D$, then $C = D$—holds for matrix addition.

7. Suppose M and N are matrices such that MN is defined. Explain why row i of MN is the row matrix we get by multiplying row i of M (thought of as a row matrix) times the matrix N.

8. Suppose that M and N are matrices such that MN is defined. Explain why column j of MN is the matrix M multiplied by column j of N (thought of as a column matrix).

9. Prove that if N is an n-by-k matrix and I is an n-by-n identity matrix, then $IN = N$.

10. Prove by induction that $I^n = I$.

11. Using A^3 in the usual way, show that

$$(A^3)_{ij} = \sum_{k=1}^{n} \sum_{h=1}^{n} A_{ik}A_{kh}A_{hj}$$

12. For numbers, we have $(x + 1)^2 = x^2 + 2x + 1$ and $(x + y)^2 = x^2 + 2xy + y^2$. Do these formulas hold for matrices? Why or why not?

Section 10-2
Matrices
and Graphs

▲ Powers of Adjacency Matrices

Matrices and matrix algebra have uses in many branches of pure and applied mathematics. We will discuss here how matrices may be applied to graphs.

Adjacency Matrices

A graph or digraph provides a visual representation of a relation; a nonvisual representation is needed if we plan to use a computer to answer questions about graphs and relations. One such representation that we already studied is the adjacency list representation. We shall now present another: the adjacency matrix of a graph or digraph. Suppose we have a graph or digraph G whose vertices are numbered 1 through n. We form a matrix A, called the **adjacency matrix** of G, by letting $A_{ij} = 1$ if there is an edge of G from vertex i to vertex j and letting $A_{ij} = 0$ if there is not an edge of G from vertex i to vertex j.

EXAMPLE 10   Find the adjacency matrix of the graph in Figure 2.

Figure 2

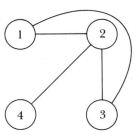

Solution   By putting a 1 in row i and column j for each i and j that are adjacent, we get

$$A = \begin{bmatrix} 0 & 1 & 1 & 0 \\ 1 & 0 & 1 & 1 \\ 1 & 1 & 0 & 0 \\ 0 & 1 & 0 & 0 \end{bmatrix}$$

Notice that A_{12} is 1, because there is an edge from vertex 1 to vertex 2, but A_{14} is 0, because there is no edge from vertex 1 to vertex 4.   ■

When we want to make it clear that the matrix we are talking about is associated with a specific graph G, not some other graph, we write $A(G)$ in place of A. The adjacency matrix of an undirected graph has a special appearance you may have noticed in the adjacency matrix of Figure 2.

A **symmetric matrix** A is one with
$$A_{ij} = A_{ji} \text{ for all } i \text{ and } j.$$

For any (undirected) *graph* G the adjacency matrix $A(G)$ is symmetric. The reason for the symmetry of $A(G)$ is that in a *graph* the edge from i to j is also an edge from j to i. For example, in the matrix A of Example 10, A_{12} is 1 and A_{21} is 1 because there is an edge between vertices 1 and 2. However, if G is a digraph, the matrix $A(G)$ need not be symmetric. As in Example 11 below, when a digraph has an edge from i to j, it need not have an edge from j to i.

EXAMPLE 11   Find the adjacency matrix of the digraph in Figure 3.

Figure 3

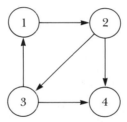

Solution   By placing a 1 in the (i,j) position if there is an edge from i to j, we get

$$A = \begin{bmatrix} 0 & 1 & 0 & 0 \\ 0 & 0 & 1 & 1 \\ 1 & 0 & 0 & 1 \\ 0 & 0 & 0 & 0 \end{bmatrix}$$

Notice that A_{12} is 1, because there is an edge from vertex 1 to vertex 2, but there is no edge from vertex 2 to vertex 1, so $A_{21} = 0$. Notice how the fact that no edges leave vertex 4 corresponds to the fact that row 4 consists entirely of zeros.   ■

Matrices are ideally suited for keeping track of multigraphs, multidigraphs, and weighted graphs and digraphs. In a multigraph or a multidigraph, we can have any number of edges from vertex i to vertex j. For a multigraph or multidigraph, we let A_{ij} be the number of edges from vertex i to vertex j. For a weighted graph, we use the weight of the edge from vertex i to vertex j in place of 1 in the adjacency matrix.

EXAMPLE 12   Give the adjacency matrix for the multigraph in Figure 4.

Figure 4

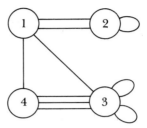

Solution   By inspecting the figure and counting the number of edges between each pair of vertices, we see that A is given by:

$$A = \begin{bmatrix} 0 & 2 & 1 & 1 \\ 2 & 1 & 0 & 0 \\ 1 & 0 & 2 & 3 \\ 1 & 0 & 3 & 0 \end{bmatrix}$$ ■

Matrix Multiplication and Walks

Matrix multiplication relates in a natural way to certain graphical counting problems. To see how this relation works, let us take an example that is easy to visualize. Suppose G is the graph in Figure 1, and let A stand for its adjacency matrix. Let us examine a typical entry of the matrix A^2, say the entry in row 1 and column 4 in A^2. Remember that this is the product of row 1 of A with column 4 of A, as shown by the highlighted area.

$$\begin{bmatrix} 0 & 1 & 1 & 0 \\ 1 & 0 & 1 & 1 \\ 1 & 1 & 0 & 0 \\ 0 & 1 & 0 & 0 \end{bmatrix}\begin{bmatrix} 0 & 1 & 1 & 0 \\ 1 & 0 & 1 & 1 \\ 1 & 1 & 0 & 0 \\ 0 & 1 & 0 & 0 \end{bmatrix} = \begin{bmatrix} \cdots & 0\cdot 0 + 1\cdot 1 + 1\cdot 0 + 0\cdot 0 \\ \cdots & \cdot \\ \cdots & \cdot \\ \cdots & \cdot \end{bmatrix}$$

In double-subscript notation, this gives us

$$(A^2)_{14} = A_{11}A_{14} + A_{12}A_{24} + A_{13}A_{34} + A_{14}A_{44}$$
$$= 0\cdot 0 + 1\cdot 1 + 1\cdot 0 + 0\cdot 0 = 1$$

We get the 1 in our final answer because there is an edge from vertex 1 to vertex 2 *and* another edge from vertex 2 to vertex 4. Thus our walk from vertex 1 to vertex 4 shows up as a 1 in row 1 and column 4 of A^2. Now if we form A^3 and ask for the number in row 1 and column 4, in the process of computing A^3 we will, for example, get the term

$$A_{13}A_{32}A_{24} = 1 \cdot 1 \cdot 1 = 1$$

so A_{14}^3 will be nonzero as well, reflecting the fact that there is a walk of length 3 from vertex 1 to vertex 4. This suggests a theorem.

Theorem 2   The number of walks of length n from vertex i to vertex j in a (multi)(di)graph with adjacency matrix M is the entry in row i and column j of M^n.

Proof   When $n = 1$, we are talking about walks of length 1 (which are edges), and by the definition of an adjacency matrix, M_{ij} is the number of edges from vertex i to vertex j. Now suppose inductively that for each i and j, the entry in row i and column j of M^{n-1} is the number of walks of length $n-1$ from vertex i to vertex j. By the double-subscript formula for matrix multiplication,

$$(M^n)_{ij} = \sum_{k=1}^{n} (M^{n-1})_{ik} M_{kj}$$

By the product principle, $(M^{n-1})_{ik} M_{kj}$ is the number of walks of length n from vertex i to vertex j whose second last vertex is vertex k. Summing this number over all k gives us both $(M^n)_{ij}$ and the number of walks of length n from vertex i to vertex j. By the principle of mathematical induction, this completes the proof.

■

EXAMPLE 13   Find the number of walks of length 4 between each two vertices of the graph of Example 10 shown in Figure 2.

Solution   We compute $A^4 = (A^2)^2$ for the adjacency matrix given in Example 10. Matrix multiplication gives

$$A^2 = \begin{bmatrix} 2 & 1 & 1 & 1 \\ 1 & 3 & 1 & 0 \\ 1 & 1 & 2 & 1 \\ 1 & 0 & 1 & 1 \end{bmatrix} \quad \text{and} \quad A^4 = \begin{bmatrix} 7 & 6 & 6 & 4 \\ 6 & 11 & 6 & 2 \\ 6 & 6 & 7 & 4 \\ 4 & 2 & 4 & 3 \end{bmatrix}$$

The entry in row i and column j is the number of walks of length 4 from vertex i to vertex j. For example, there are 11 walks of length 4 from vertex 2 back to itself and 6 walks of length 4 from vertex 1 to vertex 3.

■

B   Transitive Closure and Distances

Recall from Section 3-1 that the transitive closure of a relation contains the pair (i,j) if and only if there *is* a walk from vertex i to vertex j. For a digraph with adjacency matrix M, $M + M^2 + M^3 + \cdots + M^{n-1}$ will have the *number* of (nontrivial) walks of length $n-1$ or less from vertex i to vertex j as the entry in row i and column j. Since the most edges a walk can have without repeating vertices in an n-vertex digraph is $n-1$, the i,j entry of $M + M^2 + \cdots + M^{n-1}$ will be nonzero if and only if there is at least one (nontrivial) walk from i to j—that is, if and only if (i,j) is in the transitive closure. This gives us the following theorem.

Theorem 3   The ordered pair (i,j) is in the transitive closure of a relation whose adjacency matrix is M if and only if the i,j entry of $M + M^2 + \cdots + M^{n-1}$ is nonzero.

Proof   Given above.   ■

Finding a product of two n-by-n matrices by the usual method requires n^3 numerical multiplications. Thus an algorithm based on Theorem 3 would require $O(n^4)$ multiplications. There is a method for finding transitive closures which uses $O(n^3)$ operations of a type much faster on current computers than numerical multiplication. (There are also algorithms of lower order than n^4 based on matrix multiplication.)

Warshall's Algorithm

This method of computing transitive closures using adjacency matrices was noticed by Kleene and introduced to the computer science community by Warshall. It uses the idea of a *Boolean or* of two rows of a matrix. The **Boolean or** of row i and row j has a one wherever row i or row j *or both* have a one, and has a zero everywhere else. For example, the Boolean *or* of row 2 and row 3 of the matrix A of Example 2 is the row 1 0 1 1 of zeros and ones. Boolean *ors* are easy to compute electronically. The idea behind Warshall's algorithm is much like the idea behind algorithm Reach, which we introduced in Chapter 3; namely, if you can reach vertex j from vertex i, then anything reachable from j is also reachable from i. In Reach this meant we put everything adjacent from j onto the list of vertices reachable from i. Here it leads us to form the Boolean *or* of row i and row j and to replace row i with it, in effect, adding ones to row i for everything we know we can already reach from j.

Algorithm Warshall

Input: The adjacency matrix A of a relation R on a set with n elements.

Output: The adjacency matrix T of the transitive closure of R.

Procedure: Start with $T = A$.

For each j from 1 to n

For each i from 1 to n

If $T_{ij} = 1$, then form the Boolean *or* of row i and row j and replace row i by it.

Then go on to the next i-value.

If T_{ij} is not 1, go on to the next i-value.

Once you have processed each i-value, go on to the next j-value (and start the i's all over again.)

Theorem 4   Warshall's algorithm computes the adjacency matrix of the transitive closure of a relation.

Proof   Let us refer to the computations made for a given j value as stage j. After stage 1, A_{ik} is 1 if there is an edge from vertex i to vertex k or a two-step walk from vertex i to vertex 1 and then from vertex 1 to vertex k. After stage 2, A_{ik} is 1 if it was already 1 or if there is a two-step walk from vertex i to vertex k using both vertices 1 and 2 (in either order). Extending these observations by induction completes the proof.   ∎

EXAMPLE 14   Use algorithm Warshall to compute the transitive closure of the relation of the digraph in Figure 3.

Solution   Since there are four vertices, the four possible j-values are 1, 2, 3, and 4. The four matrices shown in Figure 5 are the matrices that result from first *all* the computations with $j = 1$, then all the computations with $j = 2$, and so on. Using the last matrix as our adjacency matrix gives us the digraph with solid *and* dotted arrows, shown in Figure 6. The solid arrows are from the original relation, and the dotted ones represent the new edges added to form the closure.   ∎

Figure 5

$$
\begin{bmatrix} 0 & 1 & 0 & 0 \\ 0 & 0 & 1 & 1 \\ 1 & 1 & 0 & 1 \\ 0 & 0 & 0 & 0 \end{bmatrix}
\quad
\begin{bmatrix} 0 & 1 & 1 & 1 \\ 0 & 0 & 1 & 1 \\ 1 & 1 & 1 & 1 \\ 0 & 0 & 0 & 0 \end{bmatrix}
\quad
\begin{bmatrix} 1 & 1 & 1 & 1 \\ 1 & 1 & 1 & 1 \\ 1 & 1 & 1 & 1 \\ 0 & 0 & 0 & 0 \end{bmatrix}
\quad
\begin{bmatrix} 1 & 1 & 1 & 1 \\ 1 & 1 & 1 & 1 \\ 1 & 1 & 1 & 1 \\ 0 & 0 & 0 & 0 \end{bmatrix}
$$

Stages: $j = 1$ $j = 2$ $j = 3$ $j = 4$

Figure 6

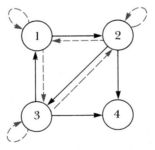

The All-Pairs Shortest Paths Algorithm

A typical application of graphs might involve a graph or digraph representing a transportation system of roads connecting stores and warehouses. Associated with each edge of this graph would be a non-negative number representing its mileage. A dispatcher might need to know which warehouses are closest to which stores; for this purpose a table of distances would be useful. In this context, the numbers associated with edges are called *weights*, and the graph or digraph is called *weighted*.

The **weight** of a walk is the sum of the weights on its edges, and the distance from vertex x to vertex y is the least weight of any walk from x to y. The idea of the Kleene-Warshall algorithm was also introduced and used by R. W. Floyd in designing the algorithm below that computes the distances between any two vertices in a graph or digraph, weighted or unweighted. (We simply regard the weight of each edge of an unweighted graph or digraph as 1. We do assume that the weights are non-negative in any case.)

Algorithm APSPaths

Input: The adjacency matrix A of a weighted digraph with nonnegative weights.

Output: The matrix D, in which D_{ij} is the (weighted) distance from vertex i to vertex j.

Procedure: Begin with $D = A$.
Set $D_{ii} = 0$ for all i.
Make D_{ij} "infinity" if vertex i and j are not adjacent or equal.
For each j from 1 to n
  For each i from 1 to n
    For each k from 1 to n
      If $D_{ij} + D_{jk} < D_{ik}$, then replace D_{ik} by $D_{ij} + D_{jk}$.
      In any case go on to the next k.
    Go on to the next i and start k over after k reaches n.
  Go on to the next j and start i over after i reaches n.

EXAMPLE 15   Compute the (directed) distances between each pair of vertices in the digraph of Figure 7.

Figure 7

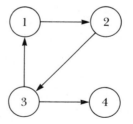

Solution   Below, we show the initial version of D and then the versions with i equal to 1, 2, 3, and 4. Note that when we are done, the distance from vertex 4 to any other vertex is ∞ because no other vertex is reachable from vertex 4.

$$
\begin{bmatrix} 0 & 1 & \infty & \infty \\ \infty & 0 & 1 & \infty \\ 1 & \infty & 0 & 1 \\ \infty & \infty & \infty & 0 \end{bmatrix}
\quad
\begin{bmatrix} 0 & 1 & \infty & \infty \\ \infty & 0 & 1 & \infty \\ 1 & 2 & 0 & 1 \\ \infty & \infty & \infty & 0 \end{bmatrix}
\quad
\begin{bmatrix} 0 & 1 & 2 & \infty \\ \infty & 0 & 1 & \infty \\ 1 & 2 & 0 & 1 \\ \infty & \infty & \infty & 0 \end{bmatrix}
\quad
\begin{bmatrix} 0 & 1 & 2 & 3 \\ 2 & 0 & 1 & 2 \\ 1 & 2 & 0 & 1 \\ \infty & \infty & \infty & 0 \end{bmatrix}
\quad
\begin{bmatrix} 0 & 1 & 2 & 3 \\ 2 & 0 & 1 & 2 \\ 1 & 2 & 0 & 1 \\ \infty & \infty & \infty & 0 \end{bmatrix}
$$

$\qquad\qquad\qquad\qquad i = 1 \qquad\qquad\quad i = 2 \qquad\qquad\quad i = 3 \qquad\qquad\quad i = 4$ ∎

Concepts Review

1. A(n) _____ _____ for a graph with vertex set $\{v_1, v_2, \ldots, v_n\}$ has a one in position i,j if v_i and v_j are adjacent.

2. The number of walks of length n from vertex i to vertex j in G is the (i,j) entry of the nth _____ of the _____ matrix of G.

3. The ordered pair (i,j) is in the transitive closure of a relation on an n-element set whose digraph has adjacency matrix M if and only if the i,j entry of _____ is nonzero.

4. Warshall's algorithm computes the _____ _____ of a relation.

5. The _____ _____ of two row matrices has a 1 in each position where at least one of the row matrices has a 1.

6. A matrix A is _____ if $A_{ij} = A_{ji}$ for all i and j.

Exercises

Ⓐ For Exercises 1–12, draw the graph or multigraph whose adjacency matrix is given,

1. $\begin{bmatrix} 0 & 1 & 0 & 0 \\ 1 & 0 & 1 & 1 \\ 0 & 1 & 0 & 1 \\ 0 & 1 & 1 & 0 \end{bmatrix}$

2. $\begin{bmatrix} 0 & 1 & 0 & 0 \\ 1 & 0 & 1 & 0 \\ 0 & 1 & 0 & 1 \\ 0 & 0 & 1 & 0 \end{bmatrix}$

3. $\begin{bmatrix} 0 & 1 & 0 & 1 \\ 1 & 0 & 1 & 0 \\ 0 & 1 & 0 & 1 \\ 1 & 0 & 1 & 0 \end{bmatrix}$

4. $\begin{bmatrix} 1 & 0 & 2 & 0 \\ 0 & 0 & 2 & 0 \\ 2 & 2 & 1 & 3 \\ 0 & 0 & 3 & 0 \end{bmatrix}$

5. $\begin{bmatrix} 0 & 1 & 0 & 0 \\ 1 & 0 & 2 & 0 \\ 0 & 2 & 0 & 3 \\ 0 & 0 & 3 & 0 \end{bmatrix}$

6. $\begin{bmatrix} 1 & 2 & 1 & 0 \\ 2 & 1 & 1 & 0 \\ 1 & 1 & 0 & 2 \\ 0 & 0 & 2 & 2 \end{bmatrix}$

7. $\begin{bmatrix} 0 & 1 & 1 & 1 \\ 1 & 0 & 0 & 0 \\ 1 & 0 & 0 & 0 \\ 1 & 0 & 0 & 0 \end{bmatrix}$

8. $\begin{bmatrix} 0 & 1 & 1 & 0 \\ 1 & 0 & 0 & 1 \\ 1 & 0 & 0 & 1 \\ 0 & 1 & 1 & 0 \end{bmatrix}$

9. $\begin{bmatrix} 0 & 1 & 1 & 0 \\ 1 & 0 & 1 & 1 \\ 1 & 1 & 0 & 1 \\ 0 & 1 & 1 & 0 \end{bmatrix}$

10. $\begin{bmatrix} 1 & 0 & 2 & 1 \\ 0 & 0 & 2 & 1 \\ 2 & 2 & 0 & 2 \\ 1 & 1 & 2 & 1 \end{bmatrix}$

11. $\begin{bmatrix} 1 & 2 & 1 & 0 \\ 2 & 0 & 0 & 1 \\ 1 & 0 & 0 & 2 \\ 0 & 1 & 2 & 1 \end{bmatrix}$

12. $\begin{bmatrix} 0 & 2 & 2 & 2 \\ 2 & 1 & 0 & 0 \\ 2 & 0 & 1 & 0 \\ 2 & 0 & 0 & 1 \end{bmatrix}$

In Exercises 13–24, write down the adjacency matrix for the graph in the figure specified.

13. Figure 8(a)

14. Figure 8(b)

15. Figure 8(c)

16. Figure 8(d)

17. Figure 8(e)

18. Figure 8(f)

19. Figure 8(g)

20. Figure 8(h)

21. Figure 8(i)

22. Figure 8(j)

23. Figure 8(k)

24. Figure 8(l)

Figure 8

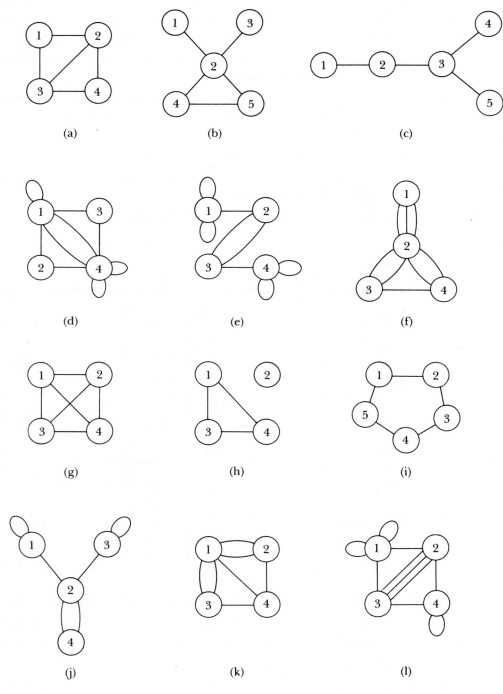

(a)   (b)   (c)

(d)   (e)   (f)

(g)   (h)   (i)

(j)   (k)   (l)

For Exercises 25–36, draw the digraph or multidigraph with the adjacency matrix given.

25. $\begin{bmatrix} 0 & 0 & 1 & 0 \\ 1 & 0 & 0 & 0 \\ 0 & 0 & 0 & 1 \\ 1 & 1 & 0 & 0 \end{bmatrix}$
26. $\begin{bmatrix} 1 & 0 & 0 & 0 \\ 1 & 1 & 0 & 0 \\ 1 & 1 & 1 & 0 \\ 1 & 1 & 1 & 1 \end{bmatrix}$
27. $\begin{bmatrix} 1 & 0 & 0 & 0 \\ 0 & 0 & 1 & 1 \\ 0 & 0 & 0 & 1 \\ 1 & 1 & 0 & 0 \end{bmatrix}$

28. $\begin{bmatrix} 1 & 0 & 0 & 0 \\ 0 & 1 & 0 & 0 \\ 1 & 1 & 0 & 0 \\ 1 & 1 & 2 & 0 \end{bmatrix}$
29. $\begin{bmatrix} 1 & 2 & 0 & 0 \\ 1 & 0 & 0 & 0 \\ 0 & 0 & 1 & 2 \\ 0 & 0 & 0 & 1 \end{bmatrix}$
30. $\begin{bmatrix} 0 & 2 & 0 & 0 \\ 0 & 0 & 2 & 1 \\ 1 & 0 & 0 & 2 \\ 2 & 0 & 0 & 0 \end{bmatrix}$

31. $\begin{bmatrix} 0 & 1 & 0 & 0 \\ 0 & 0 & 1 & 0 \\ 0 & 0 & 0 & 1 \\ 1 & 0 & 0 & 0 \end{bmatrix}$
32. $\begin{bmatrix} 0 & 2 & 1 & 0 \\ 1 & 0 & 3 & 0 \\ 0 & 0 & 0 & 1 \\ 0 & 2 & 0 & 0 \end{bmatrix}$
33. $\begin{bmatrix} 0 & 1 & 1 & 1 \\ 0 & 0 & 1 & 0 \\ 0 & 0 & 0 & 1 \\ 0 & 1 & 0 & 0 \end{bmatrix}$

34. $\begin{bmatrix} 0 & 1 & 1 & 1 \\ 1 & 0 & 1 & 0 \\ 1 & 0 & 0 & 1 \\ 1 & 1 & 0 & 0 \end{bmatrix}$
35. $\begin{bmatrix} 0 & 1 & 2 & 0 \\ 1 & 0 & 2 & 0 \\ 0 & 0 & 0 & 2 \\ 0 & 0 & 0 & 0 \end{bmatrix}$
36. $\begin{bmatrix} 1 & 1 & 0 & 0 \\ 1 & 1 & 1 & 0 \\ 1 & 0 & 1 & 0 \\ 0 & 0 & 0 & 2 \end{bmatrix}$

In Exercises 37–48, write down the adjacency matrix of the digraph or multidigraph in the figure specified.

37. Figure 9(a)   **38.** Figure 9(b)   **39.** Figure 9(c)

40. Figure 9(d)   **41.** Figure 9(e)   **42.** Figure 9(f)

43. Figure 9(g)   **44.** Figure 9(h)   **45.** Figure 9(i)

46. Figure 9(j)   **47.** Figure 9(k)   **48.** Figure 9(l)

49. Find the number of walks of length 4 from vertex 1 to vertex 4 in each of the graphs or multigraphs of the odd-numbered exercises from 1 to 11.

50. Find the number of walks of length 4 from vertex 1 to vertex 4 in each of the graphs or multigraphs of the even-numbered exercises from 2 to 12.

51. Find the number of walks of length 4 from vertex 1 to vertex 4 in each of the digraphs or multidigraphs of the odd-numbered exercises from 25 to 35.

52. Find the number of walks of length 4 from vertex 1 to vertex 4 in each of the digraphs or multidigraphs of the even-numbered exercises from 26 to 36.

B For Exercises 53–58, compute the adjacency matrix of the transitive closure of each of the graphs or digraphs whose adjacency matrix is given in the exercises specified. Draw the transitive closure. Use dotted arrows for edges in the transitive closure but not the original digraph.

53. Exercise 1   **54.** Exercise 2   **55.** Exercise 25

56. Exercise 26   **57.** Exercise 27   **58.** Exercise 9

Figure 9

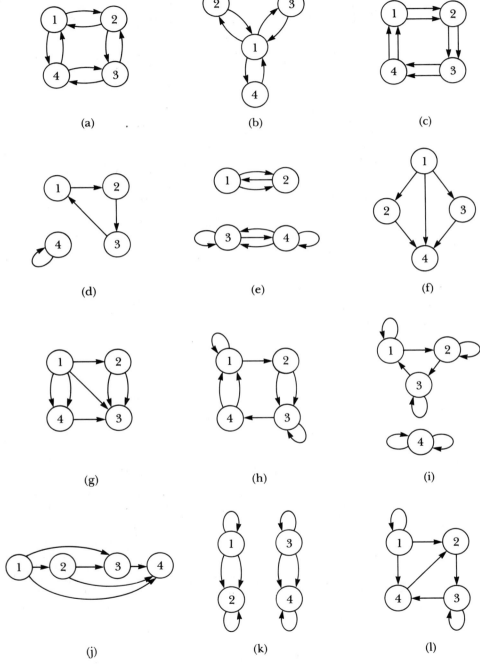

(a)

(b)

(c)

(d)

(e)

(f)

(g)

(h)

(i)

(j)

(k)

(l)

For Exercises 59–64, use Warshall's algorithm to compute the transitive closure of the relation of the graph or digraph in the exercise specified.

59. Exercise 13   **60.** Exercise 20   **61.** Exercise 42

62. Exercise 40   **63.** Exercise 48   **64.** Exercise 46

In Exercises 65–70, use Warshall's algorithm to test the digraph in the exercise specified to see if it is a digraph of a transitive relation. (It is transitive if it equals its own transitive closure.)

65. Exercise 25   **66.** Exercise 26   **67.** Exercise 42

68. Exercise 31   **69.** Exercise 33   **70.** Exercise 40

In Exercises 71–76, use algorithm APSPaths to find the distances between each pair of vertices in the graphs specified.

71. Figure 8(b)   **72.** Figure 8(i)   **73.** Figure 10(a)

74. Figure 10(b)   **75.** Figure 10(c)   **76.** Figure 10(d)

Figure 10

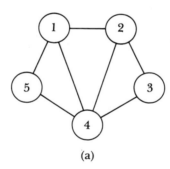

(a)

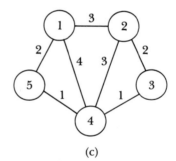

(c)

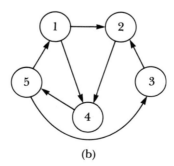

(b)

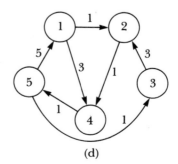

(d)

Problems

1. Explain why i is related to j in the reflexive transitive closure of a relation R (with adjacency matrix M) on an n-element set if and only if the (i,j) entry of $(I + M)^{n-1}$ is nonzero.

2. Show how to use mathematical induction to complete the proof in Theorem 4 that Warshall's algorithm computes the transitive closure of a relation.

3. True or false: If there are no changes at stage i of Warshall's algorithm, then we must still go on to stage $i + 1$ and beyond rather than stopping after stage i.

4. Is the number of stages that must be completed before we can stop with Warshall's algorithm equal to the length of the longest path? Why or why not?

5. The *trace* of a matrix is the sum of its diagonal entries. How does the trace of the cube of an adjacency matrix of a simple graph relate to the number of cycles of length 3 in the graph?

6. Discuss how your conclusion in Problem 5 must change if the graph is directed (that is, if it is a digraph).

7. Is there a result analogous to Problem 5 for cycles of length 4? Explain why not or state and prove it.

8. How does the sum of the entries of row i of an adjacency matrix relate to vertex i in the case of a multigraph? A multidigraph?

9. Prove that algorithm APSPaths results in a matrix D in which D_{ij} is the distance from vertex i to vertex j.

10. Explain how to determine paths from vertex i to each other vertex j by using the matrices A and D. (*Hint:* To get started, think about the meaning of $D_{ij} = A_{ij}$ and the meaning of $A_{ij} + A_{jk} = D_{ik}$.) Analyze the number of steps (say comparison steps) needed for this process.

11. Write a modified version of algorithm APSPaths that also computes a matrix P as it goes along, so that when we are done, P_{ij} is the number of the vertex previous to vertex j on the shortest path from vertex i to vertex j. How will the matrix P aid you in finding paths? Does this change the order of algorithm APSPaths?

Section 10-3
Matrices and Systems
of Linear Equations

◪ *Matrix Representations of Systems of Equations*

One reason for the importance of matrix multiplication is that it helps us write a system of linear equations as a matrix equation.

EXAMPLE 16 Rewrite the following systems of equations as matrix equations.

$$
\begin{array}{ll}
\text{(a)} & \begin{aligned}
x_1 - 2x_2 + x_3 &= 0 \\
2x_1 + x_2 - x_3 &= 1 \\
x_1 + x_2 + x_3 &= 6
\end{aligned}
&
\text{(b)} & \begin{aligned}
x_1 - 2x_2 + x_3 &= 0 \\
2x_1 + x_2 - x_3 &= 1 \\
x_1 + x_2 + x_3 &= 6 \\
2x_1 - x_2 + x_3 &= 3
\end{aligned}
\end{array}
$$

Solution (a) Each individual equation may be written using a product of a row matrix and a column matrix. For example, $x_1 - 2x_2 + x_3 = 0$ may be written as

$$
\begin{bmatrix} 1 & -2 & 1 \end{bmatrix} \begin{bmatrix} x_1 \\ x_2 \\ x_3 \end{bmatrix} = 0
$$

and $2x_1 + x_2 - x_3 = 1$ and $x_1 + x_2 + x_3 = 6$ may be written as

$$
\begin{bmatrix} 2 & 1 & -1 \end{bmatrix} \begin{bmatrix} x_1 \\ x_2 \\ x_3 \end{bmatrix} = 1 \quad \text{and} \quad \begin{bmatrix} 1 & 1 & 1 \end{bmatrix} \begin{bmatrix} x_1 \\ x_2 \\ x_3 \end{bmatrix} = 6
$$

The definition of the product of matrices given in Section 10-1 shows that these three equations may be written as the single matrix equation

$$
\begin{bmatrix} 1 & -2 & 1 \\ 2 & 1 & -1 \\ 1 & 1 & 1 \end{bmatrix} \begin{bmatrix} x_1 \\ x_2 \\ x_3 \end{bmatrix} = \begin{bmatrix} 0 \\ 1 \\ 6 \end{bmatrix}
$$

(b) Notice that this system of equations has all three equations from (a) and also the equation $2x_1 - x_2 + x_3 = 3$, which may be written as

$$
\begin{bmatrix} 2 & -1 & 1 \end{bmatrix} \begin{bmatrix} x_1 \\ x_2 \\ x_3 \end{bmatrix} = 3
$$

Thus the second system may be written as

$$\begin{bmatrix} 1 & -2 & 1 \\ 2 & 1 & -1 \\ 1 & 1 & 1 \\ 2 & -1 & 1 \end{bmatrix} \begin{bmatrix} x_1 \\ x_2 \\ x_3 \end{bmatrix} = \begin{bmatrix} 0 \\ 1 \\ 6 \\ 3 \end{bmatrix}$$

Notice how the matrix on the left follows exactly the pattern of the coefficients from the system of equations. ∎

Solving Equations

You are probably familiar with the *elimination* or the *elimination and substitution* method of solving a system of equations. In either method, we add multiples of one equation to or subtract multiples of one equation from another with the goal of getting an equation involving one variable. In the pure elimination method, we continue this process until each variable lies in an equation by itself. In the elimination and substitution method, we get just one variable in an equation by itself, solve for it, substitute that value into other equations, and then repeat the process to find the values of the other variables. The pure elimination method may be combined with the use of matrices to give a method that is not only fast and effective for solving the system of equations but is also especially easy to implement in a computer program. It is also easier for a person using the pure elimination method to remember what to do next at each stage.

We review several ideas from algebra before giving an example of pure elimination. A **solution** to a system of equations in variables $x_1, x_2, \ldots, x_n$ is an assignment of numbers to the variables that makes each equation a true statement about numbers. For example, $x_1 = 1$, $x_2 = 2$, $x_3 = -1$ and $x_1 = 1$, $x_2 = -1$, $x_3 = 2$ are both solutions to the system of equations

$$x_1 + x_2 + x_3 = 2$$
$$x_1 - x_2 - x_3 = 0$$

EXAMPLE 17   Check that $x_1 = 1$, $x_2 = 2$, $x_3 = -1$ is a solution to the equations above.

Solution   We substitute 1 for x_1, 2 for x_2, and -1 for x_3 in the left-hand side and simplify, giving

$$1 + 2 + (-1) = 2$$
$$1 - 2 - (-2) = 0$$

Therefore $x_1 = 1$, $x_2 = 2$, $x_3 = -1$ satisfies both equations and is thus a solution. ∎

We may check that $x_1 = 1$, $x_2 = -1$, $x_3 = 2$ is a solution similarly. In matrix terms, we would say that

$$X = \begin{bmatrix} 1 \\ 2 \\ -1 \end{bmatrix} \quad \text{and} \quad X = \begin{bmatrix} 1 \\ -1 \\ 2 \end{bmatrix}$$

are both solutions to the matrix equation

$$\begin{bmatrix} 1 & 1 & 1 \\ 1 & -1 & -1 \end{bmatrix} X = \begin{bmatrix} 2 \\ 0 \end{bmatrix}$$

EXAMPLE 18   Use matrix multiplication to verify that $\begin{bmatrix} 1 \\ -1 \\ 2 \end{bmatrix}$ is a solution to the matrix equation $\begin{bmatrix} 1 & 1 & 1 \\ 1 & -1 & -1 \end{bmatrix} X = \begin{bmatrix} 2 \\ 0 \end{bmatrix}$.

Solution   We substitute the given column matrix for X, giving

$$\begin{bmatrix} 1 & 1 & 1 \\ 1 & -1 & -1 \end{bmatrix} \begin{bmatrix} 1 \\ -1 \\ 2 \end{bmatrix} = \begin{bmatrix} 1\cdot 1 + 1\cdot(-1) & + & 1\cdot 2 \\ 1\cdot 1 + (-1)(-1) + (-1)\cdot 2 \end{bmatrix} = \begin{bmatrix} 1 - 1 + 2 \\ 1 + 1 - 2 \end{bmatrix} = \begin{bmatrix} 2 \\ 0 \end{bmatrix} \quad \blacksquare$$

> We call the set of all column matrices X satisfying a matrix equation the **solution set** of the matrix equation or system of equations.

We may think of the two equations as the compound statement

$$(x_1 + x_2 + x_3 = 2) \wedge (x_1 - x_2 - x_3 = 0)$$

The universe for this statement is all column matrices with three entries, and the truth set of this statement is the solution set of the equations. We say two systems of equations are **equivalent** if they have exactly the same solution sets. Notice that this is the same thing we mean by saying that the corresponding statements are equivalent. The two most standard ways of converting a system of equations to an equivalent system are

(1) Multiply each term of one equation by the same nonzero real number r.
(2) Add a multiple of one equation to or subtract a multiple of one equation from a second one, replacing the second equation by that sum.

We shall see many examples of these operations in Example 19. The reason why each of these operations cannot change the solution set is that each is reversible. These two operations with equations correspond to two operations we shall perform on rows of matrices in order to solve matrix equations. Let us illustrate the pure elimination method of solving systems of equations and show its effect on the matrix equations that correspond to them.

EXAMPLE 19   Solve the first system of equations from Example 16, showing the complete system of equations and its matrix representation as you go.

Solution   We write

$$
\begin{aligned}
x_1 - 2x_2 + x_3 &= 0 \\
2x_1 + x_2 - x_3 &= 1 \\
x_1 + x_2 + x_3 &= 6
\end{aligned}
\quad \text{and} \quad
\begin{bmatrix} 1 & -2 & 1 \\ 2 & 1 & -1 \\ 1 & 1 & 1 \end{bmatrix}
\begin{bmatrix} x_1 \\ x_2 \\ x_3 \end{bmatrix} =
\begin{bmatrix} 0 \\ 1 \\ 6 \end{bmatrix}
$$

Now we subtract twice the first equation from the second and write the result in place of the second equation, giving

$$
\begin{aligned}
x_1 - 2x_2 + x_3 &= 0 \\
0 + 5x_2 - 3x_3 &= 1 \\
x_1 + x_2 + x_3 &= 6
\end{aligned}
\quad \text{and} \quad
\begin{bmatrix} 1 & -2 & 1 \\ 0 & 5 & -3 \\ 1 & 1 & 1 \end{bmatrix}
\begin{bmatrix} x_1 \\ x_2 \\ x_3 \end{bmatrix} =
\begin{bmatrix} 0 \\ 1 \\ 6 \end{bmatrix}
$$

Next subtract the first equation from the third, giving

$$
\begin{aligned}
x_1 - 2x_2 + x_3 &= 0 \\
5x_2 - 3x_3 &= 1 \\
3x_2 &= 6
\end{aligned}
\quad \text{and} \quad
\begin{bmatrix} 1 & -2 & 1 \\ 0 & 5 & -3 \\ 0 & 3 & 0 \end{bmatrix}
\begin{bmatrix} x_1 \\ x_2 \\ x_3 \end{bmatrix} =
\begin{bmatrix} 0 \\ 1 \\ 6 \end{bmatrix}
$$

Now we divide the last equation by 3, giving

$$
\begin{aligned}
x_1 - 2x_2 + x_3 &= 0 \\
5x_2 - 3x_3 &= 1 \\
x_2 &= 2
\end{aligned}
\quad \text{and} \quad
\begin{bmatrix} 1 & -2 & 1 \\ 0 & 5 & -3 \\ 0 & 1 & 0 \end{bmatrix}
\begin{bmatrix} x_1 \\ x_2 \\ x_3 \end{bmatrix} =
\begin{bmatrix} 0 \\ 1 \\ 2 \end{bmatrix}
$$

Next we add twice the third equation to the first and subtract five times the third equation from the second giving

$$
\begin{aligned}
x_1 + x_3 &= 4 \\
-3x_3 &= -9 \\
x_2 &= 2
\end{aligned}
\quad \text{and} \quad
\begin{bmatrix} 1 & 0 & 1 \\ 0 & 0 & -3 \\ 0 & 1 & 0 \end{bmatrix}
\begin{bmatrix} x_1 \\ x_2 \\ x_3 \end{bmatrix} =
\begin{bmatrix} 4 \\ -9 \\ 2 \end{bmatrix}
$$

Now we divide the second equation by -3, giving

$$
\begin{aligned}
x_1 + x_3 &= 4 \\
x_3 &= 3 \\
x_2 &= 2
\end{aligned}
\quad \text{and} \quad
\begin{bmatrix} 1 & 0 & 1 \\ 0 & 0 & 1 \\ 0 & 1 & 0 \end{bmatrix}
\begin{bmatrix} x_1 \\ x_2 \\ x_3 \end{bmatrix} =
\begin{bmatrix} 4 \\ 3 \\ 2 \end{bmatrix}
$$

Next, we subtract the second equation from the first, giving

$$
\begin{aligned}
x_1 &= 1 \\
x_3 &= 3 \\
x_2 &= 2
\end{aligned}
\quad \text{and} \quad
\begin{bmatrix} 1 & 0 & 0 \\ 0 & 0 & 1 \\ 0 & 1 & 0 \end{bmatrix}
\begin{bmatrix} x_1 \\ x_2 \\ x_3 \end{bmatrix} =
\begin{bmatrix} 1 \\ 3 \\ 2 \end{bmatrix}
$$

Finally, to list our solution in order, we interchange equations 2 and 3, giving

$$\begin{aligned} x_1 &= 1 \\ x_2 &= 2 \\ x_3 &= 3 \end{aligned} \quad \text{and} \quad \begin{bmatrix} 1 & 0 & 0 \\ 0 & 1 & 0 \\ 0 & 0 & 1 \end{bmatrix} \begin{bmatrix} x_1 \\ x_2 \\ x_3 \end{bmatrix} = \begin{bmatrix} 1 \\ 2 \\ 3 \end{bmatrix}$$

In this way, we see that our system of equations has the solution $x_1 = 1$, $x_2 = 2$, and $x_3 = 3$. ∎

B Row Reduced Matrices

The Coefficient Matrix

In Example 19, we showed a matrix version of each stage of the solution process. By concentrating on how the solution process influenced the matrices, we shall be able to develop a method of solving equations that is suitable for use on a computer and is also convenient to do "by hand."

Notice that although the matrix on the left, which we shall call the **coefficient matrix,** changed as we worked through the equations and the matrix on the right (sometimes called the **matrix of constants**) changed as we worked through the equations, the matrix of variables didn't change a bit. Thus we might as well not have bothered to include the matrix of variables until the last step. Notice also that our operations first gave us exactly one *non*zero entry in the first column of the coefficient matrix, then exactly one *non*zero entry in the second column of the coefficient matrix, and finally exactly one *non*zero entry in the third column of the coefficient matrix. Each operation we performed on the equations corresponds to what we call an *elementary row operation* on both the coefficient matrix and the right-hand matrix. The three **elementary row operations** and their names are

(1) Multiply row *i* by a nonzero number: the **row multiple operation.**
(2) Add a numerical multiple of one row to another: the **row sum operation.**
(3) Interchange two rows: the **row interchange operation.**

Each operation on the equations in which we multiplied an equation by a number corresponded to a row multiple operation. Each operation in which we added a multiple of one equation to another corresponded to a row sum operation on our coefficient and right-hand matrices. Interchanging two equations corresponded to a row interchange operation.

Pivotal Entries

The fact that each row of the final matrix corresponded to the value of a different variable can be best explained in matrix terms by using the concepts of pivotal entries of a matrix and row reduced matrices.

The first nonzero entry of a row is called a **pivotal entry**.

A matrix is called **row reduced** if each *column*
containing a pivotal entry has all its other entries
equal to zero, and each pivotal entry is one.

Figure 11 shows a row reduced matrix and one that is not row reduced.

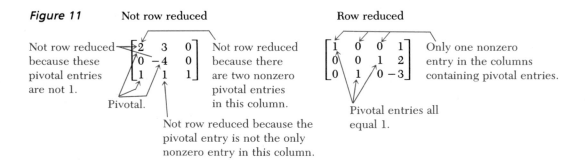

Figure 11   Not row reduced   Row reduced

Not row reduced because these pivotal entries are not 1.
$$\begin{bmatrix} 2 & 3 & 0 \\ 0 & -4 & 0 \\ 1 & 1 & 1 \end{bmatrix}$$
Pivotal.

Not row reduced because there are two nonzero pivotal entries in this column.

Not row reduced because the pivotal entry is not the only nonzero entry in this column.

$$\begin{bmatrix} 1 & 0 & 0 & 1 \\ 0 & 0 & 1 & 2 \\ 0 & 1 & 0 & -3 \end{bmatrix}$$
Only one nonzero entry in the columns containing pivotal entries.

Pivotal entries all equal 1.

The process in Example 19 of isolating all the variables into equations by themselves put the coefficient matrix into row reduced form. It is no surprise, then, that the idea of row reduced form turns out to be the foundation for our method of solving equations. What we shall do is reverse the emphasis of Example 19: We shall convert a system of equations to a matrix equation, perform row operations to put the coefficient matrix into row reduced form, and then write out the solutions to the equations on the basis of the row reduced form.

Putting a Matrix into Row Reduced Form

For now, we shall concentrate on row operations on matrices. We shall discuss the relationship with equations later. We say that a matrix M and a matrix N are **row equivalent** if there is a sequence of elementary row operations that converts M to N.

The following algorithm allows us to row reduce a matrix by imitating the pure elimination method of solving equations.

Algorithm Reduce
Input:	An m-by-n matrix M.
Output:	A row reduced m-by-n matrix that is row equivalent to M.
Procedure:	In the leftmost column containing a pivotal entry, choose one pivotal entry m_{ij}.

Divide row i by m_{ij}.

For each $k \neq i$, subtract m_{kj} times row i from row k.

Repeat this process from left to right on all columns containing pivotal entries.

Theorem 5   Applying algorithm Reduce to a matrix M yields a row reduced matrix that is row equivalent to M.

Proof   When the process is complete, each column with a pivotal entry has only one nonzero entry, and this entry is one. Thus the matrix is row reduced; since all operations performed are row operations, the resulting matrix is row equivalent to M. ∎

The process described in algorithm Reduce is called **row reduction.** The pivotal entry we choose in a column is called a **pivot.** The algorithm gives us no instructions as to which pivotal entry we should choose. In a course in numerical analysis, you may study in detail how to choose the most appropriate pivot. For our purposes, no special choices are necessary.

EXAMPLE 20   Row reduce the matrix

$$\begin{bmatrix} 2 & 1 & 3 & 4 \\ 2 & 1 & 2 & 3 \\ -2 & -1 & 1 & 1 \end{bmatrix}$$

Solution   We shall use an arrow underneath a symbol such as $\frac{1}{2}\cdot R1$, which stands for "multiply row 1 by $\frac{1}{2}$," or $(-1)R1 + R2$, which stands for "add negative one times row 1 to row 2," to describe which row operations are being performed as we row reduce our matrix. We put one symbol above and one symbol below an arrow when the arrow represents two operations. We shall blindly follow algorithm Reduce (described before Theorem 5); you may see some places where doing things in a slightly different order would save us from dealing with fractions or otherwise make our work easier. Once you understand the process, it is appropriate for you to make such minor modifications in your own work.

$$\begin{bmatrix} 2 & 1 & 3 & 4 \\ 2 & 1 & 2 & 3 \\ -2 & -1 & 1 & 1 \end{bmatrix} \xrightarrow{\frac{1}{2}\cdot R1} \begin{bmatrix} 1 & \frac{1}{2} & \frac{3}{2} & 2 \\ 2 & 1 & 2 & 3 \\ -2 & -1 & 1 & 1 \end{bmatrix} \xrightarrow[\;2R1 + R3\;]{(-2)R1 + R2}$$

$$\begin{bmatrix} 1 & \frac{1}{2} & \frac{3}{2} & 2 \\ 0 & 0 & -1 & -1 \\ 0 & 0 & 4 & 5 \end{bmatrix} \xrightarrow{-1\cdot R2} \begin{bmatrix} 1 & \frac{1}{2} & \frac{3}{2} & 2 \\ 0 & 0 & 1 & 1 \\ 0 & 0 & 4 & 5 \end{bmatrix} \xrightarrow[\;-4R2 + R3\;]{-\frac{3}{2}R2 + R1}$$

$$\begin{bmatrix} 1 & \frac{1}{2} & 0 & \frac{1}{2} \\ 0 & 0 & 1 & 1 \\ 0 & 0 & 0 & 1 \end{bmatrix} \xrightarrow[\;-1R3 + R2\;]{-\frac{1}{2}R3 + R1} \begin{bmatrix} 1 & \frac{1}{2} & 0 & 0 \\ 0 & 0 & 1 & 0 \\ 0 & 0 & 0 & 1 \end{bmatrix}$$ ∎

From the example, you see that some columns might not contain pivotal entries— the $\frac{1}{2}$ in the second column of the example is not pivotal. In our example, each row contained a pivotal entry. A row of zeros would be entirely possible in a row reduced matrix. A row of zeros cannot have a pivotal entry, but, by definition, any row of nonzero entries must contain a pivotal entry. (Why?)

◖ Solving Systems of Equations

In part A of this section, we learned how to associate matrices with systems of equations and saw how operations on equations translated into operations on matrices. In part B, we saw how these operations can be used to row reduce a matrix. Let us state precisely what we have already learned about the relationship between matrices and systems of equations, so that we may use this knowledge as a basis for solving systems of equations.

The Relationship Between Matrices and Systems of Equations

Theorem 6   Let M be an m-by-n matrix and B be a column matrix with m entries. If we perform exactly the same row operations on M and B, resulting in a row reduced m-by-n matrix N and column matrix C, then the system of equations represented by the matrix equation $MX = B$ and the system of equations represented by the matrix equation $NX = C$ are equivalent.

Proof   This theorem simply summarizes what we already know.   ∎

In some cases row reduction makes the solutions to a system of equations obvious.

EXAMPLE 21   Solve the system of equations

$$2x - y + z = 1$$
$$x + 2y - 2z = 3$$
$$3x - 2y - z = 4$$

Solution   We shall rewrite the system as the matrix equation

$$\begin{bmatrix} 2 & -1 & 1 \\ 1 & 2 & -2 \\ 3 & -2 & -1 \end{bmatrix} \begin{bmatrix} x \\ y \\ z \end{bmatrix} = \begin{bmatrix} 1 \\ 3 \\ 4 \end{bmatrix}$$

To make sure we perform the same operations on both the coefficient matrix and right-hand matrix, we shall write them together in a single matrix with a dividing line between them:

$$\begin{bmatrix} 2 & -1 & 1 & | & 1 \\ 1 & 2 & -2 & | & 3 \\ 3 & -2 & -1 & | & 4 \end{bmatrix}$$

This is called the **augmented matrix** of the system of equations. (When the matrix to the left of the vertical line is M and to the right of the line is B, we use the symbol $M|B$ to stand for the augmented matrix.)

Now we perform row operations on the augmented matrix until we have the part to the left of the line row reduced. Notice that we do not blindly follow algorithm Reduce, though we follow the pattern it suggests.

$$\begin{bmatrix} 2 & -1 & 1 & | & 1 \\ 1 & 2 & -2 & | & 3 \\ 3 & -2 & -1 & | & 4 \end{bmatrix} \xrightarrow{\frac{1}{2}R1} \begin{bmatrix} 1 & -\frac{1}{2} & \frac{1}{2} & | & \frac{1}{2} \\ 1 & 2 & -2 & | & 3 \\ 3 & -2 & -1 & | & 4 \end{bmatrix} \xrightarrow[\;(-3)R1 + R3\;]{(-1)R1 + R2}$$

$$\begin{bmatrix} 1 & -\frac{1}{2} & \frac{1}{2} & | & \frac{1}{2} \\ 0 & \frac{5}{2} & -\frac{5}{2} & | & \frac{5}{2} \\ 0 & -\frac{1}{2} & -\frac{5}{2} & | & \frac{5}{2} \end{bmatrix} \xrightarrow[\;2R3\;]{\frac{2}{5}R2} \begin{bmatrix} 1 & -\frac{1}{2} & \frac{1}{2} & | & \frac{1}{2} \\ 0 & 1 & -1 & | & 1 \\ 0 & -1 & -5 & | & 5 \end{bmatrix} \xrightarrow[\;1R2 + R3\;]{\frac{1}{2}R2 + R1}$$

$$\begin{bmatrix} 1 & 0 & 0 & | & 1 \\ 0 & 1 & -1 & | & 1 \\ 0 & 0 & -6 & | & 6 \end{bmatrix} \xrightarrow{-\frac{1}{6}R3} \begin{bmatrix} 1 & 0 & 0 & | & 1 \\ 0 & 1 & -1 & | & 1 \\ 0 & 0 & 1 & | & -1 \end{bmatrix} \xrightarrow{1R3 + R2}$$

$$\begin{bmatrix} 1 & 0 & 0 & | & 1 \\ 0 & 1 & 0 & | & 0 \\ 0 & 0 & 1 & | & -1 \end{bmatrix}$$

What does this row reduced augmented matrix tell us? By Theorem 6, we know that our original system of equations has exactly the same solutions as this new system of equations. When we write this new system down, we get

$$\begin{array}{rcr} x & = & 1 \\ y & = & 0 \\ z & = & -1 \end{array}$$

Since this system of equations is equivalent to the original system, we see that the assignment $x = 1$, $y = 0$, $z = -1$, and only that assignment, makes all three equations true, and so we have solved our system of equations. ∎

Row Reduction Always Determines All Solutions

The process we just demonstrated always provides solutions to our equations, though this fact is not always so obvious.

EXAMPLE 22   Solve the system of equations

$$\begin{array}{rcr} 2x_1 + 1x_2 + 3x_3 + 4x_4 & = & 0 \\ 2x_1 + 1x_2 + 2x_3 + 3x_4 & = & 0 \\ -2x_1 - 1x_2 + 1x_3 + 1x_4 & = & -1 \end{array}$$

Solution   We write down the augmented matrix

$$\left[\begin{array}{cccc|c} 2 & 1 & 3 & 4 & 0 \\ 2 & 1 & 2 & 3 & 0 \\ -2 & -1 & 1 & 1 & -1 \end{array}\right]$$

Since the left-hand part of the augmented matrix is the matrix of Example 20, we perform the row operations of that example on this augmented matrix to get

$$\left[\begin{array}{cccc|c} 1 & \frac{1}{2} & 0 & 0 & \frac{1}{2} \\ 0 & 0 & 1 & 0 & 1 \\ 0 & 0 & 0 & 1 & -1 \end{array}\right]$$

This corresponds to the system of equations

$$
\begin{aligned}
x_1 + \tfrac{1}{2}x_2 \quad &= \tfrac{1}{2} \\
x_3 \quad &= 1 \\
x_4 &= -1
\end{aligned}
\qquad \text{or} \qquad
\begin{aligned}
x_1 &= \tfrac{1}{2} - \tfrac{1}{2}x_2 \\
x_3 &= 1 \\
x_4 &= -1
\end{aligned}
$$

Because each of our row operations is reversible, this system of equations has exactly the same solutions as the original system. Further, if we choose some real number r and set $x_2 = r$, then our equations read $x_1 = \tfrac{1}{2} - \tfrac{1}{2}r$, $x_2 = r$, $x_3 = 1$, $x_4 = 1$. Thus whether we pick $r = \pi$, $r = -\tfrac{3}{5}$, $r = 10$, $r = \sqrt{2}$, or anything else, these four equations—$x_1 = \tfrac{1}{2} - \tfrac{1}{2}r$, $x_2 = r$, $x_3 = 1$, $x_4 = 1$—give a solution to our system of equations.   ∎

Our system of equations in Example 22 has infinitely many solutions, and by letting r stand for an arbitrary real number (often called a **parameter**), we can express our solutions in terms of r. This suggests the fundamental theorem that follows. We say that a variable x_i is **pivotal** if column i contains a pivotal entry; in Example 22, variables x_1, x_3, and x_4 were pivotal for the row reduced augmented matrix.

Theorem 7   If a system of equations has the matrix representation $MX = B$, then forming the augmented matrix $M|B$ and row reducing it to an augmented matrix $N|C$ with N in row reduced form allows us to determine the solutions to the system of equations as follows.

(1) Write down the equations corresponding to the matrix equation $NX = C$.
(2) If any of these equations has the form $0 = r$ where $r \neq 0$, then the original system of equations has no solutions.
(3) Set each nonpivotal variable equal to a different *parameter* (a symbol standing for an arbitrary real number) and express the pivotal variables in terms of these parameters. The set of column matrices described by these expressions is the solution set to the system of equations.

Proof   Since the row reduced system has the same solutions as the original system, there is nothing left to prove.   ■

EXAMPLE 23   Find all solutions to the system of equations

$$x + y = 1$$
$$x + y = 2$$

Solution   The augmented matrix is

$$\left[\begin{array}{cc|c} 1 & 1 & 1 \\ 1 & 1 & 2 \end{array}\right]$$

and row reduces to

$$\left[\begin{array}{cc|c} 1 & 1 & 1 \\ 0 & 0 & 1 \end{array}\right]$$

corresponding to $x + y = 1$ and $0 = 1$. Since $0 = 1$ is impossible, the system has *no* solutions.   ■

Having the Same Number of Unknowns as Equations Tells Us Nothing

Common examples of three equations in three unknowns have just one solution—that is, one value each for x, y, and z. This is not always the case. In Example 23 we saw that two equations with two unknowns might have no solution.

EXAMPLE 24   Solve the system of equations

$$x - y + 2z = 2$$
$$x + y - 3z = -1$$
$$5x + y - 5z = 1$$

Solution   We write

$$\left[\begin{array}{ccc|c} 1 & -1 & 2 & 2 \\ 1 & 1 & -3 & -1 \\ 5 & 1 & -5 & 1 \end{array}\right] \begin{array}{l} -1R1 + R2 \\ \xrightarrow{\hspace{2cm}} \\ -5R1 + R3 \end{array}$$

$$\left[\begin{array}{ccc|c} 1 & -1 & 2 & 2 \\ 0 & 2 & -5 & -3 \\ 0 & 6 & -15 & -9 \end{array}\right] \xrightarrow{-3R2 + R3} \left[\begin{array}{ccc|c} 1 & -1 & 2 & 2 \\ 0 & 2 & -5 & -3 \\ 0 & 0 & 0 & 0 \end{array}\right]$$

$$\xrightarrow{\frac{1}{2}R2} \left[\begin{array}{ccc|c} 1 & -1 & 2 & 2 \\ 0 & 1 & -\frac{5}{2} & -\frac{3}{2} \\ 0 & 0 & 0 & 0 \end{array}\right] \xrightarrow{1R2 + R1} \left[\begin{array}{ccc|c} 1 & 0 & -\frac{1}{2} & \frac{1}{2} \\ 0 & 1 & -\frac{5}{2} & -\frac{3}{2} \\ 0 & 0 & 0 & 0 \end{array}\right]$$

Since this is row reduced and variables x and y are the pivotal variables, we take z to be an arbitrary real number r and write down the equations

$$x - \frac{1}{2}r = \frac{1}{2}$$

$$y - \frac{5}{2}r = -\frac{3}{2}$$

After solving for x and y, we get

$$x = \frac{1}{2} + \frac{1}{2}r, \qquad y = -\frac{3}{2} + \frac{5}{2}r, \qquad z = r$$

so our system has infinitely many solutions.   ■

Of course, there is no reason why answers should involve only one parameter.

EXAMPLE 25   Find all solutions to the system of equations

$$x_1 + 2x_2 + 2x_3 - x_4 = 1$$
$$x_1 + 2x_2 + x_3 \qquad = 2$$
$$2x_1 + 4x_2 + 3x_3 - x_4 = 3$$

Solution   We apply row reduction, following the general pattern of the row reduction algorithm (but not applying it blindly), to get

$$
\begin{bmatrix} 1 & 2 & 2 & -1 & | & 1 \\ 1 & 2 & 1 & 0 & | & 2 \\ 2 & 4 & 3 & -1 & | & 3 \end{bmatrix}
\xrightarrow[\; -2R1 + R3\;]{\; -1R1 + R2\;}
\begin{bmatrix} 1 & 2 & 2 & -1 & | & 1 \\ 0 & 0 & -1 & 1 & | & 1 \\ 0 & 0 & -1 & 1 & | & 1 \end{bmatrix}
$$

$$
\xrightarrow[\; 2R2 + R1\;]{\; -1R2 + R3\;}
\begin{bmatrix} 1 & 2 & 0 & 1 & | & 3 \\ 0 & 0 & -1 & 1 & | & 1 \\ 0 & 0 & 0 & 0 & | & 0 \end{bmatrix}
\xrightarrow{\; -1R2\;}
\begin{bmatrix} 1 & 2 & 0 & 1 & | & 3 \\ 0 & 0 & 1 & -1 & | & -1 \\ 0 & 0 & 0 & 0 & | & 0 \end{bmatrix}
$$

Now our matrix is row reduced and x_2 and x_4 are our nonpivotal variables. We let them equal r and s, respectively, and we write

$$x_1 = 3 - 2r - s$$
$$x_2 = r$$
$$x_3 = -1 + s$$
$$x_4 = s$$ ■

We have now seen that a system of linear equations may have no solutions, exactly one solution, or infinitely many solutions. Further, we have seen how to find which of these three possibilities holds and how to find all solutions by row reduction for any number of equations in any number of unknowns.

Concepts Review

1. A(n) _____ to a system of equations is an assignment of numbers to the variables that makes each equation a true statement.

2. Two systems of equations are _____ if they have exactly the same solutions.

3. A row multiple _____ _____ _____ consists of multiplying a row by a number.

4. A row sum _____ _____ _____ consists of _____ _____ _____ _____ one row to another.

5. A row interchange _____ _____ _____ consists of _____ two rows.

6. The first nonzero entry in a row is called _____.

7. A matrix is _____ _____ if each column containing a pivotal entry has all its other entries equal to 0 and if all pivotal entries are _____.

8. When we choose a pivotal entry in row reduction, that entry is called the _____.

9. A variable x_i is called _____ if column i of the row reduced augmented matrix contains a pivotal entry.

10. A parameter is a symbol that stands for a _____ _____.

Exercises

A In Exercises 1–6, rewrite the given system of equations as a matrix equation.

1. $x_1 + x_2 = 4$
   $x_1 - 2x_2 = 1$

2. $2x_1 - 3x_2 = 2$
   $x_1 + x_2 = 6$

3. $x_1 - x_2 + x_3 = 1$
   $3x_1 + 2x_2 - 4x_3 = 1$
   $x_1 + 2x_2 + x_3 = 4$

4. $x_1 - 2x_2 + 3x_3 = 2$
   $x_1 - x_2 - x_3 = 2$
   $3x_1 - 2x_2 - 3x_3 = 2$

5. $x_1 \qquad + x_3 = 2$
   $x_1 - x_2 + x_3 = 2$
   $\qquad x_2 + 3x_3 = 3$
   (*Hint:* Write as $x_1 + 0x_2 + x_3 = 2$.)

6. $5x_1 + x_2 - 4x_3 = 2$
   $x_1 \qquad - x_3 = 0$
   $\qquad x_2 + 2x_3 = 3$

In Exercises 7–12, use the pure elimination method to solve the system of equations in the exercise specified and show the matrix equation that corresponds to each stage of the solution.

7. Exercise 1

8. Exercise 2

9. Exercise 3   10. Exercise 4

11. Exercise 5   12. Exercise 6

B   13. Circle the pivotal entries in each of the following matrices:

(a) $\begin{bmatrix} 0 & 2 \\ 1 & 3 \end{bmatrix}$ (b) $\begin{bmatrix} 1 & 0 & 2 & 4 \\ 0 & 1 & 3 & 5 \end{bmatrix}$ (c) $\begin{bmatrix} 1 & 0 & 1 & 2 \\ 0 & 1 & 2 & 3 \\ 0 & 0 & 0 & 2 \end{bmatrix}$ (d) $\begin{bmatrix} 1 & 0 & 1 & 0 \\ 0 & 0 & 0 & 1 \\ 0 & 1 & 3 & 0 \end{bmatrix}$

14. Circle the pivotal entries in each of the following matrices:

(a) $\begin{bmatrix} 1 & 0 \\ 0 & 1 \end{bmatrix}$ (b) $\begin{bmatrix} 1 & 0 & 2 \\ 0 & 4 & -3 \\ -3 & 2 & 0 \end{bmatrix}$ (c) $\begin{bmatrix} 1 & 2 & 0 & 1 \\ 0 & 0 & 1 & 3 \\ 0 & 0 & 0 & 0 \end{bmatrix}$ (d) $\begin{bmatrix} 1 & 2 & 0 & 1 \\ 0 & 0 & 1 & 3 \\ 0 & 1 & 0 & 1 \end{bmatrix}$

15. Which of the matrices in Exercise 13 is row reduced?

16. Which of the matrices in Exercise 14 is row reduced?

In Exercises 17–22, row reduce the matrix given.

17. $\begin{bmatrix} 1 & 2 & -1 \\ 3 & 4 & 0 \end{bmatrix}$ 18. $\begin{bmatrix} 3 & 4 \\ 2 & -1 \end{bmatrix}$

19. $\begin{bmatrix} 1 & 2 & 3 \\ 4 & 8 & 6 \\ 2 & 4 & 6 \end{bmatrix}$ 20. $\begin{bmatrix} -1 & 2 & 0 \\ 1 & -1 & 2 \\ 1 & 0 & 4 \end{bmatrix}$

21. $\begin{bmatrix} 1 & 3 & 3 & 1 \\ -1 & 2 & -3 & 2 \\ 4 & 10 & 6 & -2 \end{bmatrix}$ 22. $\begin{bmatrix} 2 & -1 & 6 & 4 \\ 4 & -2 & 4 & 2 \\ -6 & 3 & 6 & 4 \end{bmatrix}$

C   23. Rewrite each system of equations below as a matrix equation.

(a) $\begin{aligned} 2x_1 + 3x_2 - x_3 &= 4 \\ 4x_1 + 5x_2 - 4x_3 &= 5 \\ x_1 + 2x_2 + x_3 &= 4 \end{aligned}$

(b) $\begin{aligned} x_1 + 2x_2 - x_3 &= 2 \\ 2x_1 + 3x_2 + x_3 &= 1 \\ -x_1 + x_2 + x_3 &= -2 \end{aligned}$

(c) $\begin{aligned} \tfrac{1}{2}x_1 + x_2 - x_3 &= 2 \\ 3x_1 + 3x_2 - x_3 &= 5 \\ 2x_1 + 2x_2 - x_3 &= 7 \end{aligned}$

(d) $\begin{aligned} x_1 + 2x_2 + 4x_3 &= 0 \\ \tfrac{1}{2}x_1 + x_2 - x_3 &= 3 \\ x_1 + x_2 + x_3 &= 2 \end{aligned}$

24. Rewrite each system of equations below as a matrix equation.

(a) $\begin{aligned} \tfrac{1}{2}x + \tfrac{1}{3}y + z &= 2 \\ x + y + \tfrac{1}{2}z &= 0 \\ \tfrac{1}{4}x + y + \tfrac{1}{4}z &= -2 \end{aligned}$

(b) $\begin{aligned} -x + y - 2z &= -1 \\ x + y - z &= 0 \\ 2x - 3y + z &= -1 \end{aligned}$

(c) $3x_1 - 3x_2 + 6x_3 = 3$

$2x_1 + x_2 - 3x_3 = -1$

$-x_1 + 4x_2 - 2x_3 = 5$

(d) $3x_1 + x_2 - 3x_3 = 1$

$2x_1 + x_2 - x_3 = 2$

$-3x_1 - x_2 + 2x_3 = -2$

25. Solve each system of equations in Exercise 23 by row reduction of an augmented matrix.

26. Solve each system of equations in Exercise 24 by row reduction of an augmented matrix.

27. For each augmented matrix below, state whether the associated system of equations has no solutions, one solution, or infinitely many solutions.

(a) $\begin{bmatrix} 1 & 0 & 0 & 1 & 2 \\ 0 & 1 & 0 & 2 & 1 \\ 0 & 0 & 1 & -1 & 3 \end{bmatrix}$

(b) $\begin{bmatrix} 1 & 2 & 0 & 1 & 2 \\ 0 & 0 & 1 & 0 & 0 \\ 0 & 0 & 0 & 0 & 1 \end{bmatrix}$

(c) $\begin{bmatrix} 1 & 0 & 0 & 0 & 1 \\ 0 & 1 & 0 & 0 & 3 \\ 0 & 0 & 1 & 0 & 4 \end{bmatrix}$

(d) $\begin{bmatrix} 1 & 0 & 0 & 1 \\ 0 & 1 & 0 & 0 \\ 0 & 0 & 1 & 2 \end{bmatrix}$

28. For each augmented matrix below, state whether the associated system of equations has no solutions, one solution, or infinitely many solutions.

(a) $\begin{bmatrix} 1 & 0 & 1 & 2 & 3 & 2 \\ 0 & 1 & 0 & 1 & -1 & 1 \\ 0 & 0 & 0 & 0 & 0 & 0 \end{bmatrix}$

(b) $\begin{bmatrix} 1 & 0 & 1 & 2 & 3 & 2 \\ 0 & 1 & 0 & 1 & -1 & 0 \\ 0 & 0 & 0 & 0 & 0 & 1 \end{bmatrix}$

(c) $\begin{bmatrix} 1 & 0 & 0 & 0 & 1 \\ 0 & 1 & 0 & 0 & 3 \\ 0 & 0 & 1 & 0 & -3 \\ 0 & 0 & 0 & 1 & -1 \end{bmatrix}$

(d) $\begin{bmatrix} 0 & 1 & 0 & 0 & 2 & 1 \\ 0 & 0 & 1 & 1 & -1 & -1 \\ 1 & 0 & 0 & 2 & 1 & 2 \\ 0 & 0 & 0 & 0 & 0 & 0 \end{bmatrix}$

29. Write down the solutions of the systems of equations in Exercise 27 that have solutions.

30. Write down the solutions of the systems of equations in Exercise 28 that have solutions.

In Exercises 31–38, find all solutions to the system of equations given.

31. $x_1 - x_2 + x_3 - x_4 = 1$

$x_1 \quad - x_3 + 2x_4 = 1$

$x_2 + x_3 + x_4 = 3$

$2x_1 \quad + x_3 + 2x_4 = 4$

32. $x_1 + 2x_2 + 2x_3 - x_4 = 0$

$x_1 - x_2 \quad + 3x_4 = 7$

$2x_1 - x_2 + x_3 + x_4 = 6$

$2x_1 + 2x_2 + 3x_3 - 3x_4 = 4$

33. $x_1 - x_2 + x_3 - x_4 = 1$

$x_1 \quad - x_3 + 2x_4 = 1$

$x_2 + x_3 + x_4 = 3$

$2x_1 \quad + x_3 + 2x_4 = 5$

34. $x_1 + 2x_2 + 2x_3 - x_4 = 0$

$x_1 - x_2 \quad + 3x_4 = 7$

$2x_1 - x_2 + x_3 + x_4 = 6$

$2x_1 + 2x_2 + 3x_3 - 3x_4 = -1$

35. $x_1 + 2x_2 + x_3 + x_4 = 0$

$x_1 + x_2 \quad + x_4 = 0$

$2x_1 + x_2 - x_3 \quad = 0$

36. $x_1 + 2x_2 - x_3 - x_4 = 0$

$3x_1 + x_2 - x_3 - 2x_4 = 0$

$2x_1 - x_2 \quad - x_4 = 0$

37. $x_1 + 2x_2 + x_3 + x_4 = 2$

$x_1 + x_2 \quad + x_4 = 2$

$2x_1 + x_2 - x_3 \quad = 2$

38. $x_1 + 2x_2 - x_3 - x_4 = 1$

$3x_1 + x_2 - x_3 - 2x_4 = 1$

$2x_1 - x_2 \quad - x_4 = 0$

Problems

1. Milk is sold in quart and half-gallon boxes and in gallon jugs. A grocer pays 50 cents for a quart, 80 cents for a half gallon, and $1.40 for a gallon of milk.
   (a) Write an equation saying that the grocer buys x_1 quarts, x_2 half gallons, and x_3 gallons of milk for $100.
   (b) A quart of milk takes up 10 square inches of shelf space, a half gallon takes up 16 square inches, and a gallon takes up 36 square inches. Write an equation saying that the grocer has (and uses) 2800 square inches of shelf space for the milk.
   (c) Find all solutions to the equations in (a) and (b).
   (d) The grocer has observed that the numbers of half gallons and gallons sold are about equal. Write this as an equation.
   (e) Find all solutions to the equations in (a), (b), and (d).
   (f) Write an equation saying that the number of quarts ordered is half the number of half gallons.
   (g) Can the grocer make an order satisfying the conditions of equations (a), (b), (d), and (f)?

2. A company makes white, whole wheat, rye, and mixed grain bread. White bread uses only white flour, whole wheat uses $\frac{1}{3}$ white flour and $\frac{2}{3}$ whole wheat flour, rye bread uses $\frac{1}{2}$ white flour and $\frac{1}{2}$ rye flour, and mixed grain bread uses $\frac{1}{3}$ of each kind of flour. Assuming each loaf of bread uses $\frac{1}{2}$ pound of flour, write down a formula for the amount of white flour in x_1 loaves of white bread, x_2 loaves of whole wheat, x_3 loaves of rye bread, and x_4 loaves of mixed grain bread. Write formulas for the amount of rye flour and whole wheat flour used. Find all combinations of bread the company can produce using 350 pounds of white flour, 150 pounds of whole wheat flour, and 100 pounds of rye flour.

3. Which of the three possibilities (exactly one solution, infinitely many solutions, no solutions) can occur with three equations in four unknowns? What about with four equations in three unknowns?

4. Write a computer program that accepts a matrix and row reduces it to a row reduced matrix.

5. Which of the three possibilities (exactly one solution, infinitely many solutions, no solutions) can occur with a *homogeneous* system of equations (a system whose matrix equation has the form $MX = 0$)? If there is a unique solution, what must it be?

6. Show that if M is a square matrix and when $M|B$ is reduced to $M'|B'$ with M' in row reduced form, all variables are pivotal, then the rows of M' are the rows of I, perhaps in a different order.

7. Which of the three possibilities (exactly one solution, infinitely many solutions, no solutions) can occur when there are more unknowns than equations? More equations than unknowns?

8. We have seen that if we row reduce $M|B$ to $M'|B'$ and M' happens to be the identity, then B' is the solution matrix for $MX = B$. A row reduced matrix is said to be in *echelon form* if each pivotal entry occurs to the right of all pivotal entries in higher rows. Explain how you could follow the row reduction algorithm with a sorting algorithm such as selection sort, properly modified, to row reduce a matrix to row reduced echelon form.

9. Explain why a square matrix can be row reduced either to an identity matrix or a matrix with a row of zeros.

10. Prove that if $MX = B$ has a unique solution for a given column matrix B, then $MX = C$ has a unique solution for every column matrix C.

11. Row reduced echelon form is described in Problem 8. Prove that for each matrix there is one and only one row reduced echelon matrix to which it may be reduced.

Section 10-4 Inverse and Elementary Matrices

Ⓐ *Elementary Matrices*

The matrix equation $MX = B$ looks quite similar to the numerical equation $mx = b$. We solve this numerical equation by multiplying by $m^{-1} = \frac{1}{m}$ to get $x = m^{-1}b$. There is a similar way to solve some matrix equations of the form $MX = B$. The matrix M in the equation $MX = B$ has to be a special kind of square matrix, called an *invertible* matrix, for the same kind of technique to work.

M is called **invertible** if there is a matrix M^{-1}
such that $M^{-1}M = MM^{-1} = I$.

The matrix M^{-1} is called the **inverse** of M.

EXAMPLE 26 Show that the matrix

$$\begin{bmatrix} 3 & 0 \\ 0 & 1 \end{bmatrix} = M$$

has an inverse.

Solution We want a matrix M^{-1} such that $MM^{-1} = M^{-1}M = I$. We have no special way to find M^{-1}, so we try guessing. A logical guess for M^{-1} is

$$\begin{bmatrix} \frac{1}{3} & 0 \\ 0 & 1 \end{bmatrix} = M^{-1}$$

To check that we have guessed correctly, we write

$$\begin{bmatrix} 3 & 0 \\ 0 & 1 \end{bmatrix}\begin{bmatrix} \frac{1}{3} & 0 \\ 0 & 1 \end{bmatrix} = \begin{bmatrix} 3 \cdot \frac{1}{3} + 0 \cdot 0 & 3 \cdot 0 + 0 \cdot 1 \\ 0 \cdot \frac{1}{3} + 1 \cdot 0 & 0 \cdot 0 + 1 \cdot 1 \end{bmatrix} = \begin{bmatrix} 1 & 0 \\ 0 & 1 \end{bmatrix}$$

and

$$\begin{bmatrix} \frac{1}{3} & 0 \\ 0 & 1 \end{bmatrix} \begin{bmatrix} 3 & 0 \\ 0 & 1 \end{bmatrix} = \begin{bmatrix} \frac{1}{3} \cdot 3 + 0 \cdot 0 & \frac{1}{3} \cdot 0 + 0 \cdot 1 \\ 0 \cdot 3 + 1 \cdot 0 & 0 \cdot 0 + 1 \cdot 1 \end{bmatrix} = \begin{bmatrix} 1 & 0 \\ 0 & 1 \end{bmatrix}$$ ■

It will not always be so easy to guess the inverse matrix.

EXAMPLE 27   Show that the matrices

$$\begin{bmatrix} 2 & 3 \\ 4 & 2 \end{bmatrix} \quad \text{and} \quad \begin{bmatrix} \frac{1}{2} & \frac{1}{3} \\ \frac{1}{4} & \frac{1}{2} \end{bmatrix}$$

are not inverses to each other.

Solution   We multiply the two matrices to get

$$\begin{bmatrix} 2 & 3 \\ 4 & 2 \end{bmatrix} \begin{bmatrix} \frac{1}{2} & \frac{1}{3} \\ \frac{1}{4} & \frac{1}{2} \end{bmatrix} = \begin{bmatrix} 1 + \frac{3}{4} & \frac{2}{3} + \frac{3}{2} \\ 2 + \frac{1}{2} & \frac{4}{3} + 1 \end{bmatrix} \neq \begin{bmatrix} 1 & 0 \\ 0 & 1 \end{bmatrix}$$

Therefore the product of the matrices is not *I*, so they are not inverses. ■

EXAMPLE 28   Show that the matrices below are inverses to each other.

$$\begin{bmatrix} 2 & 3 \\ 4 & 2 \end{bmatrix} \quad \text{and} \quad \begin{bmatrix} -\frac{1}{4} & \frac{3}{8} \\ \frac{1}{2} & -\frac{1}{4} \end{bmatrix}$$

Solution   We multiply the two matrices in both orders to get

$$\begin{bmatrix} 2 & 3 \\ 4 & 2 \end{bmatrix} \begin{bmatrix} -\frac{1}{4} & \frac{3}{8} \\ \frac{1}{2} & -\frac{1}{4} \end{bmatrix} = \begin{bmatrix} -\frac{1}{2} + \frac{3}{2} & \frac{6}{8} - \frac{3}{4} \\ -\frac{4}{4} + \frac{2}{2} & \frac{12}{8} - \frac{1}{2} \end{bmatrix} = \begin{bmatrix} 1 & 0 \\ 0 & 1 \end{bmatrix}$$

and

$$\begin{bmatrix} -\frac{1}{4} & \frac{3}{8} \\ \frac{1}{2} & -\frac{1}{4} \end{bmatrix} \begin{bmatrix} 2 & 3 \\ 4 & 2 \end{bmatrix} \begin{bmatrix} -\frac{2}{4} & +\frac{12}{8} & -\frac{3}{4} & +\frac{6}{8} \\ \frac{3}{2} & -\frac{4}{4} & \frac{3}{2} & -\frac{2}{4} \end{bmatrix} \begin{bmatrix} 1 & 0 \\ 0 & 1 \end{bmatrix}$$ ■

Examples 27 and 28 indicate that guessing is unlikely to be a useful technique for finding inverses of matrices.

We were able to guess the inverse of the matrix *M* in Example 26 because it has a simple form. We can obtain *M* from the identity by performing the row operation of multiplying row 1 by 3, so it is not surprising that we get its inverse from the identity by performing the row operation of multiplying row 1 by $\frac{1}{3}$.

A matrix we get by performing one elementary row operation on an identity matrix is called an **elementary matrix.**

We shall soon see that each elementary matrix has an inverse. It turns out that we can use elementary matrices to develop a technique for finding inverses of all invertible matrices.

Since there are three kinds of elementary row operations, there are three types of elementary matrices. The first kind of elementary matrix is a **row multiple matrix.** We use $E(rRi)$ to stand for the result of multiplying row i of I by r. Thus the matrix M in Example 28 is $E(3R1)$ and its inverse is $E(\frac{1}{3}R1)$.

The second kind of elementary matrix is called a **row sum matrix.** We use the notation $E(rR_i + R_j)$ to stand for the result of adding r times row i of I to row j.

EXAMPLE 29   What is the 3-by-3 elementary matrix $E(4R3 + R1)$?

Solution   We add four times row 3 of the 3-by-3 identity matrix to row 1 to get

$$\begin{bmatrix} 1 & 0 & 4 \\ 0 & 1 & 0 \\ 0 & 0 & 1 \end{bmatrix}$$
∎

The third kind of elementary matrix is called a **row interchange matrix.** We use $E(R_i \leftrightarrow R_j)$ to stand for the result of exchanging row i and row j of an identity matrix.

EXAMPLE 30   What is the 4-by-4 elementary matrix $E(R2 \leftrightarrow R4)$?

Solution   We exchange row 2 and row 4 of the 4-by-4 identity matrix to get

$$\begin{bmatrix} 1 & 0 & 0 & 0 \\ 0 & 0 & 0 & 1 \\ 0 & 0 & 1 & 0 \\ 0 & 1 & 0 & 0 \end{bmatrix}$$
∎

As Theorem 8 shows, elementary matrices provide the relationship between matrix multiplication and elementary row operations.

Theorem 8   If E is an elementary matrix and the product EM is defined, then EM is the result of performing on M the elementary row operation used to define E.

Proof   Suppose we obtain E by multiplying row i of I by r. Then row i of EM is row i of E times M, which is r times row i of I times M. This is r times row i of M. Any other row of EM is the corresponding row of IM, and is therefore the corresponding row of M. We deal with the other two kinds of elementary matrices similarly.   ∎

EXAMPLE 31   Using the matrix M given below, compute the product EM for each of the three elementary matrices $E(5R1 + R2)$, $E(5R2)$ and $E(R1 \leftrightarrow R2)$.

$$M = \begin{bmatrix} 1 & 2 & 3 \\ 4 & 5 & 6 \\ 7 & 8 & 9 \end{bmatrix}$$

Solution

$$E(5R1 + R2)M = \begin{bmatrix} 1 & 0 & 0 \\ 5 & 1 & 0 \\ 0 & 0 & 1 \end{bmatrix}\begin{bmatrix} 1 & 2 & 3 \\ 4 & 5 & 6 \\ 7 & 8 & 9 \end{bmatrix} = \begin{bmatrix} 1 & 2 & 3 \\ 9 & 15 & 21 \\ 7 & 8 & 9 \end{bmatrix}$$

$$E(5R2)M = \begin{bmatrix} 1 & 0 & 0 \\ 0 & 5 & 0 \\ 0 & 0 & 1 \end{bmatrix}\begin{bmatrix} 1 & 2 & 3 \\ 4 & 5 & 6 \\ 7 & 8 & 9 \end{bmatrix} = \begin{bmatrix} 1 & 2 & 3 \\ 20 & 25 & 30 \\ 7 & 8 & 9 \end{bmatrix}$$

$$E(R1 \leftrightarrow R2)M = \begin{bmatrix} 0 & 1 & 0 \\ 1 & 0 & 0 \\ 0 & 0 & 1 \end{bmatrix}\begin{bmatrix} 1 & 2 & 3 \\ 4 & 5 & 6 \\ 7 & 8 & 9 \end{bmatrix} = \begin{bmatrix} 4 & 5 & 6 \\ 1 & 2 & 3 \\ 7 & 8 & 9 \end{bmatrix} \qquad ∎$$

Theorem 9 shows that each elementary matrix is invertible.

Theorem 9   Each elementary matrix has an inverse that is also an elementary matrix, as follows:

(a) The inverse of $E(rRi)$ is $E(\frac{1}{r}Ri)$
(b) The inverse of $E(rRi + Rj)$ is $E(-rRi + Rj)$
(c) The inverse of $E(Ri \leftrightarrow Rj)$ is $E(Ri \leftrightarrow Rj)$

Proof   We leave it to the reader to verify by using Theorem 8 that multiplying the two matrices given in (a) or (b) or (c) in either order gives an identity.   ∎

EXAMPLE 32   Write down the inverses of the matrices $E(5R1 + R2)$, $E(5R2)$, and $E(R1 \leftrightarrow R2)$ of Example 31.

Solution   By Theorem 9, we may write

$$E(5R1 + R2)^{-1} = E(-5R1 + R2) = \begin{bmatrix} 1 & 0 & 0 \\ -5 & 1 & 0 \\ 0 & 0 & 1 \end{bmatrix}$$

$$E(5R2)^{-1} = E(\tfrac{1}{5}R2) = \begin{bmatrix} 1 & 0 & 0 \\ 0 & \frac{1}{5} & 0 \\ 0 & 0 & 1 \end{bmatrix}$$

and

$$E(R1 \leftrightarrow R2)^{-1} = E(R1 \leftrightarrow R2) = \begin{bmatrix} 0 & 1 & 0 \\ 1 & 0 & 0 \\ 0 & 0 & 1 \end{bmatrix}$$

∎

⬛ Inverse Matrices

The fact that multiplying M by an elementary matrix is the same thing as performing an elementary row operation on M gives us a way to find inverses for many more matrices.

Theorem 10   Suppose the matrix M can be row reduced to the identity by multiplying by the elementary matrices $E_1, E_2, \ldots, E_n$. Then

(1) $M = E_1^{-1} E_2^{-1} \ldots E_n^{-1}$
(2) M has an inverse
(3) $M^{-1} = E_n E_{n-1} \ldots E_1$

Proof   We prove the case $n = 2$; mathematical induction may be used to extend the proof to larger n.

For $n = 2$, we are supposing that $E_2 E_1 M = I$. Multiplying by E_2^{-1} gives $E_1 M = E_2^{-1} I = E_2^{-1}$; now multiplying by E_2^{-1} gives $M = E_1^{-1} E_2^{-1}$, proving statement (1) in the case $n = 2$.

We prove statements (2) and (3) simultaneously by showing that $E_2 E_1$ is the inverse to M. By using the fact that $M = E_1^{-1} E_2^{-1}$, the associative law, and the definition of inverse matrices, we may write

$$E_2 E_1 M = (E_2 E_1)(E_1^{-1} E_2^{-1}) = E_2(E_1 E_1^{-1})E_2^{-1} = E_2 I E_2^{-1} = E_2 E_2^{-1} = I$$

and

$$ME_2 E_1 = (E_1^{-1} E_2^{-1})E_2 E_1 = E_1^{-1}(E_2^{-1} E_2)E_1 = E_1^{-1} I E_1 = E_1^{-1} E_1 = I$$

This proves statements (2) and (3).   ∎

Theorem 10 has a wide variety of applications. One of them tells us that one way to test a matrix for invertibility is to see if it may be row reduced to the identity.

EXAMPLE 33   Show that the matrix M below has an inverse.

$$M = \begin{bmatrix} 1 & 3 & 5 \\ 0 & 3 & 2 \\ 2 & 6 & 12 \end{bmatrix}$$

Solution   We use row reduction to write

$$\begin{bmatrix} 1 & 3 & 5 \\ 0 & 3 & 2 \\ 2 & 6 & 12 \end{bmatrix} \xrightarrow{\;-2R1 + R3\;} \begin{bmatrix} 1 & 3 & 5 \\ 0 & 3 & 2 \\ 0 & 0 & 2 \end{bmatrix} \xrightarrow[{-\frac{5}{2}R3 + R1}]{-R3 + R2} \begin{bmatrix} 1 & 3 & 0 \\ 0 & 3 & 0 \\ 0 & 0 & 2 \end{bmatrix} \xrightarrow{\;-R2 + R1\;}$$

$$\begin{bmatrix} 1 & 0 & 0 \\ 0 & 3 & 0 \\ 0 & 0 & 2 \end{bmatrix} \xrightarrow[{\frac{1}{2}R3}]{\frac{1}{3}R2} \begin{bmatrix} 1 & 0 & 0 \\ 0 & 1 & 0 \\ 0 & 0 & 1 \end{bmatrix}$$

Since M can be row reduced to the identity, M has an inverse.   ∎

Theorem 10 also helps us find inverse matrices by telling us how to find elementary matrices we can multiply together to find an inverse matrix.

EXAMPLE 34   Write down a list of elementary matrices whose product is the inverse M^{-1} of the matrix M in Example 33.

Solution   The elementary matrices that correspond to the row operations we performed in Example 33 are: $E_1 = E(-2R1 + R3)$, $E_2 = E(-R3 + R2)$, $E_3 = \left(-\frac{5}{2}R3 + R1\right)$, $E_4 = E(-R2 + R1)$, $E_5 = E\left(\frac{1}{3}R2\right)$, $E_6 = E\left(\frac{1}{2}R3\right)$. By Theorem 10, $M^{-1} = E_6E_5E_4E_3E_2E_1$.   ∎

Finally, Theorem 10 tells us how we can "factor" some matrices into a product of elementary matrices.

EXAMPLE 35   Write the matrix M of Example 33 as a product of elementary matrices.

Solution   By Theorem 10, $M = E_1^{-1}E_2^{-1}E_3^{-1}E_4^{-1}E_5^{-1}E_6^{-1}$, using the matrices E_i of Example 34. Using Theorem 9 to determine these inverses gives us

$$M = E(2R1 + R3) \cdot E(R3 + R2) \cdot E\left(\tfrac{2}{5}R3 + R1\right) \cdot E(R2 + R1) \cdot E(3R2) \cdot E(2R3)$$ ∎

If the instructions in Example 34 had told us to compute M^{-1} rather than give the list of matrices, we would have had considerable work to do. Fortunately, there is a way to bypass this work. Just as we solve the equation $MX = B$ for X by row reducing the augmented matrix $M|B$, we solve the equation $MM^{-1} = I$ for M^{-1} by row reducing the augmented matrix $M|I$.

Theorem 11   If M is a matrix that may be row reduced to the identity, then forming the augmented matrix $M|I$ (which has the entries of the m-by-m matrix M to the left of the line and the entries of the m-by-m identity matrix to the right of the line), and row reducing until the side to the left of the line is the identity gives the augmented matrix $I|M^{-1}$ with M^{-1} to the right-hand side of the line.

Proof Suppose $E_1, E_2, \ldots, E_n$ are the elementary matrices corresponding to the operations used to reduce M to the identity. Then performing these operations on the augmented matrix gives

$$(E_n \ldots E_2 E_1)(M|I) = (E_m \ldots E_2 E_1 M)|(E_m \ldots E_2 E_1 I)$$
$$= M^{-1} M | M^{-1} I$$
$$= I | M^{-1} \qquad \blacksquare$$

EXAMPLE 36   Find an inverse for the matrix

$$\begin{bmatrix} 2 & 3 \\ 4 & 2 \end{bmatrix} = N$$

Solution   We proceed as below to row reduce the augmented matrix.

$$\begin{bmatrix} 2 & 3 & | & 1 & 0 \\ 4 & 2 & | & 0 & 1 \end{bmatrix} \xrightarrow{-2R1 + R2} \begin{bmatrix} 2 & 3 & | & 1 & 0 \\ 0 & -4 & | & -2 & 1 \end{bmatrix}$$

$$\xrightarrow[-\frac{1}{4}R2]{\frac{1}{2}R1} \begin{bmatrix} 1 & \frac{3}{2} & | & \frac{1}{2} & 0 \\ 0 & 1 & | & \frac{1}{2} & -\frac{1}{4} \end{bmatrix} \xrightarrow{\left(-\frac{3}{2}\right)R2 + R1} \begin{bmatrix} 1 & 0 & | & -\frac{1}{4} & \frac{2}{8} \\ 0 & 1 & | & \frac{1}{2} & -\frac{1}{4} \end{bmatrix}$$

Thus by Theorem 10, N has an inverse, and by Theorem 11,

$$N^{-1} = \begin{bmatrix} -\frac{1}{4} & \frac{3}{8} \\ \frac{1}{2} & -\frac{1}{4} \end{bmatrix} \qquad \blacksquare$$

Unique Solutions and Invertible Matrices

We introduced the idea of inverse matrices in a discussion of solving a matrix equation $MX = B$ as we would solve a numerical equation $mx = b$. Theorem 12 tells us that when M is invertible, the analogy works perfectly.

Theorem 12   If an $n \times n$ matrix M has an inverse, then for each n-entry column matrix B, the matrix equation $MX = B$ has one and only one solution, $M^{-1}B$.

Proof   Multiplying $MX = B$ on the left by M^{-1} gives $X = M^{-1}B$. However, this completely specifies X as a column matrix of constants. By substitution, we see that $X = M^{-1}B$ satisfies the equation $MX = B$. Thus $X = M^{-1}B$ is the one and only solution to $MX = B$. $\qquad \blacksquare$

EXAMPLE 37   Use the inverse matrix you computed in Example 31 to solve the system of equations

$$2x + 3y = 4$$
$$4x + 2y = 8$$

Solution   This system of equations may be written as

$$\begin{bmatrix} 2 & 3 \\ 4 & 2 \end{bmatrix} \begin{bmatrix} x \\ y \end{bmatrix} = \begin{bmatrix} 4 \\ 8 \end{bmatrix}$$

Multiplying by N^{-1} gives

$$\begin{bmatrix} x \\ y \end{bmatrix} = \begin{bmatrix} -\frac{1}{4} & \frac{3}{8} \\ \frac{1}{2} & -\frac{1}{4} \end{bmatrix} \begin{bmatrix} 4 \\ 8 \end{bmatrix} = \begin{bmatrix} -1 & +3 \\ 2 & -2 \end{bmatrix} = \begin{bmatrix} 2 \\ 0 \end{bmatrix}$$

Thus the unique solution to our system of equations is $x = 2$, $y = 0$.   ∎

We have learned that if a matrix can be row reduced to the identity, then it has an inverse; further, we have an algorithm to carry out in order to find that inverse. We don't yet know whether a square matrix that cannot be row reduced to an identity matrix might still have an inverse. Theorem 13 tells us that this cannot happen.

Theorem 13   If a matrix M has an inverse, then it may be row reduced to the identity.

Proof   If M has an inverse, then the system of equations $MX = B$ has a unique solution for each column vector B. From Theorem 7, we know that this means each variable must be pivotal in the system of equations corresponding to the augmented matrix $M'|B'$ we get from row reducing $M|B$. As in Problem 6 of Section 10-3, we may conclude, from the facts that M' is square and all variables are pivotal, that the rows of M' are the rows of the identity matrix but perhaps in a different order. Thus M can be row reduced to the identity.   ∎

Theorem 10 and Theorem 13 let us reach the following conclusion.

A matrix has an inverse if and only if it
may be row reduced to the identity.

EXAMPLE 38   Is the matrix $M = \begin{bmatrix} 1 & 2 & -1 \\ 3 & 1 & -2 \\ 0 & 5 & -1 \end{bmatrix}$ invertible?

Solution   We row reduce M as follows.

$$\begin{bmatrix} 1 & 2 & -1 \\ 3 & 1 & -2 \\ 0 & 5 & -1 \end{bmatrix} \xrightarrow{-3R1 + R2} \begin{bmatrix} 1 & 2 & -1 \\ 0 & -5 & 1 \\ 0 & 5 & -1 \end{bmatrix} \xrightarrow{R2 + R3} \begin{bmatrix} 1 & 2 & -1 \\ 0 & -5 & 1 \\ 0 & 0 & 0 \end{bmatrix}$$

Since M may be row reduced to a matrix with a row of zeros, M may not be row reduced to the identity. Therefore M is not invertible.   ∎

Concepts Review

1. A matrix M is called _____ if there is a matrix N such that $MN = NM = I$.

2. If MX is defined and M' is the result of performing a certain row operation on M, then _____ is the result of performing that operation on MX.

3. A matrix has an inverse if and only if it can be _____ _____ to the identity.

4. A matrix obtained by performing an elementary row operation on an identity matrix is called an _____ matrix.

5. Multiplying M on the left by an elementary matrix E has the same effect as performing the _____ _____ _____ defining E on M.

6. The inverse of an elementary matrix of a given type is a(n) _____ _____ of the _____ type.

7. A product of elementary matrices is [Choose one: elementary, invertible, both, not necessarily, either, neither] _____ .

8. If M is invertible, then the matrix equation $MX = B$ has _____ _____ _____ _____ solution(s).

Exercises

A In Exercises 1–12, write down the 3-by-3 elementary matrix specified.

1. $E(2R1)$
2. $E(R2 \leftrightarrow R3)$
3. $E(-R1 + R2)$
4. $E(2R3 + R1)$
5. $E(R1 \leftrightarrow R3)$
6. $E(2R3)$
7. $E(-3R2)$
8. $E(R1 \leftrightarrow R2)$
9. $E(-2R1 + R3)$
10. $E(4R1)$
11. $E(R2 \leftrightarrow R1)$
12. $E(3R2 + R1)$

In Exercises 13–24, show the result of writing each of the matrices given on the left of the matrix M and performing the indicated multiplication.

$$M = \begin{bmatrix} a & b & c \\ d & e & f \\ g & h & i \end{bmatrix}$$

13. $E(2R1)$
14. $E(R2 \leftrightarrow R3)$
15. $E(-R1 + R2)$
16. $E(2R3 + R1)$
17. $E(R1 \leftrightarrow R3)$
18. $E(2R3)$
19. $E(-3R2)$
20. $E(R1 \leftrightarrow R2)$
21. $E(-2R1 + R3)$
22. $E(4R1)$
23. $E(R2 \leftrightarrow R1)$
24. $E(3R2 + R1)$

In Exercises 25–36, write down the inverse of the 3-by-3 elementary matrix specified.

25. $E(2R1)$
26. $E(R2 \leftrightarrow R3)$
27. $E(-R1 + R2)$
28. $E(2R3 + R1)$
29. $E(R1 \leftrightarrow R3)$
30. $E(2R3)$

31. $E(-3R2)$ **32.** $E(R1 \leftrightarrow R2)$ **33.** $E(-2R1 + R3)$

34. $E(4R1)$ **35.** $E(R2 \leftrightarrow R1)$ **36.** $E(3R2 + R1)$

In Exercises 37–40, verify that the pair of matrices given is a pair of inverse matrices.

37.
$$\begin{bmatrix} 1 & 2 & 0 \\ 0 & 1 & 2 \\ 2 & 1 & 0 \end{bmatrix} \quad \begin{bmatrix} -\frac{1}{3} & 0 & \frac{2}{3} \\ \frac{2}{3} & 0 & -\frac{1}{3} \\ -\frac{1}{3} & \frac{1}{2} & \frac{1}{6} \end{bmatrix}$$

38.
$$\begin{bmatrix} \frac{1}{2} & 0 & -\frac{1}{2} \\ \frac{1}{2} & 1 & 0 \\ 1 & 0 & 1 \end{bmatrix} \quad \begin{bmatrix} 1 & 0 & \frac{1}{2} \\ -\frac{1}{2} & 1 & -\frac{1}{4} \\ -1 & 0 & \frac{1}{2} \end{bmatrix}$$

39.
$$\begin{bmatrix} -1 & -1 & -1 \\ 3 & 1 & 2 \\ 1 & 0 & 1 \end{bmatrix} \quad \begin{bmatrix} 1 & 1 & -1 \\ -1 & 0 & -1 \\ -1 & -1 & 2 \end{bmatrix}$$

40.
$$\begin{bmatrix} -4 & 2 & 1 \\ -5 & 2 & 1 \\ -3 & 1 & 1 \end{bmatrix} \quad \begin{bmatrix} 1 & -1 & 0 \\ 2 & -1 & -1 \\ 1 & -2 & 2 \end{bmatrix}$$

B **41.** Show that the matrix M below is invertible by using row reduction.

$$M = \begin{bmatrix} 1 & 2 & 4 \\ 0 & 1 & 2 \\ 1 & 2 & 2 \end{bmatrix}$$

42. Show that the matrix N below is invertible by using row reduction.

$$N = \begin{bmatrix} 1 & -1 & 2 \\ -2 & 2 & -3 \\ 1 & 1 & 2 \end{bmatrix}$$

43. Use the row operations from Exercise 41 to write down a sequence $E_1, E_2, \ldots, E_n$ of matrices such that

$$E_n \ldots E_4 E_3 E_2 E_1 M = I$$

How does the product $E_n E_{n-1} \ldots E_2 E_1$ relate to M?

44. Use the row operations from Exercise 42 to write down a sequence $E_1, E_2, E_3, \ldots, E_n$ of matrices such that

$$E_n E_{n-1} \ldots E_2 E_1 N = I$$

How does the product $E_n E_{n-1} \ldots E_2 E_1$ relate to N?

45. The results of Exercises 41 and 43 allow you to write M as a product of elementary matrices. What are the matrices? In what order must they be multiplied?

46. The results of Exercises 42 and 44 allow you to write N as a product of elementary matrices. What are the matrices? In what order must they be multiplied?

In Exercises 47–54, find the inverse of each of the matrices given.

47. $\begin{bmatrix} -1 & 3 \\ 2 & -1 \end{bmatrix}$ **48.** $\begin{bmatrix} 0 & 1 \\ 1 & 0 \end{bmatrix}$

49. $\begin{bmatrix} 1 & -1 \\ 0 & 1 \end{bmatrix}$

50. $\begin{bmatrix} 1 & 2 \\ 1 & 4 \end{bmatrix}$

51. $\begin{bmatrix} 0 & -1 \\ 1 & 0 \end{bmatrix}$

52. $\begin{bmatrix} 1 & 3 \\ 0 & 1 \end{bmatrix}$

53. $\begin{bmatrix} 2 & 1 & 2 \\ 1 & 1 & 1 \\ 1 & 1 & 2 \end{bmatrix} = M$

54. $\begin{bmatrix} 1 & 2 & 3 \\ 1 & 4 & 9 \\ 1 & 8 & 27 \end{bmatrix} = N$

55. Use the matrix you computed in Exercise 47 to solve the equations

$$-x + 3y = 2$$
$$2x - y = 3$$

56. Use the matrix you computed in Exercise 50 to solve the equations

$$x + 2y = 3$$
$$x + 4y = 1$$

57. Using the matrix you computed in Exercise 53, solve the system of equations

$$MX = \begin{bmatrix} 2 \\ -2 \\ 4 \end{bmatrix}$$

58. Using the matrix you computed in Exercise 54, solve the system of equations

$$NX = \begin{bmatrix} 1 \\ -1 \\ 0 \end{bmatrix}$$

59. Determine whether each matrix below is invertible.

(a) $\begin{bmatrix} 2 & 1 & 2 \\ 1 & 1 & 1 \\ 1 & 1 & 2 \end{bmatrix}$

(b) $\begin{bmatrix} 1 & 3 & 2 & 3 \\ 1 & -1 & 4 & 1 \\ 3 & 6 & -3 & 1 \\ 3 & 2 & -1 & -1 \end{bmatrix}$

(c) $\begin{bmatrix} 1 & 2 & 3 \\ 1 & 4 & 9 \\ 1 & 8 & 27 \end{bmatrix}$

60. Determine whether each matrix below is invertible.

(a) $\begin{bmatrix} 1 & 1 & 1 & 3 \\ 1 & 2 & 1 & 4 \\ 1 & 0 & 1 & 2 \\ 1 & 1 & 1 & 4 \end{bmatrix}$

(b) $\begin{bmatrix} 1 & 4 & -2 \\ 2 & 1 & 1 \\ 1 & -3 & 4 \end{bmatrix}$

(c) $\begin{bmatrix} 1 & 1 & 1 \\ 1 & 2 & 1 \\ 2 & 1 & 2 \end{bmatrix}$

61. Find the inverse of each invertible matrix in Exercise 59.

62. Find the inverse of each invertible matrix in Exercise 60.

63. For each matrix M in Exercise 59, the matrix equation $MX = 0$, where X is a column vector of variables and 0 is a column vector of zeros, has either exactly one solution or infinitely many solutions. For each possible M, which of these is the case?

64. For each possible matrix M in Exercise 60, the matrix equation $MX = 0$, where X is a column vector of variables and 0 is a column vector of zeros, has either exactly one solution or infinitely many solutions. For each M in Exercise 60, which of these is the case?

65. Let B stand for the all-ones column vector. For each invertible matrix M in Exercise 59, use the inverse you computed in Exercise 61 to solve the system of equations $MX = B$.

66. Let B stand for the all-ones column matrix. For each invertible matrix M in Exercise 60, use the inverse you computed in Exercise 62 to solve the system of equations $MX = B$.

67. For each noninvertible matrix M in Exercise 59, determine all solutions to the matrix equation $MX = B$, with B the all-ones column vector, as in Exercise 65.

68. For each noninvertible matrix M in Exercise 60, determine all solutions to the matrix equation $MX = B$, where X and B are as in Exercise 66.

Problems

1. Prove by induction that the inverse of a product of n invertible matrices is the product of their inverses in reverse order.

2. Write out the proof that if M is a product of elementary matrices, then M may be row reduced to an identity matrix.

3. Define an elementary column matrix. Show that each elementary row matrix is also an elementary column matrix.

4. Experiment with the result of multiplying the matrices of Exercises 1–12 on the right times the matrix M of Exercises 13–24. What is the effect on a matrix M of multiplying M on the right by an elementary matrix?

5. Is it possible for more than one matrix N to serve as an inverse to a matrix M? Give an example or explain why not.

6. A *right inverse* to a matrix M is a matrix N such that $MN = I$. (*Note:* A nonsquare matrix may have a right inverse.)
   (a) Is it possible for a nonsquare matrix to have more than one right inverse? (Give examples or explain why not.)
   (b) Is it possible for a square matrix to have more than one right inverse? (Give examples or explain why not.)

7. Prove or give a counter-example: If a square matrix has a right inverse, then it is invertible. (Right inverse was defined in Problem 6.)

8. In the proof of Theorem 8, show how to deal with the other two kinds of elementary row operations.

9. What is the smallest number n such that every invertible two-by-two matrix is a product of n or fewer elementary matrices?

10. An *upper triangular* matrix M has the property that $M_{ij} = 0$ if $i > j$.
   (a) Write down a typical 3-by-3 upper triangular matrix.
   (b) Explain why a 3-by-3 upper triangular matrix is invertible if and only if the product of the entries along its main diagonal is not zero.
   (c) What is the smallest n such that every invertible 3-by-3 upper triangular matrix factors into n or fewer elementary matrices?

11. Extend the proof of Theorem 10 to the product of n elementary matrices.

12. If M is the adjacency matrix of a graph with n vertices and $I - M$ has an inverse, how does $(I - M^n)(I - M)^{-1}$ relate to the transitive closure of the graph?

13. Prove or give a counter-example: If M is the adjacency matrix of a connected graph, then $I - M$ is invertible.

Section 10-5
The Definition
of Determinants

◪ The Determinant Axioms

The ordinary (numerical) equation $mx = b$, in which m and b are numbers and x is a variable, has a unique solution if and only if $m \neq 0$. The matrix equation $MX = B$ has a unique solution if and only if M is invertible. It would be convenient if there were one number m related to M that would determine whether or not M is invertible according to whether or not that number is different from 0. You may have seen such a number for 2-by-2 matrices; people frequently are taught about *determinants* in connection with two equations in two unknowns.

Determinants of Two-by-Two Matrices

The matrix equation

$$\begin{bmatrix} a_{11} & a_{12} \\ a_{21} & a_{22} \end{bmatrix} \begin{bmatrix} x_1 \\ x_2 \end{bmatrix} = \begin{bmatrix} b_1 \\ b_2 \end{bmatrix} \qquad \text{or} \qquad AX = B$$

has a unique solution if and only if

$$a_{11}a_{22} - a_{12}a_{21} \neq 0$$

The number $a_{11}a_{22} - a_{12}a_{21}$ is called the **determinant** of the 2-by-2 matrix A and denoted by **det(A)**.

To see how it arises, consider the augmented matrix

$$\left[\begin{array}{cc|c} a_{11} & a_{12} & b_1 \\ a_{21} & a_{22} & b_2 \end{array} \right]$$

Multiplying row 2 by a_{11} and subtracting a_{21} times row 1 from it gives

$$\left[\begin{array}{cc|c} a_{11} & a_{12} & b_1 \\ 0 & a_{22}a_{11} - a_{12}a_{21} & a_{11}b_2 - a_{21}b_1 \end{array}\right]$$

If $a_{22}a_{11} - a_{12}a_{21} \neq 0$, we may divide by it and complete the row reduction to get

$$\left[\begin{array}{cc|c} 1 & 0 & \dfrac{a_{22}b_1 - a_{12}b_2}{a_{22}a_{11} - a_{12}a_{21}} \\[3ex] 0 & 1 & \dfrac{a_{11}b_2 - a_{21}b_1}{a_{22}a_{11} - a_{12}a_{21}} \end{array}\right]$$

Technically, we were assuming that a_{11} was nonzero (otherwise we would have been multiplying row 2 of the augmented matrix by zero). It is possible to work out a row reduction to get the same formula for x_1 and x_2 that we get from this row reduction in any case. Looking back, you see that if $a_{22}a_{11} - a_{12}a_{21}$ *is* zero, we get a row of zeros for our second row to the left of the line in our row reduction, so we have either no solution or infinitely many solutions. Thus $AX = 0$ has a unique solution if and only if the determinant of the coefficient matrix is nonzero. Therefore a 2-by-2 matrix is invertible if and only if its determinant is nonzero.

There are similar determinants associated with 3-by-3, 4-by-4, and larger matrices, but trying to discover formulas for them by finding general formulas for solutions to more equations in more unknowns would involve us in considerable algebra.

Rules for Computing Determinants

Fortunately, we can avoid a great deal of algebra by defining a determinant of a matrix through a set of rules (called the **determinant axioms**) for computing determinants. We shall figure out what these rules should be by analyzing how the determinants of two-by-two matrices interact with the row operations we have used for inverting matrices. Our first type of row operation consists of multiplying a row by a number. Since

$$\det \begin{bmatrix} ra_{11} & ra_{12} \\ a_{21} & a_{22} \end{bmatrix} = ra_{11}a_{22} - ra_{12}a_{21}$$

$$= r(a_{11}a_{22} - a_{12}a_{21}) = r\det \begin{bmatrix} a_{11} & a_{12} \\ a_{21} & a_{22} \end{bmatrix}$$

it is natural to write our first rule as follows.

Multiplying a Row by a Real Number

> **Determinant rule (1), the Row Multiple Rule:**
> Multiplying row i of a matrix M by the real
> number r multiplies the determinant of M by r.

In symbols, we would write

$$\text{Determinant rule (1): } \det \begin{bmatrix} R1 \\ \vdots \\ rRi \\ \vdots \\ Rn \end{bmatrix} = r\det \begin{bmatrix} R1 \\ \vdots \\ Ri \\ \vdots \\ Rn \end{bmatrix}$$

Another way to state Rule (1) is as follows.

> If M' is obtained from M by factoring r from row i
> of M, then $\det M = r\det M'$.

EXAMPLE 39 Find what happens to the determinant of the matrix

$$\begin{bmatrix} 3 & 1 \\ 4 & 3 \end{bmatrix}$$

if you multiply row 1 by 2.

Solution We know that $\det \begin{bmatrix} 3 & 1 \\ 4 & 3 \end{bmatrix} = 9 - 4 = 5$

and $\det \begin{bmatrix} 2{\cdot}3 & 2{\cdot}1 \\ 4 & 3 \end{bmatrix} = \det \begin{bmatrix} 6 & 2 \\ 4 & 3 \end{bmatrix} = 18 - 8 = 10 = 2{\cdot}5$ ∎

Adding a Row to Another Row

Our second kind of elementary row operation consists of adding a multiple of one row to another. By applying the definition of a determinant of a two-by-two matrix, we may write

$$\det \begin{bmatrix} a_{11} & a_{12} \\ a_{21} + ra_{11} & a_{22} + ra_{12} \end{bmatrix} = a_{11}(a_{22} + ra_{12}) - (a_{21} + ra_{11})a_{12}$$
$$= a_{11}a_{22} - a_{21}a_{12} + a_{11}ra_{12} - ra_{11}a_{12}$$
$$= a_{11}a_{22} - a_{21}a_{12}$$

Thus the determinant didn't change! This suggests the second rule.

Determinant rule (2), the Row Sum Rule:
Adding a numerical multiple of row i of the
matrix M to row j of the matrix M doesn't change
the determinant of M (if $i \neq j$).

In symbols, we can write

$$\textit{Determinant rule (2):}\ \det \begin{bmatrix} -R1- \\ \vdots \\ -Ri- \\ \vdots \\ -Rj + rRi- \\ \vdots \\ -Rn- \end{bmatrix} = \det \begin{bmatrix} -R1- \\ \vdots \\ -Ri- \\ \vdots \\ -Rj- \\ \vdots \\ -Rn- \end{bmatrix}$$

EXAMPLE 40   Show the effect on the determinant of adding twice row 2 to row 1 with the matrix

$$\begin{bmatrix} 2 & 3 \\ 1 & -1 \end{bmatrix}$$

Solution   We know that $\det \begin{bmatrix} 2 & 3 \\ 1 & -1 \end{bmatrix} = 2 \cdot (-1) - 3 \cdot 1 = -5$

and $\det \begin{bmatrix} 2+2 & 3-2 \\ 1 & -1 \end{bmatrix} = \det \begin{bmatrix} 4 & 1 \\ 1 & -1 \end{bmatrix} = 4(-1) - 1 \cdot 1 = -5.$ ∎

Interchanging Two Rows

Finally, if we experiment with interchanging two rows of a 2-by-2 matrix, we get

$$\det \begin{bmatrix} a_{21} & a_{22} \\ a_{11} & a_{12} \end{bmatrix} = a_{21}a_{12} - a_{22}a_{11} = -(a_{11}a_{22} - a_{21}a_{12}) = -\det \begin{bmatrix} a_{11} & a_{12} \\ a_{21} & a_{22} \end{bmatrix}$$

This suggests the general rule for determinants.

Determinant rule (3), the Row Interchange Rule:
Interchanging two rows of a matrix multiplies its
determinant by -1.

In symbols, we can write

$$\text{Determinant rule (3): } \det \begin{bmatrix} -R1- \\ \vdots \\ -Ri- \\ \vdots \\ -Rj- \\ \vdots \\ -Rn- \end{bmatrix} = -\det \begin{bmatrix} -R1- \\ \vdots \\ -Ri- \\ \vdots \\ -Rj- \\ \vdots \\ -Rn- \end{bmatrix}$$

EXAMPLE 41   Show the effect on the determinant of interchanging the rows of

$$\begin{bmatrix} 1 & 2 \\ 2 & 3 \end{bmatrix}$$

Solution   We write $\det \begin{bmatrix} 1 & 2 \\ 2 & 3 \end{bmatrix} = 1 \cdot 3 - 2 \cdot 2 = -1$

and $\det \begin{bmatrix} 2 & 3 \\ 1 & 2 \end{bmatrix} = 2 \cdot 2 - 3 \cdot 1 = 1.$ ∎

B   *Using the Rules to Compute Determinants*

Our next two examples show that the rules we have introduced so far are a considerable aid in computing determinants but are not quite sufficient.

A Row of Zeros Makes the Determinant Zero

EXAMPLE 42   Apply the rules to show what information we may learn about the determinant of

$$M = \begin{bmatrix} 1 & 3 & 2 \\ 0 & 0 & 0 \\ 1 & 0 & -1 \end{bmatrix}$$

by using row operations.

Solution   Since multiplying row 2 of the matrix M by zero doesn't change it, applying determinant rule (1) gives us

$$\det M = \det \begin{bmatrix} 1 & 3 & 2 \\ 0 \cdot 0 & 0 \cdot 0 & 0 \cdot 0 \\ 1 & 0 & -1 \end{bmatrix} = 0 \cdot \det \begin{bmatrix} 1 & 3 & 2 \\ 0 & 0 & 0 \\ 1 & 0 & -1 \end{bmatrix} = 0$$ ∎

EXAMPLE 43   Apply the rules to show what information we may learn about the determinant of

$$N = \begin{bmatrix} 1 & 6 & 5 \\ 0 & 2 & -1 \\ 0 & 0 & 4 \end{bmatrix}$$

by using row operations.

Solution   Subtracting three times the second row of N from the first row gives, by determinant rule (2),

$$\det \begin{bmatrix} 1 & 6 & 5 \\ 0 & 2 & -1 \\ 0 & 0 & 4 \end{bmatrix} = \det \begin{bmatrix} 1 & 0 & 8 \\ 0 & 2 & -1 \\ 0 & 0 & 4 \end{bmatrix}$$

Now subtracting twice row 3 from row 1 and adding a fourth of row 3 to row 2 in the last matrix, we get

$$\det \begin{bmatrix} 1 & 0 & 8 \\ 0 & 2 & -1 \\ 0 & 0 & 4 \end{bmatrix} = \det \begin{bmatrix} 1 & 0 & 0 \\ 0 & 2 & 0 \\ 0 & 0 & 4 \end{bmatrix}$$

Now, applying rule (1) twice gives

$$\det \begin{bmatrix} 1 & 0 & 0 \\ 0 & 2 & 0 \\ 0 & 0 & 4 \end{bmatrix} = 2 \cdot 4 \det \begin{bmatrix} 1 & 0 & 0 \\ 0 & 1 & 0 \\ 0 & 0 & 1 \end{bmatrix}$$

We don't know the determinant of a 3-by-3 identity matrix, so this is all we can say so far.   ■

The Determinant of an Identity Matrix

In discussing equations, we saw that a matrix can either be row reduced to a matrix with a row of zeros or else can be row reduced to an identity matrix. Thus Examples 42 and 43 suggest that, once we know what the determinant of an n-by-n identity matrix is, our rules should be complete enough to let us compute any determinant whatsoever. Since the determinant of a 2-by-2 identity matrix is 1, the most natural way of determining the determinant of an n-by-n identity matrix is the next rule.

Determinant rule (4), the Identity Matrix Rule:
The determinant of an identity matrix is 1.

In symbols, we write

Determinant rule (4): $\det I = 1$

EXAMPLE 44   Complete the computation of det$N$ in Example 42.

Solution   By following the chain of equalities in Example 42, we see that
$\det(N) = 2 \cdot 4 \det I = 2 \cdot 4 \cdot 1 = 8.$ ■

The Definition of the Determinant Function

A function defined on n-by-n matrices is called a
determinant function if it satisfies determinant rules (1) through (4).

We have seen by examples above how we can use the rules to compute determinants. The method we used in the examples may be summarized as in
Theorem 14.

Theorem 14   If there is a determinant function defined on n-by-n matrices and satisfying rules
(1) through (4), then it may be computed by the following procedure.
 Row reduce the matrix until you get a row of zeros or an identity matrix. If you
get a row of zeros, the determinant is zero. Otherwise the determinant is the
product of the following **elementary factors.** There is an elementary factor of r for
each row multiple operation in which you factor an r out of a row. There is an
elementary factor of 1 for each row sum operation and an elementary factor of -1
for each row interchange operation, interchanging two rows.

Proof   The procedure simply describes how to apply the determinant rules.   ■

EXAMPLE 45   Compute the determinant of the matrix

$$\begin{bmatrix} 2 & 8 & 9 \\ -2 & -4 & -3 \\ 2 & 12 & 12 \end{bmatrix}$$

Solution   We row reduce the matrix as follows.

$$\begin{bmatrix} 2 & 8 & 9 \\ -2 & -4 & -3 \\ 2 & 12 & 12 \end{bmatrix} \xrightarrow[-1R1 + R3]{R1 + R2} \begin{bmatrix} 2 & 8 & 9 \\ 0 & 4 & 6 \\ 0 & 4 & 3 \end{bmatrix} \xrightarrow{-1R2 + R3}$$

$$\begin{bmatrix} 2 & 8 & 9 \\ 0 & 4 & 6 \\ 0 & 0 & -3 \end{bmatrix} \xrightarrow{-2R2 + R1} \begin{bmatrix} 2 & 0 & -3 \\ 0 & 4 & 6 \\ 0 & 0 & -3 \end{bmatrix} \xrightarrow[2R3 + R2]{-1R3 + R1}$$

$$\begin{bmatrix} 2 & 0 & 0 \\ 0 & 4 & 0 \\ 0 & 0 & -3 \end{bmatrix} \xrightarrow[\left(-\frac{1}{3}\right)R3]{\begin{array}{c}\left(\frac{1}{2}\right)R1 \\ \left(\frac{1}{4}\right)R2\end{array}} \begin{bmatrix} 1 & 0 & 0 \\ 0 & 1 & 0 \\ 0 & 0 & 1 \end{bmatrix}$$

All of the operations except for the last three have elementary factors equal to 1. The elementary factors of the last three operations are, respectively, 2, 4, and -3, so the determinant is $2 \cdot 4 \cdot (-3) = -24$.

Notice how mutliplying row 1 by $\frac{1}{2}$ corresponds to factoring out a 2 from row 1 and using rule (1). This shows that multiplication by $\frac{1}{r}$ in row reduction gives an elementary factor of r. The elementary factor of 4 corresponds to factoring a four from row 2, and the elementary factor of -3 corresponds to factoring -3 from row 3.   ■

Determinants of Upper Triangular Matrices

Note how in both Example 43 and Example 45, when we had a **triangular** matrix (one with zeros below the main diagonal), the determinant we eventually got by row reduction was the product of the diagonal entries. Was this an accident, or does it gives us a shortcut for computing determinants? Fortunately, this was no accident. We call a matrix **upper triangular** if all entries below the main diagonal are zero. With this terminology, we may describe the shortcut easily.

Theorem 15   The determinant of an upper triangular matrix is the product of its diagonal entries.

Proof   The proof is similar to the computations of Example 43 and the last three steps of Example 45. It is described in Problems 5–7.   ■

EXAMPLE 46   Compute the determinant of

$$\begin{bmatrix} 2 & 4 & 6 & 8 \\ 0 & 3 & 1 & 2 \\ 0 & 0 & -1 & 4 \\ 0 & 0 & 0 & -5 \end{bmatrix}$$

Solution   By Theorem 15, the determinant is $2 \cdot 3 \cdot (-1) \cdot (-5) = 30$.   ■

In Example 45, we started out with a matrix that was not triangular and converted it to a triangular matrix with row sum operations. Thus the determinant of the original matrix and that of the triangular matrix are the same. This was no accident either; any matrix may be converted to a triangular matrix by using row sum operations. This gives us another way to compute determinants.

Theorem 16   To compute the determinant of a matrix, we row reduce it to triangular form by adding multiples of rows to other rows, then we multiply the diagonal entries together to get the determinant.

Proof   All that needs to be proved is that we can row reduce a matrix to triangular form with only row sum operations. Problems 1–4 do this.   ■

We already have an example of Theorem 16, namely Example 45. The third matrix in the chain of row reductions is upper triangular and was obtained solely by type 2 operations. Therefore the determinant is $2 \cdot 4 \cdot (-3) = -24$. If you choose to apply Theorem 16, be careful to apply *only* row sum operations in reducing the matrix to triangular form.

Concepts Review

1. The formula for the determinant of a two-by-two matrix A with entries a_{ij} is _____.

2. Multiplying row i of a matrix M by the real number r _____ the determinant of M by _____.

3. Adding a numerical multiple of row i to row j of the matrix M _____ _____ _____ the determinant of M.

4. Interchanging two rows of the matrix M _____ the determinant by _____.

5. The determinant of an identity matrix is _____.

6. There is an _____ _____ associated with each row operation on a square matrix, and multiplying them together gives the determinant of the matrix.

7. If all nonzero entries of a square matrix are on or above the main diagonal, then the matrix is called a(n) _____ _____ matrix.

8. The product of the _____ entries in an upper _____ matrix is equal to the determinant.

9. When we reduce a matrix to triangular form by using row sum elementary row operations there is _____ effect on the determinant.

Exercises

A   In Exercises 1–8, compute the determinant of the matrix given.

1. $\begin{bmatrix} 3 & 2 \\ 0 & -2 \end{bmatrix}$

2. $\begin{bmatrix} 1 & 2 \\ 3 & 4 \end{bmatrix}$

3. $\begin{bmatrix} 1 & -2 \\ 2 & 3 \end{bmatrix}$

4. $\begin{bmatrix} -2 & 0 \\ -3 & -2 \end{bmatrix}$

5. $\begin{bmatrix} 0 & 3 \\ -1 & 1 \end{bmatrix}$

6. $\begin{bmatrix} 1 & 3 \\ -1 & 0 \end{bmatrix}$

7. $\begin{bmatrix} 1 & 2 \\ 2 & 4 \end{bmatrix}$

8. $\begin{bmatrix} 1 & 1 \\ 1 & 1 \end{bmatrix}$

In Exercises 9–14, compute the two determinants and explain which determinant rule is illustrated.

9. $\det\begin{bmatrix} 1 & 6 \\ 2 & 4 \end{bmatrix}$ $\det\begin{bmatrix} 1 & 6 \\ 3 & 10 \end{bmatrix}$ 10. $\det\begin{bmatrix} 1 & 6 \\ 2 & 4 \end{bmatrix}$ $\det\begin{bmatrix} 2 & 4 \\ 1 & 6 \end{bmatrix}$

11. $\det\begin{bmatrix} 2 & 5 \\ -4 & -8 \end{bmatrix}$ $\det\begin{bmatrix} 2 & 5 \\ 2 & 4 \end{bmatrix}$ 12. $\det\begin{bmatrix} -1 & 3 \\ 2 & -2 \end{bmatrix}$ $\det\begin{bmatrix} 2 & -6 \\ 2 & -2 \end{bmatrix}$

13. $\det\begin{bmatrix} 2 & -2 \\ -1 & 3 \end{bmatrix}$ $\det\begin{bmatrix} -1 & 3 \\ 2 & -2 \end{bmatrix}$ 14. $\det\begin{bmatrix} 1 & 5 \\ 3 & 6 \end{bmatrix}$ $\det\begin{bmatrix} 1 & 5 \\ 1 & -4 \end{bmatrix}$

In Exercises 15–18, the determinants of the pairs of matrices given are related by the determinant rules. For each pair, state how det$A$ and det$B$ are related.

15. $A = \begin{bmatrix} 1 & 3 & 5 \\ -2 & -4 & -6 \\ 3 & 1 & 1 \end{bmatrix}$ $B = \begin{bmatrix} 1 & 3 & 5 \\ 1 & 2 & 3 \\ 3 & 1 & 1 \end{bmatrix}$

16. $A = \begin{bmatrix} 1 & 3 & 5 \\ -1 & -4 & -7 \\ 3 & 1 & 1 \end{bmatrix}$ $B = \begin{bmatrix} 1 & 3 & 5 \\ 1 & 2 & 3 \\ 3 & 1 & 1 \end{bmatrix}$

17. $A = \begin{bmatrix} 1 & 0 & 1 \\ 2 & -1 & 1 \\ 1 & -1 & 2 \end{bmatrix}$ $B = \begin{bmatrix} 2 & -1 & 1 \\ 1 & 0 & 1 \\ 1 & -1 & 2 \end{bmatrix}$

18. $A = \begin{bmatrix} 3 & -2 & 5 \\ 2 & -1 & 1 \\ 1 & -1 & 2 \end{bmatrix}$ $B = \begin{bmatrix} 1 & 0 & 1 \\ 2 & -1 & 1 \\ 1 & -1 & 2 \end{bmatrix}$

B   In Exercises 19–24, find the determinants of the matrices given.

19. $\begin{bmatrix} 2 & 0 & 0 \\ 0 & -3 & 0 \\ 0 & 0 & 2 \end{bmatrix}$ 20. $\begin{bmatrix} 1 & 0 & 0 & 0 \\ 0 & 3 & 0 & 0 \\ 0 & 0 & 2 & 0 \\ 0 & 0 & 0 & 2 \end{bmatrix}$ 21. $\begin{bmatrix} 2 & 3 & 0 \\ 0 & -3 & 2 \\ 0 & 0 & 2 \end{bmatrix}$

22. $\begin{bmatrix} 1 & 3 & 2 & 0 \\ 0 & 3 & 0 & 2 \\ 0 & 0 & 2 & 2 \\ 0 & 0 & 0 & 2 \end{bmatrix}$ 23. $\begin{bmatrix} 2 & 3 & 0 \\ 2 & 0 & 0 \\ 0 & 0 & 2 \end{bmatrix}$ 24. $\begin{bmatrix} 1 & 3 & 0 & 0 \\ 1 & 0 & 0 & 0 \\ 0 & 0 & 2 & 0 \\ 0 & 0 & 0 & 2 \end{bmatrix}$

For some matrices in Exercises 25–33, the determinant is the product of the diagonal elements, and for some it is not. Compute the determinants and show which ones are and are not the product of the diagonal elements $a_{11}a_{22}a_{33}$ or the reverse diagonal elements $a_{13}a_{22}a_{31}$.

25. $\begin{bmatrix} 0 & 1 \\ 1 & 2 \end{bmatrix}$ 26. $\begin{bmatrix} 0 & 0 & 2 \\ 0 & 1 & 6 \\ 3 & 8 & 2 \end{bmatrix}$ 27. $\begin{bmatrix} 1 & 0 & 0 \\ -1 & 3 & 0 \\ 3 & 4 & 2 \end{bmatrix}$

28. $\begin{bmatrix} 1 & 3 & 6 \\ 2 & 4 & 0 \\ 1 & 0 & 0 \end{bmatrix}$ **29.** $\begin{bmatrix} 2 & 0 & -1 \\ 0 & 1 & 3 \\ 0 & 0 & 3 \end{bmatrix}$ **30.** $\begin{bmatrix} 3 & 0 & 0 \\ 1 & 2 & 0 \\ 4 & 2 & -3 \end{bmatrix}$

31. $\begin{bmatrix} 1 & 3 & 2 \\ 6 & -1 & 0 \\ 3 & 0 & 0 \end{bmatrix}$ **32.** $\begin{bmatrix} 4 & 3 & 2 \\ 0 & 6 & 5 \\ 0 & 0 & 1 \end{bmatrix}$

Compute the determinants of each matrix in Exercises 33–38 by using the method of elementary factors.

33. $\begin{bmatrix} 2 & -3 & 2 \\ 4 & 3 & 4 \\ 2 & -3 & 1 \end{bmatrix}$ **34.** $\begin{bmatrix} -3 & 4 & 2 \\ 3 & 4 & 1 \\ -3 & 2 & 1 \end{bmatrix}$ **35.** $\begin{bmatrix} -1 & 2 & -3 \\ 0 & 2 & 3 \\ -1 & 4 & -3 \end{bmatrix}$

36. $\begin{bmatrix} 5 & 2 & 6 \\ 5 & 1 & 2 \\ -5 & 1 & 4 \end{bmatrix}$ **37.** $\begin{bmatrix} 1 & 3 & 1 \\ 2 & -1 & 3 \\ 3 & 2 & 4 \end{bmatrix}$ **38.** $\begin{bmatrix} 1 & 3 & 2 \\ 4 & 3 & 5 \\ 2 & -3 & 1 \end{bmatrix}$

Compute the determinant of each matrix in Exercises 39–44 by row reducing to triangular form.

39. $\begin{bmatrix} 1 & 2 & 0 \\ -1 & 0 & 1 \\ 1 & 2 & 3 \end{bmatrix}$ **40.** $\begin{bmatrix} 3 & 2 & 1 \\ 3 & 3 & 3 \\ 1 & 1 & 0 \end{bmatrix}$ **41.** $\begin{bmatrix} 3 & 3 & -6 \\ 2 & 4 & 0 \\ 1 & 1 & 6 \end{bmatrix}$

42. $\begin{bmatrix} 1 & 1 & -1 \\ 2 & 4 & -1 \\ 1 & 3 & 3 \end{bmatrix}$ **43.** $\begin{bmatrix} 1 & -1 & 1 \\ 1 & 0 & 1 \\ 2 & 0 & 3 \end{bmatrix}$ **44.** $\begin{bmatrix} 1 & 2 & 3 \\ 2 & 2 & 8 \\ 1 & 1 & 4 \end{bmatrix}$

In Exercises 45–50, compute the determinants by any appropriate method.

45. $\det \begin{bmatrix} 2 & 0 & 1 & 0 \\ 0 & 1 & 2 & 2 \\ -1 & -1 & 1 & 1 \\ 2 & -1 & 0 & 1 \end{bmatrix}$ **46.** $\det \begin{bmatrix} 0 & 2 & -1 & 0 \\ 1 & 0 & 1 & 3 \\ 2 & 1 & 0 & 0 \\ -1 & 0 & 2 & 0 \end{bmatrix}$ **47.** $\det \begin{bmatrix} 1 & 3 & 1 & 1 \\ 0 & 0 & 3 & 4 \\ 2 & -1 & 2 & 0 \\ 0 & -1 & 0 & 1 \end{bmatrix}$

48. $\det \begin{bmatrix} 1 & -1 & 2 & -2 \\ 1 & 1 & 4 & 4 \\ 1 & -1 & 8 & -8 \\ 1 & 1 & 16 & 16 \end{bmatrix}$ **49.** $\det \begin{bmatrix} x & 0 & y & 0 \\ 1 & 1 & 3 & 1 \\ 1 & 0 & 2 & 1 \\ 2 & 0 & -1 & -1 \end{bmatrix}$ **50.** $\det \begin{bmatrix} x & 1 & 3 & 4 \\ 0 & 2 & 0 & 3 \\ 0 & 0 & 3 & 2 \\ y & -1 & -1 & 1 \end{bmatrix}$

Problems

1. Describe the effect of the following sequence of row operations on a matrix:

$$Rj + Ri, \quad -1 \cdot Ri + Rj, \quad Rj + Ri, \quad -1 \cdot Rj$$

2. Explain why if a sequence of (nonzero) row multiple and row sum elementary row operations can make the entry M_{ij} of a matrix equal to zero, then a sequence of row sum elementary operations can also make M_{ij} equal to zero.

3. Prove by induction that any n-by-n matrix can be row reduced to an upper triangular matrix.

4. On the basis of Problems 1–3, explain why a matrix may be row reduced to triangular form without changing its determinant.

5. Show that if an upper triangular matrix has zero as a diagonal entry, then by row reduction we can convert the lowest row with a diagonal zero into an entire row of zeros.

6. Show that if all the diagonal entries of an upper triangular matrix are nonzero, then we may row reduce the matrix to a diagonal matrix without changing its determinant.

7. Using Problems 5 and 6, prove Theorem 15.

8. A more restricted version of determinant rule (2) is

   Rule (2′): Adding row i to row j does not change the determinant.

   Show that rules (1) and (2′) imply rule (2). (*Hint:* Examine how Problem 1 lets you prove that rules (1) and (2) imply rule (3).)

9. A still more restricted version of determinant rule (2) is

   Rule (2″). Adding a row to an adjacent row does not change the determinant.

   Show that rules (1) and (2″) imply rule (2′). (*Hint:* See how to add row i to row $i + 2$ by first adding it to $i + 1$, then adding row $i + 1$ to row $i + 2$, and finally doing some subtracting.)

10. On the basis of Problems 1, 8, and 9, show that if a function satisfies determinant rules (1), (2″), and (4), then it satisfies all the determinant rules.

11. Given a two-by-two matrix with rows $R1$ and $R2$, there is a parallelogram whose vertices are the origin, the point whose x- and y-coordinates are given by $R1$, the point whose x- and y-coordinates are given by $R2$, and the point whose x- and y-coordinates are given by $R1 + R2$.
    (a) Explain why the figure is a parallelogram.
    (b) Explain why a row sum elementary matrix operation on M gives a matrix M' whose parallelogram has the same area as M.
    (c) Explain why a row multiple elementary row operation with multiple r gives a matrix M' whose parallelogram has an area that is the absolute value of r times the area of the parallelogram of M.
    (d) Explain why a row interchange elementary row operation on M gives a matrix M' whose parallelogram has the same area as M.
    (e) Explain why the area of the parallelogram determined by M is 0 if M is not invertible and is the product of the absolute values of the elementary factors of a row reduction of M to the identity if M is invertible.
    (f) How does the area of the parallelogram relate to the determinant of M? Could we have used columns to define the parallelogram and gotten the same answer?
    (g) Make a believable conjecture about the volume of a parallelepiped (a figure having 8 corners) associated with a three-by-three matrix.
    (h) Outline the main points of the proof of your conjecture in (g).

Section 10-6 Properties of Determinants

🅐 Products and Transposes

We introduced determinants in hopes that the determinant of a matrix would be nonzero if and only if the matrix is invertible. We have learned that a matrix is invertible if and only if it is a product of elementary matrices. Now suppose the matrix M is a product of elementary matrices $M = E_1 \cdot E_2 \cdots E_n$. We know that if we first perform the elementary row operation that "undoes" E_1, then the operation that "undoes" E_2, . . . and finally the one that "undoes" E_n, we will have row reduced M to the identity. We know, from the elementary factors description of determinants, that the determinant of an elementary matrix E is the elementary factor of the row operation that converts E to the identity. Theorem 17 summarizes these remarks.

Determinants of Products of Matrices

Theorem 17 The determinant of a product of elementary matrices is the product of their determinants.

Proof Immediate from the discussion above. ∎

Theorem 18 The determinant of a matrix is nonzero if and only if it is invertible.

Proof If a matrix is invertible, then it is a product of elementary matrices and therefore, by Theorem 17 and the fact that each elementary factor is nonzero, its determinant is nonzero. If a matrix is not invertible, then it may be row reduced to a matrix with a row of zeros and therefore has determinant zero. ∎

Theorem 17 suggests a more general result that is also true.

Theorem 19 For any two square matrices M and N, $\det MN = \det M \det N$.

Proof If M and N are invertible, then Theorem 17 applied to M, N and MN gives our result. If one of M or N is not invertible, then $\det M \det N$ is zero, so for the formula to hold, $\det MN$ would have to be zero—that is, MN would have to be not invertible. In the problems, we discuss how to show that if M or N is not invertible, then MN is not invertible. ∎

EXAMPLE 47   Find the determinant of the product of the matrices M and N below without actually computing MN.

$$M = \begin{bmatrix} 1 & 2 & 3 \\ 0 & 4 & 2 \\ 0 & 0 & -1 \end{bmatrix} \quad N = \begin{bmatrix} 2 & 0 & 0 \\ 4 & 2 & 0 \\ 1 & 5 & 3 \end{bmatrix}$$

Solution   Because $\det M = 1 \cdot 4(-1) = -4$, and $\det N = 2 \cdot 2 \cdot 3 = 12$, $\det MN = -48$.   ∎

Elementary Matrices and Column Operations

We have so far concentrated all our thinking on row operations. There are three operations on the columns of matrices, called *elementary column operations*, which are defined analogously with elementary row operations. What effect do column operations have on determinants? The elementary matrix formed from I by multiplying row i by r can also be formed by multiplying column i by r. The elementary matrix formed from I by interchanging rows i and j may also be formed by interchanging columns i and j. Adding r times row i of I to row j is equivalent to adding r times column j to column i. Further, it can be shown that multiplying M by an elementary (column) matrix on the right performs the corresponding elementary column operation on M. This gives us the next theorem.

Theorem 20   Performing an elementary column operation on M multiplies the determinant of M by the determinant of the corresponding elementary matrix. That is, it has the same effect as the corresponding elementary row operation.

Proof   From the remarks above, this is a consequence of Theorem 19.   ∎

Transposes Relate Row and Column Operations to Determinants

The matrix N is called the **transpose** of the matrix M if *row i* of N has the same entries in the same order as *column i* of M. We write M^t (read as M-transpose and not as M to the t) for the transpose N of M. People say, "We get M^t from M by interchanging rows and columns."

EXAMPLE 48   Write down the transpose M^t of $M = \begin{bmatrix} 1 & 2 & 3 \\ 4 & 5 & 6 \\ 7 & 8 & 9 \end{bmatrix}$.

Solution Row 1 should be [1 4 7], row 2 should be [2 5 8], and row 3 should be [3 6 9]. This gives

$$M^t = \begin{bmatrix} 1 & 4 & 7 \\ 2 & 5 & 8 \\ 3 & 6 & 9 \end{bmatrix}$$

A useful fact about transposes is that $(MN)^t = N^t M^t$.

EXAMPLE 49 Compute M^t, N^t, and $N^t M^t$ and MN for the matrices M and N below.

$$M = \begin{bmatrix} a & b \\ c & d \end{bmatrix} \qquad N = \begin{bmatrix} w & x \\ y & z \end{bmatrix}$$

Solution We write

$$M^t = \begin{bmatrix} a & c \\ b & d \end{bmatrix} \qquad N^t = \begin{bmatrix} w & y \\ x & z \end{bmatrix}$$

by the definition of transposes. Matrix multiplication gives us

$$MN = \begin{bmatrix} a & b \\ c & d \end{bmatrix} \begin{bmatrix} w & x \\ y & z \end{bmatrix} = \begin{bmatrix} aw + by & ax + bz \\ cw + dy & cx + dz \end{bmatrix}$$

and

$$N^t M^t = \begin{bmatrix} w & y \\ x & z \end{bmatrix} \begin{bmatrix} a & c \\ b & d \end{bmatrix} = \begin{bmatrix} wa + yb & wc + yd \\ xa + zb & xc + zd \end{bmatrix}$$

This actually proves the formula $(MN)^t = N^t M^t$ for 2-by-2 matrices.

Theorem 21 If M is an m-by-m matrix and N is an n-by-k matrix, then $(MN)^t = N^t M^t$.

Proof The i,j entry of $(MN)^t$ is by definition the j,i entry of MN; that is the product of row j of M (and thus column j of M^t) with column i of N (and thus row i of N^t). Therefore $(MN)^t$ and $N^t M^t$ have the same entries, so they are equal.

Theorem 22 For any square matrix M, $\det M = \det M^t$.

Proof If M is invertible, then it is a product of elementary matrices. Since the determinant of an elementary matrix and its transpose must be equal, the theorem follows in this case directly from Theorem 19. We can show that M^t is invertible if and only if M is invertible by using Theorem 21, so $\det M = \det M^t$ if M is not invertible as well.

Theorem 22 tells us how to translate a fact involving rows of matrices and determinants into a corresponding fact about columns of matrices and determinants.

B   The Additive Property

We described the determinant function originally by stating how we hoped it would behave when we performed elementary row operations. It will be useful to have a property that describes how it reacts to a whole sequence of row operations. This description will lead us to one of the standard formulas for the determinant function and to a proof that there really is a determinant function satisfying axioms (determinant rules) (1)–(4). We shall study the case of a whole sequence of row operations, all of which affect *only* row i. Thus we might add a numerical multiple of any row, even row i itself, to row i. This replaces row i by

$$Ri + \sum_{j=1}^{n} a_j Rj$$

for some n-tuple of numbers $a_1, a_2, \ldots, a_n$. If our matrix can be row reduced to the identity, then (by row reducing to the identity and then combining rows of the identity together) we can make

$$\sum_{j=1}^{n} a_j Rj$$

into any row matrix R we choose. Thus we should be able to figure out the effect on the determinant of adding any row vector we please to row i.

The Effect of Adding an Arbitrary Row Matrix to Row i

Theorem 23   If Ri' is any row matrix and the square matrix M has rows $R1, \ldots Ri, \ldots Rn$, then

$$\det \begin{bmatrix} -R1- \\ \vdots \\ Ri + Ri' \\ \vdots \\ -Rn- \end{bmatrix} = \det \begin{bmatrix} R1 \\ \vdots \\ Ri \\ \vdots \\ Rn \end{bmatrix} + \det \begin{bmatrix} R1 \\ \vdots \\ Ri' \\ \vdots \\ Rn \end{bmatrix}$$

Proof   If M is invertible, then we may assume that Ri' is

$$\sum_{j=1}^{n} a_j R_j$$

By our second determinant axiom, applied once to each row other than row i,

$$\det \begin{bmatrix} -R1- \\ \vdots \\ Ri + \sum_{j=1}^{n} a_j R_j \\ \vdots \\ -Rn- \end{bmatrix} = \det \begin{bmatrix} -R1- \\ \vdots \\ Ri + a_i Ri \\ \vdots \\ -Rn- \end{bmatrix}$$

Then by determinant axiom (1),

$$\det \begin{bmatrix} -R1- \\ \vdots \\ Ri + \sum_{j=1}^{n} a_j R_j \\ \vdots \\ -Rn- \end{bmatrix} = (1 + a_i)\det \begin{bmatrix} R1 \\ \vdots \\ Ri \\ \vdots \\ Rn \end{bmatrix} = \det \begin{bmatrix} R1 \\ \vdots \\ Ri \\ \vdots \\ Rn \end{bmatrix} = det \begin{bmatrix} R1 \\ \vdots \\ a_i Ri \\ \vdots \\ Rn \end{bmatrix}$$

$$= \det \begin{bmatrix} R1 \\ \vdots \\ Ri \\ \vdots \\ Rn \end{bmatrix} + \det \begin{bmatrix} -R1- \\ \vdots \\ \sum_{j=1}^{n} a_j Rj \\ \vdots \\ -Rn- \end{bmatrix}$$

The last equality is by determinant rule (2) once again.

If M is not invertible, then M can be row reduced to a matrix with a row of zeros. In Problems 10 and 11, we show that the formula holds in this case as well. ∎

EXAMPLE 50 In the matrix $M = \begin{bmatrix} 1 & 1 & 1 \\ 2 & 1 & 1 \\ 1 & 0 & 3 \end{bmatrix}$, row two is the sum $[1 \quad 0 \quad 0] + [1 \quad 1 \quad 1]$. Use

this fact and the formula of Theorem 3 to compute $\det M$.

Solution   We may let $R1 = \begin{bmatrix} 1 & 1 & 1 \end{bmatrix}$, $R2 = \begin{bmatrix} 1 & 0 & 0 \end{bmatrix}$, $R2' = \begin{bmatrix} 1 & 1 & 1 \end{bmatrix}$, and $R3 = \begin{bmatrix} 1 & 0 & 3 \end{bmatrix}$. Theorem 23 tells us that

$$\det \begin{bmatrix} R1 \\ R2 + R2' \\ R3 \end{bmatrix} = \det \begin{bmatrix} R1 \\ R2 \\ R3 \end{bmatrix} + \det \begin{bmatrix} R1 \\ R2' \\ R3 \end{bmatrix}$$

$$= \det \begin{bmatrix} 1 & 1 & 1 \\ 1 & 0 & 0 \\ 1 & 0 & 3 \end{bmatrix} + \det \begin{bmatrix} 1 & 1 & 1 \\ 1 & 1 & 1 \\ 1 & 0 & 3 \end{bmatrix}$$

The second of these matrices row reduces to a matrix with a row of zeros, so $\det M$ is the determinant of the first matrix. Applying row reduction, we get

$$\det M = \det \begin{bmatrix} 1 & 1 & 1 \\ 1 & 0 & 0 \\ 1 & 0 & 3 \end{bmatrix} \xrightarrow[\; -R2 + R1 \;]{\; -R2 + R3 \;} \det \begin{bmatrix} 0 & 1 & 1 \\ 1 & 0 & 0 \\ 0 & 0 & 3 \end{bmatrix} \xrightarrow{\; R1 \leftrightarrow R2 \;} \det \begin{bmatrix} 1 & 0 & 0 \\ 0 & 1 & 1 \\ 0 & 0 & 3 \end{bmatrix}$$

Since we now have an upper triangular matrix, we see that $\det M = 3$.   ∎

Theorem 23 is often restated as follows: "The determinant of a matrix is an **additive function** of row i." This additive property together with determinant axiom (1) are often restated: "The determinant is a **linear function** of row i."

Using the Additive Property

EXAMPLE 51   Use the fact that

$$\begin{bmatrix} 1 & 2 & 3 \end{bmatrix} = \begin{bmatrix} 1 & 0 & 0 \end{bmatrix} + \begin{bmatrix} 0 & 2 & 0 \end{bmatrix} + \begin{bmatrix} 0 & 0 & 3 \end{bmatrix}$$

to help evaluate the determinant of the matrix

$$M = \begin{bmatrix} 1 & 2 & 3 \\ 0 & 2 & 1 \\ 3 & 4 & 0 \end{bmatrix}$$

Solution   We may write

$$\det M = \det \begin{bmatrix} 1 & 0 & 0 \\ 0 & 2 & 1 \\ 3 & 4 & 0 \end{bmatrix} + \det \begin{bmatrix} 0 & 2 & 0 \\ 0 & 2 & 1 \\ 3 & 4 & 0 \end{bmatrix} + \det \begin{bmatrix} 0 & 0 & 3 \\ 0 & 2 & 1 \\ 3 & 4 & 0 \end{bmatrix}$$

$$= \det \begin{bmatrix} 1 & 0 & 0 \\ 0 & 2 & 1 \\ 0 & 4 & 0 \end{bmatrix} + \det \begin{bmatrix} 0 & 2 & 0 \\ 0 & 0 & 1 \\ 3 & 0 & 0 \end{bmatrix} + \det \begin{bmatrix} 0 & 0 & 3 \\ 0 & 2 & 0 \\ 3 & 4 & 0 \end{bmatrix}$$

By interchanging columns, we may convert our matrices to triangular form:

$$\det M = -\det\begin{bmatrix} 1 & 0 & 0 \\ 0 & 1 & 2 \\ 0 & 0 & 4 \end{bmatrix} - \det\begin{bmatrix} 2 & 0 & 0 \\ 0 & 0 & 1 \\ 0 & 3 & 0 \end{bmatrix} - \det\begin{bmatrix} 3 & 0 & 0 \\ 0 & 2 & 0 \\ 0 & 4 & 3 \end{bmatrix}$$

$$= -4 + \det\begin{bmatrix} 2 & 0 & 0 \\ 0 & 1 & 0 \\ 0 & 0 & 3 \end{bmatrix} - 18$$

$$= -4 + 6 - 18 = -16 \qquad\blacksquare$$

◖ Row and Column Expansions

Computations similar to those of Example 51 give us a formula for the determinant of a 3-by-3 matrix. Theorem 23 justifies the first step that follows; the other steps are explained after the computation.

$$\det\begin{bmatrix} a_{11} & a_{12} & a_{13} \\ a_{21} & a_{22} & a_{23} \\ a_{31} & a_{32} & a_{33} \end{bmatrix} =$$

$$\det\begin{bmatrix} a_{11} & 0 & 0 \\ a_{21} & a_{22} & a_{23} \\ a_{31} & a_{32} & a_{33} \end{bmatrix} + \det\begin{bmatrix} 0 & a_{12} & 0 \\ a_{21} & a_{22} & a_{23} \\ a_{31} & a_{32} & a_{33} \end{bmatrix} + \det\begin{bmatrix} 0 & 0 & a_{13} \\ a_{21} & a_{22} & a_{23} \\ a_{31} & a_{32} & a_{33} \end{bmatrix}$$

$$= \det\begin{bmatrix} a_{11} & 0 & 0 \\ 0 & a_{22} & a_{23} \\ 0 & a_{32} & a_{33} \end{bmatrix} - \det\begin{bmatrix} a_{12} & 0 & 0 \\ 0 & a_{21} & a_{23} \\ 0 & a_{31} & a_{33} \end{bmatrix} + \det\begin{bmatrix} a_{13} & 0 & 0 \\ 0 & a_{21} & a_{22} \\ 0 & a_{31} & a_{32} \end{bmatrix}$$

$$= a_{11}\det\begin{bmatrix} 1 & 0 & 0 \\ 0 & a_{22} & a_{23} \\ 0 & a_{32} & a_{33} \end{bmatrix} - a_{12}\det\begin{bmatrix} 1 & 0 & 0 \\ 0 & a_{21} & a_{23} \\ 0 & a_{31} & a_{33} \end{bmatrix} + a_{13}\det\begin{bmatrix} 1 & 0 & 0 \\ 0 & a_{21} & a_{22} \\ 0 & a_{31} & a_{32} \end{bmatrix}$$

$$= a_{11}\det\begin{bmatrix} a_{22} & a_{23} \\ a_{32} & a_{33} \end{bmatrix} - a_{12}\det\begin{bmatrix} a_{21} & a_{23} \\ a_{31} & a_{33} \end{bmatrix} + a_{13}\det\begin{bmatrix} a_{21} & a_{22} \\ a_{31} & a_{32} \end{bmatrix}$$

The second equal sign is the result of row reduction. For example, look at the two matrices whose first row is $[a_{11} \quad 0 \quad 0]$. If a_{11} is not zero, subtracting the right multiples of row 1 from rows 2 and 3 gives the matrix with zeros below a_{11}. If, on the other hand, a_{11} is zero, then both determinants are determinants with rows of zeros, so they both equal zero. Notice that the minus sign on the middle determinant comes from interchanging rows. The third equal sign follows from determinant rule (1). The reason for the very last step is as follows. The function of the 2-by-2 matrix of a_{ij}'s given by

$$f\begin{bmatrix} a_{11} & a_{12} \\ a_{21} & a_{22} \end{bmatrix} = \det\begin{bmatrix} 1 & 0 & 0 \\ 0 & a_{11} & a_{12} \\ 0 & a_{21} & a_{22} \end{bmatrix}$$

satisfies all the axioms for a determinant function on 2-by-2 matrices. Therefore f must be the determinant function on 2-by-2 matrices. We have proved, in the 3-by-3 case, a formula called the formula for **expansion on the first row** for the computation of a determinant.

Computing a Determinant by Expansion on a First Row

From the row expansion formula above, it is just a small step to obtaining the **general row expansion formula,** which is stated as Theorem 24.

Theorem 24   If we use $A(i,j)$ to stand for the matrix obtained from the matrix A by deleting row i and column j, then for any choice of i,

$$\det A = \sum_{j=1}^{n} (-1)^{i+j} a_{ij} \det A(i,j)$$

Proof   Essentially the computation given above in the 3-by-3 case for $i=1$.   ■

The matrix $A(i,j)$ is called the *i,j minor* of A; the term $(-1)^{i+j}\det A(i,j)$ is called the **cofactor** of a_{ij}.

EXAMPLE 52   Compute the determinant

$$\det M = \det \begin{bmatrix} 2 & 3 & -1 \\ 1 & 0 & 2 \\ 3 & 2 & 1 \end{bmatrix}$$

Solution   We choose to expand on row 2 (for reasons that will become clear soon), so we apply our formula with $i = 2$. Thus we get

$$\det M = (-1)^{2+1}\cdot 1 \det \begin{bmatrix} 3 & -1 \\ 2 & 1 \end{bmatrix} + (-1)^{2+2}\cdot 0 \det \begin{bmatrix} 2 & -1 \\ 3 & 1 \end{bmatrix} + (-1)^{2+3}\cdot 2 \det \begin{bmatrix} 2 & 3 \\ 3 & 2 \end{bmatrix}$$
$$= -1(3+2) + 0 - 1\cdot 2\cdot(4-9)$$
$$= -5 + 10 = 5$$

Why did we expand on row 2? Because it had a zero, allowing us to finish the computation by using two 2-by-2 determinants rather than three.   ■

Recall that what works for rows of a matrix works for columns as well. Thus we may expand on a column as well.

EXAMPLE 53   Compute the determinant of the matrix M below by expansion on column 3.

$$M = \begin{bmatrix} 1 & 3 & 3 & 1 \\ 0 & 4 & 0 & 6 \\ 0 & 1 & 0 & 2 \\ 1 & 2 & 2 & 1 \end{bmatrix}$$

Solution

$$\det M = (-1)^{1+3} \cdot 3 \cdot \det \begin{bmatrix} 0 & 4 & 6 \\ 0 & 1 & 2 \\ 1 & 2 & 1 \end{bmatrix} + 0 + 0 + (-1)^{4+3} \cdot 2 \cdot \det \begin{bmatrix} 1 & 3 & 1 \\ 0 & 4 & 6 \\ 0 & 1 & 2 \end{bmatrix}$$

$$= 3 \cdot (-1)^{1+3}(8 - 6) - 2 \cdot (-1)^{1+1}(8 - 6)$$

$$= 3 \cdot 2 - 2 \cdot 2 = 2 \qquad \blacksquare$$

Expansion of a determinant along a row or column that contains as many zeros as possible is a good technique for evaluating determinants of matrices with a fair number of zeros. Furthermore, we have shown that if there is a determinant function on n-by-n matrices, then it may be computed recursively in terms of determinants of $(n-1)$-by-$(n-1)$ matrices. This suggests that we should be able to use the formula for 2-by-2 determinants to prove that 3-by-3 determinants exist, and so on, getting an inductive proof that there is a determinant function. Theorem 25 does this.

Theorem 25   The formula for expansion of a determinant on column 1 satisfies rules (1)–(4) for a determinant function.

Proof   Problem 10 of Section 10-5 tells us to show that a function satisfies determinant rules (1)–(4) if it satisfies rules (1), (4), and (2″)—the last one being the rule that adding a row to an adjacent row does not change the determinant. We assume inductively that the expansion formula gives a determinant function for $(n - 1)$-by-$(n - 1)$ matrices, and we note that in the case $n = 2$ it is the usual formula. Then, using the formula

$$\det A = \sum_{i=1}^{n} (-1)^{i+1} a_{i1} \det A(i,1)$$

we see that $\det I_n = (-1)^{1+1} \cdot 1 \cdot \det I_{n-1}$, where I_n and I_{n-1} denote the n-by-n and $n-1$-by-$n-1$ identity matrices. Since $\det I_{n-1} = 1$, we get that $\det I_n = 1$. Multiplying row k of A by r multiplies a_{k1} but not $\det A(k,1)$ by r; by the inductive hypothesis, it also multiplies each $\det A(i,1)$ with $i \neq k$ by r. Thus the formula satisfies rule (1). Finally, if we add row k to row $k + 1$, we don't change any of the $a_{i1}\det A(i,1)$ terms with $i \neq k$ and $i \neq k + 1$ (because the $n-1$-by-$n-1$ determinants must satisfy rule (2)). If A' is the matrix we get from A by adding row k to row $k + 1$, then

$$a'_{k1} \det A'(k,1) = a_{k1} \det A'(k,1) = a_{k1}(\det A(k,1) + \det A(k + 1,1)) \qquad (1)$$

by the additivity property for determinants of $n - 1$-by-$n - 1$ matrices. Also,

$$a'_{k+1,1} \det A'(k + 1,1) = (a_{k+1,1} + a_{k1}) \det A(k + 1,1) \qquad (2)$$

Now $a_{k1} \det A(k + 1,1)$ in (1) is multiplied by $(-1)^k$, and the $a_{k1} \det A(k + 1,1)$ in (2) is multiplied by $(-1)^{k+1}$ in the column expansion for A'. Therefore they cancel out, and the column expansion for A' is identical with that for A. Thus the formula for expansion on the first column satisfies the determinant rules. $\qquad \blacksquare$

The value of Theorem 25 is this. Until we proved it, we did not know that there *was* a determinant function; we simply knew how to compute it if there were one. Now we know that there is such a function, and since the rules determine its value, there is only one such function.

Concepts Review

1. The determinant of a product of elementary matrices is the _____ of their determinants.

2. The determinant of M times N is _____.

3. We form the _____ of a matrix by interchanging the rows and columns.

4. The _____ property tells us that if three matrices are identical except in one row, which in one matrix is the sum of the corresponding rows in the other two, then the determinant of the first matrix is the _____ of the determinants of the other two.

5. The determinant of the transpose of M is _____ to the _____ of M.

6. The transpose of the product is the _____ of the transposes in _____ _____.

7. A matrix is invertible if its determinant is _____.

8. When computing a determinant by row or column expansion, it is useful to pick a row or column with as many _____ as possible.

9. The formula for the _____ of a determinant on _____ _____ is

$$\det A = \sum_{j=1}^{n} (-1)^{i+j} a_{ij} \det A(i,j)$$

Exercises

A   For Exercises 1–18, let M, N, P, Q, R, and S be the matrices given below.

$$M = \begin{bmatrix} 1 & 2 & 3 \\ 0 & 3 & 4 \\ 0 & 5 & 6 \end{bmatrix} \quad N = \begin{bmatrix} 2 & 0 & 0 \\ -1 & 3 & 0 \\ 1 & 1 & 1 \end{bmatrix} \quad P = \begin{bmatrix} 1 & 0 & 1 \\ 0 & 2 & 2 \\ 1 & 1 & 2 \end{bmatrix}$$

$$Q = \begin{bmatrix} 1 & 1 & 1 \\ 0 & 2 & 2 \\ 0 & 0 & 3 \end{bmatrix} \quad R = \begin{bmatrix} 2 & 0 & 0 \\ -1 & -1 & 0 \\ 0 & 2 & 4 \end{bmatrix} \quad S = \begin{bmatrix} 2 & 0 & -3 \\ 0 & -3 & 1 \\ 1 & 1 & 1 \end{bmatrix}$$

1. Find the determinants of M, N, and P.
2. Find the determinants of Q, R, and S.
3. Find the determinant of MN.
4. Find the determinant of QR.
5. Find the determinant of NP.
6. Find the determinant of QS.
7. Find the determinant of MP.
8. Find the determinant of SR.
9. Find the determinant of N^2.
10. Find the determinant of Q^2.

11. Find the determinant of P^2.   **12.** Find the determinant of S^2.

13. Find MN and compute its determinant to check Exercise 3.

14. Find QR and compute its determinant to check Exercise 4.

15. Find N^2 and compute its determinant to check Exercise 9.

16. Find Q^2 and compute its determinant to check Exercise 10.

17. Find the transpose of the matrices M, N, and P in Exercise 1. What is the determinant of each of these transposes?

18. Find the transpose of the matrices Q, R, and S in Exercise 2 and the determinant of each of these transposed matrices.

B **19.** Apply the method of Example 51 using row 1 in the way $[1 \quad 2 \quad 3]$ was used for part (a), row 2 for part (b), and row 3 for part (c) to compute each of the determinants below.

(a) $\det \begin{bmatrix} 2 & 0 & 2 \\ 1 & 1 & 1 \\ -1 & 2 & -1 \end{bmatrix}$ (b) $\det \begin{bmatrix} 1 & 1 & 1 \\ 1 & -1 & 0 \\ 1 & 0 & -1 \end{bmatrix}$ (c) $\det \begin{bmatrix} 0.5 & 6.1 & 2.2 \\ 2 & -1 & 2 \\ 0 & 1 & 1 \end{bmatrix}$

20. Apply the method of Example 51 using the row containing a zero in the way the row $[1 \quad 2 \quad 3]$ was used to evaluate each of the following determinants.

(a) $\det \begin{bmatrix} 0 & 1 & 3 \\ 1 & 2 & 1 \\ \frac{1}{2} & \frac{1}{3} & \frac{1}{2} \end{bmatrix}$ (b) $\det \begin{bmatrix} \frac{1}{2} & \frac{1}{2} & 1 \\ 1 & 0 & \frac{1}{2} \\ 2 & 2 & 2 \end{bmatrix}$ (c) $\det \begin{bmatrix} 2 & 6 & 4 \\ -2 & 2 & -2 \\ \frac{1}{2} & 0 & \frac{1}{2} \end{bmatrix}$

21. In each matrix below, use the fact that $[a,b,0] = [a,0,0] + [0,b,0]$ to help evaluate the determinant of the matrix in terms of a and b. Assume that neither a nor b is 0.

(a) $\begin{bmatrix} a & b & 0 \\ 1 & 2 & 3 \\ 3 & 2 & 1 \end{bmatrix}$ (b) $\begin{bmatrix} 1 & 2 & 3 \\ a & b & 0 \\ 3 & 2 & 1 \end{bmatrix}$ (c) $\begin{bmatrix} 1 & 0 & 1 \\ 0 & 1 & -1 \\ a & b & 0 \end{bmatrix}$

22. In each matrix below, use the fact that $[c,0,d] = [c,0,0]+[0,0,d]$ to help evaluate the determinant of the matrix in terms of c and d. Assume that neither c nor d is zero.

(a) $\begin{bmatrix} c & 0 & d \\ 1 & 1 & 1 \\ 0 & 1 & -1 \end{bmatrix}$ (b) $\begin{bmatrix} 1 & 1 & 1 \\ c & 0 & d \\ 0 & 1 & -1 \end{bmatrix}$ (c) $\begin{bmatrix} 1 & 2 & 3 \\ 1 & 2 & -1 \\ c & 0 & d \end{bmatrix}$

23. Devise a method similar to the method of Example 51, but using columns, and use it to evaluate each determinant in Exercise 19 by using a column containing a zero.

24. Devise a method similar to the method of Example 51, but using columns, and use it to evaluate each determinant in Exercise 20 by using a column containing a zero.

C **25.** Use row expansion on row 1 for part (a), row 2 for part (b), and row 3 for part (c) to compute each of the determinants below.

(a) $\det \begin{bmatrix} 2 & 0 & 2 \\ 1 & 1 & 1 \\ -1 & 2 & -1 \end{bmatrix}$ (b) $\det \begin{bmatrix} 1 & 1 & 1 \\ 1 & -1 & 0 \\ 1 & 0 & -1 \end{bmatrix}$ (c) $\det \begin{bmatrix} 0.5 & 6.1 & 2.2 \\ 2 & -1 & 2 \\ 0 & 1 & 1 \end{bmatrix}$

26. Use row expansion on the row containing a zero to evaluate each of the following determinants.

(a)
$$\det \begin{bmatrix} 0 & 1 & 3 \\ 1 & 2 & 1 \\ \frac{1}{2} & \frac{1}{3} & \frac{1}{2} \end{bmatrix}$$

(b)
$$\det \begin{bmatrix} \frac{1}{2} & \frac{1}{2} & 1 \\ 1 & 0 & \frac{1}{2} \\ 2 & 2 & 2 \end{bmatrix}$$

(c)
$$\begin{bmatrix} 2 & 6 & 4 \\ -2 & 2 & -2 \\ \frac{1}{2} & 0 & \frac{1}{2} \end{bmatrix}$$

27. Use column expansion on a column containing a zero to evaluate each of the determinants in Exercise 25.

28. Use column expansion on a column containing a zero to evaluate each of the determinants in Exercise 26.

In Exercises 29–36, evaluate the determinants given by any combination of methods you feel is appropriate.

29.
$$\det \begin{bmatrix} 1 & 2 & 0 & 1 \\ 0 & 2 & 1 & 3 \\ -1 & 0 & -1 & 2 \\ 3 & 1 & .0 & 4 \end{bmatrix}$$

30.
$$\det \begin{bmatrix} \frac{1}{2} & 0 & \frac{1}{3} & 0 \\ 6 & 12 & -6 & 0 \\ 2 & 1 & 1 & 4 \\ 5 & 1 & 3 & 1 \end{bmatrix}$$

31.
$$\det \begin{bmatrix} 1 & -1 & 1 & -1 \\ 0 & 2 & 0 & 1 \\ 1 & 1 & 1 & 0 \\ 0 & 2 & 2 & -1 \end{bmatrix}$$

32.
$$\det \begin{bmatrix} 1 & 1 & -1 & -1 \\ 2 & 3 & 3 & 2 \\ 0 & 0 & 5 & 4 \\ 1 & 1 & 0 & -1 \end{bmatrix}$$

33.
$$\det \begin{bmatrix} 1 & 2 & 2 & 1 \\ 0 & 1 & 1 & 0 \\ -1 & -1 & -1 & -1 \\ 1 & 3 & 0 & 1 \end{bmatrix}$$

34.
$$\det \begin{bmatrix} 1 & 2 & -1 & -2 \\ 1 & 4 & 1 & 4 \\ 1 & 8 & -1 & -8 \\ 1 & 0 & 0 & 1 \end{bmatrix}$$

35.
$$\det \begin{bmatrix} 2 & 4 & -2 & 2 \\ 0 & 1 & 0 & 2 \\ 2 & 0 & 1 & 1 \\ 2 & 1 & 1 & 2 \end{bmatrix}$$

36.
$$\det \begin{bmatrix} 2 & 6 & 0 & 3 \\ 1 & 1 & 1 & 1 \\ 1 & 5 & 0 & 2 \\ 2 & 0 & 1 & 1 \end{bmatrix}$$

37. Derive a formula for the determinant of the upper triangular matrix

$$M = \begin{bmatrix} a & b & c \\ 0 & d & e \\ 0 & 0 & f \end{bmatrix}$$

by expanding on the first column.

38. Derive a formula for the determinant of the lower triangular matrix

$$M = \begin{bmatrix} a & 0 & 0 & 0 \\ b & c & 0 & 0 \\ d & e & f & 0 \\ g & h & i & j \end{bmatrix}$$

by expanding on the last column.

39. Consider the matrix

$$M = \begin{bmatrix} 3 & 4 & 5 \\ 2r & 3r & 4r \\ -1 & 2 & 3 \end{bmatrix}$$

Expand on the second row to show that the determinant of M is r times the determinant of

$$N = \begin{bmatrix} 3 & 4 & 5 \\ 2 & 3 & 4 \\ -1 & 2 & 3 \end{bmatrix}$$

40. Consider the matrix

$$M = \begin{bmatrix} 3 & 4r & 5 \\ 2 & 3r & 4 \\ -1 & 2r & 3 \end{bmatrix}$$

Expand on the second column to show that the determinant of M is r times the determinant of the matrix N of Exercise 39.

Problems

1. Show that a function satisfying rule (3) for determinants has the property that the function must be zero if the matrix has two equal rows.

2. Show how rules (1) and (3) and the additivity property of determinants allow you to derive rule (2).

3. Prove by induction that $\det(M_1 M_2 \cdots M_k) = \det M_1 \det M_2 \cdots \det M_k$.

4. Define the elementary column operations and describe the effect of each kind of elementary column operation on the determinant.

5. Show that determinant rule (1) and the additivity property together are equivalent to the *linearity* property:

$$\det \begin{bmatrix} - R1 - \\ \vdots \\ rRi + sRi' \\ \vdots \\ - Rn - \end{bmatrix} = r \det \begin{bmatrix} - R1 - \\ \vdots \\ - Ri - \\ \vdots \\ - Rn - \end{bmatrix} + s \det \begin{bmatrix} - R1 - \\ \vdots \\ - Ri' - \\ \vdots \\ - Rn - \end{bmatrix}$$

6. Use Theorem 21 to show that M is invertible if and only if M^t is invertible.

7. Show that if a sequence of elementary row operations reduces M to a matrix with a row of zeros, then the same sequence of elementary row operations reduces MN to a matrix with a row of zeros.

8. If the matrix M is invertible, then how does $M^{-1}(MN)$ relate to N? What do you know about a product of invertible matrices? What can you conclude about N if you know that M and MN are invertible?

9. On the basis of Problem 8, show that $\det MN = 0$ if either M or N is not invertible.

10. Suppose that it is possible to row reduce the matrix M to a matrix with a row of zeros without ever using row i in the reduction. Explain why all three determinants in the statement of Theorem 11 are zero.

11. If there is some way to reduce the matrix M to a matrix with a row of zeros, then there are numbers $a_1, a_2, \ldots, a_n$ such that $a_1 R1 + a_2 R2 + \ldots + a_n Rn = 0$.
    (a) If $a_i \neq 0$, explain why we may reduce a to a matrix with row i equal to zero without adding row i to another row or exchanging row i with another row.
    (b) If $a_i \neq 0$, explain why the left- and right-hand determinants in Theorem 11 are equal while the middle determinant is zero.
    (c) If $a_i = 0$, explain why Problem 10 completes the proof of Theorem 11.

Chapter 10
Review Exercises

For Exercises 1–12 below, use the matrices

$$R = [1 \quad 0 \quad 1 \quad 1] \qquad S = [1 \quad -1 \quad -1 \quad 2] \qquad T = [1 \quad -2]$$

$$A = \begin{bmatrix} 1 & 4 \\ -3 & 0 \end{bmatrix} \qquad B = \begin{bmatrix} 1 & 0 & 0 & 1 \\ 0 & 2 & 2 & 4 \\ 0 & 0 & 1 & -1 \\ 0 & 0 & 0 & -1 \end{bmatrix} \qquad C = \begin{bmatrix} 1 \\ 3 \\ 0 \\ -1 \end{bmatrix}$$

$$0 = \begin{bmatrix} 0 & 0 \\ 0 & 0 \end{bmatrix}$$

$$D = \begin{bmatrix} -1 & 0 \\ 2 & 1 \end{bmatrix} \qquad E = \begin{bmatrix} 1 & 2 \\ 3 & 4 \end{bmatrix} \qquad I = \begin{bmatrix} 1 & 0 \\ 0 & 1 \end{bmatrix}$$

1. Find $R + S$, $2 \cdot R$, $-3 \cdot S$.

2. Find $A + E$.

3. Find $D(A + E)$ and $DA + DE$ and explain why we should expect the two results to be the same.

4. Find IE and EI.

5. Find $0E$ and $0 + E$.

6. Find $(SB)C$ and $S(BC)$ and explain why we should expect the results to be the same.

7. Find D^2. Find D^4. What will the entry in row 1 and column 2 of D^n be for any positive integer n?

8. Which of the matrix products SC, AB, $(A + E)C$, $(AD)E$, and AS are defined?

9. Find DE and ED. What general principle is illustrated by this computation?

10. Write down the 4-by-4 identity matrix and the product IC. What will the product IB be?

11. What is B_{32}? What is B_{23}? What is C_{31}?

12. Find the value of the following.

$$\sum_{k=1}^{2} A_{2k}E_{k1}$$

In which row and column of AE do we find this entry?

13. Write the system of equations below as a matrix equation.

$$\begin{array}{rcl} 2x_1 - 3x_2 + x_3 &=& -2 \\ 2x_1 - x_3 &=& 3 \\ 4x_1 - 5x_2 + 2x_3 &=& -3 \end{array}$$

14. Write down the matrix equation that corresponds to the system of equations consisting of the first 2 equations of Exercise 13.

15. Circle the pivotal entries in the matrices M and N that follow.

$$M = \begin{bmatrix} 0 & 1 & 2 & 0 & 0 \\ 0 & 0 & 0 & 1 & 3 \\ 0 & 0 & 0 & 0 & 0 \\ 0 & 0 & 0 & 0 & 1 \end{bmatrix} \qquad N = \begin{bmatrix} 2 & 3 & 0 & 4 & 1 \\ 0 & 1 & 6 & 0 & 0 \\ 0 & 0 & 0 & 1 & 3 \\ 1 & 2 & 3 & 0 & 1 \end{bmatrix}$$

16. Which, if any, of the matrices in Exercise 15 are row reduced?

17. Row reduce the matrices M and N that follow.

$$M = \begin{bmatrix} 2 & 0 & 4 & -2 \\ 1 & 3 & -1 & 2 \\ 0 & 1 & 2 & -2 \end{bmatrix} \qquad N = \begin{bmatrix} 2 & 0 & 4 & -2 \\ 1 & 3 & -1 & 2 \\ 0 & -1 & 1 & -1 \end{bmatrix}$$

18. Write the augmented matrices corresponding to the systems of equations below.

(a) $\begin{array}{rcl} 2x_1 + 4x_3 - 2x_4 &=& 2 \\ x_1 + 3x_2 - x_3 + 2x_4 &=& 7 \\ x_2 + 2x_3 - 2x_4 &=& 5 \end{array}$
     (b) $\begin{array}{rcl} 2x_1 + 4x_3 - 2x_4 &=& 2 \\ x_1 + 3x_2 - x_3 + 2x_4 &=& 7 \\ - x_2 + x_3 - x_4 &=& 1 \end{array}$

19. Row reduce the augmented matrices you wrote in Exercise 18.

20. Which variables are pivotal in the systems of equations corresponding to the two row reduced augmented matrices in Exercise 19?

21. Find all solutions to the two systems of equations in Exercise 18.

22. Solve the system of equations in Exercise 13 by row reducing an augmented matrix.

23. For each augmented matrix below, specify whether the system of equations corresponding to it has no solutions, one solution, or infinitely many solutions.

(a) $\begin{bmatrix} 1 & 0 & 0 & | & 1 \\ 0 & 1 & 2 & | & 6 \\ 0 & 0 & 0 & | & 3 \end{bmatrix}$
     (b) $\begin{bmatrix} 1 & 0 & 0 & | & 1 \\ 0 & 1 & 2 & | & 6 \\ 0 & 0 & 0 & | & 0 \end{bmatrix}$
     (c) $\begin{bmatrix} 1 & 0 & 0 & | & 1 \\ 0 & 1 & 0 & | & 2 \\ 0 & 0 & 1 & | & 3 \end{bmatrix}$

(d) $\begin{bmatrix} 1 & 0 & 0 & | & 1 \\ 0 & 0 & 1 & | & 2 \\ 0 & 1 & 0 & | & 3 \end{bmatrix}$
     (e) $\begin{bmatrix} 1 & 0 & | & 1 \\ 0 & 1 & | & 2 \\ 0 & 0 & | & 0 \end{bmatrix}$
     (f) $\begin{bmatrix} 1 & 0 & | & 1 \\ 0 & 1 & | & 2 \\ 0 & 0 & | & 3 \end{bmatrix}$

In Exercises 24–27, find all solutions to the system of equations given.

24.
$$x_1 + x_2 - x_3 = 0$$
$$x_1 + 2x_2 - x_3 = 2$$
$$-x_1 - 2x_2 + 3x_3 = 4$$

25.
$$2x_1 + 4x_2 + 2x_3 = 8$$
$$-x_1 - 2x_2 + x_3 = 2$$
$$2x_1 + 4x_2 = 2$$

26.
$$x_1 + x_2 - x_3 - 3x_4 = -1$$
$$-2x_1 - 4x_2 + x_3 + 3x_4 = 0$$
$$2x_1 + 4x_2 - 2x_3 - 6x_4 = -2$$

27.
$$2x_1 + 2x_2 - x_3 + x_4 = 3$$
$$x_1 + x_2 + x_3 + x_4 = 3$$
$$-3x_1 - 3x_2 + x_3 - x_4 = 3$$
$$x_1 + x_2 - 2x_3 + 2x_4 = 5$$

28. Write down the following 3-by-3 elementary matrices.
   (a) $E(3R2)$ (b) $E(-R3 + R2)$ (c) $E(3R3 + R1)$ (d) $E(R1 \leftrightarrow R3)$

29. Show the effect of multiplying each of the elementary matrices of Exercise 28 on the matrix.

$$M = \begin{bmatrix} 1 & 2 & 3 \\ 4 & 5 & 6 \\ 7 & 8 & 9 \end{bmatrix}$$

30. Write down the inverses of each of the elementary matrices in Exercise 28.

31. Show that the matrix M below has an inverse by finding a sequence of row operations that row reduces it to the identity.

$$M = \begin{bmatrix} 1 & 1 & -1 \\ 1 & 2 & -1 \\ -1 & -2 & 3 \end{bmatrix}$$

32. Show that the matrix N below does not have an inverse.

$$N = \begin{bmatrix} 1 & 2 & 1 \\ -1 & -2 & 1 \\ 2 & 4 & 0 \end{bmatrix}$$

33. Write down a sequence of elementary matrices whose product is the inverse of the matrix M in Exercise 31.

34. Write down the 3-by-6 augmented matrix you could row reduce in order to compute the inverse of the matrix M in Exercise 31.

35. Use row reduction to compute the inverse of the matrix M in Exercise 31.

36. Use the inverse matrix you computed in Exercise 35 to solve the system of equations in Exercise 24.

37. Determine whether the following matrices are invertible and find their inverses if they are.
   (a) $$M = \begin{bmatrix} 2 & 3 & 0 & 4 \\ 0 & 1 & 2 & 6 \\ 0 & 0 & 1 & 3 \\ 0 & 0 & 0 & -3 \end{bmatrix}$$ (b) $$N = \begin{bmatrix} 2 & 4 & 2 \\ 3 & -2 & 1 \\ 5 & 2 & 3 \end{bmatrix}$$ (c) $$P = \begin{bmatrix} 2 & 4 & 2 \\ 3 & -2 & 1 \\ 5 & 2 & 4 \end{bmatrix}$$

38. Find the determinants of the matrices D and E of Exercises 1–12.

39. Find the determinant of the matrix DE, using D and E from Exercise 38.

40. Find the determinant of the matrix B of Exercises 1–12.

41. Find the determinant of the matrix M of Exercise 29.

42. Find the determinant of the matrix P of Exercise 37.

43. A matrix is *lower triangular* if all the entries above its main diagonal (that is, all a_{ij} with $i < j$) are zero. Explain why the determinant of a lower triangular matrix with 1's on the main diagonal is 1.

44. Using the matrix B of Exercises 1–12 and the matrix M of Exercise 37, find detMB.

45. Using the matrices M and B of Exercise 44, find detMB^t and detM^tB.

46. Write down the transpose of the matrix P of Exercise 37.

47. Write down the 3-by-3 elementary column matrices specified.
(a) $E(3C1)$ (b) $E(2C1 + C2)$ (c) $E(C2 \leftrightarrow C3)$

48. Use any method you feel is appropriate to determine the determinant of the matrix M below. Is M invertible?

$$\begin{bmatrix} 0 & 1 & 4 & 3 & 0 \\ 2 & -1 & 3 & 5 & 8 \\ 0 & 3 & 2 & -3 & 3 \\ 0 & 4 & -2 & 0 & 0 \\ 0 & -5 & 1 & -2 & 1 \end{bmatrix}$$

49. Prove by induction that $\det(M_1 \cdot M_2 \cdot \ldots \cdot M_k) = \det M_1 \cdots \det M_k$.

In Exercises 50 and 51, draw the graph or multigraph whose adjacency matrix is given.

50.
$$\begin{bmatrix} 0 & 1 & 1 & 0 & 0 & 0 \\ 1 & 0 & 0 & 0 & 1 & 0 \\ 1 & 0 & 0 & 0 & 1 & 0 \\ 0 & 0 & 0 & 1 & 0 & 1 \\ 0 & 1 & 1 & 0 & 0 & 0 \\ 0 & 0 & 0 & 1 & 0 & 1 \end{bmatrix}$$

51.
$$\begin{bmatrix} 0 & 1 & 1 & 0 & 0 \\ 1 & 0 & 3 & 1 & 0 \\ 1 & 3 & 0 & 4 & 0 \\ 0 & 1 & 4 & 0 & 2 \\ 0 & 0 & 0 & 2 & 1 \end{bmatrix}$$

In Exercises 52 and 53, draw the digraph or multidigraph whose adjacency matrix is given.

52.
$$\begin{bmatrix} 0 & 1 & 0 & 1 & 0 \\ 0 & 0 & 1 & 0 & 0 \\ 0 & 0 & 0 & 0 & 1 \\ 0 & 0 & 1 & 0 & 1 \\ 0 & 0 & 0 & 0 & 0 \end{bmatrix}$$

53.
$$\begin{bmatrix} 0 & 3 & 1 & 0 \\ 1 & 0 & 2 & 0 \\ 3 & 1 & 0 & 0 \\ 1 & 0 & 3 & 0 \end{bmatrix}$$

54. Using matrix arithmetic, find the number of 4-edge walks from vertex 1 to vertex 2 and from vertex 1 to vertex 5 in the graph of Exercise 50. Explain from the drawing why one of these anwers is 0.

55. Use matrix arithmetic to determine which pairs of vertices in the digraph of Exercise 52 have walks of length 3 between them.

56. Use Warshall's algorithm to find the transitive closure of the relation of the graph in Exercise 50. What does this tell you about the connected components of the graph?

57. Use Warshall's algorithm to find the transitive closure of the digraph of Exercise 52. Use this to tell what vertices are reachable from each vertex of the digraph.

58. Regard the entries of the matrix of Exercise 51 as weights on edges of a graph and use Floyd's algorithm to find the distance between each two vertices in the graph.

59. Regard the entries of the matrix of Exercise 53 as weights on the edges of a digraph and use Floyd's algorithm to find the distance from each vertex to each vertex which can be reached from it.

*T*he goal of probability is to give numerical measurements of how likely a statement is to be true, how likely an event is to occur, or what we should expect the outcome of a process to be. We begin our study of probability by introducing the idea of a probability measure. When the so-called uniform measure is appropriate, our probabilities take a familiar form that is likely to be recognizable from school mathematics, and our earlier work with counting principles becomes useful again. By studying the idea of conditional probability, we learn how to determine when processes depend on each other and when they are independent of each other. One of the most fundamental kinds of processes for applications of probability is the independent trials process. From coin flipping to test taking to testing memory chips, a common thread allows us to use our earlier work with binomial coefficients for efficient computation of the probabilities of significant events.

In many applications of probability, the concept of the expected value of a random variable is important. For example, in computer science, we are interested in how long a program should be expected to take (on the average) and in how much computer memory it should be expected to use. We develop enough of the theory of expected values to show, for example, that we expect insertion sort to be twice as fast as selection sort and that the expected number of comparisons made (on the average) to locate an item in a binary search tree with n entries is $O(\log_2(n))$. We conclude our discussion of expected values with a study of how different we should expect common random variables to be from their expected values, as well as a brief study of a fundamental cornerstone of statistics, the central limit theorem, and its applications to such topics as predicting performance on tests and predicting the amount of space needed for a database.

We then take up Markov chains, which are models for more sophisticated kinds of processes such as machines that represent idealized versions of a computer. Here we discover that our knowledge of matrix algebra comes in handy, for the fundamental expected values of interest to us are found by inverting an appropriate matrix.

Probability is important not only because it provides models of fundamental processes, but also because it is the foundation for statistical analysis and for discussing such concepts as the average running time of an algorithm.

Section 11-1
The Basic Concepts

◪ The Definition of Probability

Probability allows us to analyze statements that may be true statements about some elements of a universe and false statements about other elements of this universe, in order to determine how likely the statements are to be true. In one application, the universe might consist of all possible sets of inputs to an algorithm we are studying, and the statement might be about the number of computational steps used by the algorithm when it gets a certain input. In another application, the universe might consist of all possible patterns of answers to a multiple-choice test, and the statement might be about the number of questions a student could answer correctly. With a careful analysis of such situations, we can often use the methods of probability not just to decide how likely a certain outcome is, but also to decide that we should expect a certain outcome. For example, we might be able to show that we should expect a certain sorting algorithm to make $n(n - 1)/4$ interchanges with n data items, or we should expect a student who has not yet learned anything to get a grade of 50% on a true-false test. Fortunately, most of what we will learn about probability can be illustrated by simple examples of everyday processes such as flipping coins. This will make our examples more intuitive and easier to follow. We shall indicate some of the practical applications in the exercises and in some of the examples in the later sections.

Sample Spaces and Events

Since many of the early applications of probability were in laboratory experiments, when we use probability to analyze a process, the process itself is called an **experiment.** The universe of outcomes of the experiment is called the **sample space** of the experiment. Thus statements we make about the experiment are statements about the sample space.

The truth set of a statement is called an **event**.

Notice that we have defined an event to be a subset of the sample space.

EXAMPLE 1   Consider the experiment of flipping a coin three times. Represent each possible outcome as a list of three letters, each H or T. Write out the event E corresponding to the statement "Heads come up exactly twice."

Solution   An appropriate sample space is the set of all sequences of three H's or T's:

$$S = \{HHH, HHT, HTH, THH, THT, TTH, HTT, TTT\}$$

The event E will consist of the lists with exactly two H's:

$$E = \{HHT, HTH, THH\}$$

Notice that the event E consists of all circumstances that make its statement "Heads come up exactly twice" true.   ■

Before we define the word *probability*, we will define the special term *probability weight*. When we do define probability, we shall first assign probabilities to events (that is, sets) and then define the probability of a statement to be the probability of its truth set. In this way, we may guarantee that equivalent statements (those having the same truth set) will have equal probabilities.

Probability Weights

Before we begin to apply probability theory to the analysis of a certain process or experiment, we assign to each possible outcome x in the sample space S a real number $p(x)$, called a **probability weight**. The assignment is supposed to reflect the likelihood that this potential outcome will occur. The assignment of numbers must satisfy two conditions. First, for each outcome x, $p(x)$ must be a number between 0 and 1. In symbols, we assume that

$$0 \leq p(x) \leq 1$$

Second, the sum of all the assignments we have made (the sum of the weights) must be 1. If $S = \{x_1, x_2, \ldots, x_n\}$, we may write this second assumption as

$$\sum_{i=1}^{n} p(x_i) = 1$$

So that we don't have infinitely many weights to add, we assume that our sample space S is finite.

EXAMPLE 2   In discussing the experiment of flipping a coin once, our sample space is the set {H,T}. What numbers should we assign to the two outcomes as probability weights?

Solution   For a typical coin, we expect heads and tails to be equally likely. In symbols, we expect $p(H) = p(T)$. Since these two numbers must add to 1 (in symbols, $p(T) + p(H) = 1$), the only way to choose these numbers is the only way to solve the two equations $p(H) = p(T)$ and $p(T) + p(H) = 1$, namely

$$p(H) = \frac{1}{2}; \, p(T) = \frac{1}{2}$$ ■

EXAMPLE 3   Decide how to assign probability weights to the sequences of three H's and T's in Example 1.

Solution   It is natural to assume that each sequence is just as likely as each other sequence. Since we have eight sequences, the only way to assign eight equal probability weights that add to 1 is to choose each weight to be $\frac{1}{8}$.   ■

EXAMPLE 4   A student has learned to recognize the artists responsible for 80% of the slides presented in an art history course. What probabilities should we assign to the two outcomes "knows the artist" and "doesn't know the artist" for a slide chosen at random from among those presented?

Solution   Let us use K for "knows the artist" and D for "doesn't know the artist." Our sample space is thus $\{K,D\}$. To reflect the fact that the student knows the artist for 80% of the slides, we would naturally choose $p(K) = 0.8$ and $p(D) = 0.2$.   ■

As the three examples suggest, the choice of the weights assigned to the individual outcomes is one we make on the basis of our intuition. The only guidance we get from the laws of probability is that we must choose non-negative numbers whose sum is 1. After we have assigned probability weights, we can begin to apply the probability theory we shall develop.

The Definition of Probability

Remember that an event is simply the truth set of a statement, so it is a *set* of outcomes $s_1, s_2, \ldots, s_k$ chosen from the sample space.

We define the **probability** $P(E)$ of an event
$E = \{s_1, s_2, \ldots, s_k\}$ to be the sum
of the probability weights of its outcomes.

In symbols,

$$P(E) = \sum_{i=1}^{k} p(s_i)$$

Notice that E could be a one-element set $\{x\}$, in which case $s_1 = x$ and we get

$$P(\{x\}) = \sum_{i=1}^{1} p(s_i) = p(s_1) = p(x)$$

E could also be empty; we define $P(\varnothing)$ to be 0. P is a function defined on subsets of the sample space; it is called a **probability measure**. This definition may lead you to the question: "This definition tells me how to compute a probability; what does the word probability really *mean*?" The answer is that an interpretation of the meaning of the word probability comes from a study of examples and properties of probability measures. We begin such a study now.

EXAMPLE 5   In the experiment consisting of three flips of a coin in Examples 1 and 3, compute the probabilities of the events "Two heads occur," "Three heads occur," and "Four heads occur."

Solution   The event "Two heads occur" is the set $E = \{HHT, HTH, THH\}$ of Example 1. Its probability is $\frac{1}{8} + \frac{1}{8} + \frac{1}{8} = \frac{3}{8}$. The event "Three heads occur" is the set $\{HHH\}$, and its probability is $\frac{1}{8}$. The event "Four heads occur" is the empty set (that is, it is impossible), and, as above, $P(\varnothing) = 0$.   ■

B   The Uniform Measure

In many of our examples, we are able to assign equal weight to each outcome in the sample space. For instance, we assigned the same weight to each outcome in the experiment of flipping a coin once, and we assigned the same weight to each outcome in the experiment of flipping a coin three times. On the other hand, in the experiment of identifying the painter whose painting appears on a slide, we assigned different weights to the different outcomes "correct" and "incorrect."

Equiprobable Weights and the Uniform Measure

When we assign the same weight to each element of a sample space, we say we are using the **equiprobable weighting function.**

> The probability measure corresponding to the equiprobable weighting function is called the **equiprobable measure** or **uniform probability measure.**

Sometimes we have a choice of several sample spaces that are appropriate for the discussion of a certain experiment. Our first theorem in probability shows that choosing a sample space for which the equiprobable measure is appropriate makes the computation of probabilities easier.

Theorem 1   Let S be a sample space and let P be the uniform probability measure defined on S. Then for any event E, $P(E) = |E|/|S|$, the ratio of the size of E to the size of S.

Proof   Suppose the weight $p(x)$ of each x is p. When we add up all the weights of all the outcomes in the sample space S, we add together $|S|$ numbers each equal to p, so we get $|S| \cdot p$. Since the sum of all the weights of all the outcomes in S must be 1, we get

$$|S|p = 1 \qquad \text{or} \qquad p = \frac{1}{|S|}$$

Then, by substituting p for $p(s_i)$ and then $\frac{1}{|S|}$ for p in the sum below, we find that if $E = \{s_1, s_2, \ldots, s_k\}$, then $|E| = k$ and

$$P(E) = \sum_{i=1}^{k} p(s_i) = kp = |E|p = \frac{|E|}{|S|} \qquad \blacksquare$$

EXAMPLE 6   What is the probability of an odd number of heads in three tosses of a coin?

Solution   Using the sample space of Example 1, we see that there are three sequences with one H and one sequence with three H's. Thus we have four sequences in the event of "an odd number of heads come up." There are eight sequences in the sample space, so the probability is $\frac{4}{8} = \frac{1}{2}$. $\blacksquare$

A word of caution is appropriate here. Theorem 1 applies only to probabilities that come from the equiprobable weighting function. The next example shows that it does not apply in general.

EXAMPLE 7   A sample space consists of the numbers 0, 1, 2, and 3. We assign weight $\frac{1}{8}$ to 0, $\frac{3}{8}$ to 1, $\frac{3}{8}$ to 2, and $\frac{1}{8}$ to 3. What is the probability that an element of the sample space is positive? Show that this is not the result we would obtain by using the formula of Theorem 1.

Solution   The truth set of "x is positive" is the event $E = \{1,2,3\}$. The probability of E is

$$P(E) = p(1) + p(2) + p(3) = \frac{3}{8} + \frac{3}{8} + \frac{1}{8} = \frac{7}{8}$$

However, $\frac{|E|}{|S|} = \frac{3}{4}$. $\blacksquare$

Example 7 may seem to be "cooked up" in an unusual way just to prove a point. In fact, that simple space and that probability measure could easily arise in studying something as simple as coin flipping.

EXAMPLE 8   Use the set $\{0,1,2,3\}$ as a sample space for the process of flipping a coin three times and counting the number of heads. Determine the appropriate probability weights $p(0)$, $p(1)$, $p(2)$, and $p(3)$.

Solution There is one way to get the outcome 0—tails on each flip—but there are three ways to get 1 head and three ways to get 2 heads. Thus $p(1)$ and $p(2)$ should each be three times $p(0)$. There is one way to get the outcome 3—heads on each flip. Thus $p(3)$ should equal $p(0)$. We can see that this gives the weights in Example 7, but we can also write down equations we can solve to get the weights, a method likely to be useful in more complicated situations. In equations, our remarks become $p(1) = 3p(0)$, $p(2) = 3p(0)$, and $p(3) = p(0)$. We also have the equation saying that all the weights add to 1, $p(0) + p(1) + p(2) + p(3) = 1$. There is one and only one solution to these equations, $p(0) = \frac{1}{8}$, $p(1) = \frac{3}{8}$, $p(2) = \frac{3}{8}$, and $p(3) = \frac{1}{8}$. ∎

Together, Example 7 and Example 8 demonstrate that we must be careful not to apply Theorem 1 unless we are using the uniform probability measure.

Applications of Counting Techniques to Uniform Probabilities

When a problem lets us use a sample space with the equiprobable measure, the counting techniques we used in Chapter 6 allow us to compute complicated probabilities with ease. The next two examples show how some of our basic counting techniques may be used. They both concern an ordinary deck of playing cards. Such a deck consists of 52 cards, divided into four groups or suits of 13 cards each, called *clubs, diamonds, hearts,* and *spades*. Each suit contains one card each marked with the numbers 2 through 10 and one card each marked with the names *jack, queen, king,* and *ace*.

EXAMPLE 9 Using 5-element sets as a sample space, determine the probability that a "hand" of 5 cards chosen from an ordinary deck of 52 cards will consist of cards of the same suit.

Solution The sample space S consists of all 5-element sets chosen from a 52-element set. Recall that a 52-element set has $\binom{52}{5}$ subsets of size 5; $\binom{52}{5}$ may be computed from either formula

$$\frac{(52)_5}{5!} \quad \text{or} \quad \frac{52!}{5! \cdot 47!}$$

giving

$$|S| = \binom{52}{5} = \frac{(52)_5}{5!} = \frac{52 \cdot 51 \cdot 50 \cdot 49 \cdot 48}{5 \cdot 4 \cdot 3 \cdot 4 \cdot 2 \cdot 1}$$

The event E of "All cards have the same suit" will consist of all 5-element sets chosen from either the 13-element set of clubs, the 13-element set of diamonds, the 13-element set of hearts, or the 13-element set of spades. Thus the size of E is given by

$$|E| = 4\binom{13}{5} = 4\frac{(13)_5}{5!} = 4\frac{13\cdot12\cdot11\cdot10\cdot9}{5\cdot4\cdot3\cdot2\cdot1}$$

This gives

$$P(E) = \frac{|E|}{|S|} = 4\frac{13\cdot12\cdot11\cdot10\cdot9}{52\cdot51\cdot50\cdot49\cdot48} = .002 \text{ (approximately)} \quad\blacksquare$$

EXAMPLE 10   Using 5-element permutations as a sample space, determine the probability that a "hand" of 5 cards chosen from an ordinary deck of 52 cards will have all the cards from the same suit.

Solution   The sample space will consist of all 5-element permutations chosen from 52 elements, so using the formula

$$(52)_5 = \frac{52!}{(52-5)!}$$

for the number of 5-element permutations of a 52-element set, we get

$$|S| = 52\cdot51\cdot50\cdot49\cdot48$$

Now the event E will consist of all 5-element permutations chosen from one of the four suits of 13 cards each, so

$$|E| = 4(13)_5 = 4(13\cdot12\cdot11\cdot10\cdot9)$$

Thus

$$P(E) = \frac{|E|}{|S|} = \frac{4(13\cdot12\cdot11\cdot10\cdot9)}{52\cdot51\cdot50\cdot49\cdot48}$$

just as before. $\blacksquare$

The examples show us that more than one sample space can be appropriate for a certain kind of problem. However, once you choose a sample space, you should be careful to use it consistently.

◰ *Properties of a Probability Measure*

Several properties of probability measures simplify quite a few computations. We shall state each one as a theorem for future reference and give examples of how they are used.

Mutually Exclusive Events

Suppose we need to determine the probability that a student who had not yet studied a subject would get a grade of 90 or 100 on a ten-question true-false diagnostic test. A natural approach is to add the probability of exactly nine correct answers to the probability of exactly ten correct answers. The event E of getting nine correct answers and the event F of getting ten correct answers are mutually exclusive, which is another way to say $E \cap F = \emptyset$. Theorem 2 tells us that this means we *may* solve our problem by adding the probabilities.

Theorem 2   For a probability measure P on a finite sample space S, if $E \cap F = \emptyset$, then $P(E \cup F) = P(E) + P(F)$.

Proof   Since E and F have no elements in common, adding up all the weights of elements in E and all the weights of elements in F and then adding these numbers together is the same as adding up all the weights of all the elements in $E \cup F$. This proves the formula. The Venn diagram in Figure 1 helps us visualize this proof.   ∎

Figure 1 E is shaded in gray and F is shaded in color. The total weight of the shaded region may be found by adding the total weight of the gray region to the total weight of the colored region. Notice that E and F are disjoint sets.

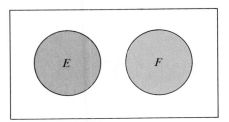

EXAMPLE 11   Using the sample space of Example 1, apply Theorem 2 to find the probability of two or three heads in three flips of a coin.

Solution   The event "two heads" is the set $\{HHT, HTH, THH\} = E$, and the set "three heads" is $\{HHH\} = F$. These two sets are disjoint and have probabilities $\frac{3}{8}$ and $\frac{1}{8}$, respectively, so $P(E \cup F) = P(E) + P(F) = \frac{3}{8} + \frac{1}{8} = \frac{1}{2}$ is the probability of two heads *or* three heads.   ∎

Overlapping Events

Of course, we may be interested in the probability of one or both of two events that are not mutually exclusive. In flipping a coin several times, for example, we may be interested in the probability that we have two heads or that heads comes up first. The Venn diagram in Figure 2 suggests how we should compute the probability of a union of overlapping events.

Figure 2   The total weight of the shaded region is the sum of total weight of the gray-only shaded region, the total weight of the doubly-shaded region, and the total weight of the color-only shaded region.

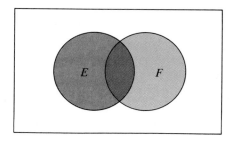

Theorem 3   For any probability measure P on a finite sample space S and for any two events E and F

$$P(E \cup F) = P(E) + P(F) - P(E \cap F) \tag{1}$$

Proof   From our study of sets, we know that if we let E' stand for $E \sim (E \cap F)$ and F' stand for $F \sim (E \cap F)$, then

$$E \cup F = E' \cup (E \cap F) \cup F'$$

and the three sets E', $E \cap F$, and F' are mutually exclusive. Thus by Theorem 2,

$$P(E \cup F) = P(E') + P(E \cap F) + P(F') \tag{2}$$

Also by Theorem 2, $P(E) = P(E') + P(E \cap F)$ and $P(F) = P(F') + P(E \cap F)$. Therefore, $P(E) + P(F) = P(E') + 2P(E \cap F) + P(F')$. Subtracting $P(E \cap F)$ from both sides and substituting the result into (2) gives Equation (1).   ■

EXAMPLE 12   Compute the probability that in three flips of a coin, there are two heads or the first flip comes up heads.

Solution   The event $E = \{HHT, HTH, THH\}$ is the event of two heads, and the event $F = \{HHH, HHT, HTH, HTT\}$ is the event of heads on the first flip. $E \cap F$ is the set $\{HHT, HTH\}$, so Equation (1) gives

$$\begin{aligned}
P(E \cup F) &= P(E) + P(F) - P(E \cap F) \\
&= \frac{3}{8} + \frac{4}{8} - \frac{2}{8} \\
&= \frac{5}{8}
\end{aligned}$$

■

EXAMPLE 13   Compute the probability of $E \cup F$ in Example 12 from the definition to verify the formula of Theorem 3 in this case.

Solution   Since $E \cup F = \{HHH, HHT, HTH, HTT, THH\}$ and each element of $E \cup F$ has weight $\frac{1}{8}$, $P(E \cup F)$ is $\frac{5}{8}$.   ∎

Complementary Probabilities

Our final property of a probability measure tells us how to compute the probability of the complement $S \sim E$ of an event E. The probabilities of E and $S \sim E$ are called **complementary probabilities.** The Venn diagram in Figure 3 suggests that the sum of these two possibilities is the probability of the universe S, which is 1.

Figure 3   Notice that $E \cap \sim E = \varnothing$ and $E \cup \sim E = S$, the universe.

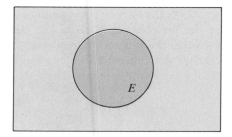

Theorem 4   For any probability measure P on a finite sample space S, $P(S \sim E) = 1 - P(E)$.

Proof   Since E and $S \sim E$ are two disjoint sets whose union is S, Theorem 2 gives us $P(S \sim E) + P(E) = P(S) = 1$. Subtraction then gives the formula $P(S \sim E) = 1 - P(E)$.   ∎

Whenever you face a good deal of work in computing a probability, it is wise to ask whether Theorem 4 would simplify the process.

EXAMPLE 14   What is the probability of at least two heads in ten flips of a coin?

Solution   It appears that we must add the probabilities of two, three, four, . . . up to ten heads in ten flips of a coin. However, if E is the event of two or more heads, then $S \sim E$ is the event of zero or one heads. Thus the probability of $S \sim E$ is easier to compute. We use the uniform measure on sequences of ten H's and T's. There are 2^{10} such sequences. The probability of 0 heads is $\frac{1}{2^{10}}$ (since there is one outcome with no H's), and that of one head is $\frac{10}{2^{10}}$ (since the one head can be on any of the ten flips). Thus, the probability of $S \sim E$ is $\frac{11}{2^{10}}$, and that of E is, by Theorem 4,

$$1 - \frac{11}{2^{10}} = \frac{1013}{1024}$$ ∎

A professor teaching probability will sometimes walk into a class of, say, 50 students and announce, "I'll bet even money that two people in this class have the same birthday." With just 50 people in the class and 365 days in the year, this may seem to be a good bet for the students.

EXAMPLE 15   Determine the probability that two people in a class have the same birthday if there are 20, 25, or 50 students in the class.

Solution   If E is the event that (at least) two people have the same birthday, then $S \sim E$ is the event that all the birthdays are different. There is a function from the students to the days of the year that assigns to each student his or her birthday. We use the possible functions as our sample space. With n students, there are 365^n such functions (ignoring leap years). A function will belong to the event that all birthdays are different if it is a one-to-one function. There are $P(365,n) = 365!/(365 - n)!$ such functions. Thus

$$P(S \sim E) = \frac{P(365,n)}{365^n} = \frac{365 \cdot 364 \cdots (365 - n + 1)}{365^n}$$

This is inconvenient to compute by hand but easy with a computer. When n is 20, 25, and 50, we get $P(S \sim E) = 0.590174, 0.432481$, and 0.00296264. Thus when n is 20, 25, and 50, Theorem 4 gives us $P(E) = 0.41, 0.57$, and 0.997, approximately. With 20 students per class, the professor will expect to win 41% of the time; with 25 students, the professor will win 57% of the time; and with 50 students, the professor will expect to win 99.7% of the time. The students in a 50-person class would be unwise to accept this wager! ∎

Concepts Review

1. In probability theory, the universe of possible outcomes of an experiment is called the _____ _____.

2. A subset of the sample space is called a(n) _____ because it is the truth set of a statement about an experiment.

3. The sum of the probability weights assigned to the elements of a sample space is _____.

4. The _____ of an event is the sum of the weights of its outcomes.

5. The _____ measure on a sample space assigns the same weight to each outcome.

6. The probability of one or the other (or perhaps both) of the events E and F is given by $P(E \cup F) = $ _____.

7. If E is an event in a sample space S with the equiprobable weight function, then $P(E) = $ _____.

8. The sum of $P(E)$ and $P(S \sim E)$ is _____.

Exercises

A

1. For the experiment of flipping a coin four times, we can represent a particular result as a sequence of four H's and T's. Write out the elements of the sample space for this experiment.

2. A penny, a nickel, a dime, and a quarter are placed in a cup, and a first coin and second coin are drawn. (The first coin is *not* replaced before the second is drawn. This is an example of what probabilists call *sampling without replacement*.) Write down the sample space of all ordered pairs of letters *P, N, D,* and *Q* that represent the outcomes.

3. Two dice are rolled, first one and then the other. Using the ordered pair (i,j) to stand for i dots on the first die and j dots on the second, write out the sample space of all possible outcomes.

4. A penny, a nickel, a dime, and a quarter are placed in a cup as in Exercise 2. One coin is taken out, examined, and put back. Then a coin is drawn once more. (This is what probabilists call *sampling with replacement*.) Write down the sample space of all ordered pairs of letters *P, N, D,* and *Q* that represent the outcomes.

5. The ace, king, queen, and jack of spades are withdrawn from a deck of playing cards.
   (a) Two of these four cards are dealt out, one on top of another. Write down the sample space of all ordered pairs of letters *A, K, Q,* and *J* that represent the outcomes.
   (b) Suppose the cards are withdrawn simultaneously. Write down the sample space of all two-element sets of letters representing the outcomes.

6. Two pennies, a nickel, and a dime are placed in a cup, and a first coin and a second coin are drawn.
   (a) Assuming we are sampling without replacement as in Exercise 2, write down the sample space of all ordered pairs of letters *P, N,* and *D* that represent the outcomes.

     (b) Suppose the coins are withdrawn simultaneously. Write down the sample space of all unordered pairs (two-element multisets) representing the outcomes.

7. Three red checkers and two black checkers are placed in a cup, and two are removed.
     (a) Using ordered pairs of *R*'s and *B*'s, write down the sample space of possible results.
     (b) Using unordered pairs (two-element multisets) of *R*'s and *B*'s, write down the sample space of possible results.

8. A student is taking three courses, each of which is graded Honors, Pass, or Fail.
     (a) Write down the ordered triples of *H*, *P*, and *F* representing the grades the student can get in each of the three courses.
     (b) Write down the three-element multisets representing the combinations of grades the student can get, ignoring which grade goes with which course.

9. For the sample space of Exercise 1, write out the following events.
     (a) At least 3 heads come up.
     (b) An even number of tails come up.
     (c) There are more heads than tails.
     (d) The first two flips are heads.

10. For the sample space of Exercise 2, write out the following events.
     (a) One coin is a penny.
     (b) The first coin is the penny.
     (c) The second coin is more valuable than the first coin.
     (d) Both coins are silver in color.

11. Assign equal weight to each outcome in the sample space in Exercise 1. What should this weight be? Compute the probability of each event in Exercise 9.

12. Assign equal weight to each outcome in the sample space in Exercise 2 and compute the probability of each event in Exercise 10.

13. For each sample space in Exercise 5, decide on the weight function that best reflects your estimate of how likely each outcome is.

14. For each sample space in Exercise 6, decide on the weight function that best reflects your estimate of how likely each outcome is.

15. For each sample space in Exercise 7, decide on the weight function that best reflects your estimate of how likely each outcome is.

16. Assume that the student of Exercise 8 is equally likely to get a passing or honors grade in any course but is only half as likely to get a failing grade. What weighting function for each sample space of Exercise 8 best fits these assumptions?

17. For the sample space from Exercise 7 given below and the weight function in Exercise 15, compute the probability of each of the following events.
     (a) Sample space (a). Event: At least one checker is red.
     (b) Sample space (b). Event: At least one checker is red.
     (c) Sample space (a). Event: The first checker is red.
     (d) Sample space (b). Event: Both checkers have the same color.

18. For the sample space from Exercise 8 given below and the weight function in Exercise 16, compute the probability of each of the following events.
     (a) Sample space (a). Event: The student gets at least one honors grade.

(b) Sample space (b). Event: The student gets at least one honors grade.
(c) Sample space (a). Event: The student fails nothing.
(d) Sample space (b). Event: The student fails nothing.

B 19. Use the fact that there are $\binom{10}{5}$ ways to have five heads in ten flips of a coin to show that the probability of five heads in ten flips of a coin is $\frac{63}{256}$.

20. Use the fact that there are $\binom{10}{6}$ ways to have six heads in ten flips of a coin to show that the probability of six heads in ten flips of a coin is $\frac{105}{512}$.

21. The face cards (jack, queen, and king) of all four suits are removed from a deck of cards. Six of these twelve cards are black. If we draw two cards from these twelve, what is the probability that both are black?

22. The honor cards (ten, jack, queen, king, and ace) of all four suits are removed from a deck of cards. Ten of these twenty cards are red. If we draw three cards from these twenty, what is the probability that all three are red?

23. How many 13-card hands chosen from a standard deck of playing cards contain all 4 aces? What is the probability of a 13-card hand with all 4 aces? (Use 13-element subsets as hands.)

24. How many five-card hands chosen from a standard deck of playing cards consist of five cards in a row (such as the nine of diamonds, the ten of clubs, jack of clubs, queen of hearts, and king of spades)? Such a hand is called a *straight*. What is the probability that a five-card hand is a straight? (Use five-element subsets as hands.)

25. Two dice are rolled. Find the probability that the total number of dots facing up on the two dice is five. Find the probability that the total number of dots facing up is odd.

26. Two dice are rolled once. Find the probability that the total number of dots facing up is 12, is 13, and is even.

27. The clubs, diamonds, hearts, and spades of an ordinary deck of cards are separated from each other into four piles, and one card is taken from each pile. For which (if any) of the sample spaces below is the equiprobable measure appropriate? Explain why or why not.
(a) Four-tuples whose entries are the numbers 2 through 10 or one of the letters J, Q, K, or A.
(b) Four-element multisets whose elements are the numbers 2 through 10 or one of the letters J, Q, K, or A.

28. I have a nickel, a dime, and a quarter in both my left pocket and my right pocket. I put one hand in each pocket and withdraw a coin from each pocket. For which (if any) of the sample spaces below is the equiprobable measure appropriate? Explain why or why not.
(a) Ordered pairs whose entries are chosen from $\{N,D,Q\}$.
(b) Two-element multisets chosen from $\{N,D,Q\}$.

29. Two nickels, one dime, and one quarter are in a cup, and two coins are drawn out. In which (if any) of the sample spaces below is the equiprobable measure appropriate? Explain why or why not.
    (a) The sample space consists of ordered pairs of letters standing for coins.
    (b) The sample space consists of two-element multisets of letters standing for coins.

30. Three red checkers and two black checkers are in a cup, and two checkers are drawn out. For which (if any) of the sample spaces below is the equiprobable measure appropriate? Explain why or why not.
    (a) Ordered pairs of the letters *R* and *B*.
    (b) Two-element multisets of the letters *R* and *B*.

C 31. A student taking a ten-question, true-false diagnostic test knows none of the answers and must guess at each answer. Compute the probability that the student gets a score of 80, 90, or 100.

32. Compute the probability that the total number of dots facing up when we roll two dice is six, seven, or eight.

33. In three flips of a coin, what is the probability that the coin comes up heads on the first flip or comes up heads on the last flip?

34. The eight kings and queens are removed from a deck of cards, and then two of these cards are selected. What is the probability that the king or the queen of spades is among the cards selected?

35. A quarter, a dime, and a nickel are in a cup. A coin is selected and returned, and then a second coin is selected. What is the probability that (at least) one of the coins selected is a quarter?

36. Two dice are rolled. What is the probability that (at least) one of them has s   dots on top?

37. The four aces are removed from an ordinary deck of playing cards, and then two cards are selected. Using complementary probabilities, find the probability that one of them is black (that is, a club or spade).

38. A student takes a ten-question true-false test and has to guess at each answer. Using complementary probabilities, determine the probability that the student's score is 70 or less.

39. Find a formula for the probability that two people in a given group of n people have birthdays in the same month. (Assume that a birthday is equally likely to be in any month.) How many people must be in the group for this probability to be at least $\frac{1}{2}$? For it to be at least $\frac{3}{4}$? For it to be 1?

40. Find the probability that if each of n people is to choose a prize from a group of ten equally desirable prizes, two will chose the same prize. How large must n be for this probability to be at least $\frac{1}{2}$? At least $\frac{3}{4}$? To be 1?

41. Show that if you roll a die twice, the probability that the first roll has an odd number of dots on top is $\frac{1}{2}$. Show that the probability that the sum of the number of dots on top in the two rolls is odd is $\frac{1}{2}$. What is the probability that the first roll is odd *and* the sum is odd? What is the probability that either the first roll or the sum (or both) is odd?

42. A bowl contains two red, two white, and two blue balls. We remove two balls. By using the probability that both are blue, find the probability that at least one is red or white. Find (directly) the probability that one is red and one is white. Note that the probability that at least one is red equals the probability that at least one is white. Using the other probabilities you have computed, compute the probability that at least one is red.

Problems

1. A die is made of a cube with a square painted on one side, a circle on two sides, and a triangle on three sides. If the die is rolled twice, what is the probability that the two shapes we see on top are the same?

2. Show that if E, F, and G are three events, then

$$P(E \cup F \cup G) =$$
$$P(E) + P(F) + P(G) - P(E \cap F) - P(E \cap G) - P(F \cap G) + P(E \cap F \cap G)$$

3. The *odds in favor* of an event with probability p are $m{:}n$ (which we read as "m to n") if $\dfrac{m}{n} = \dfrac{p}{1-p}$. Show that if we have a sample space S with an equiprobable measure, then the odds in favor of an event E are $|E|{:}|S - E|$.

4. Notice that $9 = 1 + 2 + 6 = 1 + 3 + 5 = 1 + 4 + 4 = 2 + 2 + 5 = 2 + 3 + 4 = 3 + 3 + 3$ is a list of the six ways to write 9 as a sum of three numbers between 1 and 6. Similarly, we can find six ways to write 10 as a list of three numbers. Why is it that the probability that the sum of the tops of three dice is nine and the probability that the sum of the tops of three dice is ten aren't equal?

5. Explain why the probability of any event whatsoever can never be less than zero or larger than 1.

6. Use the formula we developed in Chapter 6 for the number of functions from one set onto another to give a formula for the probability that with n people in a room, every month is someone's birth month. (Assume that all birth months are equally likely.)

7. Use the principle of inclusion and exclusion to find the probability that if n letters addressed to n people are shuffled and randomly placed in envelopes addressed to the same n people, then no letter is in the proper envelope.

8. Use calculus (power series) to show that the probability you computed in Problem 7 approaches $\frac{1}{e}$ as n increases. Use the concept of the remainder term of a Taylor polynomial to estimate the number of digits of accuracy when $\frac{1}{e}$ is used as an approximation to the probability with $n = 10$.

9. Which is more likely, or are both equally likely?
   (a) Drawing an ace and a king when you draw 2 cards from among the 13 spades or drawing an ace and a king when you draw 2 cards from a deck?
   (b) Drawing an ace and a king of the same suit when you draw 2 cards from a deck or drawing an ace and a king when you draw 2 cards from among the 13 spades?

10. Discuss the appropriateness of using the equiprobable measure on 10-element multisets chosen from a 6-element set for the following problem. If 10 identical apples are passed out to 6 children, what is the probability that each child receives at least one?

Section 11-2
Conditional Probability
and Independence

A Conditional Probability

Conditional probability tells us how the occurrence of one event influences the probabilities of another. Let us begin with an example in which we consider only one event and then extend it to one event influencing another.

EXAMPLE 16   In a certain state, there are five candidates for governor. Their names, parties, and sex are given in Table 1. A newspaper publishes a weekly interview with one of the candidates. What is the probability that the candidate is Republican? What is the probability that the candidate is a Republican male?

Table 1	Name:	Smithers	Gonzales	Patel	alFazar	Williams
	Party:	*R*	*D*	*R*	*R*	*D*
	Sex:	*M*	*F*	*F*	*M*	*M*

Solution   Our sample space is the set $\{S,G,P,aF,W\}$ of candidates. We assume that the newspaper is equally likely to interview any of them, so since there are 5 candidates, each has weight $\frac{1}{5} = 0.2$. The event that the candidate is a Republican has three elements of weight 0.2 and so has probability 0.6. The event that the candidate is a Republican male is the intersection of the set R of Republicans and the set $M = \{S,aF,W\}$ of males. This intersection is the set $\{S,aF\}$, so the probability that the interviewee is a Republican male is $.2 + .2 = .4$. ■

Construction of a New Sample Space

With this example, let us see how the occurrence of one event can affect another.

EXAMPLE 17   The newspaper decides to alternate the interviews between men and women. Given that the first interviewee is a man, what is the probability that this interviewee is Republican?

Solution   We may use the information given to change to a more appropriate sample space, the set $M = \{S,aF,W\}$ of males. This is shown in Figure 4. Since each candidate was equally likely to be interviewed in the original sample space, we expect each candidate to be equally likely to be interviewed in the new sample

Figure 4

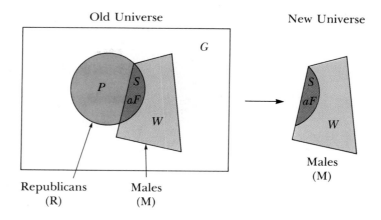

Old Universe

New Universe

Republicans
(R)

Males
(M)

Males
(M)

space. Thus we assign each candidate weight $\frac{1}{3}$ in the new space, and now the probability of a Republican is the new probability of the set $\{S, aF\}$, which is $\frac{1}{3} + \frac{1}{3} = \frac{2}{3}$.   ∎

It would be unfortunate if we always needed to construct new sample spaces with new weights each time we wanted to analyze this type of situation. We will see a pattern that saves us from most of this work if we analyze an example in which the candidates no longer have equal weights.

EXAMPLE 18   The newspaper has taken a poll and estimates the probabilities shown in Table 2 for each candidate's election. If the governor turns out to be a male, what is the probability that he is Republican?

Table 2

Candidate:	Smithers	Gonzales	Patel	alFazar	Williams
Probability:	0.1	0.3	0.2	0.1	0.3

Solution   Once again, our new sample space is $\{S, aF, W\} = M$. In Figure 5, we show the original sample space with its probability weights and then show this new sample space. However, it is not clear immediately what probability measure to use with this new sample space. We can't just copy the probabilities from the left side of Figure 5 to the right side, because the probabilities in the set M add up to 0.5, and the probabilities in a sample space must add to 1. Since in the original sample space Williams was three times as likely to be elected as Smithers, we expect that in this new sample space Williams will still be three times as likely to be elected as Smithers. In other words, we expect the ratios of the probabilities to be the same in the new sample space as the old. Doubling all the probabilities

Figure 5

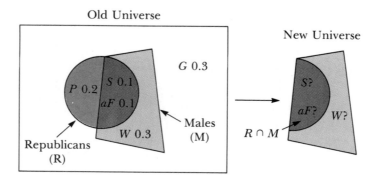

will preserve the ratios and make the new probabilities add to 1, so we now let $p(S) = 0.2$, $p(aF) = 0.2$, and $P(W) = 0.6$. In the new sample space, the event that a Republican is elected is $\{S, aF\}$, which has probability $0.2 + 0.2$. Thus the probability that a Republican is elected, given that the winner is a male, is 0.4. ∎

A General Formula to Define Conditional Probability

The crucial decision we made in Example 18 was to get the new probability weights on the set M by multiplying all the old weights by 2. In this way, we preserved the ratios of weights and made the new weights add to 1. Doubling weights won't always make them add to 1, but as we shall see, we can always choose a constant c by which we can multiply the weights in order to make them add to 1. With this in mind, we shall now figure out how to define the probability of E given F.

We want our definition to be consistent with the idea that F has occurred and we now want to know how likely E is. In this circumstance, if E occurs, the event $E \cap F$ must have occurred, since F has occurred already. Thus if we want to mimic what we did for candidates above, we will let F be our new sample space and ask for the probability of $E \cap F$ in this sample space. To compute such a probability, we must assign weights to F whose sum is 1 in order to have a probability weighting function on F. On the basis of Example 18, it may be intuitively clear that multiplying each weight of an element of F by $\frac{1}{P(F)}$ gives us new weights that sum to 1.

We can also derive the new weights algebraically from the principle that they should be proportional to the old ones. In order to keep the new weights $p'(x)$ proportional to the old weights $p(x)$, we hope to choose a constant c such that

$$p'(x) = cp(x)$$

for each x in F. Now if $F = \{s_1, s_2, \ldots, s_k\}$, the fact that it is a sample space means that

$$\sum_{i=1}^{k} p'(s_i) = 1$$

This gives us

$$\sum_{i=1}^{k} cp(s_i) = 1$$

$$c \sum_{i=1}^{k} p(s_i) = 1$$

$$cP(F) = 1$$

$$c = \frac{1}{P(F)}$$

Therefore, since $p'(x) = cp(x)$, to get $p'(x)$ from $p(x)$, we multiply $p(x)$ by $\dfrac{1}{P(F)}$; that is, we divide $p(x)$ by $P(F)$.

To get the probability of the event $E \cap F$ that interests us, we sum all these new weights $p'(x)$ for all the elements x of $E \cap F$. This is the sum of $\dfrac{p(x)}{P(F)}$ for all x in $E \cap F$. The sum gives us the old probability $P(E \cap F)$ divided by $P(F)$. This is what the new probability of $E \cap F$ will be with our new weights. We can capture all this thinking in one formula.

We define the **probability of E given F**,
written as $P(E|F)$, by

$$P(E|F) = \frac{P(E \cap F)}{P(F)} \text{ if } P(F) \neq 0.$$

This is also called the **conditional probability of E given F.** If $P(F) = 0$, then we define $P(E|F) = P(E)$.

EXAMPLE 19   Use the formula to rework Example 17—that is, to compute the probability that the interviewee is a Republican given that he is a man.

Solution   We want $P(R|M)$. This is, by definition, $P(R \cap M)/P(M)$. By adding probabilities we get $P(R \cap M) = P(\{S,aF\}) = 0.2 + 0.2 = 0.4$, and $P(M) = P(S,aF,W) = 0.2 + 0.2 + 0.2 = 0.6$. Therefore $P(R|M) = P(R \cap M)/P(M) = 0.4/0.6 = \frac{2}{3}$.   ∎

EXAMPLE 20   Use the formula to rework Example 18—that is, to compute the probability that the winner is a Republican given that he is a man.

Solution   We want $P(R|M)$, which is by definition $P(R \cap M)/P(M)$. Using the probabilities from Table 2, we find that $P(R \cap M) = P(\{S,aF\}) = 0.1 + 0.1 = 0.2$, and $P(M) = P(\{S,aF,W\}) = 0.1 + 0.1 + 0.3 = 0.5$. Therefore $P(R|M) = P(R \cap M)/P(M) = 0.2/0.5 = \frac{2}{5}$.   ∎

It is considerably easier to apply the formula than to create new sample spaces and work out new weights.

◘ *Independence*

One of the most important uses of conditional probabilities is in allowing us to define when an event does or does not depend on another event. We would say intuitively that E does not depend on F if knowing that F occurs does not change the likelihood that E occurs.

The Concept of Independence

We say that E is independent of F
if $P(E|F) = P(E)$.

We say that **E is dependent on F** if $P(E|F) \neq P(E)$. If we roll a die twice, we expect intuitively that the outcome on the second roll should be independent of the outcome of the first roll.

EXAMPLE 21   We roll two dice, first one then the other. Show that for each fixed i and j, the event $E =$ "The first die has i dots on top" is independent of the event $F =$ "The second die has j dots on top."

Solution   Our sample space is the set of all 36 ordered pairs (m, n), where m and n both vary between 1 and 6. We use the equiprobable weighting function, so each pair has weight $\frac{1}{36}$. The events E and F are

$$E = \{(i,1), (i,2), (i,3), (i,4), (i,5), (i,6)\}$$
$$F = \{(1,j), (2,j), (3,j), (4,j), (5,j), (6,j)\}$$

Each of the events E and F has probability $\frac{1}{6}$. The event $E \cap F$ is the one-element set $\{(i,j)\}$ and so has probability $\frac{1}{36}$. Thus

$$p(E|F) = \frac{p(E \cap F)}{p(F)} = \frac{\dfrac{1}{36}}{\dfrac{1}{6}} = \frac{6}{36} = \frac{1}{6}$$

Since $p(E|F) = p(E)$, the event E is independent of F.   ∎

The Product Principle for Probability

When an event E is independent of an event F, it is natural to think that F is also independent of E. This is one immediate consequence of our next theorem, the *product principle for probability.*

Theorem 5

Let E and F be events in a finite sample space S.
Then E is independent of F if and only if
$$P(E \cap F) = P(E)P(F).$$

Proof The equation $P(E) = P(E|F)$ is equivalent to $P(E) = P(E \cap F)/P(F)$ if $P(F) \neq 0$, and this equation is equivalent to $P(E \cap F) = P(E)P(F)$. If $P(F) = 0$, then by the definition of $P(E|F)$, $P(E) = P(E|F)$, so E is independent of F. But if $P(F) = 0$, then $P(E \cap F) = 0$, so the equation $P(E \cap F) = P(E)P(F)$ also holds whenever $P(F) = 0$.

Thus the equation $P(E \cap F) = P(E)P(F)$ holds in exactly the cases where $P(E) = P(E|F)$. ∎

Theorem 6 E is independent of F if and only if F is independent of E.

Proof Immediate from Theorem 6. ∎

In light of Theorem 6, we may use the phrase "E and F are independent." We may paraphrase Theorem 5 as "E and F are independent if and only if the probability of both E and F occurring is the product of their probabilities."

EXAMPLE 22 We roll two dice, first one and then the other. Show that the events given by "The total number of dots on the tops is odd" and the event "The number of dots on the top of the first die is odd" are independent.

Solution The event E consists of all (i,j) such that $i + j$ is odd; this is the set of all (i,j) such that one is even and one is odd. This event consists of half the ordered pairs (i,j) with i and j between 1 and 6, so it has probability $\frac{1}{2}$. The event F similarly has probability $\frac{1}{2}$. The event $E \cap F$ consists of the ordered pairs (i,j) with i odd and j even between 1 and 6 and has probability $\frac{1}{4}$, so that

$$P(E|F) = \frac{P(E \cap F)}{P(F)} = \frac{\frac{1}{4}}{\frac{1}{2}} = \frac{2}{4} = \frac{1}{2} = P(E)$$

Thus the two events are independent. ∎

EXAMPLE 23 In the experiment of rolling two dice, is the event E given by "The number of dots on the top of the first die is odd" independent of the event F given by "The total number of dots on the tops of the two dice is 6"?

Solution The event E has probability $\frac{1}{2}$, as above. The event F has probability $\frac{5}{36}$, because the pairs $(1,5)$, $(2,4)$, $(3,3)$, $(4,2)$, and $(5,1)$ are the only outcomes with 6 dots on top. The event $E \cap F$ is the set $\{(1,5),(3,3),(5,1)\}$, so $E \cap F$ has probability $\frac{3}{36} = \frac{1}{12}$. Thus

$$P(E|F) = \frac{P(E \cap F)}{P(F)} = \frac{\frac{1}{12}}{\frac{5}{36}} = \frac{3}{5}$$

Therefore $P(E|F) \neq P(E)$, so E and F are not independent. ∎

Independent Trials

We saw that when we use the equiprobable measure for the experiment of rolling two dice, the events of having income i at stage 1 and outcome j at stage 2 are independent. If, instead, we had rolled n dice, we would have seen that having outcome i at stage k and outcome j at stage m would be independent of each other.

A sequence of n experiments each with the same sample space $S = \{x, y, \ldots\}$ and the same probability weights is called an **independent trials process** if the events of having outcome x at stage k of the process and outcome y at stage m of the process are independent wherever k and m are different. We've seen that a sequence of dice rolls is an independent trials process. Similarly, we can show that a sequence of flips of a coin is an independent trials process. Another example of independent trials is the process of making selections, followed by replacement, of a card from a deck. (This is called **sampling with replacement.**) However, a sequence of card selections without replacing the card (**sampling without replacement**) is not an independent trials process, as we shall see later.

Knowing that we have an independent trials process allows us to use some straightforward formulas to compute probabilities. You recall that with three flips of a coin, the weight of any sequence of heads and tails is $\frac{1}{8}$; with ten flips, the weight of any sequence of heads and tails is $\frac{1}{2^{10}}$. This is just a special case of Theorem 7 below.

Theorem 7   In any independent trials process, the weight of a sequence of outcomes is the product of the weights of the outcomes in the sequence.

Proof   This proof consists of applying Theorem 5 (the product principle) and mathematical induction.   ∎

EXAMPLE 24   If we roll a die three times, what is the weight of the sequence $(1,2,3)$ of outcomes?

Solution   The probability of any particular outcome on any trial is $\frac{1}{6}$. Thus by Theorem 7, the probability of the outcome $(1,2,3)$ is $\left(\frac{1}{6}\right)^3 = \frac{1}{216}$.   ∎

EXAMPLE 25   If we roll three dice, what is the probability of seeing a single dot, a double dot, and a triple dot on the three tops?

Solution   We want to know the probability of the set of outcomes with these numbers of dots on the top. Each outcome (of the three rolls) has weight $\frac{1}{216}$ in the sample space of 3-tuples chosen from $\{1,2,3,4,5,6\}$, so the total probability is $\frac{1}{216}$ times the number of elements of the set. Each of the 6 permutations $1,2,3$, $1,3,2$, and so on of $\{1,2,3\}$ corresponds to a way to have one die come up 1, one come up 2, and one come up 3, so the event of interest to us has size 6. Thus the probability of this event is $\frac{6}{216} = \frac{1}{36}$.   ∎

Not all repeated experiments are independent trials processes.

EXAMPLE 26   Two nickels and three dimes are in a cup; we reach in and remove one. Then, without replacing it, reach in and draw another. (Here we are using *sampling without replacement*.) Draw a tree to show the possible outcomes of the process. Compute the probability of the event "dime on second draw." Is this an independent trials process?

Figure 6

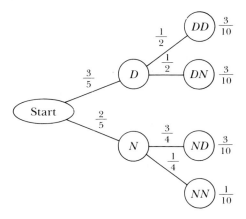

Solution   In Figure 6, we have drawn a tree diagram as in Chapter 6 to show the possible outcomes of the process. Each edge is labeled with a probability. At the start, for example, we have probability $\frac{3}{5}$ of choosing a dime and $\frac{2}{5}$ of choosing a nickel. Once we have chosen a dime, however, we have two dimes and two nickels left, so the *conditional probability* of choosing a dime, given that we have chosen a dime already, is $\frac{1}{2}$. Each other edge is similarly labelled with a conditional probability. We also have labels by the external nodes; the label $\frac{3}{10}$ by the *DD* node indicates that the event *DD* has probability $\frac{3}{10}$. Notice that $\frac{3}{10} = \frac{3}{5} \cdot \frac{1}{2}$, the product of the weights on the edges leading to *DD*. This is no accident, because the conditional probability of a dime on the second draw given a dime on the first is given by

$$P(\text{``}D\text{ second''}|\text{``}D\text{ first''}) = \frac{P(\text{``}D\text{ second''} \cap \text{``}D\text{ first''})}{P(\text{``}D\text{ first''})}$$

This gives us

$$P(\text{``}D\text{ second''}|\text{``}D\text{ first''}) \cdot P(\text{``}D\text{ first''}) = P(\text{``}D\text{ second'' and ``}D\text{ first''})$$

The right-hand side of this formula is $P(DD)$, and the left-hand side is the product of the probabilities on the edges leading to *DD*. In this way, any time we draw a tree diagram for a sequence of experiments, the probability of the sequence of events leading to an external node will be the product of the probabilities on the edges leading to it.

From our tree diagram, we see that

$$P(\text{``D second''}) = P(DD) + P(ND) = \frac{3}{10} + \frac{3}{10} = \frac{6}{10} = \frac{3}{5}$$

To determine whether we have an independent trials process, we have to see whether $P(\text{``D second''})$ is the same as $P(\text{``D second''}|\text{``D first''})$ and $P(\text{``D second''}|\text{``N first''})$. From the tree, we read that these two conditional probabilities are $\frac{1}{2}$ and $\frac{3}{4}$, not $\frac{3}{5}$. Thus we do not have an independent trials process.   ∎

EXAMPLE 27   Show that if we do return the first coin to the cup in Example 26 before the second draw, then we do have an independent trials process. (Here we are using *sampling with replacement*.)

Figure 7

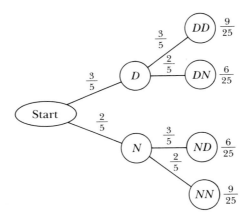

Solution   In Figure 7, we have drawn the tree once again, this time labeled with probabilities corresponding to replacing the first coin before the second draw. This time we see that $P(\text{``D second''}) = \frac{9}{25} + \frac{6}{25} = \frac{15}{25} = \frac{3}{5}$, and from the labels on the tree we see that this is $P(\text{``D second''}|\text{``D first''})$ and $P(\text{``D second''}|\text{``N first''})$. Similarly, $P(\text{``N second''})$ is independent of the events "N first" and "D first." Thus we do have an independent trials process.   ∎

Concepts Review

1. The probability of E given F is given by the formula _____ = _____ if $P(F) \neq 0$.

2. The probability of E given F is _____ if $P(F) = 0$.

3. We say that E is independent of F if $P(E|F) =$ _____.

4. If $P(E \cap F) = P(E)P(F)$, then E and F are _____.

5. We say that E and F are _____ if $P(E|F) \neq P(E)$.

6. A(n) _____ _____ process is a sequence of experiments, each with the same sample space and probability weights, so that the event of any given outcome on the ith experiment is independent of the event of any given outcome on the jth experiment for each different i and j.

7. The probability of a given sequence of outcomes in an independent trials process is the _____ of the probabilities of the outcomes in the sequence.

Exercises

A 1. A sample space consists of elements a,b,c,d,e,f. We know that $p(a) = p(b) = .1$, $p(c) = p(d) = .15$, and $p(e) = p(f) = .25$. If $E = \{c,d,f\}$ and $F = \{d,e,f\}$, find the following probabilities: $P(E)$, $P(F)$, $P(E \cap F)$, $P(E|F)$.

2. Using the sample space and probabilities of Exercise 1, if $E = \{c,d,f\}$ and $F = \{a,c,e,f\}$, find $P(E)$, $P(F)$, $P(E \cap F)$, and $P(E|F)$.

3. Consider the experiment of flipping a coin three times.
   (a) What is the probability that the first flip is heads?
   (b) What is the probability that the first flip is heads and there is an even number of heads?
   (c) What is the probability that there is an even number of heads, given that the first flip is heads?

4. Consider the experiment of flipping a coin three times.
   (a) What is the probability that there is at least one head?
   (b) What is the probability that there is at least one head and an even number of heads?
   (c) What is the probability that there is an even number of heads given that at least one flip is heads?

5. In the experiment of flipping a coin three times, find the probability that all flips are heads and the first is heads. Find the probability that the first flip is heads. Find the probability of all flips being heads, given that the first flip is heads.

6. In the experiment of rolling a die four times, find the probability of getting both an even number of dots on all rolls and an even number of dots on the first roll; the probability of an even number of dots on the first roll; and the probability of an even number of dots on all rolls, given that an even number of dots showed up on the first roll.

7. In the experiment of flipping a coin three times, we can compute the probability of at least one heads by subtracting the probability of all tails from 1. Compute the proba-

bility of heads on all three flips, given that the coin comes up heads on at least one flip.

8. In the experiment of rolling a die four times, we can compute the probability that at least one roll comes up with an even number of dots by subtracting from 1 the probability that we get an odd number of dots on each roll. Compute the probability of getting an even number of dots on all rolls, given that at least one roll has an even number of dots.

9. In three flips of a coin, what is the probability that two flips in a row are heads, given that there is an even number of heads?

10. In four rolls of a die, what is the probability that two rolls in a row come up with one dot, given that there is an even number of ones?

11. A test for a disease that affects 0.1% of the population is 99% effective on people with the disease (that is, it says that they have it with probability .99). The test gives a false reading (saying that a person who does not have the disease is affected with it) for 2% of the population without the disease. What is the probability that someone has positive test results? What is the probability that someone who has positive test results in fact has the disease? (*Hint:* Rephrase the second question as a conditional probability question and observe that the .99 and .02 are conditional probabilities also.)

12. Assume that on a true-false test, students will answer correctly any question on a subject they know. Assume that students guess at answers they do not know. For students who know 60% of the material in a course, what is the probability that they will answer a question correctly? What is the probability that they will know the answer to a question they answer correctly?

B   In Exercises 13–18, we give information about two events E and F. Determine whether E and F are independent.

13. $P(E) = .04$ $P(F) = .05$ $P(E \cap F) = .002$

14. $P(E) = \dfrac{1}{3}$ $P(F) = \dfrac{1}{3}$ $P(E \cap F) = \dfrac{1}{6}$

15. $P(E) = .04$ $P(F) = .05$ $P(E \cap F) = .01$

16. $P(E) = \dfrac{1}{3}$ $P(F) = \dfrac{2}{3}$ $P(E \cap F) = \dfrac{2}{9}$

17. $P(E) = .04$ $P(F) = .05$ $P(E \cup F) = .08$

18. $P(E) = \dfrac{1}{3}$ $P(F) = \dfrac{2}{3}$ $P(E \cup F) = \dfrac{2}{3}$

19. In the experiment of flipping a coin twice with the usual probability weights, show that the events "heads on flip 1" and "tails on flip 2" are independent.

20. In the experiment of choosing one coin from a bowl with two nickels and three dimes, replacing it, and then drawing a second coin, choose the appropriate probability measure on the sample space {*NN,ND,DN,DD*} and show that the events "Coin 1 is a nickel" and "Coin 2 is a dime" are independent.

21. In the experiment of Exercise 19, show that the event "The first flip is heads" and the event "All flips are heads" are dependent.

22. In the experiment of Exercise 20, show that the events "The first coin is a nickel" and "The coins selected are worth at least 15 cents" are dependent.

23. Each pair of events below has to do with the experiment of flipping a coin three times. State whether the events are dependent or independent.
    (a) There is an even number of heads; there is an odd number of heads.
    (b) There are at least two heads; there are two heads in a row.
    (c) The first flip is heads; the first two flips are the same.
    (d) The first and last flips are the same; there is an odd number of heads.

24. Each pair of statements below deals with the experiment of choosing two coins, first one, then the other (without replacing the first), from a penny, a nickel, a dime, and a quarter. State whether the events described by the statements are dependent or independent.
    (a) The total number of cents is odd; the first coin is a penny.
    (b) We get more than 15 cents; the first coin is the dime.
    (c) We choose the dime first; we choose the nickel second.
    (d) We choose the penny first; we choose 30 cents.

25. Assuming that the process of answering the questions on a five-question test is an independent trials process and that a student has probability .8 of answering any given question correctly, what is the probability of a sequence of four correct answers and one incorrect answer? What is the probability that a student answers exactly four questions correctly?

26. In a model for transmitting messages over so-called noisy channels we assume that each message is a sequence of zeros and ones and that the transmission of the message is an independent trials process that consists of transmitting each digit with a probability p that it is correctly transmitted and a probability $1 - p$ that it is incorrectly transmitted. If $p = .9$, what is the probability that an eight-digit message has the first bit and only the first bit incorrectly transmitted? What is the probability that an eight-digit message has exactly one error? (You may wish to use a calculator for this exercise.)

27. In n flips of a coin, what is the probability of the event "heads on flip i"? "Tails on flip i"? (Explain why without using the fact that it is an independent trials process.) What is the probability of "heads on flip i and tails on flip j"? "Heads on flip i and heads on flip j"? How do the answers to these questions help prove the statement "A sequence of n flips of a coin is an independent trials process"?

28. In n rolls of a die, what is the probability of the event "i dots occur on roll k"? What is the probability of the event "j dots occur on roll m"? If k and m are different, what is the probability of the event "i dots on roll k and j dots on roll m"? Explain why this proves that the process of rolling a die n times is an independent trials process.

29. Draw a tree diagram labeled with probabilities for the process of flipping a coin three times. Is it an independent trials process?

30. Draw a tree diagram with labels for the process of choosing a first, a second, and a third coin (without replacement) from one nickel, two dimes, and three quarters. Is this an independent trials process?

Problems

1. In a pocket, someone has two nickels and four quarters. The person pulls out two coins, one after the other. What is the probability that the person pulls out 30 cents or more if the first coin is a nickel? What is the probability that the person pulls out 30 cents or more if one of the coins is a nickel? Which is greater, the probability that the person pulls out 30 cents or more given that the first coin is a nickel or the probability that the person pulls out 30 cents or more given that at least one coin was a nickel?

2. Write down a formula for the probability that a bridge hand has four aces, given that it has one ace. Write down a formula for the probability that a bridge hand has four aces, given that it has the ace of spades. Which of these probabilities is larger? (A bridge hand contains thirteen cards chosen from an ordinary 52-card deck.)

3. If E and F are events such that $E \cap F = \emptyset$, then under what circumstances are E and F independent?

4. We define the *surprise* resulting from (or due to) an event E to be $-\log_2(p(E)) = s(E)$.
   (a) Show that the surprise resulting from an event is a non-negative number.
   (b) When is the surprise due to an event equal to 0?
   (c) Show that if E and F are independent, then the surprise due to *both* E and F (that is, the surprise due to $E \cap F$) is given by $s(E \cap F) = s(E) + s(F)$.
   (d) It is a fact that for any function f defined on the positive rational numbers with the property that $f(x \cdot y) = f(x) + f(y)$ for each pair of positive rational numbers x and y, there is some constant c such that $f(x) = c\log_2(x)$. Discuss how this relates to the formula we used to define the surprise.
   (e) Show that if E is *less* likely than F, then the surprise due to E is greater than the surprise due to F.

5. Write out the proof of Theorem 7.

6. Show that in n flips of a coin, the probability of an even number of heads, given that at least one flip is heads, is $\dfrac{2^{n-1} - 1}{2^n - 1}$.

7. Problems such as the last questions in Exercises 11 and 12 can be solved most effectively with Bayes' theorem. This theorem states that if E and F are disjoint events whose union is the sample space S, then for any event H,

$$P(E|H) = \frac{P(H|E)P(E)}{P(H|E)P(E) + P(H|F)P(F)}$$

Prove Bayes' theorem.

8. Answer the last question in Exercise 11 by using Bayes' theorem. Answer the last question in Exercise 12 by using Bayes' theorem.

9. State a generalization of Bayes' theorem in which the events E and F are replaced by n mutually exclusive events whose union is S (that is, a partition of S into n sets). Use induction to prove this version of Bayes' theorem from the version in Problem 7.

10. True or false: If E and F are independent events, then $E \cap H$ and $F \cap H$ are independent events. Either explain why or give a counter-example.

Section 11-3
Random Variables

▲ Random Variables

In many applications of probability, we ask about a numerical outcome of an experiment. We may ask for the number of heads in ten flips of a coin, the number of questions successfully answered on a test, the monetary value of a selection of coins, and so on. In deeper applications of probability, we shall ask about the number of steps taken by an algorithm, the number of errors in data transmission, or the number of characters stored in a computer memory.

The Concept of a Random Variable

A **random variable** for an experiment with a
sample space S is a function that assigns
a number to each element of S.

EXAMPLE 28   Write down the values for the random variable h that gives the number of heads in each sequence of three flips of a coin.

Solution   Our sample space is $S = \{HHH, HHT, HTH, HTT, THH, THT, TTH, TTT\}$. We may write

$$h(HHH) = 3 \quad \begin{array}{ll} h(HHT) = 2 & h(HTT) = 1 \\ h(HTH) = 2 & h(THT) = 1 \\ h(THH) = 2 & h(TTH) = 1 \end{array} \quad h(TTT) = 0$$ ■

Distribution Functions

Example 29 shows a typical question we might ask about a random variable.

EXAMPLE 29   With what probabilities do we have 0, 1, 2, 3, or 4 heads in four flips of a coin? Show these probabilities in a Cartesian graph.

Solution   The probability of zero heads is the probability of the event $\{x \mid h(x) = 0\}$, where x stands for a 4-tuple of H's and T's. Similarly, the probability of i heads is $P(\{x \mid h(x) = i\})$. A convenient shorthand for $P\{x \mid h(x) = i\}$ is $P(h(x) = i)$. In this shorthand notation, we may write

$$P(h(x) = 0) = \frac{1}{16}; \quad P(h(x) = 1) = \frac{4}{16} = \frac{1}{4}; \quad P(h(x) = 2) = \frac{6}{16} = \frac{3}{8};$$

$$P(h(x) = 3) = \frac{4}{16} = \frac{1}{4}; \quad P(h(x) = 4) = \frac{1}{16}$$

In the Cartesian graph in Figure 8(a), we show the numbers 0, 1, 2, 3, and 4 on the *x*-axis and the corresponding probabilities on the *y*-axis. In order to make the graph easier to read, in Figure 8(b) we have drawn wide vertical lines or bars up from the *x*-axis. In Figure 8(c), we have widened the bars into rectangles one unit wide. Figure 8(a) is the answer requested by the problem, but a graph such as the one in Figure 8(c) helps us visualize probabilities in a way we shall discuss briefly later.   ■

Figure 8

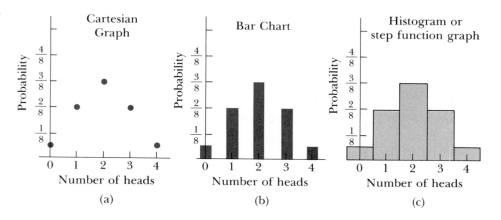

(a)   (b)   (c)

Because the values of the function are graphed on the *x*-axis, people often use the symbol *X* to stand for a random variable. Since it is confusing to think of *X* as a function, we shall not.

In Example 29, we are in fact defining a new function that relates $P(h(x) = 0)$ to the number 0, relates $P(h(x) = 1)$ to the number 1, $P(h(x) = 2)$ to the number 2, $P(h(x) = 3)$ to the number 3, and $P(h(x) = 4)$ to the number 4.

> The function that relates $P(h(x) = y)$ to each *y*
> in the image of the function *h* is called
> the **distribution function** of *h*.

In other words, the distribution function tells us the probability with which each value of the random variable *h* occurs.

The graphs in Figure 8 show several ways in which we can visualize a distribution function. The drawing in Figure 8(c) is often called the **histogram** of the distribution. We draw histograms only for integer-valued random variables; thus we can draw a rectangle with base 1 and height $P(f = i)$ for each integer value *i* of the function. Then the area of rectangle *i* is $P(f = i)$. As a result, histograms let us visualize probabilities in much the same way that Venn diagrams help us visualize sets.

EXAMPLE 30   Draw a histogram of the distribution of the "number of heads" random variable for four flips of a coin. Shade in gray the area representing the event "3 or 4 heads" and shade in color the area representing "1 or 2 heads." Which is larger, the probability of 1 or 2 heads or the probability of 3 or 4 heads?

Figure 9

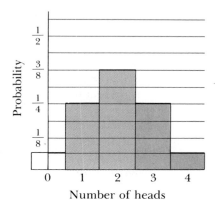

Solution In Figure 9, we have shaded in color the rectangles corresponding to 1 or 2 heads and shaded in gray the rectangles corresponding to 3 or 4 heads. The gray region is smaller in area than the colored one, so the probability of 3 or 4 heads is less than the probability of 1 or 2 heads. ■

EXAMPLE 31 Use a histogram of the "number of heads" random variable for four flips of a coin to explain why an even and an odd number of heads are equally likely in four flips of a coin.

Figure 10

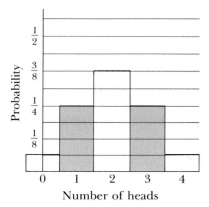

Solution In Figure 10, we have shaded the area corresponding to an odd number of heads; the remaining areas correspond to an even number of heads. Stacking the two shaded rectangles together would give the same area as stacking the three unshaded rectangles together, so the probabilities of an even number of heads and an odd number of heads are equal.   ■

B Expected Value

The running time of a computer program is a random variable defined on the sample space of possible inputs to the program. The grade on a test is a random variable defined on the sample space of possible answers to the test questions. The number of calories in a meal in a college dining hall is a random variable defined on the sample space of possible menus (and portions!). In all of these cases, we may be interested in asking what value we should *expect* the random variable to have. A simple example shows us how the idea of averaging combines with probability to provide a possible answer to the question.

EXAMPLE 32   A bag contains 2 plums, 2 tangerines, 3 nectarines, and 1 apple. A plum has 20 calories, a tangerine 40 calories, a nectarine 40 calories, and an apple 80 calories. On the average, how many calories should we expect to get if we take a piece of fruit for a snack?

Solution   There is a total of 8 pieces of fruit. We shall find the average number of calories in one piece. The plums contribute $2 \cdot 20$ to the total calories, the tangerines $2 \cdot 40$ calories, the nectarines $3 \cdot 40$ calories, and the apple $1 \cdot 80$ calories. This gives us

$$\text{Average} = \frac{\text{Total calories}}{\text{Number of fruits}} = \frac{2 \cdot 20 + 2 \cdot 40 + 3 \cdot 40 + 1 \cdot 80}{8}$$

$$= \frac{2}{8} \cdot 20 + \frac{2}{8} \cdot 40 + \frac{3}{8} \cdot 40 + \frac{1}{8} \cdot 80$$

$$= \frac{2}{8} \cdot 20 + \frac{5}{8} \cdot 40 + \frac{1}{8} \cdot 80$$

$$= 5 + 25 + 10$$

$$= 40$$

Thus, on the average, we expect a snack to have 40 calories.   ■

Expected Value as an Average

The previous example was simple enough that we could use our intuitive idea of an average to see how many calories to expect. In more complicated applications, we may have only the *probabilities* of various outcomes, not the actual numbers of outcomes as above. The second line of our computation above suggests a way to handle this problem. If we use uppercase letters to stand for fruits and use

c(snack) to stand for the number of calories of the snack, then the second line of our computation can be written

$$\text{Average} = \frac{2}{8} \cdot 20 + \frac{2}{8} \cdot 40 + \frac{3}{8} \cdot 40 + \frac{1}{8} \cdot 80$$
$$= p(P)c(P) + p(T)c(T) + p(N)c(N) + p(A)c(A)$$

This leads us to the following definition.

> The **expected value** $E(f)$ of a random variable f
> defined on a sample space $S = \{x_1, x_2, \ldots, x_n\}$
> is given by
>
> $$E(f) = \sum_{i=1}^{n} p(x_i)f(x_i) = p(x_1)f(x_1) + p(x_2)f(x_2) + \cdots + p(x_n)f(x_n)$$

Sometimes the expected value is called the **mean** or **mean value** of f and denoted by the Greek letter μ (mu) or $\mu(f)$.

EXAMPLE 33   What is the expected number of heads in two flips of a coin?

Solution   We've seen that an appropriate sample space is $\{HH, HT, TH, TT\}$, with the uniform measure giving each outcome weight $\frac{1}{4}$. If we let $h(x)$ be the number of heads in outcome x, we get

$$E(h) = \frac{1}{4} h(HH) + \frac{1}{4} h(HT) + \frac{1}{4} h(TH) + \frac{1}{4} h(TT)$$
$$= \frac{1}{4} \cdot 2 + \frac{1}{4} \cdot 1 + \frac{1}{4} \cdot 1 + \frac{1}{4} \cdot 0$$
$$= \frac{1}{4} \cdot 2 + \left(\frac{1}{4} + \frac{1}{4}\right) \cdot 1 + \frac{1}{4} \cdot 0$$
$$= 1 \qquad \blacksquare$$

A Shorter Formula for Expected Value

If we were to compute the expected number of heads in four flips of a coin in this way, we would have $2^4 = 16$ terms to add together; for 10 flips we would have $2^{10} = 1024$ terms to add together. In the third line of the computation in both Example 32 and Example 33, we see a way to reduce the arithmetic. In the third line of Example 32, we grouped together the $\frac{2}{8} \cdot 40$ and $\frac{3}{8} \cdot 40$ terms corresponding to a snack with 40 calories to get $\frac{5}{8} \cdot 40$. The term $\frac{5}{8}$ is the probability of 40 calories. The $\frac{2}{8} \cdot 20$ corresponds to a 20-calorie snack, and the $\frac{1}{8} \cdot 80$ corresponds to an 80-calorie snack. Thus the sum may be written, using the shorthand notation of Example 29 and using c for *calories*, as

$$E(c) = P(c = 20) \cdot 20 + P(c = 40) \cdot 40 + P(c = 80) \cdot 80$$

In Example 33, we grouped together the two terms with one heads to get $\left(\frac{1}{4} + \frac{1}{4}\right)\cdot 1$ or $\frac{1}{2}\cdot 1$; note that $\frac{1}{2} = P(h=1)$. Thus the third line of the computation in Example 33 may be written as

$$E(h) = P(h=2)\cdot 2 + P(h=1)\cdot 1 + P(h=0)\cdot 0$$

In general, this give us the following theorem.

Theorem 8 If f is a random variable that takes on the values $y_1, y_2, \ldots, y_k$, then

$$E(f) = \sum_{i=1}^{n} P(f=y_i)\cdot y_i = P(f=y_1)\cdot y_1 + P(f=y_2)\cdot y_2 + \cdots + P(f=y_k)\cdot y_k$$

Proof We group together terms with like probabilities, as in Examples 32 and 33. ∎

EXAMPLE 34 What is the expected number of heads in four flips of a coin?

Solution We computed the distribution function of the "number of heads" random variable h in Example 29. Using these values and Theorem 8 gives us

$$E(h) = P(h = 0)\cdot 0 + P(h = 1)\cdot 1 + P(h = 2)\cdot 2 + P(h = 3)\cdot 3 + P(h = 4)\cdot 4$$
$$= \frac{1}{16}\cdot 0 + \frac{4}{16}\cdot 1 + \frac{6}{16}\cdot 2 + \frac{4}{16}\cdot 3 + \frac{1}{16}\cdot 4$$
$$= \frac{1}{4} + \frac{3}{4} + \frac{3}{4} + \frac{1}{4} = 2$$

∎

In our examples so far, the expected value has been a possible outcome. For example, it is possible in Example 32 to choose a 40-calorie snack; it is possible in Example 34 to have two heads.

EXAMPLE 35 Compute the expected number of heads in three flips of a coin.

Solution $E(f) = 0\cdot\frac{1}{8} + 1\cdot\frac{3}{8} + 2\cdot\frac{3}{8} + 3\cdot\frac{1}{8} = \frac{3}{8} + \frac{6}{8} + \frac{3}{8} = 1\frac{1}{2}$. Notice that we say the expected number of heads is $1\frac{1}{2}$ even though it is impossible to have half a head. The point of this example is that the expected value of a random variable need not actually be a *possible* value of the function. ∎

Expected Values of Sums of Random Variables

On a test, our score is the sum of our scores on the problems. The calories in a meal are the sum of the calories in the courses. The time needed by a computer program is the sum of the times needed to carry out its various operations. We define the **sum** of two random variables f and g in the usual way we define sums of functions: $(f + g)(x) = f(x) + g(x)$. This idea lets us derive our main tool for computing expected values.

Theorem 9   The expected value of a sum of random variables is the sum of their expected values.

Proof   We suppose that f and g are random variables defined on a sample space $S = \{x_1, x_2, \ldots, x_n\}$. We may write

$$
\begin{aligned}
E(f + g) &= \sum_{i=1}^{n} (f + g)(x_i)p(x_i) \\
&= \sum_{i=1}^{n} f(x_i)p(x_i) + g(x_i)p(x_i) \\
&= \sum_{i=1}^{n} f(x_i)p(x_i) + \sum_{i=1}^{n} g(x_i)p(x_i) \\
&= E(f) + E(g)
\end{aligned}
$$

For more than two random variables, the result may be proved by induction.   ■

EXAMPLE 36   A student is taking a test with 20 questions, worth 5 points each. The student estimates that the probability of getting any given question correct is 0.8. What is the student's expected score?

Solution   The grade on the test is the sum over all questions of the number of points earned on that question. Thus if the random variable f_i is the number of points on question i, the grade is the sum of f_1 through f_{20}. The expected value of each f_i is $.8(5) + .2(0) = 4$, so by Theorem 9 the expected value of the sum of f_1 through f_{20} is the sum of 20 4's, which is 80.   ■

EXAMPLE 37   How many comparisons of two items of the list are made by the algorithm Insertion-sort below in sorting a list of n words or numbers?

Algorithm Insertion-sort
          Input: A List L of n words or numbers.
        Output: A list of the same items, sorted into order.
   Procedure: If $n = 1$ do nothing.
                      If $n > 1$, apply Insertion-sort to the first $n - 1$ positions.
                      Let Item stand for $L(n)$.
                      Beginning with $i = n - 1$, compare Item with $L(i)$ and repeat steps
                           1 and 2 below as long as Item should come before $L(i)$. (*Note:* These
                           steps tell us to move elements right until we come to where Item
                           belongs.)
                      1) Replace $L(i + 1)$ by $L(i)$.
                      2) Replace i by $i - 1$.
                      Replace $L(i + 1)$ by Item.

Solution   We are going to find a recurrence relation for the expected number c_n of comparisons with an n-element list. We assume that all possible orders of n items in a list are equally likely and take our sample space to be all these possible lists. We let $f(L)$ be the number of comparisons made in sorting the first $n - 1$

positions of L and $g(L)$ be the expected number of comparisons made after sorting the first $n - 1$ positions. Then by definition,

$$c_n = E(f + g)$$

and

$$c_{n-1} = E(f)$$

Since $E(f + g) = E(f) + E(g)$ by Theorem 9, we get

$$c_n = c_{n-1} + E(g)$$

Now we compute $E(g)$. $L(n)$ is equally likely to belong in any of the n positions of the list. If it belongs in position 1 or 2, we make $n - 1$ comparisons, comparing it with all other elements of the list. If it belongs in position i, then $n - i$ elements are moved right; thus if $i > 1$, $n - i + 1$ comparisons were made in locating its place. Therefore, for $n > 1$, the expected value of g is

$$\frac{1}{n} \cdot (n - 1) + \frac{1}{n}(n - 1) + \frac{1}{n}(n - 2) + \cdots + \frac{1}{n} \cdot 1$$

$$= \frac{1}{n}\left(n - 1 + \sum_{i=1}^{n-1} i\right)$$

$$= \frac{1}{n}\left(n - 1 + \frac{n(n-1)}{2}\right)$$

$$= 1 - \frac{1}{n} + \frac{n-1}{2} = \frac{n}{2} + \frac{1}{2} - \frac{1}{n}$$

Substituting this into the formula for c_n gives us

$$c_n = c_{n-1} + \frac{n}{2} + \frac{1}{2} - \frac{1}{n} \qquad \text{for } n > 1$$

Of course, $c_1 = 0$. From this we can prove by induction (or derive by the methods of Chapter 7) that

$$c_n = \frac{1}{2}\left(\sum_{i=1}^{n} i\right) + \frac{1}{2}n - \sum_{i=1}^{n} \frac{1}{i}$$

$$= \frac{n(n+1)}{4} + \frac{1}{2}n - \sum_{i=1}^{n} \frac{1}{i}$$

$$= \frac{n(n+3)}{4} - H_n$$

where H_n stands for the sum

$$\sum_{i=1}^{n} \frac{1}{i}$$

The numbers H_n are called the **harmonic numbers.** By using calculus and the special number $e = 2.71828 \ldots$, the base for the natural logarithm, we could prove that

$$\log_e(n) \leq H_n \leq \log_e(n) + 1$$

(There is no algebraic formula for H_n simpler than the sum we've given.) This means that the number of comparisons made on the average by insertion-sort is about half the number of comparisons made by the other sorting algorithm we've studied, selection-sort, which always makes $\dfrac{n(n-1)}{2}$ comparisons. A careful analysis of what else is done by each algorithm is required to conclude which algorithm is, on the average, faster. In general, insertion-sort is usually the faster of the two sorting algorithms.   ∎

The Expected Depth of a Node in a Binary Search Tree

In our discussion of binary trees we saw that the level or depth of any node in a well-balanced binary tree with n nodes is no more than $\log_2(n + 1)$. (Recall that the root is at level 0.) On the other hand, we saw that a node in an n-node binary search tree could be at a level as large as $n - 1$, requiring n comparisons to determine if some entry is in the tree. We remarked that the average number of comparisons needed to find an element in a binary search tree is $O(\log_2(n))$; with the concept of expected value, we can make this remark precise.

Theorem 10   Given n distinct items, if all lists of these n items are equally likely to be used to form a binary search tree, then the expected depth of an item in a binary search tree constructed from such a list is $O(\log_2(n))$.

Proof   Use d_n to stand for the maximum over all items of the expected value of the depth of an item in an n-node binary search tree. With probability $\frac{1}{n}$, the item is in the root of the tree; otherwise it is one of the $n - 1$ items in the right or left subtree of the root. In at least half these remaining cases, neither the left nor the right subtree will have more than $\lfloor \frac{3}{4}n \rfloor$ nodes. In these cases and the case where the item is in the root, the depth of the node is no more than 1 plus its depth in a binary search tree with $\lfloor \frac{3}{4}n \rfloor$ nodes, so in these cases its expected depth is no more than $1 + d_{\lfloor \frac{3}{4}n \rfloor}$. In all other cases, the node is in a left or right subtree with fewer than n vertices. Certainly in these cases, the expected depth is less than $1 + d_n$.

This lets us write the inequality

$$d_n \leq \frac{1}{2}\left(1 + d_{\lfloor \frac{3}{4}n \rfloor}\right) + \frac{1}{2}(1 + d_n)$$

$$= 1 + \frac{1}{2}d_{\lfloor \frac{3}{4}n \rfloor} + \frac{1}{2}d_n$$

or

$$\frac{1}{2}d_n \le 1 + \frac{1}{2}d_{\lfloor \frac{3}{4}n \rfloor}$$

giving

$$d_n \le 2 + d_{\lfloor \frac{3}{4}n \rfloor}$$

Applying techniques much like those we used to solve first-order linear recurrences allows us to show by induction that

$$d_n \le 2i + d_{\lfloor \left(\frac{3}{4}\right)^i n \rfloor}$$

Now if $i = \lceil \log_{4/3}(n) \rceil$, then $\left(\frac{3}{4}\right)^i n \le 1$, and since $d_1 = 0$, we get $d_n \le 2\log_{4/3}(n)$ $\le 5\log_2(n) = O(\log_2(n))$.   ∎

◀ Independent Trials with Two Outcomes

We have said that a sequence of experiments, all with the same sample space and probability weights, is an *independent trials process* if the event of each possible outcome at one stage is independent of the event of each possible outcome at each other stage. Practical uses of independent trials processes frequently have only two possible outcomes at each stage.

Examples of Independent Trials with Two Outcomes

As one example of an independent trials process, we might expect having a defect in one memory chip of a computer memory to be independent of having a defect in any other chip; here we have two outcomes for a sequence of tests of chips in a computer: "good" and "defective." Also, we might expect knowing the answer to one question on an objective test to be independent of knowing the answer to another question on the test. Here we have the two outcomes "knows" and "doesn't know." Similarly, the storage of a zero or one in one particular cell of a memory chip is likely to be independent of the storage of a zero or one in any other cell of any other chip. Here our two outcomes are "0" and "1." These kinds of examples lead us to study independent trials processes with two outcomes (also called **Bernoulli trials processes**). For most independent trials processes with two outcomes, we refer to the outcomes as *success* and *failure*. Flipping a coin is conceptually quite simple but still illustrates the essence of this important kind of process. This is one reason why coin-flipping examples occur so often in textbooks. In coin flipping examples, we shall continue to call the outcomes heads and tails.

EXAMPLE 38   What is the probability of getting two heads followed by eight tails in ten flips of a coin?

Solution In Theorem 7, we saw that the probability of a sequence of outcomes in an independent trials process is the product of the probabilities of the outcomes in the sequence. In this problem, the probability of the outcome heads is $\frac{1}{2}$ and the probability of the outcome tails is $\frac{1}{2}$. Thus the probability of two heads followed by eight tails is

$$\frac{1}{2} \cdot \frac{1}{2} \cdot \frac{1}{2} \cdot \frac{1}{2} \cdot \frac{1}{2} \cdot \frac{1}{2} \cdot \frac{1}{2} \cdot \frac{1}{2} \cdot \frac{1}{2} \cdot \frac{1}{2} = \frac{1}{2^{10}} = \frac{1}{1024} = .001 \qquad \text{(approximately)}$$

∎

EXAMPLE 39 What is the probability of getting the first eight answers correct and the last two wrong on a ten-question objective test with probability 0.9 of success on each question?

Solution For each question, the probability of success is 0.9 and the probability of failure is 0.1. Thus the probability of that particular sequence with eight successes and two failures is

$$(0.9)^8 (0.1)^2 = \frac{9^8}{10^{10}} = .0043 \qquad \text{(approximately)}$$

∎

These two examples suggest the following general result.

Theorem 11 In n independent trials with two outcomes and probability p of success, the probability of *one particular* sequence of outcomes with exactly k successes is $p^k(1 - p)^{n-k}$.

Proof If there is probability p of success, there is probability $1 - p$ of failure. Then according to Theorem 7, the probability of a given sequence with k successes and $n - k$ failures is a product including p exactly k times and $(1 - p)$ exactly $n - k$ times.

∎

The Binomial Distribution

In Example 39, it would have been much more natural to ask for the probability of a grade of 80% rather than the probability of a particular sequence of eight successes and two failures. In other words, it would have been natural to ask for the probability of exactly eight successes in our ten independent trials.

EXAMPLE 40 With probability .9 of success on each question, what is the probability that a student will answer exactly eight questions correctly on a ten-question test?

Solution There are $\binom{10}{8}$ ways to choose a sequence of eight successes (S's) and two failures. Thus the event of exactly eight S's has $\binom{10}{8}$ sequences, each with probability weight $(.9)^8(.1)^2$, so it has probability

$$\binom{10}{8}(.9)^8\,(.1)^2 = \frac{10\cdot 9}{2\cdot 1}(.9)^8\,(.1)^2 = 45\cdot.0043 = 0.19 \qquad \text{(approximately)} \quad \blacksquare$$

Theorem 12   In an independent trials process with probability p of success, the probability of exactly k successes in n trials is $\binom{n}{k}p^k(1 - p)^{n-k}$.

Proof   The proof is analogous to the computation in Example 40. $\blacksquare$

When we discuss the number of successes in n independent trials, we are associating a number (the number of successes) with each outcome in the sample space. Thus we are defining a random variable. In this language, Theorem 12 may be restated as follows.

Theorem 13   The distribution function of the "number of successes" random variable for n independent trials with two outcomes and probability p of success is given by

$$P(n,k,p) = P(\text{number of successes} = k) = \binom{n}{k}p^k(1 - p)^{n-k}$$

Proof   This is simply a restatement of Theorem 12. $\blacksquare$

Because of the binomial coefficient $\binom{n}{k}$ in this distribution function, we call it the **binomial distribution.**

EXAMPLE 41   Compute and graph the distribution function for the "number of successes" random variable for five independent trials with probability 0.8 of success. Use the x-axis for the number of successes and the y-axis for probabilities. Show the expected value on the graph.

Solution   We have $n = 5$, $p = \frac{4}{5}$, and $1 - p = \frac{1}{5}$. Using Theorem 13 with $k = 0,1,2,3,4,5$ and using f to stand for our random variable, we get

$$P(f = 0) = P\left(5,0,\frac{4}{5}\right) = \binom{5}{0}\left(\frac{4}{5}\right)^0\left(\frac{1}{5}\right)^5 = .00032$$

$$P(f = 1) = P\left(5,1,\frac{4}{5}\right) = \binom{5}{1}\left(\frac{4}{5}\right)^1\left(\frac{1}{5}\right)^4 = .0064$$

$$P(f = 2) = P\left(5,2,\frac{4}{5}\right) = \binom{5}{2}\left(\frac{4}{5}\right)^2\left(\frac{1}{5}\right)^3 = .0512$$

$$P(f=3) = P\left(5,3,\frac{4}{5}\right) = \binom{5}{3}\left(\frac{4}{5}\right)^3\left(\frac{1}{5}\right)^2 = .2048$$

$$P(f=4) = P\left(5,4,\frac{4}{5}\right) = \binom{5}{4}\left(\frac{4}{5}\right)^4\left(\frac{1}{5}\right) = .4096$$

$$P(f=5) = P\left(5,5,\frac{4}{5}\right) = \binom{5}{5}\left(\frac{4}{5}\right)^5\left(\frac{1}{5}\right)^0 = .32768$$

The function P is graphed in Figure 11.   ∎

Figure 11

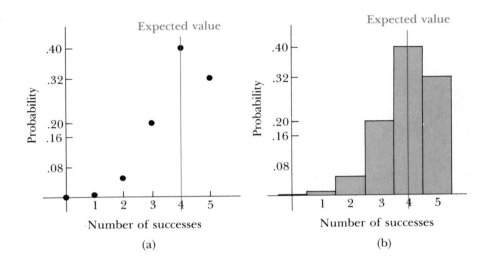

(a)   (b)

Notice in Figure 11 that the most likely outcome is 4 successes; the next most likely numbers of successes are 5 and 3. With 5 trials and probability .8 of success, it is not surprising that 4 successes is the most likely number.

The Expected Number of Successes in *n* Independent Trials

Theorem 14   The expected number of successes in n independent trials with probability p of success is np.

Proof   The proof is the computation we made in Example 36, with n in place of 20 and with p in place of 0.8.   ∎

EXAMPLE 42   If students know 80% of the material covered on a 100-question true-false test and guess at the answers they do not know, what is their expected score?

Solution   For each question, we have the possibilities that the student doesn't know the answer and gets it wrong, that the student doesn't know the answer and gets it right, or that the student does know the answer and gets it right. These possibilities have probability 0.1, 0.1, and 0.8, respectively; therefore the probability that the answer will be correct is 0.9. The expected number of right answers is $np = 100(0.9) = 90$, so the expected score is 90.   ∎

EXAMPLE 43   What is the probability that someone who knows 80% of the material being tested gets a score between 70% and 90% (inclusive) on a 10-question objective test? A 20-question objective test?

Solution   With 10 questions, the probability we want is the probability of 7, 8, or 9 correct answers. This is

$$\binom{10}{7}(.8)^7(.2)^3 + \binom{10}{8}(.8)^8(.2)^2 + \binom{10}{9}(.8)^9(.2)^1$$

$$= .20 + .30 + .27 \qquad \text{(approximately)}$$

$$= 0.77 \qquad \text{(approximately)}$$

With 20 questions, the probability is

$$\binom{20}{14}(.8)^{14}(.2)^6 + \binom{20}{15}(.8)^{15}(.2)^5 + \binom{20}{16}(.8)^{16}(.2)^4$$

$$+ \binom{20}{17}(.8)^{17}(.2)^3 + \binom{20}{18}(.8)^{18}(.2)^2$$

$$= .11 + .17 + .22 + .21 + .14 \qquad \text{(approximately)}$$

$$= 0.85 \qquad \text{(approximately)}$$ ∎

Concepts Review

1. A random variable for an experiment with sample space S is a function that assigns a(n) _____ to each element of the sample space.

2. The _____ function of a random variable f defined on a sample space tells us the probability of the event that $f(x) = z$ for each value z of f.

3. The _____ _____ of a random variable defined on a sample space $S = \{x_1, x_2, \ldots x_n\}$ is given by the formula _____ and is also the sum of the numbers $y \cdot P(f(x) = y)$ over all values y of f.

4. The expected value of a random variable f is also called the _____ of f.

5. The expected value of a sum of random variables is the _____ of their _____ _____.

6. The expected number of successes in n independent trials with probability p of success is _____.

7. The probability of exactly k successes in n independent trials, with probability p of success and $1 - p$ of failure, is equal to _____.

8. The probability distribution just described in number 7 is called the _____ distribution.

Exercises

A

1. A sample space is the set $S = \{a,b,c,d,e\}$. The table below shows $f(x)$ and $p(x)$ for each x in S. Find
   (a) $P(f(x) = 2)$ (b) $P(f(x) = 4)$
   (c) $P(f(x) = 1)$ (d) $P(f(x) = 5)$

x	a	b	c	d	e
$f(x)$	2	4	2	5	4
$p(x)$	0.1	0.3	0.1	0.2	0.3

2. A sample space is the set $S = \{x_1,x_2,x_3,x_4,x_5,x_6\}$. The table below shows $f(x)$ and $p(x)$ for each x in S. Find
   (a) $P(f(x) = 2)$ (b) $P(f(x) = 2.5)$
   (c) $P(f(x) = 6)$ (d) $P(f(x) = 6.8)$

x	x_1	x_2	x_3	x_4	x_5	x_6
$f(x)$	2.5	6.8	2.5	6.0	6.8	6.0
$p(x)$	0.1	0.2	0.2	0.3	0.1	0.1

3. Find the probability distribution for the "number of heads" random variable for five flips of a coin. Draw the Cartesian graph of this distribution function, using the y-axis for the probability and the x-axis for the value of the random variable.

4. Find the probability distribution for the "sum of tops" random variable for rolling two dice. Draw the Cartesian graph of this distribution function, using the y-axis for the probabilities and the x-axis for the values of the random variable.

5. Draw a histogram of the probability distribution you found in Exercise 3.

6. Draw a histogram of the probability distribution you found in Exercise 4.

7. Shade the region in the histogram of Exercise 5 corresponding to "There are 3 or more heads." Shade differently the region in the histogram corresponding to "The number of heads is even." Give a geometric explanation of why these two events have the same probability.

8. Shade the region in the histogram of Exercise 6 corresponding to "The sum is 6 or less." Shade differently the region corresponding to "The sum of the tops is even." Explain geometrically which of these events should have higher probability.

9. If we have a nickel, two dimes, and three quarters and draw two coins, what is the distribution of the random variable that is the monetary value of the coins we draw?

10. We have one peach, two nectarines, and three apples. A peach has 50 calories, a nectarine 100, and an apple 75. If we choose two pieces of fruit at random for a snack, what is the distribution of the "number of calories" random variable?

B   11. Find the expected value of the random variable in Exercise 1.

12. Find the expected value of the random variable in Exercise 2.

13. Find the expected value of the random variable in Exercise 3 and mark it on the x-axis of your graph from Exercise 3 and/or your histogram from Exercise 5.

14. Find the expected value of the random variable in Exercise 4 and mark it on the y-axis of your graph from Exercise 4 and/or your histogram from Exercise 6.

15. What is the expected amount of money we draw in Exercise 9?

16. What is the expected amount of calories we consume in Exercise 10?

17. Use the technique in Example 36 to compute the expected number of heads in 20 flips of a coin.

18. Use the technique in Example 36 to compute the expected number of calories we consume in 20 days if we select one fruit at random each day from among one peach, two nectarines, and three apples. Use the calorie values in Exercise 10.

19. What is the expected value of the sum of the number of dots on top in ten rolls of a die?

20. A certain computer system requires each user to have a password of 3 to 8 letters. Assuming all lengths are equally likely, what is the expected amount of space needed to store the passwords of 100 users? Assuming all possible passwords are equally likely, what is the expected amount of space needed to store the passwords of 100 users? (A calculator will be useful in answering the second question.)

C 21. Find the probability of getting exactly six heads in ten flips of a coin.

22. Find the probability of getting six answers correct on a ten-question true-false test if you are just guessing.

23. Show that the probability of six successes in ten independent trials with probability 0.8 of success is $21 \cdot 2^{26}/10^9$.

24. Show that the probability of six successes in ten independent trials with probability 0.9 of success is $7 \cdot 3^{13}/10^9$.

25. What is the expected number of successes in 200 independent trials with probability $.6$ of success?

26. What is a student's expected (percentage) score on a 50-question objective test with probability $.75$ of answering any given question correctly?

27. Show that you are equally likely to get two or three heads in five flips of a coin. (*Hint:* Compare probabilities.)

28. Show why someone who knows $\frac{1}{3}$ of the material in a course is twice as likely to get a 60% as to get a 40% on a five-question true-false quiz.

29. What is the probability of getting 8, 9, or 10 heads in ten flips of a coin?

30. If you have probability $\frac{2}{3}$ of getting a right answer on each question, what is the probability of getting four or five questions right on a six-question test?

31. Draw a graph of the binomial probability distribution with $n = 9$ and $p = \frac{1}{2}$, using the x-axis for number of successes and the y-axis for probabilities. Mark the expected value on the graph.

32. Draw a graph of the binomial probability distribution with $n = 9$ and $p = \frac{2}{3}$, using the x-axis for number of successes and the y-axis for probabilities. Mark the expected value on the graph.

Problems

1. What is your expected percentage score on a true-false test
   (a) If you guess?
   (b) If you know half the material (though not necessarily the answers to exactly half the questions), answer correctly each question whose answer you know, and guess at what you don't know? (*Hint:* In this circumstance, what is the probability you get an answer correct?)
   (c) If you know 80% of the material and guess at what you don't know?
   (d) How can a grade be calculated so that its expected value *is* the percentage you know?

2. What is your expected percentage score on a five-choice multiple-choice test if
   (a) You just guess?
   (b) You know half the material (though not necessarily the answers to exactly half the questions), answer correctly each question whose answer you know, and guess at what you don't know?

(c) You know 80% of the material and guess at what you don't know?

(d) How can a grade be calculated so that its expected value *is* the percentage you know?

3. If a restaurant has five pieces of apple pie and five pieces of cherry pie and ten customers order one piece of pie, what is the probability that the restaurant can fill all the orders if

(a) Cherry pie and apple pie are equally popular?

(b) Cherry pie is twice as popular as apple pie?

4. We say that f and g are *independent* random variables if for each value y of f and each value z of g, the event that $f(x) = y$ and the event that $g(x) = z$ are independent. Show that if f and g are independent random variables, then $E(fg) = E(f)E(g)$.

5. Give an example of two random variables f and g such that $E(fg) \neq E(f)E(g)$.

6. The surprise due to an event was defined in the problems after Section 11.2. The *entropy* of a random variable f, also called the *entropy* of the probability distribution of that random variable, is the expected value of the surprise of the event that $f(x) = y$. Show that the entropy of a random variable with range $\{y_1, y_2, \ldots, y_k\}$ is given by

$$\text{Entropy} = \sum_{i=1}^{k} -P(f(x) = y_i) \cdot \log_2(P(f(x) = y_i))$$

7. Show that the expected value of a sum of n random variables is the sum of their expected values.

8. Write out the proof of Theorem 12.

9. In the process of finding the position of the maximum element of a list by using the program fragment below,

```
Let position = 1
For i = 1 to n
If List(position) < List (i), then let position = i
Next i
```

show that the expected number of times the program executes the assignment instruction "Let position = i" satisfies $a_n = \frac{1}{n} + a_{n-1}$. What is a_n? (Assume that all lists are equally likely.)

10. In the selection-sort algorithm, we find the position of the maximum element of the list as in Problem 9, exchange it with the last element (element number n), and then apply the selection-sort algorithm to the first $n - 1$ positions. What is the order of growth of the expected number of times we carry out the assignment statement "Let position = i" (from Problem 9) in this process?

11. The sorting algorithm Quicksort has the following recursive description. To sort a list L, we first apply an algorithm called Partition, which divides and rearranges the list into three pieces such that the *second* piece consists of exactly one element that comes before each element in the third piece (in alphabetical order) and after each element in the first piece (in alphabetical order). After applying Partition, we then apply Quicksort to the first and third pieces. The element in the second piece is called the *partition element*.

(a) Assume that we design Partition as follows. We choose the partition element x by randomly choosing a place in the list and letting x be the entry in that place. Then, starting at the left side of the list, we compare each element of the list to x until we either come to an entry that *should* come after x or we come to x itself. Then we start at the right-hand side of the list and compare each element in descending order to x until we either come to an entry that *should* come before x or we come to x itself. Unless we have come to x itself in both cases, we interchange the two elements we have come to and repeat the process on the remainder of the list (including x even if x was involved in the interchange). How many times do we compare x with another element of the list? What is the maximum number of times (relative to the number of these comparisons) we carry out any other step? Explain why the number of steps in the partitioning process is of order n.

(b) Show that if E_n is the expected number of comparisons to partition elements we make in applying Quicksort to an n-element list, then

$$E_n = n - 1 + \frac{1}{n}\left(\sum_{i=1}^{n} E_{i-1} + E_{n-i}\right) = n - 1 + \frac{2}{n}\sum_{i=0}^{n-1} E_i$$

(c) Subtract the expression you get from (b) for $(n - 1)E_{n-1}$ from the expression you get from (b) for nE_n and derive the equation

$$E_n = \frac{n + 1}{n}E_{n-1} + 2 - \frac{2}{n}$$

(d) Use the formula for the solution of the general first-order linear recurrence relation (Theorem 6 of Chapter 7) to show that $E_n < 2(n + 1)H_n$.

(e) Why can you conclude that $E_n = O(n\log_e(n))$?

12. Draw the graph of $y = \frac{1}{x}$ and draw the function that has the value $\frac{1}{n}$ for each x between n and $n + 1$ $(n \geq 1)$. Explain geometrically why $H_n \geq \log_e(n)$. Now draw the graph of the function with the value $\dfrac{1}{n + 1}$ for each x between n and $n + 1$ $(n \geq 1)$. Explain geometrically why $H_n \leq \log_e(n) + 1$.

13. By using geometry and the series $\left(1 - \dfrac{1}{2}\right) + \left(\dfrac{1}{2} - \dfrac{1}{3}\right) + \left(\dfrac{1}{3} - \dfrac{1}{4}\right) + \cdots$, show that in fact $H_n \geq \log_e(n) + \dfrac{1}{2}$.

14. Find the expected number of times in the Insertion-sort algorithm (Example 37) that we move an element one place to the right.

Section 11-4
Measuring Differences
from the Expected Value

Ⓐ   *Variance*

For a number of applications of probability theory, it is useful to have a way to measure how different we should expect a random variable to be from its expected value. We shall now introduce one such measure, the *variance*. Because even the elementary applications of the variance take considerable space to explain, we shall first concentrate on defining the variance and describing its properties; then we shall discuss an important application, the central limit theorem and its statistical consequences.

Measuring the Deviation Between a Random Variable and Its Expected Value

Since we wish to measure how much difference we expect between $f(x)$ and $E(f)$, we might examine the random variable $f - E(f)$ and ask whether the expected value $E(f - E(f))$ will measure this difference. However, by Theorem 9, $E(f(x) - E(f)) = E(f) - E(f) = 0$. Thus, when we compute

$$\sum_{i=1}^{n} p(x_i)\,(f(x_i) - E(f))$$

the terms where $f(x_i) - E(f)$ is negative cancel out the terms where $f(x_i) - E(f)$ is positive. To prevent cancellation, we would like to convert $f(x) - E(f)$ into a positive quantity, so that we measure all differences between $f(x)$ and $E(f)$ by positive numbers and then find the expected value of this positive quantity. The two most common ways to convert a number to a positive number are to take its absolute value and to square it. Squares are easier to deal with in algebraic formulas, so we use squares in defining variance.

> We define the **variance** $V(f)$ of a random
> variable f to be the expected value
> $$E((f - E(f))^2) = V(f)$$

Using the "mu notation" for the expected value of f, we may write the equivalent formula

$$V(f) = E(f - \mu)^2$$

EXAMPLE 44   Compute the variance of the "number of heads" random variable for four flips of a coin.

Solution   Here, x stands for a sequence of four H's and T's, and $f(x)$ is the number of heads in that sequence. Recall that $P(f(x) = i) = \binom{4}{i}\left(\frac{1}{2}\right)^4$ and that $E(f) = 2$. This gives us

$$V(f) = E((f - E(f))^2)$$

$$= \binom{4}{0}\left(\frac{1}{2}\right)^4 (0 - 2)^2 + \binom{4}{1}\left(\frac{1}{2}\right)^4 (1 - 2)^2 + \binom{4}{2}\left(\frac{1}{2}\right)^4 (2 - 2)^2 +$$

$$\binom{4}{3}\left(\frac{1}{2}\right)^4 (3 - 2)^2 + \binom{4}{4}\left(\frac{1}{2}\right)^4 (4 - 2)^2$$

$$= \frac{1}{16}\cdot 4 + 4\cdot\frac{1}{16}\cdot 1 + 6\cdot\frac{1}{16}\cdot 0 + 4\cdot\frac{1}{16}\cdot 1 + \frac{1}{16}\cdot 4 = 1 \qquad \blacksquare$$

Examining the computations of Example 38 suggests that computing the variance for five flips of a coin would be more of a nuisance. We would have to square $\left(0 - \frac{5}{2}\right)$, $\left(1 - \frac{5}{2}\right)$, $\left(2 - \frac{5}{2}\right)$, $\left(3 - \frac{5}{2}\right)$, and $\left(4 - \frac{5}{2}\right)$. There is, however, a convenient way to avoid this.

Another Formula for the Variance

Theorem 15   For a random variable f on a sample space S, the variance is the expected value of the square of f minus the square of the expected value of f. In symbols,

$$V(f) = E(f^2) - E(f)^2$$

Proof   In the two equations

$$V(f) = E(f^2 - 2E(f)f + E(f)^2)$$
$$= E(f^2) - 2E(f)E(f) + E(f)^2$$

we first square $f - E(f)$ and then use the facts that the expected value of a sum is the sum of the expected values, that the expected value of a constant times a function is that constant times the expected value, and that the expected value of a constant (in this case the constant is $E(f)^2$) is simply that constant. But since $2E(f)E(f) = 2E(f)^2$, our formula follows immediately. $\qquad \blacksquare$

EXAMPLE 45   Compute the variance for the "number of heads" random variable for five flips of a coin.

Solution   For each sequence x of five H's and T's, we let $f(x)$ be the number of H's. The variance we want is $E(f^2) - E(f)^2$. But $E(f)$ is $\frac{5}{2}$, so $E(f)^2$ is $\frac{25}{4}$. To compute $E(f^2)$, we use the definition.

$$E(f^2) = \binom{5}{0}\cdot\frac{1}{32}\cdot 0^2 + \binom{5}{1}\cdot\frac{1}{32}\cdot 1^2 + \binom{5}{2}\cdot\frac{1}{32}\cdot 2^2 +$$

$$\binom{5}{3}\cdot\frac{1}{32}\cdot 3^2 + \binom{5}{4}\cdot\frac{1}{32}\cdot 4^2 + \binom{5}{5}\cdot\frac{1}{32}\cdot 5^2 = \frac{15}{2}$$

Thus

$$V(f) = E(f^2) - (E(f))^2 = \frac{15}{2} - \frac{25}{4} = \frac{5}{4}$$

◼

Notice that the symbolic terms $E(f^2)$ and $E(f)^2$ differ only in the location of the "squared sign." The first says "Square f and find the expected value of the result." The second says "Find the expected value of f and square the result."

Variance of a Sum

We found that knowing that the expected value of a sum is the sum of the expected values was useful for things like finding the expected number of successes in n independent trials. The variance of a sum of random variables need not be the sum of their variances. However, some random variables we have been dealing with have an additional property: being *independent* of each other. We say that f and g are **independent** if for each value y of f and each value z of g, the events that $f(x) = y$ and $g(x) = z$ are independent. When the random variables are independent, the variance of a sum is the sum of the variances.

Theorem 16   If f and g are independent random variables on the sample space S, then
$$V(f + g) = V(f) + V(g)$$

Proof   The proof is outlined in Problem 10.   ◼

EXAMPLE 46   What is the variance for the "number of heads" random variable for 10 flips of a coin? What about 100 flips?

Solution   We compute the variance for one flip of a coin. Then we add that to itself 10 or 100 times (that is, multiply by 10 or 100). Define the random variable f by $f(x) = 1$ if x is heads and $f(x) = 0$ if x is tails. Then

$$V(f) = E(f^2) - E(f)^2 = \frac{1}{2} \cdot 1^2 + \frac{1}{2} \cdot 0^2 - \left(\frac{1}{2}\right)^2 = \frac{1}{4}$$

Then if g is the "number of heads" random variable for 10 flips of a coin and h is the "number of heads" random variable for 100 flips of a coin, we may write

$$V(g) = 10V(f) = \frac{10}{4} = 2\frac{1}{2}$$

and

$$V(h) = 100V(f) = \frac{100}{4} = 25$$

◼

EXAMPLE 47 How does the computation in Example 46 change if the coin is "loaded" so that the probability of heads is $\frac{2}{3}$ and the probability of tails is $\frac{1}{3}$?

Solution   In computing $V(f)$, we would get

$$V(f) = E(f^2) - E(f)^2 = \frac{2}{3} \cdot 1^2 + \frac{1}{3} \cdot 0^2 - \left(\frac{2}{3} \cdot 1 + \frac{1}{3} \cdot 0\right)^2 = \frac{2}{3} - \frac{4}{9} = \frac{2}{9}$$

Then $V(g)$ would be $\frac{20}{9}$ and $V(h)$ would be $\frac{200}{9}$.   ■

By using the technique of the last two examples, it is possible to prove a formula for the variance of an independent trials process with two outcomes.

Theorem 17 The variance of the "number of successes" random variable for n independent trials with two outcomes and probability p of success is

$$V(\# \text{ of successes}) = np(1 - p)$$

Proof   Analogous to the preceding examples.   ■

B Standard Deviation

So far we have not been able to say what a particular numerical value of the variance means. One reason for this difficulty is that the variance itself is the expected *square* of the deviation of values of the random variable from the expected value. We shall see that in some ways its square root is more useful.

The Definition of Standard Deviation

The square root of the variance of a random
variable f is called the **standard deviation** of f.

We denote the standard deviation by the Greek letter sigma (σ). We write $\sqrt{V(f)} = \sigma(f)$ (or $\sqrt{V(f)} = \sigma$ when f is clear from context).

EXAMPLE 48 Find the standard deviation for the "number of heads" random variable for 16, 100, and 400 flips of a coin.

Solution   We know that the variance for the number of successes in n independent trials with probability p of success is $np(1 - p)$, so for the number of heads it is $n\frac{1}{2}(1 - \frac{1}{2}) = \frac{n}{4}$. Thus the variance for 16, 100, and 400 flips is 4, 25, and 100. Therefore, the standard deviation for 16, 100, and 400 flips is 2, 5, and 10.   ■

Some examples will show that the standard deviation acts somewhat like an "expected deviation."

EXAMPLE 49   For 16 flips of a coin, in what percentage of the possible outcomes is the number of heads within one standard deviation of the expected number?

Solution   This problem asks for the percentage of the outcomes of our sample space having a number of heads within one standard deviation of 8. The standard deviation is 2, so we want to know the percentage of outcomes with 6, 7, 8, 9, or 10 heads. Since we are using the equiprobable measure, this percentage is simply the probability of 6, 7, 8, 9, or 10 heads. This probability is

$$\binom{16}{6}\left(\frac{1}{2}\right)^{16} + \binom{16}{7}\left(\frac{1}{2}\right)^{16} + \binom{16}{8}\left(\frac{1}{2}\right)^{16} + \binom{16}{9}\left(\frac{1}{2}\right)^{16} + \binom{16}{10}\left(\frac{1}{2}\right)^{16}$$

Using a calculator to do these computations and adding the results together, we get approximately .79 for the probability that the number of heads is between 6 and 10.   ∎

What the Central Limit Theorem Tells Us

The computations in the example are time-consuming, even with a calculator. This is unfortunate, because it would be interesting to see whether with more flips of the coin it is still the case that the percentage of the results whose number of heads is within one standard deviation of the expected number remains around 80%. We can use a computer to add up the probabilities $\binom{n}{k} p^k (1 - p)^{n-k}$ for all k between $np - \sigma$ and $np + \sigma$. Table 3 shows the results of such a computer program. It appears that as n gets very large the percentage of coin flips in which the number of heads is between $np - \sigma$ and $np + \sigma$ gets close to 68%. It also appears that the percentage in which the number of heads is between $np - 2\sigma$ and $np + 2\sigma$ gets close to 95%. These observations are true, and, surprisingly, they don't depend on the fact that p is $\frac{1}{2}$. In fact, the **central limit theorem** tells us that for any number t, in n independent trials with probability p of success, the percentage of the outcomes in which the number of successes is between $np - t\sigma$ and $np + t\sigma$ always approaches a fixed limiting value that depends only on t.

Table 3   The percentage of coin flips in which the number of heads is within one or two standard deviations of the expected number.

Number of Coin Flips	Percent within One Standard Deviation of Expected Number	Percent within Two Standard Deviations of Expected Number
100	.728747	.9648
400	.706292	.959769
1600	.694638	.957166
6400	.688701	.955841
25600	.685705	.955173

The central limit theorem is applicable to many situations other than independent trials, but it is necessary to use calculus to state the theorem precisely and to prove it. Students who have not had calculus will want to skip over Theorem 18 and go on to the discussion of how to use Table 4.

Theorem 18   If for each positive integer i, we have a random variable f_i such that all the random variables have the same distribution (and thus all have the same expected value μ and variance v), then by choosing n large enough we may make the probability that the sum of the random variables f_1 through f_n is between $n\mu - a\sqrt{nv}$ and $n\mu + b\sqrt{nv}$ as close as we choose to

$$\frac{1}{\sqrt{2\pi}} \int_{-a}^{b} e^{-x^2/2}\, dx$$

Proof   While we do not prove the theorem, we discuss the ideas behind the proof in the case that the sum of f_1 through f_n is the number of successes in an independent trials process with variance v for each trial. As we saw in Examples 30 and 31, the probability will be the area under the histogram of a binomial distribution between $n\mu - a\sqrt{nv}$ and $n\mu + b\sqrt{nv}$. It turns out that by using an approximation for $n!$ called *Stirling's formula*, we can show that the histogram comes quite close to the graph of Je^{-Kx^2} for certain numbers J and K. Thus the area under the histogram is about equal to the area under the curve between the same bounds—and is therefore an integral. By making a change of variables, we are able to replace J, K, and some rather complicated limits of integration by the values shown in the formula above.   ■

Table 4 contains several limiting values of the probability that the number of successes is between $np - t\sigma$ and $np + t\sigma$, including those we concluded from Table 3. Note that no knowledge of calculus and no understanding of the statement of Theorem 18 is required in order to use Table 4.

Table 4

Typical t-values	1	1.65	2	2.3	2.6	3	3.1	3.3
Probability that number of successes is between $np - t\sigma$ and $np + t\sigma$	.68	.90	.95	.98	.99	.997	.998	.999

EXAMPLE 50   Estimate the probability that the number of heads in 100 flips of a coin is between 40 and 60.

Solution   Since $p = \dfrac{1}{2}$, $\sigma = \sqrt{100 \cdot \dfrac{1}{2} \cdot \dfrac{1}{2}} = 5$. Thus $40 = np - 2\sigma$ and $60 = np + 2\sigma$, so by Table 4, the probability that the number of heads is between 40 and 60 is approximately .95. Notice how close this is to the nearly exact probability we got in Table 3 by using a computer to add binomial probabilities. ∎

EXAMPLE 51   A teacher wants to be 95% sure that someone who knows 70% of the material in the course will get a grade below 80% on an n-question objective test. What must n be?

Solution   The student's expected grade on the test is 70; that is, we expect the student to have $.7n$ successes. We can be 68% sure the number of successes is between $.7n - \sigma$ and $.7n + \sigma$. We make the simplifying (and approximately correct) assumption that in half the remaining cases the number of successes is less than $.7n - \sigma$ and in the other half of the remaining cases the number of successes is greater than $.7n + \sigma$. Because $100 - 68 = 32$ and half of 32 is 16, we can be 16% sure that the grade is less than $.7n - \sigma$ and 16% sure that the grade is greater than $.7n - \sigma$. However, we want to ensure that only 5% of the possible grades are greater than $.8n$, not that 16 percent will be greater than $.8n$. Notice from Table 4 that 90% of the grades will lie between $.7n - 1.65\sigma$ and $.7n + 1.65\sigma$. Thus, based on our simplifying assumption above, 5% will be less than $.7n - 1.65\sigma$ and 5% will be greater than $.7n + 1.65\sigma$. Now the variance is given by $n(p)(1 - p) = n(.7)(.3) = .21n$. Therefore σ is given by $\sigma = \sqrt{.21n}$. To make sure that only 5% of the grades will be above 80, we want $.7n + 1.65\sigma$ to be 80% of n. Thus we want $.7n + 1.65\sqrt{.21n} = .8n$, or $1.65\sqrt{.21n} = .1n$. Solving for n by squaring both sides gives $n = 24.465$, so the test should have at least 25 questions. ∎

EXAMPLE 52   Is a score of 66 on a 100-question true-false test consistent with the hypothesis that the testee was just guessing?

Solution   If the testee just guesses, the expected score is 50 and the standard deviation is $\sqrt{\dfrac{100}{4}} = 5$. A score of 66 is therefore 3.2 standard deviations away from the expected score. The probability of being more than 3.1 standard deviations *above* the expected value is 0.001, since from Table 4 the probability of being within 3.1 standard deviations is 0.998. Therefore this score, while conceivable, is for all practical purposes inconsistent with the hypothesis. ∎

Concepts Review

1. The _____ of a random variable f is defined to be equal to the expected value of $(f - E(f))^2$.

2. The expected value of $f - E(f)$ is _____.

3. The expected value of $(f - E(f))^2$ is also equal to $E(f^2) -$ _____.

4. The variance of a sum of independent random variables is the _____ of their _____.

5. The variance of the "number of successes" random variable for n independent trials with probability p of success and probability $1 - p$ of failure is given by the formula $V =$ _____.

6. The square root of the variance of a random variable is called the _____ _____ of the random variable.

7. From the central limit theorem, we know that the probability that the number of successes in n independent trials with probability p of success and probability $1 - p$ of failure is within one _____ _____ of the expected number of successes is approximately .68.

8. The probability that the number of successes in n independent trials will be within two standard deviations of the expected value is about _____.

Exercises

A

1. Compute the variance of a random variable that takes on the values -1, 0, and 1, each with probability $\frac{1}{3}$.

2. Compute the variance for the "number of dots on top" random variable for one roll of a die.

3. A random variable takes on the values 0 through 9 with equal probability (and no other values). What is its variance?

4. A random variable takes on the values 1 through 10 with equal probability (and no other values). What is its variance?

5. A random variable takes on the values 1, 2, 3, 4, with probabilities $\frac{1}{12}$, $\frac{1}{6}$, $\frac{1}{4}$ and $\frac{1}{2}$, respectively. What are its expected value and variance?

6. We have two nickels, two dimes, and one quarter in a pocket. We reach in and remove two coins. What are the expected value and variance of the "number of cents" random variable?

7. What is the variance for the "sum of the tops" random variable for 10 rolls of a die? For 100 rolls of a die?

8. What is the variance for the "number of correct answers" random variable on a true-false test if the student is just guessing and there are 10 questions? 100 questions?

9. What are the expected value and the variance for the "total score" random variable on a 100-question true-false test when a student knows 80% of the course material and guesses at unknown answers?

10. What are the expected value and the variance for the "total score" random variable on a 100-question multiple-choice test (5 choices per question) when a student knows 75% of the test material and guesses at unknown answers?

B 11. Compute the standard deviation of a random variable that takes on the values -1 with probability $\frac{1}{9}$, 0 with probability $\frac{5}{9}$, and 1 with probability $\frac{1}{3}$.

12. Compute the standard deviation of the "number of dots on top" random variable for one roll of a die.

13. What are the expected number of successes and standard deviation of the number of successes in 100 independent trials with probability .9 of success?

14. What are the expected number of successes and the standard deviation of the number of successes in 10,000 independent trials with probability .64 of success?

15. A message is sent from one computer to another as a sequence of $2^{14} = 16,384$ zeros and ones. If the probability of error in any one digit is $2^{-10} = 1/1024$, what is the expected number of errors? What is the standard deviation of the "number of errors" random variable? What if the message has length $2^{16} = 65,536$ digits?

16. In a computer-chip manufacturing process, approximately 20% of the chips contain a defect and must be discarded. What are the expected value and standard deviation of the "number of good chips" random variable for a production run of 1000 chips? Of 10,000 chips?

17. In 9 independent trials with probability $\frac{1}{2}$ of success, what is the probability that the number of successes is within one standard deviation of the expected number? That is, in what percentage of the outcomes will the number of successes be between the expected number minus one standard deviation and the expected number plus one standard deviation? (You can compute this directly; you don't need to estimate it by using Table 4.)

18. A student knows 70% of the material covered on a 20-question objective test. What range of percentage scores corresponds to the number of right answers being within one standard deviation of the expected number? What is the probability that the student's score lies in this range? (This requires considerable arithmetic; you will need a calculator to answer it. However, you should use a calculator rather than estimating on the basis of Table 4.)

19. Use Table 4 to estimate the probability that there are 20 or fewer errors in a message of length 16,384 in Exercise 15. Estimate the probability that there are 25 or fewer errors in such a message.

20. Use Table 4 to show that the probability that in Exercise 16 there will be at least 7900 good chips in a batch of 10,000 is higher than .99.

21. Draw a graph of the binomial probability distribution for $n = 9$ and $p = \frac{1}{2}$ and mark the expected value, one standard deviation to each side of the expected value, and two standard deviations to each side of the expected value on the x-axis.

22. Draw a graph of the binomial probability distribution with $n = 9$ and $p = \frac{2}{3}$ and mark the expected value, one standard deviation, and two standard deviations to each side of the expected value on the x-axis.

23. What is the longest a message can be in Exercise 15 if we wish to be 99% sure that the number of errors is no more than two more than the expected number?

24. What is the minimum number of chips we can make in a production run of computer chips from Exercise 16 if we wish to be 99.9% sure that at least 79% of the chips are good?

Problems

1. What is the variance of a constant—that is, a random variable f with $f(x) = c$ for all x?

2. What is the variance of a constant c times a random variable f?

3. Give an example of two random variables f and g such that $V(f + g) \neq V(f) + V(g)$.

4. Prove that the variance of the "number of successes" random variable for an independent trials process with two outcomes and probability p of success is $np(1 - p)$. (See Theorem 17.)

5. Draw a graph of the equation $y = x(1 - x)$ for x between 0 and 1. What is the maximum value of y? Why does this show that the variance of the "number of successes" random variable for n independent trials is less than or equal to $n/4$?

6. This problem develops an important law of probability known as *Chebyshev's law*. Suppose we are given a real number $r > 0$ and we want to estimate the probability that the difference $|f(x) - E(f)|$ of a random variable from its expected value is more than r.
    (a) Let $S = \{x_1, x_2, \ldots, x_n\}$ be the sample space, and let $E = \{x_1, x_2, \ldots, x_k\}$ be the set of all x such that $|f(x) - E(f)| > r$. By using the formula that defines $V(f)$, show that

$$V(f) > \sum_{i=1}^{k} p(x_i)r^2 = P(E)r^2$$

    (b) Show that the probability that $|f(x) - E(f)| \geq r$ is no more than $V(f)/r^2$. This is called *Chebyshev's law*.

7. This problem derives an intuitive law of probability known as the *law of large numbers* from Chebyshev's law. Informally, the law of large numbers says if you repeat an experiment many times, the fraction of the time that an event occurs is very likely to be close to the probability of the event. In particular, we shall prove that for any positive number s, no matter how small, by making the number n of independent trials in a sequence of independent trials large enough, we can make the probability that the number of successes is between $np - ns$ and $np + ns$ as close to 1 as we choose. For example, we can make the probability that the number of successes is within 1% (or 0.1 per cent) of the expected number as close to 1 as we wish.
    (a) Show that the probability that $|f(x) - np| \geq sn$ is no more than $p(1 - p)/s^2n$.
    (b) Explain why this means that we can make the probability that $f(x)$ is between $np - sn$ and $np + sn$ as close to 1 as we want by making n large.

8. On a true-false test, the score is often computed by subtracting the number of wrong answers from the number of right ones and converting that number to a percentage of the number of questions. What is the expected score of someone who knows 80% of the material in a course? How does this scheme change the standard deviation in comparison with an objective test? What must you do to the relative number of questions on each kind of test to be able to be a certain percent sure that someone who knows 80% gets a grade within 5 points of the expected percentage score.

9. Use Problem 5 to show that in n independent trials with probability p of success,
$$P\left(\left|\frac{\# \text{ of successes} - p}{n}\right| \geq r\right) \leq \tfrac{1}{4}nr^2$$

10. Write out a proof of Theorem 17 according to the following outline. First apply algebra and Theorem 9 to get the formula
$$V(f + g) = E(f^2) + 2E(fg) + E(g^2) - E(f)^2 - 2E(f)E(g) - E(g)^2$$
Now apply Problem 4 of Section 11-3.

11. Find the variance of the random variable of Problem 14 of Section 11-3. Use the standard deviation to explain why for large values of n the number of replacements of $L(i + 1)$ by $L(i)$ in Example 37 is very close to $\frac{n^2}{4}$. What does this say about the number of comparisons?

12. Write a computer program that computes the probability of k successes in n independent trials with probability p of success and, using your program, compute the probability that the number of successes is equal to the expected number for larger and larger values of n. What does the program illustrate for large values of n?

13. Write a computer program that adds up the probability of k successes in n independent trials for each k between $np - 0.1n$ and $np + 0.1n$. What do you conclude (from running the program with larger and larger values of n) about the percentage of cases in which the actual number of successes is within 10% of the expected value?

Section 11-5
Markov Chains

A *Probability Graphs and Transition Matrices*

In some applications of graph theory, each edge of a graph has a certain number, called a *weight*, associated with it. We form the **weighted adjacency matrix** M of a weighted graph or digraph by letting M_{ij} be the weight of the edge from vertex i to vertex j. We shall describe below how certain problems in probability lead us to weighted digraphs and weighted adjacency matrices. The weights on the edges will be probabilities, so we call the graphs we work with *probability graphs*.

An Example of a Markov Chain

To begin with a concrete example, let us consider a hypothetical experiment to determine whether mice will be able to learn which chamber of a maze contains food. We place a mouse in one of the chambers of the maze shown in Figure 12; the maze has food in chamber 4. The maze is designed so that the odor of the food pervades all the chambers. The hypothesis to be tested is that after some practice the mouse will move directly to and remain in chamber 4. At the opposite extreme is the possibility that no matter how many times the mouse is placed in the maze, it moves randomly through the maze until it encounters the food. If the mouse chooses an opening at random and moves through it, then we expect that the mouse will be equally likely to pick any opening in the chamber it is in. Thus, for example, we expect the probability of moving from chamber 1 to chamber 4 to be $\frac{1}{3}$, because there are three openings in chamber 1 and one of these leads to chamber 4. We expect the probability of moving from chamber 1 to chamber 3 to be 0, because there is no opening between chambers 1 and 3. Such considerations give us the weighted digraph shown in Figure 13. We draw an edge of weight 1 from vertex 4 to itself to signify that (because of the food) the mouse stays in chamber 4 if it gets there. (Technically, this changes our description of *when* we observe the mouse; we observe it when it changes chambers or is eating.)

Figure 12

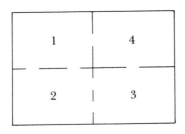

Figure 13

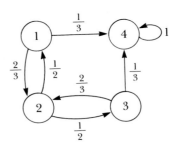

EXAMPLE 53   Write down the weighted adjacency matrix of the probability graph shown in Figure 13.

Solution   The weighted adjacency matrix of this digraph is found by putting the weight of edge (i,j) in position (i,j) of the matrix and putting a zero in position i,j if no edge connects vertex i and vertex j. This gives us

$$P = \begin{bmatrix} 0 & \frac{2}{3} & 0 & \frac{1}{3} \\ \frac{1}{2} & 0 & \frac{1}{2} & 0 \\ 0 & \frac{2}{3} & 0 & \frac{1}{3} \\ 0 & 0 & 0 & 1 \end{bmatrix}$$ ■

The weighted adjacency matrix gives us an ideal way to keep track of our probability graph in a computer. A deeper reason for studying adjacency matrices of weighted probability graphs appears in Example 54.

EXAMPLE 54   Show that the probability that a mouse starting in chamber 2 appears in chamber 4 after two observations is the entry in row 2 and column 4 of P^2.

Solution   The probability of going from chamber 2 to chamber 1 and from chamber 1 to chamber 4 is $P_{21}P_{14}$. $P_{22}P_{24}$ stands for the probability of moving from chamber 2 to chamber 2 and then going to chamber 4 (which is zero). The number $P_{23}P_{34}$ is the probability of going from chamber 2 to chamber 4 through chamber 3. $P_{24}P_{44}$ is the probability of going from chamber 2 to chamber 4 in one step (which is not possible) and then staying there. Adding up the probabilities of moving from chamber 2 to chamber 4, with a possible intermediate stop in any of the chambers, gives

$$P_{21}P_{14} + P_{22}P_{24} + P_{23}P_{34} + P_{24}P_{44}$$

Notice that this is the formula for the entry in row 2 and column 4 of the matrix power P^2. Similarly, for each other i and j, the i,j entry of P^2 contains the probability of moving from chamber i to chamber j in one or two movements.   ■

EXAMPLE 55   What is the (numerical value of) the probability that the mouse moves from chamber 2 to chamber 4 in one or two movements?

Solution   Using the matrix P of Example 53, we find that the entry in row 2 and column 4 of P^2 is

$$(P^2)_{24} = \frac{1}{2} \cdot \frac{1}{3} + 0 \cdot 0 + \frac{1}{2} \cdot \frac{1}{3} + 0 \cdot 1 = \frac{1}{6} + \frac{1}{6} = \frac{1}{3}$$ ■

A similar example arises when we consider a machine such as a computer (or more precisely, a finite state machine such as we discussed in Chapter 9) that receives random inputs. This could be a model for what happens when we use a computer to monitor equipment in a laboratory. We use the phrase *state of the machine* to describe the totality of conditions inside the computer. The state can change after each input. The state of the machine after i state changes will depend only on the previous state and the input. In this case, P_{ij} would be the conditional probability that the input would cause the machine to move to state j, given that the machine is currently in state i.

Finite Markov Chains and Transition Matrices

In both cases we have a multistage process. The outcome of each stage is restricted to a certain set S, the set of chambers or the set of states. The probability that the outcome changes from state i to state j in one stage is determined by the two states. Both of these examples are summarized by the following definition. A **finite Markov chain** with **state set S** is a multiple-stage experiment in which the outcome of each stage lies in finite set $S = \{x_1, x_2, \ldots, x_n\}$ with the property that for each k, the conditional probability that the outcome at stage $k + 1$ is x_j given that the outcome at stage k is x_i equals the probability that the outcome at stage $m + 1$ is x_j given that outcome m is x_i and given all previous outcomes. Intuitively, the probability that outcome $k + 1$ is x_j depends only on the previous outcome in a Markov chain. We call the outcome of stage k of the process the **k^{th} state** of the process. We say that the chain **moves** from state x_i to state x_j in stage m if the state after stage $m - 1$ is x_i and the state after stage m is x_j. We say that the chain *moves* from state x_i to state x_j in m steps if the state is x_i after some stage and is x_j after m additional stages.

Associated with a finite Markov chain is a matrix P, called the **transition matrix**, in which P_{ij} is the probability that the kth state will be x_j, given that state $k - 1$ is x_i. We wrote down the transition matrix P for our mouse example. As the example suggested, the powers of the matrix P are closely related to probabilities.

Theorem 19   If P is the associated probability matrix of a finite Markov chain, then the entry in row i and column j of P^m is the conditional probability that the process moves to state x_j in m steps, given that it started in state i when the states began.

Proof   The proof is by induction on m. When $m = 1$, the conclusion of the theorem is true by definition. Suppose the conclusion holds for P^{m-1}. Suppose the process is in state x_i after stage k. Then the probability that state $k + m$ of the Markov chain is x_j and state $k + m - 1$ is x_h, given that state k is x_i, is

$$(P^{m-1})_{ih} P_{hj}$$

Since state $k + m - 1$ can be one and only one of the states x_h, summing all the probabilities over all possible states x_h gives the probability that state $k + m$ is x_j, given that state k is x_i. This sum is

$$\sum_{h=1}^{n} (P^{m-1})_{ih} P_{hj} = (P^m)_{ij}$$

The theorem follows by the principle of mathematical induction. ∎

EXAMPLE 56   Using the matrix P of Example 53, find the probability that after placing the mouse in chamber 2 and making two, four, or eight observations, we find the mouse in chamber 2 again.

Solution   By successive squaring, we find that

$$P = \begin{bmatrix} 0 & \frac{2}{3} & 0 & \frac{1}{3} \\ \frac{1}{2} & 0 & \frac{1}{2} & 0 \\ 0 & \frac{2}{3} & 0 & \frac{1}{3} \\ 0 & 0 & 0 & 1 \end{bmatrix} \qquad P^2 = \begin{bmatrix} \frac{1}{3} & 0 & \frac{1}{3} & \frac{1}{3} \\ 0 & \frac{2}{3} & 0 & \frac{1}{3} \\ \frac{1}{3} & 0 & \frac{1}{3} & \frac{1}{3} \\ 0 & 0 & 0 & 1 \end{bmatrix}$$

$$P^4 = \begin{bmatrix} \frac{2}{9} & 0 & \frac{2}{9} & \frac{5}{9} \\ 0 & \frac{4}{9} & 0 & \frac{5}{9} \\ \frac{2}{9} & 0 & \frac{2}{9} & \frac{5}{9} \\ 0 & 0 & 0 & 1 \end{bmatrix} \qquad P^8 = \begin{bmatrix} \frac{8}{81} & 0 & \frac{8}{81} & \frac{65}{81} \\ 0 & \frac{16}{81} & 0 & \frac{65}{81} \\ \frac{8}{81} & 0 & \frac{8}{81} & \frac{65}{81} \\ 0 & 0 & 0 & 1 \end{bmatrix}$$

The probabilities we asked for are the entries in row 2 and column 2 of P^2, P^4, and P^8. We see that the probabilities of returning to state 2 from state 2 after two, four, or eight observations are $\frac{2}{3}$, $\frac{4}{9}$, and $\frac{16}{81}$, respectively. ∎

B   Absorbing Chains

Absorbing Chains

The matrix powers in Example 56 show an interesting pattern. The last row never changes. That bottom row of nearly all zeros makes the computation of matrix powers almost as easy as if we had just a 3-by-3 matrix. In fact, if Q is the 3-by-3 matrix

$$Q = \begin{bmatrix} 0 & \frac{2}{3} & 0 \\ \frac{1}{2} & 0 & \frac{1}{2} \\ 0 & \frac{2}{3} & 0 \end{bmatrix}$$

then its second, fourth, and eighth powers are the first three rows and columns of P^2, P^4, and P^8.

Another interesting feature of the powers of P is that the entries in the last column get closer and closer to 1. Thus the mouse is likely to end up in chamber 4 eating the food eventually, no matter where it starts. Remember, we have assumed that once the mouse finds the food in chamber 4, it stays there until the experiment is over. We say that a state of a Markov chain is an **absorbing state** if the probability of going from it to any other state is zero. Thus chamber 4 is an absorbing state. We say that a Markov chain is an **absorbing chain** if from *each* state there is a nonzero probability of eventually moving to an absorbing state. Thus our example is an absorbing chain.

Since the mouse seems likely to end up in chamber 4 eventually, how can we distinguish random movements from genuine learning? If the mouse learns, we expect that, on the average, it will go to chamber 4 rather quickly. If the mouse behaves randomly, we expect it to spend more time on the average (than if it had learned) in the nonabsorbing states until it finally enters chamber 4. It turns out that by using the matrix Q we can compute the expected number of times a randomly moving mouse will be in each chamber before reaching chamber 4. This gives us a concrete set of numbers to which we can compare our experimental results. If our experimental results are close to these numbers, we would accept the idea that the mouse moves randomly.

Theorem 20 Let P be the matrix of an absorbing Markov chain with the rows and columns arranged so that those corresponding to absorbing states come last. Let Q be the matrix obtained from P by deleting each row and column corresponding to an absorbing state. Then the matrix $I - Q$ is invertible, and the entry in row i and column j of $(I - Q)^{-1}$ is the expected number of times the chain will be in state j before reaching an absorbing state, given that it started in state i.

Proof Note that

$$(I - Q)(I + Q + Q^2 + \cdots + Q^m)$$
$$= I - Q + Q - Q^2 + Q^2 - \cdots - Q^m + Q^m - Q^{m+1} = I - Q^{m+1}$$

It is possible to use the fact that the chain will eventually enter an absorbing state to show that each entry of Q^n approaches zero as n becomes large. Thus

$$(I - Q)(I + Q + Q^2 + \cdots + Q^n) = I - Q^{n+1}$$

approaches I as n becomes large so that

$$(I - Q) \sum_{k=0}^{\infty} Q^k = I \tag{1}$$

or

$$(I - Q)^{-1} = \sum_{k=0}^{\infty} Q^k$$

(We are ignoring a few fundamental details when we write down such an infinite series of matrix powers, but all relevant details are parallel to corresponding details about power series in one numerical variable.)

Now it is possible to show that $(I + Q + Q^2 + \cdots + Q^n)_{ij}$ is the expected number of times the process will be in state j during the first m stages, given that it started in state i. Thus if we observe the process with no limits on the number of transitions, the expected number of times in state j, given state i as the starting state, is the i,j entry of

$$\sum_{k=0}^{\infty} Q^k$$

By Equation (1) above

$$\sum_{k=0}^{\infty} Q^k = (I - Q)^{-1}$$ ∎

EXAMPLE 57   Using the transition matrix from Example 53, find the expected number of times the mouse would be in chamber 2, given that it started in chamber 1. Do the same, given that it started in chamber 2.

Solution   The matrix $I - Q$ is

$$I - Q = \begin{bmatrix} 1 & -\frac{2}{3} & 0 \\ -\frac{1}{2} & 1 & -\frac{1}{2} \\ 0 & -\frac{2}{3} & 1 \end{bmatrix}$$

Inverting this gives

$$(I - Q)^{-1} = \begin{bmatrix} 2 & \mathbf{2} & 1 \\ \frac{3}{2} & \mathbf{3} & \frac{3}{2} \\ 1 & 2 & 2 \end{bmatrix}$$

We have set in boldface the entries in row 1, column 2 and row 2, column 2. We see that the expected number of times the mouse will be in state 2 if we start the mouse in state 1 is 2. The expected number of times the mouse will be in state 2 if we start the mouse in state 2 is 3. This gives us concrete projections about what we will observe if the mouse moves randomly, projections to be either confirmed or rejected by averaging the results of a large number of experiments.   ∎

There is a great deal more to the theory of Markov chains than the study of absorbing chains. An entire book is devoted to the study of finite Markov chains (*Finite Markov Chains*, by J. G. Kemeny and J. L. Snell, reprinted by Springer-Verlag, 1975). The powers and inverses of matrices like I, P, Q, and others give a great deal of information about various types of Markov chains. More up-to-date information may be found in the book *Introduction to Probability* by J. L. Snell (Random House/Birkhäuser, 1987).

Concepts Review

1. The _____ _____ _____ of a weighted graph has the weight of edge i,j as its i,j entry.

2. A finite _____ _____ is a sequence of experiments with outcomes called *states* such that the probability (given any information about the preceding states) that outcome k of the sequence has a certain value is completely determined by the state in outcome $k - 1$.

3. The possible outcomes of experiments that make up a Markov chain are called the _____ of the Markov chain.

4. The _____ _____ P of a finite Markov chain has the property that P_{ij} is the probability that the kth state is state j, given that state $k - 1$ is i.

5. A state of a Markov chain is _____ if the probability of going from it to each other state is zero.

6. A Markov chain in which it is possible to go from each state to at least one absorbing state is called a(n) _____ Markov chain.

7. If P is the matrix of a Markov chain, then the entry in row i and column j of _____ is the probability of moving from state i to state j in n changes of state.

8. If P is the matrix of an absorbing Markov chain, then the matrix Q we get by deleting the rows and columns corresponding to absorbing states has the property that $I - Q$ is _____.

9. If Q is the matrix described above, then the i,j entry of $(I - Q)^{-1}$ is the _____ _____ of _____ the Markov chain is in state j before _____, given that it started in state i.

Exercises

A **1.** Write down the weighted adjacency matrix for each of the weighted graphs or digraphs in Figure 14.

Figure 14

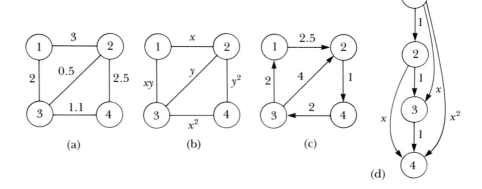

(a) (b) (c) (d)

2. Write down the weighted adjacency matrices for each of the graphs in Figure 15.

Figure 15

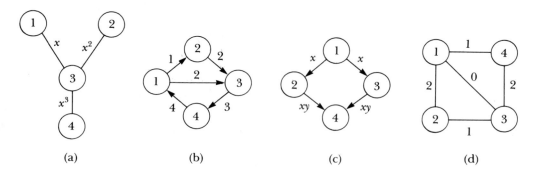

(a)   (b)   (c)   (d)

3. Write down the sum similar to the sum in Example 54 that stands for the probability of moving from chamber 1 to chamber 4 in one or two movements.

4. Write down the sum similar to the sum in Example 54 that stands for the probability of moving from chamber 3 to chamber 4 in one or two movements.

5. Each of the matrices below is the transition matrix of a Markov chain with state set $\{1,2,3\}$. Find the probability that the chain will move from state 1 to state 3 in four steps.

(a) $\begin{bmatrix} \frac{1}{2} & \frac{1}{4} & \frac{1}{4} \\ \frac{1}{2} & 0 & \frac{1}{2} \\ \frac{1}{4} & \frac{1}{2} & \frac{1}{4} \end{bmatrix}$

(b) $\begin{bmatrix} \frac{2}{5} & \frac{2}{5} & \frac{1}{5} \\ \frac{1}{2} & \frac{1}{2} & 0 \\ \frac{1}{5} & \frac{1}{5} & \frac{3}{5} \end{bmatrix}$

(c) $\begin{bmatrix} \frac{1}{3} & 0 & \frac{2}{3} \\ \frac{1}{2} & \frac{1}{2} & 0 \\ \frac{1}{3} & \frac{1}{3} & \frac{1}{3} \end{bmatrix}$

6. Each of the matrices below is the transition matrix of a Markov chain with state set $\{a,b,c\}$. Find the probability that the chain will move from state a to state c in four steps. (Assume that a is state 1, b is state 2, and c is state 3.)

(a) $\begin{bmatrix} \frac{1}{2} & \frac{1}{2} & 0 \\ \frac{1}{4} & \frac{1}{4} & \frac{1}{2} \\ 0 & 0 & 1 \end{bmatrix}$

(b) $\begin{bmatrix} \frac{1}{2} & \frac{1}{6} & \frac{1}{3} \\ \frac{1}{2} & 0 & \frac{1}{2} \\ \frac{1}{2} & \frac{1}{2} & 0 \end{bmatrix}$

(c) $\begin{bmatrix} \frac{1}{3} & \frac{2}{3} & 0 \\ \frac{1}{3} & \frac{1}{3} & \frac{1}{3} \\ 0 & \frac{1}{2} & \frac{1}{2} \end{bmatrix}$

7. Modify Figure 12 by putting an extra opening between chamber 3 and chamber 4.
   (a) Draw the weighted graph corresponding to the Markov chain that arises from the mouse problem now.
   (b) Write down the transition matrix for this Markov chain.
   (c) What is the matrix Q associated with this chain?
   (d) What is the probability of the mouse going from chamber 2 to chamber 4 in exactly four steps?

8. Modify Figure 12 by closing one of the openings between chamber 1 and chamber 2.
   (a) Draw the weighted graph corresponding to the Markov chain that arises from the mouse problem now.
   (b) Write down the transition matrix for this Markov chain.
   (c) What is the matrix Q associated with this chain?
   (d) What is the probability of the mouse going from chamber 2 to chamber 4 in exactly two steps?

9. A formal garden has pathways as shown in Figure 16. A child is walking from point to point within the garden, and whenever she comes to a corner, she chooses the direction to go at random. Draw a weighted graph that shows the corners (excluding the entrance) and shows the probabilities of going from one corner to each corner with which it is connected. Write down the transition matrix for the Markov chain in which the ith state is the ith corner the child visits. Use a computer to find the matrix in which the i,j entry is the probability that the child goes from corner i to corner j in four stages. (*Note*: If a computer is not available, then find the probability of moving from corner d to corner f in four stages.)

Figure 16

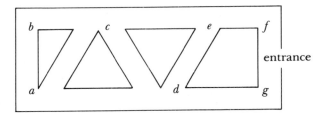

10. A puppy smells a number of neighbors barbecuing. One unsupervised grill is two houses downhill from his yard, and another unsupervised grill is three houses uphill from his yard. Because so many people are barbecuing, he goes randomly from house to house in search of food, going downhill with twice the probability that he goes uphill. We record his progress from house to house, using 0 to stand for one unsupervised grill, 2 to stand for his yard, and 5 to stand for the other unsupervised grill. Assuming that the puppy will stop and eat if and when he finds unsupervised food, write a matrix of transition probabilities of going from one house to another. Find the probability of going from his yard to the grill down the hill in two, three, or four houses of searching.

11. In a gambling game (such as coin flipping for a dollar a flip), your total fortune can go up one dollar or down one dollar (each with probability $\frac{1}{2}$) at each stage. Suppose you begin with three dollars and your opponent begins with two. Describe how a Markov chain can be used to model the game, assuming that it stops when you or your opponent loses everything. Determine the probability that you win your opponent's entire fortune by the time four coins have been flipped.

12. A computer is monitoring the temperature changes in a controlled process whose temperature must remain in the range between 20° C and 26° C. If the temperature reaches 20° C or 26° C, the computer stops the process. The temperature-measuring device measures only integer temperatures. The heating system has the property that,

during any minute, the temperature is equally likely to go up one degree, down one degree, or stay the same. Describe how a Markov chain can be used to model this process. Determine the probability that the process stops at 26° C within four minutes, given that the room is at 24° C initially.

B   13. Refer to Exercise 7 and compute the expected number of times the mouse will be in each chamber other than chamber 4 if it starts in chamber 2.

14. Refer to Exercise 8 and compute the expected number of times the mouse will be in each chamber (other than 4) if it starts in chamber 2.

15. Is the Markov chain of Exercise 9 absorbing? If so, what are the absorbing states?

16. Is the Markov chain of Exercise 10 absorbing? If so, what are the absorbing states?

17. Given that the dog in Exercise 10 begins at state 2 (his yard), what is the expected number of times the dog is one house downhill from his yard before finding food?

18. Given that the dog in Exercise 10 begins at state 2 (his yard), what is the expected number of times the dog is one house uphill from his yard before finding food?

19. What is the expected number of times the mouse in the maze shown in Figure 12 will change chambers before finding food, given that we start the mouse in chamber 2?

20. What is the expected number of houses the dog in Exercise 10 will visit before finding food?

21. How many coin flips should we expect before someone wins the game of Exercise 11?

22. How many minutes should we expect the computer to allow the process of Exercise 12 to continue, given an initial temperature of 24° C?

Problems

1. Show that if $[p_1 \ p_2 \ \ldots \ p_n]$ is the row matrix in which p_i is the probability that a Markov chain is initially in state i, then

$$[p_1 \ p_2 \ \ldots \ p_n]P^k$$

is the row matrix in which entry i is the probability of being in state i after k transitions.

2. State and prove a formula about the expected number of transitions in an absorbing Markov chain until the chain reaches an absorbing state, given that the chain starts in state j.

3. Redo Problem 2, given instead the matrix of probabilities that the Markov chain starts in each state as in Problem 1.

4. In the proof of Theorem 20, we interpreted $(I + Q + Q^2 + \cdots + Q^n)_{ij}$ as the expected number of times a Markov chain would be in state j in the first n stages, given that it started in state i. This may be proved in much the same way we proved that np is the expected number of successes in n independent trials with probability p of success. We consider a sum of random variables; random variable k is 1 if the process is in state j after k stages. We compute the expected value of the sum of these random variables. Use this technique to verify that $(I + Q + Q^2 + \cdots + Q^n)_{ij}$ is as we said.

5. A chain is *regular* if there is some number of transitions such that in that number of transitions the process can go from any given state to any other given state. Show that some power of the adjacency matrix of a Markov chain has no entries equal to zero if and only if the chain is regular.

6. It is a fact that the powers P^n of the transition matrix of a regular Markov chain (see Problem 5) approach a limit S. Explain why $SP = S$.

7. Show that all the rows of the matrix S of Problem 6 are identical.

8. Explain why if R is a row of S (in Problems 6 and 7), then $RP = R$.

9. Assume that the maze in Figure 12 is now being used for a series of experiments in whether a mouse develops sensory preferences. Each chamber in the maze is given a variation on one characteristic (four different colors, four different smoothnesses of finish on the floor, or four variations on some property). We now observe the mouse each time it moves from chamber to chamber and keep track of what percentage of the time it spends in each chamber. Draw the labeled probability graph that corresponds to assuming that each time the mouse moves, it chooses an opening randomly and moves through it.

10. Write down the transition matrix for the labeled graph in Problem 9. Is this the transition matrix of a regular Markov chain? (See Problem 5.)

11. Assume that the maze of Problem 9 has been redesigned in such a way that it is also possible to have an opening between chambers 2 and 4. Draw the probability graph associated with this version of the maze.

12. Show that the Markov chain of Problem 11 is regular. (See Problem 5.)

13. Find the transition matrix for the Markov chain of Problems 11 and 12. To what power must we raise the matrix in order to have all the entries nonzero?

14. By solving an equation $RP = R$ for the unknown row matrix R (whose entries must add to 1), find the limiting matrix for the powers P^n of the transition matrix of Problem 13.

15. Explain why the row matrix R you found in Problem 14 has the property that R_i is the expected fraction of times the mouse will be in chamber i, regardless of where it starts.

Chapter 11
Review Exercises

1. An experiment to test a 4-bit memory chip consists of storing a sequence of zeros and ones at each location within the chip and then comparing the stored sequence with the original one. A typical sequence may be written compactly as 0100. Using this notation, write down all the elements of the sample space for this experiment.

2. A fruit bowl contains two plums, two nectarines, and one tangerine. An experiment consists of removing three pieces of fruit.
   (a) Write out the sample space using three-element sequences (3-tuples) such as *PNP* to describe the possible results.
   (b) Write out the sample space using three-element multisets such as {*N,P,P*} to describe the possible results.

3. For the sample space of Exercise 1, write down the following events.
   (a) There is one or fewer zeros.
   (b) There are exactly two zeros.
   (c) There is an even number of zeros.

4. In Exercise 2, write down the events "We take a tangerine" and "The fruits we take are all different."
   (a) Using sample space (a).
   (b) Using sample space (b).

5. Assuming that all sequences are equally likely, what weight should be assigned to each outcome in the sample space in Exercise 1?

6. What is an appropriate sample space for selecting one piece of fruit from the bowl in Exercise 2? Assuming that each individual piece of fruit is equally likely to be chosen, what are the appropriate weights to use for this sample space?

7. By giving an example, explain why the uniform (or equiprobable) weighing function is inappropriate for Exercise 2.
   (a) Using the sample space in part (a).
   (b) Using the sample space in part (b).

8. For the sample space in part (a) of Exercise 2, assuming that each individual piece of fruit has an equal chance of being chosen,
   (a) Explain why $\frac{4}{60} = \frac{1}{15}$ is an appropriate weight for the outcome *PNT*.
   (b) Explain why $\frac{2}{60} = \frac{1}{30}$ is an appropriate weight for the outcome *PPT*.
   (c) Describe the remaining weights of the outcomes in Exercise 2.

9. What is the probability of each of the events in Exercise 3?

10. Using the weights you computed in Exercise 8, find the probability of each of the events in Exercise 4.

11. If we test a 16-bit chip in Exercise 1, our sample space consists of sequences of 16 zeros and ones. Use the fact that a 16-element set has $\binom{16}{8}$ subsets of size 8 to show that the probability that a sequence has exactly 8 zeros is $\dfrac{6435}{32,768}$.

12. A *flush* is a hand of playing cards all of the same suit. What is the probability that a 5-card hand chosen from an ordinary 52-card deck will be a flush?

13. Three dice—one red, one green, and one white—are rolled. Describe a sample space that is appropriate to specify the possible outcomes.

14. The maximum total number of dots facing up in Problem 13 is 18. Is the most likely total facing up equal to 9? Why or why not?

15. Explain why 10 and 11 are equally likely to be the number of dots facing up in Problem 13.

16. You are told you may have three pieces of fruit from an unlimited supply of plums, nectarines, and tangerines, but you can't choose more than two plums, two nectarines, and one tangerine. Explain which of the two possible sample spaces in Exercise 2 could be considered appropriate for use with the equiprobable measure and explain why the other one is inappropriate, assuming you are supposed to specify how many of each fruit you want.

17. What is the probability of having 1, 2, or 3 ones in a sequence of 8 bits (that is, zeros and ones)?

18. What is the probability of *at least* two ones in a sequence of 8 bits (that is, zeros and ones)?

19. In Exercises 2 and 8, what is the probability that both plums or the tangerine are selected?

20. In the fruit bowl of Exercise 2, we choose a fruit, put it back, and choose a fruit again. What is the probability of a plum on the second choice or a plum on the first choice?

21. A sample space has outcomes t,u,v,w,x,y,z. The weights of t, u, and v are each 0.1. The weights of w and z are each 0.2, and the weights of x and y are each 0.15. Suppose $E = \{t,v,x,z\}$ and $F = \{v,w,x,y\}$. Find $P(E)$, $P(F)$, $P(E \cap F)$, $P(E|F)$, and $P(F|E)$.

22. In Exercise 21, are E and F independent? Why or why not?

23. In the experiment of Exercise 1, using the uniform (equiprobable) probability measure, compute the probability of an even number of ones, of a one in the first place, of an even number of ones and a one in the first place, and of an even number of ones given that a one is in the first place. Are the events of an even number of ones and of a one in the first place independent?

24. In the experiment of Exercise 1, what is the probability of having at least three ones, given that the first place is a one? Are the events of having at least three ones and a one in the first place independent?

25. On a certain multiple-choice test, each question had 5 choices for answers, one of which was correct. If someone knew 75% of the material covered by the test, what is the probability that this person knew the answer to a question, given that the question was answered correctly?

26. Using the probability measure of Exercise 8 for the fruit bowl of Exercise 2, determine whether the event of getting at least one plum is independent of the event of getting at least one nectarine.

27. Regard the experiment of Exercise 2 as a sequence of three repeated experiments (removing one piece of fruit). Draw a tree diagram for this process. Label the edges with the appropriate conditional probabilities and label the external vertices (leaf nodes) with the appropriate probabilities. Using the tree diagram, compute the probability of drawing a plum last, the probability of drawing a nectarine first, and the probability of drawing a nectarine first and drawing a plum last. Are these events independent? Is this sequence of experiments an independent trials process?

28. Modify the sequence of experiments in Exercise 27 by returning one choice of fruit to the bowl before drawing the next fruit. Now is the process an independent trials process?

29. In the process of Exercise 28, compute the probability of drawing a tangerine, then a plum, then a nectarine. Now compute the probability of drawing three different fruits.

30. Draw the Cartesian graph and histogram for the "number of heads" random variable for six flips of a coin.

31. Shade in the region corresponding to "three or more heads in six flips of a coin" in the histogram of Exercise 30. Use the picture to explain why the probability of three or more heads in six flips of a coin is *not* $\frac{1}{2}$.

32. Assume that a plum has 20 calories, a tangerine has 40 calories, and a nectarine has 60 calories. What is the expected number of calories in one piece of fruit chosen from the bowl in Exercise 2?

33. Write down the distribution of the "number of calories" random variable for three fruits chosen from the bowl of Exercise 2. What is the expected value of this random variable?

34. What is the expected percentage grade on the test of Exercise 25?

35. Show that the probability of exactly 9 successes in 10 independent trials with probability $\frac{4}{5}$ of success is $\frac{2^{19}}{5^9}$. Assuming that the trials consist of answering test questions, show that the probability of a grade of 90% or better is $7 \cdot \frac{2^{19}}{5^{10}}$, which is approximately .376.

36. Assume that there are 100 questions on the test of Exercise 25. What is the variance of the "number right" random variable?

37. Find the variance of the "number of calories" random variable for selecting one piece of fruit in Exercise 2.

38. Use the central limit theorem to show that the probability that someone has a grade of 90 or above on the 100-question test in Exercise 36 and Exercise 25 is in fact less than .01.

39. In a certain chip manufacturing process, approximately 25% of the chips made in a production run are defective and must be discarded. What (approximately) is the probability that the number of good chips in a production run of 300 chips will be between 210 and 240?

40. Explain why a teacher can be 95% sure that a test taker who knows 75% of the material on the test of Exercise 25 will not get a grade over 85% if the test has at least 175 questions.

41. Write down the weighted adjacency matrix for each graph and digraph in Figure 17.

42. The weighted graph in Figure 17(a) is the probability graph of a Markov chain. Write down its transition matrix.

43. The weighted digraph in Figure 17(c) is the probability digraph of a Markov chain. Write down its transition matrix.

44. Find the probability of moving from state 1 to state 4 in four steps for the Markov chain of Exercise 42.

45. Is either the Markov chain of Exercise 42 or that of Exercise 43 an absorbing chain?

46. State whether each matrix below is the matrix of an absorbing Markov chain. If it is, describe which states are absorbing and determine the matrix Q.

(a) $\begin{bmatrix} 1 & 0 & 0 \\ \frac{1}{3} & \frac{1}{3} & \frac{1}{3} \\ 0 & \frac{1}{2} & \frac{1}{2} \end{bmatrix}$

(b) $\begin{bmatrix} 1 & 0 & 0 & 0 \\ 0 & \frac{1}{2} & \frac{1}{2} & 0 \\ 0 & \frac{1}{3} & \frac{1}{3} & \frac{1}{3} \\ 0 & 0 & \frac{1}{2} & \frac{1}{2} \end{bmatrix}$

(c) $\begin{bmatrix} 1 & 0 & 0 & 0 \\ .1 & .5 & .5 & 0 \\ 0 & .4 & .4 & .2 \\ 0 & 0 & 0 & 1 \end{bmatrix}$

Figure 17

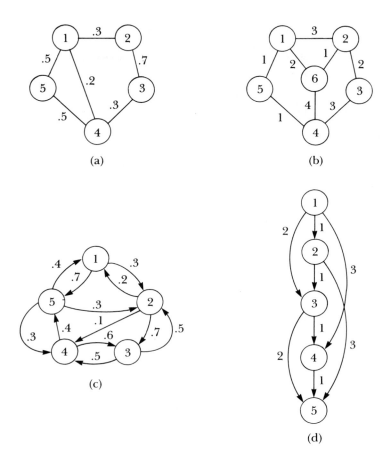

(a)

(b)

(c)

(d)

47. An amusement park has five adult attractions, two of which, an exciting roller coaster and a flume, are usually the last attractions visited before people leave the park. Figure 18 shows the paths leading among the attractions. Assuming that people are equally likely to take any path leaving an attraction and that 25% of the people who ride the roller coaster or the flume then leave the park, draw the weighted graph that shows the five attractions *and the exit* and shows the probability that someone at one vertex goes to any other vertex. Assume that someone who has exited the park does not return. Write down the transition matrix for this Markov chain.

Figure 18

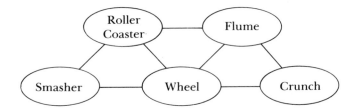

48. Find the probability that a person (in Exercise 47) who rides the roller coaster rides it once again after four changes of rides. Find the probability that someone who is now riding the roller coaster rides the wheel after changing rides four times.

49. Find the expected number of times (in Exercise 47) that someone who is now riding the roller coaster rides the wheel before leaving the park.

50. Find the expected number of rides that a person who is now riding the roller coaster (in Exercise 47) rides on any ride whatsoever before leaving the park.

CHAPTER 12
Abstract Algebra

*T*he algebra that we study in school is just one part of the branch of mathematics called *algebra*. In algebra, we study properties of operations in number systems and in other computational systems. Here we classify together mathematical structures whose operations have similar properties, leading us to brief studies of groups, rings, fields, and other algebraic systems. The knowledge we develop in our study of these systems is the foundation for our introduction to error correcting codes, one of the most significant of the many applications of modern abstract algebra.

We begin our study of algebra by recalling the properties of addition and multiplication that we used in solving equations in school. We discover that these properties are not restricted to the operations we worked with on numbers, but also can apply to the logical connectives ($\wedge$, $\vee$, $\oplus$, and so on), operations with matrices, operations with permutations, and other operations. Our study of mathematical systems called *rings*, analogous to our familiar number systems, leads us to analyze what makes the integers so special. Here we study the concepts surrounding the Euclidean algorithm, an important algorithm from number theory, which now plays a central role for schemes to encode secret messages or to allow someone to prove that he or she is the owner of a "smart" credit card or other identification card.

In abstract algebra we study the concept of *homomorphic*—we might say "essentially similar"—mathematical systems and *isomorphic*—we might say "essentially identical"—mathematical systems. The concepts of homomorphism and isomorphism, which we barely introduce here, are fundamental throughout algebra and its applications.

Of course, algebra is important for its applications, but it is also important as a unifying mode of thought, as an introduction to the concept of a mathematical system.

Section 12-1
Groups

A The Group Properties

In high school, we studied algebra in order to learn how to solve equations. We learned to use certain properties of numerical addition and multiplication in solving equations. These properties apply to operations other than numerical addition and multiplication, as well as in situations quite different from equation solving. Let us analyze the process of solving an equation in order to see exactly what properties we do use.

EXAMPLE 1   Explain why the equation $x + a = b$ has a unique integer for a solution for each pair of integers a and b.

Solution   A natural beginning step is adding $-a$ to both sides of the equation, getting

$$(x + a) + (-a) = b + (-a)$$

Next we use the associative law to get

$$x + (a + (-a)) = b + (-a)$$

Now we use the inverse property of a and $-a$ (that is, the property that $a + (-a) = 0$ and $(-a) + a = 0$) to get

$$x + 0 = b + (-a)$$

We use the identity property of 0 (that adding 0 doesn't change anything) to get

$$x = b + (-a)$$

We know that the sum of two integers is always an integer, so $b + (-a)$ is an integer (which is $b - a$, by the definition of subtraction). Thus for each a and b, $x = b + (-a)$ is the unique integer that satisfies the equation $x + a = b$. ∎

The Concept of a Binary Operation

The very first step of the example illustrates an important fact about the operation of addition. When we added $-a$ to the two equal quantities, the results were equal. Why is this? The sum $m + n$ of two integers m and n is completely determined by the pair of values m and n. Thus addition is a *function* that determines a new value from each pair m,n of values. Rather than writing $+(m,n)$ for the value of this function, we write $m + n$ for the value, to signify the idea that we are combining m and n. The equation $x + a = b$ is a statement that $x + a$ and b represent the same integer. Because addition is a function, adding $-a$ to this integer must give the same result, no matter which representation of the integer we use. In algebra, a function defined on pairs (in the way addition is defined on pairs of numbers) is called a **binary operation**. Saying that a binary operation is a function gives us the following two rules.

(1) A binary operation is defined on *each* pair of elements of its domain.
(2) A binary operation can assign *only one* value to each pair of elements in its domain.

EXAMPLE 2 Is multiplication a binary operation for the integers? Is division a binary operation for the integers? Is division a binary operation for the positive integers?

Solution For each pair of integers m and n, $m \cdot n$ is defined, and its value is determined completely by the values of m and n. Thus multiplication is a binary operation. On the other hand, for any integer n, the quotient $n \div 0$ is not defined. Thus division does not assign a value to each pair of integers, so it is not a binary operation for the integers. (Notice that division violates rule (1) above.) For the positive integers, however, division is a binary operation. ∎

Not every way of determining a new value from two given ones is a binary operation.

EXAMPLE 3 Define $m|n$ to be a positive factor of m and n for each pair of positive integers m and n. Is this a binary operation?

Solution No, because $m|n$ is not a function of m and n. For example $4|6$ could be 1 or 2 and $8|12$ could be 1, 2, or 4. Thus this description of $m|n$ violates rule (2) above. (On the other hand, $7|6$ can only be 1, but since $m|n$ is not uniquely determined for each m and n, it is not a function of m and n.) ∎

At the end of Example 1, we noted that the sum of two integers is again an integer. This is called the *closure property* of addition. A set is said to be **closed** under an operation if the result of performing the operation is always another member of the set.

EXAMPLE 4   Is the set of positive integers closed under the binary operation of multiplication? Is it closed under the binary operation of division?

Solution   Since the product of two positive integers is a positive integer, the set of positive integers is closed under multiplication. However, the quotient of two integers (say, $3/2$ or $4 \div 9$) need not be an integer. Therefore the positive integers are not closed under the operation of division.   ∎

If a set is closed under a binary operation, we say that the operation is an operation **on the set.** Thus multiplication is a binary operation on the positive integers, but division is *not* a binary operation on the positive integers.

EXAMPLE 5   Is the operation $*$ defined by $a * b = ab^2 - a^2b$ a binary operation on the integers?

Solution   For each pair of integers, ab^2 and a^2b are integers, so $ab^2 - a^2b$ is defined and is an integer. Thus the operation $*$ is a binary operation on the integers.   ∎

Other examples of binary operations are set intersection and set union on subsets of a universe, the logical operators *and* ($\wedge$), *or* ($\vee$), and exclusive *or* ($\oplus$) on statements about a universe, and addition and multiplication on n-by-n matrices. Just as we use a symbol such as x or y to stand for an arbitrary number or an element of a set, we use a symbol such as $\cdot$, $*$, $\otimes$, $\bullet$, or $\oplus$ to stand for an arbitrary binary operation. Notice that we write $a * b$ for the result of performing the operation on a and b rather than insisting on using standard notation for functions and writing $*(a,b)$ for the result of the operation. This illustrates an important point about notation: It should always be adapted to fit the situation at hand. The purpose of notation is to facilitate thinking, not get in its way.

The Group Properties

In addition to using the fact that addition is a binary operation on the integers, our example of solving an equation used three other properties of addition (described precisely below) called the *associative property,* the *identity property,* and the *inverse property.* We call these properties the **group properties,** and we refer to "the group of integers under addition" when we intend to limit our study of addition to these properties. Using the notation $*$ to stand for our binary operation, we say that a **group** consists of a set S together with a binary operation $*$ defined on S such that

(1) $g_1 * (g_2 * g_3) = (g_1 * g_2) * g_3$ for each g_1, g_2, and g_3 in S
(2) There is an element I in S such that $g * I = I * g = g$ for each g in S
(3) For each g in S, there is an element g^{-1} in S such that $g * g^{-1} = g^{-1} * g = I$.

Property (1) is called the **associative property,** property (2) is called the **identity property,** and property (3) is called the **inverse property.** With this terminology, we may write our definition of a group as follows.

A **group** consists of a set and a binary operation defined
on that set that has the associative property,
the identity property, and the inverse property.

We have seen that the set of all integers (positive, negative, and zero) with the operation + forms a group. It is traditional to use Z (Zahlen, in German, means numbers) to stand for this group.

Not every set that has a binary operation defined on it forms a group.

EXAMPLE 6 Determine which group properties are satisfied by the non-negative integers together with the + operation.

Solution Since addition is associative, property (1) is satisfied. Since 0 is a non-negative integer and $0 + n = n$ for *every* integer n, property (2) is satisfied. However, there is no non-negative integer we may add to 1 (or to any other positive integer) in order to get 0. Thus property (3) is not satisfied, so the non-negative integers do not form a group under addition. ■

Properties (1) and (2) are called the *monoid properties*. A **monoid** consists of a set S with a binary operation defined on it that is associative and has an identity. In Example 6, we verified that the non-negative integers do form a monoid under addition.

EXAMPLE 7 Which of the group and monoid properties hold for the set of positive integers with the operation of addition?

Solution Addition is associative (notice that this is true for any set of integers). However, there is no positive integer I such that $I + m = m$ for each positive integer m. Thus the identity property does not hold. Without an identity element I, the inverse property cannot hold either. ■

A **semigroup** is a set with an associative binary operation defined on it. Example 7 shows that the positive integers form a semigroup under addition. Since most (but not all) binary operations that arise in practice are associative, semigroups are one of the major building blocks of modern mathematical theories.

EXAMPLE 8 Explain why the set of n-by-n matrices is a semigroup under the operation of multiplication. Is it a monoid? Why is the set of *invertible* n-by-n matrices a group?

Solution Since multiplication is an associative binary operation on the set of n-by-n matrices, the matrices form a semigroup under this operation. Since the identity matrix acts as an identity element for multiplication, this semigroup is a monoid.

If we consider only the set of invertible matrices, multiplication is still a binary operation on this set, because a product of invertible matrices is invertible. We've already observed that multiplication is associative. Since the identity matrix is invertible, the identity property holds. The inverse property holds because we are restricting ourselves to invertible matrices. Thus the invertible matrices form a group. This famous and very important group is called the **general linear group** of degree n and is denoted by GL_n. ■

EXAMPLE 9   Show that the permutations of the set $N = \{1, 2, \ldots, n\}$ form a group under the operation of function composition.

Solution   Recall that a permutation of N is a one-to-one function from N onto N, also called a *bijection* of N. The composition of bijections is a bijection. Thus function composition is a binary operation on the set of permutations of N. To show that this operation is associative, consider three permutations f, g, and h of N. The associative law for function composition would be

$$(f \circ g) \circ h = f \circ (g \circ h)$$

Recall that $g \circ h(x) = g(h(x))$. Thus the associative law may be rewritten as

$$
\begin{aligned}
(f \circ g) \circ h(x) &= f \circ (g \circ h)(x) &&\text{for each } x \text{ in } N \\
f \circ g(h(x)) &= f(g \circ h(x)) &&\text{for each } x \text{ in } N \\
f(g(h(x))) &= f(g(h(x))) &&\text{for each } x \text{ in } N
\end{aligned}
$$

Since the left and right sides of the last equation are identical, the last equation is true; reversing the order of these equations then tells us that $(f \circ g) \circ h = f \circ (g \circ h)$. It is a small but important point that it is these equations in *reverse order* that gives the proof.

Let i stand for the function whose rule is $i(x) = x$ for each x in N. Note that

$$f \circ i(x) = f(i(x)) = f(x)$$

and

$$i \circ f(x) = i(f(x)) = f(x)$$

Therefore, $f \circ i$ equals f, and $i \circ f$ equals f. This shows that the function i is an identity for the permutations of N. A bijection of N has an inverse whose domain is N. We know that $f \circ f^{-1} = i$ and $f^{-1} \circ f = i$, so we know that the composition operation on the permutations of N has the inverse property.

Thus the permutations of $N = \{1, 2, \ldots, n\}$ form a group under the operation of composition. This group is called the **symmetric group** of degree n and is denoted by S_n. ■

EXAMPLE 10   In Chapter 3, we introduced the equivalence relation of congruence modulo m. We wrote $i \equiv j \bmod m$ to mean $i - j$ is a multiple of m. Let us use Z_m to stand for the set of equivalence classes and let us use $\underline{i}$ to stand for the equivalence class containing i. Thus $Z_m = \{\underline{0}, \underline{1}, \ldots, \underline{m-1}\}$.

(a) Under what circumstances could the rule $\underline{i} * \underline{j} = \underline{i + j}$ fail to define a binary operation on Z_m?

(b) Show that if $i \equiv i'$ and $j \equiv j'$, then $i + j \equiv i' + j'$. Explain why $\underline{i} * \underline{j} = \underline{i + j}$ does define a binary operation on Z_m.

(c) Show that Z_m forms a group under this operation.

Solution

(a) $\underline{i + j}$ is the class containing $i + j$. Thus if we pick an i' such that $\underline{i'} = \underline{i}$ and a j' such that $\underline{j'} = \underline{j}$ and discover that $\underline{i' + j'} \neq \underline{i + j}$, then the $*$ operation will not be a function, because it assigns both the value $\underline{i' + j'}$ and the value $\underline{i + j}$ to the two classes $\underline{i}$ and $\underline{j}$.

(b) If $i - i' = k_1 \cdot m$ and $j - j' = k_2 \cdot m$, then adding gives $i + j - (i' + j') = (k_1 + k_2)m$, so that $i + j \equiv i' + j'$ modulo m. This shows that the problem in part (a) cannot arise, so we have a binary operation.

(c) Since

$$(\underline{i} * \underline{j}) * \underline{k} = \underline{(i + j)} * \underline{k} = \underline{(i + j) + k} = \underline{i + (j + k)} = \underline{i} * \underline{(j + k)} = \underline{i} * (\underline{j} * \underline{k})$$

the operation is associative. Since $\underline{0} * \underline{i} = \underline{i} = \underline{i} * \underline{0}$, $\underline{0}$ is an identity for the operation. Since $\underline{i} * \underline{m - i} = \underline{m - i} * \underline{i} = \underline{m} = \underline{0}$, we may conclude that $\underline{m - i}$ is the inverse to $\underline{i}$. Therefore Z_m forms a group. This group is called the **integers modulo m**, $*$ is usually denoted by $+$, and $\underline{i}$ is usually written as i.   ∎

B   Subgroups and Homomorphisms

We have given a number of important examples of groups. Other examples arise as "special cases" of these examples.

Subgroups

EXAMPLE 11   Show that the even integers form a group under the addition operation.

Solution   The sum of two even integers is even, so the operation of addition is a binary operation on the even integers. Since we know that addition is associative for all integers, it is associative for the even integers. Since 0 is an even integer, we have an identity element. Since $-n$ is even whenever n is even, each element has an inverse. Thus the even integers form a group under addition.   ∎

A **subgroup** of a group G whose binary operation is $*$ is a subset S of G that also forms a group under the binary operation $*$. We have shown in Example 11 that the even integers form a subgroup of the group of integers. It would appear that to check that a subset of a group is a subgroup is almost as much work as checking that the original set forms a group, but there is one kind of test we can make to verify all three of the group properties simultaneously.

Theorem 1   A set S is a subgroup of the group G with the operation $*$ if $g * h^{-1}$ is in S for each g and h in S.

Proof   Suppose that $g * h^{-1}$ is in S for each g and h in S. Using $g = h$ gives us that the identity element $I = g * g^{-1}$ is in S. From this we may conclude that for each h in S, the element $I * h^{-1} = h^{-1}$ is in S as well. It is possible to derive from the group properties that $(f^{-1})^{-1} = f$. To conclude that $g * f$ is in S whenever f and g are in S, we take h equal to f^{-1} and note that saying $g * h^{-1}$ is in S is the same as saying $g * f$ is in S. This tells us that $*$ is a binary operation on S. Finally, $(g * h) * f = g * (h * f)$ for each g, h, and f in S, because this equation holds for each g, h, and f in G. Therefore S is a subgroup of G if $g * h^{-1}$ is in S for each g and h in S.   ∎

EXAMPLE 12   Six people are sitting around a table. We think of the six places at the table as being numbered one through six. If the people get up and move around and then sit back down, we obtain a permutation f of $\{1,2,3,4,5,6\}$ by letting $f(i) = j$ if the person originally in place i is now in place j. Every permutation in the symmetric group S_6 (see Example 9) can arise in this way. Show that the set G of permutations in which each person has the same neighbors before and after moving forms a subgroup of S_6.

Solution   We want to show that for each two permutations g and h in G, $g \circ h^{-1}$ is also in G. Saying that everyone has the same neighbors before and after moving according to h is the same as saying that everyone has the same neighbors after and before moving according to h^{-1}. Therefore, if each person has the same neighbors before and after we apply h and before and after we apply g, then each person has the same neighbors before and after we apply $g \circ h^{-1}$. Thus, by Theorem 1, G is a subgroup of S_6.   ∎

EXAMPLE 13   Using the arrangements of people in Example 12, we define a function φ (the Greek letter phi) from the set Z of all integers (positive, negative, and zero) to S_6 by defining $\varphi(n)$ to be the permutation which moves everyone n places to the right (or $|n|$ places to the left if n is negative). Show the following:

(a) $\varphi(m + n) = \varphi(m) \circ \varphi(n)$
(b) $\varphi(-n) = (\varphi(n))^{-1}$
(c) The image R of φ is a subgroup of S_6
(d) The image R of φ is a subgroup of G (from Example 12)

Solution If we first permute by moving everyone n places to the right and then permute by moving everyone m places to the right, this is the same as moving everyone $m + n$ places to the right. This sentence is equivalent to (a). (You may check that the sentence holds in the case that m or n is negative, with $-i$ places to the right interpreted as i places to the left.) Statement (b) says that shifting everyone n places to the left is the inverse of shifting everyone n places to the right, so (b) holds. The image R of φ is the *subset* of S_6 consisting of permutations of the form $\varphi(n)$, so to apply Theorem 1 we use (a) and (b) in writing

$$\varphi(m) \circ \varphi(n)^{-1} = \varphi(m) \circ \varphi(-n) = \varphi(m-n)$$

which is in R. Therefore, by Theorem 1, R is a subgroup of S_6. In order for Theorem 1 to tell us that R is a subgroup of G also, we need only know that R is a subset of G. (Why?) However, if we move each person some number n of places to the right, no one's neighbors will change. Thus R is a subset of G; by Theorem 1, R is a subgroup of G. ∎

A subgroup of the symmetric group S_n of all permutations of $\{1,2, \ldots ,n\}$ is called a **permutation group;** thus the groups G and R of Examples 9 and 10 are permutation groups.

Homomorphisms

Examples 11 or 12 and 13 show us two different ways to construct a new group from an old one. We may take a special kind of subset of the old group or an image of the old group under a special kind of function. The special kind of function is called a *homomorphism*. (In Greek, *homo* means similar; *morph* refers to shape.)

> A **homomorphism** from a group G with operation $*$ to a
> group H with operation $\cdot$ is a function φ from G to H
> such that $\varphi(g * h) = \varphi(g) \cdot \varphi(h)$ for each g and h in G.

Example 13 suggests that the image of a homomorphism should be a subgroup of the range (which in the definition above is H). Our next theorem shows this to be the case.

Theorem 2   If φ is a homomorphism from a group G to a group H, then the image of φ is a subgroup of H.

Proof   Condition (b) of Example 10 may be derived from condition (a). The computations we made in Example 10 may then be used to prove the theorem. ∎

EXAMPLE 14   Show that the set K of all numbers that the homomorphism φ of Example 8 sends to the identity permutation forms a subgroup of Z. Give a description of this subgroup without using φ.

Solution   The identity permutation i given by $i(x) = x$ for all x has the property that $i \circ i = i$ and $i^{-1} = i$. Thus, using (a) and (b) of Example 13, we see that if $\varphi(m) = i$ and $\varphi(n) = i$, then

$$\varphi(m + (-n)) = \varphi(m) \circ \varphi(-n) = \varphi(m) \circ \varphi(n)^{-1} = i \circ i = i$$

Therefore $m + (-n)$ is in the set K as well. Since $-n$ stands for the inverse n^{-1} of n under the operation of addition, Theorem 1 tells us that K is a subgroup of Z.

Rotating everyone 6, 12 (and so on) places to the left or right will not change anyone's place, so all multiples of 6 are in K. Any number of the form $6i + j$ with $0 < j < 6$ will rotate people j places around the table; this does not correspond to the identity permutation. Thus K consists of the multiples of 6.   ∎

The **kernel** of a homomorphism φ from a group G to a group H is the set of all g in G with $\varphi(g)$ equal to the identity element of H. Example 14 is one example of a kernel; we shall see more examples later. As Example 14 suggests, the kernel of a homomorphism is a subgroup of the domain.

Theorem 3   The kernel of a homomorphism from a group G to a group H is a subgroup of G.

Proof   Similar to the computations in Example 11.   ∎

◖C◗   Cosets

The kernel K of a homomorphism φ gives us a surprising amount of information about φ. For example, by knowing K we can determine whether $\varphi(g) = \varphi(h)$ without computing either $\varphi(g)$ or $\varphi(h)$.

Theorem 4   If φ is a homomorphism with kernel K defined on a group G with operation $*$, then $\varphi(g) = \varphi(h)$ if and only if $g * h^{-1}$ is in K.

Proof   If $\varphi(g) = \varphi(h)$, then operating on both sides with $\varphi(h)^{-1}$ gives us the equations

$$\varphi(g) * \varphi(h)^{-1} = \varphi(h)\varphi(h)^{-1} = I$$
$$\varphi(g) * \varphi(h^{-1}) = I$$
$$\varphi(g * h^{-1}) \quad = I$$

This means that $g * h^{-1}$ is in K.

Further, if $g * h^{-1}$ is in K, we may reverse the sequence of equations to get $\varphi(g) = \varphi(h)$.   ∎

EXAMPLE 15   Using the homomorphism φ of Example 13, determine whether $\varphi(36) = \varphi(52)$ and whether $\varphi(70) = \varphi(52)$.

Solution   When we use $+$ to stand for the operation, we use $-n$ rather than n^{-1} to stand for the inverse of n. In this notation, we write $m - n$ rather than $m * n^{-1}$, so we wish to determine whether $36 - 52$ is in K. In Example 14, we saw that K consists of multiples of 6. Since $36 - 52 = -16$, which is not a multiple of 6, $\varphi(36) \neq \varphi(52)$. Since $70 - 52 = 18$, which is a multiple of 6, $\varphi(70) = \varphi(52)$.   ■

Recall that for any function φ, $\varphi^{-1}(\{y\})$, called the *inverse image* of y, denotes the set of all x such that $\varphi(x) = y$. Thus the kernel of a homomorphism is the inverse image of the identity.

EXAMPLE 16   Show that the inverse image of an i-place rotation in Example 13 is the equivalence class $\underline{i}$ in Z_6, the integers modulo 6. How do we obtain the equivalence class $\underline{i}$ from the kernel?

Solution   In Example 10, $\varphi(i)$ is an i-place rotation. In Example 15, we showed that $\varphi(i) = \varphi(j)$ if and only if $i \equiv j$ mod 6. Thus $\varphi(j)$ is an i-place rotation if and only if $j \equiv i$ mod 6. Therefore j is in the inverse image of an i-place rotation if and only if $j \equiv i$ mod 6. Thus the inverse image of an i-place rotation is the equivalence class of i mod 6, the class we denote by $\underline{i}$.

The kernel is the inverse image of a zero place rotation, so it is

$$K = \underline{0} = \{\ldots, -6, 0, 6, 12, \ldots\}$$

which is the set of multiples of 6. The equivalence class of i is the set

$$\underline{i} = \{\ldots \ -6 + i, \ 0 + i, \ 6 + i, \ 12 + i, \ldots\}$$

which is the set of numbers we get by adding multiples of 6 to i. We use $K + i$ to stand for $\underline{i}$ in order to show the relationship between K and $\underline{i}$.   ■

The Concept of a Coset

The set $K + i$ in Example 16 is called a *right coset* of K.

> Given a group G with operation $*$ and a subgroup
> H of G we define the **right coset** $H * g$ by the
> formula $H * g = \{h * g \mid h \text{ is in } H\}$.

Right cosets play the same role in arbitrary groups that equivalence classes mod 6 played in Example 16. (There are also similar sets, called *left cosets*, which can play the same role.)

Theorem 5   Let φ be a homomorphism from a group G with operation $*$ to a group H with operation $\bullet$ and let K be the kernel of φ. If $\varphi(g) = h$, then the inverse image of $\{h\}$ is the right coset $K * g$.

Proof Suppose $\varphi(g') = h$. Since $\varphi(g) = h$ as well, Theorem 4 tells us that $g' * g^{-1}$ is in K. This means that $g' * g^{-1} = k$ for some k in K, or $g' = k * g$. Therefore, we may conclude that g' is in $K * g$.

Further, if g' is in $K * g$, then $g' = k * g$, so that $\varphi(g') = \varphi(k * g) = \varphi(k)\varphi(g) = I * \varphi(g) = \varphi(g)$. Thus $K * g = \{g' | \varphi(g') = \varphi(g)\}$. ∎

Theorem 5 shows that when K is the kernel of a homomorphism φ, the cosets of K are the equivalence classes of an equivalence relation, the inverse image relation of φ. Even when a subgroup K isn't the kernel of a homomorphism, its cosets are still equivalence classes. By analogy with Example 16, we say that x and y are **equivalent modulo the subgroup K** in a group G with operation $*$ if $x * y^{-1}$ is in K.

Theorem 6   Equivalence modulo K is an equivalence relation for any subgroup K of a group G, and the equivalence classes of this relation are the right cosets of K.

Proof To prove that the relation is an equivalence relation, we must prove it is reflexive, symmetric, and transitive. We explain why it is symmetric; the other two properties follow more directly from the group properties. We wish to show that if $x * y^{-1}$ is in K, then $y * x^{-1}$ is in K as well. It is a fact that $(g * h)^{-1} = h^{-1} * g^{-1}$ (notice that $(g * h) * (h^{-1} * g^{-1}) = I$) and it is a fact that $(y^{-1})^{-1} = y$ (notice that $(y^{-1}) * y = I$). Because the inverse of each element of K is also in K, if $x * y^{-1}$ is in K, then $(x * y^{-1})^{-1}$ must be in K as well. However,

$$(x * y^{-1})^{-1} = (y^{-1})^{-1} * x^{-1} = y * x^{-1}$$

Therefore if $x * y^{-1}$ is in K, then $y * x^{-1}$ is in K. Thus equivalence modulo K is symmetric. We show that the equivalence classes are cosets as in Theorem 5. ∎

EXAMPLE 17   Show that $H = \{0, 4, 8\}$ (in the notation introduced at the end of Example 10) is a subgroup of the group Z_{12}. Write down its right cosets, using the notation introduced at the end of Example 10.

Solution According to Theorem 1, we should show that the remainder mod 12 of the difference of two members of H is again in H. The differences are 0, 4, 8, -4, -8. Since $-4 \equiv 8 \bmod 12$ and $-8 \equiv 4 \bmod 12$, H is a subgroup of Z_{12}. The coset $H * 1$ will be written $H + 1$. By definition,

$$H + 1 = \{h + 1 | h \text{ is in } H\} = \{0 + 1, 4 + 1, 8 + 1\} = \{1, 5, 9\}$$

Note that

$$H + 5 = \{h + 5 | h \text{ is in } H\} = \{0 + 5, 4 + 5, 8 + 5\} = \{5, 9, 1\} = \{1, 5, 9\} = $$
$$H + 1$$

Similarly, $H + 9 = H + 1$. The other cosets are

$$H + 2 = \{2, 6, 10\} = H + 6 = H + 10$$

and

$$H + 3 = \{3, 7, 11\} = H + 7 = H + 11$$

Thus H has 4 cosets: H, $H + 1$, $H + 2$, and $H + 3$. Notice that both the size of H and the number of cosets of H are factors of 12, the size of Z_{12}—in fact, their product is the size of Z_{12}. ∎

The Size of a Subgroup of a Group

Theorem 7 (LaGrange's theorem) The size of a subgroup of a group G is a factor of the size of G.

Proof Since congruence modulo H is an equivalence relation whose equivalence classes are cosets of H, G is a union of (disjoint) cosets of H. The coset $H * g = \{h * g | h$ is in $H\}$ must have size $|H|$, because if $h_1 * g = h_2 * g$, operating with g^{-1} gives $h_1 = h_2$. The product principle tells us that the size of a union of m disjoint sets each of size n is mn. Here, m is the number of distinct cosets of H, and n is the size of H. (We did not need to show that two different cosets are disjoint because we know that two different equivalence classes must be disjoint.) Thus the size of G is mn; since n is the size of H, this proves the theorem. ∎

Isomorphism

In Example 16, we showed that the inverse image sets of the homomorphism from Z to the rotation group in Example 13 were the equivalence classes modulo 6. These equivalence classes form the 6-element group Z_6. The rotation group R contains 6 rotations—a rotation through no places, one place, and so on. In fact, we saw that the class $\underline{i}$ corresponds to rotating through i places. This suggests strongly that the two groups are essentially the same.

> A group G is **isomorphic** to a group H if there is a
> one-to-one homomorphism φ from G onto H.
> We say that φ is an **isomorphism** from G to H.

(Notice the similarity to isomorphism for graphs.) Saying that G is isomorphic to H is a precise way of saying that G and H are essentially the same. We think of the one-to-one function φ as changing the names of elements of G to the names of corresponding elements of H. The property $\varphi(g * h) = \varphi(g) \cdot \varphi(h)$ of homomorphism says that performing the operation before we change the names has the same effect as performing the operation in the other group after we change the names.

As suggested above, the group Z_6 of inverse images and the group R of rotations are isomorphic. This is just one case of the following theorem about homomorphisms, usually called the **first fundamental theorem of homomorphisms.**

Theorem 8   If φ is a homomorphism with kernel K from a group G with operation $*$ to a group H with operation $\bullet$, then

(a) The equation $(K * g) * (K * h) = K * (g * h)$ defines a binary operation on the cosets of K.

(b) The cosets of K form a group (denoted by G/K and called G modulo K) with this operation.

(c) The group G/K of (b) is isomorphic to the image of φ.

Proof

(a) The operation $*$ associates at least one coset $K * (g * h)$ to the two cosets $K * g$ and $K * h$. To show that we have a binary operation on the cosets, we must show that it associates only one coset to $K * g$ and $K * h$. Thus we must show that if $K * g = K * g'$ and $K * h = K * h'$, then $K * (g * h) = K * (g' * h')$. But $φ(g) = φ(g')$ and $φ(h) = φ(h')$; therefore

$$φ(g * h) = φ(g) \bullet φ(h) = φ(g') \bullet φ(h') = φ(g' * h')$$

Thus the inverse image $K * (g * h)$ of $φ(g * h)$ must be the same as the inverse image $K * (g' * h')$ of the equal value $φ(g' * h')$. Therefore we have a binary operation on the cosets.

(b) Verifying that G/K is a group is analogous to Example 7, part (c).

(c) Define the function $\underline{φ}$ from G/K to H by $\underline{φ}(K * g) = φ(g)$. Then $\underline{φ}(K * g * K * h) = \underline{φ}(K * (g * \overline{h})) = φ(g * h) = φ(g) \bullet φ(h) = \underline{φ}(K * g) \bullet \underline{φ}(K * h)$.

Theorem 4 tells us $\underline{φ}$ is one-to-one, so $\underline{φ}$ is an isomorphism from G/K onto its image, which is also the image of φ. ∎

EXAMPLE 18   Show that the group R of Example 13 is isomorphic to Z_6.

Solution   Since the function φ from Z to R is a homomorphism whose kernel K has the elements of Z_6 for its cosets, and since the operation defined on cosets in Z/K is identical to the addition operation defined on congruence classes in Z_6, Z/K is Z_6. By Theorem 8, Z_6 is therefore isomorphic to R. ∎

EXAMPLE 19   Table 1(a) is an example of an operation table for a group, in this case a group whose elements are named $z, o, x,$ and y. From the table we read that $z * x = x$ and $o * x = y$. In general, for an arbitrarily chosen element a and an (also arbitrarily chosen) element b, the element $a * b$ is the entry in the horizontal row that begins with a and the vertical column that begins with b. What is the identity element of the group? Show that the group is isomorphic to the group consisting of the complex numbers $\{1, -1, i = \sqrt{-1}, -i\}$ with the operation of ordinary complex number multiplication.

Table 1(a)

*	z	o	x	y
z	z	o	x	y
o	o	x	y	z
x	x	y	z	o
y	y	z	o	x

Table 1(b)

·	1	i	-1	$-i$
1	1	i	-1	$-i$
i	i	-1	$-i$	1
-1	-1	$-i$	1	i
$-i$	$-i$	1	i	-1

Table 1(c)

*	z	o	x	y
z	z	o	x	y
o	o	x	y	z
x	x	y	z	o
y	y	z	o	x

Solution   The identity for the group in Table 1(a) is the element z. We see this by observing from the table that $z * z = z$, $z * o = o$, $z * x = x$, $z * y = y$, $o * z = o$, $x * z = x$, and $y * z = y$. Having z appear as the first element in its row and column made it much easier to recognize it as the identity. It is traditional to put the identity first in this way. Table 1(b) was created by computing all possible products among the elements of the set $\{1, i, -i, -1\}$ labeling the rows and columns of a table with the four elements, and putting the product of two elements in the row and column they label. Doing this lets us notice a similarity between the two tables. In the lower rows of each table, each entry in a row equals the entry above it and to the right, except for the last element, which equals the first element in the row above it. This suggests that the elements of the two groups correspond to each other in the order listed, so we guess that the function φ given by $\varphi(1) = z$, $\varphi(i) = o$, $\varphi(-1) = x$, and $\varphi(-i) = y$ is an isomorphism. To prove that this φ is an isomorphism, we replace each element of Table 1(b) by its image under φ, getting Table 1(c). Then the entry in the row that begins with $\varphi(a)$ and the column that begins with $\varphi(b)$ will be $\varphi(a \cdot b)$. But since Table 1(c) and Table 1(a) are identical, the entry that is in the row beginning with $\varphi(a)$ and the column beginning with $\varphi(b)$ is also $\varphi(a) * \varphi(b)$. This tells us that $\varphi(a \cdot b) = \varphi(a) * \varphi(b)$. Thus φ is a homomorphism, and since it is a bijection, it is also an isomorphism. ∎

Concepts Review

1. The associative, identity, and inverse properties of operations are called the _____ properties.

2. A function from the set $S \times S$ of ordered pairs of elements of S to the set S is called a(n) _____ on S.

3. A set is _____ under an operation if the result of that operation always lies in the set.

4. A(n) _____ consists of a set with a binary operation defined on that set having the associative, identity, and inverse properties.

5. A(n) _____ consists of a set with a binary operation (defined on it) satisfying the associative and identity properties.

6. A(n) _____ consists of a set with a binary operation (defined on it) satisfying the associative property.

7. The general linear group of degree n consists of the set of n-by-n _____ _____ with the binary operation of matrix _____ .

8. The _____ group of degree n consists of the set of all permutations of the first n positive integers with the binary operation of function _____ .

9. A(n) _____ of a group G whose operation is $*$ consists of a subset of G which also forms a group under the binary operation $*$.

10. A set S is a subgroup of the group G with operation $*$ if _____ is in S for each pair of elements g and h in S.

11. A(n) _____ from a group G with operation $*$ to a group H with operation $\bullet$ is a function φ from G to H such that $\varphi(g * h) = \varphi(g) \bullet \varphi(h)$ for each g and h in G.

12. The _____ of a homomorphism φ on a group G is the set of all elements of G that φ sends to the identity element in the image.

13. The coset $H * g$ of a subgroup H of a group G determined by g is the set _____ .

14. The relation given by $g \equiv h$ if and only if $g * h^{-1}$ is in H is a(n) _____ _____ on a group G with subgroup H whose _____ _____ are the right cosets of H.

15. A one-to-one homomorphism from G onto H is called a(n) _____ from G onto H.

16. If the group G has a homomorphism whose kernel is K, then the _____ _____ of K in G form a group denoted by G/K called _____ and _____ to the image of the homomorphism.

Exercises

A 1. Explain why the positive rational numbers form a group under multiplication.

2. Define $i * j = (i + j) - 2$ on the set of integers. Show that the integers form a group under the operation *.

In Exercises 3–10, specify which (if any) of the terms *semigroup, monoid,* and *group* apply to the set and operation given.

3. Upper triangular matrices with 1's on the main diagonal; multiplication

4. Upper triangular matrices; addition

5. Elementary matrices; multiplication

6. Rational numbers; multiplication

7. Statements about a universe; $\land$

8. Subsets of a three-element set; $P \, \Delta \, Q = (P \sim Q) \cup (Q \sim P)$

9. Character strings (including the empty one) formed from the set $\{a,b,c\}$ with the operation of concatenation

10. Nonempty character strings formed from the elements of some fixed set with the operation of concatenation

11. Show that with the operation given by $\underline{i} \cdot \underline{j} = \underline{i \cdot j}$ (the class of i times the class of j is the class of $i \cdot j$), the set Z_m of congruence classes modulo m forms a monoid. Why is this monoid not a group?

12. For each statement p about a universe U, let $\underline{p}$ stand for the equivalence class of equivalent statements to p. Define $\underline{p} + \underline{q} = \underline{p \oplus q}$. Why does this define a binary operation? Why does this define a group?

B 13. Explain why the multiples of some fixed number m form a subgroup of the group of all integers under addition.

14. Show that the invertible upper triangular n-by-n matrices form a subgroup of the group of invertible n-by-n matrices under multiplication.

15. Show that the set of 2-by-2 upper triangular integer matrices with 1's on the main diagonal forms a subgroup of the group of invertible upper triangular 2-by-2 matrices under multiplication.

16. Show that if we define $S \, \Delta \, T = (S \cup T) \sim (S \cap T)$, then the subsets of a universe U form a group. Show that the subsets of even size form a subgroup. Do the subsets of odd size form a subgroup?

17. Is the set Z_4 a subgroup of the group Z_8 under addition? (See Example 7.)

18. Is the set of odd integers a subgroup of the group of integers under addition? What about the set of odd integers together with zero?

19. Find a homomorphism from the group of integers under addition onto the group Z_5 (of Example 10). What is the kernel of this homomorphism?

20. Find a homomorphism from the group of integers under addition onto the group Z_4 (of Example 10). What is the kernel of this homomorphism?

21. Find a homomorphism from the group Z_{12} onto the group Z_3.

22. Find a homomorphism from the group Z_3 into a three-element subgroup of the group Z_{12}.

23. Show that the set of permutations f of $\{1,2,3,4,5\}$ such that $f(5) = 5$ forms a subgroup of S_5. What is the size of this subgroup?

24. Show that the set of permutations f of $\{1,2,3,4,5\}$ such that $f(1) \in \{1,2\}$ forms a subgroup of S_5. What is the size of this subgroup?

C 25. Show that $\{0,3,6,9\}$ is a subgroup of Z_{12} and write down its cosets.

26. Show that $\{0,5,10\}$ is a subgroup of Z_{15} and write down its cosets.

27. If a group has 72 elements, can it have a subgroup with 32 elements? With 48 elements? With 24 elements?

28. If a group has 100 elements, can it have a subgroup with 25 elements? With 75 elements? With 40 elements? With 50 elements?

29. Table 2 describes a binary operation $*$ on the set $\{a,b,c\}$. With this operation, $\{a,b,c\}$ forms a group. The table tells us that $a * b = b$, for example, and $b * c = a$. Show that this group is isomorphic to the group Z_3.

Table 2

$*$	a	b	c
a	a	b	c
b	b	c	a
c	c	a	b

Table 3

$*$	a	b	c	d
a	a	b	c	d
b	b	c	d	a
c	c	d	a	b
d	d	a	b	c

30. Table 3 describes a binary operation $*$ on the set $\{a,b,c,d\}$. This table tells us, for example, that $b * b = c$, $c * b = d$, and $b * d = a$. With this binary operation, the set $\{a, b, c, d\}$ forms a group. Show that this group is isomorphic to the group Z_4.

31. What is the identity element of the group in Table 2? State the inverse of each element in Table 2.

32. What is the identity element of the group in Table 3? State the inverse of each element in Table 3.

33. Table 4 is a description of a group on the set $\{w, x, y, z\}$. Determine whether this group is isomorphic to the group in Table 3 and, if so, find an isomorphism.

Table 4

*	w	x	y	z
w	x	w	z	y
x	w	x	y	z
y	z	y	w	x
z	y	z	x	w

Table 5

*	w	x	y	z
w	w	x	y	z
x	x	w	z	y
y	y	z	w	x
z	z	y	x	w

34. Table 5 is a description of a group on the set $\{w, x, y, z\}$. Determine whether this group is isomorphic to the group in Table 3 and, if so, find an isomorphism.

35. Show that the binary operation defined on cosets in Theorem 8 is associative.

36. Show that the coset $K * I$ (which equals K) is an identity element for the binary operation defined in Theorem 8.

Problems

1. Show that the group S_3 of all permutations of $\{1,2,3\}$ is not isomorphic to Z_6.

2. Is the group Z_{12} isomorphic to the group G of all permutations of six people that send neighbors to neighbors in Example 12?

3. Show that if K is a subgroup of G and φ is a homomorphism from G to H, then $\varphi(K)$ (which is defined to be $\{\varphi(k)|k$ is in $K\}$) is a subgroup of H.

4. Show that if φ is a homomorphism from G to H and K is a subgroup of H, then $\varphi^{-1}(K)$ (which is defined to be $\{g|\varphi(g)$ is in $K\}$) is a subgroup of G containing the kernel of φ.

5. A group has the four elements I,a,b,c and the operation $*$. The group is not isomorphic to the group Z_4. Write down a table (similar to Tables 1–5) that describes the operation $*$.

6. The notation $\begin{pmatrix} 1 & 2 & 3 \\ a & b & c \end{pmatrix}$ stands for the permutation f with $f(1) = a$, $f(2) = b$ and $f(3) = c$. Write down the six elements of S_3 in this notation. Show that $\begin{pmatrix} 1 & 2 & 3 \\ 1 & 2 & 3 \end{pmatrix}$ and $\begin{pmatrix} 1 & 2 & 3 \\ 2 & 1 & 3 \end{pmatrix}$ form a subgroup H of S_3. Write down the cosets of this subgroup.

   Does the rule $(H * a) \cdot (H * b) = H * (a * b)$ define a binary operation on the cosets of H?

7. The left coset $g * H$ of a subgroup H of a group G with operation $*$ is by definition $g * H = \{g * h|h$ is in $H\}$. Explain why $g * H = H * g$ for each g in G if H is the kernel of a homomorphism.

8. Show that if $g * H = H * g$ for each g in the group G with subgroup H, then the rule $(H * a) \cdot (H * b) = H * (a * b)$ defines a binary operation on the cosets of H.

9. A subgroup H of a group G with operation $*$ is called **normal** if for each g in G, $g * H = H * g$. Show that a subgroup H of a group G is normal if and only if H is the kernel of a homomorphism.

10. In a group G with operation $*$, we define $g^0 = I$, and we define g^n inductively by $g^n = g^{n-1} * g$.
    (a) Show that if $g^n = I$, then $\{g, g^2, g^3, \ldots, g^n\}$ is a subgroup of G.
    (b) The order of g is defined to be the smallest positive integer n such that $g^n = I$. Prove that the order of g is a factor of the size of the group G.

11. Suppose that G is a group of permutations of $\{1, 2, \ldots, n\}$. The subset G_x of G is defined by $G_x = \{f \mid f$ is in G and $f(x) = x\}$.
    (a) Show that G_x is a subgroup of G.
    (b) Show that for each y, the set $\{f \mid f$ is in G and $f(x) = y\}$ is a coset of G_x.
    (c) The *orbit* of an element x in $\{1, 2, \ldots, n\}$ is defined by $O(x) = \{g(x) \mid g$ is in $G\}$. Show that the size of the orbit $O(x)$ is given by the formula $|O(x)| = |G|/|G_x|$—that is, the size of $O(x)$ is the size of G divided by the size of G_x.
    (d) Relate this to counting seating arrangements of people around a round table.

12. Show that if the element I' of a group G has the identity property, then $I' = I$.

13. Show that if h and h' are inverses to the same element g of a group, then $h = h'$.

14. Show that in a group G, if $g * g' = I$, then $g' = g^{-1}$. (How does this differ from Problem 13?)

Section 12-2
Rings

A The Ring Properties

We began our discussion of groups by asking what properties of addition (or multiplication) we use in solving simple equations. Solving an equation such as

$$2(x + 3) + 3(x + 2) = -3$$

requires that we mix together the operations of addition and multiplication. Furthermore, if we try to work out the solution to this equation, we will find that we want to use the commutative law $i + j = j + i$ for addition to "get all the x-terms together."

Abelian Groups

A group is called **Abelian** (pronounced uh *bee* leean) if $i * j = j * i$ for each i and j in the group. (This name is in honor of the mathematician Abel (pronounced *Ah* bull), who worked on methods for solving equations.) Nearly all the groups we studied in the last section were Abelian, but the symmetric group S_n is not Abelian if $n > 2$, and the group of n-by-n invertible matrices is not Abelian if $n > 1$.

EXAMPLE 20 Find two permutations f and g of $\{1,2,3\}$ such that $f \circ g \neq g \circ f$.

Solution Suppose $f(1) = 2$, $f(2) = 3$, and $f(3) = 1$. Suppose $g(1) = 1$, $g(2) = 3$, and $g(3) = 2$. (These two permutations can be found by experimentation.) Then $f \circ g(1) = f(g(1)) = f(1) = 2$, but $g \circ f(1) = g(f(1)) = g(2) = 3$. This tells us that $f \circ g \neq g \circ f$, since $f \circ g(1) \neq g \circ f(1)$. ∎

The Ring Properties

The *ring properties* of addition and multiplication are a number of rules that describe allowable computations we may make in such work as solving equations, even equations involving matrices or equations involving only integers. Just as the group properties led us to define a structure called a *group*, the ring properties lead us to define a structure called a *ring*. In our discussion of groups, we used a symbol $*$ to stand for an arbitrary binary operation. Here we have two binary operations. In this context, it is standard to use the symbol $+$ to stand for one binary operation and the symbol $\cdot$ to stand for the other binary operation. It is traditional to call the two operations *addition* and *multiplication*, even when they don't involve numbers, matrices, or other similar objects. Further, we will have an identity element for each operation. It is traditional to use 0 to stand for the identity of the $+$ operation and 1 to stand for the identity of the $\cdot$ operation.

A **ring** consists of a set R and two binary operations denoted by $+$ and $\cdot$ on R such that

(a) Under the operation $+$, R forms an Abelian group
(b) Under the operation $\cdot$, R forms a monoid
(c) Multiplication **distributes** over addition, that is
   $r \cdot (s + t) = r \cdot s + r \cdot t$
   $(s + t) \cdot r = s \cdot r + t \cdot r$
   for each r, s, and t in R.

EXAMPLE 21 Show where the distributive property is used and where the commutative property of addition is used in solving the equation $2(x + 3) + 3(x + 2) = -3$.

Solution A natural first step is for us to use the distributive property to write $(2x + 6) + (3x + 6) = -3$. After applying the associative law to rewrite this as $(2x + (6 + 3x)) + 6 = -3$, we use the commutative law to get $(2x + (3x + 6)) + 6 = -3$. We then use the associative law again to get $(2x + 3x) + (6 + 6) = -3$. We use the distributive law to write

$$(2x + 3x) = (2 + 3)x$$

which is $5x$ by the definition of $2 + 3$. Finally, we perform arithmetic in the group of rational numbers under addition and then in the group of nonzero rational numbers under multiplication to solve the equation $5x + 12 = -3$ and get $x = -3$.   ■

EXAMPLE 22   Explain why the integers form a ring in which $+$ and $\cdot$ have the usual meaning.

Solution   We know that the integers form a group under $+$ and that $+$ is a commutative operation. Since multiplication is associative and 1 is an identity element for multiplication, we know the integers form a monoid under $\cdot$. Finally, in Chapter 5 we derived the fact that multiplication distributes over addition by using induction. Thus the integers form a ring.   ■

EXAMPLE 23   Why is the set of even numbers not a ring under the usual $+$ and $\cdot$ operations?

Solution   There is no even integer I such that $I \cdot n = n \cdot I = n$ for each even integer n; thus the even integers do not form a monoid under the usual multiplication operation.   ■

EXAMPLE 24   Define $\underline{i} + \underline{j} = \underline{i + j}$ and $\underline{i} \cdot \underline{j} = \underline{i \cdot j}$ (as in Example 10) for each pair of congruence classes $\underline{i}$ and $\underline{j}$ modulo m. Does the set Z_m of congruence classes mod m form a ring with these operations?

Solution   In Example 10, we discussed why the equation $\underline{i} + \underline{j} = \underline{i + j}$ defines a binary operation on Z_m. In the same way, $\underline{i} \cdot \underline{j} = \underline{i \cdot j}$ defines a binary operation on Z_m. We have verified that Z_m forms a group under addition. Similarly, Z_m forms a monoid under multiplication. Notice that Z_m *can't* form a group under multiplication, because $\underline{0}$ will not have a multiplicative inverse.

To verify the distributive laws, we write

$$
\begin{aligned}
& \underline{i} \cdot (\underline{j} + \underline{k}) \\
= \ & \underline{i} \cdot (\underline{j + k}) \\
= \ & \underline{i(j + k)} \\
= \ & \underline{ij + ik} \\
= \ & \underline{ij} + \underline{ik} \\
= \ & \underline{i} \cdot \underline{j} + \underline{i} \cdot \underline{k}
\end{aligned}
\qquad \text{and} \qquad
\begin{aligned}
& (\underline{j} + \underline{k}) \cdot \underline{i} \\
= \ & (\underline{j + k}) \cdot \underline{i} \\
= \ & \underline{(j + k)i} \\
= \ & \underline{ji + ki} \\
= \ & \underline{ji} + \underline{ki} \\
= \ & \underline{j} \cdot \underline{i} + \underline{k} \cdot \underline{i}
\end{aligned}
$$

Thus we have shown that Z_m has all the properties of a ring.   ■

When it is clear from context that you are referring to elements of Z_m rather than elements of Z, it is traditional to use i, not $\underline{i}$, to stand for the congruence class of i mod m.

Commutative Rings

A ring is called **commutative** if the operation $\cdot$ is a commutative operation, that is if $x \cdot y = y \cdot x$ for all x and y in the ring. The integers, the rational numbers, the real numbers, the complex numbers, and the rings Z_m are examples of commutative rings; the ring of n-by-n matrices (for $n > 1$) is one example of a noncommutative ring.

The integers have a special property that we often use in solving equations. As an example, since $2 \cdot 3 = 6$, we solve the equation $2 \cdot x = 6$ by writing $2 \cdot 3$ in place of 6, getting $2 \cdot x = 2 \cdot 3$ and then "canceling" the two to get $1 \cdot x = 3$. The basis of this cancellation operation comes from the observation that if $2 \cdot x = 2 \cdot 3$, then $2 \cdot x - 2 \cdot 3 = 0$, or by the distributive law, $2(x - 3) = 0$. It is a fact that if the product of two integers is zero, then one of them must be zero. Since 2 isn't zero, $x - 3$ must be zero, so that x must be 3.

> A commutative ring R is called an **integral domain**
> if whenever $r \cdot s = 0$ for elements r and s of R,
> either $r = 0$ or $s = 0$.

The integers, rational numbers, and real numbers are all examples of integral domains.

EXAMPLE 25   Show that Z_6 is not an integral domain.

Solution   We use the underline notation to emphasize the fact that we are discussing equivalence classes. We know that $\underline{2} \cdot \underline{3} = \underline{6}$, but $\underline{6} = \underline{0}$ in the ring Z_6. Thus $\underline{2} \cdot \underline{3} = \underline{0}$, but neither the equivalence class $\underline{2}$ nor the equivalence class $\underline{3}$ is equal to the equivalence class $\underline{0}$. Therefore Z_6 is not an integral domain.   ∎

Notice that the equation $2x = 5$ does not have a solution in the *integers*, but it has the solution $x = 5/2$ in the *rational numbers*. We can solve the equation in the rational numbers because in the rational numbers, 2 has the multiplicative inverse 1/2, by which we multiply to solve the equation.

> A commutative ring in which each nonzero element
> has a multiplicative inverse is called a **field**.

In a field, the nonzero elements thus form a group under the operation $\cdot$. In the rational, real, and complex numbers, the reciprocal of a number is its inverse, so these number systems are fields. In the integers, no numbers but 1 and -1 have multiplicative inverses, so the integers do not form a field.

EXAMPLE 26   Which of the rings Z_2, Z_3, and Z_4 are fields?

Solution   In this example, there is no reason to underline the numbers that stand for equivalence classes in order to distinguish them from integers, so we shall follow custom and not underline them. Z_2 has two members 0 and 1, and $1 \cdot 1 = 1$, so the only nonzero member is its own multiplicative inverse. Therefore Z_2 is a field. In Z_3, we have $1 \cdot 1 = 1$ and $2 \cdot 2 = 1$ (since 4 and 1 generate the same equivalence class modulo 3). Therefore 1 and 2 both are their own inverses in Z_3, so Z_3 is a field. In Z_4, we have $2 \cdot 0 = 0$, $2 \cdot 1 = 2$, $2 \cdot 2 = 0$, and $2 \cdot 3 = 2$; thus there is no equivalence class by which we may multiply the class of 2 in order to get the class of 1. Therefore Z_4 is not a field.   ∎

B The Ring of Integers

Certain fundamental facts about the integers arise both in important applications and in a study of properties that distinguish the ring of integers from most other rings. For example, in order to work accurately with fractions on a computer, we must keep track of both the numerator and denominator, for otherwise the computer will use something similar to a decimal expansion of the fraction to keep track of it.

EXAMPLE 27   In a program to give elementary school students practice with fractions, we choose the numerator and denominator randomly. We wish to give fractions to students in lowest terms. If the numerator we choose is 28 and the denominator is 70, by what must we divide the numerator and denominator in order to reduce the fraction to lowest terms?

Solution   The largest number that is a factor of both 28 and 70 is 14; dividing 28 and 70 by 14 gives us 2/5 in lowest terms.   ∎

The example shows the importance of the greatest common factor or greatest common divisor of two positive integers m and n.

> The **greatest common divisor** of m and n is the largest number that is a factor of both m and n.

A student with a typical mathematical education would find the greatest common factor of 28 and 70 by recognizing that $28 = 4 \cdot 7$ and $70 = 7 \cdot 5 \cdot 2$, so $7 \cdot 2$ is the greatest common factor. This is an excellent method to use when we have the prime factorizations of the numbers available. The method has some drawbacks, however. In a computer program, we would not be likely to have these factorizations available in a form the computer can use. Further, suppose the fraction we wished to reduce to lowest terms had been 6887/8051. Finding the prime factorization of these two numbers is not trivial! In fact, factoring numbers has been identified by computer scientists as a problem for which no quick algorithm is likely to exist. Because of this, systems for secretly encoding messages and computer passwords have been based on the factorization of reasonably large (say about 200 digits) numbers.

Perhaps surprisingly, factorization is not a necessary part of finding greatest common divisors. Euclid observed that if a number d divides m and n, then d is a factor of $m - n$ and $n - m$ as well. This leads us to the following algorithm, sometimes called *Euclid's algorithm* (though that name is often reserved for a faster version of the algorithm).

Algorithm Euclid1
Input: Two numbers m and with $m \le n$
Output: The greatest common divisor d of m and n
Procedure: If $m = n$, then let $d = m$.
Otherwise apply Euclid1 to m and $n - m$.

It is straightforward to prove by induction that the output d of Euclid1 is the greatest common divisor of m and n.

Two traditional notations for the greatest common divisor of m and n are $gcd(m,n)$ and simply (m,n). We shall use the notation (m,n) when it is clear from context that we are discussing greatest common divisors.

EXAMPLE 28   Apply Euclid1 to the numbers 8051 and 6887.

Solution $(8051,6887) = (6887,1164) = (5723,1164) = (4559,1164) = (3395, 1164) = (2231,1164) = (1164,1067) = (1067,97) = (970,97) = (873,97) = (776,97) = (679,97) = (582,97) = (485,97) = (388,97) = (291,97) = (194,97) = (97,97) = 97$.   ■

Notice in Example 28 the long string of 1164's and the even longer string of 97's. Is there a way to avoid these? For example, could we have predicted in advance that we would subtract 1164 exactly five times? If so, we could have subtracted $5 \cdot 1164$ once. Notice that if you divide 1164 into 6887 you get a quotient of 5 and a remainder of 1067. Then if you divide 1067 into 1164 you get a quotient of 1 and a remainder of 97. If you divide 97 into 1067 you get a quotient of 11 and a remainder of zero. From this you see that $(1067,97) = 97$, so the whole string of terms with 97's is unnecessary. These considerations suggest the algorithm usually called **Euclid's algorithm.**

Algorithm Euclid2
Input: Two numbers m and n with $m \le n$.
Output: The greatest common divisor (m,n) of m and n.
Procedure: Divide m into n, getting a quotient q and a non-negative remainder $r < m$.
If $r = 0$, then let $(m,n) = m$.
Otherwise apply Euclid2 to r and m and let (m, m) be the result.

EXAMPLE 29   Apply Euclid2 to the numbers 8051 and 6887.

Solution $(8051,6887) = (6887,1164) = (1164,1067) = (1067,97) = 97$ ■

The example suggests that the algorithm is quite quick for large numbers. In the problems, we explore why the number of arithmetic operations we perform is proportional to the number of digits or (equivalently) the logarithm of the largest number involved. (Since the time needed to perform a computation such as addition is also proportional to the number of digits, the amount of time needed to carry out the computations is proportional to the square of this logarithm.) Of course, the algorithm depends on the fact that we can (quickly) divide n by m. That is, we can write

$$n = qm + r$$

for integers q and r with $0 \leq r < m$. We shall call this fact **Euclid's division principle**; it is traditionally called the *division algorithm* despite the fact that it is not an algorithm in the sense we have defined. We shall reserve the name *division algorithm* for an actual algorithm to find q and r.

Euclid's division principle lies at the heart of many of the algebraic properties (such as unique factorization into prime powers and greatest common divisors) that distinguish the integers from many other rings. The following inductive idea is the central idea of both a proof of Euclid's division principle and an algorithm for finding q and r. If $m > n$, we let $q = 0$ and $r = n$. Otherwise we find the q' and r that let us write $n - m = mq' + r$, and then we add 1 to q' to get q. The algorithm we get from this directly is as time-consuming as Euclid1 and thus would not serve to make Euclid2 faster than Euclid1. In grade school, you learned the *long division algorithm*. If n has k more digits than m, then this algorithm has about k stages, each involving at most a fixed amount of (tedious) work involving subtraction, multiplication (and so on) of integers. This algorithm is designed for people to use, but a variant of it (described in the problems) is appropriate for computers. Long division makes Euclid2 quite fast.

Euclid's Representation Theorem

Euclid's observation that a divisor of m and n divides $n - m$ lets us give an inductive proof of the following surprisingly useful fact, which we shall call **Euclid's representation theorem**.

Theorem 9   For each pair of nonzero integers m and n, there are integers (positive, negative, or zero) a and b such that $gcd(m,n) = am + bn$.

Proof   The proof is an induction on m and n whose base step is the case when m is the *gcd* of m and n. We omit the details.   ■

We say that two positive integers are **relatively prime** if they have no common factors other than 1. We say that a positive integer $p > 1$ is **prime** if its only positive factors are 1 and p. Thus a prime number is relatively prime to any other integer. The greatest common divisor of two relatively prime numbers is 1, so Euclid's representation theorem tells us the following.

If m and n are relatively prime, then there are
integers a and b such that $am + bn = 1$.

In the problems, we outline how we may derive from this equation the fact that the factorization of integers into prime powers is unique (except for the order in which they occur). We've already used strong induction to prove that there is such a factorization, so Euclid's work lets us complete our proof of this fundamental theorem of arithmetic. A second surprising application of Euclid's work tells us that there are many other fields other than the rational, real, and complex numbers studied in school.

Theorem 10   For each prime number p, the ring Z_p of integers modulo p is a field.

Proof   The ring Z_p consists of the cosets $P + 0, P + 1, \ldots, P + p - 1$ where P is the subgroup

$$\{\ldots, -p, 0, p, 2p, \ldots\}$$

(of the integers) consisting of all integer multiples of p. We must show that $P + 1$, $P + 2, \ldots, P + p - 1$ all have multiplicative inverses in this ring. However, if i is between 1 and $p - 1$ (inclusive), then i and p are relatively prime, so there are integers a and b with

$$1 = ai + bp$$

Therefore $ai \equiv 1 \bmod p$. Therefore $\underline{a} = P + a$ is a multiplicative inverse for $\underline{i} = P + i$ in Z_p.   ∎

Concepts Review

1. A group is called _____ if its operation is commutative.

2. A ring has two operations, $+$ and $\cdot$. It is a(n) _____ _____ under $+$, it is a(n) _____ under $\cdot$, and multiplication _____ over _____.

3. A ring is called commutative if its _____ operation is _____.

4. A commutative ring in which either r or s must be 0 if $rs = 0$ is a(n) _____ _____.

5. A(n) _____ is a commutative ring whose nonzero elements form a group under $\cdot$.

6. The _____ _____ _____ of m and n is the largest number that is a factor of both m and n.

7. Euclid's algorithm is an algorithm for finding the _____ _____ _____ of two numbers.

8. Euclid's division principle is sometimes called the _____ _____.

9. If d is the greatest common divisor of m and n, then there are integers a and b such that _____.

10. A positive integer is _____ if its only positive factors are 1 and itself.

11. Two numbers are called _____ _____ if they have no common factors larger than 1.

12. If p is a prime, then the ring Z_p is a _____.

Exercises

A

1. In the group S_4, let f be the permutation given by $f(1) = 2$, $f(2) = 3$, $f(3) = 4$, and $f(4) = 1$. Find a permutation g such that $f \circ g \neq g \circ f$.

2. In the group S_5 let f be the permutation given by $f(1) = 2$, $f(2) = 1$, $f(3) = 4$, $f(4) = 3$, and $f(5) = 5$. Find a permutation g such that $f \circ g \neq g \circ f$.

3. In the group $GL(2)$ of two-by-two invertible matrices, find a matrix N such that $NM \neq MN$, given that $M = \begin{bmatrix} 1 & 0 \\ 2 & 3 \end{bmatrix}$.

4. In the group $GL(2)$ of two-by-two invertible matrices, find a matrix N such that $NM \neq MN$, given that $M = \begin{bmatrix} 1 & 0 \\ 0 & 2 \end{bmatrix}$.

5. A matrix M is *upper triangular* if all entries below and to the left of the main diagonal are 0—that is, if $M_{ij} = 0$ whenever $j < i$. Is the group of 3-by-3 invertible upper triangular matrices with the operation of multiplication Abelian?

6. A matrix M is *diagonal* if all entries not on the main diagonal are zero—that is, if $M_{ij} = 0$ whenever $i \neq j$. Is the group of 3-by-3 diagonal matrices with nonzero diagonal entries and the operation of multiplication Abelian?

7. *Upper triangular* is defined in Exercise 5. Explain why the upper triangular matrices form a ring with the usual operations of multiplication and addition.

8. To add two functions from a set S to the real numbers, we define $(f + g)(x) = f(x) + g(x)$ for each x in S. To multiply two such functions, we define $f \cdot g(x) = f(x)g(x)$. Explain why the functions from a set S to the real numbers form a ring with these operations.

9. Show that if $\underline{p}$ denotes the set of statements equivalent to a statement p about a universe, then the rules $\underline{p} + \underline{q} = \underline{p \oplus q}$ and $\underline{p} \cdot \underline{q} = \underline{p \wedge q}$ define binary operations on these equivalence classes. Does this give us a ring?

10. Show that if $\underline{p}$ is defined as in Exercise 9, then the rules $\underline{p} + \underline{q} = \underline{p \oplus q}$ and $\underline{p} \vee \underline{q} = \underline{p \vee q}$ define binary operations on equivalence classes of statements. Using $\vee$ for the $\cdot$ operation, does this give us a ring?

In Problems 11 and 12, fill in the ring or field property being used in this stage of solving the equation.

11.
$$2(x + 3) + 4x = 18$$
$$(2x + 2 \cdot 3) + 4x = 18 \qquad \text{(a) } _____$$
$$(2x + 6) + 4x = 18 \qquad \text{(Arithmetic)}$$
$$2x + (6 + 4x) = 18 \qquad \text{(b) } _____$$
$$2x + (4x + 6) = 18 \qquad \text{(c) } _____$$
$$(2x + 4x) + 6 = 18 \qquad \text{(d) } _____$$

$$(2 + 4)x + 6 = 18 \qquad \text{(e)} \underline{\hspace{2cm}}$$
$$6x + 6 = 18 \qquad \text{(Arithmetic)}$$
$$(6x + 6) + -6 = 18 + -6 \qquad \text{(f) Add the } \underline{\hspace{2cm}} \text{ of 6 to each side.}$$
$$6x + (6 + -6) = 18 + -6 \qquad \text{(g)} \underline{\hspace{2cm}}$$
$$6x + \quad 0 \quad = 18 + -6 \qquad \text{(h)} \underline{\hspace{2cm}}$$
$$6x = 18 + -6 \qquad \text{(i)} \underline{\hspace{2cm}}$$
$$6x = 12 \qquad \text{(Arithmetic)}$$
$$\tfrac{1}{6}(6x) = \tfrac{1}{6}(12) \qquad \text{(j) Multiply each side by the } \underline{\hspace{2cm}} \text{ of 6.}$$
$$\left(\tfrac{1}{6}\cdot 6\right)x = \tfrac{1}{6}(12) \qquad \text{(k)} \underline{\hspace{2cm}}$$
$$1\cdot x = \tfrac{1}{6}(12) \qquad \text{(l)} \underline{\hspace{2cm}}$$
$$x = \tfrac{1}{6}(12) \qquad \text{(m)} \underline{\hspace{2cm}}$$
$$x = 2 \qquad \text{(Arithmetic)}$$

12.
$$3(2x - 3) \qquad\quad + 6 = 15$$
$$3(2x + -3) \qquad\quad + 6 = 15 \qquad \text{(Definition of subtraction)}$$
$$(3(2x) + 3(-3)) \quad + 6 = 15 \qquad \text{(a)} \underline{\hspace{2cm}}$$
$$((3\cdot 2)x + 3(-3)) \quad + 6 = 15 \qquad \text{(b)} \underline{\hspace{2cm}}$$
$$6x + \quad -9 \qquad + 6 = 15 \qquad \text{(Arithmetic)}$$
$$6x + (-9 \qquad + 6) = 15 \qquad \text{(c)} \underline{\hspace{2cm}}$$
$$6x + \qquad -3 \qquad = 15 \qquad \text{(Arithmetic)}$$
$$(6x + -3) + 3 = 15 + 3 \qquad \text{(d) Add the } \underline{\hspace{2cm}} \text{ of } -3 \text{ to each side.}$$
$$6x + (-3 + 3) = 15 + 3 \qquad \text{(e)} \underline{\hspace{2cm}}$$
$$6x + \quad 0 \quad = 15 + 3 \qquad \text{(f)} \underline{\hspace{2cm}}$$
$$6x = 15 + 3 \qquad \text{(g)} \underline{\hspace{2cm}}$$
$$6x = 18 \qquad \text{(Arithmetic)}$$
$$\tfrac{1}{6}(6x) = \tfrac{1}{6}(18) \qquad \text{(h) Multiply each side by the } \underline{\hspace{2cm}} \text{ of 6.}$$
$$\left(\tfrac{1}{6}\cdot 6\right)x = \tfrac{1}{6}(18) \qquad \text{(i)} \underline{\hspace{2cm}}$$
$$1\cdot x = \tfrac{1}{6}(18) \qquad \text{(j)} \underline{\hspace{2cm}}$$
$$x = \tfrac{1}{6}(18) \qquad \text{(k)} \underline{\hspace{2cm}}$$
$$x = 3 \qquad \text{(Arithmetic)}$$

13. Write down the addition and multiplication tables (in the form of Table 4 and Table 5 in the Exercises of Section 12-1) for Z_4. Which elements have multiplicative inverses?

14. Write down the addition and multiplication tables (in the form of Table 4 and Table 5 in the Exercises of Section 12-1) for Z_6. Which elements have multiplicative inverses?

15. A ring is determined by the addition in Table 6 and the multiplication in Table 7. Is this ring a field?

Table 6

+	0	1	x	y
0	0	1	x	y
1	1	0	y	x
x	x	y	0	1
y	y	x	1	0

Table 7

·	0	1	x	y
0	0	0	0	0
1	0	1	x	y
x	0	x	y	1
y	0	y	1	x

16. A ring is defined by the addition in Table 8 and the multiplication in Table 9. Is this ring a field?

Table 8

+	0	1	x	y	z
0	0	1	x	y	z
1	1	x	y	z	0
x	x	y	z	0	1
y	y	z	0	1	x
z	z	0	1	x	y

Table 9

$\cdot$	0	1	x	y	z
0	0	0	0	0	0
1	0	1	x	y	z
x	0	x	z	1	y
y	0	y	1	z	x
z	0	z	y	x	1

B 17. Use factoring to find the greatest common divisor of 420 and 2090.

18. Use factoring to find the greatest common divisor of 29,400 and 7920.

19. Use algorithm Euclid1 to find the greatest common divisor of 420 and 2090.

20. Use algorithm Euclid1 to find the greatest common divisor of 29,400 and 7920.

21. Use algorithm Euclid2 to find the greatest common divisor of 420 and 2090.

22. Use algorithm Euclid2 to find the greatest common divisor of 29,400 and 7920.

23. Find the greatest common divisor of 394,831 and 78,881.

24. Find the greatest common divisor of 92,213 and 357,481.

25. Give a proof by mathematical induction on n that for each pair of positive integers m and n, we may write $n = qm + r$ with $0 \le r < m$.

26. Give a proof by mathematical induction that the greatest common divisor d of two positive integers m and n may be written as $d = am + bn$ for two integers a and b.

27. The nonzero elements of Z_7 must form a group with the operation of multiplication, since Z_7 is a field. To what group that we have already studied is this group isomorphic?

28. The nonzero elements of Z_{13} must form a group under multiplication, since Z_{13} is a field. To what group that we have already studied is this group isomorphic?

Problems

1. Show that a group with four elements must be Abelian.

2. Which elements in Z_{p^2} have multiplicative inverses if p is prime?

3. Explain why the set of all symbolic statements we can form with the symbols p, q, and r is *not* a ring (with any of the *and, or,* and *exclusive or* operations as its operations). By using the concept of equivalence, show how to construct a ring from these symbolic statements, using *exclusive or* for addition and using *and* for multiplication.

4. A ring homomorphism from a ring R to a ring S is a function f from R to S such that $\varphi(x + y) = \varphi(x) + \varphi(y)$, $\varphi(x \cdot y) = \varphi(x) \cdot \varphi(y)$, and $\varphi(1) = 1$. The kernel of φ is the set $K = \{x | \varphi(x) = 0\}$.

(a) Why is the kernel a subgroup of R under addition?

(b) Show that for any element r in R and any element k in K, $r \cdot k$ is in K.

(c) Show that the cosets $K + r$ of K form a ring with the binary operations
$$(K + r) + (K + s) = K + (r + s) \quad \text{and} \quad (K + r) \cdot (K + s) = K + r \cdot s$$

5. The set of all polynomials (that is, all expressions of the form $a_0 + a_1 x + a_2 x^2 + \cdots + a_n x^n$) is denoted by $F[x]$ when the numbers $a_0, a_1, a_2, \ldots, a_n$ must come from the field F. The degree of a polynomial is the highest n such that $a_n \neq 0$. We use the notation

$$\sum_{i=0}^{n} a_i x^i$$

to stand for a typical polynomial. We define addition by the rule

$$\sum_{i=0}^{n} a_i x^i + \sum_{i=0}^{n} b_i x^i = \sum_{i=0}^{n} (a_i + b_i) x^i$$

The product is defined to be the double sum given by

$$\sum_{i=0}^{n} a_i x^i \cdot \sum_{j=0}^{m} b_j x^j = \sum_{i=0}^{n} \sum_{j=0}^{m} a_i b_j x^{i+j}$$

(a) Show that $F[x]$ is a group under addition.

(b) Show that the product is also equal to $\displaystyle\sum_{k=0}^{m+n} \left(\sum_{i=0}^{k} a_i b_{k-i} \right) x^k$

(c) Show that multiplication is associative.

(d) Show that the polynomial $1 = 1x^0$ is a multiplicative identity element.

(e) Show that multiplication distributes over addition, thus proving that $F[x]$ is a ring.

6. We have shown that if p is a prime number and p is not a factor of the integer n, then there are numbers a and b such that $ap + bn = 1$. Why does multiplying both sides of this equation by the integer m allow you to prove that if a prime is a factor of mn and is not a factor of m, then it is a factor of n? Why may you conclude that if p is a factor of the product $m_1 m_2 \ldots m_k$ of integers, then p must be a factor of one of the integers m_k?

7. Suppose p_1, q_1, p_2, and q_2 are prime numbers such that $p_1 < p_2$ and $q_1 < q_2$.

(a) Show that if $p_1 p_2 = q_1 q_2$, then $p_1 = q_1$ and $p_2 = q_2$.

(b) Show that if $p_1{}^{i_1} p_2{}^{i_2} = q_1{}^{j_1} q_2{}^{j_2}$, then $p_1 = q_1$, $p_2 = q_2$, $i_1 = j_1$, and $i_2 = j_2$.

(c) What is the correct generalization of (b) to n primes? How is it proved?

8. We use $p(x)$ to stand for an arbitrary polynomial. Prove by induction on the degree of $p(x)$ (see Problem 5) that if $p(x)$ and $s(x)$ are polynomials, then there are polynomials $q(x)$ and $r(x)$ such that $p(x) = q(x)s(x) + r(x)$ with $\deg(r(x)) < \deg(q(x))$ or $r(x) = 0$.

9. Based on Problems 5–8, what properties of the integers do you expect polynomials to have?

10. The inductive idea of the division algorithm to write $n = qm + r$ with $0 \leq r < m$ is to first write $n - m = q'm + r$ and then add 1 to q' to get q.

(a) Write out an algorithm based on this idea.

(b) If n has k more digits than m, why is m subtracted at least $10^k - 1$ times in part (a)?

(c) Write out an algorithm based on writing $n - 10^{k-1}m = q'm + r$.

(d) Show that the maximum number of subtractions made by the algorithm in part (c) is proportional to the number of digits of n.

(e) Rewrite the algorithm in (d) to subtract $10^k m$ from n if $10^k m < n$ and to subtract $10^{k-1}m$ otherwise. How does this affect the number of subtractions?

(f) Discuss how the considerations in part (e) of this problem would be irrelevant if m and n were given in binary rather than decimal representations.

11. Discuss why the algorithm discussed in Problem 10 uses a number of operations proportional to the number of digits if we count ordinary arithmetic operations with integers, but is proportional to the square of the number of digits if the only kinds of operations we count are addition and multiplication of single-digit numbers. Discuss why this means that the amount of work needed to find the greatest common divisor of two numbers is no more than the square of the logarithm of the larger number. (This is a practical problem, because working with modern schemes to encode data so that it is secret often involves applying the Euclidean algorithm to numbers with many digits or to polynomials of high degree.)

Section 12-3
Finite Fields and
Error Correcting Codes

🅐 Parity Check Matrices

The finite fields Z_2, Z_3, Z_5, and so on may appear at this point as mathematical curiosities. Table 10 and Table 11 which are the addition table and multiplication table for Z_2 (the integers mod 2), reinforce this appearance. The multiplication table appears normal, but the equation $1 + 1 = 0$ does not give one immediate faith in this system of arithmetic!

Table 10　Addition in Z_2

+	0	1
0	0	1
1	1	0

Table 11　Multiplication in Z_2

·	0	1
0	0	0
1	0	1

However, this strange equation is the basis of a number of applications. Imagine, for example, a single light switch. Think of 0 as an instruction not to touch the switch, and 1 as an instruction to flip it. If you flip it once, the lighting in the room will change (from dark to light or light to dark). If you flip it and then flip it again, however, the light in the room will be the same as when you started. This is equivalent to not flipping it at all. Symbolically, we might write

$$\text{flip} + \text{flip} = \text{noflip}$$

which is the equation $1 + 1 = 0$. In a computer, if we have a sequence of, say, 32 bits, each telling us whether one of 32 elements in a universe is or is not in a set, then to complement the set we want to change each 1 to a 0 and each 0 to a 1. We can accomplish this by adding 1 modulo two to each bit. Circuits that carry out this mod 2 addition are reasonably straightforward to construct. As you may suspect now, finite fields with two elements are the most important finite fields for applications. There are fields with 4, 8, 16, . . . elements as well, and these also arise in many applications. Fields with p^n elements for an odd prime p are also useful sometimes. The size of a finite field must be a power of a prime.

Using Finite Fields as Alphabets

One application of finite fields is to the storage, retrieval, and communication of information. Our information is in the form of words built up from a certain alphabet. In a computer, this alphabet may be $\{0,1\}$; in the case of storing English words and sentences, the alphabet may consist of the 26 usual alphabet letters together with the space character (to put a space between words and a double space between sentences), giving us an alphabet with 27 letters. Since 2 is a prime and 27 is a power of a prime, these alphabets may be thought of as symbols representing the elements of a finite field. We shall concentrate on the two-element alphabet $\{0,1\}$ in our examples.

Let us think of a message to be sent from one computer to another as a "word" consisting of a sequence of zeros and ones.

EXAMPLE 30   How many different messages may be represented as a sequence of three zeros and ones?

Solution   Since we have the two choices 0 and 1 for x_1, x_2, and x_3, we have $2 \cdot 2 \cdot 2 = 8$ possible sequences (or words) (x_1, x_2, x_3).   ∎

The message represented by a sequence such as $(0,1,0)$ may be anything—for example, "The number you have reached is not in service . . . ." Example 30 shows that eight such messages can be represented. Now when a word (sequence of bits) is sent between two devices (say a computer that recognizes which lines are in service and a computer that plays recorded messages) it is possible for external influences (called *noise*) to change a 0 to a 1 or a 1 to a 0. Similarly, it is possible that an imperfection in a memory chip may cause an item stored in a computer memory to be stored incorrectly. In order to counteract this, electrical engineers build redundancy into messages—converting a 3-bit message to 4 or 5 or more bits and using the additional information to determine whether an error has occurred.

For example, we could send the same message twice; if there is an error, we will see a difference between the two messages. If we send the same message three times and discover that one of the digits is inconsistent, we can use majority rule and decide to ignore the word with the inconsistent digit and decode the message as being the word that arrived identically twice.

Parity Check Equations

For the sake of efficiency, we should keep the redundancy to the minimum amount needed to achieve our goal. If our goal is simply to determine whether or not one error occurs, there is an approach used by engineers that is simpler than sending the message twice. In this approach, after sending our n-bit message, we send one more bit, which is a 1 if the message has an odd number of 1's and a 0 if the message has an even number of 1's. The additional information is called an **overall parity check.** (This defines the word *parity* for our purposes; in normal conversation, something has parity if it can be even or odd and the "evenness" or "oddness" is its parity.) With this parity check added, we have a sequence of $n + 1$ digits, and the $(n + 1)$-digit sequence we receive will have an even number of ones if our message is transmitted correctly. We can capture this idea with the formula

$$x_1 + x_2 + \cdots + x_n + x_{n+1} \equiv 0 \bmod 2$$

Equivalently, we may write

$$x_1 + x_2 + \cdots + x_n + x_{n+1} = 0 \text{ in } Z_2$$

When our received message does not satisfy the equation, the received message must have $1, 3, 5, \ldots$, or some odd number of errors. Unfortunately, the system does not tell us where the error is if there is one, and it does not warn us if exactly two errors have occurred. We thus ask if we can modify the system slightly, using several different "parity check bits" in such a way that different error locations will cause different parity check bits to be 1 or 0.

EXAMPLE 31   Write down equations to compute three parity checks x_4, x_5, and x_6 that check the parity of each two of the three bits x_1, x_2, and x_3 at a time.

Solution   There are three two-element sets of bits, $\{x_1, x_2\}$, $\{x_1, x_3\}$, and $\{x_2, x_3\}$. To do a parity check on each of these sets, we write (in the field Z_2)

$$
\begin{array}{llll}
x_1 + x_2 = x_4 & \text{or} & x_1 + x_2 \quad\quad + x_4 \quad\quad\quad = 0 & (1) \\
x_1 + x_3 = x_5 & \text{or} & x_1 \quad\quad + x_3 \quad\quad + x_5 \quad\quad = 0 & (2) \\
x_2 + x_3 = x_6 & \text{or} & \quad\quad x_2 + x_3 \quad\quad\quad + x_6 = 0 & (3) \quad\blacksquare
\end{array}
$$

EXAMPLE 32   Explain how to determine the position in which the error has occurred if one error occurs in sending the message $x_1 x_2 x_3 x_4 x_5 x_6$ described in Example 31.

Solution If an error occurs in x_1 alone, then the first and second equation will fail. Similarly, an error in x_2 alone or x_3 alone will make a different set of two equations fail. On the other hand, an error in x_4, x_5, or x_6 will cause only Equation (1) or only Equation (2) or only Equation (3) to fail. Thus each place where an error occurs will lead to a different pattern of failed equations, and from the pattern of failed equations we can determine which place contains the error. ■

The set of 6-tuples $(x_1, x_2, x_3, x_4, x_5, x_6)$ that satisfy the three equations in Example 31 is called a *three-dimensional code* of *length* 6 and *redundancy* 3. The set of all 4-tuples (x_1, x_2, x_3, x_4) satisfying the overall parity check equation $x_1 + x_2 + x_3 + x_4 = 0$ is a three-dimensional code of length 4 and redundancy 1. Notice that the overall parity check equation may be rewritten as the matrix equation

$$\begin{bmatrix} 1 & 1 & 1 & 1 \end{bmatrix} \begin{bmatrix} x_1 \\ x_2 \\ x_3 \\ x_4 \end{bmatrix} = 0$$

The three equations of the code of Example 32 may be written as the matrix equation

$$\begin{bmatrix} 1 & 1 & 0 & 1 & 0 & 0 \\ 1 & 0 & 1 & 0 & 1 & 0 \\ 0 & 1 & 1 & 0 & 0 & 1 \end{bmatrix} \begin{bmatrix} x_1 \\ x_2 \\ x_3 \\ x_4 \\ x_5 \\ x_6 \end{bmatrix} = 0$$

Any set of parity check equations may be converted to such a matrix equation. Notice that if we have m parity check bits, then our matrix will have m rows, one for each parity check equation. In addition, the last m columns of the matrix will form an identity matrix (because the last m x_i's are determined from the first $n - m$ x_i's).

> We define a **code of length n, redundancy m and dimension $n - m$** to be the set of all column matrices X satisfying a matrix equation $MX = 0$ in which M is an m-by-n matrix, called the **parity check matrix**, whose last m columns form (or can be row reduced to) an identity matrix.

We call a solution X of the matrix equation a **code word**. We assume that all the entries of all the matrices are chosen from some finite field F, typically Z_2 (as shown in Tables 10 and 11), called the **alphabet** of the code.

EXAMPLE 33   If C is the code described by the parity check equations of Example 31, how many code words does it contain?

Solution   We may choose x_1 to be either 0 or 1, x_2 to be either 0 or 1, and x_3 to be either 0 or 1. These choices determine the other x_i's. Thus we have $2^3 = 8$ words in the code.   ∎

The bits $x_1, x_2, \ldots, x_{n-m}$ are called the **information bits** of the code, and the bits $x_{n-m+1}, \ldots, x_n$ are called the **parity check bits** of the code. We can always choose the information bits to have any values we please, but these values then determine the parity check bits. It is typical to use k to stand for the number of information bits and to refer to a code of length n with k information bits as an **(n,k) code**. The **rate** of a code is the ratio k/n; thus the rate of a code is the fraction of its places devoted to carrying information. If all other considerations are equal, we would prefer a code with a high rate to a code with a low rate, because a high-rate code can carry more information. The code C of Examples 31–33 has rate $1/2$. By using C to send a message with three bits of information, we may correct any single error in the six bits of C; such a code is called a **single-error correcting** code.

B   Hamming Codes

We found our $(6,3)$ single-error correcting code largely by experimentation. It gives a significantly more efficient scheme than the $(9,3)$ single-error correcting code that comes from repeating a three-bit message three times. Are there, however, still more efficient schemes? Is there a $(5,3)$ single-error correcting code—that is, can we use three information bits and only two parity check bits and still correct each single error? With some experimentation, you should be able to see that since there are five bits to be corrected and only three nonempty subsets of a set of two parity check bits, we cannot hope to correct each single error among the five bits. In another direction, we might ask whether there is a $(7,4)$ or an $(8,5)$ single-error correcting code. That is, can we increase the amount of information we send without having to increase the redundancy? (This would increase the rate and so be more efficient.) Another question we can ask is what we can accomplish if we are willing to have redundancy 4. Then how much information can we send? Just four bits as our $(6,3)$ code might suggest? Or perhaps could we send ten or eleven bits of information? For questions such as these, experimentation with constructions will be at best a time-consuming way to get the answers. What we need is an overall explanation of why a code can correct errors and how families of related codes that correct these errors may be constructed. R. W. Hamming began the development of such an explanation in a series of articles appearing in the *Bell System Technical Journal* around 1950. Since then, the subject has developed so fast that the authors of a 750-page book on the subject (*The Theory of Error Correcting Codes*, by F. J. MacWilliams and N. J. A. Sloane, North Holland,

1977) had to restrict their coverage to only part of the topic! We outline the beginnings of the theory of error correcting codes.

Hamming Distance

Hamming explained why codes can be used to correct errors with a concept of distance, now called *Hamming distance*. The **distance** between two matrices of the same shape (column matrices with n entries in the case of codes) is the number of places in which their entries are different. It is standard to use $[x \ y \ z]^t$ (read as "*xyz* transpose," not "*xyz* to the t") to stand for the column matrix with entries x, y, and z.

EXAMPLE 34 Find the distance between $[0 \ 1 \ -1 \ 0]^t$ and $[1 \ 1 \ 0 \ 1]^t$.

Solution The distance between these two matrices is 3, because they are different in the first, third, and fourth places. ∎

If an error changes one place of a code word, the result is 1 unit of distance away from the original code word. If this code word is the *only* one at a distance of 1 from the changed word, then we can correct the error by decoding the changed word to the closest code word. This suggests a general principle called the **nearest neighbor principle.**

> If each possible changed word with one error is
> 1 unit of distance from only one code word, then
> decoding the changed word to the closest code
> word will correct this single error.

To apply the principle, we need a way to test whether we can change one place in one code word and get a new word just 1 unit of distance away from two different code words. To develop such a test, imagine that by changing one place in one word X in the code, we get a word Z that is 1 unit of distance from another code word Y (as well as from X). In Figure 1, you see one way to visualize this situation.

Figure 1 In geometry, the length of one side of a triangle is no more than the sum of the lengths of the other two sides.

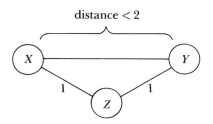

The picture suggests that if the incorrect word Z is a distance 1 from both the code word X and the code word Y, then the distance from X to Y is at most 2. Since Hamming distances must be integers, this means that the distance from X to Y must be 0, 1, or 2. This gives us our test: If there are not two words in our code that are a distance 1 or 2 from each other, then no word Z (even one not in the code) can be at a distance of 1 from each of two code words X and Y. The geometry thus suggests that if the minimum distance between any two code words is 3 or more, then decoding a received word to the closest code word will correct any single error. This is true, but in analyzing Figure 1 we made a subtle geometric assumption. In ordinary geometry, if the distance from X to Z is 1 and the distance from Z to Y is 1, then the distance from X to Y can be no more than $1 + 1$, or 2. As you see in Figure 1, the geometric property we are using is that the length of one side of a triangle is no more than the sum of the lengths of the other two sides (with equality possible if the three points lie on a line). If we use $d(X,Y)$ to stand for the distance from X to Y, then we may write our geometric property as the

triangle inequality: $d(X,Y) \leq d(X,Z) + d(Z,Y)$

If the triangle inequality holds for Hamming distance, then for Z to be a distance 1 from both X and Y, the distance from X to Y must be 2 or less.

Theorem 11   The triangle inequality holds for the Hamming distance function.

Proof   By making at most $d(X,Z) + d(Z,Y)$ changes, we can convert X to Y.   ∎

Theorem 12   If the minimum distance between each two code words of the code C is at least 3, then the code may be used to correct any single error that occurs in transmitting a code word.

Proof   Given in the discussion of Figure 1.   ∎

EXAMPLE 35   What is the minimum distance between two words of the code C of Examples 31–33, whose parity check matrix is the following?

$$M = \begin{bmatrix} 1 & 1 & 0 & 1 & 0 & 0 \\ 1 & 0 & 1 & 0 & 1 & 0 \\ 0 & 1 & 1 & 0 & 0 & 1 \end{bmatrix}$$

Solution   The column matrix $[1\ 1\ 1\ 0\ 0\ 0]^t$ is a solution to $MX = 0$. This word has three nonzero entries, so its distance from the all-zeros code word is 3. If two code words X and Y were a distance 2 apart, then subtracting one from the other would give a column matrix Z with just two nonzero entries. Since $MX = 0$ and $MY = 0$, we also have $0 = MX - MY = M(X - Y) = MZ$. However, if Z has a 1 in position i, a 1 in position j, and a 0 in each other place, then the column matrix MZ is the sum of column i and column j of M. But if $Ci + Cj = 0$, then $Ci = -Cj = Cj \pmod 2$. Since no two columns of the matrix M are equal, no two columns of the matrix can sum to 0 (mod 2). Thus Z cannot be in the code, and therefore the code cannot have two code words a distance 2 apart. Similarly, there cannot be two code words a distance 1 apart (because this would require a column of zeros). Therefore the minimum distance between two code words is 3. ∎

Notice how the example used the fact that the difference of two code words is a code word. This is exactly the test we had in Theorem 4 for a subgroup of a group, and the reason that codes are sometimes called **group codes.**

Theorem 13   A code is an Abelian group under matrix addition.

Proof   See Theorem 4 and note that if $MX = 0$ and $MY = 0$, then $M(X - Y) = 0$ also. ∎

The number of nonzero entries in a code word is called its **weight.** In the example, we converted the problem of finding the distance between two code words to finding the weight of their difference. Our next theorem tells us that this works in general.

Theorem 14   The minimum distance between two code words in a code C is the minimum weight of any nonzero word in C.

Proof   Similar to the computations of Example 35. ∎

Perhaps the most important idea in Example 35 is the tie between the 1's in a vector X and the columns we add to get MX. To be precise, we may write the following theorem.

Theorem 15   If X is the matrix $[x_1\ x_2\ \ldots\ x_n]^t$ and the matrix M has columns $C1, C2, \ldots, Cn$, then MX is the column matrix

$$\sum_{i=1}^{n} x_i Ci$$

Proof   This follows directly from the definition of matrix multiplication. ∎

We use Theorem 15 by observing that if a code word X has weight 2, say with $x_i \neq 0$ and $x_j \neq 0$, then $MX = 0$ becomes $x_i Ci + x_j Cj = 0$, or $Ci = -(x_j/x_i)Cj$. (When our alphabet is Z_2, this reduces to $Ci = Cj$.) Using this idea, Hamming explained that if all the columns of a matrix M with Z_2 entries are different from zero and each other, then $MX = 0$ is impossible if X has weight 2 or less. This led him to observe that there are seven nonzero column matrices with three entries ($2^3 = 8$, but one of the eight column matrices with three entries is the zero matrix).

Thus arranging these seven column matrices appropriately as the columns of a matrix will give us the parity check matrix

$$M' = \begin{bmatrix} 1 & 1 & 0 & 1 & 1 & 0 & 0 \\ 1 & 0 & 1 & 1 & 0 & 1 & 0 \\ 0 & 1 & 1 & 1 & 0 & 0 & 1 \end{bmatrix}$$

The matrix M' gives a (7,4) code, and since all columns are different, the code must have minimum distance 3 or more. We can find a column matrix of weight 3 in the code, so the code has minimum distance 3. Thus it is a (7,4) single-error correcting code. This shows us by example that with redundancy 3 we can have at least four information bits. The code whose parity check matrix is M' is called the **Hamming code** of length 7. Hamming also discovered a simple method for determining *where* an error occurs if one does occur.

EXAMPLE 36   Show that the Hamming code is the set of solution column matrices X to $MX = 0$ where

$$M = \begin{bmatrix} 1 & 0 & 1 & 0 & 1 & 0 & 1 \\ 0 & 1 & 1 & 0 & 0 & 1 & 1 \\ 0 & 0 & 0 & 1 & 1 & 1 & 1 \end{bmatrix}$$

Solution   We can row reduce M' to M. Row operations don't change the solutions to a matrix equation.   ■

If we start with the code word X and have one error in position i, the resulting column matrix will be $X + E_i$, where E_i has a 1 in position i and 0's elsewhere. Hamming noted that

$$M(X + E_i) = MX + ME_i = 0 + ME_i = Ci$$

However, in the order we have given the columns, Ci is the binary representation of the integer i. Thus to detect an error, we multiply M by the word Y that we receive. If we get 0, then we received a code word. If there was one error, then MY is the binary representation of the number of the bit we should change. (If there are two or more errors, then we will get a wrong answer.) In the Problems, we discuss how to modify the code so that it allows us to detect (but not correct) the fact that two errors occur if there are two errors in the received word.

We close with two observations. First, Hamming discovered an infinite family of codes; we gave the code for $m = 3$. In general, a Hamming code has length $2^m - 1$, and its parity check matrix has all the nonzero m-entry column matrices of 0's and 1's as its columns. Second, if the minimum distance of a code is more than 3, then the code may be able to correct more errors. In particular, if $d = 2e + 1$, we can correct e errors. There are families of codes, called *BCH codes*, that are similar to the Hamming codes (but with more redundancy) and can correct e errors for any e we choose. To construct these codes requires a great deal of knowledge about finite fields with p^e elements.

Concepts Review

1. In the field of integers modulo 2, 1 plus 1 is _____.

2. The equation _____ is the equation of an overall parity check on digits x_1 to x_n.

3. If the last m columns of an m-by-n matrix form an identity matrix, then the set of column matrices X such that $MX = 0$ is called a(n) _____ of length _____, dimension _____, and redundancy _____.

4. The _____ of a code is the field over which we define the _____ _____ matrix M.

5. The _____ of an (n,k) code is the ratio k/n.

6. The number of bits of information that can be communicated with an (n,k) code is _____.

7. The _____ between two code words is the number of places where they are different.

8. The _____ _____ tells us that $d(X,Y) \leq d(X,Z) + d(Z,Y)$.

9. A code can correct any single error if the minimum weight of any nonzero word in the code is at least _____.

10. The _____ _____ of length n and redundancy m has all nonzero m-tuples of 0's and 1's as the columns of its parity check matrix.

Exercises

A

1. A computer display screen has a rectangular array of spots called *pixels*, which produce white when they are glowing and black when they are not. A hypothetical graphics program represents the screen as a matrix with a 1 in row i and column j if the pixel i units over and j units up from the bottom left corner is glowing. This program lets you draw in two modes. In the "overwrite" mode, moving the drawing instrument over a pixel turns the glow off so that the pixel is dark after the motion, regardless of whether it was dark or glowing to start with. In the "reversal" mode, moving the instrument over a pixel changes a glowing spot to dark and a dark spot to glowing. Explain how these modes correspond to adding or multiplying by 0 mod 2.

2. A computer represents the truth or falsity of a statement by a logical (or *Boolean*) variable that has the value 1 if the statement is true and the value 0 if the statement is false. A set of statements gives a set of variables. Among the operations the computer can perform on variables representing the statements are *and* (from the truth values of the variables p and q, it gives the truth value of $p \land q$) and *exclusive or* (from the truth values of p and q, it gives the truth value of $p \oplus q$). Describe the relationship between these logical operations and arithmetic mod 2.

3. An alphabet for sending rudimentary English messages consists of the 26 alphabet letters, the 10 digits, and the space character. Is there a finite field that lets us represent this alphabet? If so, describe it. If not, why not?

4. A slightly less rudimentary alphabet than that in Exercise 3 consists of all lowercase and uppercase alphabet letters, the 10 digits, and the space character. Is there a finite field that lets us represent this alphabet? If so, describe it, and if not, tell why not.

5. If we add a period, a comma, and a question mark to the alphabet of Exercise 4, is there a finite field that lets us represent this alphabet? If so, describe it, and if not, tell why not.

6. An alphabet for expressions involving arithmetical computations consists of the 26 alphabet letters, the 10 digits, the space symbol, symbols for addition, subtraction, multiplication, and division, a period, and an equals sign. Is there a finite field that lets us represent this alphabet? If so, describe it, and if not, tell why not.

7. A message is to have two bits of information, x_1 and x_2. Determine whether the system of parity checks $x_3 = x_1$, $x_4 = x_2$, $x_5 = x_1 + x_2$ will allow you to correct any single error that might occur in transmitting the message $x_1x_2x_3x_4x_5$.

8. Determine whether the system of parity checks given by

$$x_5 = x_1 + x_2 + x_4, \; x_6 = x_1 + x_2 + x_3 \quad \text{and} \quad x_7 = x_2 + x_3 + x_4$$

will allow you to correct any single error made in transmitting the message $x_1x_2x_3x_4x_5x_6x_7$.

9. Suppose we add the equation $x_6 = x_1 + x_2 + x_3 + x_4 + x_5$ to the equations in Exercise 7. Show that we can correct any single error that occurs and show that if exactly two errors occur, the pattern of incorrect equations will tell us that two errors occurred rather than one but will not tell us which two digits are in error.

10. Add the equation $x_7 = x_1 + x_2 + x_3 + x_4 + x_5 + x_6$ to the equations of Example 31. Show that if any single error occurs, then we can correct it, and that if any two bits are in error, we can detect that two errors (*not* one error) have occurred, but we cannot determine which two bits are in error.

In Exercises 11–14, write down the parity check matrix for the code specified.

11. The code of Exercise 7

12. The code of Exercise 8

13. The code of Exercise 9

14. The code of Exercise 10

B   In Exercises 15–20, find the Hamming distance between the two column matrices given.

15. $\begin{bmatrix} 1 \\ 0 \\ 0 \\ 0 \\ 0 \\ 1 \end{bmatrix}$ $\begin{bmatrix} 0 \\ 1 \\ 0 \\ 1 \\ 1 \\ 0 \end{bmatrix}$ 16. $\begin{bmatrix} 1 \\ 1 \\ 1 \\ 0 \\ 0 \\ 1 \end{bmatrix}$ $\begin{bmatrix} 1 \\ 0 \\ 1 \\ 0 \\ 1 \\ 0 \end{bmatrix}$ 17. $\begin{bmatrix} 1 \\ 1 \\ 1 \\ 0 \\ 0 \\ 0 \end{bmatrix}$ $\begin{bmatrix} 0 \\ 0 \\ 0 \\ 1 \\ 1 \\ 1 \end{bmatrix}$

18. $\begin{bmatrix} 1 \\ 0 \\ 0 \\ 0 \\ 1 \end{bmatrix}$ $\begin{bmatrix} 0 \\ 1 \\ 0 \\ 1 \\ 0 \end{bmatrix}$ 19. $\begin{bmatrix} 1 \\ 2 \\ 1 \\ 1 \\ 0 \end{bmatrix}$ $\begin{bmatrix} 3 \\ 0 \\ 1 \\ 0 \\ 2 \end{bmatrix}$ 20. $\begin{bmatrix} 1 \\ -1 \\ 1 \\ 2 \\ 0 \end{bmatrix}$ $\begin{bmatrix} -1 \\ 1 \\ 1 \\ 1 \\ -1 \end{bmatrix}$

In Exercises 21–24, determine the minimum weight of a nonzero word in the code specified.

21. The code of Exercise 7

22. The code of Exercise 8

23. The code of Exercise 9 (*Hint:* What does the overall parity check equation tell you about the weight of any word in the code?)

24. The code of Exercise 10 (See hint to Exercise 23.)

25. How many nonzero column matrices of four zeros and ones are possible? Construct a parity check matrix for a $(15,11)$ code that will correct an error in any single position.

26. Using Z_3 rather than Z_2, what is the maximum number of nonzero column matrices with three entries such that no one column matrix is a multiple of any other? Construct a parity check matrix for a $(13,10)$ code over Z_3 that allows us to correct an error in any single position.

27. How many code words are in the Hamming $(7,4)$ code?

28. How many code words are there in an (n,k) code over the field Z_2?

29. Suppose we add a column of three 0's at the end of the parity check matrix of the $(7,4)$ Hamming code and then add a row of eight 1's at the bottom of the matrix, giving a 4-by-8 matrix. The code with this parity check matrix is called the *extended Hamming code*. To what new parity check equation does this last row correspond? Can the weight of a code word be an odd number? What are the length, redundancy, and minimum distance of the extended Hamming code? Use H to stand for the parity check matrix. What will the last entry of HX be if X is obtained from a code word by introducing one error? By introducing two errors? Can HX be the all-zero column matrix if X has two errors? What does this tell us about our ability to use the code to check whether two errors have occurred?

30. Apply the procedure of Exercise 29 to the parity check matrix you constructed in Exercise 25, giving a 5-by-16 matrix. Answer the questions of Exercise 29 for the code with this parity check matrix.

Problems

1. If M is the parity check matrix of an (n,k) code C and X is an n-entry column matrix, the *syndrome* of X is the matrix MX. Show that the set of all column matrices with a fixed syndrome S is a coset of C in the group of all n-by-1 matrices under addition.

2. Show that all column matrices in a coset of a code C in the group of all n-by-1 matrices under addition have the same syndrome (see Problem 1.)

3. Show that if a code C has minimum distance d, then there is at most 1 (but there may be 0) word of weight *less* than $d/2$ in each coset of C.

4. How many different syndromes (see Problem 1) may an (n,k) code over $GF(2)$ have? Must there be this many syndromes?

5. Using the $(6,3)$ code of Examples 31–33, write down a table with two rows. In row 1, write down the possible syndromes (see Problem 1). In row 2, write down a word of

minimum weight in the coset (see Problem 2) of matrices with the syndrome above it, or write down an asterisk if there are two or more words of minimum weight in that coset. Explain why the following method will decode a received column matrix Y correctly even if a single error has occurred in transmission. Compute the syndrome of Y. If there is a word E in the table below the syndrome of Y, report that $X = Y + E$. Otherwise report that more than one error occurred.

6. Repeat Problem 5 using the (7,4) Hamming code. Explain why there are no asterisks. Explain why the decoding method works.

7. On the basis of Problem 5 and Problem 6, propose a general method of decoding a received word that will correct any number of errors smaller than $d/2$. Explain why the general method works.

8. A sphere of radius r around a column matrix Y is by definition the set of all column matrices whose Hamming distance from Y is r or less. Find the spheres of radius 1 around the column vectors $[1 \ 1 \ 0 \ 1]^t$ and $[0 \ 0 \ 0 \ 0]^t$.

9. If d is the minimum distance of the code C of length n, we say that C is *perfect* if the spheres whose radii are $\lfloor (d - 1)/2 \rfloor$ (the greatest integer less than or equal to $(d - 1)/2$) and whose centers are at the code words form a partition of the n-entry column vectors. Is the (7,4) Hamming code perfect? Is the (8,4) Hamming code perfect? Is the (6,3) code of Examples 31–33 perfect?

10. Prove that if there is an (n,k) perfect code over Z_2 that has minimum distance $2t + 1$, then the numbers n, k, and t must satisfy

$$\left(\binom{n}{0} + \binom{n}{1} + \binom{n}{2} + \cdots + \binom{n}{t} \right) 2^k = 2^n$$

Chapter 12
Review Exercises

1. Using algebraic properties, explain why the matrix equation $AX = B$, in which A is an n-by-n invertible matrix and B is an n-by-k matrix, has a unique solution for an n-by-k matrix X.

In Exercises 2–6, determine which of the terms *monoid, semigroup,* and *group* apply to the structure described.

2. Upper triangular matrices; addition

3. Upper triangular matrices whose diagonal entries have a nonzero product; matrix product

4. Subsets of a set U; set intersection

5. Statements about a universe U; *and*

6. "Nonsense" words (and real words) that we can make from the alphabet; concatenation

7. Show that the m-by-m matrices whose diagonal entries are all zero form a subgroup of the group of all matrices with the addition operation.

8. The group S_4 of all permutations of $\{1, 2, 3, 4\}$ has 24 elements. Draw a square and number its vertices. Some permutations in S_4 correspond to picking the square up, moving it around in space, and putting it back down where it used to be. Show that these permutations form a subgroup of S_4. Could there be exactly 10 of these permutations?

9. Describe all subgroups of Z_8.

10. In Exercise 8, find a homomorphism from the integers into the group S_4 that has the motions that correspond to rotating the square around its center as its image. What is the kernel of this homomorphism?

11. Show that the group of rotations you found in Exercise 10 is isomorphic to Z_4.

12. Find a homomorphism from the group Z_{20} onto the group Z_5. What is the kernel of this homomorphism?

13. What are the cosets of the kernel of the homomorphism in Exercise 10? Write them down.

14. If a group has 60 elements, could it have a subgroup with 15 elements? With 20 elements? With 25 elements?

15. Table 12 describes a group with 6 elements. Is this group Abelian?

Table 12

$\cdot$	i	r_1	r_2	f_{12}	f_{13}	f_{23}
i	i	r_1	r_2	f_{12}	f_{13}	f_{23}
r_1	r_1	r_2	i	f_{13}	f_{23}	f_{12}
r_2	r_2	i	r_1	f_{23}	f_{12}	f_{13}
f_{12}	f_{12}	f_{23}	f_{13}	i	r_2	r_1
f_{13}	f_{13}	f_{12}	f_{23}	r_1	i	r_2
f_{23}	f_{23}	f_{13}	f_{12}	r_2	r_1	i

16. Table 12 describes a group with 6 elements. Is this group isomorphic to Z_6?

17. Describe a three-element subgroup of the group in Table 12.

18. How many two-element subgroups does the group in Table 12 have?

19. For each element of the group in Table 12, what is its inverse?

20. Show that the coset $K * g^{-1}$ is the inverse to the coset $K * g$ in the binary operation defined on cosets in Theorem 8.

21. Find an element of the group $GL(2)$ that does not commute with the matrix

$$\begin{bmatrix} 1 & 0 \\ 0 & 2 \end{bmatrix}$$

22. The group of 2-by-2 integer upper triangular matrices with 1's on the main diagonal and the operation of multiplication is isomorphic to another group we have discussed. Find the group, describe the isomorphism, and show that it is an isomorphism.

23. Is the set of all numbers of the form $a + b\sqrt{2}$ in which a and b are arbitrary rational numbers a ring under the operations of addition and multiplication? Is it a field?

24. Define $m \cdot n$ to be the minimum of m and n. With this operation of multiplication and the usual operation of addition, determine whether the integers (positive, negative, and zero) form a ring.

25. Fill in the ring or field properties being used in the blanks below.

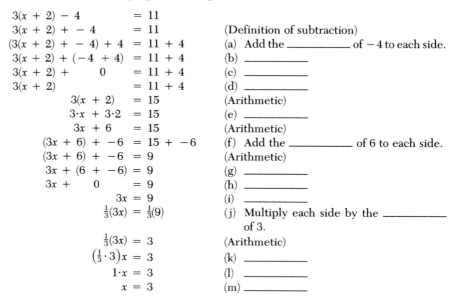

$$3(x + 2) - 4 = 11$$
$$3(x + 2) + - 4 = 11 \qquad \text{(Definition of subtraction)}$$
$$(3(x + 2) + - 4) + 4 = 11 + 4 \qquad \text{(a) Add the _____ of } -4 \text{ to each side.}$$
$$3(x + 2) + (-4 + 4) = 11 + 4 \qquad \text{(b) _____}$$
$$3(x + 2) + \qquad 0 = 11 + 4 \qquad \text{(c) _____}$$
$$3(x + 2) \qquad = 11 + 4 \qquad \text{(d) _____}$$
$$3(x + 2) = 15 \qquad \text{(Arithmetic)}$$
$$3 \cdot x + 3 \cdot 2 = 15 \qquad \text{(e) _____}$$
$$3x + 6 = 15 \qquad \text{(Arithmetic)}$$
$$(3x + 6) + -6 = 15 + -6 \qquad \text{(f) Add the _____ of 6 to each side.}$$
$$(3x + 6) + -6 = 9 \qquad \text{(Arithmetic)}$$
$$3x + (6 + -6) = 9 \qquad \text{(g) _____}$$
$$3x + \qquad 0 = 9 \qquad \text{(h) _____}$$
$$3x = 9 \qquad \text{(i) _____}$$
$$\tfrac{1}{3}(3x) = \tfrac{1}{3}(9) \qquad \text{(j) Multiply each side by the _____ of 3.}$$
$$\tfrac{1}{3}(3x) = 3 \qquad \text{(Arithmetic)}$$
$$\left(\tfrac{1}{3} \cdot 3\right)x = 3 \qquad \text{(k) _____}$$
$$1 \cdot x = 3 \qquad \text{(l) _____}$$
$$x = 3 \qquad \text{(m) _____}$$

26. Write down the addition and multiplication tables for the ring Z_8 of integers mod 8. Which elements have multiplicative inverses? Do they form a group under the operation of multiplication?

27. Find the greatest common divisor of 480 and 1225.

28. Find the greatest common divisor of 351,787 and 272,853.

29. The nonzero elements of Z_5 form a group. Is the operation addition or multiplication? To what other group we have studied is this group isomorphic? Show an isomorphism.

30. A message has digits x_1, x_2, x_3, x_4, x_5. Show that the three parity check equations $x_6 = x_1 + x_2 + x_3$, $x_7 = x_2 + x_3 + x_4$, and $x_8 = x_3 + x_4 + x_5$ will let us determine whether there is an error but will not distinguish between an error in x_5 and an error in x_8. Explain why the parity check equation $x_9 = x_1 + x_5$ remedies this difficulty.

31. Write the parity check matrix for the single-error correcting code of Exercise 30.

32. Find the minimum distance of the code of Exercise 31.

33. Suppose we add the equation $x_{10} = x_1 + x_2 + x_3 + x_4 + x_5 + x_6 + x_7 + x_8 + x_9$ to the equations of Exercise 30 (including the last one). Describe in words or write down the new parity check matrix. How does this change the minimum distance?

34. Find the Hamming distance between each two of the three matrices below.

$$[0 \ 1 \ 0 \ 1 \ 1 \ 0 \ 1]^t \qquad [0 \ 0 \ 0 \ 0 \ 0 \ 0 \ 0]^t \qquad [1 \ 0 \ 1 \ 0 \ 1 \ 0 \ 1]^t$$

35. The three parity check equations at the beginning of Exercise 30 would not let us correct all the errors. How many columns of length 3 would the parity check matrix have if three parity check equations *would* suffice to let us correct all errors? Why is this impossible?

36. How many different messages may be encoded with the code of Exercises 30 and 31?

The purpose of this appendix is to allow students who have made a thorough study of sets, functions, and relations to quickly review these topics and to learn how they and the new concept of a digraph are used in discrete mathematics. This appendix may be substituted for Sections 1-1 and 1-2, parts A and B of Section 3-1, and Sections 4-1 and 4-2.

A   Sets and Statements

In discrete mathematics we study step-by-step (or **discrete**) processes. The possible outcomes of a discrete process form a set. For example, we may represent the set of outcomes of the process of taking a four-question true-false test as

$$\{\text{TTTT, TTTF, TTFT, TTFF, TFTT, TFTF, TFFT, TFFF,}$$
$$\text{FTTT, FTTF, FTFT, FTFF, FFTT, FFTF, FFFT, FFFF}\}$$

We say we have described a **set** when we have given an unambiguous description of a collection of objects. One way to give such a description of a set is to give a list of its elements, as we did above for the possible outcomes of answering four true-false questions. Another way to describe a set is to give a statement that describes its elements. By a **statement** we mean an unambiguous declarative sentence about the possible outcomes of the process we are considering. For example, in the context of the four-question true-false test, we might consider the statement "This way of answering the question has three T's." We could write

$$\{\text{ways of answering the questions such that this way has three T's}\}$$
$$= \{\text{TTTF, TTFT, TFTT, FTTT}\}$$

However, this is obviously a cumbersome process for describing the set, and so we agree to use the notation

$$\{x | x \text{ has 3 T's}\} = \{\text{TTTF, TTFT, TFTT, FTTT}\}$$

Implicit in this notation is the fact that the variable x represents a member of (or **varies over**) the **universe** of possible ways of answering the questions. We say that the set {TTTF, TTFT, TFTT, FTTT} is the **truth set** of the statement "x has 3 T's."

Symbolic Statements

We use the upper-case letters P, Q, R, S, T to stand for sets, and when we think of them as truth sets of statements, we denote the corresponding statements by p, q, r, s, t, or $p(x)$, $q(x)$, and so on. We use the letters w, x, y, and z to stand for variables that vary over our universe. The letters p, q, r, s, t may be thought of as variables which vary over statements about our universe, and the upper-case letters P, Q, R, S, T may be thought of as variables that vary over sets chosen from our universe. Henceforth, however, the word *variable* will mean a variable representing a member of the universe unless otherwise stated.

Recall that the **intersection** $P \cap Q$ of two sets P and Q is the set of elements they have in common, and the **union** $P \cup Q$ of P and Q is the set of elements in at least one of the sets. If P and Q are given as truth sets, it would be nice to be able to decribe $P \cap Q$ and $P \cup Q$ as truth sets also. If x is in the truth sets P of p and Q of q (so that x is in $P \cap Q$), then x makes both p and q true. Thus x makes the **compound statement** "p and q" true. We use $p \wedge q$ as a shorthand for the statement "p and q" and call it the **conjunction** of p and q; this gives us a notation analogous to the one used for intersection. Similarly x is in the set $P \cup Q$ if it makes p or q or both true; thus $P \cup Q$ is the truth set of the **compound statement** "p or q or both." A shorthand notation for this compound statement is $p \vee q$, which we read as "p or q" and call the **disjunction** of p and q. This way of using the word "or" is called the **inclusive or.** There is also a notation for the other way the word *or* is used (the **exclusive or**); $p \oplus q$ stands for "p or q but not both."

EXAMPLE 1   Let $p(x)$ be the statement $x > 0$ and let $q(x)$ be the statement $x < 10$. Find the truth sets of the statements $p(x) \vee q(x)$ and $p(x) \oplus q(x)$, assuming that the universe for x is the set of integers (which means the positive, negative, and zero integers).

Solution   Since each number is either greater than zero, less than ten, or both greater than zero and less than ten, each number makes the statement $p(x) \vee q(x)$ true, and so its truth set is the set of all integers. On the other hand, since any integer x between 1 and 9 inclusive makes both $p(x)$ and $q(x)$ true, the truth set of $p(x) \oplus q(x)$ is the set of all integers less than 1 or greater than 9. Thus the two statements have different truth sets, so they have different meanings.   ■

As Example 1 shows, one way to demonstrate that two statements have different meanings is to compute their truth sets and determine whether they are different. We will often want to know when two statements have the same meaning.

EXAMPLE 2   In the universe of possible outcomes to four true-false questions, find the truth sets of the statements "The result has more trues than falses" and "The result has at most one false."

Solution   The outcomes with more trues than falses can have four trues and no falses or three trues and one false. Thus they form the set {TTTT, TTTF, TTFT, TFTT, FTTT}. The outcomes with at most one false are the outcomes {FTTT, TFTT, TTFT, TTTF, TTTT}. Since the order in which we list the members of a set is irrelevant, we see that the two sets of outcomes are exactly the same set. ∎

Example 2 shows us that we can determine that two statements mean the same thing by showing that they have same truth sets. We say that two statements are **equivalent** if they have the same truth sets. We write $p \Leftrightarrow q$ to stand for "p is equivalent to q."

Venn Diagrams

Venn diagrams provide a convenient way to visualize sets. Figure 1 shows the Venn diagram of two overlapping sets S and T. We have shaded S in color and T in grey. The set $S \cap T$ is the set which is shaded in both ways and the set $S \cup T$ is the set of all the shaded area. The nonshaded area represents the **complement** of $S \cup T$, the set of elements in the universe which are not in $S \cup T$. The area shaded in color but not in grey is usually denoted by $S{\sim}T$, and is called S **minus** T or the **difference** of S and T. This suggests using ${\sim}P$ as the notation for the complement of P, and this is the notation we shall use.

Figure 1   Visualizing unions, intersections, and complements by using a Venn diagram.

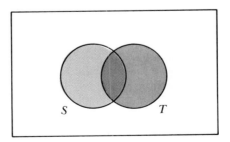

Figure 2 has two parts. Part (a) is the Venn diagram of the set $P \cap (Q \cup R)$ and part (b) is the Venn diagram of the set $(P \cap Q) \cup (P \cap R)$. In the first set, P is shaded in grey and $(Q \cup R)$ is shaded in color, so $P \cap (Q \cup R)$ is shaded in both. In the second set $P \cap Q$ is shaded in grey and $P \cap R$ is shaded in color, so that

Figure 2   The Venn diagram that illustrates the distributive law.

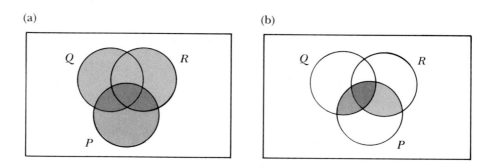

(a)   (b)

$(P \cap Q) \cup (P \cap R)$ is the total shaded region. Thus the Venn diagram makes it clear that $(P \cap Q) \cup (P \cap R) = P \cap (Q \cup R)$. This is one of two **distributive** laws for union and intersection; you obtain the other distributive law by exchanging each union sign for an intersection sign and each intersection sign for a union sign. Unfortunately, what is geometrically clear need not hold true in all cases, so this rule of set equality must be proved. To prove two sets equal, we use the **fundamental principle of set equality,** namely that to show that two sets S and T are equal, we first show that each element of S is an element of T and then show that each element of T is an element of S. In Example 3, we provide half of the proof of the distributive law.

EXAMPLE 3   Show that each element of $(P \cap Q) \cup (P \cap R)$ is also an element of $P \cap (Q \cup R)$.

Solutions   Suppose that x is in $(P \cap Q) \cup (P \cap R)$. Then x is in either $P \cap Q$ or $P \cap R$. Thus in either case x is in P, and since in one case x is in Q and in the other case x is in R, x must be in either Q or R, thus x is in $Q \cup R$. And since x is in both P and $Q \cup R$, x is in $P \cap (Q \cup R)$ by the definition of $\cap$. ∎

Sometimes it is inconvenient to say "x is in P" again and again in a proof, so we use the standard shorthand $x \in P$ to stand for "x is in P" or "x is an element of P." When every element of a set S is also in T, we say that S is a subset of T, denoted by $S \subseteq T$. Thus in Example 4 we showed that $(P \cap Q) \cup (P \cap R) \subseteq P \cap (Q \cup R)$. The fundamental principle of set equality may be phrased as "To show that $S = T$, we must show that $S \subseteq T$ and $T \subseteq S$."

When P is the truth set of a statement p, then an element x of the universe is in $\sim P$ if and only if it makes p false—or makes the statement "not p" true. We use $\neg p$ to stand for "not p." Thus $\sim P$ is the truth set of $\neg p$. Theorem 1 tells us that to convert between statements and truth sets, we interchange upper-case and lower-case letters as well as curvy and angular operation symbols.

Theorem 1   Let p and q be statements and let P and Q be their truth sets. Then

(a) $P \cap Q$ is the truth set of $p \wedge q$.
(b) $P \cup Q$ is the truth set of $p \vee q$.
(c) $\sim P$ is the truth set of $\neg p$.

Proof   We shall prove only part (a); parts (b) and (c) are proved similarly. Though much of the proof is in the discussion above, we shall give a complete proof to illustrate the fundamental principle of set equality. First, suppose x is in $P \cap Q$. We shall show that x is in the truth set of $p \wedge q$. Since x is in $P \cap Q$, it is in P and it is in Q. Thus x makes p true and x makes q true. Then x makes $p \wedge q$ true, so x is in the truth set of $p \wedge q$.

Now suppose x is in the truth set of $p \wedge q$. We shall show that x is in $P \cap Q$. Because x makes $p \wedge q$ true, it must make p true and it must make q true. Therefore x is in P and x is in Q. Therefore x is in $P \cap Q$. Thus $P \cap Q$ and the truth set of $p \wedge q$ have exactly the same elements, so by the fundamental principle of set equality they are the same set.   ■

Our study of the relationship between statements and their truth sets reminds us of one other important kind of set.

EXAMPLE 4   Using the statements $p(x)$ and $q(x)$ of Example 1, describe the truth set of $\neg p(x) \wedge \neg q(x)$ and $\neg(p(x) \vee q(x))$.

Solution   Since $\neg p(x) \wedge \neg q(x)$ is the statement that x is not greater than 0 and is not less than 10 (that is, x is both less than or equal to 0 and greater than or equal to 10), there is no x whatsoever that can satisfy the statement. Thus its truth set has no members, so it is the **empty set.** Since we saw in Example 1 that the truth set of $p(x) \vee q(x)$ is the universe, the complement of its truth set is again the empty set. Thus the two statements are equivalent. This equivalence is a special case of De Morgan's laws which say "The complement of the union is the intersection of the complements and vice versa." Similar laws hold for statements.   ■

Recall that the empty set is a subset of every set.

B   Relations

In mathematics we study relationships between sets. Relationships may be described in a wide variety of ways. For example, $y = x + 1$ and $x^2 + y^2 = 1$ are both formulas that describe a relationship between two variables that vary over sets of numbers.

EXAMPLE 5   The formulas $y = x + 2$ and $y = x^4 - 2x^3 - x^2 + 3x + 2$ each describe a relationship between the set $\{-1, 0, 1, 2\}$ (which is the universe for x) and the set $\{1, 2, 3, 4\}$ (which is the universe for y). Are these relationships different?

Solution   Both formulas relate -1 to 1, 0 to 2, 1 to 3, and 2 to 4. Thus, between the two universes given, they relate exactly the same pairs, so in some sense, they are the same.   ■

Each formula is a statement about x and y. What universe do we use for these statements? Determining the truth or falsity of either formula involves pairs of x and y values. To keep track of these pairs, we write them as **ordered pairs** (x,y) with x first and y second. This suggests that an appropriate universe is the set of all ordered pairs (x,y) with x in the domain D and y in the range R. This set is called the **Cartesian product** of D and R and is denoted by $D \times R$. The truth set of either formula may now be written as $\{(-1,1), (0,2), (1,3), (2,4)\}$.

Since two apparently different relationships resulted in the same truth set, we consider the statements defining these relationships as equivalent. We now use sets to define the concept of a relation sufficiently precisely that the relations defined by the two formulas are the same. A **relation** from a set D (called its **domain**) to a set R (called its **range**) is a set of ordered pairs (x,y) with $x \in D$ and $y \in R$, that is a subset of $D \times R$. Thus the truth set we wrote down is a relation with domain $\{-1, 0, 1, 2\}$ and range $\{1, 2, 3, 4\}$. Often a relation will have the same domain and range; then we say it is a relation **on** the set $D(= R)$.

EXAMPLE 6   The relation $\{(1,2), (1,3), (1,4), (2,3), (3,4)\}$ is a familiar relation on the set $\{1, 2, 3, 4\}$. What is a standard name for this relation?

Solution   Note that (a,b) is in the relation if and only if $a < b$. Thus our relation is the "less than" relation.   ■

EXAMPLE 7   A fraternity has a membership committee consisting of Joe, Frank, and Bill, a house committee consisting of Tony, Joe, Bill, and Andre, and a social committee consisting of Frank, Tony, and Bill. Using initials for names of people and committees, write down the "is a member of" relation from the set of people to the set of committees.

Solution   Our solution consists of the set of ordered pairs

$$\{(J,M), (F,M), (B,M), (T,H), (J,H), (B,H), (A,H), (F,S), (T,S), (B,S)\} \quad ■$$

Directed Graphs

A picture that we use to visualize a relation is often called a *graph*. The first kind of graph we shall study (which is different from the graphs studied in algebra) is called a *directed graph*, or *digraph* for short. In Figure 3 we show digraphs used to visualize the "less than" and "less than or equal to" relations on $\{1, 2, 3, 4\}$.

Figure 3 The digraph of the *less than* and *less than or equal to* relations on {1, 2, 3, 4}.

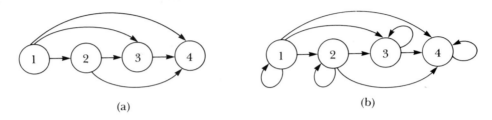

(a) (b)

To draw a digraph of a relation *on* a set we first draw a circle, called a **vertex,** for each member of the domain (and therefore range) of the relation. Thus in Figure 3 we have four circles, the vertices representing 1, 2, 3, and 4. Next, for each vertex representing a domain element we draw an arrow, called an *edge*, to each vertex representing a related range element. (As in Figure 3(b), we draw an arrow from a vertex to itself when it represents something related to itself.) Since the exact shape or placement of the circles for vertices and arrows is irrelevant, it is useful to have the following definition which doesn't mention them.

A **directed graph** (**digraph** for short) consists of a set V called a **vertex** set and a relation E on V called an **edge** set.

EXAMPLE 8 On a certain test we agree that even if one person scores 5 points below another, it is quite possible that two people have similar knowledge of the test material. If the scores are Manuel 93, Sarah 89, Rick 84, Carmela 86, and George 80, write down the relation of "possibly similar knowledge" and draw a digraph of it.

Solution Using initials to stand for peoples' names, we get the vertex set $P = \{M, S, R, C, G\}$ and the relation $\{(M,M), (S,S), (R,R), (C,C), (G,G), (M,S), (S,M), (S,R), (R,S), (S,C), (C,S), (R,C), (C,R), (R,G), (G,R)\}$. Figure 4 is a drawing of the digraph of this relation. ∎

Figure 4 The digraph of the "possibly similar knowledge" relation.

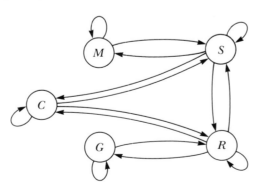

We may draw a digraph of a relation from a set A to a set B in the same way we drew the digraph of the "less than" relation; alternatively, we may begin by drawing one circle for each member of the domain and one circle for each element of the range. For example, the digraph of the relation of Example 7 is given in Figure 5(a) and a digraph of the relation of Example 8 as a relation from P to P is given in Figure 5(b). The decision of whether to draw both a domain vertex labelled x and a range vertex labelled x for an element x in both the domain and range is based on experience. Normally we use separate domain and range vertices for such an element x when drawing digraphs of functions, and the first method for other applications.

Figure 5   The digraphs of the relations of Examples 7 and 8.

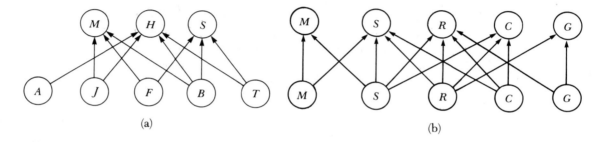

(a)   (b)

◖ Functions

One of the most useful kinds of relationships between sets that you've studied in the past is that of a function. In algebra and calculus we learn to think of a function as a relationship given by a formula such as $f(x) = x + 2$ or $y = x + 2$. We saw in Example 5 that the two apparently different formulas $y = x + 2$ and $y = x^4 - 2x^3 - x^2 + 3x + 2$ describe the same relationship between the set $\{-1, 0, 1, 2\}$ and the set $\{1, 2, 3, 4\}$. Since different formulas can define the same relationship, we will not want a definition of functions based on formulas. Instead we say

> A **function** from a set D to a set R is a relation from D to R such that each x in D is related to one and only one y in R. D is called the **domain** of the function and R is called the **range** of the function. The set of range values actually related to some domain element is called the **image** of the function.

Since we defined a relation as a set of ordered pairs, we have now defined a function as a special kind of set of ordered pairs. A standard notation for "f is a function from D to R" is $f: D \rightarrow R$.

Properties of Functions

In Figure 6 we see digraphs of four different functions.

Figure 6   Digraphs of four different kinds of functions.

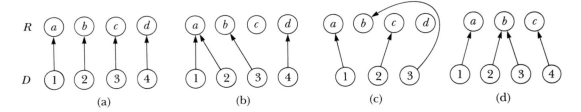

In each digraph, there is *one and only one* arrow leaving each vertex in the domain. (Note that in part (c) the domain is the set {1, 2, 3}.) This corresponds to the statement that a function relates *one and only one* element of the range to each element of the domain.

In functions (a) and (c), each element of the range receives one arrow or no arrow at all.

> A function is called an **injection** or a **one-to-one**
> function if different elements of the domain are
> related to different elements of the range.

Thus each element of the range is related to *at most one* element of the domain by a one-to-one function. Therefore functions (a) and (c) are one-to-one functions.

In functions (a) and (d), each element of the range receives *at least one* arrow.

> A function is called a **surjection** or **onto** function
> if each element of the range is related to *at least*
> *one* element of the domain.

Notice that each function is a function from its domain onto its image.

In function (a), each element of the range receives one and only one arrow.

> A function is called a **bijection**, a **one-to-one**
> **correspondence**, a **one-to-one and onto** function,
> or a **one-to-one** function from the domain **onto**
> the range if each element of the range is related
> to one and only one element of the domain.

The digraph of a relation can also show us that the relation is not a function.

EXAMPLE 9   Show that the relations {$(a,2)$, $(a,3)$, $(b,4)$, $(c,5)$} and {$(a,3)$, $(c,2)$} are not functions from the domain {a,b,c} to the range {2, 3, 4, 5}.

Solution   As you see in Figure 7(a), the relation relates both the numbers 2 and 3 in the range with the letter a in the domain. Thus a is not related to *only one* element in the range, so the first relation is not a function. As you see in Figure 7(b), the element b of the domain is not related to *any* element in the range by the second relation. Since the relation does not relate *each* element of the domain to some element of the range, it is not a function.   ■

Figure 7

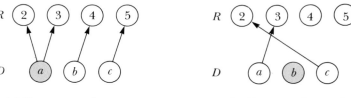

(a) Two arrows leave a.   (b) No arrow leaves b.

Sequences, n-tuples, and Sums

Many of the functions we study in discrete mathematics have sets of integers as their domains. We shall see, for example, how the amount of time needed to run a computer program with n items of input data may be profitably studied as a function of the integer n.

> A function whose domain is a set of consecutive integers is called a **sequence**.

For example, if $s(i) = i^2$ for each integer $i \geq 0$, then s is a sequence. For historical reasons and for convenience, a special notation has developed for use with sequences. Rather than use the notation $s(i)$ for the value of the sequence s at the integer i, it is customary to use the notation s_i (read as "s-eye" or "s-sub-eye"). It is also typical to refer to s_i as the ith **term** of the sequence, and to use $<s_i>$ (read as "the sequence s_i") in place of simply using s to stand for the sequence.

We frequently have sequences whose domain is the set $N = \{1, 2, \ldots, n\}$. In fact, an ordered pair may be thought of as a sequence whose domain is $\{1, 2\}$, an ordered triple is a sequence whose domain is $\{1, 2, 3\}$, and so on. A sequence whose domain is $\{1, 2, 3, \ldots, n\}$ is often called an **n-tuple** (rhymes with *quadruple*). For example $s = $ (Sam, Pam, Georgia, William, Dick) is a finite sequence of names and is called a 5-tuple. Notice that we enclosed the list in parentheses. Recall that a list enclosed in set braces represents a set and the order in which it is listed is irrelevant. Now we see that a list enclosed in parentheses represents an n-tuple and the order in which it appears is essential.

Summing Finite Sequences

In many applications of discrete mathematics we need to find sums of sequences. For example, if we need to find out how long it takes to carry out an n-stage process, we must add up the amount of time needed to carry out step number i for all i values between 1 and n. There is a special notation called *summation notation* which is used as a shorthand to describe such sums. We define the notation, which is read as "the sum from i equals m to n of a_i" by the equation

$$\sum_{i=1}^{n} a_i = a_1 + a_2 + \ldots + a_n$$

In words,

$$\sum_{i=1}^{n} a_i$$

represents the result of computing a_i for each i between 1 and n inclusive and then adding these values of a_i together.

A sum that will be important to us in Section 4-3 and later applications is

$$1 + 2 + 3 + \ldots + n = \sum_{i=1}^{n} i$$

As a child the famous mathematician Carl Friedrich Gauss (1777–1855) is said to have noticed that by writing this sum in two different orders we get

$$1 \quad + \quad 2 \quad + \quad 3 \quad + \ldots + \quad n \quad = \quad \sum_{i=1}^{n} i$$

$$+ \quad \quad n \quad + n - 1 + n - 2 + \ldots + \quad 1 \quad = \quad \sum_{i=1}^{n} i$$

$$\overline{n + 1 + n + 1 + n + 1 + \ldots + n + 1 = 2\sum_{i=1}^{n} i}$$

Since we have n terms each equal to $n + 1$ added together, we get $n(n + 1)$ and then divide by 2, giving

$$\frac{n(n + 1)}{2} = \sum_{i=1}^{n} i$$

You may put Gauss's formula to use in proving that the sum of an arithmetic series is given by the formula

$$\sum_{i=1}^{n} (ai + b) = a\frac{n(n + 1)}{2} + bn$$

Cartesian Graphs

In algebra, (analytic) geometry, and calculus we frequently study numerical functions and relations. A **numerical** function is one whose domain and range are both sets of real numbers, rational numbers, or integers. Many of these functions play an important role in discrete mathematics as well. We can visualize numerical functions and relations with a third kind of graph called a *Cartesian graph*. For this purpose, we use the usual x-y coordinate system for the plane.

> The **Cartesian graph** of a relation R consists of all points (x, y) in the plane such that x is related to y by R (in symbols, such that $(x, y) \in R$).

In Figure 8 we show the graph of the relation "x is related to y if $x^2 + y^2 = 1$"; in Figure 9 we show the graphs of the functions given by $f(x) = x$, $f(x) = x^2$ and $f(x) = x^3$.

Figure 8

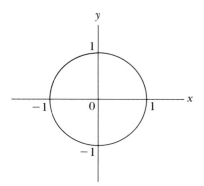

Figure 9

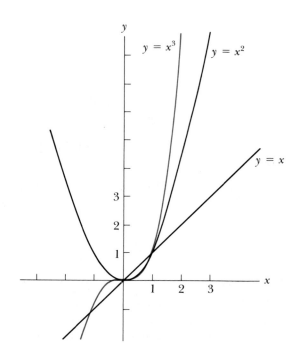

In Figures 10 and 11 we show the graphs of $y = x^2$ and $y = 2^x$ for $x \geq 0$, showing how using different scales on the x- and y-axes can be useful in order to see more information about the functions whose graphs we draw. Although Figure 10 could lead us to believe that the graphs of $y = 2^x$ and $y = x^2$ are similar, Figure 11 shows us enough of the two graphs to convince us that they are different. It appears from Figure 10 that the graph of $y = 2^x$ rises faster than the graph of $y = x^2$. Similarly, Figure 8 shows us that apparently the graph of $y = x^3$ rises faster than the graph of $y = x^2$, which in turn rises faster than the graph of $y = x$.

Figure 10

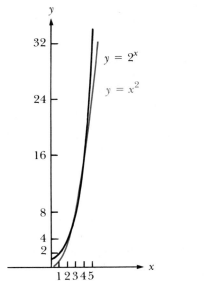

Figure 11

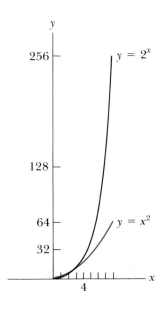

Composition

In using functions, we combine them in various ways. For example, if $f(x) = \sqrt{x}$ and $g(x) = 1 - x^2$, we may write $f(g(x)) = \sqrt{1 - x^2}$, or $f \circ g(x) = \sqrt{1 - x^2}$. In so doing, we have defined a new relation $f \circ g$.

> The **composition** of a function f with a function g
> is the relation $f \circ g$ (read as "f circle g" or
> "f composed with g") that contains the pair (x, y)
> if and only if $y = f(g(x))$ (read as "f of g of x").

So that we may compute $f(g(x))$, it is necessary that $g(x)$ be in the domain of f for each x (in the domain of g); in other words, the *image* of g must be a subset of the *domain* of f in order for $f \circ g$ to be defined.

EXAMPLE 10   Find the compositions $p \circ g$ and $g \circ p$ of the function $p(y) = \frac{y}{454}$, which converts weight in grams to weight in pounds with the function $g(x) = 454x$, which converts weight in pounds to weight in grams.

Solution $p \circ g(x) = p(g(x)) = p(454x) = \dfrac{454x}{454} = x$

$g \circ p(y) = g(p(y)) = g\left(\dfrac{y}{454}\right) = 454 \cdot \dfrac{y}{454} = y$ ∎

> Whenever f and g are two functions such that
> $f(g(x)) = x$ and $g(f(y)) = y$ for each x in the
> domain of g and each y in the domain of f, we say
> that f and g are **inverses** to each other, that f is
> the **inverse** of g, and that g is the **inverse** of f.

A shorthand notation for this is $f = g^{-1}$ or $g = f^{-1}$. (We read f^{-1} as "f inverse," not "f to the negative one.") A one-to-one function f will have an inverse whose domain is the image of f; we define $f^{-1}(y)$ to be the unique x such that $f(x) = y$. Thus (x,y) is in the relation defining f if and only if (y,x) is in the relation defining f^{-1}. This tells us that the points of the graph of f^{-1} may be obtained from the points on the graph of f by exchanging the x and y coordinates. To interpret this geometrically note that we are simply interchanging the roles of the x and y axis, so we are reflecting the figure through the line $y = x$, or, equivalently, flipping it around the line $y = x$.

EXAMPLE 11   The function given by $f(x) = 2^x$ is a one-to-one function from the set of real numbers onto the set of positive real numbers. Therefore it has an inverse function, denoted by $y = \log_2(x)$, which is a function from the set of positive real numbers to the set of real numbers. Sketch graphs of $y = 2^x$ and $y = \log_2(x)$ on the same axes.

Solution   In Figure 12 we draw the graph of $y = 2^x$ and flip it around (reflect it through) the line $y = x$ to get the graph of $y = \log_2(x)$.   ∎

Figure 12

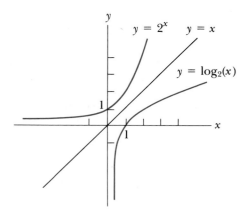

Inverse Images

There is a second important use of the notation f^{-1} for functions that are not necessarily one-to-one, which is consistent with inverse functions of one-to-one functions. If f is a function with domain X and image Y, we define the **inverse image** of an element y in Y as follows.

> The **inverse image** of y, denoted by $f^{-1}(\{y\})$, is the set of all elements x such that $f(x) = y$.

EXAMPLE 12   If $f(x) = x^2$ on the real numbers, describe the inverse image of y for each non-negative integer y.

Solution   For $y = 0$, $f^{-1}(\{0\}) = \{0\}$. However for any other y, both $\sqrt{y}$ and $-\sqrt{y}$ are sent to y by f. Thus for each other y, $f^{-1}(\{y\}) = \{-\sqrt{y}, \sqrt{y}\}$. ∎

Notice that if f is a one-to-one function, then whenever $f(x) = y$, $f^{-1}(y) = x$, and $f^{-1}(\{y\}) = \{x\}$, so the two notations are consistent and leaving the set braces out will not mislead us. Regardless of whether f is one-to-one, the relation given by x_1 is related to x_2 if and only if $f(x_1) = f(x_2)$ is an example of what we called an equivalence relation in part B of Section 3-2.

Exercises

The notation (x-y-z) after an exercise means that the answer can be found in Chapter x, Section y, Exercise z in the answer section.

A

1. In my pocket there are one nickel, two dimes, and two quarters. I reach in and pull out a coin. Then I reach in and pull out another coin. Using a notation such as *ND* to stand for getting first a nickel then a dime and *QN* for getting first a quarter then a nickel, do the following.
   (a) Write down the universe of possible results.
   (b) Show the truth set of the statement "I got a total of at least 30 cents" by circling the members of this truth set.
   (c) Show the truth set of the statement "I got a dime first" by drawing boxes around the members of this truth set. (1-1-19)

2. Use the fundamental principle of set equality to show that the set of all results of drawing at least 30 cents in Exercise 1 is equal to the set of all results with at least one quarter. (1-1-21)

3. Let p be the statement "Tom is home," let q be the statement "Dinner is served," and let r be the statement "The house is cold." Write down in symbolic form the statements below. Remember that the mathematical interpretation of the word "or" is the "inclusive or." To say $p \oplus q$ in mathematical English we must say something equivalent to "p or q but not both."
   (a) Tom is home and dinner is served.
   (b) Tom is not home and the house is cold.

(c) Dinner is not served or Tom is not home.

(d) Dinner is served and either Tom is not home or the house is cold (or both). (Remember that p and either q or r is a way of saying p and (q or r) in English.)

(e) Tom is home or both dinner is served and the house is cold. (Note again how the *both* in "both p and q" parenthesizes the statement "p and q" in English.)

(f) Tom is not home or dinner is served or both the house is not cold and Tom is home. (1-1-13)

4. Let p, q, and r be the statements of Exercise 3. Rewrite the following statements in English.

(a) $q \lor r$ (c) $q \land \neg r$ (e) $p \lor (r \land q)$

(b) $q \land r$ (d) $q \land (r \lor p)$ (f) $p \lor (\neg r \land q)$ (1-1-15)

5. By using the fundamental principle of set equality, complete the proof begun in the text that $P \cap (Q \cup R) = (P \cap Q) \cup (P \cap R)$ for any sets P, Q, and R. (1-2-21)

6. By using the fundamental principle of set equality, show the validity of the DeMorgan law that states that $\sim(P \cap Q) = \sim P \cup \sim Q$, for any sets P and Q.

7. Draw two Venn diagrams to represent the following set equalities.

(a) $\sim(P \cap Q) = (\sim P) \cup (\sim Q)$ (one of DeMorgan's two set laws)

(b) $P \cup (Q \cap R) = (P \cup Q) \cap (P \cup R)$ (1-2-55)

8. Draw a Venn diagram that illustrates the equivalence $p \lor (q \land r) \Leftrightarrow (p \lor q) \land (p \lor r)$. (1-2-57)

9. Prove that for any sets P, Q, and R, $P \cap (Q \cup R) \subseteq (P \cap Q) \cup R$. (1-Review-19)

B   10. Write down the ordered pairs of the relationship between x and y given by "x is related to y if $|x - y| \leq 1$" on $\{1, 2, 3, 4\}$.

11. The set of ordered pairs $\{(4,1), (4,2), (4,3), (3,1), (3,2), (2,1)\}$ is a familiar relation on the set $\{1, 2, 3, 4\}$. What is this relation usually called? (3-1-11)

12. Draw a digraph of the relation given by "x is related to y if $|x - y| \leq 1$" on $\{1, 2, 3, 4\}$.

13. A is a strict subset of B if $A \neq B$ but A is a subset of B. Draw a digraph of the "strict subset" relation on the set of all subsets of $\{a, b, c\}$. (3-1-21)

C   14. The floor function or greatest-integer function of a number x, denoted by $\lfloor x \rfloor$ is the greatest integer less than or equal to x. Thus, $\lfloor -1.5 \rfloor = -2$ and $\lfloor 3.5 \rfloor = 3$. Write down the ordered pairs of the floor function on the domain $\{-2, -1.5, -1, -.5, 0, .5, 1, 1.5, 2\}$. (4-1-13)

15. Write out the ordered pairs of the functions given by the rules $f(x) = x^5 - 5x^3 + 6x - 1$, $g(x) = 2x - 1$, and $h(x) = x^3 - 2x - 1$ on the domain $\{-2, -1, 0, 1, 2\}$. Which of these rules are rules for the same function on this domain? (4-1-15)

In Exercises 16–21 we give several sets D and R and relations from D to R. For each relation, state whether it is a function; for each function, state if it is one-to-one and/or if it is onto, and give its image. Draw a digraph of the relation given and explain how it illustrates your answer. (4-1-25–35, 37–47)

16. $D = \{1, 2, 3, 4, 5\}$ $R = \{a, b, c, d, e\}$ $\{(1,a), (2,b), (3,c), (4,c), (5,d)\}$

17. $D = \{1, 2, 3, 4\}$ $R \{a, b, c, d, e\}$ $\{(1,a), (2,b), (1,c), (3,d), (4,e), (5,d)\}$

18. $D = \{1, 2, 3, 4\}$ $R = \{a, b, c, d, e\}$ $\{(2,a), (1,b), (3,e), (4,c)\}$

19. $D = \{1, 2, 3, 4, 5\}$ $R = \{a, b, c, d\}$ $\{(1,a), (3,b), (2,c), (4,d)\}$

20. $D = \{1, 2, 3, 4\}$ $R = \{a, b, c, d, e\}$ $\{(1,a), (2,b), (3,c), (1,d), (4,e)\}$

21. $D = \{1, 2, 3, 4, 5\}$ $R = \{a, b, c, d\}$ $\{(1,a), (2,b), (3,c), (4,d), (5,d)\}$

22. What is $\displaystyle\sum_{i=1}^{30} (2i + 2)$? (4-1-63)

23. The composition of two functions f and g gives a new function $f \circ g$. Thus, just as the multiplication or addition of numbers produces a new number, forming the union or intersection of sets produces a new set, and forming the conjunction or disjunction of two statements produces a new statement, composition of two functions gives a new function. Prove the associative law $(f \circ g) \circ h = f \circ (g \circ h)$ by figuring out what $(f \circ g) \circ h(x)$ is and what $f \circ (g \circ h)(x)$ is.

24. Composition is an idea that makes perfectly good sense for relations. Given a relation R from W to X and a relation S from Y to Z, what condition must hold before we can define $R \circ S$? In that case, how should we define $R \circ S$?

25. The converse of a relation R is the set of all (x,y) such that (y,x) is in R. What is the converse of a one-to-one function? Use R^{converse} to stand for the converse of R. Describe the relation we get by forming $R \circ R^{\text{converse}}$. Under what circumstances will $R \circ R^{\text{converse}}$ and $R^{\text{converse}} \circ R$ be the same relation?

26. If $f(x) = \sqrt[3]{x} - 1$, which of the following is a rule for $f^{-1}(x)$? (4-2-51)
    (a) $f^{-1}(x) = x^3 + 1$

    (b) $f^{-1}(x) = \dfrac{1}{\sqrt[3]{x} - 1}$

    (c) $f^{-1}(x) = (x - 1)^3$

    (d) $f^{-1}(x) = (x + 1)^3$

    (e) $f^{-1}(x) = x^3 - 1$

27. Sketch the graph of the function given by $f(x) = (x + 1)^3$ and the line $y = x$; sketch the inverse of the function f. (4-2-61)

28. The rule for converting Kelvin temperatures to Celsius temperatures is $f(x) = x - 273$. The rule for converting Celsius temperatures to Fahrenheit temperatures is $g(x) = \frac{9}{5}x + 32$. Find the rule for converting Kelvin temperatures to Fahrenheit temperatures. (4-2-59)

29. The rule for converting Fahrenheit temperatures to Kelvin temperatures is $f(x) = \frac{5}{9}(x + 459)$. Find the inverse function of f. What conversion does the inverse function provide?

A **Symbolic Series**

With our study of symbolic series we shall begin our study of the theory of generating functions, a theory which allows us to take advantage of similarities between processes of combining arrangements of objects into new arrangements and the process of multiplying polynomials in algebra in order to compute the number of arrangements with certain specified properties. We begin with an example designed to illustrate a typical similarity. Let us imagine a student shopping in a grocery store for some fruit to take back to the dorm for snacks. Further, let us assume that the student decides not to take more than three of each fruit and, in looking over the fruit, chooses apples, pears, and tangerines.

We use the letter A to stand for the statement "The student takes an apple," AA to stand for "The student takes two apples," and AAA to stand for "The student takes three apples." Then the symbolic statement

$$A \oplus AA \oplus AAA \qquad (1)$$

stands for "the student takes one apple or two apples or three apples." (Notice our use of the *exclusive or* symbol.) This is one example of what we shall call a **symbolic series.** Rather than give a precise definition of symbolic series we shall give many examples of symbolic series.

EXAMPLE 1   Write down the symbolic series that states that the student takes 1, 2, or 3 pears and 1, 2, or 3 tangerines.

Solution   Using P for pears we write

$$P \oplus PP \oplus PPP \qquad (2)$$

and using T for tangerines we write

$$T \oplus TT \oplus TTT \qquad (3)$$

∎

Now how may we write a symbolic statement saying that the student chooses between 1 and 3 pieces of each kind of fruit? We write

$$(A \oplus AA \oplus AAA) \wedge (P \oplus PP \oplus PPP) \wedge (T \oplus TT \oplus TTT) \qquad (4)$$

Now by the distributive law, this statement is equivalent to the statement

$$A \wedge P \wedge T \oplus AA \wedge P \wedge T \oplus AAA \wedge P \wedge T \oplus \ldots \oplus AAA \wedge PPP \wedge TTT$$

(You will find it good practice to write down several more typical terms for the 27 terms of this series.) In our current context it is natural to use APT to stand for $A \wedge P \wedge T$, $AAPT$ to stand for $AA \wedge P \wedge T$ and so on. This change gives us the symbolic series

$$APT \oplus AAPT \oplus AAAPT \oplus APPT \oplus \ldots \oplus AAAPPPTTT \qquad (5)$$

There is one more notational change that algebra suggests to us. We may use

$$A^3P^3T^3 \quad \text{to stand for} \quad AAAPPPTTT$$
$$A^2PT^3 \quad \text{to stand for} \quad AAPTTT$$

and so on. This gives us the symbolic series

$$APT \oplus A^2PT \oplus A^3PT \oplus \ldots \oplus A^3P^3T^3 \qquad (6)$$

to represent the student's possible fruit choices.

Symbolic Series and Counting Problems

One way in which we use symbolic series is to answer questions about how many of the arrangements represented by the series have a certain property. For example, we might ask "In how many ways may the student choose 5 pieces of fruit?" $A^iP^jT^k$ will represent 5 pieces of fruit if and only if $i + j + k = 5$. To answer the question by finding which exponents add to 5, however, is time consuming. For a faster process imagine replacing A, P, and T *each* by the symbol x (for "unknown fruit") in expression (6) above. Next change the $\oplus$ signs to $+$ signs so you have the notation of algebra instead of the notation of logic. Now when you collect similar powers of x together, the *coefficient* of x^5 will be the *number* of $A^iP^jT^k$ terms with $i + j + k = 5$. To make it easier to find the coefficient of x^5, suppose that we change Expression (4) by the substitutions

$$\oplus \to + \qquad \wedge \to \cdot \qquad A \to x \qquad P \to x \qquad T \to x$$

We obtain

$$(x + x^2 + x^3)(x + x^2 + x^3)(x + x^2 + x^3)$$

Now since multiplication distributes over addition, multiplying this expression of x's out gives the same result as expanding out the symbolic statement (4) and *then* making the substitutions above. Thus the number of ways to choose 5 pieces of fruit is the coefficient of x^5 in $(x + x^2 + x^3)^3$.

The multinomial theorem, discussed in the problems following Section 6-4, tells us that the coefficient of $x^i y^j z^k$ in $(x + y + z)^n$ is

$$C(n; i, j, k) = \frac{n!}{i! \cdot j! \cdot k!}$$

By multiplying $(x + x^2 + x^3)^3$ out or using the multinomial theorem, we can find the coefficient of x^5. The multinomial theorem tells us how to find the coefficient of a term $a^i b^j c^k$ in $(a + b + c)^3$. If we substitute x for a, x^2 for b, and x^3 for c, the terms that give us x^5 will be $a^2 c$ and ab^2. Their coefficients are $C(3; 2, 0, 1)$ and $C(3; 1, 2, 0)$. Thus the coefficient of x^5 is

$$C(3; 2, 0, 1) + C(3; 1, 2, 0) = \frac{3!}{2! \cdot 1!} + \frac{3!}{1! \cdot 2!} = 3 + 3 = 6$$

We can ask about properties of arrangements other than the number of items in an arrangement.

EXAMPLE 2   Suppose that apples are 20 cents each, pears are 25 cents each, and tangerines are 15 cents each. How many selections of fruit cost exactly one dollar?

Solution   Our symbolic compound statement describing all the ways to choose fruit was expression (6), in which each term $A^i P^j T^k$ described one way to choose fruit. We want to choose those terms in which $20i + 25j + 15k = 100$. Note that if we use a^{20} in place of A, p^{25} in place of P, and t^{15} in place of T, the term $A^i P^j T^k$ becomes $a^{20i} p^{25j} t^{15k}$, so after we make these substitutions we want to count the symbolic choices whose three exponents add to 100. Since we want only to know how many such choices there are, we can substitute x for a, p, and t, and we will get exactly the same number of x^{100} terms as we have terms whose exponents add to 100. Once again, then, we have only used laws that we could use with "plus" and "times" instead of "or" and "and," so we go back and make the substitutions of x^{20} for A, x^{25} for P, and x^{15} for T, giving us the polynomial

$$(x^{20} + x^{40} + x^{60})(x^{25} + x^{50} + x^{75})(x^{15} + x^{30} + x^{45})$$

We want to know the coefficient of x^{100} in this product. We multiply the three polynomials by making all possible choices of one summand from each parentheses, multiplying the summands together, and adding all results. The only choices of summands that give x^{100} when multiplied together are x^{20}, x^{50}, x^{30} and x^{60}, x^{25},

x^{15}. Thus the coefficient of x^{100} in the product is 2; and there are therefore two ways to spend a dollar on fruit.   ■

B   *Power Series*

The polynomials we obtained by substituting x or powers of x into symbolic series are examples of "generating series" or "generating functions." We shall give some other examples before giving a formal definition. Suppose we consider the possibility of making a selection from an unlimited supply of apples. The natural symbolic series for us to use is

$$A \oplus AA \oplus AAA \oplus AAAA \oplus AAAAA \oplus \ldots \quad \text{or}$$
$$A^1 \oplus A^2 \oplus A^3 \oplus A^4 \oplus \ldots \oplus A^i \oplus \ldots$$

This series never stops; we refer to it as an infinite symbolic series. Thus in order to discuss selections of apples, pears, and tangerines from an unlimited supply, we would have the symbolic series

$$(A \oplus AA \oplus AAA \oplus \ldots) \, (P \oplus PP \oplus PPP \oplus \ldots) \, (T \oplus TT \oplus TTT \oplus \ldots)$$

Substituting x for each of the letters would lead us to consider the expression $(x + x^2 + \ldots)^3$.

Power Series and Generating Functions

An expression such as

$$x + x^2 + \ldots + x^i + \ldots \quad \text{or} \quad \sum_{i=1}^{\infty} x^i$$

is an example of a *power series*. More generally, if we are given a sequence $<a_i>$, defined for $i \geq 0$, we call the expression

$$p(x) = a_0 + a_1 x + a_2 x^2 + \ldots + a_i x^i + \ldots \quad \text{or}$$
$$p(x) = \sum_{i=0}^{\infty} a_i x^i$$

a **power series.** In the context of combinatorial mathematics this expression is called the **generating series** or the **generating function** for the sequence $<a_i>$. The use of the term *function* in this context is unfortunate, because a generating series *need not be* a function, putting us in the disquieting situation that a generating function is not necessarily a special kind of function. The terminology is standard, though, so we simply accept it.

EXAMPLE 3   Write down the generating function for the sequence $<a_i>$ with $a_i = 1$ for $i = 1$, 2, 3 and $a_i = 0$ otherwise.

Solution

$$a_0 x_0 + a_1 x^1 + a_2 x^2 + a_3 x^3 + a_4 x^4 \ldots = 0 + 1 \cdot x^1 + 1 \cdot x^2 + 1 \cdot x^3 + 0 \cdot x^4 + \ldots$$
$$= x + x^2 + x^3$$ ∎

EXAMPLE 4   Write down the generating function for the sequence $<a_i>$ given by $a_i = 1$ for all $i \geqslant 0$.

Solution $\displaystyle\sum_{i=0}^{\infty} a_i x^i = \sum_{i=0}^{\infty} 1 \cdot x^i = \sum_{i=0}^{\infty} x^i$

or $1 + x + x^2 + \ldots + x^i + \ldots$ ∎

On seeing Example 4 it is natural to ask, "But what does it mean?" There are two different ways people answer this. One way is to say that it is simply an expression we write down. Another way is to say that it represents the possibility of taking none of some item, or one of that item, or two of that item, or three of that item, and so on, just as we said the symbolic series

$$A \oplus A^2 \oplus A^3 \oplus \ldots \oplus A^i \oplus \ldots$$

represents taking one apple, or two apples, and so on.

In calculus and mathematical analysis you learn how to give a deeper meaning to power series; while that meaning is important for calculus and advanced discrete mathematics it is less important for much of discrete mathematics.

EXAMPLE 5   Give a formula for the sequence whose generating series is

$$x^2 + 2x^3 + 3x^4 + 4x^5 + \ldots$$

Solution   The number in front of x^i is $i - 1$, so the sequence has the formula $a_i = i - 1$.   ∎

In "summation notation" we would write the power series of Example 5 as

$$\sum_{i=2}^{\infty} (i - 1) x^i$$

Notice that just as we can start ordinary summation at an i value such as $i = 2$, we can also represent an infinite series for a sequence $<a_i>$ defined for $i \geqslant 2$ by using $i = 2$ at the bottom of the summation notation.

Algebraic Operations

From our example of distributing apples, pears, and tangerines from unlimited supplies it is clear that we must give meaning to the idea of multiplying two generating functions together, or multiplying a generating function by itself.

Let us examine how we form the product of two polynomials, say

$$p(x) = \sum_{i=0}^{n} a_i x^i \quad \text{and} \quad q(x) = \sum_{j=0}^{m} b_j x^j$$

We multiply each $a_i x^i$ by each $b_j x^j$ and then collect like powers of x together. Thus in front of x^k we get all the products $a_i b_j$ with $i + j = k$, that is with $j = k - i$. In symbols we get

$$p(x)q(x) = \sum_{k=0}^{n+m} \left(\sum_{i=0}^{k} a_i b_{k-i} \right) x^k \tag{7}$$

EXAMPLE 6   Use formula (7) to compute $x + x^2 = p(x)$ times $2x^2 + 3x^3 = q(x)$.

Solution   If we take $a_0 = 0$, $a_1 = 1$, $a_2 = 1$, and $a_i = 0$ for $i > 1$, then

$$p(x) = \sum_{i=0}^{2} a_i x^i$$

and if we take $b_0 = b_1 = 0$, $b_2 = 2$, $b_3 = 3$, and $b_j = 0$ for $j > 3$, then

$$q(x) = \sum_{j=0}^{3} b_j x^j$$

This give us

$$p(x)q(x) = \sum_{k=0}^{5} \left(\sum_{i=0}^{k} a_i b_{k-i} \right) x^k$$

$$= a_0 b_0 x^0 + (a_0 b_1 + a_1 b_0)x + (a_0 b_2 + a_1 b_1 + a_2 b_0)x^2 + (a_0 b_3 + a_1 b_2 + a_2 b_1 + a_3 b_0)x^3 + (a_0 b_4 + a_1 b_3 + a_2 b_2 + a_3 b_1 + a_4 b_0)x^4 + (a_0 b_5 + a_1 b_4 + a_2 b_3 + a_3 b_2 + a_4 b_1 + a_5 b_0)x^5$$

$$= 0 \cdot x_0 + (0 \cdot 0 + 1 \cdot 0)x + (0 \cdot 2 + 1 \cdot 0 + 1 \cdot 0)x^2 + (0 \cdot 3 + 1 \cdot 2 + 1 \cdot 0 + 0 \cdot 0)x^3 + (0 \cdot 0 + 1 \cdot 3 + 1 \cdot 2 + 0 \cdot 0 + 0 \cdot 0)x^4 + (0 \cdot 0 + 1 \cdot 0 + 1 \cdot 3 + 0 \cdot 2 + 0 \cdot 0 + 0 \cdot 0)x^5$$

$$= 2x^3 + 5x^4 + 3x^5 \qquad \blacksquare$$

Example 6 is not meant to imply that we should always go back to the formula instead of proceeding informally as you learned to do in algebra; rather it is meant to show what the symbolism in the formula means.

We shall also multiply power series by multiplying individual terms and collecting similar powers of x together. This means we may write

$$\sum_{i=0}^{\infty} a_i x^i \sum_{k=0}^{\infty} b_j x^j = \sum_{j=0}^{\infty} \left(\sum_{i=0}^{k} a_i b_{k-i} \right) x^k \tag{8}$$

(Notice that the difference from equation (7) is only the upper limit of the sum.) Just as we proceed informally in the algebra of polynomials when we multiply polynomials in x together, we can proceed in this way when we multiply power series together or multiply a power series by a polynomial.

EXAMPLE 7   Find the product of $1 + x + x^2 + \ldots + x^n + \ldots = \sum_{i=0}^{\infty} x^i$ and $1 - x$.

Solution   We proceed informally by writing

$$(1 - x)(1 + x + x^2 + \ldots + x^n + \ldots) =$$
$$1 - x + x - x^2 + x^2 - x^3 + x^3 - x^4 + \ldots$$

Each power of x (except for $x^0 = 1$) cancels out so we obtain

$$(1 - x)(1 + x + x^2 + \ldots + x^n + \ldots) = 1 \qquad \blacksquare$$

Concepts Review

1. Expressions such as $A \oplus AA \oplus AAA$, $(A \oplus AA \oplus AAA)(P \oplus PP \oplus PPP)$, or $A \oplus A^2 \oplus A^3 \oplus A^4$ in which the letters stand for objects that may be selected are called _____.

2. When we collect similar powers of x together in a polynomial, the number in front of x^i is called the _____ of x^i.

3. An expression of the form $a_0 + a_1 + a_2 x^2 + \ldots$ or $\sum_{i=0}^{\infty} a_i x^i$ is called a _____ series.

4. The _____ _____ for the sequence $<a_i>$ is the power series $\sum_{i=0}^{\infty} a_i x^i$.

5. In the product of the power series $\sum_{i=0}^{\infty} a_i x^i$ and the power series $\sum_{j=0}^{\infty} b_j x^j$, the coefficient of x^k is given by the formula $\sum_{i=0}^{k}$ _____.

Exercises

A
1. Using the letter B for bananas, write the symbolic series that says that someone chooses 1, 2, or 3 bananas.

2. Using the letter N for nectarines, write the symbolic series that says that someone chooses 1, 2, or 3 nectarines.

3. What is the symbolic series that says that someone takes between 1 and 3 each of bananas, pears, apples, and tangerines?

4. What is the symbolic series that says that someone takes between 1 and 3 each of bananas, pears, apples, tangerines, and nectarines?

5. Write down the polynomial that results from substituting x for all the letters and changing from logical to algebraic notation in Exercise 3.

6. Write down the polynomial that results from substituting x for all the letters and changing from logical to algebraic notation in Exercise 4.

7. If someone is to choose between 1 and 3 each of bananas, pears, apples, and tangerines, in how many ways may this person choose 5 pieces of fruit?

8. If someone is to choose between 1 and 3 each of bananas, pears, apples, tangerines, and nectarines, in how many ways may this person choose 7 pieces of fruit?

9. Assume in Exercise 7 that bananas and apples each cost 20 cents and pears and tangerines each cost 30 cents. In how many ways may someone select one dollar's worth of fruit?

10. Use the prices in Exercise 9 for the fruits of Exercise 8 and assume that nectarines cost 25 cents each. In how many ways may someone select one dollar's worth of fruit?

11. We have a bag of (identical) apples. If each child is allowed to take between one and three apples, show symbolically how Jo, Bill, Pat, and Sue may take apples. Use the initials J, B, P, and S instead of children's names and use, for example, J^2 to stand for the statement "Jo takes 2 apples." In how many ways may we pass out exactly 8 apples?

12. A "snack pack" has 3 packages each of potato chips, corn chips, nacho chips, and cheese twists. Show symbolically how we may choose snacks if we try at least one of each snack. (Use initials P, C, N, and T.) Make the substitution of x for each initial and show the polynomial that arises. In how many ways may we choose a total of 7 packages of snacks?

13. Redo Exercise 11 allowing us to give no apples to a child as well. For example, use J^0 to say "Jo takes no apples."

14. Redo Exercise 12 allowing us to take none of any snack as well. For example, use P^0 to say we take no potato chips.

15. Using P for pennies, N for nickels, D for dimes, and Q for quarters, write the symbolic series for making change using from 0 to 5 of each kind of coin. What should you substitute for each letter so that the coefficient of x^n in the result is the number of ways to make n cents using from 0 to 5 of each coin? What is the polynomial that results?

16. A bake shop makes four kinds of candies that weigh one ounce each, three kinds of fruit bars that weigh two ounces each, and one kind of brownies that weigh four ounces each. Using A, B, C, and D to stand for the candies, E, F, and G for the fruit bars, and H for the brownies, write a symbolic series for the ways to use between 0 and 4 of each variety to make a box of goodies. What should be substituted for each letter to answer the question "In how many ways may we choose a one-pound box?" What is the polynomial that results?

B 17. The symbolic series corresponding to taking no apples, 2 apples, 4 apples, and so on from an unlimited supply is $A^0 \oplus A^2 \oplus A^4 \oplus \ldots$. What is the generating function for the number of ways to choose an even number of apples from an unlimited supply?

18. The symbolic series corresponding to taking 1 pear, 3 pears, 5 pears, 7 pears, and so on from an unlimited supply is $P \oplus P^3 \oplus P^5 \oplus \ldots$. What is the generating function for the number of ways to choose an odd number of pears from an unlimited supply?

19. Write down the symbolic series and then the corresponding generating function for the number of ways to choose an even number of apples and any number of tangerines from unlimited supplies.

20. Write down the symbolic series and the generating function for the number of ways to choose an odd number of pears and any number of tangerines from unlimited supplies.

21. Write down the generating function for the sequence $<a_i>$ that is 0 if $i = 0, 1$; i^2 if $i = 2, 3, 4$; and 0 if $i = 5$.

22. Write down the generating function for the sequence $<a_i>$ that is i if $i = 0, 1, 2, 3, 4$; $2i - 5$ if $i = 5, 6, 7, 8$; and 0 if $i > 8$.

23. What is the sequence whose generating function is the power series $x + 2x^2 + 3x^3 + 4x^4 + \ldots$?

24. What is the sequence whose generating function is the power series $x + 4x^2 + 9x^3 + 16x^4 + \ldots$?

25. Use formula (7) to find the product of $x + 2x^2$ and $3x + x^2$.

26. Use formula (7) to find the product of $1 + x^2$ and $3 + 2x + x^2$.

27. Find the product of the polynomial $1 + x$ and the power series
$$1 - x + x^2 - x^3 + x^4 - x^5 + \ldots$$

28. Find the product of the polynomial $1 - x$ and the power series
$$x + x^2 + x^3 + x^4 + \ldots$$

Problems

1. Using $F_1, F_2, \ldots, F_n$ to stand for n different kinds of fruit, explain why
$$\prod_{i=1}^{n} (F_i^0 + F_i^1 + F_i^2 + F_i^3)$$
is a symbolic series that represents the number of ways of choosing between zero and three of n different kinds of fruit. What is the generating function for the number of ways to select fruit, taking between zero and three of each kind?

2. Modify Problem 1 by allowing someone to take any number of any of the n fruits. Write down the appropriate symbolic series and generating function.

3. Modify Problem 1 by allowing someone to take any even number of any of the n fruits. Write down the appropriate symbolic series and generating fuction.

4. What is the generating function in which the coefficient of x^i is the number of ways the sum of the tops can be i when you roll n dice?

5. By using P as the symbol for penny, N for nickel, D for dime, and Q for quarter, write down the symbolic series for the ways to choose any number of each coin. What is the generating function in which the coefficient of x^i is the number of ways to make i cents using these coins?

6. Equation (8) actually defines the meaning of $f(x) \cdot g(x)$. Write down the expression equation (8) gives for $(f(x) \cdot g(x)) \cdot h(x)$ and the expression equation (8) gives for $f(x) \cdot (g(x) \cdot h(x))$. Use this to explain why the associative law holds for the multiplication of power series.

7. Read Problem 6. Write down the expressions given by equation (8) for $f(x)g(x) + h(x)g(x)$ and $(f(x) + h(x))g(x)$. Use this to explain why the distributive law holds for multiplication and addition of power series.

8. Use the fact that $(1 - x)(1 + x + x^2 + \ldots + x^i + \ldots) = 1$ to find the value of $1 + \frac{1}{2} + \frac{1}{4} + \ldots + \left(\frac{1}{2}\right)^i + \ldots$.

9. What is the product $(1 + x)(1 - x + x^2 - x^3 + \ldots + (-1)^i x^i + \ldots)$? What does this tell you about the value of $1 - \frac{1}{2} + \frac{1}{4} - \frac{1}{8} + \ldots$?

10. Try to explain what goes wrong in Problems 8 and 9 if you replace $\frac{1}{2}$ by 2 and so attempt to compute $1 + 2 + 4 + \ldots$ or $1 - 2 + 4 - 8 + \ldots$.

Section B-2
Applications of
Generating Functions

A *Product Principle for Generating Functions*

By using symbolic series we gave two different examples of generating functions for selecting one, two, or three pieces of fruit from each of three varieties. The generating function

$$\sum_{i=0}^{\infty} a_i x^i = (x + x^2 + x^3)^3$$

had a_i equal to the number of selections with a total of i pieces of fruit. The generating function

$$\sum_{i=0}^{\infty} b_i x^i = (x^{20} + x^{40} + x^{60})(x^{25} + x^{50} + x^{75})(x^{15} + x^{30} + x^{45})$$

had b_i equal to the number of selections whose total monetary value is i cents. In both bases we were combining a selection from the set $S_1 = \{A, AA, AAA\}$ (of apple selections), the set $S_2 = \{P, PP, PPP\}$ (for pears), and the set $S_3 = \{T, TT, TTT\}$ (for tangerines) into a selection of fruit which we may regard as a member of the set

$$S = \{A^i P^j T^k \mid 1 \leqslant i \leqslant 3, 1 \leqslant j \leqslant 3, 1 \leqslant k \leqslant 3\}$$

In each case there was a numerical value (namely the number of pieces in the selection or the cost of the selection) associated with each selection we discussed. The numerical value gives a function v from the set of possible selections to the non-negative integers.

For example, when we were concerned with how many fruits we chose, we used

$$
\begin{array}{lll}
v(A) = 1 & v(AA) = 2 & v(AAA) = 3 \\
v(P) = 1 & v(PP) = 2 & v(PPP) = 3 \\
v(T) = 1 & v(TT) = 2 & v(TTT) = 3
\end{array}
$$

When we were concerned with the amount of money we spent on fruit, we used

$$
\begin{array}{lll}
v(A) = 20 & v(AA) = 40 & v(AAA) = 60 \\
v(P) = 25 & v(PP) = 50 & v(PPP) = 75 \\
v(T) = 15 & v(TT) = 30 & v(TTT) = 45
\end{array}
$$

Each final choice of fruit was an ordered triple (that is a 3-tuple) (z_1, z_2, z_3) in which z_1 was chosen from S_1, z_2 was chosen from S_2, and z_3 was chosen from S_3. For example, in $AA \wedge P \wedge TT$, z_1 is AA, z_2 is P, and z_3 is TT. The value of such an ordered triple is given by $v(z_1, z_2, z_3) = v(z_1) + v(z_2) + v(z_3)$. For example, the monetary value of (AA, P, TT) is $40 + 25 + 30 = 95$ cents.

Each of the generating functions we considered is a generating function $\sum c_i x^i$ in which c_i is the number of selections whose value is i. This is typical of the applications of generating functions. For each such generating function we consider, there will be some set S of objects and there will be a value function v from S to the set of non-negative integers. We define the **generating function for S according to** (or **by**) v to be the power series

$$
\sum_{i=0}^{\infty} a_i x^i
$$

in which a_i is the number of elements of S of value i.

Why We Multiply Generating Functions

The "product principle for generating functions" explains why in both cases we got the generating function by total value for the ordered triples (z_1, z_2, z_3) of selections by multiplying together the generating functions for S_1, for S_2, and for S_3 according to their values. Two pieces of terminology will make this principle easier to state. In Chapter 3 we defined the Cartesian product of two sets S_1 and S_2, denoted by $S_1 \times S_2$, to be the set of all ordered pairs (z_1, z_2), with z_1 in S_1, and z_2 in S_2. Similarly, we define the **product** or **Cartesian product** of n sets S_1, S_2, . . . , S_n, denoted by $S_1 \times S_2 \times \ldots \times S_n$, to be the set of n-tuples $(z_1, z_2, \ldots , z_n)$ with $z_i \in S_i$. Thus above our set of ordered triples (z_1, z_2, z_3) was the product of the 3 sets S_1, S_2, and S_3. A **value function** v_i defined on S_i is, as above, a function from S_i to the non-negative integers. Then the **total value function** v is defined on $S_1 \times S_2 \times \ldots \times S_n$ by $v(z_1, z_2, \ldots, z_n) = v_1(z_1) + v_2(z_2) + \ldots + v_n(z_n)$. Now we can state the **product principle** for generating functions as Theorem 1.

Theorem 1 If we have sets $S_1, S_2, \ldots, S_n$ with value functions $v_1, v_2, \ldots, v_n$, then the generating function for the product $S_1 \times S_2 \times \ldots \times S_n$ according to the total value function is the product of the generating functions for the sets S_i according to the value functions v_i.

Proof We prove the theorem for the case $n = 2$; the proof can be extended to all values of n by induction. Let $g_1(x)$ and $g_2(x)$ be the generating functions for S_1 and S_2 according to v_1 and v_2. We multiply

$$g_1(x) = \sum_{i=0}^{\infty} a_i x^i \quad \text{and} \quad g_2(x) = \sum_{j=0}^{\infty} b_j x^j$$

by multiplying each term from $g_1(x)$ by each term from $g_2(x)$ and collecting the terms with the same exponent on x together. Thus if

$$g(x) = g_1(x)g_2(x) = \sum_{n=0}^{\infty} c_n x^n$$

we have

$$c_n = \sum_{i=0}^{n} a_i b_{n-i}$$

The number of arrangements in S_1 with value i is a_i; b_{n-i} is the number of arrangements in S_2 that we can pair with them to get total value n. However, for a pair to have total value n, the value of its first entry (this value is i) must be an integer between 0 and n. By the (old) product principle, the product $a_i b_{n-i}$ is the number of ordered pairs of arrangements with values, respectively, i and $n - i$; adding these products gives the total number of pairs of value n. ■

EXAMPLE 8 Find the generating function (according to total amount) for the number of ways to choose fruit from 5 varieties if we may choose 1, 2, or 3 of each variety.

Solution We assume that all the fruits of a given variety are identical. Thus there is one way to take one piece, one way to take two pieces, and one way to take three pieces. Thus the generating function for the number of ways to take 1, 2, or 3 pieces of a given variety is $x + x^2 + x^3$. Then by Theorem 12, the generating function for selections of any combination of fruits is $(x + x^2 + x^3)^5$. ■

EXAMPLE 9 Find the generating function for the number of ways to choose fruit from among five different kinds if we are allowed to take any amount (including one) of each variety.

Solution   We assume that all the fruits of a given variety are identical. Thus, there is one way to choose one piece, one way to choose two pieces, and so on. There is also one way to choose none of that variety: namely, don't take any! Thus the generating function for the number of ways to take k pieces of one variety of the fruit is

$$1 + x + x^2 + \ldots + x^n + \ldots = \sum_{i=0}^{\infty} x^i$$

(The 1 is the x^0 term standing for possibly taking zero fruits of a given variety.) A selection of fruit of the five different varieties can be regarded as a 5-tuple in which the ith entry specifies the number of pieces of fruit i taken. Then by Theorem 12 the number of ways to choose k pieces of fruit is the coefficient of x^k in

$$(1 + x + x^2 + \ldots + x^n + \ldots)^5 = \left(\sum_{i=0}^{\infty} x^i \right)^5 \qquad \blacksquare$$

B   Geometric and Binomial Series

We have seen that the series

$$\sum_{i=0}^{\infty} x^i = 1 + x + x^2 + \ldots$$

which is called an **infinite geometric series** in x, arises as a generating function whenever we are discussing taking none, one, two, three, and so on of some kind of item (as in Example 9). Many of the generating functions that we need to multiply together when using the product principle are either geometric series or are closely related to geometric series. For this reason we've also seen, through both manipulations of symbolic series and the product principle for generating functions, that $(1 + x + x^2 + \ldots)^n$ arises often as a generating function. For example, if we have n different varieties of fruit, this is the generating function in which the coefficient of x^i is the number of ways to choose i pieces of fruit with no limits on the amount taken of any variety. Notice that this is simply the number of ways to choose an i-element multiset of fruit from among the n varieties. This observation is not restricted to fruit.

Theorem 2   The generating function $\sum_{i=0}^{\infty} a_i x^i$ in which a_i is the number of ways to select an i-element multiset from an n-element set is

$$(1 + x + x^2 + \ldots)^n = \left(\sum_{i=0}^{\infty} x^i \right)^n$$

Proof   Denote our n-element set as $S = \{x_1, x_2, \ldots, x_n\}$. There is one way to include the element x_j exactly i times in a multiset, so the generating function for the number of i-element multisets chosen from S and using only x_j is $1 + x + x^2 + x^3 + \ldots$. An i-element multiset from S gives an n-tuple of choices, the jth choice being to include x_j a certain number of times. By the product principle for generating functions, the generating function in which a_i is the number of multisets with i elements chosen from S is $(1 + x + x^2 + \ldots)^n$. ∎

We already have a formula, namely

$$\binom{n + i - 1}{i}$$

for the number of i-element multisets chosen from an n-element set. Combining this with Theorem 13 gives a formula for $(1 + x + x^2 + \ldots)^n$.

Theorem 3 $(1 + x + x^2 + \ldots)^n = \displaystyle\sum_{i=0}^{\infty} \binom{n + i - 1}{i} x^i.$

Proof   Given above. ∎

The Sum of a Geometric Series

In our introduction to the multiplication of power series we observed that $(1 + x + x^2 + \ldots)(1 - x) = 1$. We rewrite this by division as

$$1 + x + x^2 + \ldots = \frac{1}{1 - x} = (1 - x)^{-1}$$

This equation is often referred to as the formula for the **sum of an infinite geometric sequence.** Notice that there are some numbers, such as $x = \frac{1}{2}$, that we may substitute for x and get a sensible formula while there are other numbers such as $x = 2$ that, when substituted into the formula, give us utter nonsense. The reason for this is explained in a course in calculus. In discrete mathematics we rarely wish to substitute numbers for x so we may ignore this problem for now. Substituting $(1 - x)^{-1}$ into Theorem 2 gives us a formula for $(1 - x)^{-n}$.

Theorem 4 $(1 - x)^{-n} = \displaystyle\sum_{i=0}^{\infty} \binom{n + i - 1}{i} x^i.$

Proof   We obtain this formula by substituting $(1 - x)^{-1}$ for $1 + x + x^2 + \ldots$ in Theorem 3. ∎

EXAMPLE 10   Show that the generating function for the number of ways to choose a total of i pieces of candy from among n varieties (selecting any number of each variety) is $(1 - x)^{-n}$.

Solution   A selection of candy is simply a multiset chosen from the n varieties of candy. Thus by Theorem 4 or Theorem 2 and the formula for the sum of an infinite geometric series the generating function is $((1 - x)^{-1})^n = (1 - x)^{-n}$. ∎

EXAMPLE 11   Find the coefficient of x^4 in $(1 + x + x^2 + \ldots)^7$.

Solution   Since $(1 + x + x^2 + \ldots)^7 = (1 - x)^{-7}$, Theorem 3 or Theorem 4 tells us that the coefficient of x^4 is

$$\binom{7 + 4 - 1}{4} = \binom{10}{4} = 210$$ ∎

EXAMPLE 12   What is the generating function according to size for the number of multisets chosen from an n-element set in which each element appears an odd number of times?

Solution   Suppose the set is $\{x_1, x_2, \ldots, x_n\}$. The generating function for the number of multisets chosen from $\{x_i\}$ consisting of an odd number of x_i's is

$$x + x^3 + x^5 + \ldots = x(1 + x^2 + x^4 + \ldots) = x(1 - x^2)^{-1}$$

A choice of a multiset is the same as the choice of the n-tuple of multiplicities of $x_1, x_2, \ldots, x_n$. Thus by the product principle, the generating function according to size for the number of multisets chosen from an n-element set with the restrictions given is $x^n(1 - x^2)^{-n}$.   ∎

EXAMPLE 13   Give the generating function for the number of k-element multisets chosen from an n-element set and including each of the n elements at least twice.

Solution   A given element x_i may appear twice, three times, $\ldots$, so the generating function $g_i(x)$ for the number of times x_i appears is

$$g_i(x) = x^2 + x^3 + x^4 + \ldots = \sum_{j=2}^{\infty} x^j = x^2(1 + x + x^2 + \ldots) = x^2 \sum_{j=0}^{\infty} x^j = x^2(1 - x)^{-1}$$

Then the product of the n generating functions g_1 through g_n is

$$g(x) = x^{2n}(1 + x + x^2 + \ldots)^n = x^{2n}(1 - x)^{-n}$$ ∎

The Extended Binomial Theorem

The formula for $(1 - x)^{-n}$ in Theorem 4 looks quite similar to the formula for the binomial theorem. We can use the relationship $-(-x) = x$ to get

$$(1 + x)^{-n} = (1 - (-x))^{-n} = \sum_{i=0}^{\infty} \binom{n + i - 1}{i}(-x)^i$$

$$= \sum_{i=0}^{\infty} (-1)^i \binom{n + i - 1}{i} x^i$$

Let us expand the term $(-1)^i \binom{n+i-1}{i}$. We obtain

$$(-1)^i \binom{n+i-1}{i} = (-1)^i \frac{(n+i-1)_i}{i!} = (-1)^i \frac{(n+i-1)(n+i-2)\dots(n+i-i)}{i!}$$

$$= \frac{(-n-i+1)(-n-i+2)\dots(-n)}{i!}$$

$$= \frac{(-n)_i}{i!}$$

Now just as $\frac{(n)_i}{i!}$ is defined to be $\binom{n}{i}$, we define $\binom{-n}{i} = \frac{(-n)_i}{i!}$. The equation above says we have also defined $\binom{-n}{i} = (-1)^i \binom{n+i-1}{i}$. With this substitution for $(-1)^i \binom{n+i-1}{i}$ our formula above becomes

$$(1+x)^{-n} = \sum_{i=0}^{n} \binom{-n}{i} x_i$$

In fact we can get a formula for $(x+y)^{-n}$ as well, giving us the **binomial theorem for negative exponents.**

Theorem 5 $(x+y)^{-n} = \displaystyle\sum_{i=0}^{\infty} \binom{-n}{i} x^i y^{-n-i}$.

Proof   Since $(x+y) = y\left(1 + \dfrac{x}{y}\right)$,

$$(x+y)^{-n} = y^{-n}\left(1 + \frac{x}{y}\right)^{-n} = y^{-n} \sum_{i=0}^{\infty} \binom{-n}{i} \left(\frac{x}{y}\right)^i = \sum_{i=0}^{\infty} \binom{-n}{i} x^i y^{-n-i} \qquad \blacksquare$$

EXAMPLE 14   Expand $(x+2)^{-3}$, replacing binomial coefficients by their values.

Solution   We write

$$(x+2)^{-3} = \sum_{i=0}^{\infty} \binom{-3}{i} x^i 2^{-3-i}$$

$$= \sum_{i=0}^{\infty} \frac{1}{8} \binom{-3}{i} \frac{x^i}{2^i}$$

$$= \sum_{i=0}^{\infty} (-1)^i \frac{1}{8} \binom{2+i}{i} \frac{x^i}{2^i}$$

$$= \sum_{i=0}^{\infty} (-1)^i \frac{i^2 + 3i + 2}{16} \left(\frac{x}{2}\right)^i$$

$\blacksquare$

EXAMPLE 15   What is the coefficient of x^7 in $(x + 2)^{-3}$?

Solution   The x^7 term in the power series in Example 14 is, from the first equality in Example 14, $\binom{-3}{7} x^7 \cdot 2^{-3-7}$. Its coefficient is

$$\binom{-3}{7} \cdot 2^{-10} = (-1)^7 \binom{3 + 7 - 1}{7} \cdot 2^{-10} = (-1)^7 \binom{9}{7} \cdot \frac{1}{1024}$$

$$= (-1)^7 \cdot \frac{36}{1024} = -\frac{9}{256}$$

∎

Note that if we replace $-n$ by the symbol m in Theorem 5, we get the **binomial theorem for arbitrary exponents**:

$$(x + y)^m = \sum_{i=0}^{\infty} \binom{m}{i} x^i x^{m-i}$$

and this is a formula for the binomial theorem for positive exponents as well, because $\binom{m}{i} = 0$ if $i > m$ so that

$$\sum_{i=0}^{\infty} \binom{m}{i} x^i y^{m-i} = \sum_{i=0}^{m} \binom{m}{i} x^i y^{m-i} = (x + y)^m$$

Thus with our extended definition for binomial coefficients, we can write down the binomial theorem for positive and for negative exponents with exactly the same formula.

Applying the Binomial Theorem with Negative Exponents

With the product principle, the formulas for sums of geometric series, and the extended binomial theorem, we can answer questions which would otherwise require tedious computation.

EXAMPLE 16   If we roll 4 dice, in how many different ways may the total of the numbers of dots on the four top faces be 12?

Solution   The generating function for the number of ways *one* die may come up with i dots on top is $x + x^2 + x^3 + x^4 + x^5 + x^6$. Rolling 4 dice gives us a 4-tuple of numbers of dots; we want to know the number of such 4-tuples that add to 12. Thus we are asking for the coefficient of x^{12} in $(x + x^2 + x^3 + x^4 + x^5 + x^6)^4$. Computing this coefficient by using the multinomial theorem would be tedious; computing it by expanding the polynomial would be more tedious. Notice, however, that

$$(x + x^2 + x^3 + x^4 + x^5 + x^6)^4 = x^4 (1 + x + x^2 + x^3 + x^4 + x^5)^4$$

$$= x^4 \left(\frac{1 - x^6}{1 - x} \right)^4 = x^4 (1 - x^6)^4 (1 - x)^{-4}$$

$$= x^4(1 - 4x^6 + 6x^{12} - 4x^{18} + x^{24}) \sum_{i=0}^{\infty} \binom{4 + i - 1}{i} x^i$$

$$= x^4(1 - 4x^6 + 6x^{12} - 4x^{18} + x^{24}) \sum_{i=0}^{\infty} \binom{3 + i}{i} x^i$$

In this product the coefficient of x^{12} is

$$1 \cdot \binom{3 + 8}{8} - 4 \cdot \binom{3 + 2}{2} = \binom{11}{8} - 4 \cdot \binom{5}{2} = 165 - 4 \cdot 10 = 125 \qquad \blacksquare$$

Concepts Review

1. In the generating function $\sum_{i=0}^{\infty} a_i x^i$ for the set S according to the value v, the coefficient a_i is the _____ of elements x in S with _____.

2. If we have n sets S_i with value functions v_i then the _____ _____ function v is given on $S_1 \times S_2 \times \ldots \times S_n$ by $v(z_1, z_2, \ldots, z_n) = v_1(z_1) + v_2(z_2) + \ldots + v_n(z_n)$.

3. The symbol $S_1 \times S_2 \times \ldots \times S_n$ stands for the _____ or the _____ _____ of the sets S_i and is the set of all n-tuples $(x_1, x_2, \ldots, x_n)$ such that x_i _____.

4. The _____ principle for generating functions states that the generating function for a Cartesian product of sets by total value is the _____ of the generating functions of the individual sets by individual value.

5. The series $1 + x + x^2 + \ldots$, also written _____, is called an infinite _____ series.

6. The generating function for the number of ways to select an i-element multiset from an n-element set is $\sum_{i=0}^{\infty}$ _____ $=$ _____.

7. An infinite series representation of $(1 - x)^{-n}$ is _____.

8. The binomial theorem for arbitrary exponents gives the formula $(x + y)^m = \sum_{i=0}^{\infty}$ _____.

Exercises

A

1. Find the generating function for the number of ways to choose fruit from 4 varieties if you may take 1, 2, or 3 of each variety.

2. Find the generating function for the number of ways to choose candy from 6 varieties of candy if you may take 1, 2, or 3 of each variety.

3. Redo Exercise 1 allowing 0 of any variety as well.

4. Redo Exercise 2 allowing 0 of any variety as well.

5. What is the generating function for the number of ways to choose candy from n varieties if you may take 0 or 1 of each variety?

6. What is the generating function for the number of ways to select names from a list of n names if you may select each name zero or one time?

7. Redo Exercise 1 allowing any number of pieces of each variety.

8. Redo Exercise 2 allowing any number of pieces of each variety.

9. Use Theorem 1 to show that the generating function for the number of ways to make n cents using any number of nickels, dimes and quarters is

$$\frac{1}{1 - x^5} \cdot \frac{1}{1 - x^{10}} \cdot \frac{1}{1 - x^{25}}$$

10. Use Theorem 1 to derive a generating function for the number of ways to make i cents of postage using 20-cent, 5-cent, and 2-cent stamps.

11. Use Theorem 1 to derive a generating function for the number of ways to select any number of apples, an odd number of pears, and an even number of tangerines each from an unlimited supply.

12. Use Theorem 1 to derive a generating function for the number of ways to select an even number of apples, an even number of plums, an odd number of apples, and an odd number of tangerines each from an unlimited supply.

B   13. Use the formulas for the sums of finite and infinite geometric series to evaluate

$$\sum_{i=0}^{4} \left(\frac{1}{3}\right)^i, \quad \sum_{i=0}^{6} \left(\frac{1}{3}\right)^i, \quad \text{and} \quad \sum_{i=0}^{\infty} \left(\frac{1}{3}\right)^i$$

14. Use the formulas for the sums of finite and infinite geometric series to evaluate

$$\sum_{i=0}^{4} \left(\frac{2}{3}\right)^i, \quad \sum_{i=0}^{6} \left(\frac{2}{3}\right)^i, \quad \text{and} \quad \sum_{i=0}^{\infty} \left(\frac{2}{3}\right)^i$$

15. Expand $(1 - x)^{-3}$ as a power series without any binomial coefficient symbols.

16. Expand $(1 - x^3)^{-2}$ as a power series without any binomial coefficient symbols.

17. Find the coefficient of x^5 in $(1 + x + x^2 + \ldots)^7$.

18. Find the coefficient of x^6 in $(1 - x)^{-7}$.

19. Find the coefficient of x^k in $(1 - x)^{-7}$.

20. Find the coefficient of x^k in $(1 + x + x^2 + \ldots)^5$.

21. Find the coefficient of x^5 in $(1 + x + x^2 + \ldots)^n$.

22. Find the coefficient of x^7 in $(1 - x)^{-n}$.

C   23. Find the coefficient of x^5 in $(2 + x)^{-3}$.

24. Find the coefficient of x^6 in $(x + \sqrt{2})^{-4}$.

25. Find the coefficient of x^k in $(x + 2)^{-3}$.

26. Find the coefficient of x^5 in $(x + 2)^{-n}$.

27. What is the number of ways that the sum of the top faces of 4 dice may add up to 11?

28. What is the number of ways that the sum of the top faces of 4 dice may add up to 14?

29. Express the generating function for the number of multisets chosen from an n-element set and containing no more than 5 elements as a polynomial times $(1 - x)^{-n}$.

30. Express the generating function for the number of multisets chosen from an n-element set and including each element at least once but not more than five times as a polynomial times $(1 - x)^{-n}$.

31. We have 5 different kinds of 20-cent stamps, 2 different kinds of 10-cent stamps, and 3 different kinds of 5-cent stamps. The generating function for the number of ways to make postage using these stamps is $(1 - x^{20})^{-5}(1 - x^{10})^{-2}(1 - x^5)^{-3}$. Explain why.

32. If we have 5 different kinds of candies weighing one ounce each, 4 different kinds weighing two ounces each, and 3 different kinds weighing 5 ounces each, the generating function for the number of ways to make an n-ounce box of assorted candies is $(1 - x)^{-5}(1 - x^2)^{-4}(1 - x^5)^{-3}$. Explain why.

33. Use Theorem 1 to show that the generating function for the number of ways to make n cents by using at least one nickel, at least one dime, and at least one quarter is

$$\frac{x^{40}}{(1 - x^5)(1 - x^{10})(1 - x^{25})}$$

34. We now have one kind of 20-cent stamp, one kind of 10-cent stamp, and one kind of 5-cent stamp. What is the generating function for the number of ways to make i cents postage using at least one of each stamp?

35. What is the generating function for the number of ways of passing out oranges to n children so that each child receives an even number of oranges? (The coefficient of x^m should be the number of distributions using a total of m oranges.)

36. What is the generating function for the number of ways of passing out oranges to n children so that each child gets at least one but no more than 4 oranges? (The coefficient of x^m should be the number of distributions using a total of m oranges.)

Problems

1. Expand $(x + y)^{-3}$ as a power series without any binomial coefficient symbols.

2. Expand $(x + 2)^{-3}$ as a power series without any binomial coefficient symbols.

3. We roll n dice one at a time. What is the generating function for the number of ways in which the sum of the top faces is i?

4. A **partition** of the integer n is a multiset of positive numbers whose sum is n. The positive numbers are called the **parts** of the partition. Find the generating function for the number of partitions of an integer into parts of size 1, 2, 3, 4, or 5. The coefficient of x^n should be the number of partitions of n into parts of these sizes.

5. Partitions of integers are defined in Problem 4. Find a generating function for the number of partitions of an integer n into *even* parts of size at most 20.

6. Find a generating function for the number of partitions of an integer n into parts of size at most 10 in which each part is used an even number of times.

7. Give an explanation of the similarity of the answers to Problems 5 and 6.

8. Find the generating function for the number of multisets of zeros and ones in which the number of zeros is even.

9. Find the generating function for the number of multisets of digits and letters in which the number of letters is even.

10. Find a generating function for the number of non-negative integer solutions to the equation $w + x + y + z = n$. (A solution here is a 4-tuple of values for w, x, y, and z.)

11. By using calculus it is possible to recognize that the power series

$$\sum_{i=0}^{\infty} i x^{i-1} = \frac{1}{(1-x)^2}$$

Show how. Explain why this means that

$$\sum_{i=0}^{\infty} (i+1)x^i$$

is the generating function for the number of ways to select an i-element multiset from a 2-element set.

12. Recall that $\binom{n}{k} = \frac{(n)_k}{k!}$ and $(n)_k$ is defined as a certain product with k terms. This gives a natural way to define $(x)_k$.
    (a) Find the natural definition of $(x)_k$.

    (b) Use part (a) to define $\binom{x}{k}$.

    (c) Find a formula for $\binom{\frac{1}{2}}{k}$.

    (d) Write down the binomial theorem expansion for $(1 - 4x)^{-\frac{1}{2}}$.

    (e) Explain why $(1 - 4x)^{-\frac{1}{2}}$ is the generating function for $\binom{2n}{n}$.

13. This problem will show how generating functions lead you to the solution of first order linear recurrence equations.
    (a) Suppose $s_n = b \cdot s_{n-1}$. Let

$$f(x) = \sum_{i=0}^{\infty} s_i x_i$$

be the generating function for the sequence $<s_i>$. Show by substitution that $(1 - bx)f(x) = s_0$.

(b) Use part (a) to show that

$$f(x) = s_0 \sum_{i=0}^{\infty} b^i x^i$$

(c) Why can you conclude from part (b) that $s_i = s_0 b^i$?

(d) Repeat the steps of parts (a) − (c) with $s_n = bs_{n-1} + d(n)$ to get the formula derived in Chapter 7 for the solution to this recurrence.

14. Consider the recurrence $as_n + bs_{n-1} + cs_{n-2} = d(n)$.

(a) Show that the generating function for s_n satisfies

$$(a + bx + cx^2) \sum_{n=0}^{\infty} s_n x^n = s_0(a + b) + s_1 ax + \sum_{n=2}^{\infty} d(n)x^n$$

(b) Based on the ideas in part (a), show why the general solution to the recurrence relation $s_n - 4s_{n-1} + 4s_{n-2} = 0$ is a linear combination of 2^n and $n \cdot 2^n$.

(c) Predict the general solution of a third-order linear recurrence relation of the form $s_n - 3rs_{n-1} + 3r^2 s_{n-2} - r^3 s_{n-3} = 0$ and explain why this prediction is correct.

(d) Show that $\dfrac{1}{6x^2 - 5x + 1} = \dfrac{3}{1 - 3x} - \dfrac{2}{1 - 2x}$.

(e) Use part (d) to find the solution to the recurrence $s_n - 5s_{n-1} + 6s_{n-2} = 0$ with $s_0 = 1$ and $s_1 = 0$ and the solution with $s_0 = 1$ and $s_1 = 1$.

(f) Based on parts (a), (d), and (e), find a formula analogous to the formula for the general solution to a first-order linear constant coefficient recurrence for the general solution to $s_n - 5s_{n-1} + 6s_{n-2} = d(n)$.

(g) If you have studied partial fractions, explain how to find solutions to second-order linear recurrences with constant coefficients. Try to describe a general pattern for all constant coefficient linear recurrences.

Suggested Reading

Chapter 1

Abbot, James C. *Sets, Lattices, and Boolean Algebra*. Boston: Allyn and Bacon, 1969. A general introductory reference, intended for undergraduates but aimed at students with some mathematical experience. Starts with interesting examples of paradoxes.

Alfredo, Salvatore, and Christine Nolan. *Principles and Applications of Boolean Algebra*. New York: Hayden, 1964. Broad coverage; at least part of the book picks up where we leave off.

Douglis, Avron. *Ideas in Mathematics*. Philadelphia: W. B. Saunders, 1970. Designed for a terminal course in mathematics for students in the liberal arts, but with much to offer the student of computer science, mathematics, or any of the mathematical disciplines. Its chapter on the axiomatic method discusses circuits to test the truth of statements and some of the more elementary aspects of compound statements. Chapter 1, on logical reasoning, is a good overview of the principles of reasoning introduced in Chapters 1 and 2 of *Discrete Mathematics*.

Gillie, Angelo C. *Binary Arithmetic and Boolean Algebra*. New York: McGraw-Hill, 1965. Covers two important topics in the applications of discrete mathematics to computing and their relations to each other.

Grunbaum, B. "The Construction of Venn Diagrams." *College Math Journal* 15 (1984): 238.

Hailperin, Theodore. "Boole's Algebra Isn't Boolean Algebra." *Mathematics Magazine* 54 (1981). A fascinating discussion of just how rigorous Boole was (or wasn't) in expressing his algebraic "laws of thought."

Kemeny, J. G., J. L. Snell, and G. L. Thompson. *Introduction to Finite Mathematics*. 3d ed. Englewood Clifs: Prentice-Hall, 1974. One of the first college textbooks for freshmen to begin with sets and logic, its treatment is still among the easiest to understand.

Ralston, Anthony. "Will Discrete Mathematics Surpass Calculus in Importance?" *College Math Journal* 15 (1984): 371. The lead article in an entire issue of the journal devoted to discussing the importance of discrete mathematics.

Shwenk, Allen J. "A Venn Diagram for 5 Sets." *Mathematics Magazine* 57 (1984): 297.

Van Dalen, D., H. C. Doets, and H. De Swart. *Sets: Naive, Axiomatic, and Applied*. New York: Pergamon, 1978. While this book tackles some fairly sophicated topics, it does so in a way that makes them accessible with less background than would be expected.

Chapter 2

Korfhage, Robert. *Logic and Algorithms, with Applications to the Computer and Information Sciences*. New York: Wiley, 1966. This book appeared ten to fifteen years before its time. It covers the topics in logic relevant to students of both computer science and mathematics in an informal and straightforward way. Intended to be accessible to sophomores.

Lemmon, E. J. *Beginning Logic*. London: Nelson, 1965. A beginning book that presupposes no knowledge of philosophy or mathematics. Should be useful even to beginning students of discrete mathematics.

Manna, Zoher, and Richard Waldinger. *Deductive Reasoning*. Vol. 1 of *The Logical Basis for Computer Programming*. Reading, Mass.: Addison-Wesley, 1985. Intended for people with serious computing interests; a student who finds *Discrete Mathematics* fairly easy-going should be able to get something out of this now, and even more later.

Rose, Allen. *Computer Logic*. London: Wiley-Interscience, 1971. Intended for undergraduates (though a bit more advanced than *Discrete Mathematics*), this should provide reasonably easy access to more advanced topics in logic and computing.

Rosencrantz, Roger. *Logic Lectures*, Vol. 1. San Francisco: Ridgeview, 1970. Written originally for mathematically oriented philosophy students, this book should be a good way for students of discrete mathematics to begin a further study of logic.

Smullyan, Arthur. *Fundamentals of Logic*. Englewood Cliffs: Prentice-Hall, 1962. A brief and straightforward treatment of logic aimed at college students with little mathematics background. Has an interesting chapter on probability from a logician's viewpoint.

Chapter 3

Bogart, Kenneth P. *Introductory Combinatorics*. 2d ed. San Diego: Harcourt Brace Jovanovich, 1989. (1st ed. Boston: Pitman, 1983). This book devotes an entire chapter to partial orderings.

Cozzens, Margaret B., and Richard D. Porter. *Mathematics and Its Applications*. Lexington: D. C. Heath, 1987. This book considers primarily applications of discrete mathematics outside of computer science; its chapter on relations and functions is devoted mainly to relations.

Date, C. J. *An Introduction to Database Systems*. 4th ed. Reading, Mass.: Addison-Wesley, 1986. Discusses relational data bases, among others, and shows how *n*-ary relations (rather than just bin-ary relations) arise in database computing.

Fisher, James. *Application-Oriented Algebra*. New York: IEP, 1977. Begins with sets and binary relations and then devotes an entire chapter to partial orderings, including some of the most important classes of partial orderings that arise in applications.

Harary, Frank, Robert Z. Norman, and Dorwin Cartwright. *Structural Models: An Introduction to the Theory of Directed Graphs*. New York: Wiley, 1965. One of the few books devoted entirely to directed graphs and their applications. It is a very thorough treatment of digraphs with a behavioral science flavor, and is accessible to undergraduates.

Roberts, Fred S. *Discrete Mathematical Models*. Englewood Cliffs: Prentice-Hall 1976. One of the first textbooks in discrete applied mathematics, and still one of the best. Loaded with applications of graphs, digraphs, and partial orderings.

Rosen, Kenneth H. *Elementary Number Theory and Its Applications*. Reading, Mass.: Addison-Wesley, 1984. An excellent place to explore congruence modulo m in greater detail and to learn about some of its applications. It does not have any advanced mathematical prerequisites and would be accessible to a student who finds *Discrete Mathematics* fairly easygoing.

Stout, Quentin F., and Patricia Woodworth. "Relational Databases." *American Mathematical Monthly* 90 (1983): 101. A mathematical but readable treatment of how relations arise in database theory.

Ullman, Jeffrey D. *Database Systems*. 3d ed. Rockville, MD: Computer Science Press, 1986. A solid treatment of database theory via n-ary (rather than just bin-ary) relations.

Chapter 4

Davis, Martin. "What is a Computation?" In *Mathematics Today*, edited by Lynn A. Steen. New York: Springer-Verlag, 1978. We often think that a function is just a rule that tells us how to make a computation. This article shows us that this point of view does not simplify the situation at all.

Greene, Daniel H., and Donald E. Knuth. *Mathematics for the Analysis of Algorithms*. Boston: Birkhäuser, 1981. While this book is at the advanced undergraduate level, it contains natural extensions of many applications of discrete mathematics to the analysis of algorithms presented in *Discrete Mathematics*.

Knuth, Donald E. *The Art of Computer Programming*, Vol. 1. 2d ed. Reading, Mass.: Addison-Wesley, 1973. This book has an excellent discussion of the "big Oh" notation in the context of computer science applications. All volumes in this series (3 at this writing) have been "instant classics" and have helped set the tone for modern applications of mathematics, especially discrete mathematics, in computer science.

Wilf, Herbert S. *Algorithms and Complexity*. Englewood Cliffs: Prentice-Hall, 1986. A quick tour through selected topics in the mathematical study of algorithms and their order. Early on it has a succinct discussion of the "big Oh" notation and related notations (little oh, big omega, theta, ~). This short book extends a number of ideas introduced in *Discrete Mathematics*. It is by an author well known for his lucid expositions.

Wilf, Herbert S. "What Is an Answer?" *American Mathematical Monthly* 89 (1983): 289. What does it mean to specify a function? Here are some interesting insights.

In addition to the explicit references given, any book with a title such as *Elementary Functions, Precalculus Mathematics,* or *Functions and Graphs* will give further discussion of the basic topics such as one-to-one and onto functions, Cartesian graphs, and so on.

Chapter 5

Douglis, Avron. *Ideas in Mathematics*. Philadelphia: W. B. Saunders, 1970. Designed for a terminal course in mathematics for students in the liberal arts, but with much to offer the student of computer science, mathematics, or any of the mathematical disciplines. Its chapter on induction is straightforward and interesting.

Golvina, L. I., and I. M. Yaglom. *Induction in Geometry*. Boston: D. C. Heath, 1963. This booklet should be especially useful for those who like to think geometrically.

Henkin, Leon. "On Mathematical Induction." *American Mathematical Monthly* 67 (1960): 323. A well-known logician's rather sophisticated approach to definiton by induction.

Lewis, Harry R., and Christos H. Papadimitriou. *Elements of the Theory of Computation*. Englewood Cliffs: Prentice-Hall, 1981. A sophisticated but informal study of grammars and languages in which induction and recursion are primary techniques. Designed for undergraduates.

Polya, George. *Mathematics and Plausible Reasoning*. Princeton, NJ: Princeton University Press, 1954. A thorough discussion of the inductive way of thinking by someone famed for his insights on the "right" way to visualize and present mathematics.

Ross, Kenneth A., and Charles R. B. Wright. *Discrete Mathematics*. Englewood Cliffs: Prentice-Hall, 1985. Treats induction in two separate chapters as a branch of logic (as, in fact, it is). The treatment should be accessible to students who find our text fairly easygoing.

Sominskii, I. S. *The Method of Mathematical Induction*. Boston: D. C. Heath, 1963. A booklet devoted to presenting the concept of induction.

Wand, Michael. *Induction, Recursion, and Programming*. North Holland, NY: Elsevier, 1980. This entire book is devoted to applications of mathematical induction in computer science. It shows very well how strong the relationship is and is accessible to students of discrete mathematics.

Chapter 6

Aigner, Martin. *Combinatorial Theory*, New York: Springer-Verlag, 1979. One of the few definitive works of modern combinatorial mathematics, this is the English version of two texts originally written for students in the German Hochschul system, and thus appropriate for advanced undergraduates.

Berge, C. *Principles of Combinatorics*, New York: Academic Press, 1971. A lucid exposition of counting principles, followed by a somewhat more advanced treatment of additional problems in combinatorial enumeration theory.

Bogart, Kenneth P. *Introductory Combinatorics*. 2d ed. San Diego: Harcourt Brace Jovanovich, 1989. (1st ed. Boston: Pitman, 1983). This book extends the approach to counting techniques of *Discrete Mathematics* to more advanced topics and is suitable for use immediately after studying *Discrete Mathematics*.

Campbell, Douglas M. "The Computation of Catalan Numbers." *Mathematics Magazine* 57 (1984): 195. Here is a family of numbers based on binomial coefficients that arises in myriad applications. This paper gives a brief list of the applications (with references) and then an interesting discussion of how to obtain the numbers.

Edwards, H. W. F. *Pascal's Arithmetical Triangle*. New York: Oxford University Press, 1987. A fascinating book devoted to the history of Pascal's triangle and its uses.

Hall, Marshall. *Combinatorial Theory*. 2d ed. New York: Wiley, 1986. A new edition of a classic work. This book is aimed at advanced undergraduates and graduate students, but parts may be useful to less advanced students.

Hanson, D., K. Seyforth, and J. H. Weston. "Matching, Derangements, and Rencontres." *Mathematics Magazine* 56 (1983): 224. Some interesting inclusion-exclusion problems arising from the problem of derangements.

Liu, C. L. *Introduction to Combinatorics*. New York: McGraw-Hill, 1968. One of the first textbooks in modern combinatorics and still an excellent source. As a text it is most appropriate for advanced undergraduate students.

Ryser, Herbert J., *Combinatorial Mathematics*. Carus Mathematical Monograph no. 14. Washington: Mathematical Association of America, 1963. This gem extends the techniques of Chapter 6 in many directions beyond counting. It requires a reader with some mathematical sophistication, but little formal mathematical background.

Chapter 7

Aho, Alfred V., John E. Hopcroft, and Jeffrey D. Ullman. *Data Structures and Algorithms*. Reading, Mass.: Addison-Wesley, 1983. This widely used book provides a number of examples of the uses of recurrences in analyzing algorithms, and gives a thorough treatment of divide-and-conquer recurrences.

Call, Paul, and E. F. Ecklund, Jr. "Towers of Hanoi and the Analysis of Algorithms." *American Math Monthly* 92 (1983): 407. Though aimed at college mathematics teachers, this article has something for college math students as well.

Gardner, Martin. *Mathematical Circus*. New York: Knopf, 1979. An entertaining look at mathematics by the "resident mathematician" for *Scientific American* for many years, this book devotes a chapter to the Fibonacci sequence.

Goldberg, S. *Introduction to Difference Equations*. New York: Wiley, 1958. A well-known source which should be accessible to most undergraduates. Includes many applications.

Jean, Roger. "The Fibonacci Sequence." *UMAP Journal* 5 (1984). This article is aimed at undergraduates.

Reingold, Edward M., Jurg Nievergelt, and Narsingh Deo. *Combinatorial Algorithms: Theory and Practice*. Englewood Cliffs: Prentice-Hall, 1977. Provides a number of insights into the applications of discrete mathematics to computer science. One of the most interesting, for a student of discrete mathematics, is how Fibonacci numbers arise in the analysis of height-balanced trees.

Sandefur, James T. *Discrete Mathematics with Finite Difference Equations*. Georgetown University, 1983–1987. In this manuscript, the idea of a recurrence equation is the central idea for a course that covers many topics in discrete mathematics and a wide variety of applications.

Steinhaus, H. *Mathematical Snapshots*. London: Oxford University Press, 1960. A nice treatment of Fibonacci numbers.

Tucker, Alan. *Applied Combinatorics*. 2d ed. New York: Wiley, 1984. An informal presentation of a number of basic topics in combinatorics, including a solid but accessible chapter on recurrence equations.

Chapter 8

Aho, Alfred V., John E. Hopcroft, and Jeffrey D. Ullman. *Data Structures and Algorithms*. Reading, Mass.: Addison-Wesley, 1983. This widely used book is an authoritative reference on applications of trees in algorithms.

Harary, Frank. *Graph Theory*. Reading, Mass.: Addison-Wesley, 1969. An excellent treatment of the use of trees in graph theory.

Hopcroft, John, and J. D. Ullman. *Introduction to Automata Theory, Languages, and Computation*. Reading, Mass.: Addison-Wesley, 1977. The definitive reference.

Knuth, Donald E. *The Art of Computer Programming*, Vol. 1. 2d ed. Reading, Mass.: Addison-Wesley, 1973. This book and later books in the series are excellent references for the applications of trees in computer science.

Moon, J. W. "Various Proofs of Cayley's Formula for Counting Trees." In *A Seminar on Graph Theory*, by Frank Harary. New York: Holt, Rinehart and Winston, 1967. An account of why there are n^{n-2} trees on n vertices. Although the article is technical in places, most parts are accessible to undergraduates.

Shier, Douglas R. "Testing for Homogeneity Using Minimum Spanning Trees." *UMAP Journal* 3 (1982): 273. A good example of an application!

Chapter 9

Appel, Kenneth, and Wolfgang Haken. "The Four-Color Problem." In *Mathematics Today*, edited by Lynn A. Steen. New York: Springer-Verlag, 1978. A delightful article by the people who made the computer prove the four-color program.

Barnier, W. J. "Finite State Machines as Recognizers." *UMAP Journal* 7 (1986): 209. A nice introductory treatment of the subject.

Biggs, Norman, E. Keith Lloyd, and Robin Wilson. *Graph Theory, 1736–1936*. New York: Oxford University Press, 1976. An extremely well-done source book. Contains Kempe's attempt at the four-color theorem, Euler's article about the Königsberg bridges, and much more.

Chartrand, Gary, and Linda Lesniak. *Graphs and Digraphs*. 3d ed. Belmont, Calif.: Wadsworth, 1986. The latest edition of a well-written and popular reference in graph theory.

Cristofides, Nicos. *Graph Theory: An Algorithmic Approach*. New York: Academic Press, 1975. A good all-round reference for applied graph theory.

Fulkerson, D. R., ed. *Studies in Graph Theory*, Vols. 1 and 2. In *MAA Studies in Mathematics* 11, 12. Washington: Mathematical Association of America, 1975. An outstanding series of articles with many significant applications of graph theory and good exposition.

Harary, Frank. *Graph Theory*. Reading, Mass.: Addison-Wesley, 1969. The definitive reference.

Roberts, Fred S., *Discrete Mathematical Models*. Englewood Cliffs: Prentice-Hall, 1976. Perhaps the best source for applications of graph theory to a wide variety of subjects, done at the undergraduate level.

Stahl, Saul. "The Other Map-Coloring Theorem." *Mathematics Magazine* 58 (May 1985): 131. This is about coloring maps on more complicated surfaces than the plane; amazingly, the results came more easily.

Chapter 10

Any book on linear algebra is a potential reference for this chapter.

Hahn, Franz. *Elementary Matrix Algebra*. New York: Macmillan, 1958.

Campbell, Hugh. *An Introduction to Matrices, Vectors, and Linear Programming*. New York: Appleton Century Crofts, 1965. A straightforward and elementary approach.

Cozzens, Margaret B., and Richard D. Porter. *Mathematics and Its Applications*. Lexington: D. C. Heath, 1987. A very elementary treatment of matrices and many of their applications. A good source for an elementary treatment of linear programming.

Kemeny, J. G., J. L. Snell, and G. L. Thompson. *Introduction to Finite Mathematics*. 3d ed. Englewood Cliffs: Prentice-Hall, 1974. This book takes a matrix point of view to a wide variety of problems, and was perhaps the first to do so in order to reduce previously rather complicated mathematics to the elementary undergraduate level.

Yarmish, Rina. "Determining the Reachability Matrix of a Digraph." *UMAP Journal* 3 (1982): 357. A nice elementary discussion of the subject, aimed at undergraduates.

Chapter 11

Brunner, Jim. "Absorbing Markov Chains and the Number of Games in a World Series." *UMAP Journal* 8 (1987): 99. Suitable for undergraduates and especially appropriate for sports fans!

Chung, Kai Lai. *Elementary Probability Theory with Stochastic Process*. New York: Springer-Verlag, 1979. A standard advanced undergraduate book.

Feller, William. *An Introduction to Probability Theory and Its Applications*. New York: Wiley, 1950. The classic resource, still the bible of the subject.

Hocking, Robert L. and Neil C. Schwerton. "An Extension of the Birthday Problem to Exactly *k* Matches." *College Mathematics Journal* 17 (1986): 315.

Kemeny, John G., and J. Laurie Snell. *Finite Markov Chains*. New York: Springer-Verlag, 1976. This was the book that made the theory of Markov Chains accessible to undergraduates.

Keprer, James L. "On the Probability that the Better Team Wins the World Series." *College Mathematics Journal* 16 (1985): 250. Appropriate for baseball fans!

Milton, J. S., and J. J. Corber. "Conditional Probability and Medical Tests." *UMAP Journal* 3 (1982).

Snell, J. Laurie. *An Introduction to Probability Theory*. New York: Random House, 1987. Suitable for an undergraduate. This book extends the treatment of probability that we give here, and it inspired the treatment of probability used here.

Waffle, A. "The Pure Theory of Elevators." *Mathematics Magazine* 55 (1982): 30. Is it really more likely that the elevator is going the opposite of the way you want it to?

Zweifel, P. F. "Some Remarks about Bridge Probabilities." *Mathematics Magazine* 59 (1986). A good article for bridge players.

Chapter 12

Any book on abstract algebra is a potential reference for Chapter 12.

Arbib, Michael. *Algebraic Theory of Machines, Languages, and Semigroups*. New York: Academic Press, 1968. Somewhat advanced, but evidence that algebra pervades nearly every subject!

Birkhoff, Garrett, and Thomas Bartee. *Modern Applied Algebra*. New York: McGraw-Hill, 1970. A good general reference for many topics in applied algebra, at the advanced undergraduate level.

Deneen, Linda L. "Secret Encryption with Public Keys." *UMAP Journal* 8 (1987): 9. Discusses the exciting new applications of arithmetic mod n to virtually unbreakable secret codes. Aimed at undergraduates.

Fraleigh, *A First Course in Abstract Algebra*. 2d ed. Reading, Mass.: Addison-Wesley, 1976. Perhaps the most straightforward introduction to the subject available, but with good depth for an introductory book.

Gersting, Judith. *Mathematical Structures for Computer Science*. San Francisco: W. H. Freeman, 1982. A treatment of discrete mathematics which is simultaneously algebraic and computer scientific in its orientation.

Goldstein, Larry Joel. *Abstract Algebra*. Englewood Cliffs: Prentice-Hall, 1973. A good solid introduction to the subject.

Kleiner, Israel. "The Evolution of Group Theory: A Brief Survey." *Mathematics Magazine* 59 (June, 1986). The student who becomes interested in group theory will find this interesting, though most is a bit advanced.

Lang, Serge. *Algebraic Structures*. Reading, Mass.: Addison Wesley, 1967. A concise introduction to abstract algebra.

Larsen, M. E. "Rubik's Revenge: The Group Theoretical Solution." *American Mathematical Monthly* 92 (1983): 381. An application of group theory to Rubik's big (but less well-known) puzzle.

Lidl, Rudolf, and Harald Niederreiter. *Introduction to Finite Fields and Their Applications*. Cambridge: Cambridge University Press, 1986.

McCoy, Neal. *Introduction to Modern Algebra*. Boston: Allyn and Bacon, 1968. A standard elementary reference.

MacWilliams, F. J., and N. J. A. Sloane. *The Theory of Error-Correcting Codes,* Vols. I and II. Amsterdam: North-Holland, 1977. The classic reference. Sufficiently self-contained that an undergraduate can hope to read portions of it.

Pless, Vera. *Introduction to the Theory of Error-Correcting Codes*. New York: Wiley, 1982. This book develops needed abstract algebra and so is relatively self-contained. An ambitious freshman should not fear to try it out.

Turner, Edward, and Karen Gold. "Rubik's Groups." *American Mathematical Monthly* 92 (1985): 617. How group theory arises from a popular puzzle. This article has good references to more.

Van Lint, J. H. *Introduction to Coding Theory*. New York: Springer-Verlag, 1982. A clear introduction to the subject for somewhat advanced undergraduates.

Following are the answers for the odd-numbered exercises at the end of each section, all the concepts review questions, and all the chapter review exercises.

CHAPTER 1

Section 1-1 Concepts Review

1. discrete   2. conditional   3. statement   4. true, false   5. variable   6. answer key
7. universe   8. truth set   9. equivalent   10. element, each element, element
11. true

Section 1-1 Exercises

1. (a) statement   (b) statement   (c) not a statement   (d) not a statement   (e) statement

3. (a) statement   (b) statement   (c) statement   (d) not a statement

5. {HHH,HHT,HTH,THH,HTT, THT,TTH,TTT}

7. First write down the two two-digit numbers, one above the other, and draw a line below the bottom one. Now add the two right-hand digits. If the result has one digit, write this digit down below the right-hand digits. If this result has two digits, write a 1 above the two left-hand digits and write the second digit down below the right-hand digits. Now add the two left-hand digits, and if there is a 1 above them, increase the result by 1. Write this sum to the left of the other digit you have written below the line.

9. (a) Paul has blond hair or Cora has red hair.   (b) Paul has blond hair and Cora has red hair.   (c) Paul does not have blond hair.   (d) Paul has blond hair or Cora has red hair but not both. Or: Either Paul has blond hair or else Cora has red hair but not both.

11. (a) $p \wedge q$ (b) $p \vee q$ (c) $\neg p$ (d) $q \oplus p$

13. (a) $p \wedge q$ (b) $\neg p \wedge r$. Or: $(\neg p) \wedge r$ (c) $\neg q \vee \neg p$ (d) $q \wedge (\neg p \vee r)$
(e) $p \vee (q \wedge r)$ (f) $\neg p \vee q \vee (\neg r \wedge p)$

15. (a) Dinner is served or the house is cold.   (b) Dinner is served and the house is cold.   (c) Dinner is served and the house is not cold.   (d) Dinner is served and either the house is cold or Tom is home. Or: Dinner is served and either the house is cold or Tom is home or both.   (e) Tom is home or both the house is cold and dinner is served.   (f) Tom is home or both the house is not cold and dinner is served.

17. (a) Many answers are possible. One is {0,1,4,9,25}. Another is {4,16,64,256,1024}.
(b) One possible answer is {4, 8, 16, 32, 64}.
(c) One possible answer is {some, word, with, four, cube}.

19. (a) {*ND,NQ,DD,DN,DQ,QQ,QN,QD*}   (b) *ND,N̲Q̲,DD,DN,D̲Q̲,QD̲,QN,Q̲D̲*
(c) *ND,NQ,D̲D̲,D̲N̲,D̲Q̲,QQ,QN,QD*

21. There are two different kinds of solutions. Here is the first. The results with at least
30 cents are *NQ,DQ,QQ,QN,QD* (by part (b)). By checking each member of the
universe we see that the results with at least one quarter are *NQ,DQ,QQ,QN, QD*.
The two sets of results we listed have exactly the same elements, so they are equal.
Here is the second method. Suppose *x* is a result with 30 cents. Then *x* cannot have
two *N*'s, an *N* and a *D*, or two *D*'s. Therefore *x* must have at least one *Q*.
Furthermore, if *x* has at least one *Q*, the other coin must be worth at least a nickel,
so all results with at least one *Q* are worth at least 30 cents. Therefore the set of
results worth at least 30 cents equals the set of results with at least one *Q*.

23. (a) {*NN,ND,NQ,DD,DN,DQ,QQ,QN,QD*}   (b) Draw circles around the same results
as in Exercise 19.   (c) Draw boxes around the same results as in Exercise 19.

25. The number of zeros plus the number of ones is 16. Thus if *x* is a word with 4 ones,
then *x* is a word with 12 zeros. Furthermore if *x* is a word with 12 zeros then *x* is a
word with 4 ones. Therefore by the fundamental principle of set equality, the truth
set of "This word has exactly 4 ones" and the truth set of "This word has exactly 12
zeros" are the same. Therefore the statements "This word has exactly 4 ones" and
"This word has exactly 12 zeros" are equivalent.

Section 1-2 Concepts Review
1. intersection **2.** union **3.** complement **4.** $S \sim T$ **5.** equal **6.** $p \wedge q$ **7.** $p \vee q$
8. $\neg p$ **9.** sets, statements **10.** subset **11.** relationship, operation **12.** transitive
13. empty **14.** disjoint

Section 1-2 Exercises
1. {*a,b,c,d,e,f,g,i,k*} **3.** {*a,c,e*} **5.** {*a,b,c,d,e,f,g,h*} **7.** {*c,d,e,f*}
9. {*g,h,i,j,k,l,m,n,o,p,q,r,s,t,u,v,w,x,y,z*} **11.** {*b,c,e,f*} **13.** {*a,c,d,e*}
15. {*a*} **17.** {*a,c,d,e*} **19.** {*a*}

21. First suppose $x \in P \cap (Q \cup R)$. Then by definition of $\cap$, $x \in P$ and $x \in Q \cup R$. By
definition of $\cup$, either $x \in Q$ or $x \in R$. Therefore x is in both P and Q or x is in both
P and R. Thus by definition of $\cap$, x is in $P \cap Q$ or x is in $P \cap R$. Then by definition
of $\cup$, $x \in (P \cap Q) \cup (P \cap R)$. Next suppose $x \in (P \cap Q) \cup (P \cap R)$. Then by the
definition of $\cup$, either x is in $P \cap Q$ or x is in $P \cap R$. In the case that $x \in P \cap Q$, x is
in both P and Q, so by the definition of $Q \cup R$, x is in both P and $Q \cup R$. Then by
the definition of $\cap$, x is in $P \cap (Q \cup R)$. Similarly, in the case that $x \in P \cap R$ we
may show that x is in $P \cap (Q \cup R)$. Thus each x in $P \cap (Q \cup R)$ is in $(P \cap Q) \cup$
$(P \cap R)$ and each x in $(P \cap Q) \cup (P \cap R)$ is in $P \cap (Q \cup R)$. Thus the sets $P \cap$
$(Q \cup R)$ and $(P \cap Q) \cup (P \cap R)$ have exactly the same elements and so by the
fundamental principle of set equality, they are equal.

23.

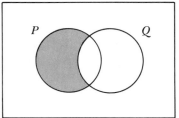

25.

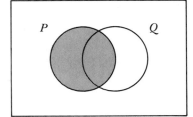

27.
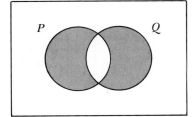

29.
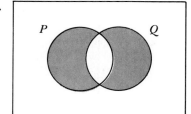

31.
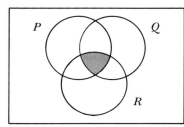

33.
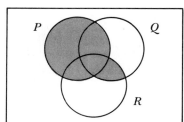

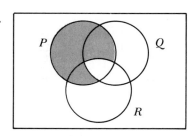

37.
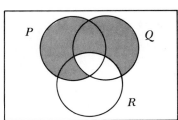

39.
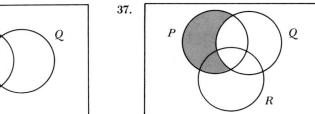

41.

43.
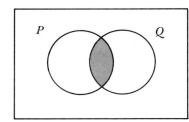

45.
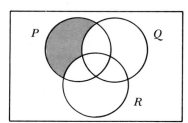

47.

49.

51.

53.

55. (a)

(b)

57.

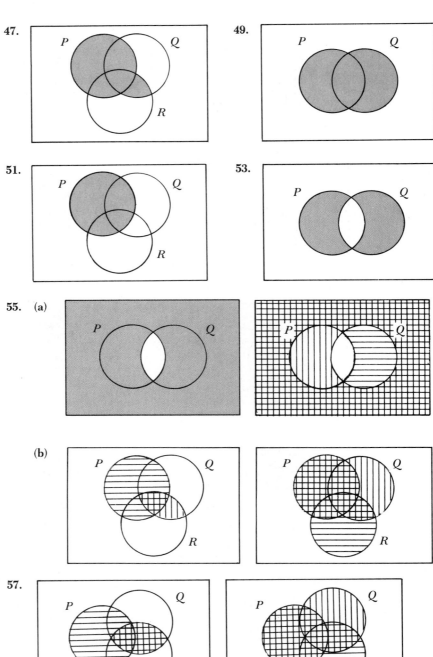

59. $P \subseteq P$, $P \subseteq T$, $Q \subseteq Q$, $Q \subseteq T$, $R \subseteq R$, $R \subseteq T$, $S \subseteq S$, $S \subseteq P$, $S \subseteq Q$, $S \subseteq T$, $T \subseteq T$

61. R and S, P and R

63. The truth sets of (b) and (c) are empty in the universe of natural numbers.

65. Let $x \in P \cap Q$. Then $x \in P$ and $x \in Q$. Therefore $x \in Q \cup {\sim}P$ by definition. But then since $x \in P$ and $x \in (Q \cup {\sim}P)$, $x \in P \cap (Q \cup {\sim}P)$ by definition. Thus each x in $P \cap Q$ is in $P \cap (Q \cup {\sim}P)$ and so $P \cap Q \subseteq (Q \cup {\sim}P)$ by definition of $\subseteq$.

67. Let $x \in (P \cap Q) \sim R$. Then x is in P and x is in Q, but x is not in R. Since x is in Q (and not in R), x is also in $Q \sim R$. Therefore x is in P and x is in $Q \sim R$, so by definition of $\cap$, $x \in P \cap (Q \sim R)$. Therefore $(P \cap Q) \sim R \subseteq P \cap (Q \sim R)$.

Section 1-3 Concepts Review

1. truth table **2.** equivalent **3.** equivalent **4.** equivalence **5.** distributive **6.** De Morgan's **7.** associative **8.** *or* gate **9.** reverse alphabetical

Section 1-3 Exercises

1. The statement $p \vee q$ is false when p and q are both false, but it is true in each other circumstance. Thus in the row of the truth table with an F under both p and q, the entry under $p \vee q$ should be F as well, and in every other row the entry under $p \vee q$ should be T.

3.

p	q	$p \oslash q$
T	T	F
T	F	F
F	T	F
F	F	T

5.

p	q	$\neg$	p	$\vee$	q
T	T	F	T	T	T
T	F	F	T	F	F
F	T	T	F	T	T
F	F	T	F	T	F
Step		2	1	3	1

7.

p	q	p	$\wedge$	$(\neg$	p	$\vee$	$q)$
T	T	T	T	F	T	T	T
T	F	T	F	F	T	F	F
F	T	F	F	T	F	T	T
F	F	F	F	T	F	T	F
Step		1	4	2	1	3	1

9.

p	q	$\neg$	p	$\wedge$	$(\neg$	$(p$	$\wedge$	$q))$
T	T	F	T	F	F	T	T	T
T	F	F	T	F	T	T	F	F
F	T	T	F	T	T	F	F	T
F	F	T	F	T	T	F	F	F
Step		2	1	4	3	1	2	1

11.

p	q	p	∨	(p	∧	q)
T	T	T	T	T	T	T
T	F	T	T	T	F	F
F	T	F	F	F	F	T
F	F	F	F	F	F	F
Step		1	3	1	2	1

13.

p	q	(p	∧	¬	q)	∨	(q	∧	¬	p)
T	T	T	F	F	T	F	T	F	F	T
T	F	T	T	T	F	T	F	F	F	T
F	T	F	F	F	T	T	T	T	T	F
F	F	F	F	T	F	F	F	F	T	F
Step		1	3	2	1	4	1	3	2	1

15.

p	q	(p	∧	q)	∨	(¬	p	∧	¬	q)
T	T	T	T	T	T	F	T	F	F	T
T	F	T	F	F	F	F	T	F	T	F
F	T	F	F	T	F	T	F	F	F	T
F	F	F	F	F	T	T	F	T	T	F
Step		1	2	1	4	2	1	3	2	1

17.

p	q	p	⊕	(p	∨	q)
T	T	T	F	T	T	T
T	F	T	F	T	T	F
F	T	F	T	F	T	T
F	F	F	F	F	F	F
Step		1	3	1	2	1

19.

p	p	∨	¬	p
T	T	T	F	T
F	F	T	T	F
Step	1	3	2	1

21.

p	q	r	p	∧	(q	∨	¬	r)
T	T	T	T	T	T	T	F	T
T	T	F	T	T	T	T	T	F
T	F	T	T	F	F	F	F	T
T	F	F	T	T	F	T	T	F
F	T	T	F	F	T	T	F	T
F	T	F	F	F	T	T	T	F
F	F	T	F	F	F	F	F	T
F	F	F	F	F	F	T	T	F
Step			1	4	1	3	2	1

23.

p	q	r	p	$\oplus$	$(q$	$\vee$	$r)$
T	T	T	T	F	T	T	T
T	T	F	T	F	T	T	F
T	F	T	T	F	F	T	T
T	F	F	T	T	F	F	F
F	T	T	F	T	T	T	T
F	T	F	F	T	T	T	F
F	F	T	F	T	F	T	T
F	F	F	F	F	F	F	F
Step			1	3	1	2	1

25.

p	q	r	$[(p$	$\wedge$	$q)$	$\vee$	$(p$	$\wedge$	$r)]$	$\vee$	$(q$	$\wedge$	$r)$
T	T	T	T	T	T	T	T	T	T	T	T	T	T
T	T	F	T	T	T	T	T	F	F	T	T	F	F
T	F	T	T	F	F	T	T	T	T	T	F	F	T
T	F	F	T	F	F	F	T	F	F	F	F	F	F
F	T	T	F	F	T	F	F	F	T	T	T	T	T
F	T	F	F	F	T	F	F	F	F	F	T	F	F
F	F	T	F	F	F	F	F	F	T	F	F	F	T
F	F	F	F	F	F	F	F	F	F	F	F	F	F
Step			1	2	1	3	1	2	1	4	1	2	1

27.

p	q	r	$(p$	$\oplus$	$q)$	$\wedge$	$\neg$	$(r$	$\oplus$	$q)$
T	T	T	T	F	T	F	T	T	F	T
T	T	F	T	F	T	F	F	F	T	T
T	F	T	T	T	F	F	F	T	T	F
T	F	F	T	T	F	T	T	F	F	F
F	T	T	F	T	T	T	T	T	F	T
F	T	F	F	T	T	F	F	F	T	T
F	F	T	F	F	F	F	F	T	T	F
F	F	F	F	F	F	F	T	F	F	F
Step			1	2	1	4	3	1	2	1

29. Yes they are equivalent. The final columns of the truth tables for $p \wedge (q \oplus r)$ and $(p \wedge q) \oplus (p \wedge r)$ are the same.

31. No they are not equivalent. For example, the truth table for $p \vee (q \oplus r)$ has a T in the final column and the row beginning TTT, while the truth table for $(p \vee q) \oplus (p \vee r)$ has an F in that place.

33. The statements $\neg(p \vee q)$ and $\neg p \wedge \neg q$ are equivalent because the truth tables have the same final column.

p	q	¬	(p	∨	q)	¬	p	∧	¬	q
T	T	F	T	T	T	F	T	F	F	T
T	F	F	T	T	F	F	T	F	T	F
F	T	F	F	T	T	T	F	F	F	T
F	F	T	F	F	F	T	F	T	T	F

35. 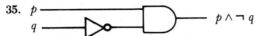 $p \wedge \neg q$

37. 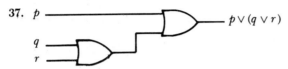 $p \vee (q \vee r)$

39.  $\neg (p \wedge q)$

41.  $\neg p \vee \neg q$

43. 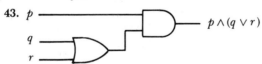 $p \wedge (q \vee r)$

45. This network is equivalent to the network in Figure 19; that is, the two networks check the truth or falsity of equivalent statements. Thus, for any input the networks have exactly the same outputs.

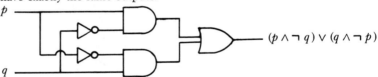 $(p \wedge \neg q) \vee (q \wedge \neg p)$

47. $\neg (p \wedge q)$

Section 1-4 Concepts Review
1. conditional **2.** conditional, biconditional **3.** equivalent **4.** equivalent
5. equivalent **6.** $\sim P \cup Q$ **7.** true, true **8.** false **9.** true, false

Section 1-4 Exercises
1. (a) $p \rightarrow q$ (b) $q \rightarrow r$ (c) $(q \wedge \neg r) \rightarrow p$ (d) $p \leftrightarrow r$ (e) $r \leftrightarrow (q \wedge \neg p)$ (f) $r \rightarrow p$
(g) $q \rightarrow r$ (h) $r \rightarrow p$

3. (a) Some digit is in error only if the first digit is in error. Or: If some digit is in error then the first digit is in error.
(b) If two (or more) digits are in error and the first digit is in error then some digit is in error. Or: Both two (or more) digits are in error and the first digit is in error only if some digit is in error.
(c) Before giving an answer we note that the negation of p is *not* "two (or more) digits are not in error." One possible answer: Both if it is not the case that two (or more) digits are in error and some digit is in error if and only if the first digit is in error.
(d) Two or more digits are in error only if both some digit is in error and the first digit is in error.

(e) No digit is in error only if the first digit is in error.

(f) No digit is in error only if both the first digit is not in error and it is not the case that two (or more) digits are in error.

5.

p	q	r	$(p$	$\rightarrow$	$q)$	$\wedge$	$(p$	$\rightarrow$	$r)$
T	T	T	T	T	T	T	T	T	T
T	T	F	T	T	T	F	T	F	F
T	F	T	T	F	F	F	T	T	T
T	F	F	T	F	F	F	T	F	F
F	T	T	F	T	T	T	F	T	T
F	T	F	F	T	T	T	F	T	F
F	F	T	F	T	F	T	F	T	T
F	F	F	F	T	F	T	F	T	F
Step			1	2	1	3	1	2	1

7.

p	q	r	p	$\rightarrow$	$(q$	$\wedge$	$r)$
T	T	T	T	T	T	T	T
T	T	F	T	F	T	F	F
T	F	T	T	F	F	F	T
T	F	F	T	F	F	F	F
F	T	T	F	T	T	T	T
F	T	F	F	T	T	F	F
F	F	T	F	T	F	F	T
F	F	F	F	T	F	F	F
Step			1	3	1	2	1

9.

p	q	r	p	$\rightarrow$	$(q$	$\vee$	$r)$
T	T	T	T	T	T	T	T
T	T	F	T	T	T	T	F
T	F	T	T	T	F	T	T
T	F	F	T	F	F	F	F
F	T	T	F	T	T	T	T
F	T	F	F	T	T	T	F
F	F	T	F	T	F	T	T
F	F	F	F	T	F	F	F
Step			1	3	1	2	1

11.

p	q	p	$\leftrightarrow$	$(q$	$\vee$	$\neg$	$p)$
T	T	T	T	T	T	F	T
T	F	T	F	F	F	F	T
F	T	F	F	T	T	T	F
F	F	F	F	F	T	T	F
Step		1	4	1	3	2	1

13.

p	q	r	$(p$	$\leftrightarrow$	$q)$	$\wedge$	$(q$	$\leftrightarrow$	$r)$
T	T	T	T	T	T	T	T	T	T
T	T	F	T	T	T	F	T	F	F
T	F	T	T	F	F	F	F	F	T
T	F	F	T	F	F	F	F	T	F
F	T	T	F	F	T	F	T	T	T
F	T	F	F	F	T	F	T	F	F
F	F	T	F	T	F	F	F	F	T
F	F	F	F	T	F	T	F	T	F
Step			1	2	1	3	1	2	1

15.

p	q	p	$\rightarrow$	$(p$	$\leftrightarrow$	$q)$
T	T	T	T	T	T	T
T	F	T	F	T	F	F
F	T	F	T	F	F	T
F	F	F	T	F	T	F
Step		1	3	1	2	1

17. equivalent **19.** not equivalent **21.** not equivalent **23.** $(\neg p \vee q) \wedge (\neg p \wedge r)$
25. $(\neg p \vee q) \wedge (\neg q \vee r)$ **27.** $\neg p \vee (q \vee r)$ **29.** $(\neg p \vee (p \wedge q)) \wedge (\neg(p \wedge q) \vee p)$
31. $\neg((\neg p \vee q) \wedge (\neg q \vee p))$

Section 1-5 Concepts Review
1. associative **2.** commutative **3.** distributive **4.** absorptive **5.** identity
6. inverse **7.** parentheses **8.** U (the universe) **9.** ~P **10.** p **11.** equivalence
12. p **13.** intersection, complement, union, complements

Section 1-5 Exercises
1. (a) (1) distributive law (2) associative law (3) inverse property (4) commutative
   law (5) associative law (6) inverse property (7) absorptive law
   (b) (1) distributive law (2) commutative law (3) associative law (4) inverse
   property (5) identity property
3. By the identity property we may substitute $P \cap U$ for P to get $U \cup P = U \cup$
   $(P \cap U)$. By the absorptive law $U \cup (P \cap U) = U$. Finally, $P \cup U = U$ by the
   commutative law applied to $U \cup P = U$.
5. Since $P \cup (P \cup Q) = (P \cup P) \cup Q$ then by substitution of P for $P \cup P$ we get
   $P \cup (P \cup Q) = P \cup Q$.
7. By the identity law $P \cap P = P \cap (P \cup \varnothing)$ and by the absorptive law
   $P \cap (P \cup \varnothing) = P$.
9. (a) distributive law (b) distributive law (c) inverse property (d) inverse
   property (e) commutative law (f) identity property (g) identity property
   (h) De Morgan's law (i) commutative law
11. (a) identity property (b) commutative law (c) absorptive law
13. q **15.** $p \vee q$ **17.** $p \vee (r \wedge q)$
19. If $x \wedge p \Leftrightarrow \underline{0}$ for all p, then $x \wedge \underline{1} \Leftrightarrow \underline{0}$. But $x \wedge \underline{1} \Leftrightarrow x$, so that $x \Leftrightarrow \underline{0}$.
21. $x \Leftrightarrow x \wedge (p \vee \neg p) \Leftrightarrow (x \wedge p) \vee (x \wedge \neg p) \Leftrightarrow \underline{0} \vee (x \wedge \neg p) \Leftrightarrow (p \wedge \neg p) \vee (x \wedge \neg p)$
   $\Leftrightarrow (x \vee p) \wedge \neg p = \underline{1} \wedge \neg p \Leftrightarrow \neg p$.

Chapter 1 Review Exercises

1. (a) statement (b) statement (c) not a statement (d) statement (e) not a statement
2. (a) not a statement (b) statement (c) statement (d) statement (e) statement
    (f) not a statement
3. (b) {3} (c) Ø (d) {0, 1} (e) Ø
4. 000, 001, 010, 100, 011, 101, 110, 111
5. (a) $p \wedge q$ (b) $p \wedge (q \oplus r)$ (c) $\neg q \wedge r$ (d) $r \rightarrow \neg q$ (e) $p \leftrightarrow \neg r$ (f) $(p \wedge r) \rightarrow \neg q$
6. (a) This network has seven nodes and either this network uses three-bit addresses or
    the last bit is a parity check bit (or both).
    (b) This network has seven nodes or both this network uses three-bit addresses and
    the last bit is a parity check bit.
    (c) If this network has seven nodes and this network uses three-bit addresses, then
    the last bit is not a parity check bit.
    (d) This network has seven nodes if and only if both this network does not use three-
    bit addresses and the last bit is a parity check bit.
7. (a) {000, 011, 101, 110}   (b) {011, 101, 110}   (c) {001, 010, 100, 011, 101, 110, 111}
    (d) {011, 101, 110}
8. The total number of digits is three. If n is the number of zeros, then $3 - n$ is the
    number of ones. Because 3 is odd, $3 - n$ is odd if and only if n is even. Therefore
    the sequences with an odd number of zeros are exactly the same as the sequences
    with an even number of ones. Thus the two statements "The number of zeros is odd"
    and "The number of ones is even" have exactly the same truth sets. Therefore they
    are equivalent.
9. {1,2,3,4,5,7,9}   **10.** {4,6}   **11.** {3,5,7}   **12.** Both are {2,4}   **13.** {0,1,2,3,4,5,6,7,8,9}
14. yes, no   **15.** R and S are disjoint
16.

(a)

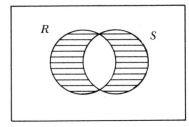

(b)

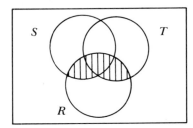

(c)

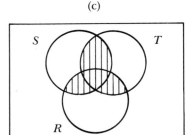

(d)

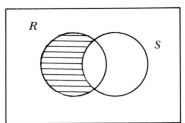

17. They are equal.

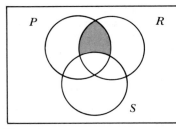 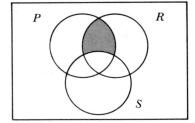

18. Equivalent.

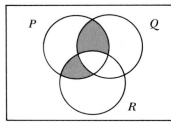 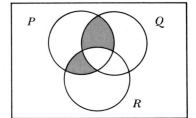

19. Suppose $x \in P \cap (Q \cup R)$. Then $x \in P$ and $x \in Q \cup R$. Thus it is either the case that x is in both P and Q or the case that x is in both P and R. Therefore it is either the case that x is in $P \cap Q$ or the case that x is in R. Therfore x is in $(P \cap Q) \cup R$. Then, by the definition of subset, $P \cap (Q \cup R)$ is a subset of $(P \cap Q) \cup R$.

20. Suppose $x \in S \sim T$. Then x is in S and x is not in T, so x is in $S \cap \sim T$. Now suppose $x \in S \cap \sim T$. Then x is in S, and since $x \in \sim T$, x is not in T, so x is in $S \sim T$. Therefore $S \sim T$ and $S \cap \sim T$ have exactly the same elements. Therefore $S \sim T = S \cap \sim T$ by the fundamental principle of set equality.

21.

p	q	p	↑	q
T	T		F	
T	F		T	
F	T		F	
F	F		F	

22.

p	q	¬	p	∧	q
T	T	F	T	F	T
T	F	F	T	F	F
F	T	T	F	T	T
F	F	T	F	F	F
Step		2	1	3	1

23.

p	q	p	∧	[(p	∧	q)	→	q]
T	T	T	T	T	T	T	T	T
T	F	T	T	T	F	F	T	F
F	T	F	F	F	F	T	T	T
F	F	F	F	F	F	F	T	F
Step		1	4	1	2	1	3	1

24.

p	q	r	p	∧	¬	(q	∧	r)
T	T	T	T	F	F	T	T	T
T	T	F	T	T	T	T	F	F
T	F	T	T	T	T	F	F	T
T	F	F	T	T	T	F	F	F
F	T	T	F	F	F	T	T	T
F	T	F	F	F	T	T	F	F
F	F	T	F	F	T	F	F	T
F	F	F	F	F	T	F	F	F
Step			1	4	3	1	2	1

25.

p	q	r	p	∧	(q	→	r)
T	T	T	T	T	T	T	T
T	T	F	T	F	T	F	F
T	F	T	T	T	F	T	T
T	F	F	T	T	F	T	F
F	T	T	F	F	T	T	T
F	T	F	F	F	T	F	F
F	F	T	F	F	F	T	T
F	F	F	F	F	F	T	F
Step			1	3	1	2	1

26. The law is not valid because the two final columns are different (in the last four rows).

p	q	r	p	∧	(q	→	r)	(p	∧	q)	→	(p	∧	r)
T	T	T	T	T	T	T	T	T	T	T	T	T	T	T
T	T	F	T	F	T	F	F	T	T	T	F	T	F	F
T	F	T	T	T	F	T	T	T	F	F	T	T	T	T
T	F	F	T	T	F	T	F	T	F	F	T	T	F	F
F	T	T	F	F	T	T	T	F	F	T	T	F	F	T
F	T	F	F	F	T	F	F	F	F	T	T	F	F	F
F	F	T	F	F	F	T	T	F	F	F	T	F	F	T
F	F	F	F	F	F	T	F	F	F	F	T	F	F	F
Step			1	3	1	2	1	1	2	1	3	1	2	1

27.

(a)

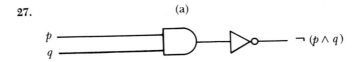

$\neg\,(p \wedge q)$

(b)

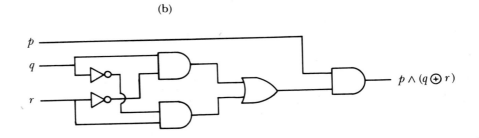

$p \wedge (q \oplus r)$

(c)

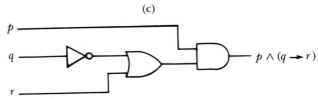

$p \wedge (q \rightarrow r)$

28. $(p \wedge q) \vee \neg(q \wedge r)$ **29.** $(\neg p \vee q) \wedge (\neg q \vee r) \wedge (q \vee \neg r)$

30. Not equivalent.

p	r	$\neg$	$(p$	$\leftrightarrow$	$r)$	$\neg$	p	$\leftrightarrow$	$\neg$	r
T	T	F	T	T	T	F	T	T	F	T
T	F	T	T	F	F	F	T	F	T	F
F	T	T	F	F	T	T	F	F	F	T
F	F	F	F	T	F	T	F	T	T	F
Step		3	1	2	1	2	1	3	2	1

31. Since $(P \cup Q) \cap P = P$, we may substitute $\varnothing$ for Q to get $P = (P \cup \varnothing) \cap P = P \cap P$. The formula $P = P \cup P$ is similarly derived.

32. (a) distributive law   (b) associative law   (c) inverse property   (d) zero property
(e) identity property   (f) distributive property   (g) associative law
(h) commutative law   (i) associative law   (j) inverse property   (k) zero property
(l) identity property   (m) associative law   (n) commutative law   (o) associative law
(p) associative law   (q) distributive law   (r) definition of $\oplus$

33. $p \wedge q$

34. $(P \cap Q) \cup (P \cap R) = [(P \cap Q) \cup P] \cap [(P \cap Q) \cup R]$ ∪-distributive
$= P \cap [(P \cap Q) \cup R]$ absorptive
$= P \cap [(P \cup R) \cap (Q \cup R)]$ ∪-distributive
$= [P \cap (P \cup R)] \cap (Q \cup R)$ associative
$= P \cap (Q \cup R)$ absorptive

CHAPTER 2

Section 2-1 Concepts Review

1. universally   2. empty   3. tautology   4. contradiction   5. universally
6. universally equivalent   7. implies   8. universally implies   9. symbolically implies
10. relationship, operation (or connective)   11. relationship, operation (or connective)
12. within   13. universally true, tautology   14. universally true, tautology

Section 2-1 Exercises

1. (a) universally true   (b) universally false   (c) neither   (d) neither   (e) neither
(f) neither
3. neither   5. tautology   7. neither   9. tautology   11. neither   13. contradiction
15. We shall use s to stand for the first statement and t for the second. (a) $s \Rightarrow t$
(b) $t \Rightarrow s$ (c) neither   (d) $s \Rightarrow t$ and $t \Rightarrow s$ (e) $t \Rightarrow s$ (because t is universally false
so the truth set of t is empty)
17. neither   19. $p \oplus q \Rightarrow p \vee q$ 21. $p \wedge (q \vee r) \Rightarrow (p \wedge q) \vee r$ 23. each implies the
other   25. $(p \wedge q) \to (p \vee q \vee r)$ 27. $[(p \wedge q) \vee (p \wedge r)] \to [p \wedge (p \vee q \vee r)]$
29. Neither shaded region is a subset of the other.

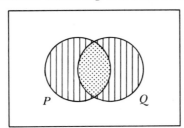

31. The lined region is a subset of the dotted region.

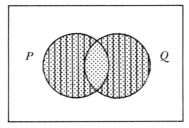

33. The lined region is a subset of the dotted region.

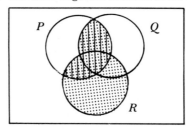

35. The lined and dotted regions are identical.

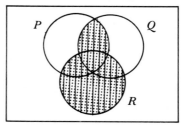

37. The lined and dotted regions are identical.

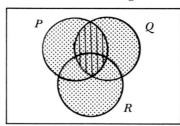

39. There is no dotted region because the truth set of the first statement in Exercise 27 is empty.

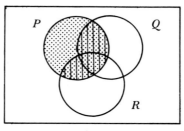

41. (a) $s \rightarrow t$ is universally true.   (b) $t \rightarrow s$ is universally true.   (c) Neither is a tautology.
(d) Both $s \rightarrow t$ and $t \rightarrow s$ are tautologies.   (e) $t \rightarrow s$ is a tautology.
43. Neither is a tautology.   **45.** $p \oplus q \rightarrow p \vee q$ is a tautology.
47. $p \wedge (q \vee r) \rightarrow (p \wedge q) \vee r$ is a tautology.   **49.** Both are tautologies.
51. $p \wedge (p \vee q \vee r) \rightarrow p$ is a tautology.   **53.** $\neg p \wedge \neg q \wedge (p \vee q) \rightarrow p$ is a tautology.

Section 2-2 Concepts Review
1. direct inference   2. theorem   3. hypotheses, direct inference   4. converse
5. sometimes   6. counter-example   7. counter-example   8. contrapositive
9. contrapositive   10. contradiction

Section 2-2 Exercises
1. (a) $n = 3$ (b) $n = 7$

3. If m is even then $m = 2i$ for some i, and if n is even then $n = 2j$ for some j. But m is even and n is even (by assumption), so $m + n = 2i + 2j = 2(i + j) = 2 \cdot k$. Therefore $m + n = 2k$ for the integer $k = i + j$. If $m + n = 2k$ for some integer k, then $m + n$ is even. Therefore $m + n$ is even.

5. If $p \Rightarrow q$ and $(\neg p \vee q) \wedge (\neg q \vee p)$ have the same final column in their truth tables then they are equivalent. Examination of the truth tables shows they have the same final column. Therefore $p \leftrightarrow q$ and $(\neg p \vee q) \wedge (\neg q \vee p)$ are equivalent.

p q	$p \leftrightarrow q$	$(\neg$	p	$\vee$	$q)$	$\wedge$	$(\neg$	q	$\vee$	$p)$
T T	T	F	T	T	T	T	F	T	T	T
T F	F	F	T	F	F	F	T	F	T	T
F T	F	T	F	T	T	F	F	T	F	F
F F	T	T	F	T	F	T	T	F	T	F
Step		2	1	3	1	4	2	1	3	1

7. If m is even then there is a j such that $m = 2j$. Since m is even, $m = 2j$. Therefore $m^2 = 2j \cdot 2j = 4j^2$. If $m^2 = 2k$ then m^2 is even. But $4j^2 = 2k$ if $k = 2j^2$. Therefore m^2 is even.

9. Assume that A, B, and C are the angles of one triangle and A', B', and C' are the angles of another triangle. If A, B, and C are the angles of one triangle then $m(A) + m(B) + m(C) = \pi$ radians. Thus $m(A) + m(B) + m(C) = \pi$. Therefore by subtraction $m(C) = \pi - m(A) - m(B)$. Similarly $m(C') = \pi - m(A') - m(B')$. We are assuming that $m(A) = m(A')$ and $m(B) = m(B')$. Then by substitution $\pi - m(A') - m(B') = \pi - m(A) - m(B)$. Therefore $m(C) = m(C')$. But if $m(A) = m(A')$, $m(B) = m(B')$, and $m(C) = m(C')$ then the two triangles are similar. Therefore the two triangles are similar.

11. (a) If the hose will reach the tomatoes then the hose is 60 feet long. If the hose will not reach the tomatoes, then the hose is not 60 feet long.
    (b) If Bill weighs at least 210 then George weighs 160 pounds. If Bill does not weigh at least 210, then George does not weigh 160 pounds.
    (c) Mary goes for a walk only if George goes for a walk. Mary does not go for a walk if George does not go for a walk.
    (d) Andre asks for a poem if Pamela recites a poem. Andre does not ask for a poem if Pamela does not recite a poem.

13. Assume that m is even and n is odd. If m is even then $m = 2i$ for some integer i. If n is odd then $n = 2j + 1$ for some integer j. Therefore $m = 2i$ and $n = 2j + 1$. By addition $m + n = 2k + 1$ for some integer k. If $m + n = 2k + 1$ then $m + n$ is odd by definition. Therefore $m + n$ is odd.

15. Suppose $n^2 < 9$. Suppose n is not less than 3. Then $n \geq 3$. Therefore by arithmetic, $n \cdot n \geq 3 \cdot 3 = 9$. Then $n^2 \geq 9$. This contradicts the assumption that $n^2 < 9$. Therefore n must be less than 3.

17. Assume $\frac{m}{n} = \sqrt{2}$ in lowest terms. Then $m^2 = n^2 \cdot 2$. Since 2 is a factor of $2n^2$ it must be a factor of m^2. But then 2 must be a factor of m because 2 is prime. But if 2 is a factor of m, then $m = 2k$. Therefore $m^2 = 2k \cdot 2k = 4k^2$. This gives by substitution $4k^2 = n^2 \cdot 2$ or by division $2k^2 = n^2$. By a similar argument we may deduce that 2 is a factor of n. This contradicts the definition of lowest terms. But every fraction may be written in lowest terms. Therefore the assumption $\frac{m}{n} = \sqrt{2}$ must be incorrect. Therefore $\sqrt{2}$ is not rational.

19. The proof is very similar to the proof in 17, except that we have $m^3 = n^3 \cdot 2$ which gives us $4k^3 = n^3$. Once again since $4 = 2 \cdot 2$, this gives us 2 is a factor of n^3 and we proceed as above.

Section 2-3 Concepts Review
1. universally quantified   2. existentially quantified   **3.** $\exists$ **4.** bound   **5.** scope
6. bind   7. universally true   8. empty   9. true   10. equivalent

Section 2-3 Exercises
1. (a) $\forall x \, (s(x))$ (b) $\exists x \, (s(x))$ (c) $\neg \exists x \, (s(x))$ (d) $\forall x \, (\neg s(x))$ (e) $\neg \exists x \, (s(x))$

3. (a) $\forall y \, (\exists x \, (q(x,y)) \rightarrow r(y))$ (b) $\forall x \, (\exists y \, (q(x,y)) \rightarrow r(x))$ (c) $\exists x \, (q(x,y)) \rightarrow r(y)$
   (d) $\forall x \, (\forall y \, (q(x,y) \rightarrow t(x,y)))$ (e) $\neg \exists x \, (r(x) \wedge s(x))$

5. (a) $\forall y \, (t(0,y))$ (b) $t(2,3)$ (c) $t(4,2)$ (d) $\neg \exists x \, (t(x,3))$ (e) $\exists x \, (t(x,4))$

7. (a) Scope of $\forall x$: remainder of formula; scope of $\exists y$: $q(x,y) \wedge r(x)$; all variables are bound.
   (b) Scope of $\exists x$: remainder of formula; scope of $\forall y$: $q(x,y) \wedge t(x,y)$; all variables are bound.
   (c) Scope of $\forall y$: $t(u,y) \vee r(v)$; u, v, and x are not bound. y is bound.
   (d) Scope of $\forall x$: remainder of formula; scope of $\exists z$: $t(y,z)$; y is not bound; x and z are bound.

9. (a) For all x there is a y such that $y = x^2$ and x is a square.
   (b) There is no x such that for all y, $y = x^2$ and $x \leq y$ and x is an even integer.
   (c) u is an even integer and for all y, $u \leq y$ or v is a square, and $x \leq v$.
   (d) For all x, $y = x^2$ and there is a z such that $y \leq z$.

11. $\exists x \, ((p(x) \wedge q(x)) \wedge \forall y \, (p(y) \wedge q(y)) \rightarrow r(x, y))$

13. The definition of "P is a subset of Q" is that every element of P is an element of Q. The "every" translates to the $\forall$ symbol in $\forall x \, (x \in P \rightarrow x \in Q)$.

15. Suppose that $x \in S \cap (T \sim U)$. Then $x \in S$ and $x \in T \sim U$. Since $x \in T \sim U$, x is in T and x is not in U. Thus x is in $S \cap T$ (since it is in both S and T) and x is not in $S \cap U$ (since x is not in U). Therefore $x \in S \cap T \sim (S \cap U)$. Thus $S \cap (T \sim U) \subseteq (S \cap T) \sim (S \cap U)$.

17. (a) True   (b) True   (c) True   (d) False

19. (See Example 24.) $\forall x \, (\neg s(x))$ is true if and only if $s(x)$ is false for every x in the universe. $\neg \exists x \, (s(x))$ is true if and only if there is no x in the universe that makes $s(x)$ true. Since $s(x)$ is false for all x in the universe if and only if no x makes it true, the two statements are true in exactly the same circumstances, so they are equivalent.

21. Take the universe to be the positive integers (or all the integers). Let $p(x)$ stand for "x is even" and $q(x)$ stand for "x is odd." Then $\forall x \, (p(x))$ is false, $\forall y \, (q(y))$ is false and so $\forall x \, (p(x)) \vee \forall y \, (p(y))$ is false. However $p(x) \vee q(x)$ is true for each x since each integer is either even or odd. Thus $\forall z \, (p(z) \vee q(z))$ is true. Therefore the symbolic statements cannot be equivalent.

23. No. (Experiment with $p(x)$ standing for "x is even" and $q(x)$ standing for "x is a square.")

Chapter 2 Review Exercises

1. (a) universally true   (b) neither   (c) neither   (d) neither   (e) universally true   (f) universally false

2. tautology   **3.** neither   **4.** tautology   **5.** neither

6. Use s for the first statement; t for the second.   (a) neither   (b) $s \Rightarrow t$ (c) $t \Rightarrow s$ (d) $s \Rightarrow t$ (e) $t \Rightarrow s$ (f) $s \Rightarrow t$, $t \Rightarrow s$, equivalent

7. $p \leftrightarrow q \Rightarrow p \rightarrow q$ **8.** $p \wedge (q \vee r) \Rightarrow (p \wedge r) \vee q$ **9.** neither   **10.** $p \wedge (q \vee r) \Rightarrow (p \wedge q) \vee (p \wedge r) \vee (q \wedge r)$

11. Lined region lies within dotted region.   **12.** Dotted region lies within lined region.

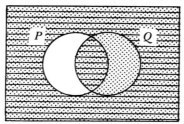 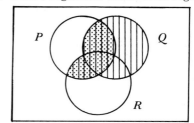

13. Neither region lies within the other.   **14.** Lined region lies within dotted region.

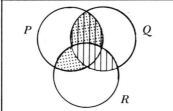 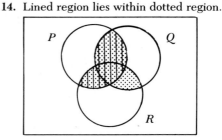

15. $(p \leftrightarrow q) \rightarrow (p \rightarrow q)$ is the only tautology.

16. $(p \wedge (q \vee r)) \rightarrow ((p \wedge r) \vee q)$ is the only tautology.

17. None is a tautology.

18. $(p \wedge (q \vee r)) \rightarrow ((p \wedge q) \vee (p \wedge r) \vee (q \wedge r))$ is the only tautology.

19. (a) none   (b) $s \rightarrow t$ is universally true.   (c) $t \rightarrow s$ is universally true.   (d) $s \rightarrow t$ is universally true.   (e) $t \rightarrow s$ is universally true.   (f) All 3 are universally true.

20. (a) 100   (b) 000   (c) 111

21. Assume m is a square and n is a square. If m is a square there is a number i such that $m = i^2$. Then $m = i^2$. If n is a square there is a number j such that $n = j^2$. Then $n = j^2$. Thus $mn = i^2 j^2 = (ij)^2$ by arithmetic. But if we use k to stand for ij this tells us $mn = k^2$. However if $mn = k^2$ then by definition mn is a square. Therefore mn is a square.

22. No, because 4 is a square and 9 is a square but $4 + 9 = 13$ is not.

23. Converse: If the sum of the digits is odd then the first digit is in error.
Contrapositive: If the sum of the digits is not odd then the first digit is not in error.

24. Assume that mn is negative. Assume further that m is positive and n is positive. If m

is positive and n is positive, then mn is positive (an accepted fact of arithmetic). But "mn is positive" contradicts "mn is negative." This is a contradiction, so both m and n cannot be positive. Therefore m is negative or n is negative.

25. Suppose $\sqrt{7} = \frac{n}{m}$ in lowest terms. Then $m\sqrt{7} = n$. Squaring gives $7m^2 = n^2$. Since 7 is a prime, for 7 to be a factor of n^2, 7 must be a factor of n. But for 7 to be a factor of n, n must be $7k$ for some integer k. Thus $7m^2 = (7k)^2 = 49k^2$. Cancellation gives $m^2 = 7k^2$. But then, as with n, 7 must be a factor of m. Therefore 7 must be a common factor of m and n, contradicting the definition of lowest terms. Since each fraction may be expressed in lowest terms, the assumption that $\sqrt{7} = \frac{n}{m}$ cannot be true. Therefore $\sqrt{7}$ is not rational.

26. By the transitive law, if $P \subseteq R$ and $R \subseteq S$, then $P \subseteq S$. But $P \subseteq R$ and $R \subseteq S$. Therefore $P \subseteq S$. By the transitive law, if $P \subseteq S$ and $S \subseteq T$, the $P \subseteq T$. But $P \subseteq S$ and $S \subseteq T$. Therefore $P \subseteq T$.

27. (a) $p(x, y) \lor r(x, y)$
(b) $\forall x\, (q(x, S) \rightarrow \exists y\, (q(y, S) \land (p(x, y) \lor r(x, y))))$
(c) $\exists z\, [q(z, S) \land \forall x\, [(q(x, S) \land \neg r(x, z)) \rightarrow p(z, x)]]$
(d) $\exists z\, [q(z, S) \land \forall x\, [q(x, S) \rightarrow (p(x, z) \lor r(x, z))]]$

28. (a) For each y in x, x is less than y.
(b) There is an x in S such that for all y, if y is in S and different from x, then x is less than y. In more standard English: S has a unique minimum element.
(c) For all x in X, x is less than or equal to y. In more standard English: y is greater than or equal to all members of X.

29. (a) Scope of $\forall y$ is remainder of expression. S is free; x is free; y is bound.
(b) Scope of $\exists x$ is remainder of expression. Scope of $\forall y$ is remainder of expression. S is free; x and y are bound.
(c) Scope of $\forall x$ is remainder of expression. S and y are free; x is bound.

30. $\forall x\, ((p(x, S) \rightarrow p(x, T)) \land (p(x, T) \rightarrow p(x, S)))$. Another natural correct answer is:
$\forall x\, (p(x, S) \rightarrow p(x, T)) \land \forall y\, (p(y, T) \rightarrow p(y, S))$.

31. (a) Suppose x is in $R \cap (S \cup T)$. Then x is in R and x is in $S \cup T$. Therefore x is in both R and S or x is in both R and T. Therefore x is in $R \cap S$ or x is in $R \cap T$. Thus $x \in (R \cap S) \cup R \cap T$.
(b) Suppose $x \in (R \cap S) \cup (R \cap T)$. Then x is in $R \cap S$ or x is in $R \cap T$. In other words, x is in both R and S or x is in both R and T. In either case x is in R. Since x is in S or x is in T, x is in $S \cup T$ as well. Therefore by definition, x is in $R \cap (S \cup T)$.
(c) Together (a) and (b) tell us that $R \cap (S \cup T) = (R \cap S) \cup (R \cap T)$.

32. (a) true (b) false (c) true (This says there is one and only one even prime.)
(d) true (This says there is an odd prime which is greater than every even prime.)

33. Take the universe for x to be the integers and $p(x)$ to be "x is even." Then $\neg \exists x\, (p(x))$ says "There is no even integer" and is false, but $\exists x\, (\neg p(x))$ says "There is an integer which is not even" and is true.

34. Take the universe for x and y to be the integers and take $p(x)$ to be "x is even" and $q(x)$ to be "x is odd." Then $\exists x\, (p(x)) \lor \exists y\, (q(y))$ says there is an even number or there is an odd number—which is true—while $\exists z\, (p(z) \land q(z))$ says there is a number which is both even and odd—which is false. Note that changing $\lor$ to $\land$ in the first statement leaves a true statement. Thus in either case the two statements are not equivalent.

35. The first statement is true if at least one x makes $p(x)$ true and also $q(y)$ is universally true. The second statement is true if $q(y)$ is universally true and there is at least one x that makes $p(x)$ true. Therefore they are equivalent.

CHAPTER 3
Section 3-1 Concepts Review
1. ordered pair   **2.** Cartesian product, $A \times B$ **3.** relation   **4.** domain, range
5. relation   **6.** vertices, edges   **7.** ordered pair   **8.** adjacent to, adjacent from
9. adjacency list   **10.** directed walk   **11.** reachable   **12.** path   **13.** reach
14. transitive   **15.** transitive   **16.** transitive closure

Section 3-1 Exercises
1. $\{(2,1), (3,1), (4,1), (5,1), (3,2), (4,2), (5,2), (4,3), (5,3), (5,4)\}$

3. $\{(1,1), (2,2), (3,3), (4,4), (5,5)\}$

5. $\{(\varnothing,\varnothing), (\{1\},\varnothing), (\{2\},\varnothing), (\{1,2\},\varnothing), (\{1\},\{1\}), (\{1,2\},\{1\}), (\{1,2\},\{2\}), (\{1,2\},\{1,2\})\}$

7. $\{(0,0), (1,1), (1,-1), (2,2), (2,-2), (3,3), (3,-3), (4,4), (4,-4)\}$

9. $\{(\varnothing, \{a\}), (\varnothing,\{b\}), (\varnothing,\{c\}), (\varnothing,\{a,b\}), (\varnothing,\{a,c\}), (\varnothing,\{b,c\}), (\varnothing,\{a,b,c\}), (\{a\},\{a,b\}),$
$(\{a\},\{a,c\}), (\{a\},\{a,b,c\}), (\{b\},\{a,b\}), (\{b\},\{b,c\}), (\{b\},\{a,b,c\}), (\{c\},\{a,c\}), (\{c\},\{b,c\}),$
$(\{c\},\{a,b,c\}), (\{a,b\},\{a,b,c\}), (\{a,c\},\{a,b,c\}), (\{b,c\},\{a,b,c\})\}$

11. greater than

13. (a) $\{(1,2), (2,4), (1,4), (4,1), (4,3), (3,1)\}$
   (b) $\{(a,1), (a,2), (b,1), (b,3), (c,2), (c,3)\}$
   (c) $\{(a,b), (b,c), (c,d), (a,d), (e,a), (e,d)\}$
   (d) $\{(1,1), (1,3), (3,1), (3,2), (2,2), (1,2)\}$

15.

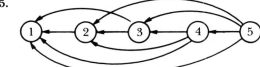

17.

19.

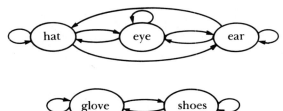

21.

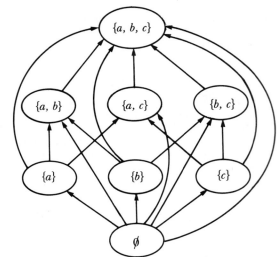

23. (a) 1: 2,4; 2: 4; 3: 1; 4: 1,3   (b) *a*: 1,2; *b*: 1,3; *c*: 2,3   (c) *a*: *b*,*d*; *b*: *c*; *c*: *d*; *e*: *a*,*d*
    (d) 1: 1,2,3; 2: 2; 3: 1,2

25. 2, 4, 3, and 1   **27.** *b*, *c*, and *d*   **29.** 4, 2, 5, 3, and 1   **31.** 2, 3, and 4

33. 4(4,3)3(3,1)1; yes, it is a path.

35. 4(4,3)3(3,1)1(1,4)4(4,1)1(1,2)2; no, it is not a path.

37. 2

39. (a) {(1,1), (1,2), (1,3), (1,4), (2,2), (2,3), (2,4), (2,1), (3,3), (3,4), (3,1), (3,2), (4,4), (4,1),
      (4,2), (4,3)}
    (b) {(*a*,1), (*a*,2), (*b*,1), (*b*,3), (*c*,2), (*c*,3)}
    (c) {(*a*,*b*), (*a*,*c*), (*a*,*d*), (*b*,*c*), (*b*,*d*), (*c*,*d*), (*e*,*a*), (*e*,*b*), (*e*,*c*), (*e*,*d*)}
    (d) {(1,1), (1,2), (1,3), (2,2), (3,1), (3,2), (3,3)}

41. Not transitive. 1 is reachable from 1, but (1,1) is not an edge. Similarly (2,4) and (4,1)
    are edges so that 1 is reachable from 2 but (2,1) is not an edge.

43. Transitive: we never have two edges (x,y) and (y,z) with a common "middle" vertex y.

45. Intransitive. (a,b) and (b,c) are edges but (a,c) is not.

47. Intransitive. (3,1) and (1,3) are edges but (3,3) is not.

49.   **51.**

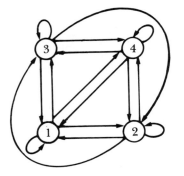
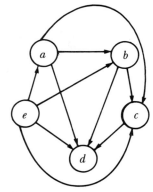

53. If $a > b$ then $a - b$ is positive. If $b > c$ then $b - c$ is positive. Assume $a > b$ and
    $b > c$; therefore $a - b$ and $b - c$ are positive. Notice that $a - c = (a - b) +$

$(b - c)$. A sum of positive numbers is positive. Therefore $a - c$ is positive. But if $(a - c)$ is positive then $a > c$. Therefore the assumption $a > b$ and $b > c$ leads to the conclusion that $a > c$. Therefore the relation is transitive.

55. No, 1 is related to 2 and 2 is related to 3 but 1 is not related to 3.

57. Yes. If $x - y = i \cdot 3$ and $y - z = j \cdot 3$ then $(x - y) + (y - z) = (i + j) \cdot 3$ but $(x - y) + (y - z) = x - z$ as well so $x - z$ is a multiple of 3.

Section 3-2 Concepts Review

1. symmetric **2.** sets **3.** two- **4.** walk **5.** connected

6. connectivity class (Connected component is very close to being correct also.)

7. one and only one **8.** connected **9.** reflexive **10.** equivalence relation

11. equivalence (While reflexive, symmetric, and transitive are all technically correct ways to fill in the blank, equivalence is the intended answer.) **12.** edge

Section 3-2 Exercises

1.

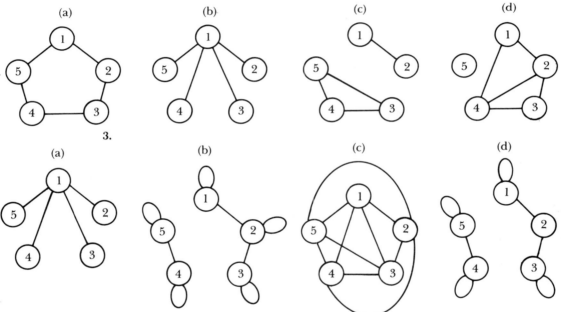

3.

5. (a) $\{\{1,4\}, \{1,5\}, \{2,4\}, \{2,5\}, \{3,4\}, \{3,5\}\}$; $\{(1,4), (4,1), (1,5), (5,1), (2,4), (4,2), (2,5),$
$(5,2), (3,4), (4,3), (3,5), (5,3)\}$
(b) $\{\{1,2\}, \{1,3\}, \{1,4\}, \{1,5\}, \{2,3\}, \{2,4\}, \{2,5\}, \{3,4\}, \{3,5\}, \{4,5\}\}$; $\{(1,2), (2,1), (1,3),$
$(3,1), (1,4), (4,1), (1,5), (5,1), (2,3), (3,2), (2,4), (4,2), (2,5), (5,2), (3,4), (4,3), (3,5),$
$(5,3), (4,5), (5,4)\}$
(c) $\{\{1,2\}, \{1,3\}, \{1,4\}, \{1,5\}, \{2\}, \{3\}, \{4\}, \{5\}\}$; $\{(1,2), (2,1), (1,3), (3,1), (1,4), (4,1),$
$(1,5), (5,1), (2,2), (3,3), (4,4), (5,5)\}$
(d) $\{\{1,2\}, \{2,3\}, \{3,4\}, \{4,5\}\}$; $\{(1,2), (2,1), (2,3), (3,2), (3,4), (4,3), (4,5), (5,4)\}$

7. (a) connected graph (b) not connected; $\{1,2,3\}$, $\{4,5\}$ are components (c) connected graph (d) not connected; $\{1,2,3\}$, $\{4,5\}$ are components

9. (a) 1,4,2,5,3 (b) 1,2,5,4,3 (c) 1{1,5}5{5,1}1{1,3}3{3}3
(d) 1{1,2}2{2,3}3{3,4}4{4,3}3

11. a and b are connected; c and d are not.

13. (a) If $x + y$ is divisible by 3 then so is $y + x$ since $x + y = y + x$. Therefore R is symmetric.
(b)

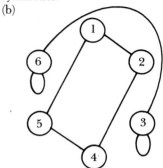

(c) $\{1,2,4,5\}\{3,6\}$

15. (a) equivalence relation   (b) not an equivalence relation   (c) not an equivalence relation   (d) equivalence relation

17. (a) There are edges from 1 to 2 and 2 to 3 but not 1 to 3.   (b) not reflexive
(c) equivalence relation

(a)   (b)   (c)

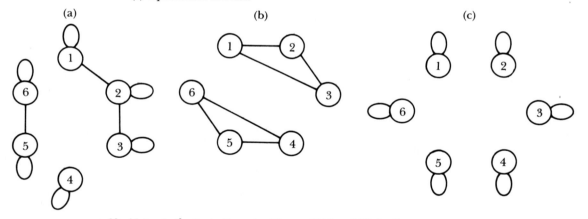

19. Note similarity to Exercise 13; see 13(a) and (b) for first two questions. Not an equivalence relation.

Section 3-3 Concepts Review

1. equivalence class   **2.** equivalence class   **3.** equivalent   **4.** not   **5.** partition
6. partition   **7.** equivalence classes   **8.** congruent, modulo   **9.** equivalence (also congruence)   **10.** congruence   **11.** solutions   **12.** 0, $m - 1$

Section 3-3 Exercises

1. $\{1,3,5\}\{4,6,2\}$ **3.** $\{1,3\}\{2\}\{4\}\{5\}\{6\}$

5. (a) $\{(1,1), (2,2), (3,3), (4,4), (5,5)\}$
(b) $\{(1,2), (2,1), (1,1), (2,2), (3,3), (4,4), (5,5), (3,4), (4,3), (3,5), (5,3), (4,5), (5,4)\}$
(c) $\{(1,1), (2,2), (3,3), (4,4), (5,5), (2,3), (3,2), (5,4), (4,5)\}$
(d) $\{(1,1), (2,2), (3,3), (4,4), (5,5), (2,3), (3,2), (2,4), (4,2), (2,5), (5,2), (3,4), (4,3), (3,5), (5,3), (4,5), (5,4)\}$

7. (a) not a partition   (b) partition   (c) not a partition   (d) partition

9. (a) True; says $5 \equiv 5$ (b) True; says $3 \equiv 3$ (c) True; says $0 \equiv 0$

(d) False; says $12 \equiv 21$ mod 27   (e) True; says $12 \equiv 12$ (f) True; says $12 \equiv 12$
(g) True; says $2 \equiv 2$ (h) False; says $6 \equiv 8$ mod 12   (i) True; says $8 \equiv 8$

11. 2; $\{\cdots -6,2,10,\cdots\}$ **13.** 3; $\{\cdots -3,3,9,15,\cdots\}$ **15.** 4; $\{\cdots -3,4,11,\cdots\}$
17. 2; $\{\cdots -7,2,11,\cdots\}$ **19.** 14; $\{\cdots -26,14,54,\cdots\}$ **21.** 3; $\{\cdots -5,3,11,\cdots\}$
23. 4; $\{\cdots -1,4,9,\cdots\}$

25. (a) $3, -6, 12$; 3 principal   (b) $-1, 8, -10$; 8 principal   (c) $2, -7, 11$; 2 principal
(d) $-3, 6, -12$; 6 principal   (e) $0, -9, 9$; 0 principal

27. $x = 5, 8,$ and 11 are all examples.

29. To say $x \equiv y$ mod m means $x - y = km$ for some k. Then $(x - n) - (y - n) = x - y = km$. Therefore $(x - n) \equiv (y - n)$ mod m.

Section 3-4 Concepts Review

1. irreflexive   **2.** irreflexive transitive   **3.** linear, total   **4.** antisymmetric
5. reflexive partial ordering   **6.** minimal   **7.** second element   **8.** covers   **9.** covering
10. linear extension

Section 3-4 Exercises

1. We must check the irreflexive and transitive properties. Since $x - x = 0$, $x \not> x$. Therefore $>$ is irreflexive. If $x > y$ and $y > z$ then $x - y$ is positive and $y - z$ is positive; then since $x - z = (x - y) + (y - z)$ is a sum of two positive numbers, $x - z$ is positive, so $x > z$.

3. $x - x = 0$ which is non-negative, so $\geq$ is reflexive. If $x - y$ is non-negative and $y - x$ is non-negative we must have $x - y = 0$, so $x = y$. Thus if x and y are two different numbers we cannot have $x \geq y$ and $y \geq x$; therefore $\geq$ is antisymmetric. Transitivity is as in Exercise 1.

5. No (x,x) pairs, so it is irreflexive. To check for transitivity: the pair (a,b) is in R; the pair (b,f) is the only one with b first and (a,f) is in R. The pair (a,c) is in R; the pair (c,f) is the only one with c first and (a,f) is in R. The pair (a,d) is in R; (d,f) is the only one in R with d first and (a,f) is in R. The pair (a,e) is in R; and (e,f) is the only pair in R with e first and (a,f) is in R. All other pairs have f as their second entry; f is not the first entry of any pair, so no need to check the transitive law. We have checked all possible applications of the transitive law and verified it.

7. (a) strict partial ordering   (b) neither   (c) neither   (d) strict partial ordering
(e) reflexive partial ordering   (f) strict partial ordering

9. $\{(a,a), (a,b), (a,c), (a,d), (a,e), (b,b), (c,c), (d,d), (e,e), (c,e), (d,e)\}$

11. (a) neither   (b) irreflexive   (c) reflexive

13. (a) symmetric   (b) antisymmetric   (c) neither

15. (a) 1, 4   (b) 1   (c) 1, 4

17.

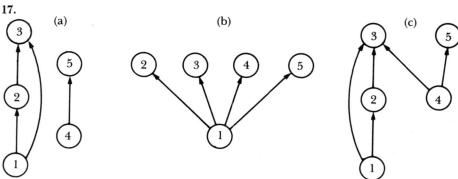

19.

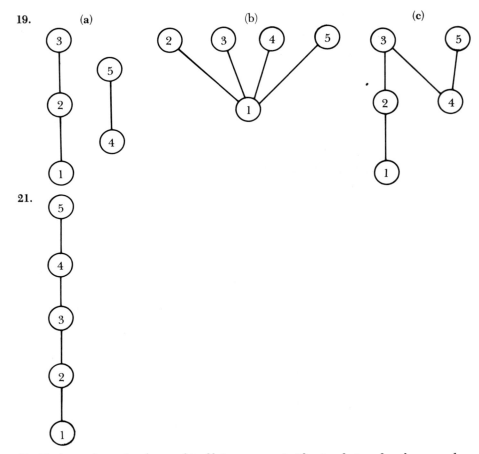

21.

23. Each number n is a factor of itself since $n = n \cdot 1$. If m is a factor of n, then $n = km$ and if n is a factor of m, then $m = k'n$. Substitution gives $n = kk'n$ or $kk' = 1$. Since k and k' are positive integers, both must be 1. This shows that unless $m = n$ we cannot have (m,n) and (n,m) in our relation. To show the relation is transitive assume m is a factor of n and j is a factor of m. Then $n = km$ and $m = k'j$ so that $n = kk'j$; thus j is a factor of n. The relation is $\{(1,1), (2,2), (3,3), (4,4), (6,6), (12,12), (1,2), (1,3), (1,4), (1,6), (1,12), (2,4), (2,6), (2,12), (3,6), (3,12), (4,12), (6,12)\}$.

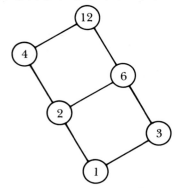

25. (a) One answer is {(1,2), (1,3), (1,4), (1,5), (2,3), (2,4), (2,5), (3,4), (3,5), (4,5)} (i.e. <).
(b) The same answer as (a) is possible.
(c) {(1,2), (1,3), (1,4), (1,5), (2,3), (2,4), (2,5), (4,3), (4,5), (3,5)}

Chapter 3 Review Exercises

1. {(−3,−3), (−2,−2), (−1,−1), (0,0), (1,1), (2,2), (3,3), (−3,3), (−2,2), (−1,1), (1,−1), (2,−2), (3,−3)}

2. {(−3,−3), (−2,−2), (−1,−1), (0,0), (1,1), (2,2), (3,3), (−3,−2), (−3,−1), (−2,−1), (−2,0), (−2,−3), (−1,−3), (−1,−2), (−1,0), (−1,1), (0,−2), (0,−1), (0,1), (0,2), (1,−1), (1,0), (1,2), (1,3), (2,0), (2,1), (2,3), (3,1), (3,2)}

3. {(3,27), (3,12), (12,27), (h,x)}

4. Equivalence relation; Classes: {0}, {1,−1}, {2,−2}, {3,−3}

5. Not an equivalence relation; not transitive. For example, has (−2,0), (0,2) but not (−2,2) in it.

6. Not an equivalence relation; neither reflexive not symmetric. For example, does not have (3,3) and has (3,27) but not (27,3).

7. (a) {(a,a), (a,b), (b,d), (a,c), (c,a), (c,d)}   (b) {(a,b), (b,e), (a,c), (c,d), (d,e)}
(c) {(a,b), (b,a), (d,c), (c,e), (e,d)}

8. (a) {(a,a), (c,c), (a,b), (a,d), (b,d), (a,c), (c,a), (c,d), (c,b)}
(b) {(a,b), (a,c), (a,d), (a,e), (b,e), (c,d), (c,e), (d,e)}
(c) {(a,a), (b,b), (a,b), (b,a), (c,c), (d,d), (e,e), (c,e), (e,c), (c,d), (d,c), (e,d), (d,e)}

9.

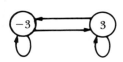 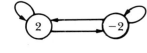 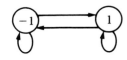

10.

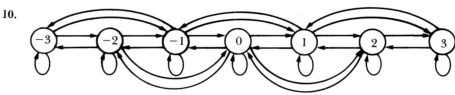

11. a,b,c,d; d

12. b,c,d,e; e

13. a(a,c)c(c,d)d(d,e)e. It is also correct to write *acde*.

14. a(a,c)c(c,a)a(a,a)a(a,c)c(c,d)d

15. (a) Not an equivalence relation; neither reflexive (doesn't contain (d,d)) nor symmetric (contains (b,d) but not (d,b)).
(b) Not an equivalence relation; neither reflexive (contains no (x,x) pairs) nor symmetric (contains no (x,y) and (y,x) pairs).
(c) Equivalence relation: classes are {a,b} and {c,d,e}.

16. Not reflexive; not irreflexive; symmetric; not antisymmetric; not transitive

17. The relation is reflexive: each sequence has the same number of zeros as itself. It is symmetric: if sequence 2 has the same number of zeros as sequence 1, then sequence 1 has the same number of zeros as sequence 2. Similarly, it is transitive. The equivalence classes are {110010,110001,001110} and {100010,100001,110000}.

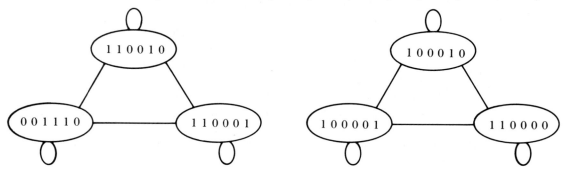

18. The relation is not reflexive; for example $1 + 1$ is not a multiple of 4. The relation is not transitive; for example $1 + 3$ is a multiple of 4 and $3 + 5$ is a multiple of 4 but $1 + 5$ is not a multiple of 4. The connected components are {1,3,5,7} {2,5} {4,8}.

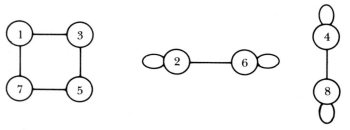

19. In the symmetric relation we write down the ordered pairs (a,b) and (b,a) if a and b are connected by an edge; in the edge set we write down $\{a,b\}$ (and don't write down a second symbol $\{b,a\}$) if a and b are connected by an edge.

20. (a) {{1,2}, {3,4}, {4,6}, {6,5}, {3,5}}
    (b) {{1,2}, {2,4}, {4,3}, {3,1}, {3,5}, {4,5}}
    (c) {{1,2}, {1,3}, {3,4}, {2,4}, {5,6}, {6,7}, {7,5}, {9,8}, {9,10}, {8,10}}

21. Only graph (b) is connected. Connected components of (a) are {1,2} {3,4,5,6} and of (c) are {1,2,3,4} {5,6,7} {8,9,10}.

22. (a) {(1,1), (2,2), (3,3), (4,4), (5,5), (6,6), (1,5), (5,1), (4,2), (2,4), (4,6), (6,4), (2,6), (6,2)}
    (b) {(1,1), (2,2), (3,3), (4,4)}

23. (a) not a partition   (b) partition   (c) not a partition

24. (a) false   (b) true   (c) true   (d) true

25. 5   26. 5   27. 1   28. 6   29. $x = 7$ is a counterexample

30. We know that $x - y$ is a multiple of m. Say that $x - y = km$, then $(ax + b) - (ay + b) = ax - ay = a(x - y) = akm$ which is a multiple of m as well, so $ax + b \equiv ay + b \bmod m$.

31. The relation is irreflexive because it has no (x,x) pairs. To have (x,y) and (y,z) in the relation, (x,y) must be (c,a) [in which case (a,e) is the only choice for (y,z)] or (b,h) [in which case (h,f) is the only choice for (y,z)] because the second elements of ordered pairs other than a and h do not appear as first elements of ordered pairs as well.

Thus to verify the transitive law we must check that (a,e) and (h,f) are in the relation, but they are so the relation is transitive. Therefore the relation is a partial ordering.

32. $\{(a,a), (b,b), (c,c), (e,e), (f,f), (g,g), (h,h), (c,a), (a,e), (c,e), (b,h), (h,f), (b,f)\}$ This is a reflexive partial ordering.

33. Since $a - a$ is non-negative, $a \leq a$. If $a - b$ is non-negative and $b - a$ is non-negative, then either both are zero in which case $a = b$ or one is positive. If $a - b$ is positive, then $-(a - b)$ is negative so $b - a$ is negative, contrary to assumption. Therefore the relation is antisymmetric. If $a \leq b$ and $b \leq c$ then $b - a$ and $c - b$ are non-negative; therefore $(b - a) + (c - b)$ is non-negative. This says that $c - a$ is non-negative so $a \leq c$. Therefore the relation is transitive. Since the relation is reflexive, antisymmetric, and transitive, it is a reflexive partial ordering.

34. c, b, and g

35.

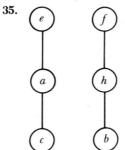

36. $\{(b,a), (e,d), (d,c), (e,c), (h,f), (f,c), (h,c), (h,g), (f,g), (i,g)\}$

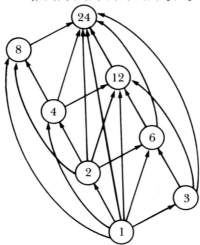 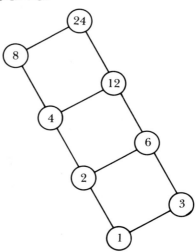

38. Read from left to right: $b < a < e < d < h < f < c < i < g$ (Include all consequences of the transitive law as well.)

39. If m is a factor of n, then $n = mk$, so m and k are both less than or equal to n. Thus whenever m is a factor of n, m is less than n as well. Therefore each ordered pair in the "is a factor of" relation is also in the "less than" relation. Since the "less than" relation is linear, this means it is a linear extension of the "is a factor of" relation.

CHAPTER 4

Section 4-1 Concepts Review

1. function 2. domain, function, range, function 3. exactly one 4. onto, at least one
5. injection, one-to-one 6. bijection 7. image 8. image, range 9. sequence
10. sum, m, n 11. arithmetic

Section 4-1 Exercises

1. $f = \{(1,1), (2,4), (3,9), (4,16), (5,25)\}$

3. $g = \{(1,1.5), (2,.5), (3,-.5), (4,-1.5), (5,-2.5)\}$

5. $h = \{(1,2), (2,1), (3,0), (4,1), (5,2)\}$

7. $\{(1,2), (2,4), (3,6), (4,8), (5,10)\}$

9. $\{(1,1), (2,3), (3,7), (4,13), (5,21)\}$

11. $\{(1,0), (2,0), (3,0), (4,0), (5,0)\}$

13. $\{(-2,-2), (-1.5,-2), (-1,-1), (-.5,-1), (0,0), (.5,0), (1,1), (1.5,1), (2,2)\}$

15. $f = \{(-2,-5), (-1,-3), (0,-1), (1,1), (2,3)\}$ $g = \{(-2,-5), (-1,-3), (0,-1), (1,1), (2,3)\}$ $h = \{(-2,-5), (-1,0), (0,-1), (1,-2), (2,3)\}$ $f = g$ on this domain

17. bijection (both one-to-one and onto); image $= \{a,b,c,d\}$

19. neither; image $= \{a,c,d\}$ 21. onto (surjection); image $= \{a,b,c\}$

23. neither; image $= \{a,c\}$ 25. function; neither; image $= \{a,b,c,d\}$

27. not a function 29. function; one-to-one (injection); image $= \{a,b,c,e\}$

31. not a function 33. not a function

35. function; onto (surjection); image $= \{a,b,c,d\}$

37. One arrow leaves each domain element, one range element gets no arrow and another gets two arrows.

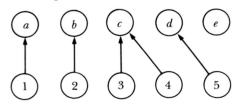

39. Vertex 1 has two arrows leaving it.

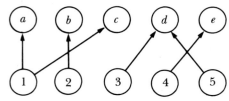

41. One arrow leaves each domain element; each range element has at most one arrow coming in and one has no arrow.

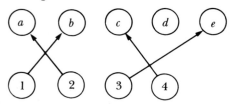

43. No arrow leaves vertex 5.

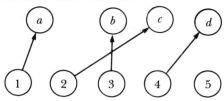

45. Two arrows leave vertex 1.

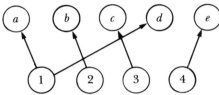

47. One arrow leaves each domain element. One range element gets two arrows; each range element gets at least one arrow.

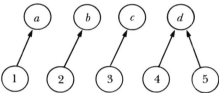

49. Start with $i = 1$. $0,3,8,15,24$ **51.** Start with $i = 0$. $1,2,5,10,17$ **53.** $1, \frac{1}{32}$ **55.** 125
57. 31   **59.** 160   **61.** 1225   **63.** 990   **65.** 775; should be 5 less than number 64
67. 112

Section 4-2 *Concepts Review*

1. Cartesian   **2.** Cartesian   **3.** significantly faster than   **4.** exactly once   **5.** one to one
6. onto (the real numbers)   **7.** composition   **8.** range, domain
9. inverses, domain, domain   **10.** exchanging   **11.** binary representation

Section 4-2 *Exercises*

1.

(a)

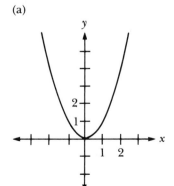

(b)

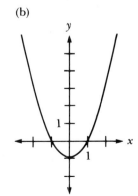

(c)

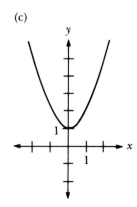

3.

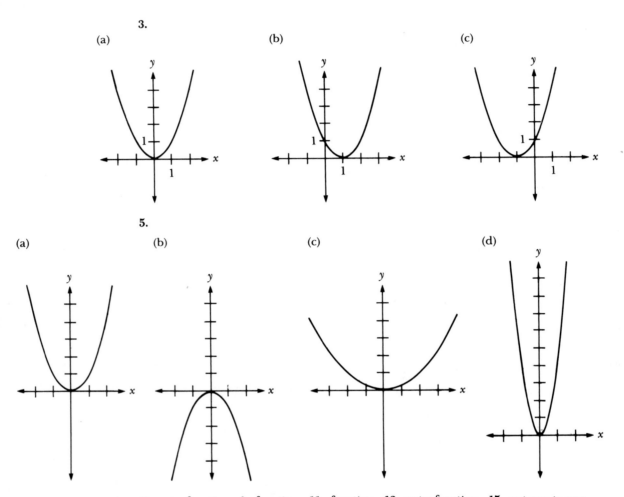

5.

7. not a function   9. function   11. function   13. not a function   15. not one-to-one
17. one-to-one   19. one-to-one   21. one-to-one

23. $f(x)$ is larger

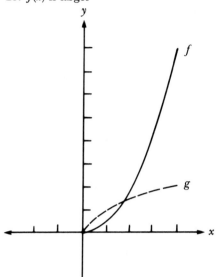

25. $g(x)$ is larger

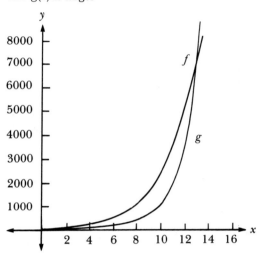

27. $g(x)$ is larger

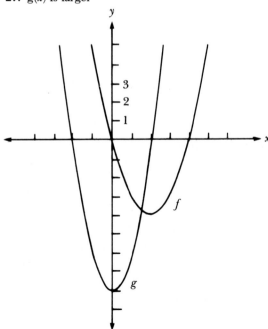

29. $f(x)$ is larger

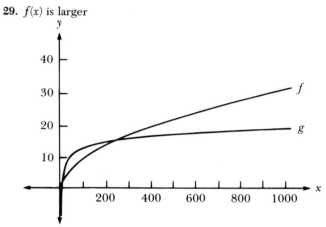

31.

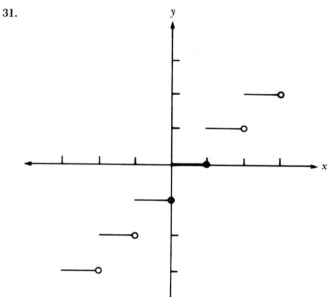

33. $f \circ g(x) = x + 3$ **35.** $f \circ g(x) = x^2 + 4x$ **37.** $f \circ g = \{(a,2), (b,3), (c,6), (d,4)\}$
39. $f \circ g = \{(a,2), (b,3), (c,6)\}$ **41.** yes **43.** no **45.** yes **47.** yes **49.** $\lceil \lfloor x \rfloor \rceil = \lfloor x \rfloor$
51. (d)
53. (a) 5 (b) 15 (c) 8 (d) 13
55. (a) 1000 (b) 111 (c) 1010 (d) 1011 (e) 10001
57. $g^{-1} = \frac{9}{5}t + 32$; Celsius to Fahrenheit
59. $g \circ f(x) = \frac{1}{5}(9x - 2297)$ or $g \circ f(x) = \frac{9}{5}x - 459.4$

61.

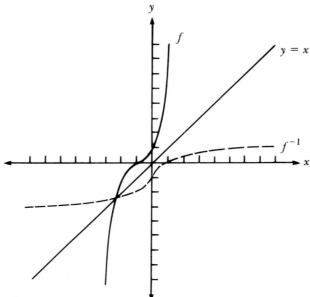

Section 4-3 Concepts Review

1. polynomial, degree **2.** two **3.** one **4.** lower bound, upper bound
5. significantly more slowly than **6.** $O(g(x))$ **7.** faster **8.** $O(g)$, $O(f)$ **9.** $f(x)$, $g(x)$
10. $g(x)$, $f(x)$

Section 4-3 Exercises

1. The word in the blank is largest. Applying it to 4321 gives 3214.

3. $n - 1$, $n - 1$

5. Result is 1,2,3,4,5. The output is a list of the same numbers in order.

7. $1 + 2 + \cdots + n - 1 = \dfrac{n(n - 1)}{2}$

9. $\dfrac{n(n - 1)}{2}$

11. 4 seconds for cn^2; 2^{20} seconds $=$ a bit over 12 days for $d \cdot 2^n$.

13. The $dn \log_2(n)$ method in both cases.

15. (a) 2 (or any larger constant) (b) $\frac{3}{2}$ (or any larger constant)
    (c) $\frac{3}{2}$ (or any larger constant) (d) 2 (or any larger constant)

17. $g(x) = O(f(x))$ **19.** $f(x) = O(g(x))$ **21.** $f(x) = O(g(x))$ **23.** $g(x) = O(f(x))$

25. True **27.** False **29.** True **31.** True **33.** True **35.** False **37.** True **39.** True

41. False **43.** 2 **45.** 2 **47.** 0 **49.** 2

51. (a) same (b) different (c) different (d) same

53. approaches 6 **55.** becomes infinite **57.** approaches $\frac{1}{4}$ **59.** approaches 0

Chapter 4 Review Exercises

1. (a) $\{(0,4), (1,1), (2,0), (3,1), (4,4)\}$ (b) $\{(0,1), (1,2), (2,4), (3,8), (4,16)\}$
   (c) $\{(0,3), (1,2), (2,1), (3,0), (4,1)\}$

2. (a) onto; image $= \{a,b,c\}$ (b) neither; image $= \{a,b\}$ (c) neither; image $= \{a,c,d\}$
   (d) one-to-one and onto; image $= \{a,b,c,d\}$ (e) one-to-one; image $= \{a,b,c,e\}$

3. (a) each vertex in range gets an arrow; not $1 - 1$ since a gets 2 arrows
   (b) c does not get an arrow (not onto) and a and b get 2 arrows each (not one-to-one)
   (c) b gets no arrow and d gets 2
   (d) each range vertex has exactly one arrow coming in
   (e) vertex e has no arrows, all others have exactly one (not onto but one-to-one)

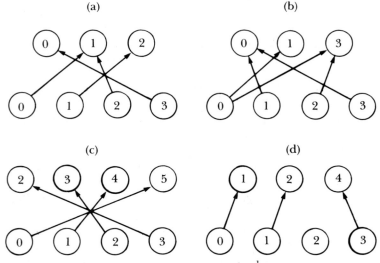

4. (a) function   (b) not function   (c) function   (d) not function
5. (a) one arrow leaves each vertex   (b) two arrows leave vertex 0   (c) one arrow leaves
   each vertex   (d) no arrow leaves vertex 2

6. For integers and half integers, i.e., integers plus $\frac{1}{2}$
7. f and g define the same function; h is different.
8. $S_0 = 0$. Fourth term is $S_4 = 4 \cdot 3 = 12$; 0,0,2,6,12
9. $\frac{31}{32}$ **10.** 575   **11.** $575 - (2 \cdot 1 - 3) - (2 \cdot 2 - 3) = 575$ **12.** 97

13. (a) *g* is larger

(b) *g* is larger

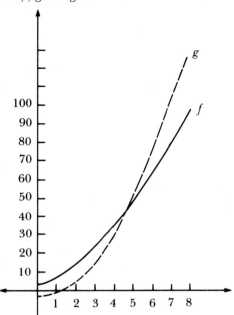

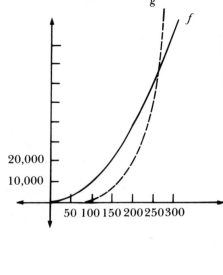

(c) *f* is larger

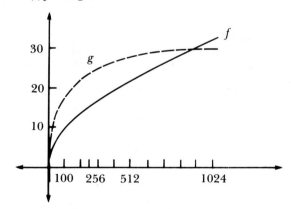

14. $f \circ g = \{(a,1),(b,1),(c,3),(d,2),(e,4)\}$

15. You get the graph of $f \circ g$ by shifting the graph of *g* 2 units down. You get the graph of $g \circ f$ by shifting the graph of *g* 2 units right.

16. $f^{-1}(x) = \sqrt[3]{x-4}$; all real numbers   **17.** 1101,1110   **18.** 10,17

19.

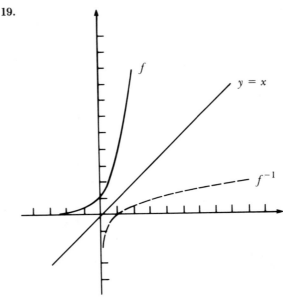

20. The largest member among those originally in positions i to j of the list.

21. $4, j - 1, j - 1$ changes maximum plus the first assignment if you consider it a change.

22. $2,3,4,7,8,14,17$

23. The same numbers but in increasing order. $\dfrac{n(n-1)}{2}$; $\dfrac{n(n-1)}{2}$ (don't count initial assignment), $n - 1$.

24. This makes the same number of comparisons and changes as bubblesort makes comparisons and exchanges. Thus the comparing and changing takes half as long. Next we add in relatively few exchanges, and as n gets large this number is dwarfed by $\dfrac{n(n-1)}{2}$, so this sorting method is almost twice as fast.

25. The second is fastest with 16; the third is fastest with 32 or more.

26. (a) $2\sqrt{2}$ or any larger constant   (b) 2 or any larger constant   (c) $\dfrac{3\sqrt{2}}{2}$ or any larger constant.

27. pair (b) only

28. (a) $g(x) = O(f(x))$ (b) $g(x) = O(f(x))$ (c) $f(x) = O(g(x))$ (d) $g(x) = O(f(x))$
(e) $f(x) = O(g(x))$; $g(x) = O(f(x))$; same order of growth   (f) $g(x) = O(f(x))$

CHAPTER 5

Section 5-1 Concepts Review

1. implies, $s(k)$ 2. base   3. inductive hypothesis   4. inductive   5. geometric

6. $\dfrac{1 - r^{n+1}}{1 - r}$

Section 5-1 Exercises

1. The base step is the two sentences beginning "If $n = 1$ . . . ." The inductive hypothesis is the sentence beginning "Now suppose the equation is true when $n =$

$k - 1 \ldots$." The inductive step begins with the inductive hypothesis and ends with the sentence "Thus our original equation is true when $n = k$." The inductive conclusion is the last sentence.

3. When $n = 1$ the formula reads $2 - 1 = 1^2$ which is true. Now suppose that $1 + 3 + \cdots + 2(k - 1) - 1 = (k - 1)^2$. Adding $2k - 1$ to each side gives $1 + 3 + \cdots + 2k - 1 = (k - 1)^2 + 2k - 1 = k^2 - 2k + 1 + 2k - 1 = k^2$. Thus whenever the formula is true with $n = k - 1$, it is true with $n = k$. Therefore by the principle of mathematical induction, $1 + 3 + \cdots + 2n - 1 = n^2$ for all positive integers n.

5. For $n = 1$ the formula reads $\frac{1}{2} = 1 - \frac{1}{2}$ which is true. Assume the formula is true when $n = k - 1$, i.e., $\frac{1}{2} + \cdots + \left(\frac{1}{2}\right)^{k-1} = 1 - \left(\frac{1}{2}\right)^{k-1}$. Adding $\left(\frac{1}{2}\right)^k$ to each side gives $\frac{1}{2} + \cdots + \left(\frac{1}{2}\right)^k = 1 - \left(\frac{1}{2}\right)^{k-1} + \left(\frac{1}{2}\right)^k = 1 - \left(\frac{1}{2}\right)^{k-1}\left(-1 + \frac{1}{2}\right) = 1 - \left(\frac{1}{2}\right)^k$. Therefore the formula is true when $n = k$ so by the principle of mathematical induction, the formula is true for all positive n.

7. When $n = 1$ the formula reads $2 = \dfrac{4 + 2}{3}$, which is true. Assume the formula holds when $n = k - 1$ and subtract $(-2)^k$ from both sides to get

$$
\begin{aligned}
2 - 4 + \cdots - (-2)^k &= \frac{(-2)^k + 2}{3} - (-2)^k \\
&= \frac{(-2)^k - 3(-2)^k + 2}{3} \\
&= \frac{(-2)^k(1 - 3) + 2}{3} \\
&= \frac{(-2)^{k+1} + 2}{3}
\end{aligned}
$$

Thus the formula holds when $n = k$ as well and so by the principle of mathematical induction, the formula holds for all positive integers n.

9. When $n = 1$ the formula reads $1 = 2 - 1$ which is true. Assume that the formula is true when $n = k - 1$ and add $4k - 3$ to both sides to get $1 + 5 + 9 + \cdots + 4k - 3 = 2(k - 1)^2 - (k - 1) + 4k - 3 = 2k^2 - 4k + 2 - k + 1 + 4k - 3 = 2k^2 - k$. Therefore the formula holds when $n = k$ as well and so by the principle of mathematical induction it holds for all positive n.

11. For $n = 1$ the formula reads $1 = \dfrac{1 \cdot 2^2}{4}$ which is true. Assume the formula holds when $n = k - 1$ and add k^3 to both sides to get

$$
\begin{aligned}
1^3 + 2^3 + \cdots + k^3 &= \frac{(k - 1)^2 \cdot k^2}{4} + k^3 \\
&= \frac{(k^2 - 2k + 1) \cdot k^2}{4} + k^3 \\
&= \frac{k^4 - 2k^3 + k^2 + 4k^3}{4} \\
&= \frac{k^4 + 2k^3 + k^2}{4} \\
&= \frac{k^2(k + 1)^2}{4}
\end{aligned}
$$

Therefore the formula holds when $n = k$ as well, and so by the principle of mathematical induction it holds for all positive n.

13. When $n = 2$ the inequality reads $4 < 8$, which is true. (Since we were to prove it for $n > 1$, our base step is $n = 2$.) [Now assume $(k - 1)^2 < (k - 1)^3$, or $k^2 - 2k + 1 < k^3 - 3k^2 + 3k - 1$ and add $2k - 1$ to both sides to get $k^2 < k^3 - 3k^2 + 5k - 2$. It looks difficult to show that this is less than k^3, so we ignore the assumption that the inequality is true when $n = k - 1$ and start over making the assumption that $n = k$.] Now assume $k^2 < k^3$. Adding $2k + 1$ to each side gives $k^2 + 2k + 1 < k^3 + 2k + 1$ but $2k + 1 < 3k^2 + 3k + 1$ for all $k > 0$, so by transitivity, $k^2 + 2k + 1 < k^3 + 3k^2 + 3k + 1 = (k + 1)^3$. Therefore the inequality with $n = k$ implies the inequality with $n = k + 1$ and so by the principle of mathematical induction, the inequality holds for all $n > 1$.

15. When $n = 1$ the inequality reads $1 < 2$, which is true. Now suppose the inequality is true when $n = k - 1$ and $k \geq 2$ so that $k - 1 < 2^{k-1}$. Adding 1 to both sides gives $k < 2^{k-1} + 1$. But since $k \geq 2$, $1 < 2^{k-1}$. Therefore by substitution, $k < 2^{k-1} + 1 < 2^{k-1} + 2^{k-1} = 2 \cdot 2^{k-1} = 2^k$. Therefore the inequality holds when $n = k$ as well so by the principle of mathematical induction the inequality is true for all positive integers.

17. Let us try 1 for the constant c. Thus we will try to prove $1^3 + 2^3 + \cdots + n^3 \leq n^4$. When $n = 1$ this states $1^3 \leq 1^4$ which is true. Assume the inequality holds when $n = k$ and add $(k + 1)^3$ to both sides, giving

$$1^3 + 2^3 + \cdots + k^3 + (k + 1)^3 \leq k^4 + (k + 1)^3 = k^4 + k^3 + 3k^2 + 3k + 1$$
$$\leq k^4 + 4k^3 + 6k^2 + 4k + 1$$
$$= (k + 1)^4$$

Therefore the inequality holds when $n = k + 1$ as well so by the principle of mathematical induction, the inequality holds for all positive n. Therefore $1^3 + 2^3 + \cdots + n^3 < 1 \cdot n^4$ for all n so that $1^3 + 2^3 + \cdots + n^3 = O(n^4)$.

19. To show that $\sum_{i=0}^{n} (2i + 1)^2 = O(n^3)$, we must find a constant c such that $\sum_{i=0}^{n} (2i + 1)^2 \leq cn^3$. Since for $n = 1$ this reads $1^2 + 3^2 \leq c \cdot 1^3$, it makes sense to try to prove the inequality $\sum_{i=1}^{n} (2i + 1)^2 \leq 10n^3$. For $n = 1$ we have $1^2 + 3^2 \leq 10 \cdot 1^3$, so we assume it is true for $n = k$ and add $(2(k + 1) + 1)^2$ to both sides to get

$$\sum_{i=0}^{k} (2i + 1)^2 + (2(k + 1) + 1)^2 \leq 10k^3 + (2k + 3)^2 = 10k^3 + 4k^2 + 12k + 9$$
$$\leq 10(k^3 + 3k^2 + 3k + 1)$$
$$= 10(k + 1)^3$$

Thus the inequality holds when $n = k + 1$ as well and so by the principle of mathematical induction the inequality holds for all n. Therefore $\sum_{i=0}^{n} (2i + 1)^2 = O(n^3)$.

21. When $n = 2$ the formula reads $(1 + x)^2 > 1 + 2x$, and since $(1 + x)^2 = 1 + 2x + x^2$, $(1 + x)^2$ is greater than $1 + 2x$ because x^2 must be positive. Now assume inductively that $(1 + x)^k > 1 + kx$ for the positive integer k. Multiply both sides by $1 + x$ (which is greater than 0 since $x > -1$) to get $(1 + x)^{k+1} > (1 + kx)(1 + x) =$

$1 + kx + x + kx^2 = 1 + (k + 1)x + kx^2 > 1 + (k + 1)x$ since k is positive. Therefore the inequality with $n = k$ implies the inequality with $n = k + 1$ and so by the principle of mathematical induction is true for all $n > 1$.

Section 5-2 Concepts Review

1. strong mathematical induction 2. $\sum_{i=1}^{m-1} a_i$ 3. recursive 4. recursive
5. well-formed formula

Section 5-2 Exercises

1. If $n = 2$ then $n = 1{\cdot}2 + 0{\cdot}3$ and so the statement that n is a non-negative multiple of 2 plus a non-negative multiple of 3 holds. If $n = 3$ then it holds as well. Now assume that $k \geq 4$ and that our statement that n is a non-negative multiple of 2 plus a non-negative multiple of 3 holds for all n between 2 and $k - 1$. Since $k - 2$ is between 2 and $k - 1$ (that is why we assumed $k \geq 4$ and handled $k = 3$ separately) we have assumed $k - 2 = i{\cdot}2 + j{\cdot}3$ for non-negative integers i and j. Therefore $k = (i + 1){\cdot}2 + j{\cdot}3$ so that k is a non-negative multiple of 2 plus a non-negative multiple of 3. Thus by the strong principle of mathematical induction, every integer $n > 1$ is a non-negative multiple of 2 plus a non-negative multiple of 3.

3. $8 = 1{\cdot}3 + 1{\cdot}5$. Therefore 8 is a non-negative multiple of 3 plus a non-negative multiple of 5. Further, $9 = 3{\cdot}3 + 0{\cdot}5$ and $10 = 0{\cdot}3 + 2{\cdot}5$. Now assume that $k > 10$ and that for each n between 8 and $k - 1$, n is a non-negative multiple of 3 plus a non-negative multiple of 5. Since $k - 3$ is greater than 7 and less than k, it is between 8 and $k - 1$, so we may write $k - 3 = 3i + 5j$. Therefore $k = 3(i + 1) + 5j$ so that k is a non-negative multiple of 3 plus a non-negative multiple of 5 as well. Therefore by the strong principle of mathematical induction, each integer greater than 7 is a non-negative multiple of 3 plus a non-negative multiple of 5.

5. As in Example 8 we induct on the number m of edges. If $m = 0$ then we may have only one vertex so $n = m + 1$ (otherwise the graph could not be connected). Now assume that a tree with k edges has $k + 1$ vertices for $k = 0, 1, \ldots, m - 1$. Let G be a tree with n vertices and m edges and remove one edge. By the definition of "tree" this gives us a disconnected graph. Since putting the edge back in could join only two components together to form one, removing the edge breaks G into two connected components: G_1 with n_1 vertices and m_1 edges, and G_2 with n_2 vertices and m_2 edges. Since $m_1 \leq m - 1$ and $m_2 \leq m - 1$, and since G_1 and G_2 must be trees, $n_1 = m_1 + 1$ and $n_2 = m_2 + 1$. Therefore $n_1 + n_2$, which is n, equals $m_1 + 1 + m_2 + 1 = m_1 + m_2 + 2$. But $m_1 + m_2 + 1 = m$, so $n = m + 1$. Thus a tree with m edges has $m + 1$ vertices. Therefore by the principle of mathematical induction, for all non-negative integers m, a tree with m edges has $m + 1$ vertices. (Note: It was not necessary here to induct on the number of edges; carrying out induction on the number of vertices works equally well and may be less cumbersome; however we preferred to have the analogy with Example 8.)

7. We don't know in advance whether to try strong induction or ordinary induction. Since strong induction includes ordinary induction as a special case, we shall try a proof by strong induction. Let's use n to stand for the number of vertices, m for the number of edges, and c for the number of components. We wish to show that $m + c \geq n$. Example 8 suggests we try induction on m. If $m = 0$ then the graph has no edges so that each connected component is a vertex; therefore $c = n$ and our inequality holds. Now assume that the inequality holds whenever $m = 0, 1, 2, \ldots, k - 1$ and let G be a k-edge graph with c connected components and n vertices.

Removing an edge either increases the number of connected components by 1 or doesn't change the number of connected components. If removing an edge doesn't change the number of connected components, then our inductive hypothesis gives $(k - 1) + c \geq n$ or $k + c \geq n + 1 \geq n$. Thus in this case the desired inequality holds. If removing one edge does increase c by one, then our inductive hypothesis gives us $(k - 1) + c + 1 \geq n$ or $k + c \geq n$. Therefore the inequality $k + c \geq n$ holds in this case as well. Therefore by the principle of mathematical induction, for all graphs the number of edges plus the number of connected components is at least the number of vertices.

9. A nontrivial walk is one with one or more edges. If there is a nontrivial walk from x to y with one edge, then by the definition of walk, (x,y) is that edge so (x,y) is in the relation. Now suppose that whenever a walk from x to y has fewer than n edges then (x,y) is in the relation and let $x e_1 x_1 e_2 x_2 \cdots e_{n-1} x_{n-1} e_n y$ be an n-edge walk from x to y. By the induction hypothesis (x, x_{n-1}) is in the relation and by the definition of walk, (x_{n-1}, y) is in the relation. Therefore by the definition of transitive, (x,y) is in the relation as well. Thus by the principle of mathematical induction, whenever there is a nontrivial walk from x to y in the digraph of a transitive relation, then (x,y) is in the relation as well.

11. $\prod\limits_{i=1}^{1} a_i = a_1$. If $n > 1$, then $\prod\limits_{i=1}^{n} a_i = \left(\prod\limits_{i=1}^{n-1} a_i \right) \cdot a_n$; 576

13. $\bigcap\limits_{i=1}^{1} A_i = A_1$. If $n > 1$, then $\bigcap\limits_{i=1}^{n} A_i = \left(\bigcap\limits_{i=1}^{n-1} A_i \right) \cap A_n$.

15. We prove the distributive law by induction on n. If $n = 1$, the law states that

$$A \cap \left(\bigcup_{i=1}^{1} B_i \right) = \bigcup_{i=1}^{1} (A \cap B_i)$$ which, according to the inductive definition of unions,

says $A \cap B_1 = A \cap B_1$, which is true. Now suppose the law holds when $n = k - 1$ (and $n \geq 2$). Then for $n > 1$ we get

$$A \cap \left(\bigcup_{i=1}^{1} B_i \right) = A \cap \left[\left(\bigcup_{i=1}^{n-1} B_i \right) \cup B_n \right]$$

By the two-set distributive law this may be rewritten as

$$A \cap \left(\bigcup_{i=1}^{n} B_i \right) = \left[A \cap \left(\bigcup_{i=1}^{n-1} B_i \right) \right] \cup (A \cap B_n)$$

By the inductive hypothesis this may be rewritten as

$$A \cap \left(\bigcup_{i=1}^{n} B_i \right) = \left[\bigcup_{i=1}^{n-1} (A \cap B_i) \right] \cup (A \cap B_n)$$

By the inductive definition of union this may be rewritten as

$$A \cap \left(\bigcup_{i=1}^{n} B_i \right) = \bigcup_{i=1}^{n} (A \cap B_i)$$

Thus by the principle of mathematical induction, the n-set distributive law holds for all positive integers n.

17. $a^0 = 1$. If $n > 0$, then $a^n = a^{n-1} \cdot a$.

19. For $n = 0$ we get $a^m \cdot a^0 = a^m \cdot 1 = a^m = a^{m+0}$. Now assume $k > 0$ and assume the formula $a^m a^{k-1} = a^{m+(k-1)}$ holds. Then we may write

$$\begin{aligned} a^n a^k &= a^m(a^{k-1} \cdot a) \\ &= (a^m a^{k-1}) \cdot a \\ &= a^{m+(k-1)} \cdot a \\ &= a^{(m+k)-1} \cdot a \\ &= a^{m+k} \end{aligned}$$

Thus whenever the law $a^m a^n = a^{m+m}$ holds for $n = k - 1$, it holds for $n = k$ as well. Therefore by the principle of mathematical induction, the law $a^{m+n} = a^m a^n$ holds for all non-negative integers n.

21. We prove by induction on n that "$\bigcap\limits_{i=1}^{n} A_i$ is the set of elements x such that x is in each A_i with i between 1 and n inclusive" by using the inductive definition of $\cap$ and induction on n. For $n = 1$ the statement in quotes is equivalent to "A_1 is the set of elements x such that x is in each A_i with i between 1 and 1 inclusive," which is certainly true. Now assume $n \geq 2$ and the statement in quotes is true when $n = k - 1$. For $n = 2$ the equivalence follows from the two-set definition of $\cap$ (which we are assuming as well). Now $\bigcap\limits_{i=1}^{n} A_i = \left(\bigcap\limits_{i=1}^{n-1} A_i \right) \cap A_n$. By the two-set definition of intersection this is the set of all elements x in both the set $\bigcap\limits_{i=1}^{n-1} A_i$ and the set A_n. By the inductive hypothesis this is the set of all elements x in each of the sets A_i for i between 1 and $n - 1$ inclusive *and* in the set A_n. This is, however, the set of all elements x in each of the sets A_i for i between 1 and n inclusive. Therefore by the principle of mathematical induction, $\bigcap\limits_{i=1}^{n} A_i$ is the set of all elements in each of the sets A_i for i between 1 and n inclusive.

23. Many answers are correct. A typical one is $(((3 + 2) + 1) + (2 \cdot 3))$. Check the following. Do parentheses balance? Does each operator correspond to a pair of parentheses? Are there 4 operators?

25. Yes

27. No because (4) is not.

29. 1 operator: $-(2)$; 2 operators: $(-(2)) + (x)$; 3 operators: $(z) \cdot ((-(2)) + (x))$

31. No; not enough parentheses. However $(x) + (1)$ is legal by the rules of Exercise 29.

33. No, it needs parentheses around $(x) \cdot (y)$ (or perhaps around $(y) + (1)$).

Section 5-3 Concepts Review

1. recursive **2.** binary search **3.** Backus Naur **4.** concatenating **5.** smallest, first, selection sort **6.** $n + 1$ (including the final comparison to see if the element located is equal to the target) **7.** can be, or

Section 5-3 Exercises

1. Procedure: If $n = 1$ do nothing.
If $n > 1$ apply Bubble to the portion of the list between 1 and $n - 1$.
If $L(n) < L(n - 1)$ exchange $L(n)$ and $L(n - 1)$; otherwise do nothing.

3. Algorithm Bubblesort (recursive)
Input: A list L and a number n.
Output: A list L of the same n numbers in increasing order.

Procedure: If $n = 1$ do nothing; otherwise apply Bubble to the portion of L from 1 to n, then apply Bubblesort to L and $n - 1$.

5. The statement we wish to prove by induction on n is "When applied to a list of n items, the algorithm places the largest member of positions 1 through n inclusive of the list into position n." If $n = 1$, the algorithm does nothing and the element in position 1 is the largest member of positions 1 through n inclusive. Now suppose the statement is true with $n = k - 1$. Thus when Bubble is applied to the first $k - 1$ positions of L, the largest element appears in position $k - 1$. When positions $k - 1$ and k are compared, the larger of these two elements will thus be the largest element of the list; according to the algorithm it will be placed in position k. Thus by the principle of mathematical induction, for all positive integers n, applying Bubble to a list of length n places the largest item in position n.

7. The statement about n we wish to prove is "If we apply Bubblesort to positions 1 through n of a list, the entries in these positions will be sorted into increasing order." If $n = 1$, the algorithm does nothing and the single position is (trivially) sorted. Suppose the statement is true when $n = k - 1$. Applying Bubblesort to positions 1 to k of a list first applies Bubble to these positions. By Exercise 5, the largest element among positions 1 through n now appears in position n. By the inductive hypothesis, applying Bubblesort to positions 1 through $n - 1$ sorts these positions into increasing order, and since the element in position n is at least as large as all of these, all n positions have been sorted into increasing order. Thus by the principle of mathematical induction, applying Bubblesort to positions 1 through n of a list sorts these positions into increasing order.

9. (a) goat, pony, horse, (pony)   (b) goat, pony, horse, hog, (horse)   (c) goat, pony, rat, (rat)   (d) goat, pony, rat, (tiger)   *Note:* Parenthesized words examined with $i = j$, not as entry $\lfloor \frac{i + j}{2} \rfloor$.

11. A positive integer can be a positive integer followed by a digit, and a digit can be a positive digit which can be 3. Thus a positive integer can be a positive integer followed by 3. A positive integer can be a positive digit and a positive digit can be 2 giving us 23.

   An integer can be a positive integer or $-\langle$positive integer$\rangle$. Since a positive integer can be a positive integer followed by a digit and a digit can be a positive digit which can be 3, an integer can be $-\langle$positive integer$\rangle$3. Since a positive integer can be a positive integer followed by a digit and a digit can be 0, an integer can be $-\langle$positive integer$\rangle$03. Since a positive integer can be a positive digit and a positive digit can be 2, an integer can be -203.

13. (a) There are 2 characters, 0 is in the set $\{0,1,2,3,4,5,6,7,8,9\}$. Since 2 is in the set $\{1,2,3,4,5,6,7,8,9\}$, we output "yes."
   (b) This has more than one character and 0 is in the set $\{0,1,2,3,4,5,6,7,8,9\}$ so we can apply PosInt to $2++$. This has more than one character and $+$ is not in $\{0,1,2,3,4,5,6,7,8,9\}$ so we output "no" and stop.
   (c) Similar to (b).
   (d) We continue removing digits till we get to $-$ which is not in the set $\{1,2,3,4,5,6,7,8,9\}$ so we output "no" and stop.

15. $\langle$Alpha letter$\rangle := A \mid B \mid C \mid D \mid E \mid F \mid G \mid H \mid I \mid J \mid K \mid L \mid M \mid N \mid O \mid P \mid Q \mid R \mid S \mid$
      $T \mid U \mid V \mid W \mid X \mid Y \mid Z \mid$
   $\langle$Digit$\rangle := 0 \mid 1 \mid 2 \mid 3 \mid 4 \mid 5 \mid 6 \mid 7 \mid 8 \mid 9 \mid$
   $\langle$Variable name$\rangle := \langle$Alpha letter$\rangle \mid \langle$Variable name$\rangle \_ \mid \langle$Variable name$\rangle\langle$Alpha letter$\rangle \mid$
      $\langle$Variable name$\rangle\langle$Digit$\rangle$

17. Algorithm Varitest

Input: A symbol string

Output: "Yes" if the symbol string represents a variable. "No" otherwise.

Procedure: If the string has length 1, then output "yes" if its character is in the set $\{A, B, \ldots, Z\}$. Otherwise output "no." If the string has length more than 1, then output "no" unless the last character is in the set $\{A, B, \ldots, Z, 0, 1, 2, 3, 4, 5, 6, 7, 8, 9, \_\}$ and in this case remove the last character and apply Varitest to the string that remains.

19. Algorithm Integer

Input: A symbol string

Output: "Yes" if the symbol string represents an integer and "no" otherwise.

Procedure: If the symbol string has more than one character and the first character is $-$, discard this character and apply Algorithm PosInt to what remains (and output the output of PosInt). In any other case, apply PosInt to the symbol string (and output the output of PosInt).

Chapter 5 Review Exercises

1. The base step consists of the first two sentences. The inductive hypothesis is the third sentence. The inductive step is the third sentence through the sentence "Thus the formula holds when $n = k$." The inductive conclusion is the last sentence.

2. The formula may be written as $\sum_{i=1}^{n} \frac{1}{3^i} = \frac{3^n - 1}{2 \cdot 3^n}$. When $n = 1$ this formula gives $\frac{1}{3} = \frac{3 - 1}{2 \cdot 3} = \frac{1}{3}$ which is true. Suppose now the formula holds when $n = k - 1$ so that

$$\sum_{i=1}^{k-1} \frac{1}{3^i} = \frac{3^{k-1} - 1}{2 \cdot 3^{k-1}}$$

Adding $\frac{1}{3^k}$ to each side gives

$$\sum_{i=1}^{k} \frac{1}{3^i} = \frac{3^{k-1} - 1}{2 \cdot 3^{k-1}} + \frac{1}{3^k} = \frac{3 \cdot 3^{k-1} - 3 \cdot 1 + 2 \cdot 1}{2 \cdot 3^k} = \frac{3^k - 1}{2 \cdot 3^k}$$

Thus the formula holds for $n = k$ whenever it holds for $n = k - 1$. Thus by the principle of mathematical induction the formula holds for all positive integers n.

3. When $n = 1$ the formula is $2 = 1^2(1 + 1)$ which is true. Now suppose the formula holds when $n = k - 1$ so that

$$2 + 10 + \ldots + 3(k - 1)^2 - (k - 1) = (k - 1)^2 k$$

Adding $3k^2 - k$ to both sides gives

$$\begin{aligned} 2 + 10 + \ldots + 3k^2 - k &= (k^2 - 2k + 1)k + 3k^2 - k \\ &= k^3 - 2k^2 + k + 3k^2 - k \\ &= k^3 + k^2 \\ &= k^2(k + 1) \end{aligned}$$

Thus the formula holds when $n = k$ as well, so the formula holds for all positive integers n by the principle of mathematical induction.

4. For $n = 3$ the inequality reads $3^2 + 3 \cdot 3 < 3^3$, which is true. Now suppose the inequality holds when $n = k$, so that $k^2 + 3k < k^3$. Since we wish to have $(k + 1)^2 + 3(k + 1) = k^2 + 5k + 4$ on the left-hand side we add $2k + 4$ to both sides of $k^3 + 3k < k^3$,

getting the inequality

$$
\begin{aligned}
k^2 + 5k + 4 &< k^3 + 2k + 4 \\
&< k^3 + 2k + 3k^2 + 1 \\
&< k^3 + 3k^2 + 3k + 1 \\
&= (k + 1)^3
\end{aligned}
$$

Thus the inequality holds when $n = k + 1$ as well, so by the principle of mathematical induction, $n^2 + 3n < n^3$ for all integers $n \geq 3$.

5. When $n = 10$ the inequality reads $10^3 < 2^{10}$ which is true since $1000 < 1024$. Now suppose the formula is true when $n = k$. To get $(k + 1)^3 = k^3 + 3k^2 + 3k + 1$ on the left-hand side, we add $3k^2 + 3k + 1$ to both sides of the inequality $k^3 < 2^k$, getting

$$
\begin{aligned}
(k + 1)^3 = k^3 + 3k^2 + 3k + 1 &< 2^k + 3k^2 + 3k + 1 \\
&< 2^k + 3k^2 + 3k^2 + 1k^2 \\
&< 2^k + 7k^2 \\
&< 2^k + k^3 \quad \text{(since } k \geq 10) \\
&< 2^k + 2^k \\
&= 2 \cdot 2^k = 2^{k+1}
\end{aligned}
$$

Thus the inequality holds when $n = k + 1$ as well, and so by the principle of mathematical induction, the formula holds for all integers $n > 10$.

6. We must prove that for some c (and large enough n) $1 \cdot 2 \cdot 3 + \ldots + n(n + 1)(n + 2) \leq cn^4$. Since with $n = 1$ this reads $6 \leq cn^4$, we try $c = 6$ so that we can try to prove the inequality for all positive n. When $n = 1$ the inequality reads $1 \cdot 2 \cdot 3 \leq 6 \cdot 1$ which is true. Now assume the formula holds when $n = k$ so that

$$
1 \cdot 2 \cdot 3 + \ldots + k(k + 1)(k + 2) \leq 6k^4
$$

Adding $(k + 1)(k + 2)(k + 3)$ to both sides gives

$$
\begin{aligned}
1 \cdot 2 \cdot 3 + \ldots + (k + 1)(k + 2)(k + 3) &\leq 6k^4 + k^3 + 6k^2 + 11k + 6 \\
&\leq 6k^4 + 6k^3 + 6k^2 + 12k + 6 \\
&= 6(k^4 + k^3 + k^2 + 2k + 1) \\
&\leq 6(k^4 + 4k^3 + 6k^2 + 4k + 1) \\
&= 6(k + 1)^4
\end{aligned}
$$

Therefore the inequality holds when $n = k + 1$ as well, and so by the principle of mathematical induction, the inequality holds for all $n \geq 1$. Therefore $1 \cdot 2 \cdot 3 + \ldots + n(n + 1)(n + 2) = O(n^4)$.

7. Here, once again, we must first determine the value of c. This is a bit tricky, because the cases $n = 1$, $n = 2$, and $n = 3$ suggest that c can be 1 because we have $1^4 < 1 \cdot 2 \cdot 3$, $2^4 < 6 + 24 = 30$, $3^4 < 6 + 24 + 60$. Notice that, relatively speaking, the inequalities are coming closer and closer to equalities. For $n = 4$, we have $4^4 = 256$ while $1 \cdot 2 \cdot 3 + \ldots + 4 \cdot 5 \cdot 6 = 210$. To see what *will* make a good c, we notice we will want to go from $n^4 \leq c \cdot something$ to $(n + 1)^4 \leq c \cdot something$. Since $(n + 1)^4 = n^4 + 4n^3 + 6n^2 + 4n + 1 \leq n^4 + (4 + 6 + 4 + 1)n^3 = n^4 + 15n^3$, the quantity we will add to the left-hand side of the equation will be no more than $15n^3$. The quantity we may add to the right-hand side is $c(n + 1)(n + 2)(n + 3)$ which is more than cn^3. Thus $c = 15$ should be sufficient. We try now to prove by induction that

$$
n^4 \leq 15(1 \cdot 2 \cdot 3 + 2 \cdot 3 \cdot 4 + \ldots + n(n + 1)(n + 2))
$$

for all $n \geq 1$. For $n = 1$ we get $1 \leq 90$ which is certainly true. Suppose the inequality holds when $n = k$ so that $k^4 \leq 15(1 \cdot 2 \cdot 3 + \ldots + k(k + 1)(k + 2))$. Then adding $4k^3 + 6k^2 + 4k + 1$ to both sides of the inequality gives

$$
\begin{aligned}
(k + 1)^4 &= k^4 + 4k^3 + 6k^2 + 4k + 1 \\
&\leq 15(1 \cdot 2 \cdot 3 + \ldots + k(k + 1)(k + 2)) + 4k^3 + 6k^2 + 4k + 1 \\
&\leq 15(1 \cdot 2 \cdot 3 + \ldots + k(k + 1)(k + 2)) + (4 + 6 + 4 + 1)k^3 \\
&\leq 15(1 \cdot 2 \cdot 3 + \ldots + k(k + 1)(k + 2) + 15(k + 1)(k + 2)(k + 3)) \\
&= 15(1 \cdot 2 \cdot 3 + \ldots + (k + 1)(k + 2)(k + 3))
\end{aligned}
$$

and so the inequality holds when $n = k$ as well. Therefore by the principle of mathematical induction, $n^4 \leq 15(1 \cdot 2 \cdot 3 + \ldots + n(n + 1)(n + 2))$ for all $n \geq 1$ so $n^4 = O(1 \cdot 2 \cdot 3 + \ldots + n(n + 1)(n + 2))$.

8. We wish to prove the statement "If a graph has n vertices, it has at most $\dfrac{n(n + 1)}{2}$ edges." If the graph has one vertex, it can have at most one edge—the edge connecting that vertex to itself. Since $\dfrac{1(1 + 1)}{2}$ is 1, the statement is true with $n = 1$. Suppose now the statement is true when $n = k - 1$ and suppose G is a graph with k vertices. Choose an arbitrary vertex x and remove x and all the edges it touches. There can be at most one edge between any vertex and x, so we have removed at most k edges. Since the resulting graph has $k - 1$ vertices, it has, by hypothesis, at most $\dfrac{(k - 1)k}{2}$ edges. Replacing x and its edges thus gives at most

$$
\frac{(k - 1)k}{2} + k = \frac{k^2 - k}{2} + \frac{2k}{2} = \frac{k^2 + k}{2}
$$

edges. Therefore the statement is true when $n = k$ as well and so by the principle of mathematical induction, for all integers n a graph with n vertices has at most $\dfrac{n^2 + n}{2}$ edges.

9. The statement about m we wish to prove is that if a uniquely connected graph has m edges, then it has at least two vertices of degree 1. If $m = 1$, we have 1 edge so we have exactly two vertices of degree 1. Now assume that if a uniquely connected graph has between 1 and $k - 1$ edges, then it has two vertices of degree 1. Now let G be a uniquely connected graph with k edges. Choose an edge connecting vertices x and y and delete this edge. Since this edge must have been the unique path from x to y, x and y lie in different connected components of the resulting graph. Each connected component must still be uniquely connected. Each connected component has fewer than k edges and so is either a single vertex or has at least two vertices of degree 1. Adding $\{x, y\}$ back into the edge set can remove at most one degree-1 vertex from each component, and if a component were $\{x\}$ or $\{y\}$ it would *add* a degree-1 vertex to that component. Thus in the resulting graph at least one vertex in the component containing x has degree 1 now and at least one vertex in the component containing y has degree 1 now. Therefore we have at least two vertices of degree 1 in our k-edge graph. Thus by the principle of mathematical induction, for all $m \geq 1$, a uniquely connected graph with m edges has at least 2 vertices of degree 1.

10. First, $\bigwedge_{i=1}^{1} p_i$ means p_1. Second, if $k > 1$, $\bigwedge_{i=1}^{k} p_i = \left(\bigwedge_{i=1}^{k-1} p_i \right) \wedge p_k$. (We assume that $p \wedge q$ has been defined independently.)

11. We wish to prove the statement

$$q \vee \left(\bigwedge_{i=1}^{n} p_i \right) \Leftrightarrow \bigwedge_{i=1}^{n} (q \vee p_i)$$

which we proved in Chapter 1 for $n = 2$. For $n = 1$ it states

$$q \vee \left(\bigwedge_{i=1}^{1} p_i \right) \Leftrightarrow \bigwedge_{i=1}^{1} (q \vee p_i) \quad \text{or} \quad q \vee p_1 \Leftrightarrow q \vee p_1$$

which is certainly true. Assume that the equivalence holds if $n = k - 1$. Then

$$q \vee \left(\bigwedge_{i=1}^{k} p_i \right) = q \vee \left[\left(\bigwedge_{i=1}^{k-1} p_i \right) \wedge p_k \right]$$

$$\Leftrightarrow \left[q \vee \left(\bigwedge_{i=1}^{k-1} p_i \right) \right] \wedge [q \vee p_k]$$

$$\Leftrightarrow \left[\bigwedge_{i=1}^{k-1} (q \vee p_i) \right] \wedge (q \vee p_k)$$

$$\Leftrightarrow \bigwedge_{i=1}^{k} (q \vee p_i)$$

Thus the equivalence with $n = k - 1$ implies the equivalence with $n = k$, so that by the principle of mathematical induction, the equivalence holds for all integers n.

12. We proved in the text the distributive law $(a + b)n = an + bn$. Thus we shall assume the distributive law $b(a + c) = ba + bc$ as well. We wish to prove the statement

$$b \sum_{i=1}^{n} a_i = \sum_{i=1}^{n} ba_i$$

When $n = 1$ this statement becomes $ba_1 = ba_1$ which is true. Now assume the statement is true when $n = k - 1$. Then, by the definition of summation

$$b \sum_{i=1}^{k} a_i = b \left(\sum_{i=1}^{k-1} a_i + a_k \right)$$

By the ordinary distributive law this is

$$\left(b \sum_{i=1}^{k-1} a_i \right) + ba_k$$

By the inductive hypothesis this must equal

$$\left(\sum_{i=1}^{k-1} ba_i \right) + ba_k$$

By the inductive definition of summation notation, this is

$$\sum_{i=1}^{k} ba_i$$

Thus the truth of the statement for $n = k - 1$ implies the truth of the statement for $n = k$. Therefore by the principle of mathematical induction, for all positive integers n,

$$b \sum_{i=1}^{n} a_i = \sum_{i=1}^{n} ba_i$$

13. (a) well formed   (b) not well formed   (c) well formed   (d) well formed
    (e) not well formed

14. 1 operator: $(\sim A)$. 2 operators: $(B \cup (\sim A))$. 3 operators: $(A \cap (B \cup (\sim A)))$

15. (a) no   (b) yes   (c) no   (d) yes

16. $L(k)$ is the largest element of the list. We wish to prove by induction on n the statement that if Nameless is applied to the list L with the integer n then $L(k)$ is the maximum element among the first n elements of L. If $n = 1$, then Nameless sets k to 1 and the statement is true. Assume the statement is true when $n = m - 1$. Then when we apply Nameless to L with $n = m$, we first get $L(k)$ to be the largest element among the first $m - 1$. Next we compare $L(k)$ to $L(m)$, and if $L(m)$ is larger we change k to m, and otherwise we don't change k. Thus $L(k)$ will be the largest element of the list of length m. Therefore by the principle of mathematical induction, when Nameless is applied to a list L and an integer n, $L(k)$ is the largest element among the first n entries of L.

17. The effect of algorithm Exercise is to sort the list. We prove by induction on n the statement that "applying algorithm Exercise to a list L and the integer n produces a list whose first n entries are the first n entries of L sorted into increasing order." If $n = 1$, the algorithm does nothing and any list with just one entry is sorted into increasing order trivially. Assume that when $n = m - 1$ the statement is true. If $m > 1$, algorithm Exercise applied to L and m first uses algorithm Nameless to find the largest element of L and then exchanges the largest element with element m. Then it applies Exercise to the first $m - 1$ positions, and by our inductive hypothesis this sorts these positions into increasing order. Further, none of the elements in these first $m - 1$ positions could come after the largest element, so now the first m positions are sorted into increasing order. Therefore, by the principle of mathematical induction, for all $n > 0$ if we apply Nameless to a list L (with at least n entries) and the integer n, then the first n positions of L will be sorted into increasing order.

18. (a) Is Sue after Robert? Is Sue after Sally? Is Sue equal to Walter?   (b) Is Robert after Robert? Is Robert after Charles? Is Robert equal to Robert?   (c) Is Ralph after Robert? Is Ralph after Charles? Is Ralph equal to Robert?   (d) Is Bill after Robert? Is Bill after Charles? Is Bill after Ann? Is Bill equal to Charles?

19. $\langle \text{expression} \rangle := a \mid b \cdots \mid z$
    $\langle \text{expression} \rangle := (\neg \langle \text{expression} \rangle)$
    $\langle \text{expression} \rangle := (\langle \text{expression} \rangle \vee \langle \text{expression} \rangle) \mid (\langle \text{expression} \rangle \wedge \langle \text{expression} \rangle)$
    Note: the three different kinds of descriptions were put on three lines for convenience and visual emphasis of their differences.

20. First write down Rules 1–3 describing positive integers. Then write

$$\langle\text{stem}\rangle := \langle\text{positive digit}\rangle\langle\text{digit}\rangle \mid \langle\text{stem}\rangle\langle\text{digit}\rangle$$
$$\langle\text{decimal}\rangle := \langle\text{stem}\rangle.\langle\text{positive digit}\rangle \mid -\langle\text{stem}\rangle.\langle\text{positive digit}\rangle$$
$$\langle\text{exponent}\rangle := e\langle\text{positive integer}\rangle \mid e -\langle\text{positive integer}\rangle$$
$$\langle\text{base}\rangle := \langle\text{positive digit}\rangle \mid \langle\text{decimal}\rangle \mid -\langle\text{positive digit}\rangle$$
$$\langle\text{CSnumber}\rangle := \langle\text{base}\rangle \mid \langle\text{base}\rangle\langle\text{exponent}\rangle$$

21. If the expression has one symbol, then output "yes" if the symbol is a lower case letter and "no" otherwise. If the expression has more than one symbol, then unless the first and last symbols are left and right parentheses, output "no." If the first and last expressions are parentheses, then remove them. Now if the first character is a $\neg$ sign, apply this algorithm to the remainder of the expression. Otherwise, read from the left to the right, counting the left and right parentheses until you have the same number of each. (Output "no" if the numbers are never equal.) If the next symbol is $\wedge$ or $\vee$, apply this algorithm to everything preceding the symbol and everything following the symbol. If both outputs would be "yes," then output "yes." In all other cases output "no."

CHAPTER 6
Section 6-1 Concepts Review
1. counting function **2.** size **3.** same size **4.** sum principle **5.** product principle
6. product principle **7.** Cartesian product **8.** $\prod_{i=1}^{m} n_i$ **9.** permutation **10.** $\dfrac{n!}{(n-m)!}$
11. n^m

Section 6-1 Exercises
1. $\{(1,a), (2,b), (3,c), (4,d), (5,e), (6,f), (7,g)\}$. Many other answers are possible.
3. $\{(\varnothing,\text{TTT}), (\{1\},\text{HTT}), (\{2\},\text{THT}), (\{3\},\text{TTH}), (\{1,2\},\text{HHT}), (\{1,3\},\text{HTH}), (\{2,3\},\text{THH}),$
$(\{1,2,3\},\text{HHH})\}$.
5. $\{(a,1), (a,2), (a,3), (a,4), (b,1), (b,2), (b,3), (b,4)\}$. We see $R \times S$ has 8 elements and 8 $= 2\cdot4$.
7. 35 **9.** 56 **11.** $20\cdot19 = 380$
13. 12 use $\{a,b,c,d\}$ for set. $ab,ac,ad,\ ba,bc,bd,\ ca,cb,cd,\ da,db,dc$
15. 60 **17.** 120 **19.** 20 **21.** 20 **23.** 210 **25.** 380 **27.** $n(n-1)$
29. $n(n-1)(n-2)$ **31.** $n(n-1)$ **33.** 1 **35.** 5 **37.** 120 **39.** 5040 **41.** 24, 64
43. 256 **45.** 240

Section 6-2 Concepts Review
1. 2^n **2.** $\dfrac{n!}{(n-m)!m!}$ or $\dbinom{n}{k}$ **3.** binomial coefficient **4.** combinations **5.** product
6. sum **7.** multiset **8.** $\dbinom{n+k-1}{k}$

Section 6-2 Exercises
1. 10, $\{1,2,3\}\ \{1,2,4\}\ \{1,2,5\}\ \{1,3,4\}\ \{1,3,5\}\ \{1,4,5\}\ \{2,3,4\}\ \{2,3,5\}\ \{2,4,5\}\ \{3,4,5\}$
3. 20 **5.** 20 **7.** 20 **9.** 190
11. $\dfrac{n(n-1)}{2}$ **13.** $\dfrac{n(n-1)}{2}$ **15.** $n(n-1)$
17. 655 **19.** 5 **21.** 120 **23.** 5 **25.** 5 **27.** $C(10,4) = 210$ **29.** $C(8,4) = 70$
31. $C(10,3)\cdot C(10,4) = 25{,}200;\ C(10,3)\cdot C(7,4) = 4200$

33. (a) permutations (one-to-one functions) (b) k-tuples (functions) (c) subsets
(d) none
For Exercises 35–41, see answers to Exercises 13–19 in Section 6-3.
43. $\dbinom{8 + 5 - 1}{8} = 495$ **45.** (d) **47.** $12 \cdot C(11, 3) = 1980$

49. Same as Exercise 31 but in opposite order. **51.** $(10)_2 \cdot C(8,3) = 5040$
53. 10 possible outcomes

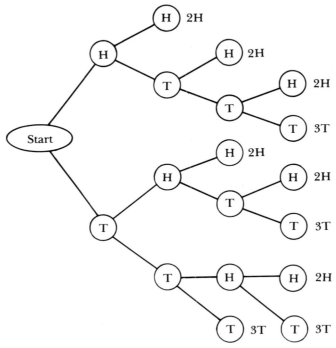

55. $5 + 3 = 8$ **57.** $15 + 90 = 105$

Section 6-3 Concepts Review
1. single-ring, one-way **2.** double-ring **3.** $\dfrac{p}{r}$ **4.** permutations **5.** function
6. function, permutation **7.** $\dfrac{n + k - 1!}{k!}$ **8.** multiplicity **9.** multiset
10. $\dbinom{n + k - 1}{k}$

Section 6-3 Exercises
1. (a) 120 (b) 360 (c) 60 **3.** 6

5. Imagine the vertical surface of the wastebasket removed, cut vertically along a seam and flattened out. A coloring of the wastebasket gives several equivalent colorings of the strip. A typical class is {RBWY, BWYR, WYRB, YRBW}.

7. $\frac{4!}{2} = 12$. Two colorings of the wire may become equivalent when it is bent into a bracelet because rotating the bracelet or flipping it over doesn't change the coloring;

however two different patterns of colors in the straight wire can be made to coincide by rotation or flipping after the wire is bent. The equivalence classes of straight-line color patterns correspond with the bracelet colorings.

9. $\{ab,ba\}$ $\{ac,ca\}$ $\{ad,da\}$ $\{bc,cb\}$ $\{bd,db\}$ $\{cd,dc\}$ 11. $(n-1)!$
13. $m(a) = 2$, $m(c) = 2$, $m(e) = 2$, $m(b) = 1$, $m(i) = 1$, $m(p) = 2$, $m(r) = 2$, $m(s) = 1$, $m(t) = 1$, $m(letter) = 0$ for each letter
15. 35   17. 66   19. 1540   21. 56, 20   23. 1680   25. 6720   27. 6720   29. 2002

Section 6-4 Concepts Review

1. monomial   2. binomial   3. binomial theorem   4. $x^{n-i}y^i$ 5. in, out of
6. $\binom{n-1}{k-1} + \binom{n-1}{k}$ 7. Pascal's triangle   8. Pascal's triangle

Section 6-4 Exercises

1. $x^7 + 7x^6y + 21x^5y^2 + 35x^4y^3 + 35x^3y^4 + 21x^2y^5 + 7xy^6 + y^7$
3. $x^4 + 8x^3 + 24x^2 + 32x + 16$
5. $64x^6 - 576x^5 + 2160x^4 - 4320x^3 + 4860x^2 - 2916x + 729$
7. $49 + 20\sqrt{6}$
9. $x^8 - 8x^7 + 28x^6 - 56x^5 + 70x^4 - 56x^3 + 28x^2 - 8x + 1$. Another valid answer is

$$x^8 - \binom{8}{1}x^7 + \binom{8}{2}x^6 - \binom{8}{3}x^5 + \binom{8}{4}x^4 - \binom{8}{5}x^3 + \binom{8}{6}x^2 - \binom{8}{7}x + 1$$

Substituting in $x = 1$ gives

$$\binom{8}{0} - \binom{8}{1} + \ldots + \binom{8}{8} = 0$$

11. $x^n - \binom{n}{1}x^{n-1} + \binom{n}{2}x^{n-2} - \binom{n}{3}x^{n-3} + \ldots$. Substituting in $x = 1$ gives

$$0 = (1-1)^n = 1 - \binom{n}{1} + \binom{n}{2} - \binom{n}{3} \ldots$$

13. 1140, 1140   15. 220, 220   17. 1, 10, 45, 120, 210, 252, 210, 120, 45, 10, 1   19. 15504
21. 352,716

23. $\dfrac{n!}{(n-k)!(n-(n-k))!} = \dfrac{n!}{(n-k)!k!} = \dfrac{n!}{k!(n-k)!}$

25. $x^8 + 16x^7 + 112x^6 + 448x^5 + 1120x^4 + 1792x^3 + 1792x^2 + 1024x + 256$

Section 6-5 Concepts Review

1. $|C| + |D| - |C \cap D|$
2. $|R| + |S| + |T| - |R \cap S| - |R \cap T| - |S \cap T| + |R \cap S \cap T|$
3. derangement   4. $\displaystyle\sum_{i<j \in N} |S_i \cap S_j|$
5. inclusion exclusion, $\displaystyle -\sum_{i<j \in N} |S_i \cap S_j| + \sum_{i<j<k \in N} |S_i \cap S_j \cap S_j|$

Section 6-5 Exercises

1. 15, 5   3. 2   5. 27, 21, 35, 13   7. 28, 7   9. 50, 10   11. 5

11. 5

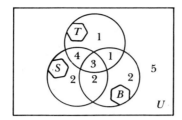

13.

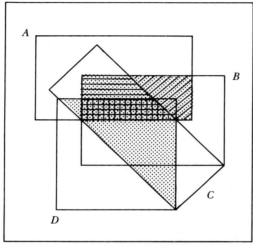

$A \cap B \cap C$: Horizontal
$A \cap B \cap C \sim (A \cap B \cap C \cap D)$: Horizontal and not vertical
$A \cap B \cap \sim C$: Slanted
$(A \cap B) \cup (C \cap D)$: Dotted

15. 8

17.

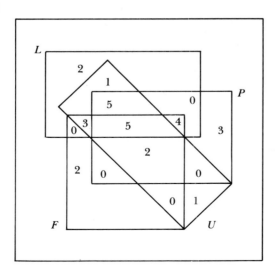

19. 44

21. 60, assuming no plots are needed for no treatment whatsoever.

23. $4 \cdot 32 - 6 \cdot 29 + 4 \cdot 12 - 6 = -4$, so there would be a negative number of garden plots used.

25. $\displaystyle\sum_{i=0}^{n} (-1)^i \frac{n!}{i!}$

27. $\displaystyle\sum_{i=0}^{5} (-1)^i \binom{5}{i} \cdot 5^{5-i} = 1024$

29. $C(10,3) - 3 \cdot C(5,3) = 90$

31. $\displaystyle\sum_{i=0}^{4} (-1)^i \binom{4}{i} (4-i)^8 = 40824$

Chapter 6 Review Exercises

1. $\{(1,a), (2,s), (3,d), (4,f), (5,g), (6,h), (7,j), (8,k), (9,l)\}$

2. $\{(1,1), (2,2), (10,3), (11,4), (12,5), (20,6), (21,7), (22,8)\}$

3. 6 $\{(1,a), (1,z), (2,a), (2,z), (3,a), (3,z)\}$

4. 240 **5.** 1,814,400 **6.** $n(n-1)(n-2) = n^3 - 3n^2 + 2n$ **7.** 720 **8.** 15

9. $\dfrac{n(n-1)(n-2)}{6} = \dfrac{n^3}{6} - \dfrac{n^2}{2} + \dfrac{n}{3}$

10. Same as Exercise 9 **11.** 6840 **12.** 1140 **13.** 720, 1000 **14.** 120, 220 **15.** 64

16. $(8)_3 \cdot C(5,4) = 1680$, $(8)_3 \cdot C(8,4) = 23520$

17. (a) k-element permutations $(n)_k = \dfrac{n!}{(n-k)!}$ (b) k-tuples; n^k (c) None of the methods. This is a problem in ordered distributions of k objects to n recipients; $\dfrac{(n+k-1)!}{(n-1)!}$ (d) k-element subsets $C(n,k) = \dfrac{n!}{k!(n-k)!}$ (e) k-element multisets $C(n+k-1,k) = \dfrac{(n+k-1)!}{k!(n-1)!}$

18. 5 outcomes are possible.

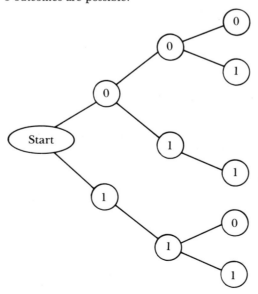

19. 720, 360, 2520
20. $m(a) = 2$, $m(e) = 2$, $m(h) = 1$, $m(l) = 1$, $m(m) = 1$, $m(p) = 2$, $m(r) = 1$, $m(s) = 2$, $m(letter) = 0$ for each other letter.
21. 3456
22. $x^9 + 9xy^8 + 36x^2y^7 + 84x^3y^6 + 126x^4y^5 + 126x^5y^4 + 84x^6y^3 + 36x^7y^2 + 9x^8y + y^9$
23. $243x^5 - 810x^4 + 1080x^3 - 720x^2 + 240x - 32$
24. $\sum_{i=0}^{5} \binom{5}{i} x^i$; $\sum_{i=0}^{5} \binom{5}{i} = 2^5$. The number of subsets of a five element set is 2^5.
25. (a) 18564 (b) 15504 (c) 15504 (d) 20349
26. 2520 **27.** 21, 4 **28.** 3 **29.** 1, 2
30. $\sum_{i=0}^{6} (-1)^i \binom{6}{i} 6^{6-i} = 15625$

31. In the answer to Exercise 30, replace 6^{6-i} by $\dfrac{6!}{i!}$.

32. $\sum_{i=0}^{m} (-1)^i \binom{m}{i} (n-i)_{m-i} = \sum_{i=0}^{m} (-1)^i \dfrac{m!(n-i)!}{i!(m-i)!(n-m)!}$

CHAPTER 7

Section 7-1 Concepts Review
1. recurrence **2.** first order **3.** order **4.** linear **5.** driving **6.** $b_i(n)$
7. homogeneous **8.** solution **9.** general solution **10.** logarithm

Section 7-1 Exercises
1. We begin by comparing item one to item two (and maybe exchanging), two to three, three to four, and so on. Thus the number of comparisons before we get to the end of the list and start over is the number of pairs of adject integers between 1 and n which is $n - 1$. But when we start over we apply Bubblesort to the first $n - 1$ positions, so we use c_{n-1} comparisons to finish the job. Thus we have $n - 1 + c_{n-1}$ comparisons in total.

3. Think of the jobs as numbered 1 through n. There are 3 choices for where we assign job n. Then there are J_{n-1} choices for where we assign the first $n - 1$ jobs. Since for any choice of how we assign the last job there are J_{n-1} ways to assign the first $n - 1$, the *product principle* tells us there are $3 \cdot J_{n-1}$ ways to assign the jobs.

5. (a) first order (b) second order (c) second order (d) has no order (e) first order (f) second order
7. (a), (b), (c), and (d) **9.** 0, 1, 3, 6, 10 **11.** 1, 1, 2, 3, 5, 8, 13, 21
13. If $b_n = n!$ then $nb_{n-1} = n \cdot (n-1)! = n! = b_n$, so that $b_n = nb_{n-1}$.
15. If $S_n = 3 \cdot 2^{n-1} - 1$, then $2S_{i-1} + 1 = 2(3 \cdot 2^{i-2} - 1) + 1 = 3 \cdot 2^{i-1} - 2 + 1 = 3 \cdot 2^{i-1} - 1 = S_i$; therefore $S_i = 2S_{i-1} + 1$.
17. (a) nonhomogeneous (b) homogeneous (c) homogeneous (d) nonhomogeneous (e) homogeneous (f) homogeneous
19. (a) constant (b) constant (c) not (d) not (e) constant (f) not
21. Each year p percent is added. Thus if S_n is the population in year n, we have that $S_n = S_{n-1} + \frac{p}{100}S_{n-1} = (1 + .01p)S_{n-1}$.
23. $\$10,000 \cdot (1.1)^{20} = \$67,275$ to the nearest cent
25. 6, 18, 54, 162, 486
27. $a_n = 2 \cdot 3^n$

29. Since $a_n = 2^n a_0$ we get $96 = 2^5 a_0 = 32 a_0$ so that $a_0 = 3$.

31. $a_n = 4\sqrt{n!}$

33.

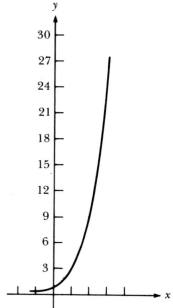

35. 10^5 **37.** 10^6 **39.** 2^9 **41.** 10^8 **43.** $10^{2.5}$ **45.** 2^6

47. $\log_{10}(3) = .477$ from Example 10; $\log_{10}(15) = \log_{10}(3) + \log_{10}(5) = .477 + .699 = 1.176$ approximately

49. $2 \cdot (.699) = 1.398$

51. Because $2 \cdot 5 = 10$ and the base 10 log of 10 is 1.

53. Use the facts that $y = 3^{\log_3(y)} = 10^{\log_{10}(y)}$ and $3 = 10^{\log_{10}(3)}$ to write $3^{\log_3(y)} = (10^{\log_{10}(3)})^{\log_3(y)} = 10^{\log_{10}(y)}$ so that $\log_{10}(3)\log_3(y) = \log_{10}(y)$ or $\log_3(y) = \dfrac{\log_{10}(y)}{\log_{10}(3)}$.

Second Solution: To use the method of Example 14, write $y = 3^x$, so $\log_{10}(y) = x \log_{10}(3)$ and $x = \log_3(y)$. By substitution you get $\log_{10}(y) = \log_3(y)\log_{10}(3)$ or $\log_3(y) = \dfrac{\log_{10}(y)}{\log_{10}(3)}$.

55. a^8 **57.** 2   **59.** 6^{32} **61.** 7   **63.** $2^{\log_4(3)} = 4^{\frac{1}{2}\log_4(3)} = (4^{\log_4(3)})^{\frac{1}{2}} = 3^{\frac{1}{2}} = \sqrt{3}$ **65.** 17

67. 1

69. $1 + \log_6(10)$ **71.** 4

73. $f(x) = a_0(.9)^x$ where a_0 is the amount present on day 0. Setting $\frac{1}{2}a_0 = a_0(.9)^x$, dividing by a_0 and taking logs gives $x = \dfrac{\log_b(\frac{1}{2})}{\log_b(.9)} = 6.58$ approximately.

75. If $10,000 \cdot (1.1)^n = 25,000$, then $n = \dfrac{\log_b(2.5)}{\log_b(1.1)} = 9.6$, so to the next biggest year, n must be 10.

77. We are given $\frac{1}{2}a_0 = a_0(p)^3$, where p is the unknown percent (fraction) that is left after one day. This gives $\log_{10}(p) = \dfrac{\log_{10}(\frac{1}{2})}{3} = \dfrac{-.609}{3} = -.303$ approximately (therefore $p = .498$ approximately). Now we want $.1a_0 = a_0 p^n$, so that $n = \dfrac{\log_{10}(.1)}{\log_{10}(p)} = \dfrac{-1}{-.303} = 3.3$ approximately. Notice we didn't use the fact that $p = .498$, only the fact that $\log_{10}(p) = -.303$.

79. $10{,}000(1.01)^{12} = 11{,}268.25$ approximately; 12.6825.

Section 7-2 Concepts Review

1. initial **2.** divide and conquer **3.** merge **4.** growth **5.** nb^n **6.** $n \log_b(n)$

Section 7-2 Exercises

1. $S_n = 3^n \left(S_0 + \displaystyle\sum_{i=1}^{n} 3^{-i}(3)^i \right) = 3^n(S_0 + n);\ 3^n + n \cdot 3^n$

3. $S_n = 3^n \left(S_0 + \displaystyle\sum_{i=1}^{n} 3^{-i} \cdot 3^i \cdot i \right) = 3^n \left(S_0 + \dfrac{n(n+1)}{2} \right);\ 3^{n-1} + \dfrac{n^2 - n}{2} \cdot 3^n$

5. $S_n = 2^n \left(S_0 + \displaystyle\sum_{i=1}^{n} 2^{-i} \cdot 1 \right) = 2^n \left(S_0 + 1 - \left(\dfrac{1}{2} \right)^n \right) = 2^n(S_0 + 1) - 1;\ 2^{n+1} - 1$

7. $S_n = \left(\dfrac{1}{2} \right)^n \left(S_0 + \displaystyle\sum_{i=1}^{n} 2^i \cdot 2^i \right) = 2^{-n} \left(S_0 + \dfrac{4^{n+1} - 4}{3} \right) =$
$\left(S_0 - \dfrac{4}{3} \right) 2^{-n} + \dfrac{2^{n+2}}{3};\ \dfrac{8}{3} 2^{-n} + \dfrac{1}{3} 2^{n+1}$

9. $S_n = (1.01)S_{n-1} - 200$

11. $t_n = .9 t_{n-1} + 300$

13. $b_k = b_{k-1} + 2$ with $n = 3^k$; valid for n a power for 3.

15. $b_k = 2b_{k-1} + 3^k$ with $n = 3^k$; valid for n a power of 3.

17. $b_k = 3b_{k-1} + 1$ with $n = 3^k$; valid for n a power of 3.

19. $b_k = 2k + b_0$; therefore $a_n = 2 \cdot \log_3(n) + a_1;\ a_n = 2 \log_3(n) + 3$

21. $b_k = 2^k \left(b_0 + \displaystyle\sum_{i=1}^{k} 2^{-i} \cdot 3^i \right) = (b_0 - 3) \cdot 2^k + 2 \cdot \left(\dfrac{3}{2} \right)^{k+1}$. This gives $a_n = (b_0 - 3)2^{\log_3(n)} + 3\left(\dfrac{3}{2} \right)^{\log_3(n)} = (a_1 - 3)n^{\log_3(2)} + 3n^{1-\log_3(2)}$. (Notice the final form of the answer was obtained by substituting $3^{\log_3(2)}$ for 2. Other final forms are possible and correct but each should be convertible into this form.)

23. $b_k = 3^k \left(b_0 + \displaystyle\sum_{i=1}^{k} 3^{-i} \right) = \left(b_0 + \dfrac{1}{2} \right) \cdot 3^k - \dfrac{1}{2} = \left(a_1 + \dfrac{1}{2} \right)n - \dfrac{1}{2}$. Since $\left(a_1 + \dfrac{1}{2} \right) \cdot 2 - \dfrac{1}{2} = 6$, $a_1 = \dfrac{11}{4}$, so $a_n = \dfrac{13}{4}n - \dfrac{1}{2}$.

25. The solution we gave was obtained by letting $n = 3^k$. Thus since $3^k \neq 0$ for any k, $n = 0$ is not of the form $n = 3^k$ and thus the solution we gave is not related in any way to a_0.

27. Divide n by 2, find $i^{\frac{n}{2}}$, and square it. Then $s_n = s_{\frac{n}{2}} + 1$. This gives $s_n = \log_2(n)$.

Thus the algorithm is desirable since $\log_2(n)$ grows more slowly than n.

29. $s_n = 3^n \left(s_0 + \displaystyle\sum_{i=1}^{n} 3^{-i} \cdot 3^i \right) = 3^n(s_0 + n) = O(n \cdot 3^n)$

31. $S_n = 2^n\left(S_0 + \sum_{i=1}^{n} 2^{-i} \cdot i^2 2^{i-1}\right) = 2^n\left(S_0 + \sum_{i=1}^{n} \frac{i^2}{2}\right) = O(2^n \cdot n^3)$

33. S_n is of order $n^3 \cdot 2^n$ **35.** S_n is of order 3^n **37.** S_n is of order $n \cdot 3^n$

39. S_n is of order 2^n

Section 7-3 Concepts Review

1. Fibonacci **2.** linear combination **3.** linear combination **4.** $r^2 + br + c = 0$

5. $c_1 r_1^n + c_2 r_2^n$ **6.** $c_1 r^n + c_2 n r^n$ **7.** $x^2 + bx + c$

Section 7-3 Exercises

1. Since $s_n = -2s_{n-1} - s_{n-2}$, $s_2 = -7$, $s_3 = 11$, $s_4 = -15$, $s_5 = 19$

3. yes **5.** no **7.** no **9.** no

11. linear, homogeneous, constant coefficient, second order

13. homogeneous, linear, second order, constant coefficient

15. linear, first order, neither constant coefficient nor homogeneous

17. homogeneous, linear, not constant coefficient, has no order

19. linear, constant coefficient, not homogeneous, has no order

21. linear, constant coefficient, third order, not homogeneous

23. linear, homogeneous, second order, not constant coefficient

25. linear, homogeneous, constant coefficient, second order

27. linear, constant coefficient, not homogeneous, has no order

29. $s_n = 1.5(s_{n-1} - s_{n-2}) + s_{n-1} = 2.5s_{n-1} - 1.5s_{n-2}$

31. $r_n = r_{n-1} + 2r_{n-2}$

33. $r_n = r_{n-1} + r_{n-2} + r_{n-3}$

35. $c(b^n - 5b^{n-1} + 6b^{n-2}) = 0$ gives either $c = 0$ or else $b^2 - 5b + 6 = 0$ so that $b = 2$ or $b = 3$

37. $c(b^n - 4b^{n-1} + 4b^{n-2}) = 0$ gives either $c = 0$ or else $b^2 - 4b + 4 = 0$ so that $b = 2$

39. $s_n = 2^n + 3^n$ **41.** $a_n = c_1 \cdot 2^n + c_2 \cdot 3^n$

43. $s_n = c_1 + c_2 \cdot 5^n$ **45.** $a_n = c_1(-1)^n + c_2 \cdot 5^n$

47. $s_n = c_1 \cdot 4^n + c_2(-3)^n$ **49.** $a_n = -(2^n) + 3^n$

51. $s_n = -5 + 5^n$ **53.** $a_n = 2 \cdot (-1)^n + 2 \cdot 5^n$

55. $s_n = 3 \cdot 4^n + 2(-3)^n$

57. $a_n = c_1\left(\dfrac{3 + \sqrt{5}}{2}\right)^n + c_2\left(\dfrac{3 - \sqrt{5}}{2}\right)^n$

59. $s_n = c_1(2 + \sqrt{2})^n + c_2(2 - \sqrt{2})^n$

61. $a_n = c_1\left(\dfrac{1 + i\sqrt{3}}{2}\right)^n + c_2\left(\dfrac{1 - i\sqrt{3}}{2}\right)^n$

63. $a_n = c_1(2 + i)^n + c_2(2 - i)^n$

65. $a_n = 2\left(\dfrac{3 + \sqrt{5}}{2}\right)^n + 2\left(\dfrac{3 - \sqrt{5}}{2}\right)^n$

67. $s_n = (1 - \sqrt{2})(2 + \sqrt{2})^n + (1 + \sqrt{2})(2 - \sqrt{2})^n$

69. $a_n = \dfrac{-i\sqrt{3}}{3}\left(\dfrac{1 + i\sqrt{3}}{2}\right)^n + \dfrac{i\sqrt{3}}{3}\left(\dfrac{1 - i\sqrt{3}}{2}\right)^n$

71. $a_n = (1 + i)(2 + i)^n + (1 - i)(2 - i)^n$

Chapter 7 Review Exercises

1. n comparisons if the element should come first; 1 comparison in the best case. In sorting the first $n - 1$ elements we make at most W_{n-1} comparisons to sort the first $n - 1$ elements, then at most $n - 1$ comparisons to insert the last word. Thus in the worst case we have $W_{n-1} + n - 1$ comparisons. In the best case we make b_{n-1} comparisons to sort the first $n - 1$ places and 1 comparison to insert the last element. Thus we have $b_{n-1} + 1$ comparisons to make in the best case.

2. $j_n = mj_{n-1}$ (There are j_{n-1} ways to assign the first $n - 1$ jobs and m ways to assign the last one.) [For the ordered distribution there are $m + n - 1$ ways to assign the last one, giving $j_n = (m + n - 1)j_{n-1}$.]

3. first order, linear, constant coefficient, homogeneous

4. first order, linear, homogeneous

5. first order, linear, constant coefficient

6. second order, linear, constant coefficient, homogeneous

7. second order, linear, constant coefficient

8. first order, homogeneous

9. second order, homogeneous

10. no order, linear, not constant coefficient (signs change as n increases), homogeneous

11. $a_0 = 3$, $a_1 = 9$, $a_2 = 27$, $a_3 = 81$, $a_4 = 243$;
    $a_0 = 3$, $a_1 = 3$, $a_2 = 12$, $a_3 = 108$, $a_4 = 1728$

12. Since $a_{n-1} = \dfrac{(n - 1)^2 n^2}{4}$, we may write

$$
\begin{aligned}
a_{n-1} + n^3 &= \frac{(n - 1)^2 n^2}{4} + n^3 \\
&= \frac{n^4}{4} - \frac{n^3}{2} + \frac{n^2}{4} + n^3 \\
&= \frac{n^4}{4} + \frac{n^3}{2} + \frac{n^2}{4} \\
&= \frac{n^2(n + 1)^2}{4}
\end{aligned}
$$

13. $a_n = (n + 1)!$ 14. 2^{14} 15. 5   16. 25   17. 1

18. Since $40 = 5 \cdot 8 = 5 \cdot 2^3$, $\log_{10}(40) = \log_{10}(5) + 3 \log_{10}(2) = .699 + .903 = 1.602$ approximately.

19. If $y = 8^x$, then $x = \log_8(y)$ and $\log_{10}(y) = x \log_{10}(8)$, or $\log_8(y) = x = \dfrac{\log_{10}(y)}{\log_{10}(8)}$.

20. $a_n = a_0(.8)^n$; $\dfrac{\log_b(.5)}{\log_b(.8)} = 3.1$ hours approximately

21. $v_n = 1000(1.08)^n$; Doubling time: $n = \dfrac{\log_b(2)}{\log_b(1008)} = 9$ years approximately

22. $s_n = 3^n \left(s_0 + \displaystyle\sum_{i=1}^{n} 3^{-i} 2^i \right) = (s_0 + 2) \cdot 3^n - 2^{n+1}$; $5 \cdot 3^n - 2^{n+1}$

23. $s_n = 3^n \left(s_0 + \displaystyle\sum_{i=1}^{n} 3^{-i} \right) = (s_0 + \tfrac{1}{2}) \cdot 3^n - \tfrac{1}{2}$; $s_n = \tfrac{13}{2} \cdot 3^{n-1} - \tfrac{1}{2}$

24. $s_n = 3^n\left(s_0 + \sum_{i=1}^{n} 3^{-i}\cdot 3^i\right) = s_0\cdot 3^n + n\cdot 3^n; \ s_n = n\cdot 3^n - 4\cdot 3^{n-1}$

25. $a_n = 1.08\cdot a_{n-1} + 200$

$$a_n = (1.08)^n\left(1000 + 200\cdot 12.5\left(1 - \left(\frac{1}{1.08}\right)^n\right)\right) = (3500)(1.08)^n - 2500$$

$$n = \frac{\log_b(55) - \log_b(35)}{\log_b(1.08)} = 5.87 \text{ years approximately}$$

26. $s_k = 3s_{k-1} + 4$, valid for $n = 2^k$ **27.** $b_k = 3b_{k-1} + 4$, valid for $n = 3^k$

28. $b_k = 3b_{k-1} + 4$, valid for $n = 4^k$ **29.** $b_k = 3b_{k-1} + 2^k$, valid for $n = 2^k$

30. Solving for s_k gives $s_k = 3^{k+1} - 2$. Since $3 = 2^{\log_2(3)}$, s_k may be written as $s_k = 2^{(k+1)\log_2(3)} - 2 = 3\cdot 2^{k\cdot\log_2(3)} - 2 = 3\cdot n^{\log_2(3)} - 2$.

31. Solving for b_k gives $b_k = 3^k(b_0 + 2) - 2$. (Note similarity to Exercise 30.) Since $n = 3^k$ this gives $a_n = n(a_1 + 2) - 2$, and $a_3 = 7$ gives $a_1 = 1$, so that $a_n = 3n - 2$.

32. Solving for b_k gives $b_k = 3^k(b_0 + 2) - 2$ again as in Exercise 31. Now $n = 4^k$ and since $3 = 4^{\log_4(3)}$ we may write c_n as

$$c_n = 4^{k\cdot\log_4(3)}(c_1 + 2) - 2 = n^{\log_4(3)}(c_1 + 2) - 2 = 3n^{\log_4(3)} - 2$$

33. Solving for b_k gives $b_k = 3^k(b_0 + 2 - 2(\frac{2}{3})^k) = 3^k(b_0 + 2) - 2\cdot 2^k$. Since $b_0 = c_1$ and $c_4 = 28$, we use the recurrence backwards to compute c_2 and c_1, getting $c_1 = 2$. Thus $b_k = 4\cdot 3^k - 2\cdot 2^k$. Now using $n = 2^k$ and $3 = 2^{\log_2(3)}$ gives us $c_n = 4n^{\log_2(3)} - 2n$.

34. By part 1 of Theorem 7, s_n is of order 3^n.

35. By part 1 of Theorem 7, a_i is of order 3^i.

36. By part 3 of Theorem 7, the growth rate of a_i is no more than $\left(\sum_{j=1}^{i} j3^j\right)^2$. The formula for the general solution shows us that the solution grows at the rate of $2^n\sum_{i=1}^{n} i\left(\frac{3}{2}\right)^i$, this product has the same order of growth as 3^i.

37. Since $\log_2(3) > 1$, part 1 of Theorem 8 tells us t_n has order $n^{\log_2(3)}$.

38. Since $n^2 > n^{\log_2(3)}$, none of Theorem 8 applies, but the computations in Example 20 and 21 show that the order of growth of t_n is n^2.

39. $a_2 = 8$; $a_3 = 20$, $a_4 = 68$, $a_5 = 188$, $a_6 = 596$

40. $3^{n-1} + 6\cdot 3^{n-2} = 3^{n-1} + 2\cdot 3^{n-1} = (1 + 2)3^{n-1} = 3\cdot 3^{n-1} = 3^n$.

41. Substitution of $a_n = r^n$ gives $r = 3$ or $r = -2$ so that $a_n = c_1\cdot 3^n + c_2(-2)^n$. Solving for c_1 and c_2 gives $a_n = \frac{4}{5}\cdot 3^n + \frac{1}{5}(-2)^n$.

42. $a_n = (1.08)a_{n-1} + (.02)a_{n-2}$. If $a_0 = 1000$ and $a_{-1} = 0$, then $a_1 = 1080$, $a_2 = 1186.40$, $a_3 = 1302.912$, $a_4 = 1430.873$; $a_5 = 1571.401$ (computations to the nearest tenth of a penny).

CHAPTER 8

Section 8-1 Concepts Review

1. tree **2.** closed walk **3.** cycle **4.** spanning tree **5.** $n - 1$ **6.** $n - 1$ **7.** $n - 1$
8. tree **9.** path

Section 8-1 Exercises

1.

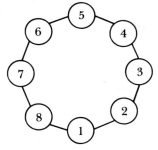

3. (a) Not a tree. Cycles are 124531, 124631, 36453. (b) A tree (c) Not a tree. Cycle is 35463. (d) Not a tree. Cycles are 12351, 123462, 1264351.

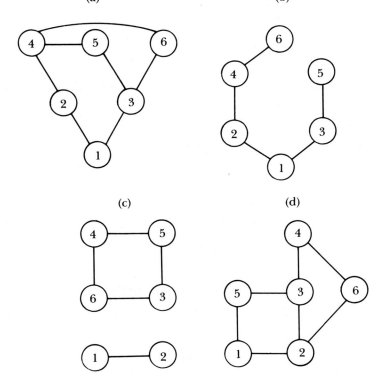

5. (a) 136, 13546, 1246, 124536 (b) 1246 (c) No path; 1 and 6 lie in different connected components. (d) 126, 12346, 15326, 15346

7. (a) Not a tree   (b) tree   (c) tree

(a)   (b)   (c)

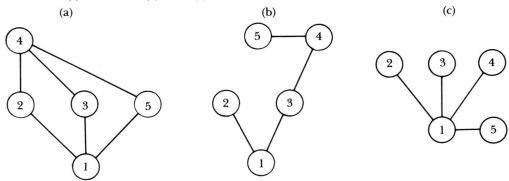

9. (a) 1243131   (b) 4543134   (c) 1414141 (many other answers are also correct)

11. (a) 3   (b) 1   (c) 1

13. (a) no, contains a cycle   (b) no, {1,5} is not an edge of G (c) yes, spanning tree
(d) yes, spanning tree

15. (a) Edge set given by Spantree beginning at 1 is {{1,2},{1,3},{2,4},{3,6},{3,5}} which is the edge set of a tree.
(b) Edge set given by Spantree is {{1,2},{1,3},{2,4},{4,6},{3,5}} when we begin at vertex 1. Thus the graph is its own spanning tree.
(c) Applying Spantree to vertex 1 gives {{1,2}} for an edge set. Thus the vertex set of the connected component containing 1 is also {1,2}.
(d) Edge set given by Spantree starting at vertex 1 is {{1,2},{2,3},{3,4},{3,5},{4,6}}. Note: Other spanning trees are possible correct answers for (a) and (d).

17. (a) We get the adjacency lists 1: 2,3,5; 2: 1,4; 3: 1,6; 4: 2; 5: 1; 6: 3. The graph is connected, the adjacency lists of a spanning tree are given. The graph is not a tree and it does have cycles. (Any edges not in the spanning tree create a cycle with the tree.)
(b) Adjacency lists are: 1: 2,5; 2: 1,3,6; 3: 2,4; 4: 3; 5: 1; 6: 2. The graph is connected, the adjacency lists of a spanning tree were given above, the graph is not a tree and it has cycles.
(c) Adjacency lists for Spantree are: 1: 2,3; 2: 1; 3: 1. The graph is not connected, not a tree and has cycles (because the connected component {1,2,3} has edges that were not given by Spantree).
(d) Adjacency lists from Spantree are: 1: 2; 2: 1,3,4; 3: 2,5; 4: 2,6; 5: 3; 6: 4. Graph is connected, adjacency lists for spanning tree are given. Graph is a tree because it has the same edges as the spanning tree given.

Section 8-2 Concepts Review

1. rooted, root   **2.** ancestor, descendant, unique   **3.** child   **4.** parent
5. one and only one   **6.** ancestor, descendant   **7.** external, leaf   **8.** internal
9. level, level   **10.** height, depth   **11.** binary, right, left   **12.** right child, descendants
13. come before, come after

Section 8-2 Exercises

1.

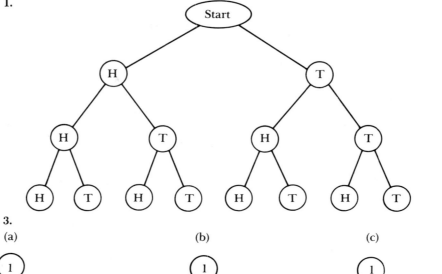

3.

(a) 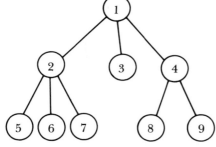 (b) 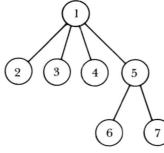 (c)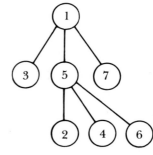

5. 3 and 4 children, 1 is only ancestor, 3, 4, 5, and 6 are descendants

7. 2 and 7 have level 1, 3, 4, 8, and 9 have level 2, 5 and 6 have level 3. Height of tree is 3

9. 1, 2, 7; and 4 are internal; 3, 5, 6, 8, and 9 are external

11. (a) 6 (b) 7 (c) 4, 7, b, f, g (d) 6, 8, e, h, l

13.

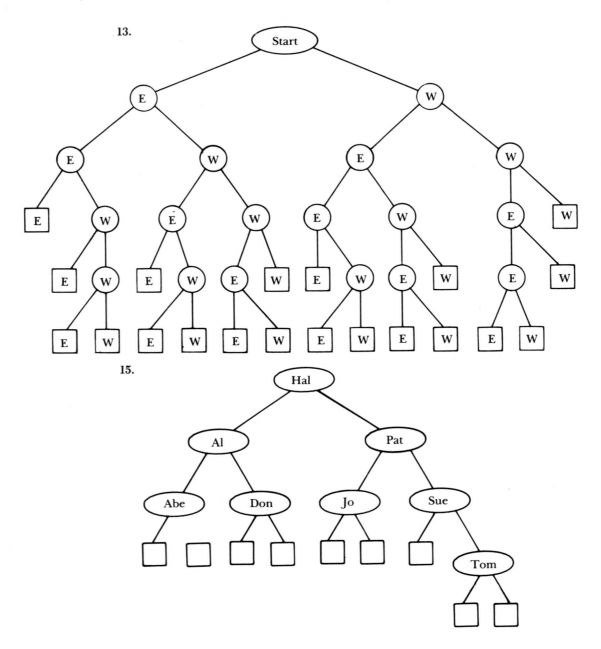

15.

17. No, you couldn't get this tree. (For one thing, it is too unbalanced; for another, it has the wrong root for illustrating binary search on the new list.)

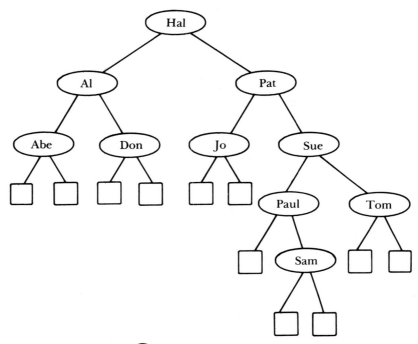

19.

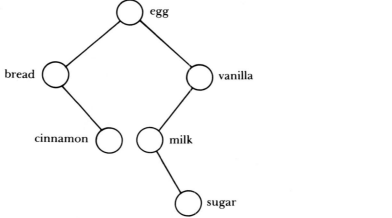

21. egg, vanilla, milk, sugar, bread, cinnamon; and egg, bread, vanilla, cinnamon, milk, sugar (Other answers are possible too.)

Section 8-3 Concepts Review

1. traversing **2.** preorder **3.** postorder **4.** inorder **5.** ordered **6.** binary ternary

7. binary ternary search, come before, between, come after **8.** binary ternary

9. quaternary **10.** two three **11.** $\log_2(m + 1) - 1$, $\log_3(2m + 1) - 1$

Section 8-3 Exercises

1. *FDGBEAJIKCLHM*   **3.** *ABDFGECIJKHLM*   **5.** *FGDEBJKILMHCA*

7. Circle, hexagon, parallelogram, pentagon, rectangle, sphere, square, triangle. (This list is in alphabetical order.)

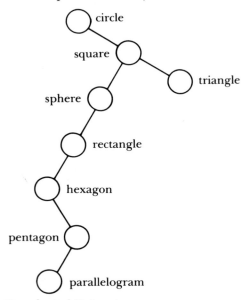

9. Hypothetical University
    Arts and Sciences
        Art, Literature, Math
    Business
        Accounting, Marketing
    Engineering
        Chemical, Electrical
    Medicine
        Internal, External
This is the usual "outline form" of organization of a university catalog.

11.

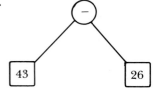

13.

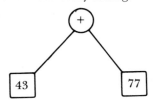

15.

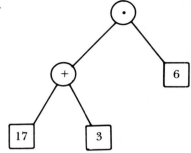

17.

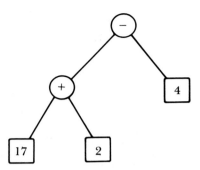

19.

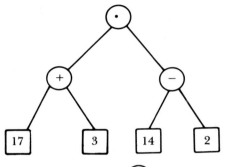

21.

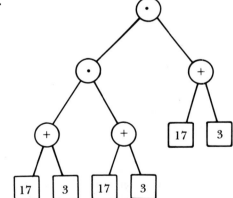

23. $43 - 26 = 17$ **25.** $43 + 77 = 120$ **27.** $17 + 3 = 20; 20 \cdot 6 = 120$

29. $17 + 2 = 19; 19 - 4 = 15$ **31.** $17 + 3 = 20; 14 - 2 = 12; 20 \cdot 12 = 240;$

33. $17 + 3 = 20; 17 + 3 = 20; 20 \cdot 20 = 400; 17 + 3 = 20; 400 \cdot 20 = 8000$

35. Nodes examined are 1, 5, 7, 8   **37.** Nodes examined are 1, 5, 6, right child of 6

39.

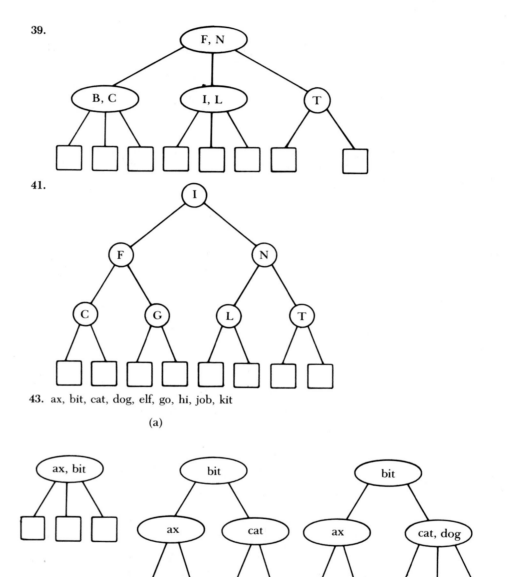

41.

43. ax, bit, cat, dog, elf, go, hi, job, kit

(a)

(*continued*)

(continued)

(b)

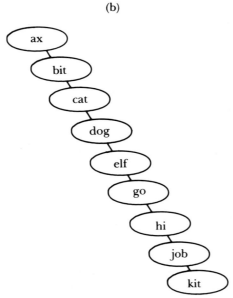

Section 8-4 Concepts Review
1. weighted   2. minimum total weight   3. greedy   4. distance   5. length (or weight)
6. distance   7. minimum path weight

Section 8-4 Exercises
1. 10, {d,e}

3. 58, could replace {b,e} by {d,e}

5. Edge set is {{c,f}, { a,c}, {a,b}, {b,d}, {d,e}}

7. Same answer as for Exercise 5, except that the edges are found in reverse order; same total weight; by Theorem 10, the algorithm produces a minimum cost spanning tree no matter where we start.

9. Give tree by adjacency lists: *d*: *b,g,c*; *b*: *d,a*; *g*: *d,f*; *a*: *b*; *f*: *g*; *c*: *d*. Other answers are possible.

11. *abcd, abcgd, abced, afed, afecd, afecgd.* Path *abcd* is as short as any path and has 3 edges.

13. Distance from *a* to *b* in graph is 11 but distance from *a* to *b* in tree is 22.

15. Edge set is {{b,c}, {b,a}, {b,d}, {b,f}, {c,e}, {f,g}}.   17. Path is *b*{*b,f*}*f*{*f,g*}*g* Length is 12 + 10 = 22   19. Edge set is {{b,c}, {b,a}, {a,d}, {c,f}, {e,f}, {f,g}. Path from *b* to *d* is *b,a,d* of weight 21, minimum weight path in graph is *b,d* of weight 12.

21. The tree we find has the edge set {{d,c}, {b,c}, {b,a}}. In this tree the path from *d* to *c* has weight 2. However in the graph the path {*d,a*}, {*a,b*}, {*b,c*} has weight −7.

Chapter 8 Review Exercises

1. Cycles are 1231 and 4564, is not a tree.   **2.** No cycles; is a tree.

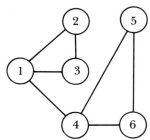

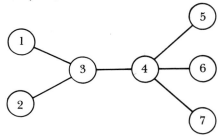

3. No cycles; is not a tree.   **4.** No cycles; is a tree.

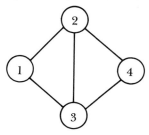

5. Cycles 1231, 12431, 2342; is not a tree.

6. 145, 1465

7. (a) spanning tree   (b) not spanning tree; has a cycle   (c) spanning tree   (d) not spanning tree; not enough edges

8. (a) Connected. Adjacency lists of spanning tree 1: 5,2; 2: 1,4; 3: 4; 4: 2,3,5; 5: 4,1
(b) Not connected. Component is {1,2,3,4} and all edges joining two of these vertices.
(c) Connected. Spanning tree: 1: 2,3; 2: 1,4; 3: 1; 4: 2,5,6; 5: 4; 6: 4
(d) Not connected. Component is {1,2,3} with adjacency lists 1: 2,3; 2: 1,3; 3: 1,2.

9.

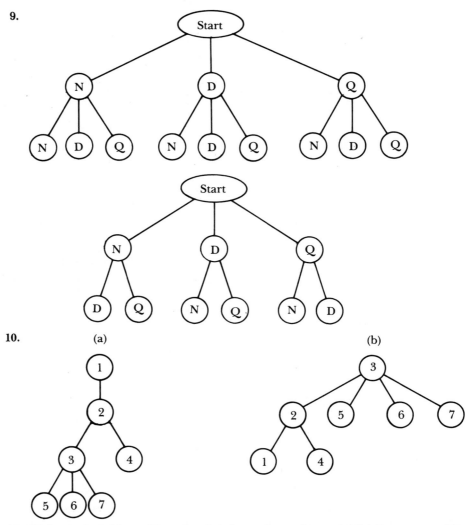

10.   (a)   (b)

11. With root 1, children of 2 are 3 and 4; descendants of 2 are 3,4,5,6,7; ancestors of 5 are 3,2,1. Internal vertices are 1,2,3; external vertices are 4,5,6,7. With root 3, descendants of 2 are 1 and 4; ancestor of 5 is 3; internal vertices are 2 and 3; external vertices are 1,4,5,6,7.

12. Right child is *f*; *g,e,h,c,f* have empty left children.

13. No, it would not look different.

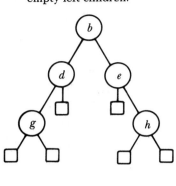

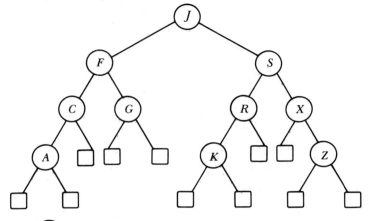

14. Yes, it would look different.

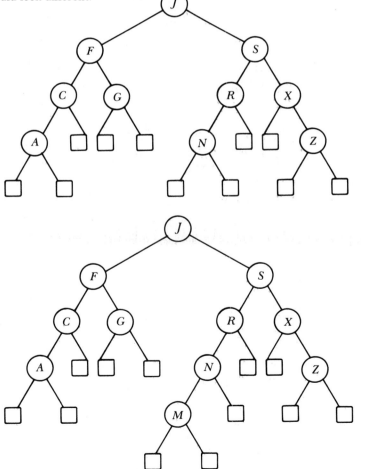

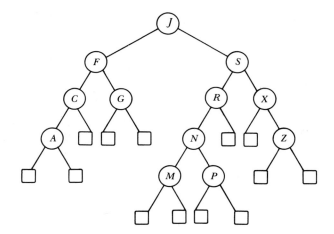

15. The first tree could arise from the order E,J,M,H,C,A,D and from many other orders.

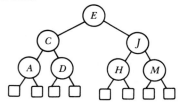

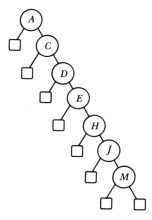

16. a,b,d,g,e,h,c,f; g,d,b,e,h,a,c,f; g,d,h,e,b,f,c,a

17. A,C,D,E,H,J,M; no, all binary search trees give alphabetical order.

18.

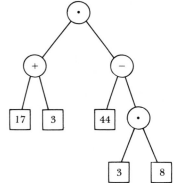

19. $17 + 3 = 20$; $3 \cdot 8 = 24$; $44 - 24 = 20$; $20 \cdot 20 = 400$

20.

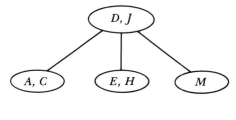

21.

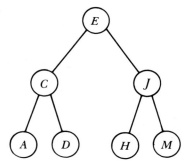

22. 1,2,4,5,7; 1,2,4,5,6,7; 1,3,4,5,7; 1,3,4,5,6,7. Minimum length path has length 4.

23. four more paths

24. No; $\{a,b\}$ in place of $\{a,d\}$ would reduce the total weight.

25. No; d,c,a is a minimum weight path from vertex d to vertex a and is not in the tree.

26. Edge set is $\{\{d,c\}, \{d,b\}, \{c,a\}, \{d,f\}, \{d,e\}, \{g,e\}\}$ and the edges are given in the order they were chosen.

27. Edge set is $\{\{d,c\}, \{d,b\}, \{c,a\}, \{d,f\}, \{d,e\}, \{e,g\}\}$ and the edges are given in the order they were chosen.

28. *abdca*

CHAPTER 9

Section 9-1 Concepts Review

1. multigraph **2.** multidigraph **3.** isomorphism **4.** isomorphic
5. number, two, twice, number, one **6.** equal **7.** outdegree

Section 9-1 Exercises

1. graph **3.** simple graph **5.** multigraph

7. $\{\{1,2\}, \{3,3\}, \{3,4\}, \{4,4\}\}$

9. $\{\{1,2\}, \{1,3\}, \{1,4\}, \{2,3\}, \{2,4\}, \{3,4\}\}$

11. $\{\{1,1\}, \{1,1\}, \{1,2\}, \{2,2\}, \{2,3\}, \{3,3\}, \{3,4\}, \{4,4\}, \{4,1\}\}$

13. multidigraph (examine edges between 2 and 4)

15. multidigraph **17.** digraph

19. $\{(1,3), (3,1), (3,3), (2,4), (4,4), (2,4), (4,5), (5,2)\}$

21. $\{(1,2), (2,1), (2,4), (4,2), (4,2), (4,3), (3,2), (4,5), (5,4), (1,5), (1,4)\}$

23. $\{(1,2), (2,1), (2,3), (3,2), (1,3), (4,1), (3,4), (4,3), (3,1)\}$

25. Connected

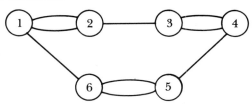

27. Connected

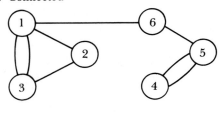

29. Connected

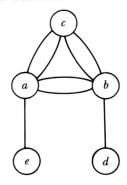

31. 1, 2 and 3 are reachable from 1

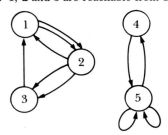

33. 2 and 3 are reachable from 1

35. Everything is reachable from *a*.

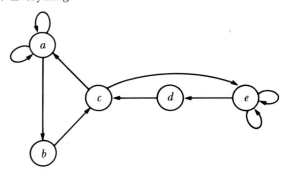

37. 1: 2; 2: 1; 3: 3, 4; 4: 4,3

39. 1: 2,3,4; 2: 1,3,4; 3: 1,2,4; 4: 1,2,3

41. 1: 2,2,3,4; 2: 1,1,3,5; 3: 1,2,4,5; 4: 1,3,5,5; 5: 2,3,4,4

43. 1: 3; 2: 4,4; 3: 3,1; 4: 4,5; 5: 2

45. 1: 2,4,5; 2: 1,4; 3: 2; 4: 2,2,3,5; 5: 4

47. 1: 2,3; 2: 1,3; 3: 1,2,4; 4: 1,3

49. $d(1) = 1$; $d(2) = 1$; $d(3) = 3$; $d(4) = 3$

51. $d(1) = 3;\ d(2) = 3;\ d(3) = 3;\ d(4) = 3$

53. $id(1) = 1,\ od(1) = 1,\ id(3) = 2,\ od(3) = 2,\ id(2) = 1,\ od(2) = 2,\ id(4) = 3,\ od(4) = 2,\ id(5) = 1,\ od(5) = 1$

55. $id(1) = 2,\ od(1) = 3;\ id(2) = 3,\ od(2) = 2,\ id(3) = 1,\ od(3) = 2;\ id(4) = 4,\ od(4) = 2$

57. $\{f(1),f(2)\} = \{a,b\}$, an edge; $\{f(1),f(5)\} = \{a,d\}$, an edge; $\{f(1),f(4)\} = \{a,e\}$, an edge; $\{f(2),f(3)\} = \{b,c\}$, an edge; $\{f(2),f(5)\} = \{b,d\}$ an edge; $\{f(3),\ f(4)\} = \{c,e\}$, an edge; $\{f(3),\ f(5)\} = \{c,d\}$ an edge. Every edge of graph (b) is $\{f(i),f(j)\}$ for some edge $\{i,j\}$ of graph (a). Therefore f is an isomorphism.

59. 3 is in 3 edges but $d = f(3)$ is in 4 edges. Thus there is an edge containing d which is not $\{f(3),f(j)\}$ for any vertex j of the first graph.

61. c has degree 4; no vertex of the second graph has degree 4.

63. The graph on the left has two cycles with 4 vertices and one cycle with 6 vertices. The graph on the right has 1 cycle with 4 vertices and two cycles with 5 vertices.

65. If f is an isomorphism from G to H, then it is a bijection from the vertex set of G to the vertex set of H. Thus by the definition of size, the two vertex sets have the same size.

67. All three are isomorphic.

69. If f is the isomorphism and (x',y') and (y',z') are edges of H with $f(x) = x'$, $f(y) = y'$, $f(z) = z'$, then since $(f(a),f(b))$ is an edge of H *if and only if* (a,b) is an edge of G, (x,y) and (y,z) must be edges of G. Therefore (x,z) is an edge of G by transitivity and so $(x',z') = (f(x),f(z))$ is an edge of H by isomorphism.

71. One tree has edge set $\{\{1,2\},\{2,3\},\{3,4\},\{4,5\}\}$. Another has edge set $\{\{2,1\},\{2,5\},\{2,3\},\{5,4\}\}$. They do not give isomorphic trees because 2 has degree 3 in one tree and there are no vertices of degree 3 in the other.

Section 9-2 Concepts Review

1. Eulerian **2.** Eulerian tour **3.** even number **4.** two **5.** edge tour
6. minimum weight **7.** exactly once **8.** Hamiltonian path

Section 9-2 Exercises

1.

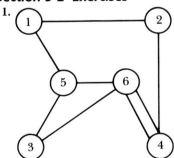

3. Using the labels of the figure for the answer to Exercise 1, an Eulerian walk is 512465364.

5. No

7. This makes an Eulerian walk possible but not an Eulerian tour.

9. $1\,a\,2\,c\,3\,j\,6\,r\,8\,p\,7\,m\,4\,e\,1\,b\,2\,d\,3\,i\,8\,q\,5\,o\,7\,n\,4\,k\,5\,l\,6\,h\,2\,g\,5\,f\,1$

11. (Note that the islands have to be moved!)

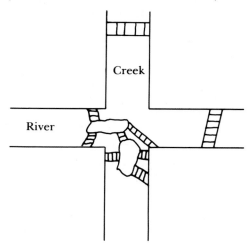

Creek

River

13. 23

15. (a) edge tour (b) not edge tour (c) edge tour (d) edge tour

17. duplicate (1,2) and (4,5) **19.** {{1,5}, {2,3}, {3,4}} **21.** {{1,2}, {4,5}}

23. 1,4,3,2,1,5,2,3,4,5,1 **25.** 1,5,4,3,2,1,4,5,2,1

27. (a) Hamiltonian tour (b) none (c) none (d) Hamiltonian tour
(e) Hamiltonian path

29. (d)

31. *a* is a minimum weight Hamiltonian tour.

33. 1-2-3-6-5-4-1; 1-4-5-6-3-2-1; 1-5-3-6-2-4-1; 1-4-2-6-3-5-1; 1-2-6-3-5-4-1;
1-4-5-3-6-2-1; 1-5-6-3-2-4-1; 1-4-2-3-6-5-1

35.

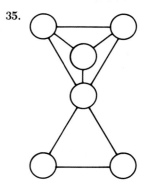

Section 9-3 Concepts Review

1. intersection graph, nonempty intersection **2.** proper coloring, edge
3. chromatic number, proper coloring **4.** clique **5.** chromatic number
6. planar drawing, cross **7.** planar drawing **8.** faces **9.** Euler's, 2,
vertices, edges, faces

Section 9-3 Exercises

1. The sets are named in alphabetical order as given in Exercise 1.

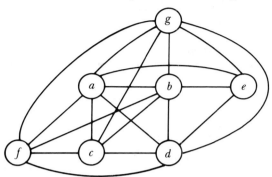

3.

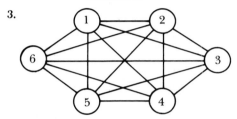

5. 1: {2,4,8,9,10} 2: {1,2,3,4,5,6,7,8} 3: {1,2,3,4,5,10} 4: {5,6,9} 5: {1,3,4,6,7,10} 6: {7,8,9,10}

7. This graph is identical with the figure for the answer to Exercise 3.

9. 1R; 2B; 3G; 4R; 5G

11. Chromatic number is 3.

13. Planar

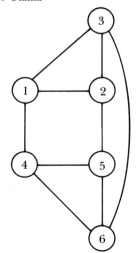

15. If the graph had a planar drawing, removing the edges from 1 to 4 and 5 and the edges from 3 to 7 and from 2 to 6 leaves a polygon with 7 sides. The edge from 2 to 6 is either inside or outside the polygon. If the edge is drawn inside, then the edge from 3 to 7 must be drawn outside. Now {1,4} or {1,5} cannot be inside the polygon for it would cross {2,6} and it cannot be outside for then it would cross {3,7}. Similarly if {2,6} is drawn on the outside, then {3,7} is drawn on the inside and there is no possible place where {1,5} can be drawn. Thus the graph does not have a planar drawing.

17.

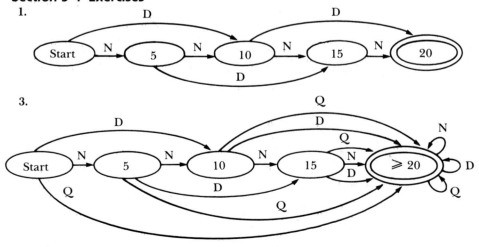

19. Since $10 - 20 + f = 2$, it has 12 faces.

21. Since $v = 7$, $3v - 6 = 15$. Further, $e = 11$ and $11 < 15$. However the graph is not planar as shown in Exercise 15.

23. Since the graph has 13 edges and 6 vertices and $13 \nleq 3 \cdot 6 - 6$, the graph is not planar.

Section 9-4 Concepts Review

1. states   **2.** input alphabet   **3.** deterministic   **4.** automaton   **5.** accepts   **6.** terminal
7. productions   **8.** regular   **9.** regular grammar   **10.** regular, automaton

Section 9-4 Exercises

1.

3.

5. *NNNN, DD, NDN, NND, DNN*

7. State set: {Start,A1,A2,A3,B1,B2,C} input alphabet {a,b}. Strings of a's and b's in which each occurrence of a's consists of some number $3m$ of a's in a row and each occurrence of b's consists of some number $2n$ of b's in a row (and either m or n is not zero).

9. (Note: State c and edges touching it may be replaced by an arrow from "start" to "start" with label 0.)

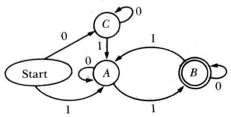

11. $\langle \text{Start} \rangle := \langle A \rangle := a\langle B\rangle a := abba$

13.
$$\langle \text{Start} \rangle := 0\langle A\rangle \,|\, 1\langle B\rangle$$
$$\langle A \rangle := 0\langle A\rangle \,|\, 1\langle B\rangle \,|\, 0 \,|\, \lambda$$
$$\langle B \rangle := 0\langle D\rangle \,|\, 1\langle C\rangle$$
$$\langle C \rangle := \lambda \,|\, 1\langle B\rangle \,|\, 0\langle A\rangle$$
$$\langle D \rangle := 0\langle D\rangle \,|\, 1\langle D\rangle$$

The language consists of non-empty character strings that alternate between strings of an even number of ones and strings of any number of zeros.

15.
$$\langle \text{Start} \rangle := a\langle A\rangle \,|\, b\langle B\rangle \,|\, c\langle C\rangle$$
$$\langle A \rangle := b\langle B\rangle \,|\, a\langle D\rangle \,|\, a\langle A\rangle$$
$$\langle B \rangle := c\langle C\rangle \,|\, a\langle D\rangle \,|\, \lambda$$
$$\langle C \rangle := b\langle B\rangle$$

The language consists of strings of cb's or else a string of 0 or more a's followed by a single b, perhaps followed by a string of cb's.

17. The language consists of all non-empty strings of zeros and ones. Grammar is regular and automaton is deterministic.

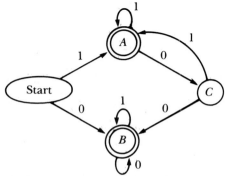

19. Grammar is regular, automaton is non-deterministic. A string in the language ends with either two zeros or two ones; removing the last two entries gives a string of

zeros and ones such that whenever 0 appears, it appears $3n$ times in a row for some n and whenever 1 appears it appears $3n$ times in a row for some n.

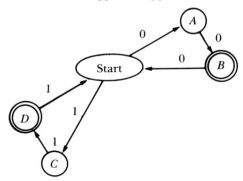

Chapter 9 Review Exercises

1. (a) simple connected graph   (b) connected multigraph   (c) simple disconnected graph   (d) simple connected graph

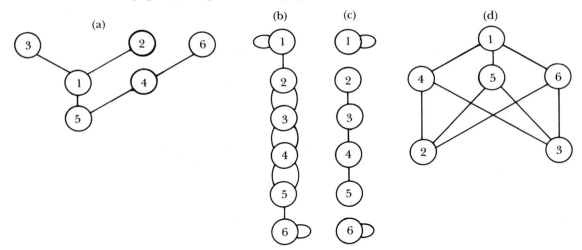

2. (a) Digraph. All vertices are reachable from vertex 1; only vertex 5 is reachable from vertex 5.

(b) Digraph. Vertices 1 and 2 are reachable from vertex 1. Vertices 3, 4, and 5 are reachable from vertex 5.

(c) Multidigraph. Vertices 2, 3, 4, and 5 are reachable from vertex 1, no vertices, not even vertex 5, are reachable from vertex 1.

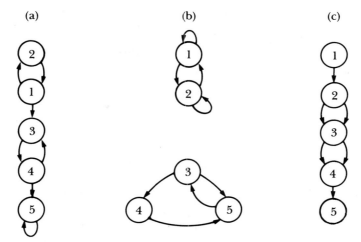

(a)   (b)   (c)

3. (a) 1: 5,2,3; 2: 3,1; 3: 1,2; 4: 5,6; 5: 4,1; 6: 4   (b) 1: 1,2; 2: 1,3,3; 3: 2,2,4,4;
4: 3,3,5,5; 5: 4,4,6; 6: 5,6   (c) 1: 2,3; 2: 1; 3: 4; 4: 3,5; 5: 5   (d) 1: 2; 2: 3,3;
3: 4,4; 4: 5; 5:

4. $(\{(f(1), f(2)\}, \{f(2), f(3)\}, \{f(1), f(5)\}, \{f(2), f(5)\}, \{f(4), f(5)\},$
$\{f(3), f(4)\}, \{f(2), f(4)\}, \{f(1), f(3)\}) = (\{a_1,a_2\}, \{a_2,a_3\}, \{a_1,a_5\}, \{a_2,a_5\},$
$\{a_3,a_4\}, \{a_2,a_4\}, \{a_1,a_3\})$ which is the edge set of the graph H in the same order. Also
$f(1) = a_3, f(2) = a_2, f(3) = a_4, f(4) = a_5, f(5) = a_4$ is an isomorphism.

5. Since 1 is adjacent to 2, 3 and 5, $f(1)$ should be adjacent to $f(2) = a_2, f(3) = a_1$ and
$f(5) = a_5$. However $f(1) = a_3$ and a_3 is not adjacent to a_5.

6. Not isomorphic, the first has a vertex of degree 5 and the second does not.

7. Isomorphic; $f(1) = c, f(3) = a, f(2) = e, f(4) = d, f(5) = f, f(6) = b$.

8. Not isomorphic. The second graph has two adjacent vertices of degree 2, namely 4
and 5, but the first graph does not.

9. If $x = x_1, x_2, \ldots, x_n = y$ is a sequence of vertices with edges from x_i to x_{i+1}, then
$f(x) = f(x_1), f(x_2), \ldots, f(x_n) = f(y)$ is a sequence of vertices with edges from $f(x_i)$ to
$f(x_{i+1})$.

10. For each four-cycle $x_1x_2x_3x_4x_1$ of G, the sequence $f(x_1)f(x_2)f(x_3)f(x_4)f(x_1)$ is a four-
cycle of H and for each four-cycle $f(y_1)f(y_2)f(y_3)f(y_4)f(y_1)$ of H, $y_1y_2y_3y_4y_1$ must be a
four-cycle of G. Thus F is a bijection between the four-cycles of G and the four-
cycles of H.

11.

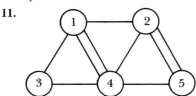

12. Eulerian walk, no Eulerian tour.

13. 5254314124

14.

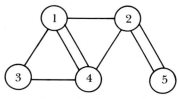

15. If we add an edge touching neither vertex 4 nor 5 then the graph will have neither an Eulerian walk nor an Eulerian tour. There are $\binom{3}{2} = 3$ ways to add edges without counting loops; $\binom{3}{2} + \binom{3}{1} = 6$ ways if we allow loops. (Whether or not you include loops depends on whether you want the edges to represent bridges; the problem does not tell you how to choose so either answer is correct.)

16. 33

17. We must duplicate three edges and in so doing eliminate all vertices of odd degree. Duplicating {1,2}, {3,5}, and {5,6} does this.

18. No tour is actually needed to answer the question, the cost is the sum of the costs of the edges of the graph plus the costs of the three duplicated edges. This gives $25 + 3 + 3 + 2 = 33$.

19. The edge tour must cover every edge at least once, for a weight of 25, and must duplicate 3 edges for a minimum weight of 3 more or a total weight of at least 28. However duplicating exactly 3 edges requires the total weight of 33 given in Exercise 18. Thus we must duplicate at least 4 edges to get a smaller total weight. There is no four element set of weight 1 edges whose duplication eliminates all vertices of odd degree, but duplicating the set {{3,7},{1,7},{2,4},{2,5},{2,6}} eliminates all vertices of odd degree for a total weight of 30. Thus a minimum weight tour is 1-4-3-7-1-8-6-5-1-2-5-2-6-2-4-2-3-7-1.

20. 2-4-3-7-1-8-6-5-2

21. 15

22. (a) Not a tour or a path (or even a walk).   (b) Not a tour, not a Hamiltonian path or walk.   (c) Hamiltonian path   (d) Not a vertex tour; therefore not a Hamiltonian tour.

23. 14

24. There are 3 weight 1 edges touching vertex 2; at most 2 edges of a Hamiltonian path could touch vertex 2.

25. A Hamiltonian path would have 7 edges. At most 5 (by Exercise 23) could have weight 1 and possibly the other two could have weight 2 for a total weight of 9. In fact, a Hamiltonian path of weight 9 exists, namely 8-6-5-2-4-1-7-3.

26.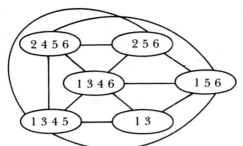

27.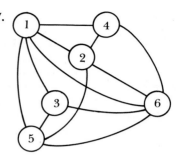

28. 1: {A,C,E,G,H} 2: {B,C,D,F,H} 3: {E,G,I} 4: {A,B,C,F} 5: {D,E,H} 6: {D,F,G,I}. The two graphs are isomorphic.

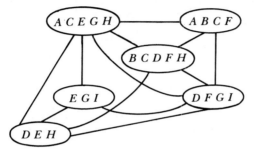

29. 1: *R*, 2: *R*, 3: *R*, 4: *B*, 6: *B*, 5: *G*, 7: *G*. If the numbers represented 7 committees and the edges represented people they have in common, then we would need at least 3 different time slots to schedule committee meetings so that each person could attend all meetings of each committee he or she is on.

30. Must be at least 4 because {1,2,4,6} forms a clique (complete subgraph); however the coloring 1: *R*, 4: *B*, 2: *G*, 6: *Y*, 5: *B*, 3: *G* suffices, chromatic number is 4.

31.

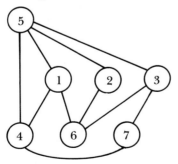

32. No, since $e = 16$ and $3v - 6 = 15$

33. $9 - 12 + f = 2$ so that $f = 5$

34. Yes, $12 < 3 \cdot 9 - 6$, no the graph is not planar. To see why, assume there is a planar drawing and remove vertices 7, 8 and 9. Then the resulting graph will be a 6-sided figure with an inside and outside. Vertex 7 will be either inside or outside that figure. Assume it is inside and draw it and its edges back in. Now the path from vertex 1 to vertex 4 cannot cross the path from vertex 2 to vertex 5, so this path must be outside the 6-sided figure. Thus draw vertex 8 and its edges back in outside the figure. The path from vertex 3 to vertex 6 cannot pass inside the 6-sided figure since it would have to cross the path from vertex 2 to vertex 5. Thus vertex 9 must be drawn outside the 6-sided figure. However the path 1-8-4 divides the outside into 2 regions, one containing 3 but not 6 and one containing 6 but not 3. If we draw vertex 9 in the region containing 3 then we can't draw the edge to 6; and if we draw vertex 9 in the region containing 6 then we can't draw the edge to 3; therefore the graph is not planar.

35.

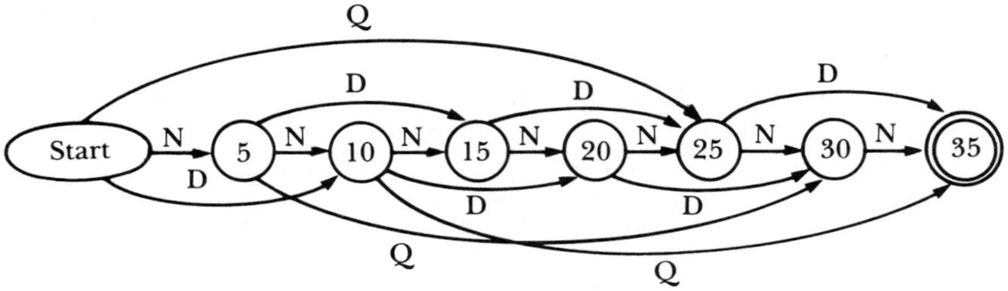

36. *NNNNNNN*, any sequence of 5 *N*'s and 1 *D*, 3 *N*'s and 2 *D*'s, 1 *N* and 3 *D*'s, also *DQ*, *QD*, *QNN*, *NQN*, *NNQ*. The language consists of all ways to make exact change for 35 cents using nickels, dimes, and quarters.

37. State set {Start,A,B,C,D}; Input Alphabet {0,1}. Not deterministic because two arrows labelled 0 leave A and two arrows labelled 1 leave B. Accepts any string of length 2 or more consisting entirely of zeros or entirely of ones.

38.

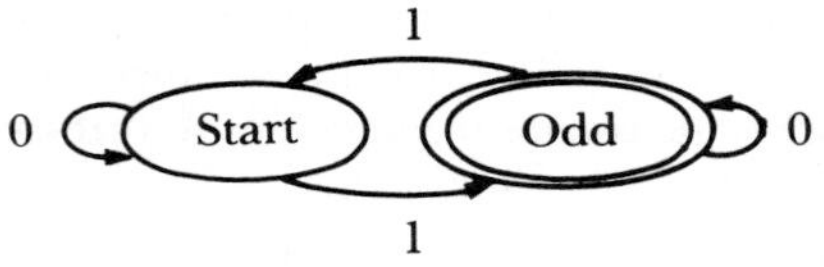

39. $\langle \text{Start} \rangle := b\langle B \rangle := bb\langle B \rangle := bbb\langle B \rangle := bbba\langle A_1 \rangle := bbbaa\langle A_2 \rangle := bbbaaa\langle A_3 \rangle :=$ *bbbaaa*. No sequence of replacements leads to *bbaa*.

40. Automaton is deterministic.

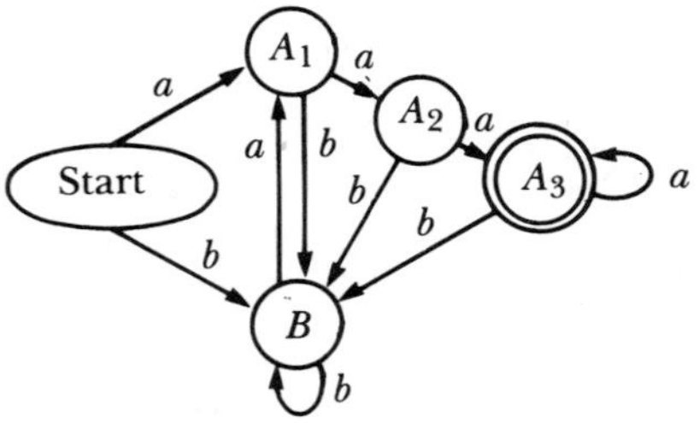

41. Now the language consists of all non-empty strings consisting entirely of zeros or entirely of ones.

42. $\langle \text{Start} \rangle := 0\langle A \rangle \mid 1\langle B \rangle$
$\langle A \rangle := 0\langle A \rangle \mid 1\langle C \rangle \mid \lambda$
$\langle B \rangle := 1\langle B \rangle \mid 0\langle C \rangle \mid \lambda$
$\langle C \rangle := 0\langle C \rangle \mid 1\langle C \rangle$

43. Yes it is regular.

44. Regular and not deterministic. Language: Any positive number of ones followed by a zero.

$$\langle \text{Start}\rangle := 1\langle A\rangle$$
$$\langle A\rangle := 1\langle A\rangle \,|\, 0\langle B\rangle \,|\, 0\langle C\rangle$$
$$\langle B\rangle := \lambda$$
$$\langle C\rangle := 1\langle C\rangle$$

For a 3-state automaton.

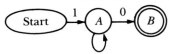

45. Start $:= 1\langle A\rangle$
$A := 1\langle B\rangle$
$B := 1\langle A\rangle \,|\, 0\langle \text{Start}\rangle \,|\, 0\langle B\rangle \,|\, \lambda$

Language: Those strings of zeros and ones for which, whenever 1 occurs it occurs an even number of times in a row. Fails because: No arrow leaves Start with a 0, no arrow leaves A with a 0, two arrows leave B with a 0.

46. All nonempty strings of a'a and b's ending with b.

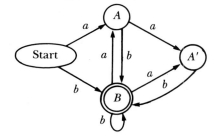

CHAPTER 10
Section 10-1 Concepts Review
1. matrix **2.** sum **3.** m, n **4.** $r_1c_1 + r_2c_2 + \ldots + r_nc_n$ **5.** n, r **6.** row i, column j
7. row, column **8.** main diagonal **9.** identity, A **10.** i, j, AB
Section 10-1 Exercises
1. $[2\ \ 1\ \ 3\ \ 1]\ \ [0\ \ 2\ \ 1\ \ 1]$
3. $(R + S) + T = [2\ \ 1\ \ 3\ \ 1] + [1\ \ 0\ \ 1\ \ 0] = [3\ \ 1\ \ 4\ \ 1]$
$R + (S + T) = [1\ \ 2\ \ 2\ \ 1] + [2\ \ -1\ \ 2\ \ 0] = [3\ \ 1\ \ 4\ \ 1]$
5. $S + 0 = S$, illustrating that the matrix 0 behaves like zero.
7. not defined **9.** defined **11.** not defined
13. not defined **15.** $\begin{bmatrix} 1 & -3 \\ -4 & 1 \end{bmatrix}, \begin{bmatrix} 3 & 5 \\ 4 & 3 \end{bmatrix}$ **17.** 14 **19.** -2
21. $\begin{bmatrix} 13 \\ 1 \\ 3 \end{bmatrix}$ **23.** $N^2 = \begin{bmatrix} 17 & 8 \\ 8 & 17 \end{bmatrix}$ $N^4 = \begin{bmatrix} 353 & 272 \\ 272 & 353 \end{bmatrix}$

25. $P \cdot (C + E) = \begin{bmatrix} 16 \\ 4 \\ 9 \end{bmatrix}$; $PC + PE = \begin{bmatrix} 13 \\ 1 \\ 3 \end{bmatrix} + \begin{bmatrix} 3 \\ 3 \\ 6 \end{bmatrix} = \begin{bmatrix} 16 \\ 4 \\ 9 \end{bmatrix}$; illustrates distributive law.

27. not defined   **29.** not defined   **31.** not defined

33. $\begin{bmatrix} 9 & 6 \\ 3 & -3 \\ 2 & 8 \\ 4 & 1 \end{bmatrix}$; not defined   **35.** $\begin{bmatrix} 9 & 3 \\ 6 & -3 \end{bmatrix}$, $\begin{bmatrix} -3 & 3 \\ 6 & 9 \end{bmatrix}$; multiplication is not commutative.

37. $(LN)Q = \begin{bmatrix} -6 & 9 \\ 8 & 2 \end{bmatrix} \begin{bmatrix} 1 & -1 \\ 2 & 1 \end{bmatrix} = \begin{bmatrix} 24 & 3 \\ 12 & -6 \end{bmatrix}$; $L(NQ) = \begin{bmatrix} 2 & 1 \\ 0 & 2 \end{bmatrix} \begin{bmatrix} 9 & 3 \\ 6 & -3 \end{bmatrix} = \begin{bmatrix} 24 & 3 \\ 12 & 6 \end{bmatrix}$; illustrates associative law.

39. $(R + S)M = \begin{bmatrix} 2 & 1 & 3 & 1 \end{bmatrix} \begin{bmatrix} 1 & 2 \\ -1 & 1 \\ 2 & 0 \\ 0 & 1 \end{bmatrix} = \begin{bmatrix} 7 & 6 \end{bmatrix}$;

$RM + SM = \begin{bmatrix} 3 & 5 \end{bmatrix} + \begin{bmatrix} 4 & 1 \end{bmatrix} = \begin{bmatrix} 7 & 6 \end{bmatrix}$; illustrates distributive law.

41. $\begin{bmatrix} 1 & 0 & 0 \\ 0 & 1 & 0 \\ 0 & 0 & 1 \end{bmatrix} = I$; $IP = P$ **43.** 1, 2   **45.** $-1 + 2 = 1$; row 1, column 2

Section 10-2 Concepts Review
1. adjacency matrix   **2.** power, adjacency   **3.** M^n **4.** transitive closure   **5.** Boolean *or*
6. symmetric

Section 10-2 Exercises

1.

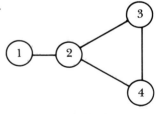

3.

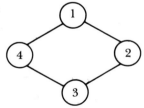

5.

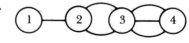

7.

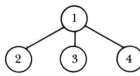

9.

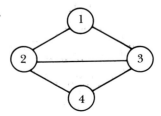

11.

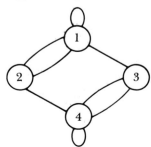

13. $\begin{bmatrix} 0 & 1 & 1 & 0 \\ 1 & 0 & 1 & 1 \\ 1 & 1 & 0 & 1 \\ 0 & 1 & 1 & 0 \end{bmatrix}$

15. $\begin{bmatrix} 0 & 1 & 0 & 0 & 0 \\ 1 & 0 & 1 & 0 & 0 \\ 0 & 1 & 0 & 1 & 1 \\ 0 & 0 & 1 & 0 & 0 \\ 0 & 0 & 1 & 0 & 0 \end{bmatrix}$

17. $\begin{bmatrix} 2 & 1 & 0 & 0 \\ 1 & 0 & 2 & 0 \\ 0 & 2 & 0 & 1 \\ 0 & 0 & 1 & 2 \end{bmatrix}$

19. $\begin{bmatrix} 0 & 1 & 1 & 1 \\ 1 & 0 & 1 & 1 \\ 1 & 1 & 0 & 1 \\ 1 & 1 & 1 & 0 \end{bmatrix}$

21. $\begin{bmatrix} 0 & 1 & 0 & 0 & 1 \\ 1 & 0 & 1 & 0 & 0 \\ 0 & 1 & 0 & 1 & 0 \\ 0 & 0 & 1 & 0 & 1 \\ 1 & 0 & 0 & 1 & 0 \end{bmatrix}$

23. $\begin{bmatrix} 0 & 2 & 2 & 1 \\ 2 & 0 & 0 & 1 \\ 2 & 0 & 0 & 1 \\ 1 & 1 & 1 & 0 \end{bmatrix}$

25.

27.

29.

31.

33.

35.

37. $\begin{bmatrix} 0 & 1 & 0 & 1 \\ 1 & 0 & 1 & 0 \\ 0 & 1 & 0 & 1 \\ 1 & 0 & 1 & 0 \end{bmatrix}$

39. $\begin{bmatrix} 0 & 2 & 0 & 0 \\ 0 & 0 & 2 & 0 \\ 0 & 0 & 0 & 2 \\ 2 & 0 & 0 & 0 \end{bmatrix}$

41. $\begin{bmatrix} 0 & 2 & 0 & 0 \\ 1 & 0 & 0 & 0 \\ 0 & 0 & 1 & 1 \\ 0 & 0 & 2 & 1 \end{bmatrix}$

43. $\begin{bmatrix} 0 & 1 & 1 & 2 \\ 0 & 0 & 2 & 0 \\ 0 & 0 & 0 & 0 \\ 0 & 0 & 1 & 0 \end{bmatrix}$

45. $\begin{bmatrix} 1 & 1 & 0 & 0 \\ 0 & 1 & 1 & 0 \\ 1 & 0 & 1 & 0 \\ 0 & 0 & 0 & 2 \end{bmatrix}$

47. $\begin{bmatrix} 1 & 2 & 0 & 0 \\ 0 & 1 & 0 & 0 \\ 0 & 0 & 1 & 2 \\ 0 & 0 & 0 & 1 \end{bmatrix}$

49. 4 walks of length 4 in number 1,   0 walks of length 4 in number 3,   0 walks of length 4 in number 5,   0 walks of length 4 in number 7,   10 walks of length 4 in number 9,   52 walks of length 4 in number 11

51. 0 walks of length 4 in numbers 25 through 31,   1 walk of length 4 in number 33, 4 walks of length 4 in number 35

53. $\begin{bmatrix} 1 & 1 & 1 & 1 \\ 1 & 1 & 1 & 1 \\ 1 & 1 & 1 & 1 \\ 1 & 1 & 1 & 1 \end{bmatrix}$

55. $\begin{bmatrix} 1 & 1 & 1 & 1 \\ 1 & 1 & 1 & 1 \\ 1 & 1 & 1 & 1 \\ 1 & 1 & 1 & 1 \end{bmatrix}$

57. $\begin{bmatrix} 1 & 0 & 0 & 0 \\ 1 & 1 & 1 & 1 \\ 1 & 1 & 1 & 1 \\ 1 & 1 & 1 & 1 \end{bmatrix}$

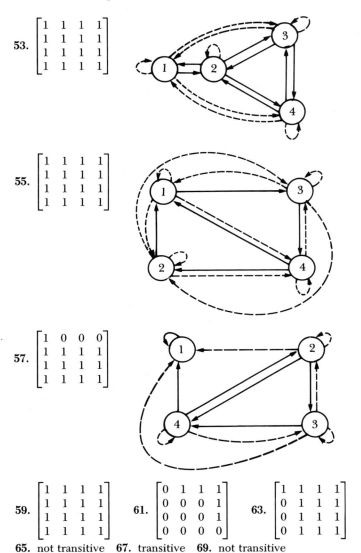

59. $\begin{bmatrix} 1 & 1 & 1 & 1 \\ 1 & 1 & 1 & 1 \\ 1 & 1 & 1 & 1 \\ 1 & 1 & 1 & 1 \end{bmatrix}$ **61.** $\begin{bmatrix} 0 & 1 & 1 & 1 \\ 0 & 0 & 0 & 1 \\ 0 & 0 & 0 & 1 \\ 0 & 0 & 0 & 0 \end{bmatrix}$ **63.** $\begin{bmatrix} 1 & 1 & 1 & 1 \\ 0 & 1 & 1 & 1 \\ 0 & 1 & 1 & 1 \\ 0 & 1 & 1 & 1 \end{bmatrix}$

65. not transitive   **67.** transitive   **69.** not transitive

In Exercises 71–75 we give the matrix of distances.

71. $\begin{bmatrix} 0 & 1 & 2 & 2 & 2 \\ 1 & 0 & 1 & 1 & 1 \\ 2 & 1 & 0 & 2 & 2 \\ 2 & 1 & 2 & 0 & 1 \\ 2 & 1 & 2 & 1 & 0 \end{bmatrix}$ **73.** $\begin{bmatrix} 0 & 1 & 2 & 1 & 1 \\ 1 & 0 & 1 & 1 & 2 \\ 2 & 1 & 0 & 1 & 2 \\ 1 & 1 & 1 & 0 & 1 \\ 1 & 2 & 2 & 1 & 0 \end{bmatrix}$ **75.** $\begin{bmatrix} 0 & 3 & 4 & 3 & 2 \\ 3 & 0 & 2 & 3 & 4 \\ 4 & 2 & 0 & 1 & 2 \\ 3 & 3 & 1 & 0 & 1 \\ 2 & 4 & 2 & 1 & 0 \end{bmatrix}$

Section 10-3 Concepts Review
1. solution 2. equivalent 3. elementary row operation 4. elementary row operation, adding a multiple of 5. elementary row operation, interchanging
6. pivotal 7. row reduced, one 8. pivot 9. pivotal 10. real number

Section 10-3 Exercises

1. $\begin{bmatrix} 1 & 1 \\ 1 & -2 \end{bmatrix} \begin{bmatrix} x_1 \\ x_2 \end{bmatrix} = \begin{bmatrix} 4 \\ 1 \end{bmatrix}$ 3. $\begin{bmatrix} 1 & -1 & 1 \\ 3 & 2 & -4 \\ 1 & 2 & 1 \end{bmatrix} \begin{bmatrix} x_1 \\ x_2 \\ x_3 \end{bmatrix} = \begin{bmatrix} 1 \\ 1 \\ 4 \end{bmatrix}$

5. $\begin{bmatrix} 1 & 0 & 1 \\ 1 & -1 & 1 \\ 0 & 1 & 3 \end{bmatrix} \begin{bmatrix} x_1 \\ x_2 \\ x_3 \end{bmatrix} = \begin{bmatrix} 2 \\ 2 \\ 3 \end{bmatrix}$

7. $x_1 = 3, x_2 = 1$ 9. $x_1 = 1, x_2 = 1, x_3 = 1$ 11. $x_1 = 1, x_2 = 0, x_3 = 1$

13. (a) the 1 and 2 are pivotal (b) the two ones are pivotal (c) the 1,1 entry, 2,2 entry, and 3,4 entry are pivotal. (d) the 1,1 entry, 2,4 entry, and 3,2 entry are pivotal

15. (b) and (d) are row reduced

17. $\begin{bmatrix} 1 & 0 & 2 \\ 0 & 1 & -\frac{3}{2} \end{bmatrix}$ 19. $\begin{bmatrix} 1 & 2 & 0 \\ 0 & 0 & 1 \\ 0 & 0 & 0 \end{bmatrix}$ 21. $\begin{bmatrix} 1 & 0 & 0 & -\frac{16}{5} \\ 0 & 0 & 1 & \frac{4}{5} \\ 0 & 1 & 0 & \frac{3}{5} \end{bmatrix}$

23. (a) $\begin{bmatrix} 2 & 3 & -1 \\ 4 & 5 & -4 \\ 1 & 2 & 1 \end{bmatrix} \begin{bmatrix} x_1 \\ x_2 \\ x_3 \end{bmatrix} = \begin{bmatrix} 4 \\ 5 \\ 4 \end{bmatrix}$ (b) $\begin{bmatrix} 1 & 2 & -1 \\ 2 & 3 & 1 \\ -1 & 1 & 1 \end{bmatrix} \begin{bmatrix} x_1 \\ x_2 \\ x_3 \end{bmatrix} = \begin{bmatrix} 2 \\ 1 \\ -2 \end{bmatrix}$

(c) $\begin{bmatrix} \frac{1}{2} & 1 & -1 \\ 3 & 3 & -1 \\ 2 & 2 & -1 \end{bmatrix} \begin{bmatrix} x_1 \\ x_2 \\ x_3 \end{bmatrix} = \begin{bmatrix} 2 \\ 5 \\ 7 \end{bmatrix}$ (d) $\begin{bmatrix} 1 & 2 & 4 \\ \frac{1}{2} & 1 & -1 \\ 1 & 1 & 1 \end{bmatrix} \begin{bmatrix} x_1 \\ x_2 \\ x_3 \end{bmatrix} = \begin{bmatrix} 0 \\ 3 \\ 2 \end{bmatrix}$

25. (a) $x_1 = 1, x_2 = 1, x_3 = 1$ (b) $x_1 = 1, x_2 = 0, x_3 = -1$ (c) $x_1 = 14, x_2 = -16, x_3 = -11$ (d) $x_1 = 2, x_2 = 1, x_3 = -1$

27. (a) infinitely many (b) none (c) infinitely many (d) exactly one

29. (a) $x_1 = 2 - r, x_2 = 1 - 2r, x_3 = 3 + r, x_4 = r, r$ any real number (c) $x_1 = 1, x_2 = 3, x_3 = 4, x_4 = r, r$ any real number (d) $x_1 = 1, x_2 = 0, x_3 = 2$

31. no solutions

33. $x_1 = 2 - \frac{4}{3}r, x_2 = 2 - \frac{5}{3}r, x_3 = 1 + \frac{2}{3}r, x_4 = r, r$ any real number

35. $x_1 = r, x_2 = -r, x_3 = r, x_4 = 0, r$ any real number

37. $x_1 = -1 + r, x_2 = 4 - r, x_3 = r, x_4 = -1, r$ any real number

Section 10-4 Concepts Review
1. invertible 2. M′ 3. row reduced 4. elementary 5. elementary row operation
6. elementary matrix, same 7. invertible 8. one and only one

Section 10-4 Exercises

1. $\begin{bmatrix} 2 & 0 & 0 \\ 0 & 1 & 0 \\ 0 & 0 & 1 \end{bmatrix}$ 3. $\begin{bmatrix} 1 & 0 & 0 \\ -1 & 1 & 0 \\ 0 & 0 & 1 \end{bmatrix}$ 5. $\begin{bmatrix} 0 & 0 & 1 \\ 0 & 1 & 0 \\ 1 & 0 & 0 \end{bmatrix}$ 7. $\begin{bmatrix} 1 & 0 & 0 \\ 0 & -3 & 0 \\ 0 & 0 & 1 \end{bmatrix}$

9. $\begin{bmatrix} 1 & 0 & 0 \\ 0 & 1 & 0 \\ -2 & 0 & 1 \end{bmatrix}$ 11. $\begin{bmatrix} 0 & 1 & 0 \\ 1 & 0 & 0 \\ 0 & 0 & 1 \end{bmatrix}$ 13. $\begin{bmatrix} 2a & 2b & 2c \\ d & e & f \\ g & h & i \end{bmatrix}$

15. $\begin{bmatrix} a & b & c \\ d-a & e-b & f-c \\ g & h & i \end{bmatrix}$　**17.** $\begin{bmatrix} g & h & i \\ d & e & f \\ a & b & c \end{bmatrix}$　**19.** $\begin{bmatrix} a & b & c \\ -3d & -3e & -3f \\ g & h & i \end{bmatrix}$

21. $\begin{bmatrix} a & b & c \\ d & e & f \\ g-2a & h-2b & i-2c \end{bmatrix}$　**23.** $\begin{bmatrix} d & e & f \\ a & b & c \\ g & h & i \end{bmatrix}$

25. $E(\frac{1}{2}R1)$　**27.** $E(R1+R2)$　**29.** $E(R1 \leftrightarrow R3)$

31. $E(-\frac{1}{3}R2)$　**33.** $E(2R1+R3)$　**35.** $E(R2 \leftrightarrow R1)$

37. The product is the three-by-three identity matrix (in both orders).

39. The product is the three-by-three identity matrix (in both orders).

41. $\begin{bmatrix} 1 & 2 & 4 \\ 0 & 1 & 2 \\ 1 & 2 & 2 \end{bmatrix} \xrightarrow{-R1+R3} \begin{bmatrix} 1 & 2 & 4 \\ 0 & 1 & 2 \\ 0 & 0 & -2 \end{bmatrix} \xrightarrow[2R3+R1]{R3+R2} \begin{bmatrix} 1 & 2 & 0 \\ 0 & 1 & 2 \\ 0 & 0 & -2 \end{bmatrix}$

$\xrightarrow[-\frac{1}{2}R3]{-2R2+R1} \begin{bmatrix} 1 & 0 & 0 \\ 0 & 1 & 0 \\ 0 & 0 & 1 \end{bmatrix}$

43. $E(-\frac{1}{2}R3)E(-2R2+R1)E(2R3+R1)E(R3+R2)E(-R1+R3)$. The product is M^{-1}.

45. The matrices are the inverses of the matrices in Exercise 43 and they must be multiplied in the opposite order.

$M = E(R1+R3)E(-R3+R2)E(-2R3+R1)E(2R2+R1)E(-2R3)$

47. $\begin{bmatrix} \frac{1}{5} & \frac{3}{5} \\ \frac{2}{5} & \frac{1}{5} \end{bmatrix}$　**49.** $\begin{bmatrix} 1 & 1 \\ 0 & 1 \end{bmatrix}$　**51.** $\begin{bmatrix} 0 & 1 \\ -1 & 0 \end{bmatrix}$　**53.** $\begin{bmatrix} 1 & 0 & -1 \\ -1 & 2 & 0 \\ 0 & -1 & 1 \end{bmatrix}$

55. $x = \frac{11}{5}; y = \frac{7}{5}$　**57.** $x = \begin{bmatrix} -2 \\ -6 \\ 6 \end{bmatrix}$

59. (a) invertible　(b) not invertible　(c) invertible

61. (a) $\begin{bmatrix} 1 & 0 & -1 \\ -1 & 2 & 0 \\ 0 & -1 & 1 \end{bmatrix}$　(c) $\begin{bmatrix} 3 & -\frac{5}{2} & \frac{1}{2} \\ -\frac{3}{2} & 2 & -\frac{1}{2} \\ \frac{1}{3} & -\frac{1}{2} & \frac{1}{6} \end{bmatrix}$

63. (a) exactly one　(b) infinitely many　(c) exactly one

65. (a) $\begin{bmatrix} 0 \\ 1 \\ 0 \end{bmatrix}$　(c) $\begin{bmatrix} 1 \\ 0 \\ 0 \end{bmatrix}$

67. $x_1 = \frac{1}{3} + \frac{2}{3}r$; $x_2 = \frac{2}{21} - \frac{17}{21}r$; $x_3 = \frac{4}{21} - \frac{13}{21}r$; $x_4 = r$, r any real number

Section 10-5 Concepts Review

1. $a_{11}a_{22} - a_{12}a_{21}$　**2.** multiplies, r　**3.** does not change　**4.** multiplies, -1　**5.** 1
6. elementary factor　**7.** upper triangular　**8.** diagonal, triangular　**9.** no

Section 10-5 Exercises

1. -6　**3.** 7　**5.** 3　**7.** 0

9. $4 - 12 = -8$; $10 - 18 = -8$, the row sum rule, rule 2

11. $-16 + 20 = 4$; $8 - 10 = -2$, the row multiple rule, rule 1

13. $6 - 2 = 4; 2 - 6 = - 4$, the row interchange rule, rule 3

15. $\det A = -2 \det B$ **17.** $\det A = - \det B$ **19.** -12 **21.** -12 **23.** -12 **25.** not either diagonal product **27.** diagonal product $a_{11}a_{22}a_{33}$ **29.** diagonal product $a_{11}a_{22}a_{33}$ **31.** not either diagonal product **33.** -18 **35.** 6 **37.** 0 **39.** 6 **41.** 48 **43.** 1 **45.** 15 **47.** 27 **49.** $-x + 3y$

Section 10-6 Concepts Review

1. product **2.** detMdetN **3.** transpose **4.** additivity (linearity), sum **5.** equal, determinant **6.** product, reverse order **7.** nonzero **8.** zeros **9.** expansion, *i*th row

Section 10-6 Exercises

1. $\det(M) = -2$, $\det(N) = 6$, $\det(P) = 0$ **3.** -12 **5.** 0 **7.** 0 **9.** 36 **11.** 0

13. $MN = \begin{bmatrix} 3 & 9 & 3 \\ 1 & 13 & 4 \\ 1 & 21 & 6 \end{bmatrix}$, **15.** $N^2 = \begin{bmatrix} 4 & 0 & 0 \\ -5 & 9 & 0 \\ 2 & 4 & 1 \end{bmatrix}$,

$\det MN = -12$, as in Exercise 3. $\det N^2 = 36$, as in Exercise 9.

17. $M^t = \begin{bmatrix} 1 & 0 & 0 \\ 2 & 3 & 5 \\ 3 & 4 & 6 \end{bmatrix}$, $N^t = \begin{bmatrix} 2 & -1 & 1 \\ 0 & 3 & 1 \\ 0 & 0 & 1 \end{bmatrix}$, $P^t = \begin{bmatrix} 1 & 0 & 1 \\ 0 & 2 & 1 \\ 1 & 2 & 2 \end{bmatrix}$, $\det M^t = -2$, $\det N^t = 6$,

$\det P^t = 0$

19. (a) $\det \begin{bmatrix} 2 & 0 & 0 \\ 0 & 1 & 1 \\ 0 & 2 & -1 \end{bmatrix} + \det \begin{bmatrix} 0 & 0 & 2 \\ 1 & 1 & 0 \\ -1 & 2 & 0 \end{bmatrix} = -6 + 6 = 0$

(b) $\det \begin{bmatrix} 0 & 1 & 1 \\ 0 & -1 & 0 \\ 1 & 0 & -1 \end{bmatrix} + \det \begin{bmatrix} 1 & 0 & 1 \\ 0 & -1 & 0 \\ 1 & 0 & 1 \end{bmatrix} = 1 + 2 = 3$

(c) $\det \begin{bmatrix} .5 & 0 & 2.2 \\ 2 & 0 & 2 \\ 0 & 1 & 0 \end{bmatrix} + \det \begin{bmatrix} .5 & 6.1 & 0 \\ 2 & -1 & 0 \\ 0 & 0 & 1 \end{bmatrix} = 3.4 - 12.7 = -9.3$

21. (a) $-4a + 8b$ (b) $4a - 8b$ (c) $-a + b$

23. (a) Use column 2; determinant $= 0$ (b) Use either column 2 or column 3, determinant $= 3$ (c) Use column 1, determinant $= -9.3$

25. (a) 0 (b) 3 (c) -9.3 **27.** (a) 0 (b) 3 (c) -9.3 **29.** -34 **31.** 0 **33.** 0 **35.** -6

37. $a\det \begin{bmatrix} d & e \\ 0 & f \end{bmatrix} = adf$

39. $2r \det \begin{bmatrix} 4 & 5 \\ 2 & 3 \end{bmatrix} + 3r \det \begin{bmatrix} 3 & 5 \\ -1 & 3 \end{bmatrix} + 4r \det \begin{bmatrix} 3 & 4 \\ -1 & 2 \end{bmatrix} = r \cdot \left(2 \det \begin{bmatrix} 4 & 5 \\ 2 & 3 \end{bmatrix} + 3 \det \begin{bmatrix} 3 & 5 \\ -1 & 3 \end{bmatrix} + 4 \det \begin{bmatrix} 3 & 4 \\ -1 & 2 \end{bmatrix} \right)$

Chapter 10 Review Exercises

1. $[2 \ \ -1 \ \ 0 \ \ 3]$ $[2 \ \ 0 \ \ 2 \ \ 2]$ $[3 \ \ -3 \ \ -3 \ \ 6]$ **2.** $\begin{bmatrix} 2 & 6 \\ 0 & 4 \end{bmatrix}$

3. $D(A + E) = \begin{bmatrix} -2 & -6 \\ 4 & 16 \end{bmatrix}$ $DA + DE = \begin{bmatrix} -1 & -4 \\ -1 & 8 \end{bmatrix} + \begin{bmatrix} -1 & -2 \\ 5 & 8 \end{bmatrix} = \begin{bmatrix} -2 & -6 \\ 4 & 16 \end{bmatrix}$

The distributive law tells us they should be the same.

4. *E, E*   **5.** $\begin{bmatrix} 0 & 0 \\ 0 & 0 \end{bmatrix}, \begin{bmatrix} 1 & 2 \\ 3 & 4 \end{bmatrix}$

6. Both products are -1; the equality follows from the associative law.

7. $\begin{bmatrix} 1 & 0 \\ 0 & 1 \end{bmatrix}, \begin{bmatrix} 1 & 0 \\ 0 & 1 \end{bmatrix}$, zero. (Note that the same cannot be said for the entry in row 2 and column 1.)

8. *SC* and *(AD)E* are defined; the other products are not.

9. $DE = \begin{bmatrix} -1 & -2 \\ 5 & 8 \end{bmatrix}, ED = \begin{bmatrix} 3 & 2 \\ 5 & 4 \end{bmatrix}$ Matrix multiplication is not commutative.

10. $\begin{bmatrix} 1 & 0 & 0 & 0 \\ 0 & 1 & 0 & 0 \\ 0 & 0 & 1 & 0 \\ 0 & 0 & 0 & 1 \end{bmatrix} = I; IC = C, IB = B$

11. 0, 2; 0

12. $-3 + 0 = -3$, row 2 and column 1.

13. $\begin{bmatrix} 2 & -3 & 1 \\ 2 & 0 & -1 \\ 4 & -5 & 2 \end{bmatrix} \begin{bmatrix} x_1 \\ x_2 \\ x_3 \end{bmatrix} = \begin{bmatrix} -2 \\ 3 \\ -3 \end{bmatrix}$

14. $\begin{bmatrix} 2 & -3 & 1 \\ 2 & 0 & -1 \end{bmatrix} \begin{bmatrix} x_1 \\ x_2 \\ x_3 \end{bmatrix} = \begin{bmatrix} -2 \\ 3 \end{bmatrix}$

15. All the 1's are the pivotal entries of *M*. The pivotal entries of *N* are in row 1, column 1, row 2, column 2, row 3, column 4, and row 4, column 1.

16. neither

17. $\begin{bmatrix} 1 & 0 & 0 & 1 \\ 0 & 1 & 0 & 0 \\ 0 & 0 & 1 & -1 \end{bmatrix} \begin{bmatrix} 1 & 0 & 2 & -1 \\ 0 & 1 & -1 & 1 \\ 0 & 0 & 0 & 0 \end{bmatrix}$

18. (a) $\begin{bmatrix} 2 & 0 & 4 & -2 & | & 2 \\ 1 & 3 & -1 & 2 & | & 7 \\ 0 & 1 & 2 & -2 & | & 5 \end{bmatrix}$ (b) $\begin{bmatrix} 2 & 0 & 4 & -2 & | & 2 \\ 1 & 3 & -1 & 2 & | & 7 \\ 0 & -1 & 1 & -1 & | & 1 \end{bmatrix}$

19. (a) $\begin{bmatrix} 1 & 0 & 0 & 1 & | & -1 \\ 0 & 1 & 0 & 0 & | & 3 \\ 0 & 0 & 1 & -1 & | & 1 \end{bmatrix}$ (b) $\begin{bmatrix} 1 & 0 & 2 & -1 & | & 1 \\ 0 & 1 & -1 & 1 & | & 2 \\ 0 & 0 & 0 & 0 & | & 3 \end{bmatrix}$

20. (a) $x_1, x_2,$ and x_3 (b) x_1 and x_2

21. (a) $x_1 = -1 - r, x_2 = 3, x_3 = 1 + r, x_4 = r$, r any real number   (b) no solutions

22. $x_1 = 1, x_2 = 1, x_3 = -1$

23. (a) no solutions   (b) infinitely many solutions   (c) exactly one solution   (d) exactly one solution   (e) exactly one solution   (f) no solutions

24. $x_1 = 1, x_2 = 2, x_3 = 3$

25. $x_1 = 1 - 2r, x_2 = r, x_3 = 3$

26. $x_1 = 1, x_2 = 0, x_3 = 2 - 3r, x_4 = r$

27. no solutions

28. (a) $\begin{bmatrix} 1 & 0 & 0 \\ 0 & 3 & 0 \\ 0 & 0 & 1 \end{bmatrix}$ (b) $\begin{bmatrix} 1 & 0 & 0 \\ 0 & 1 & -1 \\ 0 & 0 & 1 \end{bmatrix}$ (c) $\begin{bmatrix} 1 & 0 & 3 \\ 0 & 1 & 0 \\ 0 & 0 & 1 \end{bmatrix}$ (d) $\begin{bmatrix} 0 & 0 & 1 \\ 0 & 1 & 0 \\ 1 & 0 & 0 \end{bmatrix}$

29. (a) $\begin{bmatrix} 1 & 2 & 3 \\ 12 & 15 & 18 \\ 7 & 8 & 9 \end{bmatrix}$ (b) $\begin{bmatrix} 1 & 2 & 3 \\ -3 & -3 & -3 \\ 7 & 8 & 9 \end{bmatrix}$ (c) $\begin{bmatrix} 22 & 26 & 30 \\ 4 & 5 & 6 \\ 7 & 8 & 9 \end{bmatrix}$

(d) $\begin{bmatrix} 7 & 8 & 9 \\ 4 & 5 & 6 \\ 1 & 2 & 3 \end{bmatrix}$

30. (a) $\begin{bmatrix} 1 & 0 & 0 \\ 0 & \frac{1}{3} & 0 \\ 0 & 0 & 1 \end{bmatrix}$ (b) $\begin{bmatrix} 1 & 0 & 0 \\ 0 & 1 & 1 \\ 0 & 0 & 1 \end{bmatrix}$ (c) $\begin{bmatrix} 1 & 0 & -3 \\ 0 & 1 & 0 \\ 0 & 0 & 1 \end{bmatrix}$ (d) $\begin{bmatrix} 0 & 0 & 1 \\ 0 & 1 & 0 \\ 1 & 0 & 0 \end{bmatrix}$

31. One set of operations is: $R3 + R2$, $R1 + R3$, $-R2 + R3$, $\frac{1}{2}R2$, $R2 + R1$, $R3 + R1$, $-R3$, $R2 \leftrightarrow R3$.

32. Subtracting half of $R3$ from $R1$ and adding half of $R3$ to $R2$ gives a matrix with two equal rows; one more operation gives a row of zeros.

33. $E(R2\leftrightarrow R3)E(-1R3)E(R3 + R1)E(R2 + R1)E(\frac{1}{2}R2)E(-R2 + R3)E(R1 + R3)E(R3 + R2)$

34. $\begin{bmatrix} 1 & 1 & -1 & 1 & 0 & 0 \\ 1 & 2 & -1 & 0 & 1 & 0 \\ -1 & -2 & 3 & 0 & 0 & 1 \end{bmatrix}$ **35.** $\begin{bmatrix} 2 & -\frac{1}{2} & \frac{1}{2} \\ -1 & 1 & 0 \\ 0 & \frac{1}{2} & \frac{1}{2} \end{bmatrix}$

36. Multiply M^{-1} by $\begin{bmatrix} 0 \\ 2 \\ 4 \end{bmatrix}$ to get $\begin{bmatrix} 1 \\ 2 \\ 3 \end{bmatrix}$

37. (a) Invertible $\begin{bmatrix} \frac{1}{2} & \frac{3}{2} & 3 & \frac{2}{3} \\ 0 & 1 & -2 & 0 \\ 0 & 0 & 1 & 1 \\ 0 & 0 & 0 & -\frac{1}{3} \end{bmatrix}$ (b) not invertible

(c) invertible $\begin{bmatrix} \frac{5}{8} & \frac{3}{4} & -\frac{1}{2} \\ \frac{7}{16} & \frac{1}{8} & -\frac{1}{4} \\ -1 & -1 & 1 \end{bmatrix}$

38. $-1, -2$ **39.** $(-1)(-2) = 2$ **40.** -2 **41.** 0 **42.** -16

43. We can row reduce the matrix without changing the diagonal elements but making all non-diagonal elements zero entirely by row-sum operations.

44. $(-6)(-2) = 12$ **45.** $12, 12$

46. $\begin{bmatrix} 2 & 3 & 5 \\ 4 & -2 & 2 \\ 2 & 1 & 4 \end{bmatrix}$ **47.** (a) $\begin{bmatrix} 3 & 0 & 0 \\ 0 & 1 & 0 \\ 0 & 0 & 1 \end{bmatrix}$ (b) $\begin{bmatrix} 1 & 0 & 0 \\ 0 & 2 & 0 \\ 0 & 0 & 1 \end{bmatrix}$ (c) $\begin{bmatrix} 1 & 0 & 0 \\ 0 & 0 & 1 \\ 0 & 1 & 0 \end{bmatrix}$

48. 84

49. If $k = 1$ the statement reads $\det M_1 = \det M_1$, which is true. Now assume inductively that $\det(M_1 M_2 \cdots M_{k-1}) = \det M_1 \det M_2 \cdots \det M_{k-1}$. Then since $\det(AB) = $

det$A$ det$B$, it follows that $\det((M_1\ M_2 \cdots M_{k-1})\ M_k) = \det(M_1 \cdots M_{k-1})\ \det M_k = \det M_1\ \det M_2 \cdots \det M_{k-1}\ \det M_k.$

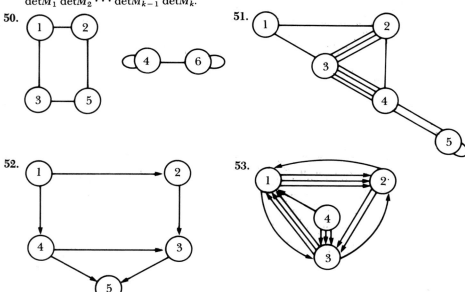

50.

51.

52.

53.

54. 0, 8. Any walk from vertex 1 to vertex 2 must have an odd number of edges.

55. There are two walks of length 3 from vertex 1 to vertex 5 and that is all.

56. {(1,1), (1,2), (1,3), (1,5), (2,1), (2,2), (2,3), (2,5), (3,1), (3,2), (3,3), (3,5), (5,1), (5,2), (5,3), (5,5), (4,4), (4,6), (6,4), (6,6)}. The connected components are {1,2,3,5} and {4,6}.

57. {(1,2), (1,3), (1,4), (1,5), (2,3), (2,5), (3,5), (4,3), (4,5)}. All other vertices are reachable from vertex 1; 3 and 5 are reachable from both 2 and 4; 5 is reachable from 3; and nothing is reachable from 5.

58. The matrix of distances is $\begin{bmatrix} 0 & 1 & 1 & 5 & 7 \\ 1 & 0 & 2 & 6 & 8 \\ 1 & 2 & 0 & 4 & 6 \\ 5 & 6 & 4 & 0 & 2 \\ 7 & 8 & 6 & 2 & 0 \end{bmatrix}$.

Notice that the loop at vertex 5 is irrelevant.

59. The matrix of distances is $\begin{bmatrix} 0 & 2 & 1 & \infty \\ 1 & 0 & 2 & \infty \\ 2 & 1 & 0 & \infty \\ 1 & 3 & 2 & 0 \end{bmatrix}$.

CHAPTER 11
Section 11-1 Concepts Review
1. sample space **2.** event **3.** one **4.** probability **5.** uniform **6.** $P(E) + P(F) - P(E \cap F)$ **7.** $\dfrac{|E|}{|S|}$ **8.** one

Section 11-1 Exercises
1. {HHHH, HHHT, HHTH, HTHH, THHH, HHTT, HTHT, HTTH, THHT, THTH, TTHH, HTTT, THTT, TTHT, TTTH, TTTT}

3. {(1,1), (1,2), (1,3), (1,4), (1,5), (1,6), (2,1), (2,2), (2,3), (2,4), (2,5), (2,6), (3,1), (3,2), (3,3), (3,4), (3,5), (3,6), (4,1), (4,2), (4,3), (4,4), (4,5), (4,6), (5,1), (5,2), (5,3), (5,4), (5,5), (5,6), (6,1), (6,2), (6,3), (6,4), (6,5), (6,6)}

5. (a) {(A,K), (A,Q), (A,J), (K,A), (K,Q), (K,J), (Q,A), (Q,K), (Q,J), (J,A), (J,K), (J,Q)}
   (b) {{A,K}, {A,Q}, {A,J}, {K,Q}, {K,J}, {Q,J}}

7. (a) {(R,R), (R,B), (B,R), (B,B)   (b) {{R,R}, {R,B.}, {B,B}}

9. (a) {HHHH, HHHT, HHTH, HTHH, THHH} (b) {HHHH, HHTT, HTHT, HTTH, THHT, THTH, TTHH, TTTT} (c) {HHHH, HHHT, HHTH, HTHH, THHH} (d) {HHHH, HHHT, HHTH, HHTT}

11. $\frac{1}{16}$; (a) $\frac{5}{16}$ (b) $\frac{1}{2}$ (c) $\frac{5}{16}$ (d) $\frac{1}{4}$

13. (a) The weight of each ordered pair is $\frac{1}{12}$.   (b) The weight of each two element multiset is $\frac{1}{6}$.

15. (a) $p((RR)) = \frac{3}{10}$, $p((R,B)) = \frac{3}{10}$, $p((B,R)) = \frac{3}{10}$, $p((B,B)) = \frac{1}{10}$ (b) $p(\{R,R\}) = \frac{3}{10}$, $p(\{R,B\}) = \frac{6}{10}$, $p(\{B,B\}) = \frac{1}{10}$

17. (a) P(at least one red) $= \frac{3}{10} + \frac{3}{10} + \frac{3}{10} = \frac{9}{10}$ (b) P(at least one red) $= \frac{3}{10} + \frac{6}{10} = \frac{9}{10}$
   (c) P(first is red) $= \frac{3}{10} + \frac{3}{10} = \frac{6}{10}$ (d) P(both same) $= \frac{3}{10} + \frac{1}{10} = \frac{2}{5}$

19. $\binom{10}{5} \cdot \frac{1}{2^{10}} = \frac{10!}{5!5!}\frac{1}{1024} = \frac{63}{256}$

21. $\frac{30}{12\cdot 11} = \frac{5}{22}$ since each possibility has weight $\frac{1}{12\cdot 11}$

23. $\binom{48}{9}$ since this is the number of ways to choose the remaining cards.

$$\frac{\binom{48}{9}}{\binom{52}{13}} = \frac{13\cdot 12\cdot 11\cdot 10}{52\cdot 51\cdot 50\cdot 49} = .002641 \text{ approximately.}$$

25. $\frac{4}{36} = \frac{1}{9}$, $\frac{18}{36} = \frac{1}{2}$

27. (a) Appropriate because the ith position corresponds to the ith pile, and all possibilities are equally likely from all piles.   (b) Inappropriate. There is only one way to get {A,A,A,A}, but there are many ways to get {2,3,4,5}.

29. Not appropriate for either because getting a nickel and a dime is more likely than a quarter and a dime.

31. $\binom{10}{8}\frac{1}{2^{10}} + \binom{10}{9}\frac{1}{2^{10}} + \binom{10}{10}\frac{1}{2^{10}} = \frac{56}{1024} = \frac{7}{128} = .0547$ approximately

33. $\frac{1}{2} + \frac{1}{2} - \frac{1}{4} = \frac{3}{4}$

35. $\frac{1}{3} + \frac{1}{3} - \frac{1}{9} = \frac{5}{9}$

37. $1 - P$(both red) $= 1 - \frac{1}{6} = \frac{5}{6}$ (this is the probability that at least one is black.)

39. $1 - \frac{(12)_n}{12^n}$; 5 people, 6 people, 13 people.

41. The pairs $(1,n)$, $(3,n)$, and $(5,n)$ are half the pairs (m,n) you could get by rolling a die twice. The pairs (i,j) form four classes of equal size (even, odd), (even, even), (odd, odd), and (odd, even). Two (and only two) of these classes give the odd sums. For the sum to be odd and the first roll to be odd the second term (n) must be even, and a fourth of the pairs (m,n) have the property that m is odd and n is even. $\frac{1}{2} + \frac{1}{2} - \frac{1}{4} = \frac{3}{4}$

Section 11-2 Concepts Review

1. $P(E|F)$; $\dfrac{P(E \cap F)}{P(F)}$ 2. $P(E)$ 3. $P(E)$ 4. independent   5. dependent

6. independent trials   7. product

Section 11-2 Exercises

1. .55, .65, .40, $\dfrac{.40}{.65} = \dfrac{8}{13} = .6154$ approximately

3. $\dfrac{1}{2}$, $\dfrac{1}{4}$, $\dfrac{\frac{1}{4}}{\frac{1}{2}} = \dfrac{1}{2}$ 5. $\dfrac{1}{8}$, $\dfrac{1}{2}$, $\dfrac{1}{4}$ 7. $\dfrac{\frac{1}{8}}{\frac{7}{8}} = \dfrac{1}{7}$ 9. $\dfrac{\frac{1}{4}}{\frac{1}{2}} = \dfrac{1}{2}$

11. $(.001)(.99) + (.999)(.02) = .02097$, P(positive and disease) =

    P(positive|disease) P (disease) = $(.99)(.001) = .00099$ P(disease|positive) = $\dfrac{.00099}{.02097}$ = .0472 approximately

13. independent   15. not independent   17. not independent (if they were, $P(E \cup F)$ would be .0898)

19. Two outcomes out of four have heads on flip 1 so that P(heads on flip 1) = $\frac{1}{2}$; similarly, P(tails on flip 2) = $\frac{1}{2}$. Only one outcome has heads on flip 1 and tails on flip 2, so that P(heads on flip 1 and tails on flip 2) = $\frac{1}{4}$, and $\frac{1}{4} = \frac{1}{2} \cdot \frac{1}{2}$.

21. P(first flip is heads) = $\frac{1}{2}$, P(all flips are heads) = $\frac{1}{4}$, and P(first flip is heads and all flips are heads) = $\frac{1}{4} \neq \frac{1}{2} \cdot \frac{1}{4}$.   23. (a) dependent   (b) dependent   (c) independent (d) independent   25. $(.8)^4(.2) = .08192$; $5 \cdot (.8)^4(.2) = .4096$ 27. $\frac{1}{2}$, $\frac{1}{2}$, (We are using the equiprobable measure, and each of these events comprises exactly half the cases.) $\frac{1}{4}$, $\frac{1}{4}$. They show that the event "heads on flip i" is independent of the event "tails on flip j."

29. Yes it is an independent trials process.

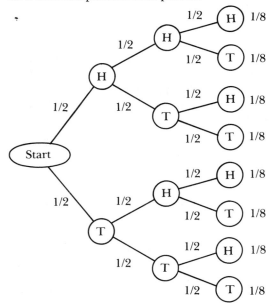

Section 11-3 Concepts Review

1. number **2.** distribution **3.** expected value, $\sum_{i=1}^{n} p_i f(x_i)$ **4.** mean **5.** sum, expected

values **6.** np **7.** $\binom{n}{k}p^k(1-p)^{n-k}$ **8.** binomial

Section 11-3 Exercises

1. (a) 0.2 (b) 0.6 (c) 0 (d) 0.2

3. $P(0) = P(5) = \frac{1}{32}$, $P(1) = P(4) = \frac{5}{32}$, and $P(2) = P(3) = \frac{5}{16}$

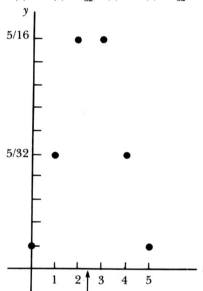

5.

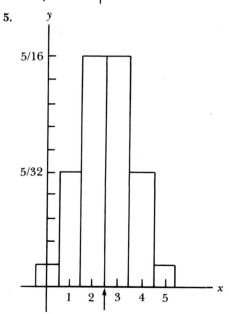

7. Diagonal shading for 3 or more heads; horizontal shading for even number of heads. The three rectangles with horizontal shading have the same total area as the three rectangles with diagonal shading.

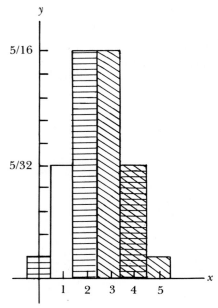

9. $P(.15) = \frac{2}{15}$, $P(.20) = \frac{1}{15}$, $P(.30) = \frac{1}{5}$, $P(.35) = \frac{2}{5}$, $P(.50) = \frac{1}{5}$ 11. 3.8

13. See arrows in answers to Exercises 3 and 5. Expected value is $\frac{5}{2}$ or $2\frac{1}{2}$.

15. Expected value is one third of a dollar, or $33\frac{1}{3}$ cents.

17. $\frac{1}{2} \cdot 20 = 10$

19. 35

21. $\binom{10}{6} \frac{1}{2^{10}} = \frac{105}{512} = .205$ approximately

23. $\left(\frac{4}{5}\right)^6 \left(\frac{2}{5}\right)^4 \cdot 210 = \frac{21 \cdot 2 \cdot 2^{12} \cdot 2^4}{5^9} = 21 \cdot \frac{2^{26}}{10^9}$ 25. 120

27. $\binom{5}{2} \frac{1}{2^5} = \binom{5}{3} \frac{1}{2^5}$

29. $\binom{10}{8} \frac{1}{2^{10}} + \binom{10}{9} \frac{1}{2^{10}} + \binom{10}{10} \frac{1}{2^{10}} = \frac{56}{2^{10}} = \frac{7}{128}$

31. $\frac{1}{2^9} = \frac{1}{512}$; $\frac{9}{2^9} = \frac{9}{512}$; $\frac{36}{2^9} = \frac{9}{2^7} = \frac{9}{128}$; $\frac{84}{2^9} = \frac{21}{128}$; $\frac{126}{2^9} = \frac{63}{256}$

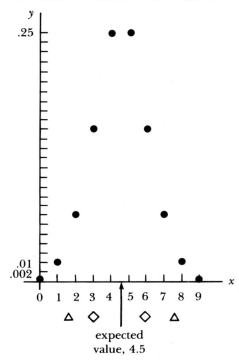

expected
value, 4.5

Section 11-4 Concepts Review

1. variance **2.** zero **3.** $E(f)^2$ **4.** sum, variances **5.** $np(1 - p)$ **6.** standard deviation **7.** standard deviation **8.** .95 (or .955)

Section 11-4 Exercises

1. $\frac{2}{3}$ **3.** 8.25 **5.** $\frac{19}{6}, \frac{35}{36}$ **7.** $\frac{350}{12} = \frac{175}{6}, \frac{3500}{12} = \frac{875}{3}$

9. 90, 9 **11.** $\dfrac{4\sqrt{2}}{9}$ **13.** 90; 3

15. $2^4 = 16$; $\sqrt{2^4(1 - 2^{-10})} = 4$ approximately; with 16 digits, $2^6 = 64$, $\sqrt{2^6(1 - 2^{-10})} = 8$ approximately.

17. Expected number 4.5, standard deviation 1.5; 3, 4, 5, or 6 successes has probability

$$\left[\binom{9}{3} + \binom{9}{4} + \binom{9}{5} + \binom{9}{6}\right]\frac{1}{2^9} = \frac{420}{2^9} = \frac{105}{2^7} = .82 \text{ approximately.}$$

19. Since the standard deviation is 4, 20 errors is one standard deviation above the expected value of 16. Therefore the probability is .84. Since 2.3 standard deviations is 9.2 and $16 + 9.2 = 25.2$, the probability of 25 or fewer errors is $1 - \frac{1}{2}(1 - .98) = .99$ approximately.

21. In the figure for the answer to Exercise 31 in Section 11-3, an arrow marks the expected value, diamonds mark one standard deviation to each side of the expected value, and triangles mark 2 standard deviations.

23. We want to adjust the length so that 2.3 times the standard deviation is no more than 2. Thus we want $\sqrt{n \cdot 2^{-10}(1 - 2^{-10})} = \dfrac{2}{2.3}$ approximately, and using $1 - 2^{-10} = 1$ approximately, we get $\sqrt{n} = 2^5 \cdot \dfrac{2}{2.3}$, giving $n = \dfrac{2^{12}}{5.29} = 795$ approximately.

Section 11-5 Concepts Review

1. weighted adjacency matrix   2. Markov chain   3. states   4. transition matrix
5. absorbing   6. absorbing   7. P^n 8. invertible   9. expected number, times, absorption

Section 11-5 Exercises

1. (a) $\begin{bmatrix} 0 & 3 & 2 & 0 \\ 3 & 0 & .5 & 2.5 \\ 2 & .5 & 0 & 1.1 \\ 0 & 2.5 & 1.1 & 0 \end{bmatrix}$ (b) $\begin{bmatrix} 0 & x & xy & 0 \\ x & 0 & y & y^2 \\ xy & y & 0 & x^2 \\ 0 & y^2 & x^2 & 0 \end{bmatrix}$

(c) $\begin{bmatrix} 0 & 2.5 & 0 & 0 \\ 0 & 0 & 0 & 1 \\ 2 & 4 & 0 & 0 \\ 0 & 0 & 2 & 0 \end{bmatrix}$ (d) $\begin{bmatrix} 0 & 1 & x & x^2 \\ 0 & 0 & 1 & x \\ 0 & 0 & 0 & 1 \\ 0 & 0 & 0 & 0 \end{bmatrix}$

3. $P_{11}P_{14} + P_{12}P_{24} + P_{13}P_{34} + P_{14}P_{44}$

5. Squaring the matrix and computing the 1,3 entry of the square of that square gives
(a) $\frac{81}{256}$ (b) $\frac{1}{5}$ (c) $\frac{10}{27}$

7. (a)

(b) $\begin{bmatrix} 0 & \frac{2}{3} & 0 & \frac{1}{3} \\ \frac{1}{2} & 0 & \frac{1}{2} & 1 \\ 0 & \frac{1}{2} & 0 \\ 0 & 0 & 0 & \frac{5}{2} \end{bmatrix}$ (c) $\begin{bmatrix} 0 & \frac{2}{3} & 0 \\ \frac{1}{2} & 0 & \frac{1}{2} \\ 0 & \frac{1}{2} & 0 \end{bmatrix}$ (d) $\frac{95}{144}$

9. Taking the states in alphabetical order, we get the transition matrix that follows.

$$\begin{bmatrix} 0 & \frac{1}{3} & \frac{1}{3} & \frac{1}{3} & 0 & 0 & 0 \\ \frac{1}{2} & 0 & \frac{1}{2} & 0 & 0 & 0 & 0 \\ \frac{1}{4} & \frac{1}{4} & 0 & \frac{1}{4} & \frac{1}{4} & 0 & 0 \\ \frac{1}{4} & 0 & \frac{1}{4} & 0 & \frac{1}{4} & 0 & \frac{1}{4} \\ 0 & 0 & \frac{1}{3} & \frac{1}{3} & 0 & \frac{1}{3} & 0 \\ 0 & 0 & 0 & 0 & \frac{1}{2} & 0 & \frac{1}{2} \\ 0 & 0 & 0 & \frac{1}{2} & 0 & \frac{1}{2} & 0 \end{bmatrix}$$

The fourth power is the matrix

$$
\begin{bmatrix}
.211806 & .098958 & .223958 & .137153 & .173611 & .038194 & .116319 \\
.148437 & .162326 & .197917 & .236979 & .127604 & .074653 & .052083 \\
.167969 & .098958 & .240885 & .197917 & .11849 & .098958 & .076823 \\
.102865 & .11849 & .197917 & .292969 & .082031 & .174479 & .03125 \\
.173611 & .085069 & .157986 & .109375 & .253472 & .024306 & .196181 \\
.057292 & .074653 & .197917 & .348958 & .036458 & .274306 & .010417 \\
.174479 & .052083 & .153646 & .0625 & .294271 & .010417 & .252604
\end{bmatrix}
$$

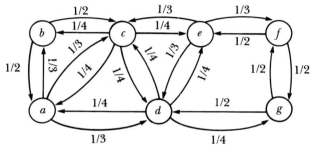

11. The states are your total fortune, either 0, 1, 2, 3, 4, or 5 dollars. The probability of going from state i to state $i + 1$ or $i - 1$ is $\frac{1}{2}$ unless $i = 0$ or $i = 5$. The probability of staying at state 0 or 5 is 1 and all other transition probabilities are 0. Since we stay in state 5 if we get there, the probability of winning your opponent's fortune in four or fewer flips is the 3, 5 entry of the fourth power of the transition matrix (assuming we consider the rows and columns as labelled with 0 through 5), and this probability is $\frac{3}{8}$.

13. The mouse will be in chamber 1 on the average 1.2 times, chamber 2 on the average 2.4 times and chamber 3 on the average 1.2 times before ending in chamber 4, assuming it starts in chamber 2.

15. No, the chain in Exercise 9 is not absorbing.

17. The expected number of times the dog is one house downhill before finding food is $\frac{42}{31}$, the entry in row 2 and column 1 of $(I - Q)^{-1}$.

19. The expected number of changes is the expected total number of times the mouse is in any of the nonabsorbing states until it is absorbed. This is the sum of the entries in row 2 of $(I - Q)^{-1}$ which, from Example 57, is 6.

21. This should be the sum of the entries in row 3 of the matrix $(I - Q)^{-1}$. This sum is 6.

Chapter 11 Review Exercises

1. {0000, 0001, 0010, 0100, 1000, 0011, 0101, 1001, 0110, 1010, 1100, 0111, 1011, 1101, 1110, 1111}

2. (a) {PNT, NTP, TPN, NPT, PTN, TNP, PPT, PTP, TPP, NNT, NTN, TNN, PPN, PNP, NPP, NNP, NPN, PNN}   (b) {{P,N,T}, {P,P,T}, {N,N,T}, {P,P,N}, {N,N,P}}

3. (a) {1111, 1110, 1101, 1011, 0111}   (b) {0011, 0101, 1001, 0110, 1010, 1100}
   (c) {0000, 0011, 0101, 1001, 0110, 1010, 1100, 1111}

4. (a) {PNT, NTP, TPN, NPT, PTN, TNP, PPT, PTP, TPP, NNT, NTN, TNN}, {PNT, NTP, TPN, NPT, PTN, TNP}   (b) {{P,N,T}, {P,P,T}, {N,N,T}},   {{P,N,T}} (Notice that this is a set containing a 3-element multiset.)

5. $\frac{1}{16}$ 6. {N,P,T}, $p(N) = \frac{2}{5}$, $p(P) = \frac{2}{5}$, $p(T) = \frac{1}{5}$

7. (a) Because there are 4 ways to get *PNT* but just two ways to get *TNN* if we simply choose a first, second, and third piece of fruit. (b) The multiset {*P,N,T*} arises from 4 different selections of fruit, but other multisets, such as {*T,N,N*}, arise from other numbers, such as 1, of fruit selections.

8. (a) With 5 choices for first fruit, 4 for second fruit and 3 for the third, we have 60 ways to select fruit. Four of these ways give a *P* first and then an *N*, so *PNT* has weight $\frac{4}{60} = \frac{1}{15}$. (b) With 60 ways to select fruit, we can select the 2 *P*'s in two orders, so *PPT* arises in 2 ways, giving it weight $\frac{2}{60} = \frac{1}{30}$. (c) The probability of any 3 different fruits is $\frac{1}{15}$, the probability of two of one fruit with a *T* is $\frac{1}{30}$ and the probability of any arrangement without a *T* is $\frac{1}{15}$.

9. (a) $\frac{5}{16}$ (b) $\frac{3}{8}$ (c) $\frac{1}{2}$

10. $\frac{3}{5}, \frac{2}{5}$

11. There are $2^{16} = 65,536$ sequences of 16 zeros and ones. Of these, $\binom{16}{8} = \frac{16!}{8!8!} = 12,870$ have exactly 8 ones, and $\frac{12,870}{65,536} = \frac{6435}{32,768}$.

12. There are $4 \cdot \binom{13}{5}$ flushes and $\binom{52}{5}$ hands. This gives $\frac{33}{16,660} = .00198$ approximately.

13. Ordered triples (i, j, k) in which i, j, and k are integers between 1 and 6 inclusive.

14. The expected total is 10.5; the most likely number is 10 or 11. (In a probability course you may see examples where the most likely values are far from the expected values.)

15. The ordered triples adding to 10 are the ordered triples formed from the multisets {1,3,6}, {1,4,5}, {2,2,6}, {2,3,5}, {2,4,4}, and {3,3,4}. Those adding to 11 correspond to the multisets {1,4,6}, {1,5,5}, {2,3,6}, {2,4,5}, {3,4,4} and {3,3,5}. Since we have the same numbers of multisets with 2 distinct elements and the same numbers of multisets with 3 distinct elements, we have the same number of triples adding to 10 as to 11.

16. If we make the assumption that you are equally likely to choose any specification, then we are assuming any multiset is equally likely. Thus this assumption leads us to use the equiprobable measure for the sample space in part (b).

17. $\left(\binom{8}{1} + \binom{8}{2} + \binom{8}{3}\right)\frac{1}{2^8} = \frac{92}{256} = .359375$

18. $1 - \left(\binom{8}{1} + \binom{8}{0}\right)\frac{1}{2^8} = \frac{247}{256} = .9648375$

19. P(both plums) $= \frac{1}{10} + \frac{1}{5} = \frac{3}{10}$, P(tangerine) $= \frac{3}{5}$, P(both plums and tangerine) $= \frac{1}{10}$, P(both plums or tangerine) $= \frac{3}{10} + \frac{3}{5} - \frac{1}{10} = \frac{4}{5}$

20. $\frac{2}{5} + \frac{2}{5} - \frac{4}{25} = \frac{16}{25}$

21. $P(E) = .55$, $P(F) = .60$, $P(E \cap F) = .25$, $P(E|F) = \frac{5}{12}$, $P(F|E) = \frac{5}{11}$

22. Not independent because $P(E \cap F) \neq P(E)P(F)$

23. $\frac{1}{2}, \frac{1}{2}, \frac{1}{4}, \frac{1}{2}$, yes

24. $\frac{2}{2}$, no 25. $\frac{15}{16}$ 26. not independent

27. $P(\text{Plum last}) = \frac{1}{30} + \frac{1}{15} + \frac{1}{30} + \frac{1}{15} + \frac{1}{15} + \frac{1}{15} + \frac{1}{15} = \frac{2}{5}$, $P(N \text{ first}) = 5 \cdot \frac{1}{15} +$
$2 \cdot \frac{1}{30} = \frac{2}{5}$, $p(N \text{ first and Plum last}) = 3 \cdot \frac{1}{15} = \frac{1}{5} \neq \frac{4}{25}$. Not independent, not independent trials

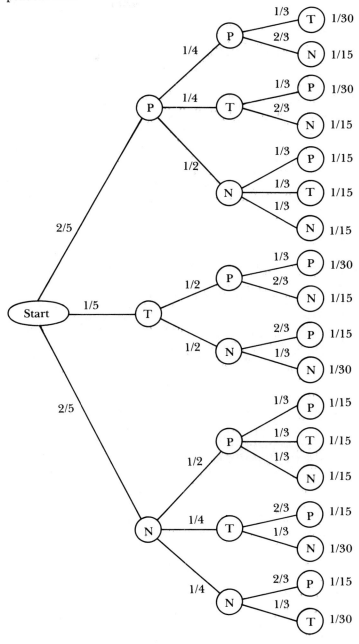

28. independent trials.   **29.** $\dfrac{4}{125}, \dfrac{24}{125}$

30.

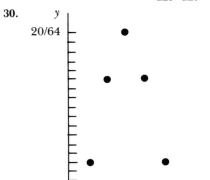
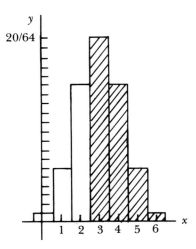

31. See answer to Review Exercise 30. More than half the area is shaded.

32. $\frac{2}{5}\cdot20 + \frac{1}{5}\cdot40 + \frac{2}{5}\cdot60 = 40$ calories

33. $P(80) = \frac{1}{10}$, $P(100) = \frac{1}{5}$, $P(120) = \frac{2}{5}$, $P(140) = \frac{1}{5}$, $P(160) = \frac{1}{10}$; 120

34. 80%

35. $\dbinom{10}{9}\left(\dfrac{4}{5}\right)^9\left(\dfrac{1}{5}\right) = \dfrac{10\cdot4^9}{5^{10}} = \dfrac{2^9}{5^9}$. Probability of all right is $\dfrac{4^{10}}{5^{10}}$. Thus probability of 90% or better $= 5\cdot\dfrac{2^{19}}{5^{10}} + 2\cdot\dfrac{2^{19}}{5^{10}} = 7\cdot\dfrac{2^{19}}{5^{10}}$

36. $\sqrt{100(.8)(.2)} = 4$ **37.** 320

38. A grade of 90 or above is at least $2\frac{1}{2}$ standard deviations above the expected grade of 80. Since the probability of being within 2.3 standard deviations of the expected value is about .98, the probability of being more than 2.3 standard deviations above is about .01, so the probability of being more than $2\frac{1}{2}$ standard deviations above the expected value is less than .01.

39. About .95

40. The teacher can be 95% sure that the student will not be more than 1.65 standard deviations above the expected value. Thus n can be any number greater than or equal to the solution to the equation $.8n = 1.65\sqrt{n(.8)(.2)} = .85n$. This gives $n = 174.24$, approximately, so 175 questions will suffice.

41. (a) $\begin{bmatrix} 0 & .3 & 0 & .2 & .5 \\ .3 & 0 & .7 & 0 & 0 \\ 0 & .7 & 0 & .3 & 0 \\ .2 & 0 & .3 & 0 & .5 \\ .5 & 0 & 0 & .5 & 0 \end{bmatrix}$ (b) $\begin{bmatrix} 0 & 3 & 0 & 0 & 1 & 2 \\ 3 & 0 & 2 & 0 & 0 & 1 \\ 0 & 2 & 0 & 3 & 0 & 0 \\ 0 & 0 & 3 & 0 & 1 & 4 \\ 1 & 0 & 0 & 1 & 0 & 0 \\ 2 & 1 & 0 & 4 & 0 & 0 \end{bmatrix}$

(c) $\begin{bmatrix} 0 & .3 & 0 & 0 & .7 \\ .2 & 0 & .7 & .1 & 0 \\ 0 & .5 & 0 & .5 & 0 \\ 0 & 0 & .6 & 0 & .4 \\ .4 & .3 & 0 & .3 & 0 \end{bmatrix}$ (d) $\begin{bmatrix} 0 & 1 & 2 & 3 & 0 \\ 0 & 0 & 1 & 0 & 3 \\ 0 & 0 & 0 & 1 & 2 \\ 0 & 0 & 0 & 0 & 1 \\ 0 & 0 & 0 & 0 & 0 \end{bmatrix}$

42. See 41(a) **43.** See 41(c). **44.** 0.1535 **45.** No, neither has an absorbing state.

46. (a) absorbing, state 1, $\begin{bmatrix} \frac{1}{3} & \frac{1}{3} \\ \frac{1}{2} & \frac{1}{2} \end{bmatrix}$ (b) Not absorbing (c) absorbing,

states 1 and 4 $\begin{bmatrix} .5 & .5 \\ .4 & .4 \end{bmatrix}$

47. The word *usually* calls for some interpretation. The interpretation which is easiest to use is "always," and this is the one we use. Note that the numbering of vertices in the figure corresponds to numbering of rows in matrix.

$\begin{bmatrix} 0 & \frac{1}{2} & 0 & \frac{1}{2} & 0 & 0 \\ \frac{1}{4} & 0 & \frac{1}{4} & \frac{1}{4} & \frac{1}{4} & 0 \\ 0 & \frac{1}{2} & 0 & 0 & \frac{1}{2} & 0 \\ \frac{1}{4} & \frac{1}{4} & 0 & 0 & \frac{1}{4} & \frac{1}{4} \\ 0 & \frac{1}{4} & \frac{1}{4} & \frac{1}{4} & 0 & \frac{1}{4} \\ 0 & 0 & 0 & 0 & 0 & 1 \end{bmatrix}$

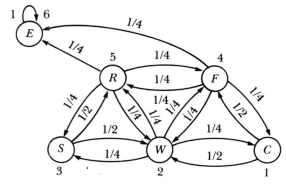

48. $\frac{9}{64}, \frac{17}{128}$ **49.** 2 times **50.** 8 rides

CHAPTER 12

Section 12-1 Concepts Review
1. group **2.** operation (or binary operation) **3.** closed **4.** group **5.** monoid
6. semigroup **7.** invertible matrices, multiplication **8.** symmetric, composition
9. subgroup **10.** $g*h^{-1}$ **11.** homomorphism **12.** kernel **13.** $\{h*g \mid h \in H\}$
14. equivalence relation, equivalence classes **15.** isomorphism **16.** right cosets, G modulo K, isomorphic

Section 12-1 Exercises

1. Multiplication of two positive rational numbers gives a positive rational number, so multiplication is a binary operation *on* the positive rational numbers. Multiplication is associative, so the multiplication of positive rational numbers is associative. 1 is a positive rational number and $1 \cdot r = r = r \cdot 1$ for every positive rational number r. If $\frac{p}{q}$ is a positive rational number, then $\frac{q}{p}$ is a positive rational number and $\frac{p}{q} \cdot \frac{q}{p} = 1 = \frac{q}{p} \cdot \frac{p}{q}$ so that every positive rational number has an inverse. Therefore the positive rational numbers form a group.

3. Semigroup, monoid, and group.

5. Since the product of elementary matrices need not be elementary, the set is not closed under multiplication so that none of the terms applies.

7. Since $a \wedge (b \wedge c)$ is a *different*, even though equivalent, statement from $(a \wedge b) \wedge c$, none of the terms applies. If we consider equivalence classes of statements, then the associative and identity laws hold and we have a monoid (and therefore a semigroup also).

9. Since ab concatenated with c, a concatenated with bc, both give the string abc, and the empty string is an identity, we have a monoid, and therefore a semigroup also.

11. First, we must observe that we have a binary operation, so that $i \cdot j$ is an equivalence class mod m and if $i = i'$ and $j = j'$, then $i \bullet j = i' \bullet j'$. By definition, $\overline{i \cdot j}$ is an equivalence class mod $\overline{m}$. If $i - i' = k_1 m$ and $j - j' = k_2 m$ then $ij - i'j' = ij - i'j + i'j - i'j' = (i - i')j + i'(j - j') = (k_1 j + k_2 i')m$. Therefore $i \cdot j$ is congruent to $i' \cdot j'$. Since multiplication is associative in the integers, we get $i \bullet (j \bullet k) = i \bullet \overline{(j \cdot k)} = \overline{i \cdot (j \cdot k)} = \overline{(i \cdot j) \cdot k} = \overline{(i \cdot j)} \bullet k = (i \bullet j) \bullet k$. Thus multiplication is associative for equivalence classes. Since $\overline{1 \bullet i} = \overline{1 \cdot i} = i = \overline{i \cdot 1} = i \bullet 1$, 1 is an identity and so we have a monoid. The monoid is not a group because $\overline{0}$ has no inverse (except in the trivial case $m = 1$).

13. We must explain why $im + -(jn)$ is again a multiple of m so that we may apply Theorem 1, using $+$ as the operation $*$ and $-(jm)$ for the inverse of jm under addition. However, in the integers, $-(jm) = (-j)m$ and thus we may write $im + -(jm) = im + (-j)m = [i + -j]m$ which is again a multiple of m.

15. Since $\begin{bmatrix} 1 & a \\ 0 & 1 \end{bmatrix}^{-1} = \begin{bmatrix} 1 & -a \\ 0 & 1 \end{bmatrix}$, we observe that $\begin{bmatrix} 1 & b \\ 0 & 1 \end{bmatrix}\begin{bmatrix} 1 & -a \\ 0 & 1 \end{bmatrix} = \begin{bmatrix} 1 & b-a \\ 0 & 1 \end{bmatrix}$

    and this (according to Theorem 1) shows we have a subgroup.

17. No, the elements of Z_4 are congruence classes mod 4 while the elements of Z_8 are congruence classes mod 8. For example, the congruence class $\{\ldots, -4, 0, 4, 8, \ldots\}$ is not a congruence class mod 8.

19. Define $\varphi(i) = i$, the congruence class of i mod 5. Since $\overline{i \cdot j} = i \bullet j$, this means that $\varphi(i \cdot j) = \varphi(i) \bullet \varphi(j)$. The kernel is the congruence class $\{\ldots, -5, 0, 5, 10, \ldots\}$ of 0 mod 5.

21. We define φ of the equivalence class of i mod 12 to be the equivalence class of i mod 3. We need a different notation for the equivalence class of i mod 12 and the equivalence class of i mod 3 in order to write a formula for φ. Let us use i for the equivalence class of i mod 12 and $\langle i \rangle$ for the equivalence class of i mod 3. Thus we may write $\varphi(i) = \langle i \rangle$. With this notation we can show that when $i = i'$, then $\varphi(i) = \varphi(i')$. Since $i = 12k + i'$, $\langle i \rangle = \langle 12k + i' \rangle = \langle 12k \rangle + \langle i' \rangle = \langle 0 \rangle + \langle i' \rangle = \langle i' \rangle$. Thus $\varphi(\underline{i + j}) = \varphi(\overline{i + j}) = \langle i + j \rangle = \langle i \rangle + \langle j \rangle$. Notice that we would not get a

function φ if $\langle i \rangle$ stood for the class of i modulo a nondivisor of 12—say mod 5—because $\langle 12k \rangle$ would not necessarily be $\langle 0 \rangle$.

23. If $f(5) = 5$ and $g(5) = 5$, then $g^{-1}(5) = 5$ as well and $f \circ g^{-1}(5) = f(g^{-1}(5)) = f(5) = 5$. Thus by Theorem 1 this set of permutations is a subgroup of S_5. The size is 24.

25. To show that $S = \{0,3,6,9\}$ is a subgroup of Z_{12} we must show that the difference of two elements in S is again in S. If i and j are in S and $i \geq j$ then clearly $i - j$ is again in S. If $j > i$ then $i - j$ is -9, -6, or -3. However recall that we are using -9 to stand for the equivalence class $\overline{-9}$ as well as the integer -9, using context to determine which we mean. Recall that $\overline{-9} = \overline{3}$, $\overline{-6} = \overline{6}$ and $\overline{-3} = \overline{9}$. thus $i - j$ is in S whenever i and j are in S, so that S is a subgroup of Z_{12}. The cosets are $\{0,\overline{3},6,9\} + 0 = \{0,3,6,9\}$, $\{0,3,6,9\} + 1 = \{1,4,7,10\}$, and $\{0,3,6,9\} + 2 = \{2,5,8,11\}$.

27. Impossible with 32 or 48 elements; possible with 24 elements since $3 \cdot 24 = 72$.

29. To show two groups are isomorphic, we must describe a function φ from one to the other and show that it is an isomorphism. Let us define $\varphi(a) = 0$, $\varphi(b) = 1$, $\varphi(c) = 2$. Then φ is clearly a one-to-one and onto function. To check that φ is an isomorphism, observe that $\varphi(a*a) = \varphi(a) = 0 = 0 + 0 = \varphi(a) + \varphi(a)$, $\varphi(b*b) = \varphi(c) = 2 = 1 + 1 = \varphi(b) + \varphi(b)$, and $\varphi(c*c) = \varphi(b) = 1 = 2 + 2 = \varphi(c) + \varphi(c)$. Further, $\varphi(a*b) = \varphi(b) = 1 = 0 + 1 = \varphi(a) + \varphi(b)$ and similarly for $\varphi(a*c)$, $\varphi(b*a)$ and $\varphi(c*a)$. Finally, $\varphi(b*c) = \varphi(a) = 0 = 1 + 2 = \varphi(b) + \varphi(c)$ and similarly for $\varphi(c*b)$.

31. a is the identity. The inverse of a is a, of b is c, and of c is b.

33. Notice that x is the identity for the group in Table 4 while a is the identity for the group in Table 3. Notice also that $w*w = x$ and $c*c = a$, while no other element has w or a for its "square." Thus if there is a homomorphism φ, then $\varphi(x) = a$ and $\varphi(w) = c$. We have two choices for $\varphi(y)$, namely b and d. Let us try $\varphi(y) = b$. Thus we define φ by $\varphi(x) = a$, $\varphi(w) = c$, $\varphi(y) = b$, $\varphi(z) = d$. Because x and a are identities, $\varphi(x*anything) = \varphi(anything*x) = \varphi(anything) = \varphi(anything)*a = a*\varphi(anything) = \varphi(x)*\varphi(anything) = \varphi(anything)*\varphi(x)$. Also, $\varphi(y*y) = \varphi(z*z) = \varphi(w) = c = b*b = d*d = \varphi(y)\varphi(y) = \varphi(z)\varphi(z)$. Now $\varphi(z*w)$, $\varphi(w*y)$, $\varphi(y*w)$, $\varphi(w*w)$, $\varphi(w*z)$, $\varphi(y*z)$, and $\varphi(z*y)$ may be checked similarly to show that φ is a homomorphism; since φ is one-to-one and onto, it is an isomorphism.

35. $(K*f)*[(K*g)(K*h)] = (K*f)*(K*(g*h)) = K*[f*(g*h)] = K*[(f*g)*h] = [K*(f*g)]*K*h = [(K*f)*(K*g)]*K*h$.

Section 12-2 Concepts Review

1. abelian   **2.** abelian group, monoid, distributes, addition   **3.** multiplication, commutative   **4.** integral domain   **5.** field   **6.** greatest common divisor (greatest common factor)   **7.** greatest common divisor   **8.** division algorithm **9.** $am + bn = 1$ **10.** prime   **11.** relatively prime   **12.** field

Section 12-2 Exercises

1. We want a permutation g such that $f(g(i)) \neq g(f(i))$ for some integer i. Since $g(f(1)) = g(2)$, let us try to define g so that $f(g(1)) \neq g(2)$. If, for example, we have $g(1) = 2$ and $g(2) = 1$, then $g(f(1)) = g(2) = 1$ but $f(g(1)) = f(2) = 3$. Thus we define $g(1) = 2$, $g(2) = 1$, $g(3) = 4$ and $g(4) = 3$ and in this way get a permutation g such that $f \circ g \neq g \circ f$.

3. There are many such matrices M; one possibility is $M = \begin{bmatrix} 2 & 0 \\ 0 & 1 \end{bmatrix}$; any other matrix with two different elements on the diagonal and zeros off the diagonal will work, as will still other possibilities.

5. No; in the case of *lower* triangular matrices, Exercise 3 gives an example which shows why.

7. The difference of upper triangular matrices is upper triangular, so they form a subgroup of the group of n-by-n matrices under addition. Further, I is upper triangular and the product of upper triangular matrices is upper triangular, so they form a submonoid of the monoid of n-by-n matrices under multiplication. Finally, since matrix multiplication distributes over addition for *all* matrices, it does so for the upper triangular matrices. Thus the upper triangular matrices form a ring.

9. Yes. The important things to note are that (1) the additive inverse of $\underline{p}$ is $\underline{p}$; since $p \oplus p$ is false for every statement p, $p \oplus p$ is equivalent to 0 for any chosen false statement 0, giving $\underline{p} \oplus \underline{p} = \underline{0}$, and (2) multiplication distributes over addition because $p \wedge (q \oplus r)$ is equivalent to $(p \wedge q) \oplus (p \wedge r)$. The other ring properties are easy to verify.

11. (a) distributive (b) associative (c) commutative (d) associative (e) distributive (f) (additive) inverse (g) associative (h) inverse property (i) identity property (j) (multiplicative) inverse (k) associative (l) inverse property (m) identity property.

13.

+	0	1	2	3
0	0	1	2	3
1	1	2	3	0
2	2	3	0	1
3	3	0	1	2

$\cdot$	0	1	2	3
0	0	0	0	0
1	0	1	2	3
2	0	2	0	2
3	0	3	2	1

1 and 3 have multiplicative inverses.

15. Yes, because the multiplication is commutative and every element has a multiplicative inverse.

17. $420 = 7 \cdot 5 \cdot 3 \cdot 2^2$; $2090 = 11 \cdot 19 \cdot 2 \cdot 5$; $GCD = 10$

19. $(420, 2090) = (420, 1670) = (420, 1250) = (420, 830) = (420, 410) = (10, 410) = (10, 400) = (10, 390) = \ldots = (10, 20) = (10, 10) = 10$

21. $(420, 2090) = (420, 410) = (410, 10) = 10$

23. $(394{,}831, 78{,}881) = (78{,}881, 426) = (426, 71) = 6$

25. We shall prove by strong induction on n that if m and n are positive, then there are integers q and r such that $n = qm + r$ with $0 \le r < m$. If $n = 1$, then we have two cases. If $m = 1$, then $n = 1 \cdot 1 + 0$ and $0 = r < m = 1$. Otherwise $m > 1$ and $1 = 0 \cdot m + 1$ and $1 = r < m$. Now suppose the formula holds for $n < k$ and assume $n = k$. If $k < m$, then setting $q = 0$ and $r = k$ gives us $k = q \cdot m + r$ with $r < m$. Otherwise $k = m$ or $k > m$. If $k = m$, then $k = 1 \cdot m + 0$, as required. If $k > m$, then $k - m$ is positive and so there are numbers q' and r such that $k - m = q'm + r$ with $0 \le r < m$, giving the desired formula with $q = q' + 1$. Thus by the principle of mathematical induction, the formula holds for all integers $n > 0$.

27. The only groups with 6 elements we have studied are the symmetric group S_3 and the group Z_6 of integers mod 6. Since S_3 is not commutative, the answer must be Z_6. To prove this is true we must demonstrate an isomorphism between Z_6 with the operation $+$ and the group of *nonzero* elements of Z_7 with the operation $\cdot$. How can we find such an isomorphism? The crucial step is to note that if $\varphi(1) = a$, then $\varphi(2) = a \cdot a = a^2$, $\varphi(3) = a^3$, and so on. Thus we must find an integer a such that the set $\{a, a^2, a^3, a^4, a^5, a^6\}$, taken mod 7, is the set $\{1, 2, 3, 4, 5, 6\}$. Of course a can't be 1. We try $a = 2$ and discover that $\{2, 4, 8, 16, 32, 64\}$ is the multiset $\{2, 4, 1, 2, 4, 1\}$ mod 7. However $\{3, 9, 27, 81, 243, 729\} = \{3, 2, 6, 4, 5, 1\}$ mod 7, so we try letting $\varphi(i) = 3^i$, the congruence class of 3^i mod 7. We have just seen that φ is a bijection. Further, $\varphi(i + j) = 3^{i+j} = 3^i 3^j = 3^i \cdot 3^j = \varphi(i)\,\varphi(j)$. Therefore φ is an isomorphism.

Section 12-3 Concepts Review

1. 0   **2.** $x_1 + x_2 + \ldots + x_n = 0$ **3.** code, n, $n - m$, m **4.** alphabet, parity check
5. rate   **6.** k **7.** distance   **8.** triangle inequality   **9.** 3   **10.** Hamming code

Section 12-3 Exercises

1. In overwrite mode, the program multiplies by zero because it turns off (that is, turns to zero) every pixel it encounters. In reversal mode it changes each zero to a one and each one to a zero. This is the same as adding one mod 2.

3. Yes, it is the integers mod 37.

5. This would require 66 symbols, and 66 is not a power of a prime.

7. If x_1 is received incorrectly, then the parity checks x_3 and x_5 will be inconsistent, if x_2 is received incorrectly, then the parity checks x_4 and x_5 will be inconsistent, if x_3, x_4, or x_5 is received incorrectly, then it will be the only inconsistent parity check and thus each single error gives rise to a different set of inconsistent parity checks. Therefore we can correct any single error.

9. We have already shown above that we can correct any single error among digits x_1 to x_5; if digit x_6 is incorrectly received then it will be the only inconsistent parity check digit and so we can correct that error. If exactly one error is made in positions 1–5, then in addition to the pattern of incorrect digits described in the solution to Exercise 7 above, x_6 will be inconsistent also. Thus in *all* cases with a single error, x_6 will be *inconsistent*. If two errors are made among x_1 through x_5, then these two errors will cancel each other in the sum $x_6 = x_1 + x_2 + x_3 + x_4 + x_5$, and thus the digit x_6 will satisfy its parity check equation. Similarly, if one of the digits x_1 through x_5 is received incorrectly and x_6 is as well, then x_6 will satisfy its parity check equation. Thus in *all* cases with two errors, x_6 will be *consistent* with its parity check equation. Now the four words of the code are 000000, 101011, 010111, and 111100. Thus if two errors are made in transmitting a codeword we will not get a codeword as a result so we will know that some error (or errors) has (have) been made in transmitting the codeword and thus we can distinguish between one or two errors because with two errors the digit x_6 will be consistent with its parity check equation and with one error it won't.

11. $\begin{bmatrix} 1 & 0 & 1 & 0 & 0 \\ 0 & 1 & 0 & 1 & 0 \\ 1 & 1 & 0 & 0 & 1 \end{bmatrix}$ **13.** $\begin{bmatrix} 1 & 0 & 1 & 0 & 0 & 0 \\ 0 & 1 & 0 & 1 & 0 & 0 \\ 1 & 1 & 0 & 0 & 1 & 0 \\ 1 & 1 & 1 & 1 & 1 & 1 \end{bmatrix}$

15. 5   **17.** 6   **19.** 4   **21.** 3   **23.** 4

25. $2^4 - 1 = 15$;
$$\begin{bmatrix} 1 & 0 & 1 & 0 & 1 & 0 & 1 & 0 & 1 & 0 & 1 & 0 & 1 & 0 & 1 \\ 0 & 1 & 1 & 0 & 0 & 1 & 1 & 0 & 0 & 1 & 1 & 0 & 0 & 1 & 1 \\ 0 & 0 & 0 & 1 & 1 & 1 & 1 & 0 & 0 & 0 & 0 & 1 & 1 & 1 & 1 \\ 0 & 0 & 0 & 0 & 0 & 0 & 0 & 1 & 1 & 1 & 1 & 1 & 1 & 1 & 1 \end{bmatrix}$$

27. $2^4 = 16$

29. $x_8 = x_1 + x_2 + x_3 + x_4 + x_5 + x_6 + x_7$ No, only a word of even weight can satisfy the equation for x_8. Length is 8, redundancy is 4, minimum distance is 4. Last entry of HX is 1 if X has one error. Last entry of HX will be 0 if x has two errors. HX cannot be the zero column matrix if X has two errors because if X differs from a codeword in two places, then X can't itself be in the code (since the minimum distance is 4). Thus if two errors are made we will know that some sort of error has been made and it is not exactly one error since the last entry of HX is 0.

Chapter 12 Review Exercises

1. Since A is invertible, there is a matrix A^{-1} such that $A^{-1}A = I$. Because multiplication is a binary operation and $AX = B$, $A^{-1}(AX) = (A^{-1}A)X$ and since $A^{-1}A = I$, we have $A^{-1}(AX) = IX$. Since I is a multiplicative identity we have $X = A^{-1}(AX) = A^{-1}B$, so there is one and only one X that satisfies the equation $AX = B$, namely $X = A^{-1}B$.

2. semigroup, monoid, group   **3.** semigroup, monoid, group

4. semigroup, monoid   **5.** None of the terms apply.

6. semigroup (not a monoid because the empty string is not made from alphabet letters)

7. If A and B are m-by-n matrices with zero diagonal, then so is $A - B$. Therefore the matrices with zero diagonal form a subgroup.

8. Picking up the square and putting it back down on the same place it used to be gives a function which makes the number which used to be in a certain place correspond to the number now in that place. Thus the result of each motion may be represented by a permutation. The inverse of such a permutation corresponds to the reversal of the motion. Following one motion by another results in sending a vertex to its image under the composition of the two permutations. Thus the set of permutations corresponding to motions contains $\varphi \circ \rho^{-1}$ whenever it contains φ and ρ. Thus it is a subgroup of S_4. Since 10 is not a factor of 24, the size of S_4, there cannot be exactly 10 such permutations.

9. $\{\underline{0}\}$ is a subgroup, $\{\underline{0}, \underline{4}\}$ is a subgroup, and $\{\underline{0}, \underline{2}, \underline{4}, \underline{6}\}$ is a subgroup. If a subgroup contains the equivalence class of an odd number, then it contains the class of $\underline{1}$ (for example if a subgroup contains $\underline{5}$, then it contains $\underline{5} + \underline{5}, \underline{5} + \underline{5} + \underline{5}, \underline{5} + \underline{5} + \underline{5} + \underline{5}$, and $\underline{5} + \underline{5} + \underline{5} + \underline{5} + \underline{5} = \underline{25} = \underline{1}$ as well as some other elements; the classes $\underline{3}$ and $\underline{7}$ are dealt with similarly.) A subgroup containing $\underline{1}$ will contain every element of Z_8. Thus a subgroup must be Z_8, or if it contains $\underline{2}$ but not $\underline{1}$ must be the set $\{\underline{0}, \underline{2}, \underline{4}, \underline{6}\}$ (because it must contain this 4-element set and $\underline{4}$ is the largest proper factor of 8). Similarly a class containing $\underline{6}$ but not $\underline{1}$ must be this set. Similarly, a subgroup containing $\underline{4}$ but not $\underline{2}$ must be the set $\{\underline{0}, \underline{4}\}$. Finally a subgroup which does not contain $\underline{4}$ must be $\{\underline{0}\}$.

10. Let $\varphi(i)$ be the permutation which sends j to the remainder of $j + i$ mod 4. For example, $\varphi(9)$ sends 0 to the remainder of $0 + 9 = 9$ or 1, sends 1 to the remainder of $1 + 9 = 10$ or 2, 2 to the remainder of $2 + 9 = 11$ or 3, and 3 to the remainder of 12 mod 12, or 0. Thus if $\varphi(9)$ is the permutation f, we have that $f(0) = 1$, $f(1) = $

2, $f(2) = 3$, and $f(3) = 0$. Thus $\varphi(i)$ is the permutation that corresponds to rotating the square through $i \cdot 90$ degrees.

11. The kernel of φ is the set of integers whose remainder mod 4 is zero, that is, the kernel is the equivalence class $\underline{4}$ mod 4. But then by the first fundamental theorem of homomorphisms, the image must be isomorphic to $Z/\underline{4} = Z_4$.

12. Let us use i for the class of i mod 20 and $\langle i \rangle$ for the class of i mod 5. We may define $\varphi(i) = \langle i \rangle$; in this way we get a function because if $i = j$ then $i = j + k \cdot 20$ for some integer k and $\langle i + k \cdot 20 \rangle = \langle i \rangle + \langle k \cdot 20 \rangle = \langle i \rangle + \langle \bar{k} \cdot 4 \rangle \langle \bar{5} \rangle = \langle i \rangle + \langle k \cdot 4 \rangle \langle 0 \rangle = \langle i \rangle + \langle 0 \rangle = 0$. Then φ is a homomorphism because $\varphi(i + j) = \varphi(\underline{i + j}) = \langle i + j \rangle = \langle i \rangle = \langle j \rangle$. The kernel is $\{\underline{0}, \underline{5}, \underline{10}, \underline{15}\}$

13. $\{\underline{0}, \underline{5}, \underline{10}, \underline{15}\}, \{\underline{1}, \underline{6}, \underline{11}, \underline{16}\}, \{\underline{2}, \underline{7}, \underline{12}, \underline{17}\}, \{\underline{3}, \underline{8}, \underline{13}, \underline{18}\}, \{\underline{4}, \underline{9}, \underline{14}, \underline{19}\}$

14. yes, yes, no   15. No, notice that $f_{12} \cdot r_1 = f_{23}$, but $r_1 \cdot f_{12} = f_{13}$.

16. No, because Z_6 is commutative.   17. $\{i, r_1, r_2\}$

18. three   19. $i^{-1} = i; r_1^{-1} = r_2; r_2^{-1} = r_1; f_{ij}^{-1} = f_{ij}$

20. Since $(K * g^{-1}) * (K * g) = (K * (g^{-1} * g)) = K$ and $(K * g)(K * g^{-1}) = K$ and K acts as the identity in G/K, $K * g^{-1}$ must be the inverse to $K * g$.

21. One answer is $\begin{bmatrix} 1 & 1 \\ 0 & 1 \end{bmatrix}$; many other answers are possible.

22. It is isomorphic to Z, the integers under the operation of addition, and $\varphi(i) = \begin{bmatrix} 1 & i \\ 0 & 1 \end{bmatrix}$ is the isomorphism. To show it is an isomorphism, we need only show that $\varphi(i + j) = \varphi(i)\varphi(j)$ since it is clearly a bijection. But $\varphi(i)\varphi(j) = \begin{bmatrix} 1 & i \\ 0 & 1 \end{bmatrix}\begin{bmatrix} 1 & j \\ 0 & 1 \end{bmatrix} = \begin{bmatrix} 1 + i \cdot 0 & 1 \cdot j + i \cdot 1 \\ 0 + 0 & 0 + 1 \end{bmatrix} = \begin{bmatrix} 1 & i + j \\ 0 & 1 \end{bmatrix} = \varphi(i + j)$.

23. Yes it is a ring because it is a subgroup of the real numbers under addition and is closed under multiplication (of real numbers) so the addition and multiplication operations are defined *on* the set and will satisfy all the ring properties. To see that it is a field, we must show that $a + b\sqrt{2}$ has an inverse of the form $a' + b'\sqrt{2}$. However, $\dfrac{1}{a + b\sqrt{2}} = \dfrac{a - b\sqrt{2}}{a^2 - 2b^2} = \dfrac{a}{a^2 - 2b^2} + \dfrac{-b}{a^2 - 2b^2}\sqrt{2}$. Since $\sqrt{2}$ is not rational, $a^2 - 2b^2$ cannot be zero, so we may take $a' = \dfrac{a}{a^2 - 2b^2}$ and $b' = \dfrac{-b}{a^2 - 2b^2}$ and $a' + b'\sqrt{2}$ is $(a + b\sqrt{2})^{-1}$.

24. There is no integer i such that min $(i, n) = n$ for every integer n. Thus we have no multiplicative identity. Further, with $i = 2, j = 2, k = 3$, you may show that $(i + j) \cdot k = \min(i + j, k) \neq i \cdot k + j \cdot k = \min(i, k) + \min(j, k)$.

25. (a) additive inverse   (b) associative   (c) inverse property for addition   (d) identity (for addition)   (e) distributive   (f) additive inverse   (g) associative   (h) inverse property (for addition)   (i) identity (for addition)   (j) multiplicative inverse   (k) associative   (l) inverse property (for multiplication)   (m) identity (for multiplication)

26. The odd numbers have multiplicative inverses and form a group under multiplication. (1 is the identity and the multiplication operation is an associative binary operation *on* the odd numbers.)

+	0	1	2	3	4	5	6	7
0	0	1	2	3	4	5	6	7
1	1	2	3	4	5	6	7	0
2	2	3	4	5	6	7	0	1
3	3	4	5	6	7	0	1	2
4	4	5	6	7	0	1	2	3
5	5	6	7	0	1	2	3	4
6	6	7	0	1	2	3	4	5
7	7	0	1	2	3	4	5	6

+	0	1	2	3	4	5	6	7
0	0	0	0	0	0	0	0	0
1	0	1	2	3	4	5	6	7
2	0	2	4	6	0	2	4	6
3	0	3	6	1	4	7	2	5
4	0	4	0	4	0	4	0	4
5	0	5	2	7	4	1	6	3
6	0	6	4	2	0	6	4	2
7	0	7	6	5	4	3	2	1

27. $(480,1225) = (265,480) = (215,265) = (215,50) = (15,50) = (15,5) = 5$

28. $(351,787; 272,853) = (272,853; 78,934) = (78,934; 36,051) = (36,051; 6832) = (6832,1891) = (1891,1159) = (1159,732) = (427,732) = (427,305) = (305,122) = (122,61) = 61$

29. multiplication, Z_4 with the addition operation. Notice that in Z_5, $\underline{2}$, $\underline{2^2} = \underline{4}$, $\underline{2^3} = \underline{3}$, and $\underline{2^4} = \underline{1}$, comprise the nonzero elements of Z_5, while in Z_4 (under addition) the elements are $\langle 1 \rangle$, $\langle 1 \rangle + \langle 1 \rangle = \langle 2 \rangle$, $\langle 1 \rangle + \langle 1 \rangle + \langle 1 \rangle = \langle 3 \rangle$, $\langle 1 \rangle + \langle 1 \rangle + \langle 1 \rangle + \langle 1 \rangle = \langle 4 \rangle = \langle 0 \rangle$. This suggests we define $\varphi(\langle i \rangle) = \underline{2^i}$ from Z_4 to the nonzero elements of Z_5. For this definition to make sense we must know that when $\langle i \rangle = \langle j \rangle$, then $\underline{2^i} = \underline{2^j}$. If, however, $\langle i \rangle = \langle j \rangle$, then $\underline{2^i} = \underline{2^{j+4k}} = \underline{2^j \cdot 2^{4k}} = \underline{2^j \cdot (2^4)^k} \equiv \underline{2^j 1^k} = \underline{2^j}$ (with the congruence mod 5). Thus the definition makes sense. Further, we have seen that φ is a bijection and we see that $\varphi(\langle i \rangle + \langle j \rangle) = \varphi(\langle i + j \rangle) = \underline{2^{i+j}} = \underline{2^i \cdot 2^j} = \underline{2^i \cdot 2^j} = \varphi(\langle i \rangle) \cdot \varphi(\langle j \rangle)$ so that φ is an isomorphism.

30. If exactly one of the digits is changed, then one or more of the parity check equations will fail to hold. However having either x_5 or x_8 changed will result in the equation that defines x_8 failing and no other equation failing, so we cannot distinguish between these two possibilities. Adding the equation for x_9 will make the equations for x_9 and x_8 fail if x_5 is wrong, only x_8 fail if x_8 is wrong and only x_9 fail if x_9 is wrong. Further, errors in x_1, x_2, x_3, x_4, x_5, x_6, or x_7 make the following sets of checks fail: $\{x_6, x_9\}$, $\{x_6, x_7\}$, $\{x_6, x_7, x_8\}$, $\{x_7, x_8\}$, $\{x_6\}$, $\{x_7\}$ so each wrong digit makes different set of parity check equations fail.

31.
$$\begin{bmatrix} 1 & 1 & 1 & 0 & 0 & 1 & 0 & 0 & 0 \\ 0 & 1 & 1 & 1 & 0 & 0 & 1 & 0 & 0 \\ 0 & 0 & 1 & 1 & 1 & 0 & 0 & 1 & 0 \\ 1 & 0 & 0 & 0 & 1 & 0 & 0 & 0 & 1 \end{bmatrix}$$

32. Minimum distance is three because it corrects one error but the word 100001001 is in the code.

33. Add a column of zeros and then a row of ones to the matrix of Exercise 31. Minimum distance is now 4.

$$\begin{bmatrix} 1 & 1 & 1 & 0 & 0 & 1 & 0 & 0 & 0 & 0 \\ 0 & 1 & 1 & 1 & 0 & 0 & 1 & 0 & 0 & 0 \\ 0 & 0 & 1 & 1 & 1 & 0 & 0 & 1 & 0 & 0 \\ 1 & 0 & 0 & 0 & 1 & 0 & 0 & 0 & 1 & 0 \\ 1 & 1 & 1 & 1 & 1 & 1 & 1 & 1 & 1 & 1 \end{bmatrix}$$

34. d(first, second) = 4; d(first, third) = 4; d(second, third) = 4.

35. To correct all errors we would need enough columns beyond column 5 so that the set of parity check columns had at least 5 nonempty subsets so that we have 5 different patterns to correspond to errors in the first 5 places. In addition we would need one more nonempty subset to correct an error for each parity check digit we add. Thus if we add three parity check columns, we would need 8 nonempty subsets—but a set of 3 columns has only 7 nonempty subsets! Therefore we need 9 columns. Now, however, since there are only seven possible different columns containing 3 zeros or ones, neither 8 nor 9 columns are possible. (Note: if we repeated some columns so we had nine columns with two repeats, the code would contain a word of weight 2 and so could not correct each single error.)

36. $2^5 = 32$

APPENDIX B

Section B-1 Concepts Review

1. symbolic series **2.** coefficient **3.** power **4.** generating function (generating series)
5. $a_i b_{k-i}$

Section B-2 Concepts Review

1. number, value i **2.** total value **3.** product, Cartesian product, $\in S_i$ **4.** product, product **5.** $\sum_{i=0}^{n} x^i$ or $\dfrac{1}{1-x}$, geometric **6.** $\dbinom{n+i-1}{i} x^i$, $(1-x)^{-n}$

7. $\sum_{i=0}^{\infty} \dbinom{n+i-1}{i} x^i$ **8.** $\dbinom{m}{i} x^i y^{m-i}$

Index

Useful Formulas and Notation

Sets

U	universe	
$\sim S$	$\{x \mid x \in U \text{ and } x \notin S\}$	complement of S
$S \cup T$	$\{x \mid x \in S \text{ or } x \in T\}$	union of S and T
$S \cap T$	$\{x \mid x \in S \text{ and } x \in T\}$	intersection of S and T
$S \times T$	$\{(x,y) \mid x \in S \text{ and } y \in T\}$	Cartesian product of S and T
$S \sim T$	$\{x \mid x \in S \text{ and } x \notin T\}$	difference of S and T

De Morgan's Laws: $\sim(S \cup T) = \sim S \cap \sim T$ Distributive Laws: $R \cap (S \cup T) = (R \cap S) \cup (R \cap T)$

$\sim(S \cap T) = \sim S \cup \sim T$ $R \cup (S \cap T) = (R \cup S) \cap (R \cup T)$

Functions

$f \circ g(x)$ $f(g(x))$ composition of f with g $f^{-1} \circ f = f \circ f^{-1} = $ identity function

f^{-1} $\{(y, x) \mid (x, y) \in f\}$ inverse function

Table of growth rates

name	constant	logarithmic	polylog	root	linear	power	exponential	factorial
example	c	$\log_b(n)$	$\log_b(n)^k$	$n^{1/m}$	n	n^r	b^n	$n!$

Note: Each example is Big Oh of all the examples to its right.

Sums

$$\sum_{i=0}^{n} 1 = n + 1 \qquad \sum_{i=0}^{n} i = \frac{n(n+1)}{2} \qquad \sum_{i=0}^{n} i^2 = \frac{n(n+1)(2n+1)}{6} \qquad \sum_{i=0}^{n} r^i = \frac{1 - r^{n+1}}{1 - r}$$

Logic

$p \wedge q$	p and q	De Morgan's Laws
$p \vee q$	p or q	$\neg(r \vee s) \Leftrightarrow \neg r \wedge \neg s$
$p \oplus q$	p exclusive or q	$\neg(r \wedge s) \Leftrightarrow \neg r \vee \neg s$
$\neg p$	not p	$\neg \exists x \, (s(x)) \Leftrightarrow \forall x \, (\neg s(x))$ etc.
$p \rightarrow q$	p only if q or if p then q	
$p \leftrightarrow q$	p if and only if q	
$\Leftrightarrow$	is equivalent to	Distributive laws
$\Rightarrow$	implies	$r \wedge (s \vee t) \Leftrightarrow (r \wedge s) \vee (r \wedge t)$
$\exists x$	There exists x	$r \vee (s \wedge t) \Leftrightarrow (r \vee s) \wedge (r \vee t)$
$\forall x$	For all x	

Recurrences

First-order linear constant coefficient homogeneous: $a_n = ba_{n-1}; a_n = a_0 b^n$

First-order linear constant coefficient: $a_n = ba_{n-1} + d(n); a_n = b^n(a_0 + \sum_{i=1}^{n} b^{-i}d(i))$

Divide and conquer: $s_n = bs_{n/a} + d(n)$; convert to first-order linear by letting $n = a^k$

Second-order linear homogeneous constant coefficient: $s_n + bs_{n-1} + cs_{n-2} \doteq 0$; solve by substituting
    $s_n = r^n$ and solving for r; form linear combination of solutions